A Brief Guide to **Getting the Most** from this Book

1   Read the Book

Feature	Description	Benefit
Section-Opening Scenarios	Every section opens with a scenario presenting a unique application of algebra in your life outside the classroom.	Realizing that algebra is everywhere will help motivate your learning. (See page 105.)
Detailed Worked-Out Examples	Examples are clearly written and provide step-by-step solutions. No steps are omitted, and each step is thoroughly explained to the right of the mathematics.	The blue annotations will help you understand the solutions by providing the reason why every algebraic step is true. (See page 110.)
Applications Using Real-World Data	Interesting applications from nearly every discipline, supported by up-to-date real-world data, are included in every section.	Ever wondered how you'll use algebra? This feature will show you how algebra can solve real problems. (See page 253.)
Great Question!	NEW to this Edition. Answers to students' questions offer suggestions for problem solving, point out common errors to avoid, and provide informal hints and suggestions.	By seeing common mistakes, you'll be able to avoid them. This feature should help you not to feel anxious or threatened when asking questions in class. (See page 108.)
Explanatory Voice Balloons	Voice balloons help to demystify algebra. They translate algebraic language into plain English, clarify problem-solving procedures, and present alternative ways of understanding.	Does math ever look foreign to you? This feature often translates math into everyday English. (See page 194.)
Learning Objectives	Every section begins with a list of objectives. Each objective is restated in the margin where the objective is covered.	The objectives focus your reading by emphasizing what is most important and where to find it. (See page 122.)
Technology	The screens displayed in the technology boxes show how graphing utilities verify and visualize algebraic results.	Even if you are not using a graphing utility in the course, this feature will help you understand different approaches to problem solving. (See page 109.)

2   Work the Problems

Feature	Description	Benefit
Check Point Examples	Each example is followed by a similar matched problem, called a Check Point, that offers you the opportunity to work a similar exercise. The answers to the Check Points are provided in the answer section.	You learn best by doing. You'll solidify your understanding of worked examples if you try a similar problem right away to be sure you understand what you've just read. (See page 276.)
Concept and Vocabulary Checks	NEW to this Edition. These short-answer questions, mainly fill-in-the-blank and true/false items, assess your understanding of the definitions and concepts presented in each section.	It is difficult to learn algebra without knowing its special language. These exercises test your understanding of the vocabulary and concepts. (See page 223.)
Extensive and Varied Exercise Sets	An abundant collection of exercises is included in an Exercise Set at the end of each section. Exercises are organized within several categories. Your instructor will usually provide guidance on which exercises to work. The exercises in the first category, Practice Exercises, follow the same order as the section's worked examples.	The parallel order of the Practice Exercises lets you refer to the worked examples and use them as models for solving these problems. (See page 360.)
Practice Plus Problems	This category of exercises contains more challenging problems that often require you to combine several skills or concepts.	It is important to dig in and develop your problem-solving skills. Practice Plus Exercises provide you with ample opportunity to do so. (See page 387.)
Preview Problems	Each Exercise Set concludes with three problems to help you prepare for the next section.	These exercises let you review previously covered material that you'll need to be successful for the forthcoming section. Some of these problems will get you thinking about concepts you'll soon encounter. (See page 300.)

3   Review for Quizzes and Tests

Feature	Description	Benefit
Mid-Chapter Check Points	At approximately the midway point in the chapter, an integrated set of review exercises allows you to review the skills and concepts you learned separately over several sections.	By combining exercises from the first half of the chapter, the Mid-Chapter Check Points give a comprehensive review before you move on to the material in the remainder of the chapter. **(See page 269.)**
Chapter Review Grids	Each chapter contains a review chart that summarizes the definitions and concepts in every section of the chapter. Examples that illustrate these key concepts are also referenced in the chart.	Review this chart and you'll know the most important material in the chapter! **(See page 583.)**
Chapter Review Exercises	A comprehensive collection of review exercises for each of the chapter's sections follows the grid.	Practice makes perfect. These exercises contain the most significant problems for each of the chapter's sections. **(See page 202.)**
Chapter Tests	Each chapter contains a practice test with approximately 25 problems that cover the important concepts in the chapter. Take the practice test, check your answers, and then watch the Chapter Test Prep Videos to see worked-out solutions for any exercises you miss.	You can use the chapter test to determine whether you have mastered the material covered in the chapter. **(See page 206.)**
Chapter Test Prep Videos	These videos contain worked-out solutions to every exercise in each chapter test and can be found in MyMathLab and on YouTube.	The videos let you review any exercises you miss on the chapter test.
Cumulative Review Exercises	Beginning with Chapter 2, each chapter concludes with a comprehensive collection of mixed cumulative review exercises. These exercises combine problems from previous chapters and the present chapter, providing an ongoing cumulative review.	Ever forget what you've learned? These exercises ensure that you are not forgetting anything as you move forward. **(See page 440.)**

Robert Blitzer

College Algebra
Math 1302

Second Custom Edition for
University of Arkansas Little Rock

Taken from:
College Algebra, Sixth Edition
by Robert Blitzer

Cover Art: Courtesy of Office of Communications, University of Arkansas Little Rock.

Taken from:

College Algebra, Sixth Edition
by Robert Blitzer
Copyright © 2014, 2010, 2007 by Pearson Education, Inc.
Boston, Massachusetts 02116

This special edition published in cooperation with Pearson Learning Solutions.

Pearson Learning Solutions, 501 Boylston Street, Suite 900, Boston, MA 02116
A Pearson Education Company
www.pearsoned.com

Printed in the United States of America

3 4 5 6 7 8 9 10 V092 16 15 14

000200010271846651

ML

ISBN 10: 1-269-62079-7
ISBN 13: 978-1-269-62079-6

DEDICATION

For Jerid (1985–2012)
And for those who have loved their pets
and have been loved by them

CONTENTS

4 Exponential and Logarithmic Functions 441

3 Polynomial and Rational Functions 329

PREFACE

I've written **College Algebra, Sixth Edition**, to help diverse students, with different backgrounds and future goals, to succeed. The book has three fundamental goals:

1. To help students acquire a solid foundation in algebra, preparing them for other courses such as calculus, business calculus, and finite mathematics.
2. To show students how algebra can model and solve authentic real-world problems.
3. To enable students to develop problem-solving skills, while fostering critical thinking, within an interesting setting.

One major obstacle in the way of achieving these goals is the fact that very few students actually read their textbook. This has been a regular source of frustration for me and for my colleagues in the classroom. Anecdotal evidence gathered over years highlights two basic reasons that students do not take advantage of their textbook:

- "I'll never use this information."
- "I can't follow the explanations."

I've written every page of the Sixth Edition with the intent of eliminating these two objections. The ideas and tools I've used to do so are described for the student in "A Brief Guide to Getting the Most from This Book," which appears at the front of the book.

What's New in the Sixth Edition?

New Applications and Real-World Data. I'm on a constant search for data that can be used to illustrate unique algebraic applications. I researched hundreds of books, magazines, newspapers, almanacs, and online sites to prepare the Sixth Edition. Among the 108 worked-out examples and exercises based on new data sets, you'll find applications involving modeling blood-alcohol concentration (Section P.1), starting salaries for college graduates (Section 1.3), the world's vanishing tiger population (Section 3.2), and the year humans become immortal (Section 4.1).

Concept and Vocabulary Checks. The Sixth Edition contains 470 new short-answer exercises, mainly fill-in-the-blank and true/false items, that assess students' understanding of the definitions and concepts presented in each section.

The Concept and Vocabulary Checks appear as separate features preceding the Exercise Sets.

Great Question! This feature takes the content of each Study Tip in the Fifth Edition and presents it in the context of a student question. Answers to questions offer suggestions for problem solving, point out common errors to avoid, and provide informal hints and suggestions. 'Great Question!' should draw students' attention and curiosity more than the 'Study Tips.' As a secondary benefit, this new feature should help students not to feel anxious or threatened when asking questions in class.

New Chapter-Opening and Section-Opening Scenarios. Every chapter and every section open with a scenario based on an application, many of which are unique to the Sixth Edition. These scenarios are revisited in the course of the chapter or section in one of the book's new examples, exercises, or discussions. The often humorous tone of these openers is intended to help fearful and reluctant students overcome their negative perceptions about math.

New Blitzer Bonuses. The Sixth Edition contains a variety of new but optional enrichment essays. Examples include "Using Algebra to Measure Blood-Alcohol Concentration" (Section P.1), "Seven Ways to Spend \$1 Trillion" (Section P.2), "Addressing Stress Parabolically" (Section 3.1), "Five Things Scientists Learned from the Hubble Space Telescope" (Section 7.3), and "Ponzi Schemes and Geometric Sequences" (Section 8.3).

Sample Homework Assignments. Within each Exercise Set, I have chosen odd-numbered problems, primarily from the Practice Exercises, that can serve as sample homework assignments. These are indicated by a <u>blue underline</u> in the Annotated Instructor's Edition. Based on the goals and objectives of your course, you may wish to enrich each sample homework assignment with additional exercises from the other categories in the Exercise Set.

New Interactive Figures. These new figures bring mathematical concepts to life and are included in MyMathLab. Used as a lecture tool, the figures help engage students more fully and save the time spent drawing figures by hand. Questions pertaining to each figure are assignable in MyMathLab and reinforce active learning and critical thinking. Each figure has an accompanying Exploratory Exercise that encourages further study and can be used as a presentation tool or as an open-ended learning assignment.

What Content and Organizational Changes Have Been Made to the Sixth Edition?

- **Section P.1 (Algebraic Expressions, Mathematical Models, and Real Numbers)** contains a new essay, now called a Blitzer Bonus, on using algebra to measure blood-alcohol concentration. This Blitzer Bonus should set the stage for the book's engaging collection of unique applications.

- **Section P.6 (Rational Expressions)** presents a new example on excluding numbers from a rational expression with a trinomial denominator.

- **Section 1.2 (Linear Equations and Rational Equations)** contains examples involving both inconsistent equations and identities.

- **Section 2.5 (Transformations of Functions)** has a more thoroughly developed discussion of how stretching or shrinking changes a graph's shape.

- **Section 2.6 (Combinations of Functions; Composite Functions)** has a new example on finding the domain of a function with a square root in the denominator. There is also a new example that ties in with the section opener (number of births and deaths in the United States) and illustrates an application of the algebra of functions.

- **Section 3.2 (Polynomial Functions and Their Graphs)** contains a new example on graphing $f(x) = -2(x - 1)^2(x + 2)$, a polynomial function whose equation is given in factored form.

- **Section 3.5 (Rational Functions and Their Graphs)** has a variety of exercises where students must factor to find vertical asymptotes or holes.

- **Section 3.6 (Polynomial and Rational Inequalities)** contains a new example on solving a polynomial inequality with irrational boundary points that requires the use of the quadratic formula.

- **Section 4.1 (Exponential Functions)** presents an intriguing new Blitzer Bonus on the year humans become immortal. The section also contains a new table clarifying interest plans in which interest is paid more than once a year.

- **Section 4.4 (Exponential and Logarithmic Equations)** has a new discussion (within the context of the Great Question! feature) on whether a negative number can belong to the solution set of a logarithmic equation.

- **Section 5.3 (Partial Fractions)** uses the Great Question! feature to include a discussion on speeding up the process of finding partial fraction decompositions.

What Familiar Features Have Been Retained in the Sixth Edition?

- **Detailed Worked-Out Examples.** Each worked example is titled, making clear the purpose of the example. Examples are clearly written and provide students with detailed step-by-step solutions. No steps are omitted and key steps are thoroughly explained to the right of the mathematics.

- **Explanatory Voice Balloons.** Voice balloons are used in a variety of ways to demystify mathematics. They translate algebraic ideas into everyday English, help clarify problem-solving procedures, present alternative ways of understanding concepts, and connect problem solving to concepts students have already learned.

- **Check Point Examples.** Each example is followed by a similar matched problem, called a Check Point, offering students the opportunity to test their understanding of the example by working a similar exercise. The answers to the Check Points are provided in the answer section.

- **Extensive and Varied Exercise Sets.** An abundant collection of exercises is included in an Exercise Set at the end of each section. Exercises are organized within eight category types: Practice Exercises, Practice Plus Exercises, Application Exercises, Writing in Mathematics, Technology Exercises, Critical Thinking Exercises, Group Exercises, and Preview Exercises. This format makes it easy to create well-rounded homework assignments. The order of the Practice Exercises is exactly the same as the order of the section's worked examples. This parallel order enables students to refer to the titled examples and their detailed explanations to achieve success working the Practice Exercises.

- **Practice Plus Problems.** This category of exercises contains more challenging practice problems that often require students to combine several skills or concepts. With an average of ten Practice Plus problems per Exercise Set, instructors are provided with the option of creating assignments that take Practice Exercises to a more challenging level.

- **Mid-Chapter Check Points.** At approximately the midway point in each chapter, an integrated set of Review Exercises allows students to review and assimilate the skills and concepts they learned separately over several sections.

- **Graphing and Functions.** Graphing is introduced in Chapter 1 and functions are introduced in Chapter 2, with an integrated graphing functional approach emphasized throughout the book. Graphs and functions that model data appear in nearly every section and Exercise Set. Examples and exercises use graphs of functions to explore relationships between data and to provide ways of visualizing a problem's solution. Because functions are the core of this course, students are repeatedly shown how functions relate to equations and graphs.

- **Section Objectives.** Learning objectives are clearly stated at the beginning of each section. These objectives help students recognize and focus on the section's most important ideas. The objectives are restated in the margin at their point of use.

- **Integration of Technology Using Graphic and Numerical Approaches to Problems.** Side-by-side features in the Technology boxes connect algebraic solutions to graphic and numerical approaches to problems. Although the use of graphing utilities is optional, students can use the explanatory voice balloons to understand different approaches to problems even if they are not using a graphing utility in the course.

- **Chapter Summaries.** Each chapter contains a review chart that summarizes the definitions and concepts in every section of the chapter. Examples that illustrate these key concepts are also referenced in the chart.

- **End-of-Chapter Materials.** A comprehensive collection of Review Exercises for each of the chapter's sections follows the Summary. This is followed by a Chapter Test that enables students to test their understanding of the material covered in the chapter. Beginning with Chapter 2, each chapter concludes with a comprehensive collection of mixed Cumulative Review Exercises.

- **Discovery.** Discovery boxes, found throughout the text, encourage students to further explore algebraic concepts. These explorations are optional and their omission does not interfere with the continuity of the topic at hand.

I hope that my passion for teaching, as well as my respect for the diversity of students I have taught and learned from over the years, is apparent throughout this new edition. By connecting algebra to the whole spectrum of learning, it is my intent to show students that their world is profoundly mathematical, and indeed, π is in the sky.

Robert Blitzer

Acknowledgments

An enormous benefit of authoring a successful series is the broad-based feedback I receive from the students, dedicated users, and reviewers. Every change to this edition is the result of their thoughtful comments and suggestions. I would like to express my appreciation to all the reviewers, whose collective insights form the backbone of this revision. In particular, I would like to thank the following people for reviewing *College Algebra, Algebra and Trigonometry, Precalculus,* and *Trigonometry.*

Barnhill, Kayoko Yates, Clark College
Beaver, Timothy, Isothermal Community College
Becan, Jaromir, University of Texas-San Antonio
Benjelloun, Imad, Delaware Valley College
Best, Lloyd, Pacific Union College
Brown, Denise, Collin College, Spring Creek Campus
Burgin, Bill, Gaston College
Cabaniss, Jennifer, Central Texas College
Chang, Jimmy, St. Petersburg College
Colt, Diana, University of Minnesota-Duluth
Cornell, Shannon, Amarillo College
Davidson, Wendy, Georgia Perimeter College-Newton
Densmore, Donna, Bossier Parish Community College
Enegren, Disa, Rose State College
Erickson, Keith A., Georgia Gwinnett College
Fisher, Nancy, University of Alabama
Gerken, Donna, Miami Dade College
Glickman, Cynthia, Community College of Southern Nevada
Goel, Sudhir Kumar, Valdosta State University
Gordon, Donald, Manatee Community College
Gross, David L., University of Connecticut
Groves, Jason W., South Plains College
Haack, Joel K., University of Northern Iowa
Haefner, Jeremy, University of Colorado
Hague, Joyce, University of Wisconsin at River Falls
Hall, Mike, University of Mississippi
Hassani, Mahshid, Hillsborough Community College
Hayes, Tom, Montana State University
Hay-Jahans, Christopher N., University of South Dakota
Hernandez, Celeste, Richland College
Horney, Jo Beth, South Plains College
Howard, Heidi, Florida State College at Jacksonville, South Campus
Ihlow, Winfield A., SUNY College at Oswego
Johnson, Nancy Raye, Manatee Community College
Larue, Dennine, Fairmont State University
Leesburg, Mary, Manatee Community College
Lehman, Christine Heinecke, Purdue University North Central
Levichev, Alexander, Boston University
Lin, Zongzhu, Kansas State University
Marlin, Benjamin, Northwestern Oklahoma State University
Massey, Marilyn, Collin County Community College
McCarthy-Germaine, Yvelyne, University of New Orleans

Mertens, Owen, Missouri State University-Springfield
Miller, James, West Virginia University
Nega, Martha, Georgia Perimeter College-Decatur
Peterman, Shahla, University of Missouri St. Louis
Pharo, Debra A., Northwestern Michigan College
Phoenix, Gloria, North Carolina Agricultural and Technical State University
Platt, David, Front Range Community College
Pohjanpelto, Juha, Oregon State University
Quinlan, Brooke, Hillsborough Community College
Rech, Janice, University of Nebraska at Omaha
Rody, Joseph W., Arizona State University
Rouhani, Behnaz, Georgia Perimeter College-Dunwoody
Salmon, Judith, Fitchburg State University
Schramm, Michael, Indian River State College
Schultz, Cynthia, Illinois Valley Community College
Shelton, Pat, North Carolina Agricultural and Technical State University
Spillman, Caroline, Georgia Perimeter College-Clarkston
Stadler, Jonathan, Capital University
Stallworth, Franotis R., Gwinnett Technical College
Stump, Chris, Bethel College
Sykes, Scott, University of West Georgia
Townsend, Richard, North Carolina Central University
Trim, Pamela, Southwest Tennessee Community College
Turner, Chris, Arkansas State University
Van Lommel, Richard E., California State University-Sacramento
Van Peursem, Dan, University of South Dakota
Van Veldhuizen, Philip, University of Nevada at Reno
Weaver, Jeffrey, Baton Rouge Community College
Wheeler, Amanda, Amarillo College
White, David, The Victoria College
Wienckowski, Tracy, University of Buffalo

Additional acknowledgments are extended to Dan Miller and Kelly Barber for preparing the solutions manuals; Brad Davis for preparing the answer section, serving as accuracy checker, and writing the new learning guide; cMPreparé formatting team for the book's brilliant paging; Brian Morris and Kevin Morris at Scientific Illustrators for superbly illustrating the book; Sheila Norman, photo researcher, for obtaining the book's new photographs; Rebecca Dunn, project manager, and Kathleen Manley, production editor, whose collective talents kept every aspect of this complex project moving through its many stages.

I would like to thank my editors at Pearson, Katie O'Connor and Dawn Murrin, who, with the assistance of Joseph Colella, guided and coordinated the book from manuscript through production. Thanks to Beth Paquin for the beautiful covers and interior design. Finally, thanks to Peggy Lucas for her innovative marketing efforts and to the entire Pearson sales force for their confidence and enthusiasm about the book.

Robert Blitzer

DYNAMIC RESOURCES

MyMathLab® Online Course (access code required)

MyMathLab delivers **proven results** in helping individual students succeed. It provides **engaging experiences** that personalize, stimulate, and measure learning for each student. And it comes from a **trusted partner** with educational expertise and an eye on the future.

To learn more about how MyMathLab combines proven learning applications with powerful assessment, visit **www.mymathlab.com** or contact your Pearson representative.

In Blitzer's **MyMathLab®** course, you have access to the most cutting-edge, innovative study solutions proven to increase student success. Noteworthy features include the following:

Ready to Go Courses.

These new courses provide students with all the same great MyMathLab features that you're used to but make it easier for instructors to get started. Each course includes author-chosen, preassigned homework, integrated review questions, quizzes, and cumulative review exercises to make creating your course even simpler.

Interactive Figures.

These *Mathematica*-based figures make the figures from the text come alive. Used during a lecture, interactive figures engage students more fully and save time that would otherwise be spent drawing them by hand. Exercises pertaining to each interactive figure are assignable in MyMathLab to reinforce active learning, critical thinking, and conceptual reasoning.

Integrated Review.

Skill review quizzes are assignable throughout the course, testing students on prerequisite knowledge. From these quizzes, each student receives a personalized, just-in-time review assignment, allowing them to refresh forgotten concepts.

MathTalk Videos.

Engaging videos connect mathematics to real-life events and interesting applications. These fun, instructional videos show students that math is relevant to their daily lives and are assignable in MyMathLab.

Video Assessment.

Assignable MXL exercises are available for MathTalk videos to help students retain valuable information presented in the videos.

Section-Lecture Videos.

These videos provide lectures for each section of the text to help students review important concepts and procedures 24/7.

Concept and Vocabulary Check.

New and assignable in MyMathLab, these short-answer and fill-in-the blank exercises provide a quick check for understanding of concepts. These questions also test for reading comprehension before the student moves on to the exercises.

Chapter Test Prep Videos.

Students can watch instructors work through step-by-step solutions to all the Chapter Test exercises from the textbook. These are available in MyMathLab and on YouTube.

www.youtube.com/BlitzerCollegeAlg6e

Instructor Resources

Additional resources can be downloaded from www.pearsonhighered.com or hardcopy resources can be ordered from your sales representative.

TestGen.

Enables instructors to build, edit, print, and administer tests using a computerized bank of algorithmic questions developed to cover all the objectives of the text.

PowerPoint Lecture Slides.

Fully editable lecture slides that correlate to the textbook.

Instructor's Solutions Manual.

Fully worked solutions to all textbook exercises.

Mini Lecture Notes.

Additional examples and helpful teaching tips for each section.

Annotated Instructor's Edition.

Shorter answers are on the page beside the exercises. Longer answers are in the back of the text.

LEARNING GUIDE

Blitzer

Charles B. Davis

Student Resources

Additional resources to help student success are available to be packaged with the Blitzer textbook and MyMathLab access code.

Student's Solutions Manual.

Fully worked solutions to odd-numbered exercises and available to be packaged with the textbook.

Learning Guide.

This note-taking guide is organized by objective and begins each chapter with an engaging application, providing additional examples and exercises for students to work through for greater conceptual understanding and mastery of mathematical topics. The Learning Guide is available as PDFs and customizable Word files in MyMathLab. They can also be packaged with the textbook and MyMathLab access code.

TO THE STUDENT

The bar graph shows some of the qualities that students say make a great teacher. It was my goal to incorporate each of these qualities throughout the pages of this book.

Explains Things Clearly

I understand that your primary purpose in reading *College Algebra* is to acquire a solid understanding of the required topics in your algebra course. In order to achieve this goal, I've carefully explained each topic. Important definitions and procedures are set off in boxes, and worked-out examples that present solutions in a step-by-step manner appear in every section. Each example is followed by a similar matched problem, called a Check Point, for you to try so that you can actively participate in the learning process as you read the book. (Answers to all Check Points appear in the back of the book.)

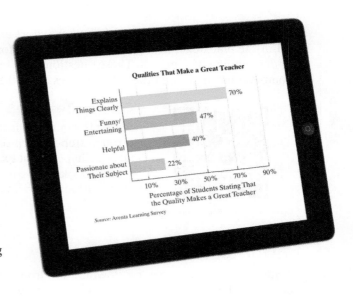

Funny & Entertaining

Who says that an algebra textbook can't be entertaining? From our quirky cover to the photos in the chapter and section openers, prepare to expect the unexpected. I hope some of the book's enrichment essays, called Blitzer Bonuses, will put a smile on your face from time to time.

Helpful

I designed the book's features to help you acquire knowledge of college algebra, as well as to show you how algebra can solve authentic problems that apply to your life. These helpful features include

- **Explanatory Voice Balloons:** Voice balloons are used in a variety of ways to make math less intimidating. They translate algebraic language into everyday English, help clarify problem-solving procedures, present alternative ways of understanding concepts, and connect new concepts to concepts you have already learned.

- **Great Question!:** The book's Great Question! boxes are based on questions students ask in class. The answers to these questions give suggestions for problem solving, point out common errors to avoid, and provide informal hints and suggestions.

- **Chapter Summaries:** Each chapter contains a review chart that summarizes the definitions and concepts in every section of the chapter. Examples from the chapter that illustrate these key concepts are also referenced in the chart. Review these summaries and you'll know the most important material in the chapter!

Passionate about the Subject

I passionately believe that no other discipline comes close to math in offering a more extensive set of tools for application and development of your mind. I wrote the book in Point Reyes National Seashore, 40 miles north of San Francisco. The park consists of 75,000 acres with miles of pristine surf-washed beaches, forested ridges, and bays bordered by white cliffs. It was my hope to convey the beauty and excitement of mathematics using nature's unspoiled beauty as a source of inspiration and creativity. Enjoy the pages that follow as you empower yourself with the algebra needed to succeed in college, your career, and your life.

Regards,

Bob

Robert Blitzer

ABOUT THE AUTHOR

Bob Blitzer is a native of Manhattan and received a Bachelor of Arts degree with dual majors in mathematics and psychology (minor: English literature) from the City College of New York. His unusual combination of academic interests led him toward a Master of Arts in mathematics from the University of Miami and a doctorate in behavioral sciences from Nova University. Bob's love for teaching mathematics was nourished for nearly 30 years at Miami Dade College, where he received numerous teaching awards, including Innovator of the Year from the League for Innovations in the Community College and an endowed chair based on excellence in the classroom. In addition to

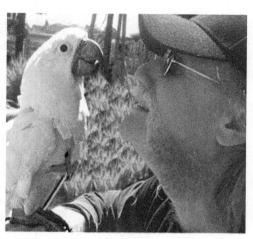

Bob and his buddy Casper Cockatoo

College Algebra, Bob has written textbooks covering introductory algebra, intermediate algebra, trigonometry, algebra and trigonometry, precalculus, and liberal arts mathematics, all published by Pearson. When not secluded in his Northern California writer's cabin, Bob can be found hiking the beaches and trails of Point Reyes National Seashore and tending to the chores required by his beloved entourage of horses, chickens, and irritable roosters.

APPLICATIONS INDEX

FUNCTIONS AND GRAPHS

HERE'S WHERE YOU'LL FIND THESE APPLICATIONS:

A mathematical model involving global warming is developed in Example 9 in Section 2.3.

Using mathematics in a way that is similar to making a movie is discussed in the Blitzer Bonus on page 266.

A vast expanse of open water at the top of our world was once covered with ice. The melting of the Arctic ice caps has forced polar bears to swim as far as 40 miles, causing them to drown in significant numbers. Such deaths were rare in the past.

There is strong scientific consensus that human activities are changing the Earth's climate. Scientists now believe that there is a striking correlation between atmospheric carbon dioxide concentration and global temperature. As both of these variables increase at significant rates, there are warnings of a planetary emergency that threatens to condemn coming generations to a catastrophically diminished future.*

In this chapter, you'll learn to approach our climate crisis mathematically by creating formulas, called functions, that model data for average global temperature and carbon dioxide concentration over time. Understanding the concept of a function will give you a new perspective on many situations, ranging from global warming to using mathematics in a way that is similar to making a movie.

*Sources: Al Gore, *An Inconvenient Truth*, Rodale, 2006; *Time*, April 3, 2006

SECTION 2.1   Basics of Functions and Their Graphs

Objectives

① Find the domain and range of a relation.

② Determine whether a relation is a function.

③ Determine whether an equation represents a function.

④ Evaluate a function.

⑤ Graph functions by plotting points.

⑥ Use the vertical line test to identify functions.

⑦ Obtain information about a function from its graph.

⑧ Identify the domain and range of a function from its graph.

⑨ Identify intercepts from a function's graph.

Magnified 6000 times, this color-scanned image shows a T-lymphocyte blood cell (green) infected with the HIV virus (red). Depletion of the number of T cells causes destruction of the immune system.

The average number of T cells in a person with HIV is a *function* of time after infection. In this section, you will be introduced to the basics of functions and their graphs. We will analyze the graph of a function using an example that illustrates the progression of HIV and T cell count. Much of our work in this course will be devoted to the important topic of functions and how they model your world.

Relations

Forbes magazine published a list of the highest-paid TV celebrities between June 2010 and June 2011. The results are shown in **Figure 2.1**.

① Find the domain and range of a relation.

Highest Paid TV Celebrities between June 2010 and June 2011

FIGURE 2.1
Source: *Forbes*

The graph indicates a correspondence between a TV celebrity and that person's earnings, in millions of dollars. We can write this correspondence using a set of ordered pairs:

{(Winfrey, 315), (Cowell, 80), (McGraw, 80), (DeGeneres, 55), (Seacrest, 51)}.

These braces indicate we are representing a set.

The mathematical term for a set of ordered pairs is a *relation*.

Definition of a Relation

A **relation** is any set of ordered pairs. The set of all first components of the ordered pairs is called the **domain** of the relation and the set of all second components is called the **range** of the relation.

EXAMPLE 1   Finding the Domain and Range of a Relation

Find the domain and range of the relation:

{(Winfrey, 315), (Cowell, 80), (McGraw, 80), (DeGeneres, 55), (Seacrest, 51)}.

SOLUTION

The domain is the set of all first components. Thus, the domain is

{Winfrey, Cowell, McGraw, DeGeneres, Seacrest}.

The range is the set of all second components. Thus, the range is

{315, 80, 55, 51}.

> Although Cowell and McGraw both earned $80 million, it is not necessary to list 80 twice.

• • •

⊘ Check Point **1** Find the domain and range of the relation:
{(0, 9.1), (10, 6.7), (20, 10.7), (30, 13.2), (40, 21.2)}.

As you worked Check Point 1, did you wonder if there was a rule that assigned the "inputs" in the domain to the "outputs" in the range? For example, for the ordered pair (30, 13.2), how does the output 13.2 depend on the input 30? The ordered pair is based on the data in **Figure 2.2(a)**, which shows the percentage of first-year U.S. college students claiming no religious affiliation.

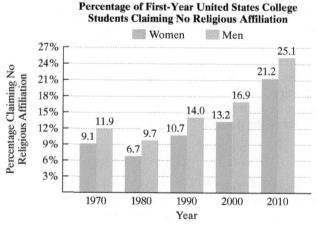

FIGURE 2.2(a) Data for women and men
Source: John Macionis, *Sociology*, Fourteenth Edition, Pearson, 2012.

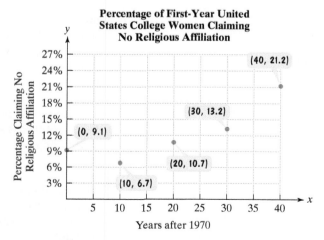

FIGURE 2.2(b) Visually representing the relation for the women's data

Percentage of First-Year United States College Women Claiming No Religious Affiliation

FIGURE 2.2(b) (repeated)
Visually representing the relation for the women's data

In **Figure 2.2(b)**, we used the data for college women to create the following ordered pairs:

$$\left(\text{years after 1970,} \quad \begin{array}{l} \text{percentage of first-year college} \\ \text{women claiming no religious} \\ \text{affiliation} \end{array} \right).$$

Consider, for example, the ordered pair (30, 13.2).

(30, 13.2)

The five points in **Figure 2.2(b)** visually represent the relation formed from the women's data. Another way to visually represent the relation is as follows:

Domain	Range
0	9.1
10	6.7
20	10.7
30	13.2
40	21.2

② Determine whether a relation is a function.

Table 2.1 Highest-Paid TV Celebrities

Celebrity	Earnings (millions of dollars)
Winfrey	315
Cowell	80
McGraw	80
DeGeneres	55
Seacrest	51

Functions

Table 2.1, based on our earlier discussion, shows the highest-paid TV celebrities and their earnings between June 2010 and June 2011, in millions of dollars. We've used this information to define two relations.

Figure 2.3(a) shows a correspondence between celebrities and their earnings. **Figure 2.3(b)** shows a correspondence between earnings and celebrities.

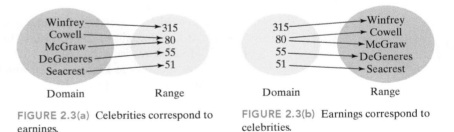

FIGURE 2.3(a) Celebrities correspond to earnings.

FIGURE 2.3(b) Earnings correspond to celebrities.

A relation in which each member of the domain corresponds to exactly one member of the range is a **function**. Can you see that the relation in **Figure 2.3(a)** is a function? Each celebrity in the domain corresponds to exactly one earnings amount in the range: If we know the celebrity, we can be sure of his or her earnings. Notice that more than one element in the domain can correspond to the same element in the range: Cowell and McGraw both earned $80 million.

Is the relation in **Figure 2.3(b)** a function? Does each member of the domain correspond to precisely one member of the range? This relation is not a function because there is a member of the domain that corresponds to two different members of the range:

(80, Cowell)   (80, McGraw).

The member of the domain 80 corresponds to both Cowell and McGraw in the range. If we know that earnings are $80 million, we cannot be sure of the celebrity. Because **a function is a relation in which no two ordered pairs have the same first component and different second components**, the ordered pairs (80, Cowell) and (80, McGraw) are not ordered pairs of a function.

Same first component

$(80, \text{Cowell})$ $(80, \text{McGraw})$

Different second components

Definition of a Function

A **function** is a correspondence from a first set, called the **domain**, to a second set, called the **range**, such that each element in the domain corresponds to *exactly one* element in the range.

In Check Point 1, we considered a relation that gave a correspondence between years after 1970 and the percentage of first-year college women claiming no religious affiliation. Can you see that this relation is a function?

Each element in the domain

$\{(0, 9.1), (10, 6.7), (20, 10.7), (30, 13.2), (40, 21.2)\}$

corresponds to exactly one element in the range.

However, Example 2 illustrates that not every correspondence between sets is a function.

EXAMPLE 2   Determining Whether a Relation Is a Function

Determine whether each relation is a function:

a. $\{(1, 6), (2, 6), (3, 8), (4, 9)\}$ **b.** $\{(6, 1), (6, 2), (8, 3), (9, 4)\}$.

SOLUTION

We begin by making a figure for each relation that shows the domain and the range (**Figure 2.4**).

Domain   Range

FIGURE 2.4(a)

Domain   Range

FIGURE 2.4(b)

a. Figure 2.4(a) shows that every element in the domain corresponds to exactly one element in the range. The element 1 in the domain corresponds to the element 6 in the range. Furthermore, 2 corresponds to 6, 3 corresponds to 8, and 4 corresponds to 9. No two ordered pairs in the given relation have the same first component and different second components. Thus, the relation is a function.

b. Figure 2.4(b) shows that 6 corresponds to both 1 and 2. If any element in the domain corresponds to more than one element in the range, the relation is not a function. This relation is not a function; two ordered pairs have the same first component and different second components.

Same first component

$(6, 1)$ $(6, 2)$

Different second components

• • •

Look at **Figure 2.4(a)** again. The fact that 1 and 2 in the domain correspond to the same number, 6, in the range does not violate the definition of a function. **A function can have two different first components with the same second component.** By contrast, a relation is not a function when two different ordered pairs have the same first component and different second components. Thus, the relation in **Figure 2.4(b)** is not a function.

GREAT QUESTION!

If I reverse a function's components, will this new relation be a function?

If a relation is a function, reversing the components in each of its ordered pairs may result in a relation that is not a function.

⊘ Check Point **2** Determine whether each relation is a function:

    a. $\{(1, 2), (3, 4), (5, 6), (5, 8)\}$ **b.** $\{(1, 2), (3, 4), (6, 5), (8, 5)\}$.

③ Determine whether an equation represents a function.

Functions as Equations

Functions are usually given in terms of equations rather than as sets of ordered pairs. For example, here is an equation that models the percentage of first-year college women claiming no religious affiliation as a function of time:

$$y = 0.014x^2 - 0.24x + 8.8.$$

The variable x represents the number of years after 1970. The variable y represents the percentage of first-year college women claiming no religious affiliation. The variable y is a function of the variable x. For each value of x, there is one and only one value of y. The variable x is called the **independent variable** because it can be assigned any value from the domain. Thus, x can be assigned any nonnegative integer representing the number of years after 1970. The variable y is called the **dependent variable** because its value depends on x. The percentage claiming no religious affiliation depends on the number of years after 1970. The value of the dependent variable, y, is calculated after selecting a value for the independent variable, x.

We have seen that not every set of ordered pairs defines a function. Similarly, not all equations with the variables x and y define functions. If an equation is solved for y and more than one value of y can be obtained for a given x, then the equation does not define y as a function of x.

EXAMPLE 3   Determining Whether an Equation Represents a Function

Determine whether each equation defines y as a function of x:

    a. $x^2 + y = 4$ **b.** $x^2 + y^2 = 4$.

SOLUTION

Solve each equation for y in terms of x. If two or more values of y can be obtained for a given x, the equation is not a function.

a. $x^2 + y = 4$ This is the given equation.

     $x^2 + y - x^2 = 4 - x^2$ Solve for y by subtracting x^2 from both sides.

     $y = 4 - x^2$ Simplify.

From this last equation we can see that for each value of x, there is one and only one value of y. For example, if $x = 1$, then $y = 4 - 1^2 = 3$. The equation defines y as a function of x.

b. $x^2 + y^2 = 4$ This is the given equation.

     $x^2 + y^2 - x^2 = 4 - x^2$ Isolate y^2 by subtracting x^2 from both sides.

     $y^2 = 4 - x^2$ Simplify.

     $y = \pm\sqrt{4 - x^2}$ Apply the square root property: If $u^2 = d$, then $u = \pm\sqrt{d}$.

The $\pm$ in this last equation shows that for certain values of x (all values between -2 and 2), there are two values of y. For example, if $x = 1$, then $y = \pm\sqrt{4 - 1^2} = \pm\sqrt{3}$. For this reason, the equation does not define y as a function of x.

• • •

⊘ Check Point **3** Solve each equation for y and then determine whether the equation defines y as a function of x:

a. $2x + y = 6$ **b.** $x^2 + y^2 = 1$.

④ Evaluate a function.

Function Notation

If an equation in x and y gives one and only one value of y for each value of x, then the variable y is a function of the variable x. When an equation represents a function, the function is often named by a letter such as f, g, h, F, G, or H. Any letter can be used to name a function. Suppose that f names a function. Think of the domain as the set of the function's inputs and the range as the set of the function's outputs. As shown in **Figure 2.5**, input is represented by x and the output by $f(x)$. The special notation $f(x)$, read "f of x" or "f at x," represents the **value of the function at the number x**.

Let's make this clearer by considering a specific example. We know that the equation

$$y = 0.014x^2 - 0.24x + 8.8$$

defines y as a function of x. We'll name the function f. Now, we can apply our new function notation.

FIGURE 2.5 A "function machine" with inputs and outputs

GREAT QUESTION!

Doesn't $f(x)$ indicate that I need to multiply f and x?

The notation $f(x)$ does *not* mean "f times x." The notation describes the value of the function at x.

Input	Output	Equation
x	$f(x)$	$f(x) = 0.014x^2 - 0.24x + 8.8$

We read this equation as "f of x equals $0.014x^2 - 0.24x + 8.8$."

Suppose we are interested in finding $f(30)$, the function's output when the input is 30. To find the value of the function at 30, we substitute 30 for x. We are **evaluating the function** at 30.

$f(x) = 0.014x^2 - 0.24x + 8.8$ This is the given function.

$f(30) = 0.014(30)^2 - 0.24(30) + 8.8$ Replace each occurrence of x with 30.

$= 0.014(900) - 0.24(30) + 8.8$ Evaluate the exponential expression: $30^2 = 30 \cdot 30 = 900$.

$= 12.6 - 7.2 + 8.8$ Perform the multiplications.

$f(30) = 14.2$ Subtract and add from left to right.

The statement $f(30) = 14.2$, read "f of 30 equals 14.2," tells us that the value of the function at 30 is 14.2. When the function's input is 30, its output is 14.2. **Figure 2.6** illustrates the input and output in terms of a function machine.

Input $x = 30$ $f(x) = 0.014x^2 - 0.24x + 8.8$

$0.014(30)^2 - 0.24(30) + 8.8$

Output $f(30) = 14.2$

FIGURE 2.6 A function machine at work

$$f(30) = 14.2$$

30 years after 1970, or in 2000,   14.2% of first-year college women claimed no religious affiliation.

We have seen that in 2000, 13.2% actually claimed nonaffiliation, so our function that models the data slightly overestimates the percent for 2000.

TECHNOLOGY

Graphing utilities can be used to evaluate functions. The screens below show the evaluation of

$$f(x) = 0.014x^2 - 0.24x + 8.8$$

at 30 on a TI-84 Plus graphing calculator. The function f is named Y_1.

 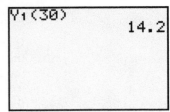

We used $f(x) = 0.014x^2 - 0.24x + 8.8$ to find $f(30)$. To find other function values, such as $f(40)$ or $f(55)$, substitute the specified input value, 40 or 55, for x in the function's equation.

If a function is named f and x represents the independent variable, the notation $f(x)$ corresponds to the y-value for a given x. Thus,

$$f(x) = 0.014x^2 - 0.24x + 8.8 \quad \text{and} \quad y = 0.014x^2 - 0.24x + 8.8$$

define the same function. This function may be written as

$$y = f(x) = 0.014x^2 - 0.24x + 8.8.$$

EXAMPLE 4 Evaluating a Function

If $f(x) = x^2 + 3x + 5$, evaluate each of the following:

    a. $f(2)$ **b.** $f(x + 3)$ **c.** $f(-x)$.

SOLUTION

We substitute 2, $x + 3$, and $-x$ for x in the equation for f. When replacing x with a variable or an algebraic expression, you might find it helpful to think of the function's equation as

$$f(x) = \boxed{x}^2 + 3\boxed{x} + 5.$$

a. We find $f(2)$ by substituting 2 for x in the equation.

$$f(2) = 2^2 + 3 \cdot 2 + 5 = 4 + 6 + 5 = 15$$

   Thus, $f(2) = 15$.

b. We find $f(x + 3)$ by substituting $x + 3$ for x in the equation.

$$f(x + 3) = (x + 3)^2 + 3(x + 3) + 5$$

   Equivalently,

$$f(x + 3) = (x + 3)^2 + 3(x + 3) + 5$$
$$= x^2 + 6x + 9 + 3x + 9 + 5 \quad \text{Square } x + 3 \text{ using}$$
$$(A + B)^2 = A^2 + 2AB + B^2.$$
$$\text{Distribute 3 throughout the parentheses.}$$
$$= x^2 + 9x + 23. \quad \text{Combine like terms.}$$

c. We find $f(-x)$ by substituting $-x$ for x in the equation.

$$f(-x) = (-x)^2 + 3(-x) + 5$$

   Equivalently,

$$f(-x) = (-x)^2 + 3(-x) + 5$$
$$= x^2 - 3x + 5.$$

      • • •

DISCOVERY

Using $f(x) = x^2 + 3x + 5$ and the answers in parts (b) and (c):

1. Is $f(x + 3)$ equal to $f(x) + f(3)$?

2. Is $f(-x)$ equal to $-f(x)$?

⌀ Check Point **4** If $f(x) = x^2 - 2x + 7$, evaluate each of the following:

    a. $f(-5)$ **b.** $f(x + 4)$ **c.** $f(-x)$.

⑤ Graph functions by plotting points.

Graphs of Functions

The **graph of a function** is the graph of its ordered pairs. For example, the graph of $f(x) = 2x$ is the set of points (x, y) in the rectangular coordinate system satisfying $y = 2x$. Similarly, the graph of $g(x) = 2x + 4$ is the set of points (x, y) in the rectangular coordinate system satisfying the equation $y = 2x + 4$. In the next example, we graph both of these functions in the same rectangular coordinate system.

EXAMPLE 5   Graphing Functions

Graph the functions $f(x) = 2x$ and $g(x) = 2x + 4$ in the same rectangular coordinate system. Select integers for x, starting with -2 and ending with 2.

SOLUTION

We begin by setting up a partial table of coordinates for each function. Then we plot the five points in each table and connect them, as shown in **Figure 2.7**. The graph of each function is a straight line. Do you see a relationship between the two graphs? The graph of g is the graph of f shifted vertically up by 4 units.

FIGURE 2.7

x	$f(x) = 2x$	(x, y) or $(x, f(x))$
-2	$f(-2) = 2(-2) = -4$	$(-2, -4)$
-1	$f(-1) = 2(-1) = -2$	$(-1, -2)$
0	$f(0) = 2 \cdot 0 = 0$	$(0, 0)$
1	$f(1) = 2 \cdot 1 = 2$	$(1, 2)$
2	$f(2) = 2 \cdot 2 = 4$	$(2, 4)$

Choose x.   Compute $f(x)$ by evaluating f at x.   Form the ordered pair.

x	$g(x) = 2x + 4$	(x, y) or $(x, g(x))$
-2	$g(-2) = 2(-2) + 4 = 0$	$(-2, 0)$
-1	$g(-1) = 2(-1) + 4 = 2$	$(-1, 2)$
0	$g(0) = 2 \cdot 0 + 4 = 4$	$(0, 4)$
1	$g(1) = 2 \cdot 1 + 4 = 6$	$(1, 6)$
2	$g(2) = 2 \cdot 2 + 4 = 8$	$(2, 8)$

Choose x.   Compute $g(x)$ by evaluating g at x.   Form the ordered pair.

• • •

The graphs in Example 5 are straight lines. All functions with equations of the form $f(x) = mx + b$ graph as straight lines. Such functions, called **linear functions**, will be discussed in detail in Section 2.3.

TECHNOLOGY

We can use a graphing utility to check the tables and the graphs in Example 5 for the functions

$$f(x) = 2x \quad \text{and} \quad g(x) = 2x + 4.$$

Enter $y_1 = 2x$ in the $\boxed{y=}$ screen.   Enter $y_2 = 2x + 4$ in the $\boxed{y=}$ screen.

We entered -2 for the starting x-value and 1 as an increment between x-values to check our tables in Example 5.

Checking Tables

Use the first five ordered pairs (x, y_1) to check the first table.

Use the first five ordered pairs (x, y_2) to check the second table.

Checking Graphs

$y_2 = 2x + 4$

$y_1 = 2x$

$[-6, 6, 1]$ by $[-6, 9, 1]$

We selected this viewing rectangle, or window, to match **Figure 2.7**.

Check Point **5** Graph the functions $f(x) = 2x$ and $g(x) = 2x - 3$ in the same rectangular coordinate system. Select integers for x, starting with -2 and ending with 2. How is the graph of g related to the graph of f?

⑥ Use the vertical line test to identify functions.

The Vertical Line Test

Not every graph in the rectangular coordinate system is the graph of a function. The definition of a function specifies that no value of x can be paired with two or more different values of y. Consequently, if a graph contains two or more different points with the same first coordinate, the graph cannot represent a function. This is illustrated in **Figure 2.8**. Observe that points sharing a common first coordinate are vertically above or below each other.

This observation is the basis of a useful test for determining whether a graph defines y as a function of x. The test is called the **vertical line test**.

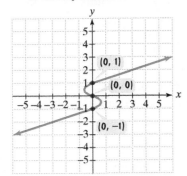

FIGURE 2.8 y is not a function of x because 0 is paired with three values of y, namely, $1, 0,$ and -1.

The Vertical Line Test for Functions

If any vertical line intersects a graph in more than one point, the graph does not define y as a function of x.

EXAMPLE 6   Using the Vertical Line Test

Use the vertical line test to identify graphs in which y is a function of x.

a.   b.   c.   d.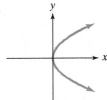

SOLUTION

y is a function of x for the graphs in (b) and (c).

a.   b.   c.   d.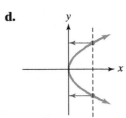

y is **not a function** of x.
Two values of y
correspond to an x-value.

y is **a function** of x.

y is **a function** of x.

y is **not a function of** x.
Two values of y
correspond to an x-value.

• • •

 Check Point **6** Use the vertical line test to identify graphs in which y is a function of x.

a.   b.   c.   d.

7 Obtain information about a function from its graph.

Obtaining Information from Graphs

You can obtain information about a function from its graph. At the right or left of a graph, you will find closed dots, open dots, or arrows.

- A closed dot indicates that the graph does not extend beyond this point and the point belongs to the graph.
- An open dot indicates that the graph does not extend beyond this point and the point does not belong to the graph.
- An arrow indicates that the graph extends indefinitely in the direction in which the arrow points.

EXAMPLE 7 Analyzing the Graph of a Function

The human immunodeficiency virus, or HIV, infects and kills helper T cells. Because T cells stimulate the immune system to produce antibodies, their destruction disables the body's defenses against other pathogens. By counting the number of T cells that remain active in the body, the progression of HIV can be monitored. The fewer helper T cells, the more advanced the disease. **Figure 2.9** shows a graph that is used to monitor the average progression of the disease. The average number of T cells, $f(x)$, is a function of time after infection, x.

FIGURE 2.9

Source: B. E. Pruitt et al., *Human Sexuality,* Prentice Hall, 2007.

a. Explain why f represents the graph of a function.
b. Use the graph to find $f(8)$.
c. For what value of x is $f(x) = 350$?
d. Describe the general trend shown by the graph.

SOLUTION

a. No vertical line can be drawn that intersects the graph of f more than once. By the vertical line test, f represents the graph of a function.

b. To find $f(8)$, or f of 8, we locate 8 on the x-axis. **Figure 2.10** shows the point on the graph of f for which 8 is the first coordinate. From this point, we look to the y-axis to find the corresponding y-coordinate. We see that the y-coordinate is 200. Thus,

$$f(8) = 200.$$

When the time after infection is 8 years, the average T cell count is 200 cells per milliliter of blood. (AIDS clinical diagnosis is given at a T cell count of 200 or below.)

FIGURE 2.10 Finding $f(8)$

c. To find the value of x for which $f(x) = 350$, we find the approximate location of 350 on the y-axis. **Figure 2.11** shows that there is one point on the graph of f for which 350 is the second coordinate. From this point, we look to the x-axis to find the corresponding x-coordinate. We see that the x-coordinate is 6. Thus,

$$f(x) = 350 \text{ for } x = 6.$$

An average T cell count of 350 occurs 6 years after infection.

FIGURE 2.11 Finding x for which $f(x) = 350$

d. **Figure 2.12** uses voice balloons to describe the general trend shown by the graph.

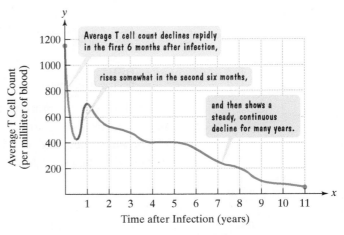

FIGURE 2.12 Describing changing T cell count over time in a person infected with HIV

$\bullet\bullet\bullet$

✓ Check Point 7

a. Use the graph of f in **Figure 2.9** on page 219 to find $f(5)$.

b. For what value of x is $f(x) = 100$?

c. Estimate the minimum average T cell count during the asymptomatic stage.

⑧ Identify the domain and range of a function from its graph.

Identifying Domain and Range from a Function's Graph

GREAT QUESTION!

I peeked below and saw that you are using interval notation. What should I already know about this notation?

Recall that square brackets indicate endpoints that are included in an interval. Parentheses indicate endpoints that are not included in an interval. Parentheses are always used with ∞ or $-\infty$. For more detail on interval notation, see Section 1.7, pages 183–184.

Figure 2.13 illustrates how the graph of a function is used to determine the function's domain and its range.

Domain: set of inputs

Found on the x-axis

Range: set of outputs

Found on the y-axis

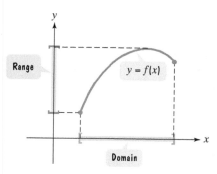

FIGURE 2.13 Domain and range of f

Let's apply these ideas to the graph of the function shown in **Figure 2.14**. To find the domain, look for all the inputs on the x-axis that correspond to points on the graph. Can you see that they extend from -4 to 2, inclusive? The function's domain can be represented as follows:

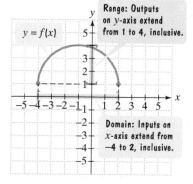

FIGURE 2.14 Domain and range of f

Using Set-Builder Notation

$$\{\, x \mid -4 \leq x \leq 2 \,\}$$

The set of all x such that x is greater than or equal to -4 and less than or equal to 2.

Using Interval Notation

$$[-4, 2].$$

The square brackets indicate -4 and 2 are included. Note the square brackets on the x-axis in **Figure 2.14**.

To find the range, look for all the outputs on the y-axis that correspond to points on the graph. They extend from 1 to 4, inclusive. The function's range can be represented as follows:

Using Set-Builder Notation

$$\{\, y \mid 1 \leq y \leq 4 \,\}$$

The set of all y such that y is greater than or equal to 1 and less than or equal to 4.

Using Interval Notation

$$[1, 4].$$

The square brackets indicate 1 and 4 are included. Note the square brackets on the y-axis in **Figure 2.14**.

EXAMPLE 8 Identifying the Domain and Range of a Function from Its Graph

Use the graph of each function to identify its domain and its range.

a.

b.

c.

d.

e.

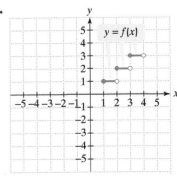

SOLUTION

For the graph of each function, the domain is highlighted in purple on the *x*-axis and the range is highlighted in green on the *y*-axis.

a.

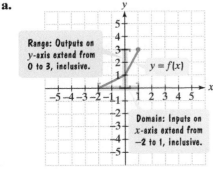

Range: Outputs on y-axis extend from 0 to 3, inclusive.

Domain: Inputs on x-axis extend from −2 to 1, inclusive.

Domain = $\{x | -2 \le x \le 1\}$ or $[-2, 1]$
Range = $\{y | 0 \le y \le 3\}$ or $[0, 3]$

b.

Range: Outputs on y-axis extend from 1, excluding 1, to 2, including 2.

Domain: Inputs on x-axis extend from −3, excluding −3, to 2, including 2.

Domain = $\{x | -3 < x \le 2\}$ or $(-3, 2]$
Range = $\{y | 1 < y \le 2\}$ or $(1, 2]$

c.

Range: Outputs on y-axis extend from 1 to 5, inclusive.

Domain: Inputs on x-axis extend from −2, including −2, to 1, excluding 1.

Domain = $\{x | -2 \le x < 1\}$ or $[-2, 1)$
Range = $\{y | 1 \le y \le 5\}$ or $[1, 5]$

GREAT QUESTION!

The range in Example 8(e) was identified as $\{y | y = 1, 2, 3\}$. Why didn't you also use interval notation like you did in the other parts of Example 8?

Interval notation is not appropriate for describing a set of distinct numbers such as $\{1, 2, 3\}$. Interval notation, $[1, 3]$, would mean that numbers such as 1.5 and 2.99 are in the range, but they are not. That's why we only used set-builder notation.

d.

Range: Outputs on y-axis include real numbers greater than or equal to 0.

Domain: Inputs on x-axis include real numbers less than or equal to 4.

Domain = $\{x | x \le 4\}$ or $(-\infty, 4]$
Range = $\{y | y \ge 0\}$ or $[0, \infty)$

e.

Range: Outputs on y-axis "step" from 1 to 2 to 3.

Domain: Inputs on x-axis extend from 1, including 1, to 4, excluding 4.

Domain = $\{x | 1 \le x < 4\}$ or $[1, 4)$
Range = $\{y | y = 1, 2, 3\}$

• • •

Ⓞ Check Point **8** Use the graph of each function to identify its domain and its range.

a.

b.

c.
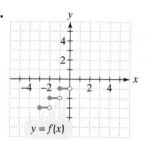

⑨ Identify intercepts from a function's graph.

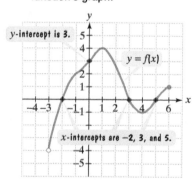

FIGURE 2.15 Identifying intercepts

Identifying Intercepts from a Function's Graph

Figure 2.15 illustrates how we can identify intercepts from a function's graph. To find the x-intercepts, look for the points at which the graph crosses the x-axis. There are three such points: $(-2, 0)$, $(3, 0)$, and $(5, 0)$. Thus, the x-intercepts are $-2, 3$, and 5. We express this in function notation by writing $f(-2) = 0$, $f(3) = 0$, and $f(5) = 0$. We say that $-2, 3$, and 5 are the *zeros of the function*. The **zeros of a function** f are the x-values for which $f(x) = 0$. Thus, the real zeros are the x-intercepts.

To find the y-intercept, look for the point at which the graph crosses the y-axis. This occurs at $(0, 3)$. Thus, the y-intercept is 3. We express this in function notation by writing $f(0) = 3$.

By the definition of a function, for each value of x we can have at most one value for y. What does this mean in terms of intercepts? **A function can have more than one x-intercept but at most one y-intercept.**

CONCEPT AND VOCABULARY CHECK

Fill in each blank so that the resulting statement is true.

1. Any set of ordered pairs is called a/an _____. The set of all first components of the ordered pairs is called the _____. The set of all second components of the ordered pairs is called the _____.
2. A set of ordered pairs in which each member of the set of first components corresponds to exactly one member of the set of second components is called a/an _____.
3. The notation $f(x)$ describes the value of _____ at _____.
4. True or false: $y = x^2 - 1$ defines y as a function of x. _____
5. True or false : $y = \pm\sqrt{x^2 - 1}$ defines y as a function of x. _____
6. If $f(x) = x^2 - 5x + 4$, we can find $f(x + 6)$ by replacing each occurrence of _____ by _____.
7. The graph of a function is the graph of its _____.
8. If any vertical line intersects a graph _____, the graph does not define y as a/an _____ of x.

9. The shaded set of numbers shown on the x-axis can be expressed in interval notation as _____. This set represents the function's _____.

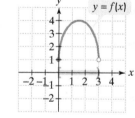

10. The shaded set of numbers shown on the y-axis can be expressed in interval notation as _____. This set represents the function's _____.

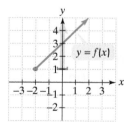

11. If the x-intercepts of a function are -1 and 3, then $f(-1) = $ ____ and $f(3) = $ ____. The x-intercepts, -1 and 3, are called the _____ of the function.
12. True or false: A function can have more than one y-intercept. _____

EXERCISE SET 2.1

Practice Exercises

In Exercises 1–10, determine whether each relation is a function. Give the domain and range for each relation.

1. $\{(1, 2), (3, 4), (5, 5)\}$
2. $\{(4, 5), (6, 7), (8, 8)\}$
3. $\{(3, 4), (3, 5), (4, 4), (4, 5)\}$
4. $\{(5, 6), (5, 7), (6, 6), (6, 7)\}$
5. $\{(3, -2), (5, -2), (7, 1), (4, 9)\}$
6. $\{(10, 4), (-2, 4), (-1, 1), (5, 6)\}$
7. $\{(-3, -3), (-2, -2), (-1, -1), (0, 0)\}$
8. $\{(-7, -7), (-5, -5), (-3, -3), (0, 0)\}$
9. $\{(1, 4), (1, 5), (1, 6)\}$
10. $\{(4, 1), (5, 1), (6, 1)\}$

In Exercises 11–26, determine whether each equation defines y as a function of x.

11. $x + y = 16$
12. $x + y = 25$
13. $x^2 + y = 16$
14. $x^2 + y = 25$
15. $x^2 + y^2 = 16$
16. $x^2 + y^2 = 25$
17. $x = y^2$
18. $4x = y^2$
19. $y = \sqrt{x + 4}$
20. $y = -\sqrt{x + 4}$
21. $x + y^3 = 8$
22. $x + y^3 = 27$
23. $xy + 2y = 1$
24. $xy - 5y = 1$
25. $|x| - y = 2$
26. $|x| - y = 5$

In Exercises 27–38, evaluate each function at the given values of the independent variable and simplify.

27. $f(x) = 4x + 5$
  a. $f(6)$ **b.** $f(x + 1)$ **c.** $f(-x)$

28. $f(x) = 3x + 7$
  a. $f(4)$ **b.** $f(x + 1)$ **c.** $f(-x)$

29. $g(x) = x^2 + 2x + 3$
  a. $g(-1)$ **b.** $g(x + 5)$ **c.** $g(-x)$

30. $g(x) = x^2 - 10x - 3$
  a. $g(-1)$ **b.** $g(x + 2)$ **c.** $g(-x)$

31. $h(x) = x^4 - x^2 + 1$
  a. $h(2)$ **b.** $h(-1)$
  c. $h(-x)$ **d.** $h(3a)$

32. $h(x) = x^3 - x + 1$
  a. $h(3)$ **b.** $h(-2)$
  c. $h(-x)$ **d.** $h(3a)$

33. $f(r) = \sqrt{r + 6} + 3$
  a. $f(-6)$ **b.** $f(10)$ **c.** $f(x - 6)$

34. $f(r) = \sqrt{25 - r} - 6$
  a. $f(16)$ **b.** $f(-24)$ **c.** $f(25 - 2x)$

35. $f(x) = \dfrac{4x^2 - 1}{x^2}$
  a. $f(2)$ **b.** $f(-2)$ **c.** $f(-x)$

36. $f(x) = \dfrac{4x^3 + 1}{x^3}$
  a. $f(2)$ **b.** $f(-2)$ **c.** $f(-x)$

37. $f(x) = \dfrac{x}{|x|}$
  a. $f(6)$ **b.** $f(-6)$ **c.** $f(r^2)$

38. $f(x) = \dfrac{|x + 3|}{x + 3}$
  a. $f(5)$ **b.** $f(-5)$ **c.** $f(-9 - x)$

In Exercises 39–50, graph the given functions, f and g, in the same rectangular coordinate system. Select integers for x, starting with −2 and ending with 2. Once you have obtained your graphs, describe how the graph of g is related to the graph of f.

39. $f(x) = x, g(x) = x + 3$
40. $f(x) = x, g(x) = x - 4$
41. $f(x) = -2x, g(x) = -2x - 1$
42. $f(x) = -2x, g(x) = -2x + 3$
43. $f(x) = x^2, g(x) = x^2 + 1$
44. $f(x) = x^2, g(x) = x^2 - 2$
45. $f(x) = |x|, g(x) = |x| - 2$
46. $f(x) = |x|, g(x) = |x| + 1$
47. $f(x) = x^3, g(x) = x^3 + 2$
48. $f(x) = x^3, g(x) = x^3 - 1$
49. $f(x) = 3, g(x) = 5$
50. $f(x) = -1, g(x) = 4$

In Exercises 51–54, graph the given square root functions, f and g, in the same rectangular coordinate system. Use the integer values of x given to the right of each function to obtain ordered pairs. Because only nonnegative numbers have square roots that are real numbers, be sure that each graph appears only for values of x that cause the expression under the radical sign to be greater than or equal to zero. Once you have obtained your graphs, describe how the graph of g is related to the graph of f.

51. $f(x) = \sqrt{x}$ $(x = 0, 1, 4, 9)$ and
    $g(x) = \sqrt{x} - 1$ $(x = 0, 1, 4, 9)$

52. $f(x) = \sqrt{x}$ $(x = 0, 1, 4, 9)$ and
    $g(x) = \sqrt{x} + 2$ $(x = 0, 1, 4, 9)$

53. $f(x) = \sqrt{x}$ $(x = 0, 1, 4, 9)$ and
    $g(x) = \sqrt{x - 1}$ $(x = 1, 2, 5, 10)$

54. $f(x) = \sqrt{x}$ $(x = 0, 1, 4, 9)$ and
    $g(x) = \sqrt{x + 2}$ $(x = -2, -1, 2, 7)$

In Exercises 55–64, use the vertical line test to identify graphs in which y is a function of x.

55.

56.

57.

58.

59.

60.

61.

62.

63.

64.

In Exercises 65–70, use the graph of f to find each indicated function value.

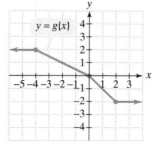

65. $f(-2)$

66. $f(2)$

67. $f(4)$

68. $f(-4)$

69. $f(-3)$

70. $f(-1)$

Use the graph of g to solve Exercises 71–76.

71. Find $g(-4)$.

72. Find $g(2)$.

73. Find $g(-10)$.

74. Find $g(10)$.

75. For what value of x is $g(x) = 1$?

76. For what value of x is $g(x) = -1$?

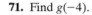

In Exercises 77–92, use the graph to determine **a.** the function's domain; **b.** the function's range; **c.** the x-intercepts, if any; **d.** the y-intercept, if any; and **e.** the missing function values, indicated by question marks, below each graph.

77.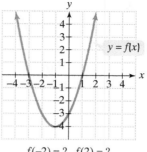

$f(-2) = ?$ $f(2) = ?$

78.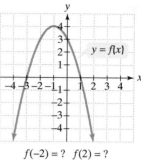

$f(-2) = ?$ $f(2) = ?$

79.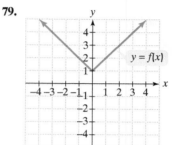

$f(-1) = ?$ $f(3) = ?$

80.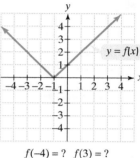

$f(-4) = ?$ $f(3) = ?$

81.

$f(3) = ?$

82.

$f(-4) = ?$

83.

$f(4) = ?$

84.

$f(3) = ?$

85.

$f(-1) = ?$

86.

$f(-2) = ?$

87.

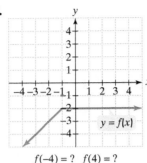

$f(-4) = ?$ $f(4) = ?$

88.

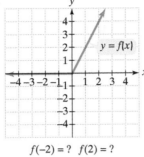

$f(-2) = ?$ $f(2) = ?$

89.

Graph approaches but never touches the x-axis.

$f(4) = ?$

90.

Graph approaches but never touches the dashed vertical line.

On both sides, graph never touches the x-axis.

$f(2) = ?$

91.

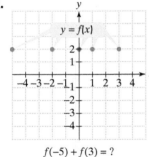

$f(-5) + f(3) = ?$

92.

$f(-5) + f(4) = ?$

Practice Plus

In Exercises 93–94, let $f(x) = x^2 - x + 4$ and $g(x) = 3x - 5$.

93. Find $g(1)$ and $f(g(1))$.   **94.** Find $g(-1)$ and $f(g(-1))$.

In Exercises 95–96, let f and g be defined by the following table:

x	$f(x)$	$g(x)$
-2	6	0
-1	3	4
0	-1	1
1	-4	-3
2	0	-6

95. Find $\sqrt{f(-1) - f(0)} - [g(2)]^2 + f(-2) \div g(2) \cdot g(-1)$.

96. Find $|f(1) - f(0)| - [g(1)]^2 + g(1) \div f(-1) \cdot g(2)$.

In Exercises 97–98, find $f(-x) - f(x)$ for the given function f. Then simplify the expression.

97. $f(x) = x^3 + x - 5$

98. $f(x) = x^2 - 3x + 7$

Application Exercises

The bar graph shows minimum legal ages for sex and marriage in five selected countries. Use this information to solve Exercises 99–100. (We did not include data for the United States because the legal age of sexual consent varies according to state law. Furthermore, women are allowed to marry younger than men: 16 for women and 18 for men.)

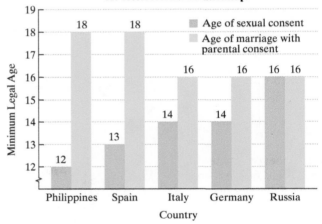

Minimum Legal Ages for Sex and Marriage, for Heterosexual Relationships

Source: Mitchell Beazley, *Snapshot: The Visual Almanac for Our World Today*. Octopus Publishing, 2009

99. a. Write a set of five ordered pairs in which countries correspond to the minimum legal age of sexual consent. Each ordered pair should be in the form

(country, minimum legal age of sexual consent).

   b. Is the relation in part (a) a function? Explain your answer.

   c. Write a set of five ordered pairs in which the minimum legal age of sexual consent corresponds to a country. Each ordered pair should be in the form

(minimum legal age of sexual consent, country).

   d. Is the relation in part (c) a function?

100. a. Write a set of five ordered pairs in which countries correspond to the minimum legal age of marriage with parental consent. Each ordered pair should be in the form

(country, minimum legal age of marriage with parental consent).

b. Is the relation in part (a) a function? Explain your answer.

c. Write a set of five ordered pairs in which the minimum legal age of marriage with parental consent corresponds to a country. Each ordered pair should be in the form

(minimum legal age of marriage with parental consent, country).

d. Is the relation in part (c) a function?

The bar graph shows your chances of surviving to various ages once you reach 60.

Chances of 60-Year-Olds Surviving to Various Ages

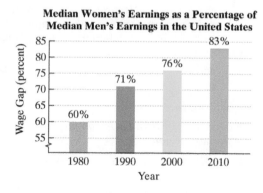

Source: National Center for Health Statistics

The functions

$$f(x) = -2.9x + 286$$

$$\text{and} \quad g(x) = 0.01x^2 - 4.9x + 370$$

model the chance, as a percent, that a 60-year-old will survive to age x. Use this information to solve Exercises 101–102.

101. a. Find and interpret $f(70)$.
   b. Find and interpret $g(70)$.
   c. Which function serves as a better model for the chance of surviving to age 70?

102. a. Find and interpret $f(90)$.
   b. Find and interpret $g(90)$.
   c. Which function serves as a better model for the chance of surviving to age 90?

The wage gap is used to compare the status of women's earnings relative to men's. The wage gap is expressed as a percent and is calculated by dividing the median, or middlemost, annual earnings for women by the median annual earnings for men. The bar graph shows the wage gap for selected years from 1980 through 2010.

Median Women's Earnings as a Percentage of Median Men's Earnings in the United States

The Graph of a Function Modeling the Data

$G(x) = -0.01x^2 + x + 60$

Years after 1980

Source: Bureau of Labor Statistics

The function $G(x) = -0.01x^2 + x + 60$ *models the wage gap, as a percent, x years after 1980. The graph of function G is shown to the right of the actual data. Use this information to solve Exercises 103–104.*

103. a. Find and interpret $G(30)$. Identify this information as a point on the graph of the function.
   b. Does $G(30)$ overestimate or underestimate the actual data shown by the bar graph? By how much?

104. a. Find and interpret $G(10)$. Identify this information as a point on the graph of the function.
   b. Does $G(10)$ overestimate or underestimate the actual data shown by the bar graph? By how much?

In Exercises 105–108, you will be developing functions that model given conditions.

105. A company that manufactures bicycles has a fixed cost of $100,000. It costs $100 to produce each bicycle. The total cost for the company is the sum of its fixed cost and variable costs. Write the total cost, C, as a function of the number of bicycles produced, x. Then find and interpret $C(90)$.

106. A car was purchased for $22,500. The value of the car decreased by $3200 per year for the first six years. Write a function that describes the value of the car, V, after x years, where $0 \le x \le 6$. Then find and interpret $V(3)$.

107. You commute to work a distance of 40 miles and return on the same route at the end of the day. Your average rate on the return trip is 30 miles per hour faster than your average rate on the outgoing trip. Write the total time, T, in hours, devoted to your outgoing and return trips as a function of your rate on the outgoing trip, x. Then find and interpret $T(30)$. Hint:

$$\text{Time traveled} = \frac{\text{Distance traveled}}{\text{Rate of travel}}.$$

108. A chemist working on a flu vaccine needs to mix a 10% sodium-iodine solution with a 60% sodium-iodine solution to obtain a 50-milliliter mixture. Write the amount of sodium iodine in the mixture, S, in milliliters, as a function of the number of milliliters of the 10% solution used, x. Then find and interpret $S(30)$.

Writing in Mathematics

109. What is a relation? Describe what is meant by its domain and its range.

110. Explain how to determine whether a relation is a function. What is a function?

111. How do you determine if an equation in x and y defines y as a function of x?

112. Does $f(x)$ mean f times x when referring to a function f? If not, what does $f(x)$ mean? Provide an example with your explanation.

113. What is the graph of a function?

114. Explain how the vertical line test is used to determine whether a graph represents a function.

115. Explain how to identify the domain and range of a function from its graph.

116. For people filing a single return, federal income tax is a function of adjusted gross income because for each value of adjusted gross income there is a specific tax to be paid. By contrast, the price of a house is not a function of the lot size on which the house sits because houses on same-sized lots can sell for many different prices.
   a. Describe an everyday situation between variables that is a function.
   b. Describe an everyday situation between variables that is not a function.

Technology Exercise

117. Use a graphing utility to verify any five pairs of graphs that you drew by hand in Exercises 39–54.

Critical Thinking Exercises

Make Sense? *In Exercises 118–121, determine whether each statement makes sense or does not make sense, and explain your reasoning.*

118. My body temperature is a function of the time of day.

119. Using $f(x) = 3x + 2$, I found $f(50)$ by applying the distributive property to $(3x + 2)50$.

120. I graphed a function showing how paid vacation days depend on the number of years a person works for a company. The domain was the number of paid vacation days.

121. I graphed a function showing how the average number of annual physician visits depends on a person's age. The domain was the average number of annual physician visits.

Use the graph of f to determine whether each statement in Exercises 122–125 is true or false.

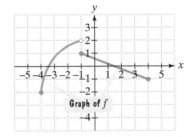

122. The domain of f is $[-4, -1) \cup (-1, 4]$.

123. The range of f is $[-2, 2]$.

124. $f(-1) - f(4) = 2$

125. $f(0) = 2.1$

126. If $f(x) = 3x + 7$, find $\dfrac{f(a + h) - f(a)}{h}$.

127. Give an example of a relation with the following characteristics: The relation is a function containing two ordered pairs. Reversing the components in each ordered pair results in a relation that is not a function.

128. If $f(x + y) = f(x) + f(y)$ and $f(1) = 3$, find $f(2), f(3)$, and $f(4)$. Is $f(x + y) = f(x) + f(y)$ for all functions?

Preview Exercises

Exercises 129–131 will help you prepare for the material covered in the next section.

129. The function $C(t) = 20 + 0.40 (t - 60)$ describes the monthly cost, $C(t)$, in dollars, for a cellphone plan for t calling minutes, where $t > 60$. Find and interpret $C(100)$.

130. Use point plotting to graph $f(x) = x + 2$ if $x \le 1$.

131. Simplify: $2(x + h)^2 + 3(x + h) + 5 - (2x^2 + 3x + 5)$.

SECTION 2.2   More on Functions and Their Graphs

Objectives

1. Identify intervals on which a function increases, decreases, or is constant.
2. Use graphs to locate relative maxima or minima.
3. Identify even or odd functions and recognize their symmetries.
4. Understand and use piecewise functions.
5. Find and simplify a function's difference quotient.

It's hard to believe that this gas-guzzler, with its huge fins and overstated design, was available in 1957 for approximately $1800. The line graph in **Figure 2.16** shows the average fuel efficiency, in miles per gallon, of new U.S. passenger cars for selected years from 1955 through 2009. Based on the averages shown by the graph, it's unlikely that this classic 1957 Chevy got more than 15 miles per gallon.

FIGURE 2.16
Source: U.S. Department of Transportation

You are probably familiar with the words used to describe the graph in **Figure 2.16**:

> decreased   increased   minimum   maximum

In this section, you will enhance your intuitive understanding of ways of describing graphs by viewing these descriptions from the perspective of functions.

1. Identify intervals on which a function increases, decreases, or is constant.

Increasing and Decreasing Functions

Too late for that flu shot now! It's only 8 A.M. and you're feeling lousy. Your temperature is 101°F. Fascinated by the way that algebra models the world (your author is projecting a bit here), you decide to construct graphs showing your body temperature as a function of the time of day. You decide to let x represent the number of hours after 8 A.M. and $f(x)$ your temperature at time x.

At 8 A.M. your temperature is 101°F and you are not feeling well. However, your temperature starts to decrease. It reaches normal (98.6°F) by 11 A.M. Feeling energized, you construct the graph shown on the right, indicating decreasing temperature for $\{x \mid 0 < x < 3\}$, or on the interval $(0, 3)$.

Temperature decreases on $(0, 3)$, reaching 98.6° by 11 A.M.

Did creating that first graph drain you of your energy? Your temperature starts to rise after 11 A.M. By 1 P.M., 5 hours after 8 A.M., your temperature reaches 100°F. However, you keep plotting points on your graph. At the right, we can see that your temperature increases for $\{x \mid 3 < x < 5\}$, or on the interval $(3, 5)$.

The graph of f is decreasing to the left of $x = 3$ and increasing to the right of $x = 3$. Thus, your temperature 3 hours after 8 A.M. was at its lowest point. Your relative minimum temperature was 98.6°.

Temperature increases on $(3, 5)$.

By 3 P.M., your temperature is no worse than it was at 1 P.M.: It is still 100°F. (Of course, it's no better, either.) Your temperature remained the same, or constant, for $\{x \mid 5 < x < 7\}$, or on the interval $(5, 7)$.

The time-temperature flu scenario illustrates that a function f is increasing when its graph rises from left to right, decreasing when its graph falls from left to right, and remains constant when it neither rises nor falls. Let's now provide a more precise algebraic description for these intuitive concepts.

Temperature remains constant at 100° on $(5, 7)$.

Increasing, Decreasing, and Constant Functions

1. A function is **increasing** on an open interval, I, if $f(x_1) < f(x_2)$ whenever $x_1 < x_2$ for any x_1 and x_2 in the interval.
2. A function is **decreasing** on an open interval, I, if $f(x_1) > f(x_2)$ whenever $x_1 < x_2$ for any x_1 and x_2 in the interval.
3. A function is **constant** on an open interval, I, if $f(x_1) = f(x_2)$ for any x_1 and x_2 in the interval.

Increasing	**Decreasing**	**Constant**
(1) For $x_1 < x_2$ in I, $f(x_1) < f(x_2)$; f is increasing on I.	**(2)** For $x_1 < x_2$ in I, $f(x_1) > f(x_2)$; f is decreasing on I.	**(3)** For x_1 and x_2 in I, $f(x_1) = f(x_2)$; f is constant on I.

EXAMPLE 1 Intervals on Which a Function Increases, Decreases, or Is Constant

State the intervals on which each given function is increasing, decreasing, or constant.

a.

b.

(0, 2) belongs to the graph of f; (0, 0) does not.

SOLUTION

a. The function is decreasing on the interval $(-\infty, 0)$, increasing on the interval $(0, 2)$, and decreasing on the interval $(2, \infty)$.

b. Although the function's equations are not given, the graph indicates that the function is defined in two pieces. The part of the graph to the left of the y-axis shows that the function is constant on the interval $(-\infty, 0)$. The part to the right of the y-axis shows that the function is increasing on the interval $(0, \infty)$. • • •

Check Point 1 State the intervals on which the given function is increasing, decreasing, or constant.

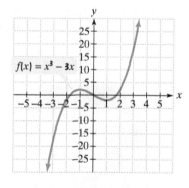

$f(x) = x^3 - 3x$

2 Use graphs to locate relative maxima or minima.

Relative Maxima and Relative Minima

The points at which a function changes its increasing or decreasing behavior can be used to find any *relative maximum* or *relative minimum* values of the function.

Definitions of Relative Maximum and Relative Minimum

1. A function value $f(a)$ is a **relative maximum** of f if there exists an open interval containing a such that $f(a) > f(x)$ for all $x \neq a$ in the open interval.

2. A function value $f(b)$ is a **relative minimum** of f if there exists an open interval containing b such that $f(b) < f(x)$ for all $x \neq b$ in the open interval.

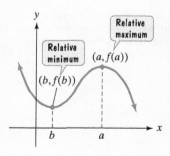

The word *local* is sometimes used instead of *relative* when describing maxima or minima.

What's the difference between where a function has a relative maximum or minimum and the relative maximum or minimum?

- If $f(a)$ is greater than all other values of f near a, then f has a relative maximum at the input value, a. The relative maximum is the output value, $f(a)$. Equivalently, $f(a)$ is a relative maximum *value* of the function.
- If $f(b)$ is less than all other values of f near b, then f has a relative minimum at the input value, b. The relative minimum is the output value, $f(b)$. Equivalently, $f(b)$ is a relative minimum *value* of the function.

If the graph of a function is given, we can often visually locate the number(s) at which the function has a relative maximum or a relative minimum. For example, the graph of f in **Figure 2.17** shows that

- f has a relative maximum at $\dfrac{\pi}{2}$.

  The relative maximum is $f\left(\dfrac{\pi}{2}\right) = 1$.

- f has a relative minimum at $-\dfrac{\pi}{2}$.

  The relative minimum is $f\left(-\dfrac{\pi}{2}\right) = -1$.

FIGURE 2.17 Using a graph to locate where a function has a relative maximum or minimum

Notice that f does not have a relative maximum or minimum at $-\pi, 0,$ and π, the x-intercepts, or zeros, of the function.

③ Identify even or odd functions and recognize their symmetries.

Even and Odd Functions and Symmetry

Is beauty in the eye of the beholder? Or are there certain objects (or people) that are so well balanced and proportioned that they are universally pleasing to the eye? What constitutes an attractive human face? In **Figure 2.18**, we've drawn lines between paired features and marked the midpoints. Notice how the features line up almost perfectly. Each half of the face is a mirror image of the other half through the white vertical line.

Did you know that graphs of some equations exhibit exactly the kind of symmetry shown by the attractive face in **Figure 2.18**? The word *symmetry* comes from the Greek *symmetria*, meaning "the same measure." We can identify a function whose graph has symmetry by looking at the function's equation and determining if the function is *even* or *odd*.

FIGURE 2.18 To most people, an attractive face is one in which each half is an almost perfect mirror image of the other half.

Definitions of Even and Odd Functions

The function f is an **even function** if
$$f(-x) = f(x) \quad \text{for all } x \text{ in the domain of } f.$$
The right side of the equation of an even function does not change if x is replaced with $-x$.

The function f is an **odd function** if
$$f(-x) = -f(x) \quad \text{for all } x \text{ in the domain of } f.$$
Every term on the right side of the equation of an odd function changes sign if x is replaced with $-x$.

EXAMPLE 2   Identifying Even or Odd Functions

Determine whether each of the following functions is even, odd, or neither:

    a. $f(x) = x^3 - 6x$ **b.** $g(x) = x^4 - 2x^2$ **c.** $h(x) = x^2 + 2x + 1.$

SOLUTION

In each case, replace x with $-x$ and simplify. If the right side of the equation stays the same, the function is even. If every term on the right side changes sign, the function is odd.

a. We use the given function's equation, $f(x) = x^3 - 6x$, to find $f(-x)$.

Use $f(x) = x^3 - 6x$.

> Replace x with $-x$.

$$f(-x) = (-x)^3 - 6(-x) = (-x)(-x)(-x) - 6(-x) = -x^3 + 6x$$

There are two terms on the right side of the given equation, $f(x) = x^3 - 6x$, and each term changed sign when we replaced x with $-x$. Because $f(-x) = -f(x)$, f is an odd function.

b. We use the given function's equation, $g(x) = x^4 - 2x^2$, to find $g(-x)$.

Use $g(x) = x^4 - 2x^2$.

> Replace x with $-x$.

$$g(-x) = (-x)^4 - 2(-x)^2 = (-x)(-x)(-x)(-x) - 2(-x)(-x)$$
$$= x^4 - 2x^2$$

The right side of the equation of the given function, $g(x) = x^4 - 2x^2$, did not change when we replaced x with $-x$. Because $g(-x) = g(x)$, g is an even function.

c. We use the given function's equation, $h(x) = x^2 + 2x + 1$, to find $h(-x)$.

Use $h(x) = x^2 + 2x + 1$.

> Replace x with $-x$.

$$h(-x) = (-x)^2 + 2(-x) + 1 = x^2 - 2x + 1$$

The right side of the equation of the given function, $h(x) = x^2 + 2x + 1$, changed when we replaced x with $-x$. Thus, $h(-x) \neq h(x)$, so h is not an even function. The sign of *each* of the three terms in the equation for $h(x)$ did not change when we replaced x with $-x$. Only the second term changed signs. Thus, $h(-x) \neq -h(x)$, so h is not an odd function. We conclude that h is neither an even nor an odd function.   •••

 Check Point 2 Determine whether each of the following functions is even, odd, or neither:

a. $f(x) = x^2 + 6$ **b.** $g(x) = 7x^3 - x$ **c.** $h(x) = x^5 + 1$.

Now, let's see what even and odd functions tell us about a function's graph. Begin with the even function $f(x) = x^2 - 4$, shown in **Figure 2.19**. The function is even because

$$f(-x) = (-x)^2 - 4 = x^2 - 4 = f(x).$$

Examine the pairs of points shown, such as $(3, 5)$ and $(-3, 5)$. Notice that we obtain the same y-coordinate whenever we evaluate the function at a value of x and the value of its opposite, $-x$. Like the attractive face, each half of the graph is a mirror image of the other half through the y-axis. If we were to fold the paper along the y-axis, the two halves of the graph would coincide. This is what it means for the graph to be *symmetric with respect to the y-axis*. A graph is **symmetric with respect to the y-axis** if, for every point (x, y) on the graph, the point $(-x, y)$ is also on the graph. All even functions have graphs with this kind of symmetry.

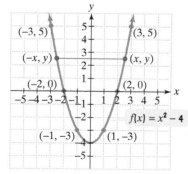

FIGURE 2.19 y-axis symmetry with $f(-x) = f(x)$

Even Functions and y-Axis Symmetry

The graph of an even function in which $f(-x) = f(x)$ is symmetric with respect to the y-axis.

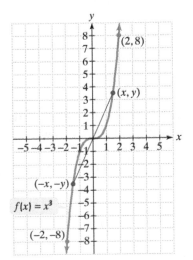

FIGURE 2.20 Origin symmetry with $f(-x) = -f(x)$

Now, consider the graph of the function $f(x) = x^3$, shown in **Figure 2.20**. The function is odd because

$$f(-x) = (-x)^3 = (-x)(-x)(-x) = -x^3 = -f(x).$$

Although the graph in **Figure 2.20** is not symmetric with respect to the y-axis, it is symmetric in another way. Look at the pairs of points, such as $(2, 8)$ and $(-2, -8)$. For each point (x, y) on the graph, the point $(-x, -y)$ is also on the graph. The points $(2, 8)$ and $(-2, -8)$ are reflections of one another through the origin. This means that the origin is the midpoint of the line segment connecting the points.

A graph is **symmetric with respect to the origin** if, for every point (x, y) on the graph, the point $(-x, -y)$ is also on the graph. Observe that the first- and third-quadrant portions of $f(x) = x^3$ are reflections of one another with respect to the origin. Notice that $f(x)$ and $f(-x)$ have opposite signs, so that $f(-x) = -f(x)$. All odd functions have graphs with origin symmetry.

Odd Functions and Origin Symmetry

The graph of an odd function in which $f(-x) = -f(x)$ is symmetric with respect to the origin.

4 Understand and use piecewise functions.

Piecewise Functions

A cellphone company offers the following plan:

- $20 per month buys 60 minutes.
- Additional time costs $0.40 per minute.

We can represent this plan mathematically by writing the total monthly cost, C, as a function of the number of calling minutes, t.

FIGURE 2.21

$$C(t) = \begin{cases} 20 & \text{if } 0 \leq t \leq 60 \\ 20 + 0.40(t - 60) & \text{if } t > 60 \end{cases}$$

The cost is $20 for up to and including 60 calling minutes.

The cost is $20 plus $0.40 per minute for additional time for more than 60 calling minutes.

$20 for first 60 minutes $0.40 per minute   times the number of calling minutes exceeding 60

A function that is defined by two (or more) equations over a specified domain is called a **piecewise function**. Many cellphone plans can be represented with piecewise functions. The graph of the piecewise function described above is shown in **Figure 2.21**.

EXAMPLE 3 Evaluating a Piecewise Function

Use the function that describes the cellphone plan

$$C(t) = \begin{cases} 20 & \text{if } 0 \leq t \leq 60 \\ 20 + 0.40(t - 60) & \text{if } t > 60 \end{cases}$$

to find and interpret each of the following:

a. $C(30)$ **b.** $C(100)$.

SOLUTION

a. To find $C(30)$, we let $t = 30$. Because 30 lies between 0 and 60, we use the first line of the piecewise function.

$$C(t) = 20 \qquad \text{This is the function's equation for } 0 \le t \le 60.$$
$$C(30) = 20 \qquad \text{Replace } t \text{ with 30. Regardless of this function's input, the constant output is 20.}$$

This means that with 30 calling minutes, the monthly cost is \$20. This can be visually represented by the point $(30, 20)$ on the first piece of the graph in **Figure 2.21**.

b. To find $C(100)$, we let $t = 100$. Because 100 is greater than 60, we use the second line of the piecewise function.

$$C(t) = 20 + 0.40(t - 60) \qquad \text{This is the function's equation for } t > 60.$$
$$C(100) = 20 + 0.40(100 - 60) \qquad \text{Replace } t \text{ with 100.}$$
$$= 20 + 0.40(40) \qquad \text{Subtract within parentheses: } 100 - 60 = 40.$$
$$= 20 + 16 \qquad \text{Multiply: } 0.40(40) = 16.$$
$$= 36 \qquad \text{Add: } 20 + 16 = 36.$$

Thus, $C(100) = 36$. This means that with 100 calling minutes, the monthly cost is \$36. This can be visually represented by the point $(100, 36)$ on the second piece of the graph in **Figure 2.21**. ● ● ●

Check Point 3 Use the function in Example 3 to find and interpret each of the following:

a. $C(40)$ **b.** $C(80)$.

Identify your solutions by points on the graph in **Figure 2.21**.

EXAMPLE 4   Graphing a Piecewise Function

Graph the piecewise function defined by

$$f(x) = \begin{cases} x + 2 & \text{if} \quad x \le 1 \\ 4 & \text{if} \quad x > 1. \end{cases}$$

SOLUTION

We graph f in two parts, using a partial table of coordinates to create each piece. The tables of coordinates and the completed graph are shown in **Figure 2.22**.

Graph $f(x) = x + 2$ for $x \le 1$.
Domain $= (-\infty, 1]$

x $(x \le 1)$	$f(x) = x + 2$	$(x, f(x))$
1	$f(1) = 1 + 2 = 3$	$(1, 3)$
0	$f(0) = 0 + 2 = 2$	$(0, 2)$
−1	$f(-1) = -1 + 2 = 1$	$(-1, 1)$
−2	$f(-2) = -2 + 2 = 0$	$(-2, 0)$
−3	$f(-3) = -3 + 2 = -1$	$(-3, -1)$
−4	$f(-4) = -4 + 2 = -2$	$(-4, -2)$

Graph $f(x) = 4$ for $x > 1$.
Domain $= (1, \infty)$

x $(x > 1)$	$f(x) = 4$	$(x, f(x))$
1.5	$f(1.5) = 4$	$(1.5, 4)$
2	$f(2) = 4$	$(2, 4)$
3	$f(3) = 4$	$(3, 4)$
4	$f(4) = 4$	$(4, 4)$
5	$f(5) = 4$	$(5, 4)$

FIGURE 2.22 Graphing a piecewise function ● ● ●

GREAT QUESTION!

When I graphed the function in Example 4, here's what I got:

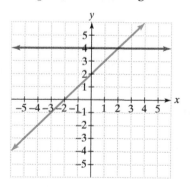

Is my graph ok?

No. You incorrectly ignored the domain for each piece of the function and graphed each equation as if its domain was $(-\infty, \infty)$.

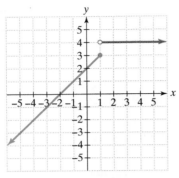

FIGURE 2.22 (repeated)

We can use the graph of the piecewise function in **Figure 2.22** to find the range of f. The range of the blue piece on the left is $\{y \mid y \leq 3\}$. The range of the red horizontal piece on the right is $\{y \mid y = 4\}$. Thus, the range of f is

$$\{y \mid y \leq 3\} \cup \{y \mid y = 4\}, \text{ or } (-\infty, 3] \cup \{4\}.$$

⊘ Check Point **4** Graph the piecewise function defined by

$$f(x) = \begin{cases} 3 & \text{if} \quad x \leq -1 \\ x - 2 & \text{if} \quad x > -1. \end{cases}$$

Some piecewise functions are called **step functions** because their graphs form discontinuous steps. One such function is called the **greatest integer function**, symbolized by $\text{int}(x)$ or $[\![x]\!]$, where

$$\text{int}(x) = \text{the greatest integer that is less than or equal to } x.$$

For example,

$$\text{int}(1) = 1, \quad \text{int}(1.3) = 1, \quad \text{int}(1.5) = 1, \quad \text{int}(1.9) = 1.$$

> 1 is the greatest integer that is less than or equal to 1, 1.3, 1.5, and 1.9.

Here are some additional examples:

$$\text{int}(2) = 2, \quad \text{int}(2.3) = 2, \quad \text{int}(2.5) = 2, \quad \text{int}(2.9) = 2.$$

> 2 is the greatest integer that is less than or equal to 2, 2.3, 2.5, and 2.9.

Notice how we jumped from 1 to 2 in the function values for $\text{int}(x)$. In particular,

$$\text{If } 1 \leq x < 2, \quad \text{then} \quad \text{int}(x) = 1.$$
$$\text{If } 2 \leq x < 3, \quad \text{then} \quad \text{int}(x) = 2.$$

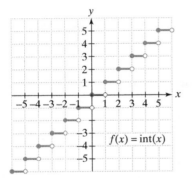

FIGURE 2.23 The graph of the greatest integer function

The graph of $f(x) = \text{int}(x)$ is shown in **Figure 2.23**. The graph of the greatest integer function jumps vertically one unit at each integer. However, the graph is constant between each pair of consecutive integers. The rightmost horizontal step shown in the graph illustrates that

$$\text{If } 5 \leq x < 6, \quad \text{then} \quad \text{int}(x) = 5.$$

In general,

$$\text{If } n \leq x < n + 1, \text{ where } n \text{ is an integer,} \quad \text{then} \quad \text{int}(x) = n.$$

⑤ Find and simplify a function's difference quotient.

Functions and Difference Quotients

In Section 2.4, we will be studying the average rate of change of a function. A ratio, called the *difference quotient*, plays an important role in understanding the rate at which functions change.

Definition of the Difference Quotient of a Function

The expression

$$\frac{f(x + h) - f(x)}{h}$$

for $h \neq 0$ is called the **difference quotient** of the function f.

EXAMPLE 5   Evaluating and Simplifying a Difference Quotient

If $f(x) = 2x^2 - x + 3$, find and simplify each expression:

a. $f(x + h)$ **b.** $\dfrac{f(x + h) - f(x)}{h}, h \neq 0.$

SOLUTION

a. We find $f(x + h)$ by replacing x with $x + h$ each time that x appears in the equation.

$$f(x) = 2x^2 \quad - \quad x \quad\quad + 3$$

| Replace x with $x + h$. | Replace x with $x + h$. | Replace x with $x + h$. | Copy the 3. There is no x in this term. |

$$f(x + h) = 2(x + h)^2 - (x + h) \quad + 3$$
$$= 2(x^2 + 2xh + h^2) - x - h + 3$$
$$= 2x^2 + 4xh + 2h^2 - x - h + 3$$

b. Using our result from part (a), we obtain the following:

This is $f(x + h)$ from part (a).

This is $f(x)$ from the given equation.

$$\frac{f(x + h) - f(x)}{h} = \frac{\boxed{2x^2 + 4xh + 2h^2 - x - h + 3} - (2x^2 - x + 3)}{h}$$

$$= \frac{2x^2 + 4xh + 2h^2 - x - h + 3 - 2x^2 + x - 3}{h} \qquad \text{Remove parentheses and change the sign of each term in the parentheses.}$$

$$= \frac{(2x^2 - 2x^2) + (-x + x) + (3 - 3) + 4xh + 2h^2 - h}{h} \qquad \text{Group like terms.}$$

$$= \frac{4xh + 2h^2 - 1h}{h} \qquad \text{Simplify.}$$

We wrote $-h$ as $-1h$ to avoid possible errors in the next factoring step.

$$= \frac{h(4x + 2h - 1)}{h} \qquad \text{Factor } h \text{ from the numerator.}$$

$$= 4x + 2h - 1 \qquad \text{Divide out identical factors of } h \text{ in the numerator and denominator.} \qquad \bullet\bullet\bullet$$

⊘ Check Point **5** If $f(x) = -2x^2 + x + 5$, find and simplify each expression:

a. $f(x + h)$ **b.** $\dfrac{f(x + h) - f(x)}{h}, h \neq 0.$

CONCEPT AND VOCABULARY CHECK

Fill in each blank so that the resulting statement is true.

1. Assume that f is a function defined on an open interval I and x_1 and x_2 are any elements in the interval I.
f is increasing on I if $f(x_1)$ _____ when $x_1 < x_2$.
f is decreasing on I if $f(x_1)$ _____ when $x_1 < x_2$.
f is constant on I if $f(x_1)$ _____.

2. If $f(a) > f(x)$ in an open interval containing $a, x \neq a$, then the function value $f(a)$ is a relative _____ of f.
If $f(b) < f(x)$ in an open interval containing $b, x \neq b$, then the function value $f(b)$ is a relative _____ of f.

3. If f is an even function, then $f(-x) =$ _____. Such a function is symmetric with respect to the _____.

4. If f is an odd function, then $f(-x) =$ _____. The graph of such a function is symmetric with respect to the _____.

5. A function defined by two or more equations over a specified domain is called a/an _____ function.

6. The greatest integer function is defined by $\text{int}(x) =$ the greatest integer that is _____.
For example, $\text{int}(2.5) =$ ___, $\text{int}(-2.5) =$ ___, and $\text{int}(0.5) =$ ___.

7. The expression
$$\frac{f(x + h) - f(x)}{h}, h \neq 0,$$
is called the _____ of the function f. We find this expression by replacing x with _____ each time x appears in the function's equation. Then we subtract _____. After simplifying, we factor ___ from the numerator and divide out identical factors of ___ in the numerator and denominator.

8. True or false: $f(x + h) = f(x) + h$ _____

9. True or false: $f(x + h) = f(x) + f(h)$ _____

EXERCISE SET 2.2

Practice Exercises

In Exercises 1–12, use the graph to determine

    a. *intervals on which the function is increasing, if any.*
    b. *intervals on which the function is decreasing, if any.*
    c. *intervals on which the function is constant, if any.*

1.

2.

3.

4.

5.

6.

7.

8.

9.

10.

11.

12.
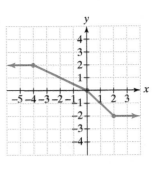

In Exercises 13–16, the graph of a function f is given. Use the graph to find each of the following:

    a. *The numbers, if any, at which f has a relative maximum. What are these relative maxima?*
    b. *The numbers, if any, at which f has a relative minimum. What are these relative minima?*

13.

14.

15.

$f(x) = 2x^3 + 3x^2 - 12x + 1$

$[-4, 4, 1]$ by $[-15, 25, 5]$

16.

$$f(x) = 2x^3 - 15x^2 + 24x + 19$$

[−2, 6, 1] by [−15, 35, 5]

In Exercises 17–28, determine whether each function is even, odd, or neither.

17. $f(x) = x^3 + x$

18. $f(x) = x^3 - x$

19. $g(x) = x^2 + x$

20. $g(x) = x^2 - x$

21. $h(x) = x^2 - x^4$

22. $h(x) = 2x^2 + x^4$

23. $f(x) = x^2 - x^4 + 1$

24. $f(x) = 2x^2 + x^4 + 1$

25. $f(x) = \frac{1}{5}x^6 - 3x^2$

26. $f(x) = 2x^3 - 6x^5$

27. $f(x) = x\sqrt{1 - x^2}$

28. $f(x) = x^2\sqrt{1 - x^2}$

In Exercises 29–32, use possible symmetry to determine whether each graph is the graph of an even function, an odd function, or a function that is neither even nor odd.

29.

30.

31.

32.

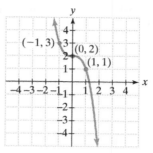

33. Use the graph of f to determine each of the following. Where applicable, use interval notation.

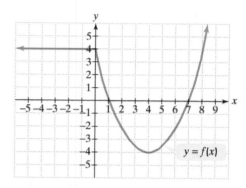

a. the domain of f

b. the range of f

c. the x-intercepts

d. the y-intercept

e. intervals on which f is increasing

f. intervals on which f is decreasing

g. intervals on which f is constant

h. the number at which f has a relative minimum

i. the relative minimum of f

j. $f(-3)$

k. the values of x for which $f(x) = -2$

l. Is f even, odd, or neither?

34. Use the graph of f to determine each of the following. Where applicable, use interval notation.

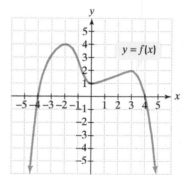

a. the domain of f

b. the range of f

c. the x-intercepts

d. the y-intercept

e. intervals on which f is increasing

f. intervals on which f is decreasing

g. values of x for which $f(x) \le 0$

h. the numbers at which f has a relative maximum

i. the relative maxima of f

j. $f(-2)$

k. the values of x for which $f(x) = 0$

l. Is f even, odd, or neither?

35. Use the graph of f to determine each of the following. Where applicable, use interval notation.

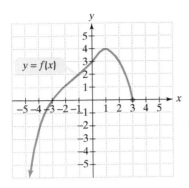

a. the domain of f
b. the range of f
c. the zeros of f
d. $f(0)$
e. intervals on which f is increasing
f. intervals on which f is decreasing
g. values of x for which $f(x) \le 0$
h. any relative maxima and the numbers at which they occur
i. the value of x for which $f(x) = 4$
j. Is $f(-1)$ positive or negative?

36. Use the graph of f to determine each of the following. Where applicable, use interval notation.

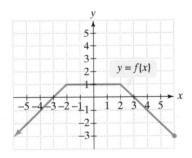

a. the domain of f
b. the range of f
c. the zeros of f
d. $f(0)$
e. intervals on which f is increasing
f. intervals on which f is decreasing
g. intervals on which f is constant
h. values of x for which $f(x) > 0$
i. values of x for which $f(x) = -2$
j. Is $f(4)$ positive or negative?
k. Is f even, odd, or neither?
l. Is $f(2)$ a relative maximum?

In Exercises 37–42, evaluate each piecewise function at the given values of the independent variable.

37. $f(x) = \begin{cases} 3x + 5 & \text{if } x < 0 \\ 4x + 7 & \text{if } x \ge 0 \end{cases}$

    a. $f(-2)$ **b.** $f(0)$ **c.** $f(3)$

38. $f(x) = \begin{cases} 6x - 1 & \text{if } x < 0 \\ 7x + 3 & \text{if } x \ge 0 \end{cases}$

    a. $f(-3)$ **b.** $f(0)$ **c.** $f(4)$

39. $g(x) = \begin{cases} x + 3 & \text{if } x \ge -3 \\ -(x + 3) & \text{if } x < -3 \end{cases}$

    a. $g(0)$ **b.** $g(-6)$ **c.** $g(-3)$

40. $g(x) = \begin{cases} x + 5 & \text{if } x \ge -5 \\ -(x + 5) & \text{if } x < -5 \end{cases}$

    a. $g(0)$ **b.** $g(-6)$ **c.** $g(-5)$

41. $h(x) = \begin{cases} \dfrac{x^2 - 9}{x - 3} & \text{if } x \ne 3 \\ 6 & \text{if } x = 3 \end{cases}$

    a. $h(5)$ **b.** $h(0)$ **c.** $h(3)$

42. $h(x) = \begin{cases} \dfrac{x^2 - 25}{x - 5} & \text{if } x \ne 5 \\ 10 & \text{if } x = 5 \end{cases}$

    a. $h(7)$ **b.** $h(0)$ **c.** $h(5)$

In Exercises 43–54, the domain of each piecewise function is $(-\infty, \infty)$.

    a. Graph each function.
    b. Use your graph to determine the function's range.

43. $f(x) = \begin{cases} -x & \text{if } x < 0 \\ x & \text{if } x \ge 0 \end{cases}$

44. $f(x) = \begin{cases} x & \text{if } x < 0 \\ -x & \text{if } x \ge 0 \end{cases}$

45. $f(x) = \begin{cases} 2x & \text{if } x \le 0 \\ 2 & \text{if } x > 0 \end{cases}$

46. $f(x) = \begin{cases} \frac{1}{2}x & \text{if } x \le 0 \\ 3 & \text{if } x > 0 \end{cases}$

47. $f(x) = \begin{cases} x + 3 & \text{if } x < -2 \\ x - 3 & \text{if } x \ge -2 \end{cases}$

48. $f(x) = \begin{cases} x + 2 & \text{if } x < -3 \\ x - 2 & \text{if } x \ge -3 \end{cases}$

49. $f(x) = \begin{cases} 3 & \text{if } x \le -1 \\ -3 & \text{if } x > -1 \end{cases}$

50. $f(x) = \begin{cases} 4 & \text{if } x \le -1 \\ -4 & \text{if } x > -1 \end{cases}$

51. $f(x) = \begin{cases} \frac{1}{2}x^2 & \text{if } x < 1 \\ 2x - 1 & \text{if } x \ge 1 \end{cases}$

52. $f(x) = \begin{cases} -\frac{1}{2}x^2 & \text{if } x < 1 \\ 2x + 1 & \text{if } x \ge 1 \end{cases}$

53. $f(x) = \begin{cases} 0 & \text{if } x < -4 \\ -x & \text{if } -4 \le x < 0 \\ x^2 & \text{if } x \ge 0 \end{cases}$

54. $f(x) = \begin{cases} 0 & \text{if } x < -3 \\ -x & \text{if } -3 \le x < 0 \\ x^2 - 1 & \text{if } x \ge 0 \end{cases}$

In Exercises 55–76, find and simplify the difference quotient

$$\frac{f(x + h) - f(x)}{h}, h \ne 0$$

for the given function.

55. $f(x) = 4x$

56. $f(x) = 7x$

57. $f(x) = 3x + 7$

58. $f(x) = 6x + 1$

59. $f(x) = x^2$

60. $f(x) = 2x^2$

61. $f(x) = x^2 - 4x + 3$

62. $f(x) = x^2 - 5x + 8$

63. $f(x) = 2x^2 + x - 1$

64. $f(x) = 3x^2 + x + 5$

65. $f(x) = -x^2 + 2x + 4$

66. $f(x) = -x^2 - 3x + 1$

67. $f(x) = -2x^2 + 5x + 7$

68. $f(x) = -3x^2 + 2x - 1$

69. $f(x) = -2x^2 - x + 3$

70. $f(x) = -3x^2 + x - 1$

71. $f(x) = 6$

72. $f(x) = 7$

73. $f(x) = \dfrac{1}{x}$

74. $f(x) = \dfrac{1}{2x}$

75. $f(x) = \sqrt{x}$

76. $f(x) = \sqrt{x - 1}$

Practice Plus

In Exercises 77–78, let f be defined by the following graph:

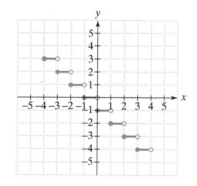

77. Find

$$\sqrt{f(-1.5) + f(-0.9)} - [f(\pi)]^2 + f(-3) \div f(1) \cdot f(-\pi).$$

78. Find

$$\sqrt{f(-2.5) - f(1.9)} - [f(-\pi)]^2 + f(-3) \div f(1) \cdot f(\pi).$$

A cellphone company offers the following plans. Also given are the piecewise functions that model these plans. Use this information to solve Exercises 79–80.

Plan A

- *$30 per month buys 120 minutes.*
- *Additional time costs $0.30 per minute.*

$$C(t) = \begin{cases} 30 & \text{if } 0 \le t \le 120 \\ 30 + 0.30(t - 120) & \text{if } t > 120 \end{cases}$$

Plan B

- *$40 per month buys 200 minutes.*
- *Additional time costs $0.30 per minute.*

$$C(t) = \begin{cases} 40 & \text{if } 0 \le t \le 200 \\ 40 + 0.30(t - 200) & \text{if } t > 200 \end{cases}$$

79. Simplify the algebraic expression in the second line of the piecewise function for plan A. Then use point-plotting to graph the function.

80. Simplify the algebraic expression in the second line of the piecewise function for plan B. Then use point-plotting to graph the function.

In Exercises 81–82, write a piecewise function that models each cellphone billing plan. Then graph the function.

81. $50 per month buys 400 minutes. Additional time costs $0.30 per minute.

82. $60 per month buys 450 minutes. Additional time costs $0.35 per minute.

Application Exercises

With aging, body fat increases and muscle mass declines. The line graphs show the percent body fat in adult women and men as they age from 25 to 75 years. Use the graphs to solve Exercises 83–90.

Percent Body Fat in Adults

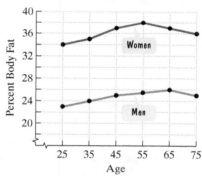

Source: Thompson et al., *The Science of Nutrition,* Benjamin Cummings, 2008

83. State the intervals on which the graph giving the percent body fat in women is increasing and decreasing.

84. State the intervals on which the graph giving the percent body fat in men is increasing and decreasing.

85. For what age does the percent body fat in women reach a maximum? What is the percent body fat for that age?

86. At what age does the percent body fat in men reach a maximum? What is the percent body fat for that age?

87. Use interval notation to give the domain and the range for the graph of the function for women.

88. Use interval notation to give the domain and the range for the graph of the function for men.

89. The function $p(x) = -0.002x^2 + 0.15x + 22.86$ models percent body fat, $p(x)$, where x is the number of years a person's age exceeds 25. Use the graphs to determine whether this model describes percent body fat in women or in men.

90. The function $p(x) = -0.004x^2 + 0.25x + 33.64$ models percent body fat, $p(x)$, where x is the number of years a person's age exceeds 25. Use the graphs to determine whether this model describes percent body fat in women or in men.

Here is the 2011 Federal Tax Rate Schedule X that specifies the tax owed by a single taxpayer.

If Your Taxable Income Is Over	But Not Over	The Tax You Owe Is	Of the Amount Over
$ 0	$ 8500	10%	$ 0
$ 8500	$ 34,500	$ 850.00 + 15%	$ 8500
$ 34,500	$ 83,600	$ 4750.00 + 25%	$ 34,500
$ 83,600	$174,400	$ 17,025.00 + 28%	$ 83,600
$174,400	$379,150	$ 42,449.00 + 33%	$174,400
$379,150	—	$110,016.50 + 35%	$379,150

The preceding tax table can be modeled by a piecewise function, where x represents the taxable income of a single taxpayer and T(x) is the tax owed:

$$T(x) = \begin{cases} 0.10x & \text{if} & 0 < x \le 8500 \\ 850.00 + 0.15(x - 8500) & \text{if} & 8500 < x \le 34,500 \\ 4750.00 + 0.25(x - 34,500) & \text{if} & 34,500 < x \le 83,600 \\ 17,025.00 + 0.28(x - 83,600) & \text{if} & 83,600 < x \le 174,400 \\ \underline{\hspace{2cm}?} & \text{if} & 174,400 < x \le 379,150 \\ \underline{\hspace{2cm}?} & \text{if} & x > 379,150. \end{cases}$$

Use this information to solve Exercises 91–94.

91. Find and interpret $T(20,000)$.

92. Find and interpret $T(50,000)$.

In Exercises 93–94, refer to the preceding tax table.

93. Find the algebraic expression for the missing piece of $T(x)$ that models tax owed for the domain (174,400, 379,150].

94. Find the algebraic expression for the missing piece of $T(x)$ that models tax owed for the domain (379,150, ∞).

The figure shows the cost of mailing a first-class letter, f(x), as a function of its weight, x, in ounces. Use the graph to solve Exercises 95–98.

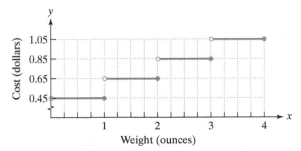

Source: Lynn E. Baring, Postmaster, Inverness, CA

95. Find $f(3)$. What does this mean in terms of the variables in this situation?

96. Find $f(3.5)$. What does this mean in terms of the variables in this situation?

97. What is the cost of mailing a letter that weighs 1.5 ounces?

98. What is the cost of mailing a letter that weighs 1.8 ounces?

99. Furry Finances A pet insurance policy has a monthly rate that is a function of the age of the insured dog or cat. For pets whose age does not exceed 4, the monthly cost is $20. The cost then increases by $2 for each successive year of the pet's age.

Age Not Exceeding	Monthly Cost
4	$20
5	$22
6	$24

The cost schedule continues in this manner for ages not exceeding 10. The cost for pets whose ages exceed 10 is $40. Use this information to create a graph that shows the monthly cost of the insurance, $f(x)$, for a pet of age x, where the function's domain is [0, 14].

Writing in Mathematics

100. What does it mean if a function f is increasing on an interval?

101. Suppose that a function f whose graph contains no breaks or gaps on (a, c) is increasing on (a, b), decreasing on (b, c), and defined at b. Describe what occurs at $x = b$. What does the function value $f(b)$ represent?

102. If you are given a function's equation, how do you determine if the function is even, odd, or neither?

103. If you are given a function's graph, how do you determine if the function is even, odd, or neither?

104. What is a piecewise function?

105. Explain how to find the difference quotient of a function f, $\dfrac{f(x + h) - f(x)}{h}$, if an equation for f is given.

Technology Exercises

106. The function
$$f(x) = -0.00002x^3 + 0.008x^2 - 0.3x + 6.95$$
models the number of annual physician visits, $f(x)$, by a person of age x. Graph the function in a [0, 100, 5] by [0, 40, 2] viewing rectangle. What does the shape of the graph indicate about the relationship between one's age and the number of annual physician visits? Use the ⎍TABLE⎍ or minimum function capability to find the coordinates of the minimum point on the graph of the function. What does this mean?

In Exercises 107–112, use a graphing utility to graph each function. Use a [−5, 5, 1] by [−5, 5, 1] viewing rectangle. Then find the intervals on which the function is increasing, decreasing, or constant.

107. $f(x) = x^3 - 6x^2 + 9x + 1$

108. $g(x) = |4 - x^2|$

109. $h(x) = |x - 2| + |x + 2|$

110. $f(x) = x^{\frac{1}{3}}(x - 4)$

111. $g(x) = x^{\frac{2}{3}}$

112. $h(x) = 2 - x^{\frac{2}{5}}$

113. a. Graph the functions $f(x) = x^n$ for $n = 2, 4,$ and 6 in a $[-2, 2, 1]$ by $[-1, 3, 1]$ viewing rectangle.

b. Graph the functions $f(x) = x^n$ for $n = 1, 3,$ and 5 in a $[-2, 2, 1]$ by $[-2, 2, 1]$ viewing rectangle.

c. If n is positive and even, where is the graph of $f(x) = x^n$ increasing and where is it decreasing?

d. If n is positive and odd, what can you conclude about the graph of $f(x) = x^n$ in terms of increasing or decreasing behavior?

e. Graph all six functions in a $[-1, 3, 1]$ by $[-1, 3, 1]$ viewing rectangle. What do you observe about the graphs in terms of how flat or how steep they are?

Critical Thinking Exercises

Make Sense? *In Exercises 114–117, determine whether each statement makes sense or does not make sense, and explain your reasoning.*

114. My graph is decreasing on $(-\infty, a)$ and increasing on (a, ∞), so $f(a)$ must be a relative maximum.

115. This work by artist Scott Kim (1955–) has the same kind of symmetry as an even function.

"DYSLEXIA," 1981

116. I graphed

$$f(x) = \begin{cases} 2 & \text{if } x \neq 4 \\ 3 & \text{if } x = 4 \end{cases}$$

and one piece of my graph is a single point.

117. I noticed that the difference quotient is always zero if $f(x) = c$, where c is any constant.

118. Sketch the graph of f using the following properties. (More than one correct graph is possible.) f is a piecewise function that is decreasing on $(-\infty, 2), f(2) = 0, f$ is increasing on $(2, \infty)$, and the range of f is $[0, \infty)$.

119. Define a piecewise function on the intervals $(-\infty, 2], (2, 5),$ and $[5, \infty)$ that does not "jump" at 2 or 5 such that one piece is a constant function, another piece is an increasing function, and the third piece is a decreasing function.

120. Suppose that $h(x) = \dfrac{f(x)}{g(x)}$. The function f can be even, odd, or neither. The same is true for the function g.

a. Under what conditions is h definitely an even function?

b. Under what conditions is h definitely an odd function?

Group Exercise

121. (For assistance with this exercise, refer to the discussion of piecewise functions beginning on page 234, as well as to Exercises 79–80.) Group members who have cellphone plans should describe the total monthly cost of the plan as follows:

$_____ per month buys _____ minutes. Additional time costs $_____ per minute.

(For simplicity, ignore other charges.) The group should select any three plans, from "basic" to "premier." For each plan selected, write a piecewise function that describes the plan and graph the function. Graph the three functions in the same rectangular coordinate system. Now examine the graphs. For any given number of calling minutes, the best plan is the one whose graph is lowest at that point. Compare the three calling plans. Is one plan always a better deal than the other two? If not, determine the interval of calling minutes for which each plan is the best deal. (You can check out cellphone plans by visiting www.point.com.)

Preview Exercises

Exercises 122–124 will help you prepare for the material covered in the next section.

122. If $(x_1, y_1) = (-3, 1)$ and $(x_2, y_2) = (-2, 4)$, find $\dfrac{y_2 - y_1}{x_2 - x_1}$.

123. Find the ordered pairs (_____, 0) and (0, _____) satisfying $4x - 3y - 6 = 0$.

124. Solve for y: $3x + 2y - 4 = 0$.

Objectives

❶ Calculate a line's slope.

❷ Write the point-slope form of the equation of a line.

❸ Write and graph the slope-intercept form of the equation of a line.

❹ Graph horizontal or vertical lines.

❺ Recognize and use the general form of a line's equation.

❻ Use intercepts to graph the general form of a line's equation.

❼ Model data with linear functions and make predictions.

Is there a relationship between literacy and child mortality? As the percentage of adult females who are literate increases, does the mortality of children under five decrease? **Figure 2.24** indicates that this is, indeed, the case. Each point in the figure represents one country.

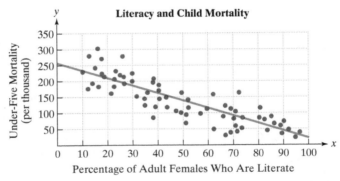

Literacy and Child Mortality

FIGURE 2.24
Source: United Nations

Data presented in a visual form as a set of points is called a **scatter plot**. Also shown in **Figure 2.24** is a line that passes through or near the points. A line that best fits the data points in a scatter plot is called a **regression line**. By writing the equation of this line, we can obtain a model for the data and make predictions about child mortality based on the percentage of literate adult females in a country.

Data often fall on or near a line. In this section, we will use functions to model such data and make predictions. We begin with a discussion of a line's steepness.

❶ Calculate a line's slope.

The Slope of a Line

Mathematicians have developed a useful measure of the steepness of a line, called the *slope* of the line. Slope compares the vertical change (the **rise**) to the horizontal change (the **run**) when moving from one fixed point to another along the line. To calculate the slope of a line, we use a ratio that compares the change in y (the rise) to the corresponding change in x (the run).

Definition of Slope

The **slope** of the line through the distinct points (x_1, y_1) and (x_2, y_2) is

$$\frac{\text{Change in } y}{\text{Change in } x} = \frac{\text{Rise}}{\text{Run}} \quad \begin{array}{l}\text{Vertical change} \\ \text{Horizontal change}\end{array}$$

$$= \frac{y_2 - y_1}{x_2 - x_1},$$

where $x_2 - x_1 \neq 0$.

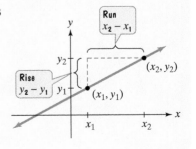

It is common notation to let the letter m represent the slope of a line. The letter m is used because it is the first letter of the French verb *monter*, meaning "to rise" or "to ascend."

EXAMPLE 1 Using the Definition of Slope

Find the slope of the line passing through each pair of points:

a. $(-3, -1)$ and $(-2, 4)$ **b.** $(-3, 4)$ and $(2, -2)$.

SOLUTION

a. Let $(x_1, y_1) = (-3, -1)$ and $(x_2, y_2) = (-2, 4)$. We obtain the slope as follows:

$$m = \frac{\text{Change in } y}{\text{Change in } x} = \frac{y_2 - y_1}{x_2 - x_1} = \frac{4 - (-1)}{-2 - (-3)} = \frac{4 + 1}{-2 + 3} = \frac{5}{1} = 5.$$

The situation is illustrated in **Figure 2.25**. The slope of the line is 5. For every vertical change, or rise, of 5 units, there is a corresponding horizontal change, or run, of 1 unit. The slope is positive and the line rises from left to right.

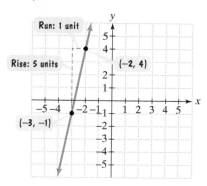

FIGURE 2.25 Visualizing a slope of 5

GREAT QUESTION!

When using the definition of slope, how do I know which point to call (x_1, y_1) and which point to call (x_2, y_2)?

When computing slope, it makes no difference which point you call (x_1, y_1) and which point you call (x_2, y_2). If we let $(x_1, y_1) = (-2, 4)$ and $(x_2, y_2) = (-3, -1)$, the slope is still 5:

$$m = \frac{\text{Change in } y}{\text{Change in } x} = \frac{y_2 - y_1}{x_2 - x_1} = \frac{-1 - 4}{-3 - (-2)} = \frac{-5}{-1} = 5.$$

However, you should not subtract in one order in the numerator ($y_2 - y_1$) and then in a different order in the denominator ($x_1 - x_2$).

$$\frac{-1 - 4}{-2 - (-3)} = \frac{-5}{1} = -5. \quad \text{Incorrect! The slope is not } -5.$$

b. To find the slope of the line passing through $(-3, 4)$ and $(2, -2)$, we can let $(x_1, y_1) = (-3, 4)$ and $(x_2, y_2) = (2, -2)$. The slope of the line is computed as follows:

$$m = \frac{\text{Change in } y}{\text{Change in } x} = \frac{y_2 - y_1}{x_2 - x_1} = \frac{-2 - 4}{2 - (-3)} = \frac{-6}{5} = -\frac{6}{5}.$$

The situation is illustrated in **Figure 2.26**. The slope of the line is $-\frac{6}{5}$. For every vertical change of -6 units (6 units down), there is a corresponding horizontal change of 5 units. The slope is negative and the line falls from left to right.

● ● ●

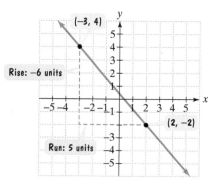

FIGURE 2.26 Visualizing a slope of $-\frac{6}{5}$

GREAT QUESTION!

Is it OK to say that a vertical line has no slope?

Always be clear in the way you use language, especially in mathematics. For example, it's not a good idea to say that a line has "no slope." This could mean that the slope is zero or that the slope is undefined.

☑ Check Point **1** Find the slope of the line passing through each pair of points:

a. $(-3, 4)$ and $(-4, -2)$ **b.** $(4, -2)$ and $(-1, 5)$.

Example 1 illustrates that a line with a positive slope is increasing and a line with a negative slope is decreasing. By contrast, a horizontal line is a constant function and has a slope of zero. A vertical line has no horizontal change, so $x_2 - x_1 = 0$ in the formula for slope. Because we cannot divide by zero, the slope of a vertical line is undefined. This discussion is summarized in **Table 2.2** at the top of the next page.

Table 2.2 Possibilities for a Line's Slope

Positive Slope	Negative Slope	Zero Slope	Undefined Slope
$m > 0$	$m < 0$	$m = 0$	m is undefined.
Line rises from left to right.	Line falls from left to right.	Line is horizontal.	Line is vertical.

2   Write the point-slope form of the equation of a line.

The Point-Slope Form of the Equation of a Line

We can use the slope of a line to obtain various forms of the line's equation. For example, consider a nonvertical line that has slope m and that contains the point (x_1, y_1).

The line in **Figure 2.27** has slope m and contains the point (x_1, y_1). Let (x, y) represent any other point on the line.

Regardless of where the point (x, y) is located, the steepness of the line in **Figure 2.27** remains the same. Thus, the ratio for the slope stays a constant m. This means that for all points (x, y) along the line

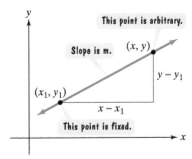

This point is arbitrary.
Slope is m. (x, y)
$y - y_1$
(x_1, y_1)
$x - x_1$
This point is fixed.

FIGURE 2.27 A line passing through (x_1, y_1) with slope m

$$m = \frac{\text{Change in } y}{\text{Change in } x} = \frac{y - y_1}{x - x_1}.$$

We used (x, y) instead of (x_2, y_2) because (x_2, y_2) represents a fixed point and (x, y) is not a fixed point on the line.

We can clear the fraction by multiplying both sides by $x - x_1$, the least common denominator.

$$m = \frac{y - y_1}{x - x_1} \qquad \text{This is the slope of the line in Figure 2.27.}$$

$$m(x - x_1) = \frac{y - y_1}{x - x_1} \cdot (x - x_1) \qquad \text{Multiply both sides by } x - x_1.$$

$$m(x - x_1) = y - y_1 \qquad \text{Simplify: } \frac{y - y_1}{x - x_1} \cdot (x - x_1) = y - y_1.$$

Now, if we reverse the two sides, we obtain the *point-slope form* of the equation of a line.

GREAT QUESTION!

When using $y - y_1 = m(x - x_1)$, for which variables do I substitute numbers?

When writing the point-slope form of a line's equation, you will never substitute numbers for x and y. You will substitute values for $x_1, y_1,$ and m.

Point-Slope Form of the Equation of a Line

The **point-slope form of the equation** of a nonvertical line with slope m that passes through the point (x_1, y_1) is

$$y - y_1 = m(x - x_1).$$

For example, the point-slope form of the equation of the line passing through $(1, 5)$ with slope 2 $(m = 2)$ is

$$y - 5 = 2(x - 1).$$

We will soon be expressing the equation of a nonvertical line in function notation. To do so, we need to solve the point-slope form of a line's equation for y. Example 2 illustrates how to isolate y on one side of the equal sign.

EXAMPLE 2   Writing an Equation for a Line in Point-Slope Form

Write an equation in point-slope form for the line with slope 4 that passes through the point $(-1, 3)$. Then solve the equation for y.

SOLUTION

We use the point-slope form of the equation of a line with $m = 4$, $x_1 = -1$, and $y_1 = 3$.

$$y - y_1 = m(x - x_1)$$ This is the point-slope form of the equation.

$$y - 3 = 4[x - (-1)]$$ Substitute the given values: $m = 4$ and $(x_1, y_1) = (-1, 3)$.

$$y - 3 = 4(x + 1)$$ We now have an equation in point-slope form for the given line.

Now we solve this equation for y.

We need to isolate y.

$$y - 3 = 4(x + 1)$$ This is the point-slope form of the equation.

$$y - 3 = 4x + 4$$ Use the distributive property.

$$y = 4x + 7$$ Add 3 to both sides.   • • •

🔘 Check Point 2 Write an equation in point-slope form for the line with slope 6 that passes through the point $(2, -5)$. Then solve the equation for y.

EXAMPLE 3   Writing an Equation for a Line in Point-Slope Form

Write an equation in point-slope form for the line passing through the points $(4, -3)$ and $(-2, 6)$. (See **Figure 2.28**.) Then solve the equation for y.

SOLUTION

To use the point-slope form, we need to find the slope. The slope is the change in the y-coordinates divided by the corresponding change in the x-coordinates.

$$m = \frac{6 - (-3)}{-2 - 4} = \frac{9}{-6} = -\frac{3}{2}$$ This is the definition of slope using $(4, -3)$ and $(-2, 6)$.

We can take either point on the line to be (x_1, y_1). Let's use $(x_1, y_1) = (4, -3)$. Now, we are ready to write the point-slope form of the equation.

$$y - y_1 = m(x - x_1)$$ This is the point-slope form of the equation.

$$y - (-3) = -\tfrac{3}{2}(x - 4)$$ Substitute: $(x_1, y_1) = (4, -3)$ and $m = -\tfrac{3}{2}$.

$$y + 3 = -\tfrac{3}{2}(x - 4)$$ Simplify.

We now have an equation in point-slope form for the line shown in **Figure 2.28**. Now, we solve this equation for y.

We need to isolate y.

$$y + 3 = -\tfrac{3}{2}(x - 4)$$ This is the point-slope form of the equation.

$$y + 3 = -\tfrac{3}{2}x + 6$$ Use the distributive property.

$$y = -\tfrac{3}{2}x + 3$$ Subtract 3 from both sides.   • • •

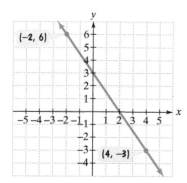

FIGURE 2.28 Write an equation in point-slope form for this line.

DISCOVERY

You can use either point for (x_1, y_1) when you write a point-slope equation for a line. Rework Example 3 using $(-2, 6)$ for (x_1, y_1). Once you solve for y, you should still obtain

$$y = -\tfrac{3}{2}x + 3.$$

🔘 Check Point 3 Write an equation in point-slope form for the line passing through the points $(-2, -1)$ and $(-1, -6)$. Then solve the equation for y.

③ Write and graph the slope-intercept form of the equation of a line.

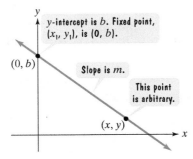

FIGURE 2.29 A line with slope m and y-intercept b

The Slope-Intercept Form of the Equation of a Line

Let's write the point-slope form of the equation of a nonvertical line with slope m and y-intercept b. The line is shown in **Figure 2.29**. Because the y-intercept is b, the line passes through $(0, b)$. We use the point-slope form with $x_1 = 0$ and $y_1 = b$.

$$y - y_1 = m(x - x_1)$$

Let $y_1 = b$.   Let $x_1 = 0$.

We obtain

$$y - b = m(x - 0).$$

Simplifying on the right side gives us

$$y - b = mx.$$

Finally, we solve for y by adding b to both sides.

$$y = mx + b$$

Thus, if a line's equation is written with y isolated on one side, the coefficient of x is the line's slope and the constant term is the y-intercept. This form of a line's equation is called the *slope-intercept form* of the line.

> ### Slope-Intercept Form of the Equation of a Line
>
> The **slope-intercept form of the equation** of a nonvertical line with slope m and y-intercept b is
>
> $$y = mx + b.$$

The slope-intercept form of a line's equation, $y = mx + b$, can be expressed in function notation by replacing y with $f(x)$:

$$f(x) = mx + b.$$

We have seen that functions in this form are called **linear functions**. Thus, in the equation of a linear function, the coefficient of x is the line's slope and the constant term is the y-intercept. Here are two examples:

$$y = 2x - 4 \qquad\qquad f(x) = \tfrac{1}{2}x + 2.$$

The slope is 2.   The y-intercept is −4.   The slope is $\tfrac{1}{2}$.   The y-intercept is 2.

If a linear function's equation is in slope-intercept form, we can use the y-intercept and the slope to obtain its graph.

GREAT QUESTION!

If the slope is an integer, such as 2, why should I express it as $\frac{2}{1}$ for graphing purposes?

Writing the slope, m, as a fraction allows you to identify the rise (the fraction's numerator) and the run (the fraction's denominator).

Graphing $y = mx + b$ Using the Slope and y-Intercept

1. Plot the point containing the y-intercept on the y-axis. This is the point $(0, b)$.
2. Obtain a second point using the slope, m. Write m as a fraction, and use rise over run, starting at the point containing the y-intercept, to plot this point.
3. Use a straightedge to draw a line through the two points. Draw arrowheads at the ends of the line to show that the line continues indefinitely in both directions.

EXAMPLE 4   Graphing Using the Slope and y-Intercept

Graph the linear function: $f(x) = -\dfrac{3}{2}x + 2.$

SOLUTION

The equation of the line is in the form $f(x) = mx + b$. We can find the slope, m, by identifying the coefficient of x. We can find the y-intercept, b, by identifying the constant term.

$$f(x) = -\frac{3}{2}x + 2$$

The slope is $-\frac{3}{2}$.

The y-intercept is **2**.

Now that we have identified the slope, $-\frac{3}{2}$, and the y-intercept, 2, we use the three-step procedure to graph the equation.

Step 1   Plot the point containing the y-intercept on the y-axis. The y-intercept is 2. We plot $(0, 2)$, shown in **Figure 2.30**.

Step 2   Obtain a second point using the slope, m. Write m as a fraction, and use rise over run, starting at the point containing the y-intercept, to plot this point. The slope, $-\frac{3}{2}$, is already written as a fraction.

$$m = -\frac{3}{2} = \frac{-3}{2} = \frac{\text{Rise}}{\text{Run}}$$

We plot the second point on the line by starting at $(0, 2)$, the first point. Based on the slope, we move 3 units *down* (the rise) and 2 units to the *right* (the run). This puts us at a second point on the line, $(2, -1)$, shown in **Figure 2.30**.

Step 3   Use a straightedge to draw a line through the two points. The graph of the linear function $f(x) = -\frac{3}{2}x + 2$ is shown as a blue line in **Figure 2.30**.   • • •

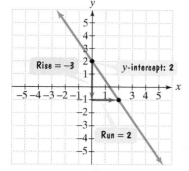

FIGURE 2.30 The graph of $f(x) = -\frac{3}{2}x + 2$

✓ Check Point **4**   Graph the linear function: $f(x) = \frac{3}{5}x + 1$.

④ Graph horizontal or vertical lines.

Equations of Horizontal and Vertical Lines

If a line is horizontal, its slope is zero: $m = 0$. Thus, the equation $y = mx + b$ becomes $y = b$, where b is the y-intercept. All horizontal lines have equations of the form $y = b$.

EXAMPLE 5   Graphing a Horizontal Line

Graph $y = -4$ in the rectangular coordinate system.

SOLUTION

All ordered pairs that are solutions of $y = -4$ have a value of y that is always -4. Any value can be used for x. In the table on the right, we have selected three of the possible values for x: $-2, 0$, and 3. The table shows that three ordered pairs that are solutions of $y = -4$ are $(-2, -4)$, $(0, -4)$, and $(3, -4)$. Drawing a line that passes through the three points gives the horizontal line shown in **Figure 2.31**.

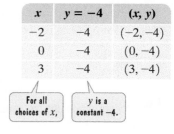

x	$y = -4$	(x, y)
-2	-4	$(-2, -4)$
0	-4	$(0, -4)$
3	-4	$(3, -4)$

For all choices of x,

y is a constant -4.

FIGURE 2.31 The graph of $y = -4$ or $f(x) = -4$

✓ Check Point **5**   Graph $y = 3$ in the rectangular coordinate system.

Equation of a Horizontal Line

A horizontal line is given by an equation of the form

$$y = b,$$

where b is the y-intercept of the line. The slope of a horizontal line is zero.

Because any vertical line can intersect the graph of a horizontal line $y = b$ only once, a horizontal line is the graph of a function. Thus, we can express the equation $y = b$ as $f(x) = b$. This linear function is often called a **constant function**.

Next, let's see what we can discover about the graph of an equation of the form $x = a$ by looking at an example.

EXAMPLE 6 Graphing a Vertical Line

Graph the linear equation: $x = 2$.

SOLUTION

All ordered pairs that are solutions of $x = 2$ have a value of x that is always 2. Any value can be used for y. In the table on the right, we have selected three of the possible values for y: $-2, 0$, and 3. The table shows that three ordered pairs that are solutions of $x = 2$ are $(2, -2)$, $(2, 0)$,

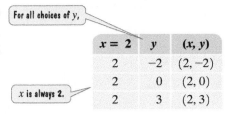

and $(2, 3)$. Drawing a line that passes through the three points gives the vertical line shown in **Figure 2.32**.

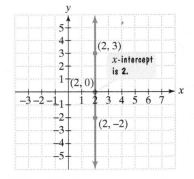

FIGURE 2.32 The graph of $x = 2$

Equation of a Vertical Line

A vertical line is given by an equation of the form

$$x = a,$$

where a is the x-intercept of the line. The slope of a vertical line is undefined.

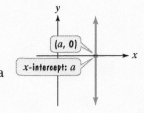

Does a vertical line represent the graph of a linear function? No. Look at the graph of $x = 2$ in **Figure 2.32**. A vertical line drawn through $(2, 0)$ intersects the graph infinitely many times. This shows that infinitely many outputs are associated with the input 2. **No vertical line represents a linear function.**

✓ Check Point 6 Graph the linear equation: $x = -3$.

⑤ Recognize and use the general form of a line's equation.

The General Form of the Equation of a Line

The vertical line whose equation is $x = 5$ cannot be written in slope-intercept form, $y = mx + b$, because its slope is undefined. However, every line has an equation that can be expressed in the form $Ax + By + C = 0$. For example, $x = 5$ can be expressed as $1x + 0y - 5 = 0$, or $x - 5 = 0$. The equation $Ax + By + C = 0$ is called the *general form* of the equation of a line.

General Form of the Equation of a Line

Every line has an equation that can be written in the **general form**

$$Ax + By + C = 0,$$

where A, B, and C are real numbers, and A and B are not both zero.

If the equation of a nonvertical line is given in general form, it is possible to find the slope, m, and the y-intercept, b, for the line. We solve the equation for y, transforming it into the slope-intercept form $y = mx + b$. In this form, the coefficient of x is the slope of the line and the constant term is its y-intercept.

EXAMPLE 7 Finding the Slope and the y-Intercept

Find the slope and the y-intercept of the line whose equation is $3x + 2y - 4 = 0$.

SOLUTION

The equation is given in general form. We begin by rewriting it in the form $y = mx + b$. We need to solve for y.

Our goal is to isolate y.

$3x + 2y - 4 = 0$	This is the given equation.
$2y = -3x + 4$	Isolate the term containing y by adding $-3x + 4$ to both sides.
$\dfrac{2y}{2} = \dfrac{-3x + 4}{2}$	Divide both sides by 2.
$y = -\dfrac{3}{2}x + 2$	On the right, divide each term in the numerator by 2 to obtain slope-intercept form.

slope   y-intercept

The coefficient of x, $-\frac{3}{2}$, is the slope and the constant term, 2, is the y-intercept. This is the form of the equation that we graphed in **Figure 2.30** on page 249. •••

☑ Check Point **7** Find the slope and the y-intercept of the line whose equation is $3x + 6y - 12 = 0$. Then use the y-intercept and the slope to graph the equation.

6 Use intercepts to graph the general form of a line's equation.

Using Intercepts to Graph $Ax + By + C = 0$

Example 7 and Check Point 7 illustrate that one way to graph the general form of a line's equation is to convert to slope-intercept form, $y = mx + b$. Then use the slope and the y-intercept to obtain the graph.

A second method for graphing $Ax + By + C = 0$ uses intercepts. This method does not require rewriting the general form in a different form.

Using Intercepts to Graph $Ax + By + C = 0$

1. Find the x-intercept. Let $y = 0$ and solve for x. Plot the point containing the x-intercept on the x-axis.

2. Find the y-intercept. Let $x = 0$ and solve for y. Plot the point containing the y-intercept on the y-axis.

3. Use a straightedge to draw a line through the two points containing the intercepts. Draw arrowheads at the ends of the line to show that the line continues indefinitely in both directions.

EXAMPLE 8 Using Intercepts to Graph a Linear Equation

Graph using intercepts: $4x - 3y - 6 = 0$.

SOLUTION

Step 1 Find the *x*-intercept. Let *y* = 0 and solve for *x*.

$$4x - 3 \cdot 0 - 6 = 0 \qquad \text{Replace } y \text{ with 0 in } 4x - 3y - 6 = 0.$$
$$4x - 6 = 0 \qquad \text{Simplify.}$$
$$4x = 6 \qquad \text{Add 6 to both sides.}$$
$$x = \frac{6}{4} = \frac{3}{2} \qquad \text{Divide both sides by 4.}$$

The *x*-intercept is $\frac{3}{2}$, so the line passes through $\left(\frac{3}{2}, 0\right)$ or $(1.5, 0)$, as shown in **Figure 2.33**.

Step 2 Find the *y*-intercept. Let *x* = 0 and solve for *y*.

$$4 \cdot 0 - 3y - 6 = 0 \qquad \text{Replace } x \text{ with 0 in } 4x - 3y - 6 = 0.$$
$$-3y - 6 = 0 \qquad \text{Simplify.}$$
$$-3y = 6 \qquad \text{Add 6 to both sides.}$$
$$y = -2 \qquad \text{Divide both sides by } -3.$$

The *y*-intercept is -2, so the line passes through $(0, -2)$, as shown in **Figure 2.33**.

Step 3 Graph the equation by drawing a line through the two points containing the intercepts. The graph of $4x - 3y - 6 = 0$ is shown in **Figure 2.33**. • • •

FIGURE 2.33 The graph of
$4x - 3y - 6 = 0$

⊘ **Check Point 8** Graph using intercepts: $3x - 2y - 6 = 0$.

We've covered a lot of territory. Let's take a moment to summarize the various forms for equations of lines.

Equations of Lines

1. Point-slope form	$y - y_1 = m(x - x_1)$
2. Slope-intercept form	$y = mx + b$ or $f(x) = mx + b$
3. Horizontal line	$y = b$
4. Vertical line	$x = a$
5. General form	$Ax + By + C = 0$

⑦ Model data with linear functions and make predictions.

Applications

Linear functions are useful for modeling data that fall on or near a line.

EXAMPLE 9 Modeling Global Warming

The amount of carbon dioxide in the atmosphere, measured in parts per million, has been increasing as a result of the burning of oil and coal. The buildup of gases and particles traps heat and raises the planet's temperature. The bar graph in **Figure 2.34(a)** at the top of the next page gives the average atmospheric concentration of carbon dioxide and the average global temperature for six selected years. The data are displayed as a set of six points in a rectangular coordinate system in **Figure 2.34(b)**.

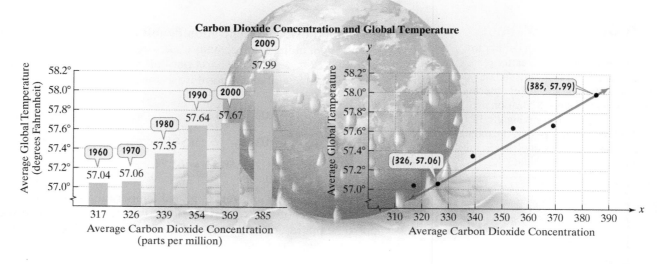

FIGURE 2.34(a)
Source: National Oceanic and Atmospheric Administration

FIGURE 2.34(b)

a. Shown on the scatter plot in **Figure 2.34(b)** is a line that passes through or near the six points. Write the slope-intercept form of this equation using function notation.

b. The preindustrial concentration of atmospheric carbon dioxide was 280 parts per million. The United Nations' Intergovernmental Panel on Climate Change predicts global temperatures will rise between 2°F and 5°F if carbon dioxide concentration doubles from the preindustrial level. Compared to the average global temperature of 57.99°F for 2009, how well does the function from part (a) model this prediction?

SOLUTION

a. The line in **Figure 2.34(b)** passes through (326, 57.06) and (385, 57.99). We start by finding its slope.

$$m = \frac{\text{Change in } y}{\text{Change in } x} = \frac{57.99 - 57.06}{385 - 326} = \frac{0.93}{59} \approx 0.02$$

The slope indicates that for each increase of one part per million in carbon dioxide concentration, the average global temperature is increasing by approximately 0.02°F.

Now we write the line's equation in slope-intercept form.

$$y - y_1 = m(x - x_1)$$ Begin with the point-slope form.

$$y - 57.06 = 0.02(x - 326)$$ Either ordered pair can be (x_1, y_1). Let $(x_1, y_1) = (326, 57.06)$. From above, $m \approx 0.02$.

$$y - 57.06 = 0.02x - 6.52$$ Apply the distributive property: $0.02(326) = 6.52$.

$$y = 0.02x + 50.54$$ Add 57.06 to both sides and solve for y.

A linear function that models average global temperature, $f(x)$, for an atmospheric carbon dioxide concentration of x parts per million is

$$f(x) = 0.02x + 50.54.$$

TECHNOLOGY

You can use a graphing utility to obtain a model for a scatter plot in which the data points fall on or near a straight line. After entering the data in **Figure 2.34(a)** on the previous page, a graphing utility displays a scatter plot of the data and the regression line, that is, the line that best fits the data.

[310, 390, 10] by [56.8, 58.4, 0.2]

Also displayed is the regression line's equation.

b. If carbon dioxide concentration doubles from its preindustrial level of 280 parts per million, which many experts deem very likely, the concentration will reach 280×2, or 560 parts per million. We use the linear function to predict average global temperature at this concentration.

$$f(x) = 0.02x + 50.54 \qquad \text{Use the function from part (a).}$$

$$f(560) = 0.02(560) + 50.54 \qquad \text{Substitute 560 for x.}$$

$$= 11.2 + 50.54 = 61.74$$

Our model projects an average global temperature of 61.74°F for a carbon dioxide concentration of 560 parts per million. Compared to the average global temperature of 57.99° for 2009 shown in **Figure 2.34(a)** on the previous page, this is an increase of

$$61.74°F - 57.99°F = 3.75°F.$$

This is consistent with a rise between 2°F and 5°F as predicted by the Intergovernmental Panel on Climate Change. • • •

 Check Point **9** Use the data points (317, 57.04) and (354, 57.64), shown, but not labeled, in **Figure 2.34(b)** on the previous page to obtain a linear function that models average global temperature, $f(x)$, for an atmospheric carbon dioxide concentration of x parts per million. Round m to three decimal places and b to one decimal place. Then use the function to project average global temperature at a concentration of 600 parts per million.

CONCEPT AND VOCABULARY CHECK

Fill in each blank so that the resulting statement is true.

1. Data presented in a visual form as a set of points is called a/an _____. A line that best fits this set of points is called a/an _____ line.
2. The slope, m, of a line through the distinct points (x_1, y_1) and (x_2, y_2) is given by the formula $m = $ _____.
3. If a line rises from left to right, the line has _____ slope.
4. If a line falls from left to right, the line has _____ slope.
5. The slope of a horizontal line is _____.
6. The slope of a vertical line is _____.
7. The point-slope form of the equation of a nonvertical line with slope m that passes through the point (x_1, y_1) is _____.

8. The slope-intercept form of the equation of a line is _____, where m represents the _____ and b represents the _____.
9. In order to graph the line whose equation is
   $y = \dfrac{2}{5}x + 3$, begin by plotting the point _____.
   From this point, we move _____ units up (the rise) and _____ units to the right (the run).
10. The graph of the equation $y = 3$ is a/an _____ line.
11. The graph of the equation $x = -2$ is a/an _____ line.
12. The equation $Ax + By + C = 0$, where A and B are not both zero, is called the _____ form of the equation of a line.

EXERCISE SET 2.3

Practice Exercises

In Exercises 1–10, find the slope of the line passing through each pair of points or state that the slope is undefined. Then indicate whether the line through the points rises, falls, is horizontal, or is vertical.

1. $(4, 7)$ and $(8, 10)$
2. $(2, 1)$ and $(3, 4)$
3. $(-2, 1)$ and $(2, 2)$
4. $(-1, 3)$ and $(2, 4)$
5. $(4, -2)$ and $(3, -2)$
6. $(4, -1)$ and $(3, -1)$
7. $(-2, 4)$ and $(-1, -1)$
8. $(6, -4)$ and $(4, -2)$
9. $(5, 3)$ and $(5, -2)$
10. $(3, -4)$ and $(3, 5)$

In Exercises 11–38, use the given conditions to write an equation for each line in point-slope form and slope-intercept form.

11. Slope $= 2$, passing through $(3, 5)$
12. Slope $= 4$, passing through $(1, 3)$
13. Slope $= 6$, passing through $(-2, 5)$
14. Slope $= 8$, passing through $(4, -1)$
15. Slope $= -3$, passing through $(-2, -3)$
16. Slope $= -5$, passing through $(-4, -2)$
17. Slope $= -4$, passing through $(-4, 0)$
18. Slope $= -2$, passing through $(0, -3)$
19. Slope $= -1$, passing through $\left(-\frac{1}{2}, -2\right)$
20. Slope $= -1$, passing through $\left(-4, -\frac{1}{4}\right)$
21. Slope $= \frac{1}{2}$, passing through the origin
22. Slope $= \frac{1}{3}$, passing through the origin
23. Slope $= -\frac{2}{3}$, passing through $(6, -2)$
24. Slope $= -\frac{3}{5}$, passing through $(10, -4)$
25. Passing through $(1, 2)$ and $(5, 10)$
26. Passing through $(3, 5)$ and $(8, 15)$
27. Passing through $(-3, 0)$ and $(0, 3)$
28. Passing through $(-2, 0)$ and $(0, 2)$
29. Passing through $(-3, -1)$ and $(2, 4)$
30. Passing through $(-2, -4)$ and $(1, -1)$
31. Passing through $(-3, -2)$ and $(3, 6)$
32. Passing through $(-3, 6)$ and $(3, -2)$
33. Passing through $(-3, -1)$ and $(4, -1)$
34. Passing through $(-2, -5)$ and $(6, -5)$
35. Passing through $(2, 4)$ with x-intercept $= -2$
36. Passing through $(1, -3)$ with x-intercept $= -1$
37. x-intercept $= -\frac{1}{2}$ and y-intercept $= 4$
38. x-intercept $= 4$ and y-intercept $= -2$

In Exercises 39–48, give the slope and y-intercept of each line whose equation is given. Then graph the linear function.

39. $y = 2x + 1$
40. $y = 3x + 2$
41. $f(x) = -2x + 1$
42. $f(x) = -3x + 2$
43. $f(x) = \frac{3}{4}x - 2$
44. $f(x) = \frac{3}{4}x - 3$
45. $y = -\frac{3}{5}x + 7$
46. $y = -\frac{2}{5}x + 6$
47. $g(x) = -\frac{1}{2}x$
48. $g(x) = -\frac{1}{3}x$

In Exercises 49–58, graph each equation in a rectangular coordinate system.

49. $y = -2$
50. $y = 4$
51. $x = -3$
52. $x = 5$
53. $y = 0$
54. $x = 0$
55. $f(x) = 1$
56. $f(x) = 3$
57. $3x - 18 = 0$
58. $3x + 12 = 0$

In Exercises 59–66,

  a. *Rewrite the given equation in slope-intercept form.*
  b. *Give the slope and y-intercept.*
  c. *Use the slope and y-intercept to graph the linear function.*

59. $3x + y - 5 = 0$
60. $4x + y - 6 = 0$
61. $2x + 3y - 18 = 0$
62. $4x + 6y + 12 = 0$
63. $8x - 4y - 12 = 0$
64. $6x - 5y - 20 = 0$
65. $3y - 9 = 0$
66. $4y + 28 = 0$

In Exercises 67–72, use intercepts to graph each equation.

67. $6x - 2y - 12 = 0$
68. $6x - 9y - 18 = 0$
69. $2x + 3y + 6 = 0$
70. $3x + 5y + 15 = 0$
71. $8x - 2y + 12 = 0$
72. $6x - 3y + 15 = 0$

Practice Plus

In Exercises 73–76, find the slope of the line passing through each pair of points or state that the slope is undefined. Assume that all variables represent positive real numbers. Then indicate whether the line through the points rises, falls, is horizontal, or is vertical.

73. $(0, a)$ and $(b, 0)$
74. $(-a, 0)$ and $(0, -b)$
75. (a, b) and $(a, b + c)$
76. $(a - b, c)$ and $(a, a + c)$

In Exercises 77–78, give the slope and y-intercept of each line whose equation is given. Assume that $B \neq 0$.

77. $Ax + By = C$
78. $Ax = By - C$

In Exercises 79–80, find the value of y if the line through the two given points is to have the indicated slope.

79. $(3, y)$ and $(1, 4), m = -3$
80. $(-2, y)$ and $(4, -4), m = \frac{1}{3}$

In Exercises 81–82, graph each linear function.

81. $3x - 4f(x) - 6 = 0$
82. $6x - 5f(x) - 20 = 0$

83. If one point on a line is $(3, -1)$ and the line's slope is -2, find the y-intercept.

84. If one point on a line is $(2, -6)$ and the line's slope is $-\frac{3}{2}$, find the y-intercept.

Use the figure to make the lists in Exercises 85–86.

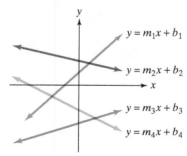

85. List the slopes m_1, m_2, m_3, and m_4 in order of decreasing size.
86. List the y-intercepts b_1, b_2, b_3, and b_4 in order of decreasing size.

Application Exercises

Americans are getting married later in life or not getting married at all. In 2008, nearly half of Americans ages 25 through 29 were unmarried. The following bar graph shows the percentage of never-married men and women in this age group. The data are displayed as two sets of four points each, one scatter plot for the percentage of never-married American men and one for the percentage of never-married American women. Also shown for each scatter plot is a line that passes through or near the four points. Use these lines to solve Exercises 87–88.

Percentage of United States Population Never Married, Ages 25–29

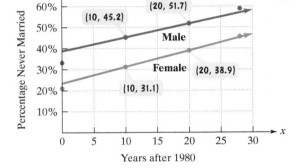

Source: U.S. Census Bureau

87. In this exercise, you will use the blue line for the women shown on the scatter plot to develop a model for the percentage of never-married American females ages 25–29.

   a. Use the two points whose coordinates are shown by the voice balloons to find the point-slope form of the equation of the line that models the percentage of never-married American females ages 25–29, *y*, *x* years after 1980.

   b. Write the equation from part (a) in slope-intercept form. Use function notation.

   c. Use the linear function to predict the percentage of never-married American females, ages 25–29, in 2020.

The bar graph gives the life expectancy for American men and women born in six selected years. In Exercises 89–90, you will use the data to obtain models for life expectancy and make predictions about how long American men and women will live in the future.

Life Expectancy in the United States, by Year of Birth

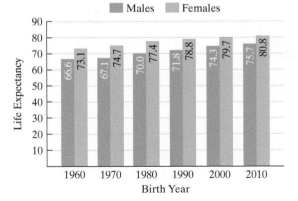

Source: National Center for Health Statistics

88. In this exercise, you will use the red line for the men shown on the scatter plot to develop a model for the percentage of never-married American males ages 25–29.

   a. Use the two points whose coordinates are shown by the voice balloons to find the point-slope form of the equation of the line that models the percentage of never-married American males ages 25–29, *y*, *x* years after 1980.

   b. Write the equation from part (a) in slope-intercept form. Use function notation.

   c. Use the linear function to predict the percentage of never-married American males, ages 25–29, in 2015.

89. Use the data for males shown in the bar graph at the bottom of the previous column to solve this exercise.

   a. Let *x* represent the number of birth years after 1960 and let *y* represent male life expectancy. Create a scatter plot that displays the data as a set of six points in a rectangular coordinate system.

   b. Draw a line through the two points that show male life expectancies for 1980 and 2000. Use the coordinates of these points to write a linear function that models life expectancy, *E*(*x*), for American men born *x* years after 1960.

   c. Use the function from part (b) to project the life expectancy of American men born in 2020.

90. Use the data for females shown in the bar graph at the bottom of the previous column to solve this exercise.

   a. Let *x* represent the number of birth years after 1960 and let *y* represent female life expectancy. Create a scatter plot that displays the data as a set of six points in a rectangular coordinate system.

   b. Draw a line through the two points that show female life expectancies for 1970 and 2000. Use the coordinates of these points to write a linear function that models life expectancy, *E*(*x*), for American women born *x* years after 1960. Round the slope to two decimal places.

   c. Use the function from part (b) to project the life expectancy of American women born in 2020.

91. Shown, again, is the scatter plot that indicates a relationship between the percentage of adult females in a country who are literate and the mortality of children under five. Also shown is a line that passes through or near the points. Find a linear function that models the data by finding the slope-intercept form of the line's equation. Use the function to make a prediction about child mortality based on the percentage of adult females in a country who are literate.

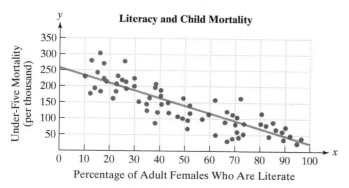

Source: United Nations

92. Just as money doesn't buy happiness for individuals, the two don't necessarily go together for countries either. However, the scatter plot does show a relationship between a country's annual per capita income and the percentage of people in that country who call themselves "happy."

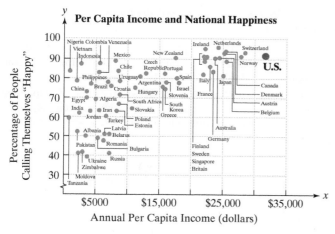

Source: Richard Layard, *Happiness: Lessons from a New Science*, Penguin, 2005

Draw a line that fits the data so that the spread of the data points around the line is as small as possible. Use the coordinates of two points along your line to write the slope-intercept form of its equation. Express the equation in function notation and use the linear function to make a prediction about national happiness based on per capita income.

Writing in Mathematics

93. What is the slope of a line and how is it found?

94. Describe how to write the equation of a line if the coordinates of two points along the line are known.

95. Explain how to derive the slope-intercept form of a line's equation, $y = mx + b$, from the point-slope form

$$y - y_1 = m(x - x_1).$$

96. Explain how to graph the equation $x = 2$. Can this equation be expressed in slope-intercept form? Explain.

97. Explain how to use the general form of a line's equation to find the line's slope and y-intercept.

98. Explain how to use intercepts to graph the general form of a line's equation.

99. Take another look at the scatter plot in Exercise 91. Although there is a relationship between literacy and child mortality, we cannot conclude that increased literacy causes child mortality to decrease. Offer two or more possible explanations for the data in the scatter plot.

Technology Exercises

Use a graphing utility to graph each equation in Exercises 100–103. Then use the TRACE *feature to trace along the line and find the coordinates of two points. Use these points to compute the line's slope. Check your result by using the coefficient of x in the line's equation.*

100. $y = 2x + 4$

101. $y = -3x + 6$

102. $y = -\frac{1}{2}x - 5$

103. $y = \frac{3}{4}x - 2$

104. Is there a relationship between wine consumption and deaths from heart disease? The table gives data from 19 developed countries.

France

Country	A	B	C	D	E	F	G
Liters of alcohol from drinking wine, per person per year (x)	2.5	3.9	2.9	2.4	2.9	0.8	9.1
Deaths from heart disease, per 100,000 people per year (y)	211	167	131	191	220	297	71

U.S.

Country	H	I	J	K	L	M	N	O	P	Q	R	S
(x)	0.8	0.7	7.9	1.8	1.9	0.8	6.5	1.6	5.8	1.3	1.2	2.7
(y)	211	300	107	167	266	227	86	207	115	285	199	172

Source: *New York Times*

a. Use the statistical menu of your graphing utility to enter the 19 ordered pairs of data items shown in the table.

b. Use the scatter plot capability to draw a scatter plot of the data.

c. Select the linear regression option. Use your utility to obtain values for a and b for the equation of the regression line, $y = ax + b$. You may also be given a **correlation coefficient**, r. Values of r close to 1 indicate that the points can be described by a linear relationship and the regression line has a positive slope. Values of r close to -1 indicate that the points can be described by a linear relationship and the regression line has a negative slope. Values of r close to 0 indicate no linear relationship between the variables. In this case, a linear model does not accurately describe the data.

d. Use the appropriate sequence (consult your manual) to graph the regression equation on top of the points in the scatter plot.

Critical Thinking Exercises

Make Sense? *In Exercises 105–108, determine whether each statement makes sense or does not make sense, and explain your reasoning.*

105. The graph of my linear function at first increased, reached a maximum point, and then decreased.

106. A linear function that models tuition and fees at public four-year colleges from 2000 through 2012 has negative slope.

107. Because the variable m does not appear in $Ax + By + C = 0$, equations in this form make it impossible to determine the line's slope.

108. The federal minimum wage was \$5.15 per hour from 1997 through 2006, so $f(x) = 5.15$ models the minimum wage, $f(x)$, in dollars, for the domain $\{1997, 1998, 1999, \ldots, 2006\}$.

In Exercises 109–112, determine whether each statement is true or false. If the statement is false, make the necessary change(s) to produce a true statement.

109. The equation $y = mx + b$ shows that no line can have a y-intercept that is numerically equal to its slope.

110. Every line in the rectangular coordinate system has an equation that can be expressed in slope-intercept form.

111. The graph of the linear function $5x + 6y - 30 = 0$ is a line passing through the point $(6, 0)$ with slope $-\frac{5}{6}$.

112. The graph of $x = 7$ in the rectangular coordinate system is the single point $(7, 0)$.

In Exercises 113–114, find the coefficients that must be placed in each shaded area so that the function's graph will be a line satisfying the specified conditions.

113. $\boxed{}\, x + \boxed{}\, y - 12 = 0$; x-intercept $= -2$; y-intercept $= 4$

114. $\boxed{}\, x + \boxed{}\, y - 12 = 0$; y-intercept $= -6$; slope $= \dfrac{1}{2}$

115. Prove that the equation of a line passing through $(a, 0)$ and $(0, b)(a \neq 0, b \neq 0)$ can be written in the form $\dfrac{x}{a} + \dfrac{y}{b} = 1$. Why is this called the *intercept form* of a line?

116. Excited about the success of celebrity stamps, post office officials were rumored to have put forth a plan to institute two new types of thermometers. On these new scales, $°E$ represents degrees Elvis and $°M$ represents degrees Madonna. If it is known that $40°E = 25°M, 280°E = 125°M$, and degrees Elvis is linearly related to degrees Madonna, write an equation expressing E in terms of M.

Group Exercise

117. In Exercises 87–88, we used the data in a bar graph to develop linear functions that modeled the percentage of never-married American females and males, ages 25–29. For this group exercise, you might find it helpful to pattern your work after Exercises 87 and 88. Group members should begin by consulting an almanac, newspaper, magazine, or the Internet to find data that appear to lie approximately on or near a line. Working by hand or using a graphing utility, group members should construct scatter plots for the data that were assembled. If working by hand, draw a line that approximately fits the data in each scatter plot and then write its equation as a function in slope-intercept form. If using a graphing utility, obtain the equation of each regression line. Then use each linear function's equation to make predictions about what might occur in the future. Are there circumstances that might affect the accuracy of the prediction? List some of these circumstances.

Preview Exercises

Exercises 118–120 will help you prepare for the material covered in the next section.

118. Write the slope-intercept form of the equation of the line passing through $(-3, 1)$ whose slope is the same as the line whose equation is $y = 2x + 1$.

119. Write an equation in general form of the line passing through $(3, -5)$ whose slope is the negative reciprocal (the reciprocal with the opposite sign) of $-\frac{1}{4}$.

120. If $f(x) = x^2$, find

$$\frac{f(x_2) - f(x_1)}{x_2 - x_1},$$

where $x_1 = 1$ and $x_2 = 4$.

SECTION 2.4   More on Slope

Objectives

① Find slopes and equations of parallel and perpendicular lines.

② Interpret slope as rate of change.

③ Find a function's average rate of change.

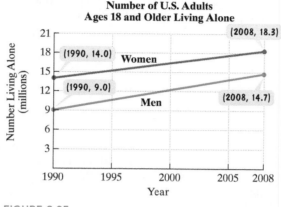

Number of U.S. Adults Ages 18 and Older Living Alone

(2008, 18.3)

(1990, 14.0)   Women

(1990, 9.0)

Men

(2008, 14.7)

Year

FIGURE 2.35
Source: U.S. Census Bureau

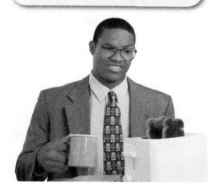

A best guess at the future of our nation indicates that the numbers of men and women living alone will increase each year. **Figure 2.35** shows that in 2008, 14.7 million men and 18.3 million women lived alone, an increase over the numbers displayed in the graph for 1990.

Take a second look at **Figure 2.35**. Can you tell that the green graph representing men has a greater slope than the red graph representing women? This indicates a greater rate of change in the number of men living alone than in the number of women living alone over the period from 1990 through 2008. In this section, you will learn to interpret slope as a rate of change. You will also explore the relationships between slopes of parallel and perpendicular lines.

① Find slopes and equations of parallel and perpendicular lines.

Parallel and Perpendicular Lines

Two nonintersecting lines that lie in the same plane are **parallel**. If two lines do not intersect, the ratio of the vertical change to the horizontal change is the same for both lines. Because two parallel lines have the same "steepness," they must have the same slope.

Slope and Parallel Lines

1. If two nonvertical lines are parallel, then they have the same slope.

2. If two distinct nonvertical lines have the same slope, then they are parallel.

3. Two distinct vertical lines, both with undefined slopes, are parallel.

EXAMPLE 1   Writing Equations of a Line Parallel to a Given Line

Write an equation of the line passing through $(-3, 1)$ and parallel to the line whose equation is $y = 2x + 1$. Express the equation in point-slope form and slope-intercept form.

SOLUTION

The situation is illustrated in **Figure 2.36**. We are looking for the equation of the red line passing through $(-3, 1)$ and parallel to the blue line whose equation is $y = 2x + 1$. How do we obtain the equation of this red line? Notice that the line passes through the point $(-3, 1)$. Using the point-slope form of the line's equation, we have $x_1 = -3$ and $y_1 = 1$.

$$y - y_1 = m(x - x_1)$$

$y_1 = 1 \qquad x_1 = -3$

The equation of this line is given: $y = 2x + 1$.

$(-3, 1)$

We must write the equation of this line.

FIGURE 2.36

With $(x_1, y_1) = (-3, 1)$, the only thing missing from the equation of the red line is m, the slope. Do we know anything about the slope of either line in **Figure 2.36**? The answer is yes; we know the slope of the blue line on the right, whose equation is given.

$$y = 2x + 1$$

The slope of the blue line on the right in **Figure 2.36** is 2.

Parallel lines have the same slope. Because the slope of the blue line is 2, the slope of the red line, the line whose equation we must write, is also 2: $m = 2$. We now have values for x_1, y_1, and m for the red line.

$$y - y_1 = m(x - x_1)$$

$y_1 = 1 \qquad m = 2 \qquad x_1 = -3$

The point-slope form of the red line's equation is

$$y - 1 = 2[x - (-3)] \text{ or}$$
$$y - 1 = 2(x + 3).$$

Solving for y, we obtain the slope-intercept form of the equation.

$$y - 1 = 2x + 6 \quad \text{Apply the distributive property.}$$
$$y = 2x + 7 \quad \text{Add 1 to both sides. This is the slope-intercept}$$
form, $y = mx + b$, of the equation. Using function
notation, the equation is $f(x) = 2x + 7$. • • •

⊘ Check Point **1** Write an equation of the line passing through $(-2, 5)$ and parallel to the line whose equation is $y = 3x + 1$. Express the equation in point-slope form and slope-intercept form.

Two lines that intersect at a right angle (90°) are said to be **perpendicular**, shown in **Figure 2.37**. The relationship between the slopes of perpendicular lines is not as obvious as the relationship between parallel lines. **Figure 2.37** shows line AB, with slope $\frac{c}{d}$. Rotate line AB counterclockwise 90° to the left to obtain line $A'B'$, perpendicular to line AB. The figure indicates that the rise and the run of the new line are reversed from the original line, but the former rise, the new run, is now negative. This means that the slope of the new line is $-\frac{d}{c}$. Notice that the product of the slopes of the two perpendicular lines is -1:

$$\left(\frac{c}{d}\right)\left(-\frac{d}{c}\right) = -1.$$

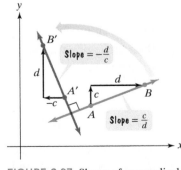

FIGURE 2.37 Slopes of perpendicular lines

This relationship holds for all perpendicular lines and is summarized in the box at the top of the next page.

Slope and Perpendicular Lines

1. If two nonvertical lines are perpendicular, then the product of their slopes is −1.

2. If the product of the slopes of two lines is −1, then the lines are perpendicular.

3. A horizontal line having zero slope is perpendicular to a vertical line having undefined slope.

An equivalent way of stating this relationship is to say that **one line is perpendicular to another line if its slope is the** *negative reciprocal* **of the slope of the other line**. For example, if a line has slope 5, any line having slope $-\frac{1}{5}$ is perpendicular to it. Similarly, if a line has slope $-\frac{3}{4}$, any line having slope $\frac{4}{3}$ is perpendicular to it.

EXAMPLE 2   Writing Equations of a Line Perpendicular to a Given Line

a. Find the slope of any line that is perpendicular to the line whose equation is $x + 4y - 8 = 0$.

b. Write the equation of the line passing through $(3, -5)$ and perpendicular to the line whose equation is $x + 4y - 8 = 0$. Express the equation in general form.

SOLUTION

a. We begin by writing the equation of the given line, $x + 4y - 8 = 0$, in slope-intercept form. Solve for y.

$$x + 4y - 8 = 0 \qquad \text{This is the given equation.}$$
$$4y = -x + 8 \qquad \text{To isolate the } y\text{-term, subtract } x \text{ and add 8 on both sides.}$$
$$y = -\frac{1}{4}x + 2 \qquad \text{Divide both sides by 4.}$$

Slope is $-\frac{1}{4}$.

The given line has slope $-\frac{1}{4}$. Any line perpendicular to this line has a slope that is the negative reciprocal of $-\frac{1}{4}$. Thus, the slope of any perpendicular line is 4.

b. Let's begin by writing the point-slope form of the perpendicular line's equation. Because the line passes through the point $(3, -5)$, we have $x_1 = 3$ and $y_1 = -5$. In part (a), we determined that the slope of any line perpendicular to $x + 4y - 8 = 0$ is 4, so the slope of this particular perpendicular line must also be 4: $m = 4$.

$$y - y_1 = m(x - x_1)$$

$y_1 = -5$ $m = 4$ $x_1 = 3$

The point-slope form of the perpendicular line's equation is

$$y - (-5) = 4(x - 3) \text{ or}$$
$$y + 5 = 4(x - 3).$$

How can we express this equation, $y + 5 = 4(x - 3)$, in general form ($Ax + By + C = 0$)? We need to obtain zero on one side of the equation. Let's do this and keep A, the coefficient of x, positive.

$y + 5 = 4(x - 3)$	This is the point-slope form of the line's equation.
$y + 5 = 4x - 12$	Apply the distributive property.
$y - y + 5 - 5 = 4x - y - 12 - 5$	To obtain 0 on the left, subtract y and subtract 5 on both sides.
$0 = 4x - y - 17$	Simplify.

In general form, the equation of the perpendicular line is $4x - y - 17 = 0$.

• • •

Check Point 2

a. Find the slope of any line that is perpendicular to the line whose equation is $x + 3y - 12 = 0$.

b. Write the equation of the line passing through $(-2, -6)$ and perpendicular to the line whose equation is $x + 3y - 12 = 0$. Express the equation in general form.

2 Interpret slope as rate of change.

Slope as Rate of Change

Slope is defined as the ratio of a change in y to a corresponding change in x. It describes how fast y is changing with respect to x. For a linear function, slope may be interpreted as the rate of change of the dependent variable per unit change in the independent variable.

Our next example shows how slope can be interpreted as a rate of change in an applied situation. When calculating slope in applied problems, keep track of the units in the numerator and the denominator.

EXAMPLE 3 Slope as a Rate of Change

The line graphs for the number of women and men living alone are shown again in **Figure 2.38**. Find the slope of the line segment for the women. Describe what this slope represents.

SOLUTION

We let x represent a year and y the number of women living alone in that year. The two points shown on the line segment for women have the following coordinates:

$$(1990, 14.0) \qquad (2008, 18.3).$$

In 1990, 14 million U.S. women lived alone.

In 2008, 18.3 million U.S. women lived alone.

Now we compute the slope:

$$m = \frac{\text{Change in } y}{\text{Change in } x} = \frac{18.3 - 14.0}{2008 - 1990}$$

The unit in the numerator is *million women*.

The unit in the denominator is *year*.

$$= \frac{4.3}{18} \approx \frac{0.24 \text{ million women}}{\text{year}}.$$

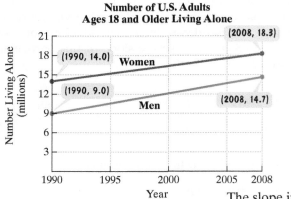

Number of U.S. Adults Ages 18 and Older Living Alone

FIGURE 2.38

The slope indicates that the number of American women living alone increased at a rate of approximately 0.24 million each year for the period from 1990 through 2008. The rate of change is 0.24 million women per year.

• • •

⌀ Check Point **3** Use the ordered pairs in **Figure 2.38** to find the slope of the green line segment for the men. Express the slope correct to two decimal places and describe what it represents.

In Check Point 3, did you find that the slope of the line segment for the men is different from that of the women? The rate of change for the number of men living alone is greater than the rate of change for the number of women living alone. The green line segment representing men in **Figure 2.38** is steeper than the red line segment representing women. If you extend the line segments far enough, the resulting lines will intersect. They are not parallel.

③ Find a function's average rate of change.

The Average Rate of Change of a Function

If the graph of a function is not a straight line, the **average rate of change** between any two points is the slope of the line containing the two points. This line is called a **secant line**. For example, **Figure 2.39** shows the graph of a particular man's height, in inches, as a function of his age, in years. Two points on the graph are labeled: $(13, 57)$ and $(18, 76)$. At age 13, this man was 57 inches tall and at age 18, he was 76 inches tall.

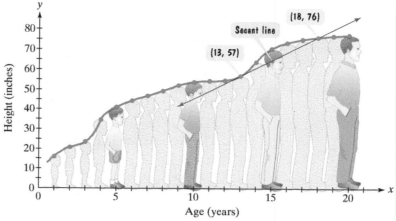

FIGURE 2.39 Height as a function of age

The man's average growth rate between ages 13 and 18 is the slope of the secant line containing $(13, 57)$ and $(18, 76)$:

$$m = \frac{\text{Change in } y}{\text{Change in } x} = \frac{76 - 57}{18 - 13} = \frac{19}{5} = 3\frac{4}{5}.$$

This man's average rate of change, or average growth rate, from age 13 to age 18 was $3\frac{4}{5}$, or 3.8, inches per year.

The Average Rate of Change of a Function

Let $(x_1, f(x_1))$ and $(x_2, f(x_2))$ be distinct points on the graph of a function f. (See **Figure 2.40.**) The **average rate of change of f** from x_1 to x_2 is

$$\frac{f(x_2) - f(x_1)}{x_2 - x_1}.$$

FIGURE 2.40

EXAMPLE 4   Finding the Average Rate of Change

Find the average rate of change of $f(x) = x^2$ from

a. $x_1 = 0$ to $x_2 = 1$ **b.** $x_1 = 1$ to $x_2 = 2$ **c.** $x_1 = -2$ to $x_2 = 0$.

SOLUTION

a. The average rate of change of $f(x) = x^2$ from $x_1 = 0$ to $x_2 = 1$ is

$$\frac{f(x_2) - f(x_1)}{x_2 - x_1} = \frac{f(1) - f(0)}{1 - 0} = \frac{1^2 - 0^2}{1} = 1.$$

Figure 2.41(a) shows the secant line of $f(x) = x^2$ from $x_1 = 0$ to $x_2 = 1$. The average rate of change is positive and the function is increasing on the interval $(0, 1)$.

b. The average rate of change of $f(x) = x^2$ from $x_1 = 1$ to $x_2 = 2$ is

$$\frac{f(x_2) - f(x_1)}{x_2 - x_1} = \frac{f(2) - f(1)}{2 - 1} = \frac{2^2 - 1^2}{1} = 3.$$

Figure 2.41(b) shows the secant line of $f(x) = x^2$ from $x_1 = 1$ to $x_2 = 2$. The average rate of change is positive and the function is increasing on the interval $(1, 2)$. Can you see that the graph rises more steeply on the interval $(1, 2)$ than on $(0, 1)$? This is because the average rate of change from $x_1 = 1$ to $x_2 = 2$ is greater than the average rate of change from $x_1 = 0$ to $x_2 = 1$.

c. The average rate of change of $f(x) = x^2$ from $x_1 = -2$ to $x_2 = 0$ is

$$\frac{f(x_2) - f(x_1)}{x_2 - x_1} = \frac{f(0) - f(-2)}{0 - (-2)} = \frac{0^2 - (-2)^2}{2} = \frac{-4}{2} = -2.$$

Figure 2.41(c) shows the secant line of $f(x) = x^2$ from $x_1 = -2$ to $x_2 = 0$. The average rate of change is negative and the function is decreasing on the interval $(-2, 0)$.

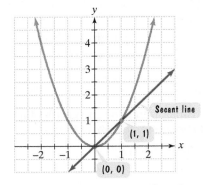

FIGURE 2.41(a) The secant line of $f(x) = x^2$ from $x_1 = 0$ to $x_2 = 1$

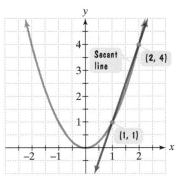

FIGURE 2.41(b) The secant line of $f(x) = x^2$ from $x_1 = 1$ to $x_2 = 2$

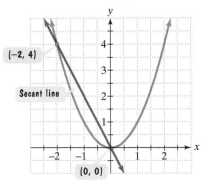

FIGURE 2.41(c) The secant line of $f(x) = x^2$ from $x_1 = -2$ to $x_2 = 0$ ● ● ●

Check Point **4** Find the average rate of change of $f(x) = x^3$ from

a. $x_1 = 0$ to $x_2 = 1$ **b.** $x_1 = 1$ to $x_2 = 2$ **c.** $x_1 = -2$ to $x_2 = 0$.

Suppose we are interested in the average rate of change of f from $x_1 = x$ to $x_2 = x + h$. In this case, the average rate of change is

$$\frac{f(x_2) - f(x_1)}{x_2 - x_1} = \frac{f(x + h) - f(x)}{x + h - x} = \frac{f(x + h) - f(x)}{h}.$$

Do you recognize the last expression? It is the difference quotient that you used in Section 2.2. Thus, the difference quotient gives the average rate of change of a function from x to $x + h$. In the difference quotient, h is thought of as a number very close to 0. In this way, the average rate of change can be found for a very short interval.

EXAMPLE 5   Finding the Average Rate of Change

When a person receives a drug injected into a muscle, the concentration of the drug in the body, measured in milligrams per 100 milliliters, is a function of the time elapsed after the injection, measured in hours. **Figure 2.42** shows the graph of such a function, where x represents hours after the injection and $f(x)$ is the drug's concentration at time x. Find the average rate of change in the drug's concentration between 3 and 7 hours.

SOLUTION

At 3 hours, the drug's concentration is 0.05 and at 7 hours, the concentration is 0.02. The average rate of change in its concentration between 3 and 7 hours is

$$\frac{f(x_2) - f(x_1)}{x_2 - x_1} = \frac{f(7) - f(3)}{7 - 3} = \frac{0.02 - 0.05}{7 - 3} = \frac{-0.03}{4} = -0.0075.$$

The average rate of change is -0.0075. This means that the drug's concentration is decreasing at an average rate of 0.0075 milligram per 100 milliliters per hour.   • • •

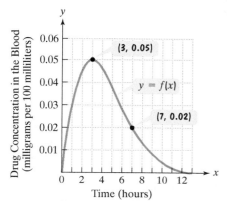

FIGURE 2.42 Concentration of a drug as a function of time

GREAT QUESTION!

Can you clarify how you determine the units that you use when describing slope as a rate of change?

Units used to describe x and y tend to "pile up" when expressing the rate of change of y with respect to x. The unit used to express the rate of change of y with respect to x is

the unit used
to describe y **per**   the unit used
to describe x.

In **Figure 2.42**, y, or drug concentration,
is described in milligrams per 100 milliliters.   In **Figure 2.42**, x, or
time, is described in hours.

In Example 5, the rate of change is described in terms of milligrams per 100 milliliters per hour.

⊘ Check Point **5** Use **Figure 2.42** to find the average rate of change in the drug's concentration between 1 hour and 3 hours.

Blitzer Bonus ‖ How Calculus Studies Change

Take a rapid sequence of still photographs of a moving scene and project them onto a screen at thirty shots a second or faster. Our eyes see the results as continuous motion. The small difference between one frame and the next cannot be detected by the human visual system. The idea of calculus likewise regards continuous motion as made up of a sequence of still configurations. Calculus masters the mystery of movement by "freezing the frame" of a continuous changing process, instant by instant. For example, **Figure 2.43** shows a male's changing height over intervals of time. Over the period of time from P to D, his average rate of growth is his change in height—that is, his height at time D minus his height at time P—divided by the change in time from P to D. This is the slope of secant line PD.

The secant lines PD, PC, PB, and PA shown in **Figure 2.43** have slopes that show average growth rates for successively shorter periods of time. Calculus makes these time frames so small that they approach a single point—that is, a single instant in time. This point is shown as point P in **Figure 2.43**. The slope of the line that touches the graph at P gives the male's growth rate at one instant in time, P.

FIGURE 2.43 Analyzing continuous growth over intervals of time and at an instant in time

CONCEPT AND VOCABULARY CHECK

Fill in each blank so that the resulting statement is true.

1. If two nonvertical lines are parallel, then they have _____ slope.
2. If two nonvertical lines are perpendicular, then the product of their slopes is ____.
3. Consider the line whose equation is $y = -\frac{1}{3}x + 5$. The slope of any line that is parallel to this line is ____. The slope of any line that is perpendicular to this line is ____.

4. Consider the line whose equation is $2x + y - 6 = 0$. The slope of any line that is parallel to this line is ____. The slope of any line that is perpendicular to this line is ____.
5. The slope of the line through the distinct points (x_1, y_1) and (x_2, y_2) can be interpreted as the rate of change in ____ with respect to ____.
6. If $(x_1, f(x_1))$ and $(x_2, f(x_2))$ are distinct points on the graph of a function f, the average rate of change of f from x_1 to x_2 is _____.

EXERCISE SET 2.4

Practice Exercises

In Exercises 1–4, write an equation for line L in point-slope form and slope-intercept form.

1.

L is parallel to $y = 2x$.

2.
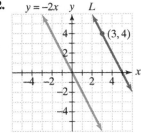
L is parallel to $y = -2x$.

3.
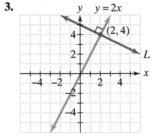
L is perpendicular to $y = 2x$.

4.
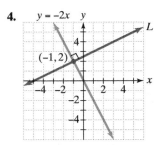
L is perpendicular to $y = -2x$.

In Exercises 5–8, use the given conditions to write an equation for each line in point-slope form and slope-intercept form.

5. Passing through $(-8, -10)$ and parallel to the line whose equation is $y = -4x + 3$

6. Passing through $(-2, -7)$ and parallel to the line whose equation is $y = -5x + 4$

7. Passing through $(2, -3)$ and perpendicular to the line whose equation is $y = \frac{1}{5}x + 6$

8. Passing through $(-4, 2)$ and perpendicular to the line whose equation is $y = \frac{1}{3}x + 7$

In Exercises 9–12, use the given conditions to write an equation for each line in point-slope form and general form.

9. Passing through $(-2, 2)$ and parallel to the line whose equation is $2x - 3y - 7 = 0$

10. Passing through $(-1, 3)$ and parallel to the line whose equation is $3x - 2y - 5 = 0$

11. Passing through $(4, -7)$ and perpendicular to the line whose equation is $x - 2y - 3 = 0$

12. Passing through $(5, -9)$ and perpendicular to the line whose equation is $x + 7y - 12 = 0$

In Exercises 13–18, find the average rate of change of the function from x_1 to x_2.

13. $f(x) = 3x$ from $x_1 = 0$ to $x_2 = 5$

14. $f(x) = 6x$ from $x_1 = 0$ to $x_2 = 4$

15. $f(x) = x^2 + 2x$ from $x_1 = 3$ to $x_2 = 5$

16. $f(x) = x^2 - 2x$ from $x_1 = 3$ to $x_2 = 6$

17. $f(x) = \sqrt{x}$ from $x_1 = 4$ to $x_2 = 9$

18. $f(x) = \sqrt{x}$ from $x_1 = 9$ to $x_2 = 16$

Practice Plus

In Exercises 19–24, write an equation in slope-intercept form of a linear function f whose graph satisfies the given conditions.

19. The graph of f passes through $(-1, 5)$ and is perpendicular to the line whose equation is $x = 6$.

20. The graph of f passes through $(-2, 6)$ and is perpendicular to the line whose equation is $x = -4$.

21. The graph of f passes through $(-6, 4)$ and is perpendicular to the line that has an x-intercept of 2 and a y-intercept of -4.

22. The graph of f passes through $(-5, 6)$ and is perpendicular to the line that has an x-intercept of 3 and a y-intercept of -9.

23. The graph of f is perpendicular to the line whose equation is $3x - 2y - 4 = 0$ and has the same y-intercept as this line.

24. The graph of f is perpendicular to the line whose equation is $4x - y - 6 = 0$ and has the same y-intercept as this line.

Application Exercises

The bar graph shows that as costs changed over the decades, Americans devoted less of their budget to groceries and more to health care.

Percentage of Total Spending in the United States on Food and Health Care

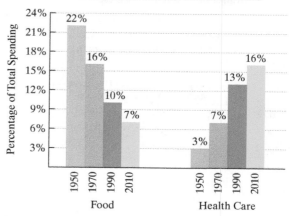

Source: *Time*, October 10, 2011

In Exercises 25–26, find a linear function in slope-intercept form that models the given description. Each function should model the percentage of total spending, $p(x)$, by Americans x years after 1950.

25. In 1950, Americans spent 22% of their budget on food. This has decreased at an average rate of approximately 0.25% per year since then.

26. In 1950, Americans spent 3% of their budget on health care. This has increased at an average rate of approximately 0.22% per year since then.

The stated intent of the 1994 "don't ask, don't tell" policy was to reduce the number of discharges of gay men and lesbians from the military. Nearly 14,000 active-duty gay servicemembers were dismissed under the policy, which officially ended in 2011, after 18 years. The line graph shows the number of discharges under "don't ask, don't tell" from 1994 through 2010. Use the data displayed by the graph to solve Exercises 27–28.

Number of Active-Duty Gay Servicemembers Discharged from the Military for Homosexuality

Source: General Accountability Office

(In Exercises 27–28, be sure to refer to the graph at the bottom of the previous page.)

27. Find the average rate of change, rounded to the nearest whole number, from 1994 through 1998. Describe what this means.

28. Find the average rate of change, rounded to the nearest whole number, from 2001 through 2006. Describe what this means.

The function $f(x) = 1.1x^3 - 35x^2 + 264x + 557$ models the number of discharges, $f(x)$, under "don't ask, don't tell" x years after 1994. Use this model and its graph, shown on the domain $[0, 12]$, to solve Exercises 29–30.

Graph of a Model for Discharges under "Don't Ask, Don't Tell"

29. a. Find the slope of the secant line, rounded to the nearest whole number, from $x_1 = 0$ to $x_2 = 4$.

    b. Does the slope from part (a) underestimate or overestimate the average yearly increase that you determined in Exercise 27? By how much?

30. a. Find the slope of the secant line, rounded to the nearest whole number, from $x_1 = 7$ to $x_2 = 12$.

    b. Does the slope from part (b) underestimate or overestimate the average yearly decrease that you determined in Exercise 28? By how much?

Writing in Mathematics

31. If two lines are parallel, describe the relationship between their slopes.

32. If two lines are perpendicular, describe the relationship between their slopes.

33. If you know a point on a line and you know the equation of a line perpendicular to this line, explain how to write the line's equation.

34. A formula in the form $y = mx + b$ models the average retail price, y, of a new car x years after 2000. Would you expect m to be positive, negative, or zero? Explain your answer.

35. What is a secant line?

36. What is the average rate of change of a function?

Technology Exercise

37. a. Why are the lines whose equations are $y = \frac{1}{3}x + 1$ and $y = -3x - 2$ perpendicular?

    b. Use a graphing utility to graph the equations in a $[-10, 10, 1]$ by $[-10, 10, 1]$ viewing rectangle. Do the lines appear to be perpendicular?

    c. Now use the zoom square feature of your utility. Describe what happens to the graphs. Explain why this is so.

Critical Thinking Exercises

Make Sense? *In Exercises 38–41, determine whether each statement makes sense or does not make sense, and explain your reasoning.*

38. Some of the steel girders in this photo of the Eiffel Tower appear to have slopes that are negative reciprocals of each other.

39. I have linear functions that model changes for men and women over the same time period. The functions have the same slope, so their graphs are parallel lines, indicating that the rate of change for men is the same as the rate of change for women.

40. The graph of my function is not a straight line, so I cannot use slope to analyze its rates of change.

41. According to the Blitzer Bonus on page 266, calculus studies change by analyzing slopes of secant lines over successively shorter intervals.

42. What is the slope of a line that is perpendicular to the line whose equation is $Ax + By + C = 0$, $A \neq 0$ and $B \neq 0$?

43. Determine the value of A so that the line whose equation is $Ax + y - 2 = 0$ is perpendicular to the line containing the points $(1, -3)$ and $(-2, 4)$.

Preview Exercises

Exercises 44–46 will help you prepare for the material covered in the next section. In each exercise, graph the functions in parts (a) and (b) in the same rectangular coordinate system.

44. a. Graph $f(x) = |x|$ using the ordered pairs $(-3, f(-3))$, $(-2, f(-2))$, $(-1, f(-1))$, $(0, f(0))$, $(1, f(1))$, $(2, f(2))$, and $(3, f(3))$.

    b. Subtract 4 from each y-coordinate of the ordered pairs in part (a). Then graph the ordered pairs and connect them with two linear pieces.

    c. Describe the relationship between the graph in part (b) and the graph in part (a).

45. a. Graph $f(x) = x^2$ using the ordered pairs $(-3, f(-3))$, $(-2, f(-2))$, $(-1, f(-1))$, $(0, f(0))$, $(1, f(1))$, $(2, f(2))$, and $(3, f(3))$.

    b. Add 2 to each x-coordinate of the ordered pairs in part (a). Then graph the ordered pairs and connect them with a smooth curve.

    c. Describe the relationship between the graph in part (b) and the graph in part (a).

46. a. Graph $f(x) = x^3$ using the ordered pairs $(-2, f(-2))$, $(-1, f(-1))$, $(0, f(0))$, $(1, f(1))$, and $(2, f(2))$.

b. Replace each x-coordinate of the ordered pairs in part (a) with its opposite, or additive inverse. Then graph the ordered pairs and connect them with a smooth curve.

c. Describe the relationship between the graph in part (b) and the graph in part (a).

CHAPTER 2 Mid-Chapter Check Point

WHAT YOU KNOW: We learned that a function is a relation in which no two ordered pairs have the same first component and different second components. We represented functions as equations and used function notation. We graphed functions and applied the vertical line test to identify graphs of functions. We determined the domain and range of a function from its graph, using inputs on the x-axis for the domain and outputs on the y-axis for the range. We used graphs to identify intervals on which functions increase, decrease, or are constant, as well as to locate relative maxima or minima. We identified even functions [$f(-x) = f(x)$: y-axis symmetry] and odd functions [$f(-x) = -f(x)$: origin symmetry]. Finally, we studied linear functions and slope, using slope (change in y divided by change in x) to develop various forms for equations of lines:

Point-slope form	Slope-intercept form	Horizontal line	Vertical line	General form
$y - y_1 = m(x - x_1)$	$y = f(x) = mx + b$	$y = f(x) = b$	$x = a$	$Ax + By + C = 0.$

We saw that parallel lines have the same slope and that perpendicular lines have slopes that are negative reciprocals. For linear functions, slope was interpreted as the rate of change of the dependent variable per unit change in the independent variable. For nonlinear functions, the slope of the secant line between $(x_1, f(x_1))$ and $(x_2, f(x_2))$ described the average rate of change of f from x_1 to x_2: $\dfrac{f(x_2) - f(x_1)}{x_2 - x_1}$.

In Exercises 1–6, determine whether each relation is a function. Give the domain and range for each relation.

1. $\{(2, 6), (1, 4), (2, -6)\}$

2. $\{(0, 1), (2, 1), (3, 4)\}$

3.

4.

5.

6.

In Exercises 7–8, determine whether each equation defines y as a function of x.

7. $x^2 + y = 5$

8. $x + y^2 = 5$

Use the graph of f to solve Exercises 9–24. Where applicable, use interval notation.

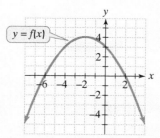

9. Explain why f represents the graph of a function.

10. Find the domain of f.

11. Find the range of f.

12. Find the x-intercept(s).

13. Find the y-intercept.

14. Find the interval(s) on which f is increasing.

15. Find the interval(s) on which f is decreasing.

16. At what number does f have a relative maximum?

17. What is the relative maximum of f?

18. Find $f(-4)$.

19. For what value or values of x is $f(x) = -2$?

20. For what value or values of x is $f(x) = 0$?

21. For what values of x is $f(x) > 0$?

22. Is $f(100)$ positive or negative?

23. Is f even, odd, or neither?

24. Find the average rate of change of f from $x_1 = -4$ to $x_2 = 4$.

In Exercises 25–36, graph each equation in a rectangular coordinate system.

25. $y = -2x$

26. $y = -2$

27. $x + y = -2$

28. $y = \frac{1}{3}x - 2$

29. $x = 3.5$

30. $4x - 2y = 8$

31. $f(x) = x^2 - 4$

32. $f(x) = x - 4$

33. $f(x) = |x| - 4$

34. $5y = -3x$

35. $5y = 20$

36. $f(x) = \begin{cases} -1 & \text{if} \quad x \le 0 \\ 2x + 1 & \text{if} \quad x > 0 \end{cases}$

37. Let $f(x) = -2x^2 + x - 5$.

   a. Find $f(-x)$. Is f even, odd, or neither?

   b. Find $\dfrac{f(x + h) - f(x)}{h}$, $h \ne 0$.

38. Let $C(x) = \begin{cases} 30 & \text{if} \quad 0 \le x \le 200 \\ 30 + 0.40(x - 200) & \text{if} \quad x > 200 \end{cases}$.

   a. Find $C(150)$.   **b.** Find $C(250)$.

In Exercises 39–42, write a function in slope-intercept form whose graph satisfies the given conditions.

39. Slope $= -2$, passing through $(-4, 3)$

40. Passing through $(-1, -5)$ and $(2, 1)$

41. Passing through $(3, -4)$ and parallel to the line whose equation is $3x - y - 5 = 0$

42. Passing through $(-4, -3)$ and perpendicular to the line whose equation is $2x - 5y - 10 = 0$

43. Determine whether the line through $(2, -4)$ and $(7, 0)$ is parallel to a second line through $(-4, 2)$ and $(1, 6)$.

44. Exercise is useful not only in preventing depression, but also as a treatment. The following graphs show the percentage of patients with depression in remission when exercise (brisk walking) was used as a treatment. (The control group that engaged in no exercise had 11% of the patients in remission.)

   a. Find the slope of the line passing through the two points shown by the voice balloons. Express the slope as a decimal.

Exercise and Percentage of Patients with Depression in Remission

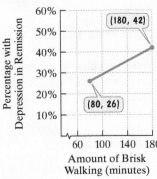

Source: *Newsweek*, March 26, 2007

   b. Use your answer from part (a) to complete this statement: For each minute of brisk walking, the percentage of patients with depression in remission increased by _____%. The rate of change is _____% per _____.

45. Find the average rate of change of $f(x) = 3x^2 - x$ from $x_1 = -1$ to $x_2 = 2$.

Objectives

1. Recognize graphs of common functions.
2. Use vertical shifts to graph functions.
3. Use horizontal shifts to graph functions.
4. Use reflections to graph functions.
5. Use vertical stretching and shrinking to graph functions.
6. Use horizontal stretching and shrinking to graph functions.
7. Graph functions involving a sequence of transformations.

Have you seen *Terminator 2, The Mask,* or *The Matrix?* These were among the first films to use spectacular effects in which a character or object having one shape was transformed in a fluid fashion into a quite different shape. The name for such a transformation is **morphing**. The effect allows a real actor to be seamlessly transformed into a computer-generated animation. The animation can be made to perform impossible feats before it is morphed back to the conventionally filmed image.

Like transformed movie images, the graph of one function can be turned into the graph of a different function. To do this, we need to rely on a function's equation. Knowing that a graph is a transformation of a familiar graph makes graphing easier.

① Recognize graphs of common functions.

Graphs of Common Functions

Table 2.3 gives names to seven frequently encountered functions in algebra. The table shows each function's graph and lists characteristics of the function. Study the shape of each graph and take a few minutes to verify the function's characteristics from its graph. Knowing these graphs is essential for analyzing their transformations into more complicated graphs.

Table 2.3 Algebra's Common Graphs

- Domain: $(-\infty, \infty)$
- Range: the single number c
- Constant on $(-\infty, \infty)$
- Even function

- Domain: $(-\infty, \infty)$
- Range: $(-\infty, \infty)$
- Increasing on $(-\infty, \infty)$
- Odd function

- Domain: $(-\infty, \infty)$
- Range: $[0, \infty)$
- Decreasing on $(-\infty, 0)$ and increasing on $(0, \infty)$
- Even function

- Domain: $(-\infty, \infty)$
- Range: $[0, \infty)$
- Decreasing on $(-\infty, 0)$ and increasing on $(0, \infty)$
- Even function

- Domain: $[0, \infty)$
- Range: $[0, \infty)$
- Increasing on $(0, \infty)$
- Neither even nor odd

- Domain: $(-\infty, \infty)$
- Range: $(-\infty, \infty)$
- Increasing on $(-\infty, \infty)$
- Odd function

- Domain: $(-\infty, \infty)$
- Range: $(-\infty, \infty)$
- Increasing on $(-\infty, \infty)$
- Odd function

DISCOVERY

The study of how changing a function's equation can affect its graph can be explored with a graphing utility. Use your graphing utility to verify the hand-drawn graphs as you read this section.

② Use vertical shifts to graph functions.

Vertical Shifts

Let's begin by looking at three graphs whose shapes are the same. **Figure 2.44** on the next page shows the graphs. The black graph in the middle is the standard quadratic function, $f(x) = x^2$. Now, look at the blue graph on the top. The equation of this graph, $g(x) = x^2 + 2$, adds 2 to the right side of $f(x) = x^2$. The y-coordinate of each

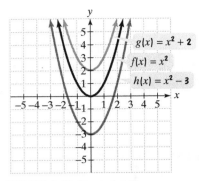

FIGURE 2.44 Vertical shifts

point of g is 2 more than the corresponding y-coordinate of each point of f. What effect does this have on the graph of f? It shifts the graph vertically up by 2 units.

$$g(x) = x^2 + 2 = f(x) + 2$$

The graph of g | shifts the graph of f up 2 units.

Finally, look at the red graph on the bottom in **Figure 2.44**. The equation of this graph, $h(x) = x^2 - 3$, subtracts 3 from the right side of $f(x) = x^2$. The y-coordinate of each point of h is 3 less than the corresponding y-coordinate of each point of f. What effect does this have on the graph of f? It shifts the graph vertically down by 3 units.

$$h(x) = x^2 - 3 = f(x) - 3$$

The graph of h | shifts the graph of f down 3 units.

In general, if c is positive, $y = f(x) + c$ shifts the graph of f upward c units and $y = f(x) - c$ shifts the graph of f downward c units. These are called **vertical shifts** of the graph of f.

Vertical Shifts

Let f be a function and c a positive real number.

- The graph of $y = f(x) + c$ is the graph of $y = f(x)$ shifted c units vertically upward.
- The graph of $y = f(x) - c$ is the graph of $y = f(x)$ shifted c units vertically downward.

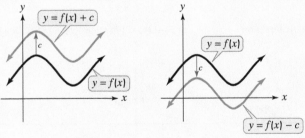

GREAT QUESTION!

If I'm using the graph of a familiar function, how do I actually obtain the graph of a transformation?

To keep track of transformations and obtain their graphs, identify a number of points on the given function's graph. Then analyze what happens to the coordinates of these points with each transformation.

EXAMPLE 1 Vertical Shift Downward

Use the graph of $f(x) = |x|$ to obtain the graph of $g(x) = |x| - 4$.

SOLUTION

The graph of $g(x) = |x| - 4$ has the same shape as the graph of $f(x) = |x|$. However, it is shifted down vertically 4 units.

• • •

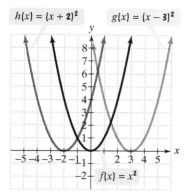

3 Use horizontal shifts to graph functions.

FIGURE 2.45 Horizontal shifts

✐ Check Point 1 Use the graph of $f(x) = |x|$ to obtain the graph of $g(x) = |x| + 3$.

Horizontal Shifts

We return to the graph of $f(x) = x^2$, the standard quadratic function. In **Figure 2.45**, the graph of function f is in the middle of the three graphs. By contrast to the vertical shift situation, this time there are graphs to the left and to the right of the graph of f. Look at the blue graph on the right. The equation of this graph, $g(x) = (x - 3)^2$, subtracts 3 from each value of x before squaring it. What effect does this have on the graph of $f(x) = x^2$? It shifts the graph horizontally to the right by 3 units.

$$g(x) = (x - 3)^2 = f(x - 3)$$

The graph of g shifts the graph of f 3 units to the right.

Does it seem strange that *subtracting* 3 in the domain causes a shift of 3 units to the *right*? Perhaps a partial table of coordinates for each function will numerically convince you of this shift.

x	$f(x) = x^2$
−2	$(-2)^2 = 4$
−1	$(-1)^2 = 1$
0	$0^2 = 0$
1	$1^2 = 1$
2	$2^2 = 4$

x	$g(x) = (x - 3)^2$
1	$(1 - 3)^2 = (-2)^2 = 4$
2	$(2 - 3)^2 = (-1)^2 = 1$
3	$(3 - 3)^2 = \quad 0^2 = 0$
4	$(4 - 3)^2 = \quad 1^2 = 1$
5	$(5 - 3)^2 = \quad 2^2 = 4$

Notice that for the values of $f(x)$ and $g(x)$ to be the same, the values of x used in graphing g must each be 3 units greater than those used to graph f. For this reason, the graph of g is the graph of f shifted 3 units to the right.

Now, look at the red graph on the left in **Figure 2.45**. The equation of this graph, $h(x) = (x + 2)^2$, adds 2 to each value of x before squaring it. What effect does this have on the graph of $f(x) = x^2$? It shifts the graph horizontally to the left by 2 units.

$$h(x) = (x + 2)^2 = f(x + 2)$$

The graph of h shifts the graph of f 2 units to the left.

In general, if c is positive, $y = f(x + c)$ shifts the graph of f to the left c units and $y = f(x - c)$ shifts the graph of f to the right c units. These are called **horizontal shifts** of the graph of f.

GREAT QUESTION!

Using my intuition, it seems that $f(x + c)$ should cause a shift to the right and $f(x - c)$ should cause a shift to the left. Is my intuition on target when it comes to these horizontal shifts?

No. On a number line, if x represents a number and c is positive, then $x + c$ lies c units to the right of x and $x - c$ lies c units to the left of x. This orientation does not apply to horizontal shifts: $f(x + c)$ causes a shift of c units to the left and $f(x - c)$ causes a shift of c units to the right.

Horizontal Shifts

Let f be a function and c a positive real number.

- The graph of $y = f(x + c)$ is the graph of $y = f(x)$ shifted to the left c units.
- The graph of $y = f(x - c)$ is the graph of $y = f(x)$ shifted to the right c units.

EXAMPLE 2   Horizontal Shift to the Left

Use the graph of $f(x) = \sqrt{x}$ to obtain the graph of $g(x) = \sqrt{x + 5}$.

SOLUTION

Compare the equations for $f(x) = \sqrt{x}$ and $g(x) = \sqrt{x + 5}$. The equation for g adds 5 to each value of x before taking the square root.

$$y = g(x) = \sqrt{x + 5} = f(x + 5)$$

 The graph of g shifts the graph of f 5 units to the left.

The graph of $g(x) = \sqrt{x + 5}$ has the same shape as the graph of $f(x) = \sqrt{x}$. However, it is shifted horizontally to the left 5 units.

Graph $g(x) = \sqrt{x + 5}$. Shift f 5 units left. Subtract 5 from each x-coordinate.

The graph of $f(x) = \sqrt{x}$ with three points identified

The graph of $g(x) = \sqrt{x + 5}$

GREAT QUESTION!

What's the difference between $f(x) + c$ and $f(x + c)$?

- $y = f(x) + c$ shifts the graph of $y = f(x)$ c units vertically upward.
- $y = f(x + c)$ shifts the graph of $y = f(x)$ c units horizontally to the left.

There are analogous differences between $f(x) - c$ and $f(x - c)$.

Check Point 2 Use the graph of $f(x) = \sqrt{x}$ to obtain the graph of $g(x) = \sqrt{x - 4}$.

Some functions can be graphed by combining horizontal and vertical shifts. These functions will be variations of a function whose equation you know how to graph, such as the standard quadratic function, the standard cubic function, the square root function, the cube root function, or the absolute value function.

In our next example, we will use the graph of the standard quadratic function, $f(x) = x^2$, to obtain the graph of $h(x) = (x + 1)^2 - 3$. We will graph three functions:

$$f(x) = x^2 \qquad g(x) = (x + 1)^2 \qquad h(x) = (x + 1)^2 - 3.$$

Start by graphing the standard quadratic function.

Shift the graph of f horizontally one unit to the left.

Shift the graph of g vertically down 3 units.

Combining Horizontal and Vertical Shifts

Use the graph of $f(x) = x^2$ to obtain the graph of $h(x) = (x + 1)^2 - 3$.

SOLUTION

The graph of $f(x) = x^2$ with three points identified

Graph $g(x) = (x + 1)^2$. Shift f horizontally 1 unit left. Subtract 1 from each x-coordinate.

The graph of $g(x) = (x + 1)^2$

Graph $h(x) = (x + 1)^2 - 3$. Shift g vertically down 3 units. Subtract 3 from each y-coordinate.

The graph of $h(x) = (x + 1)^2 - 3$

• • •

DISCOVERY

Work Example 3 by first shifting the graph of $f(x) = x^2$ three units down, graphing $g(x) = x^2 - 3$. Now, shift this graph one unit left to graph $h(x) = (x + 1)^2 - 3$. Did you obtain the last graph shown in the solution of Example 3? What can you conclude?

✓ Check Point **3** Use the graph of $f(x) = \sqrt{x}$ to obtain the graph of $h(x) = \sqrt{x - 1} - 2$.

4 Use reflections to graph functions.

Reflections of Graphs

This photograph shows a reflection of an old bridge in a Maryland river. This perfect reflection occurs because the surface of the water is absolutely still. A mild breeze rippling the water's surface would distort the reflection.

Is it possible for graphs to have mirror-like qualities? Yes. **Figure 2.46** shows the graphs of $f(x) = x^2$ and $g(x) = -x^2$. The graph of g is a **reflection about the x-axis** of the graph of f. For corresponding values of x, the y-coordinates of g are the opposites of the y-coordinates of f. In general, the graph of $y = -f(x)$ reflects the graph of f about the x-axis. Thus, the graph of g is a reflection of the graph of f about the x-axis because

$$g(x) = -x^2 = -f(x).$$

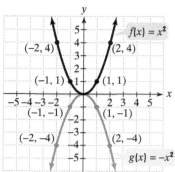

FIGURE 2.46 Reflection about the x-axis

Reflection about the x-Axis

The graph of $y = -f(x)$ is the graph of $y = f(x)$ reflected about the x-axis.

EXAMPLE 4   Reflection about the x-Axis

Use the graph of $f(x) = \sqrt[3]{x}$ to obtain the graph of $g(x) = -\sqrt[3]{x}$.

SOLUTION

Compare the equations for $f(x) = \sqrt[3]{x}$ and $g(x) = -\sqrt[3]{x}$. The graph of g is a reflection about the x-axis of the graph of f because

$$g(x) = -\sqrt[3]{x} = -f(x).$$

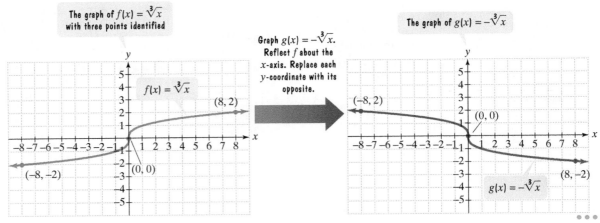

 Check Point **4** Use the graph of $f(x) = |x|$ to obtain the graph of $g(x) = -|x|$.

It is also possible to reflect graphs about the y-axis.

Reflection about the y-Axis

The graph of $y = f(-x)$ is the graph of $y = f(x)$ reflected about the y-axis.

For each point (x, y) on the graph of $y = f(x)$, the point $(-x, y)$ is on the graph of $y = f(-x)$.

EXAMPLE 5   Reflection about the y-Axis

Use the graph of $f(x) = \sqrt{x}$ to obtain the graph of $h(x) = \sqrt{-x}$.

SOLUTION

Compare the equations for $f(x) = \sqrt{x}$ and $h(x) = \sqrt{-x}$. The graph of h is a reflection about the y-axis of the graph of f because

$$h(x) = \sqrt{-x} = f(-x).$$

 Check Point **5** Use the graph of $f(x) = \sqrt[3]{x}$ to obtain the graph of $h(x) = \sqrt[3]{-x}$.

⑤ Use vertical stretching and shrinking to graph functions.

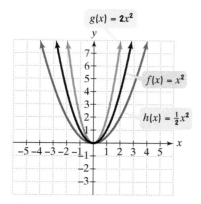

$g(x) = 2x^2$

$f(x) = x^2$

$h(x) = \frac{1}{2}x^2$

FIGURE 2.47 Vertically stretching and shrinking $f(x) = x^2$

GREAT QUESTION!

Does vertical stretching or shrinking change a graph's shape?

Yes. A vertical stretch moves a function's graph away from the x-axis. A vertical shrink compresses a function's graph toward the x-axis. The other transformations we have discussed (vertical shifts, horizontal shifts, and reflections) change only the position of a function's graph without changing the shape of the basic graph.

Vertical Stretching and Shrinking

Morphing does much more than move an image horizontally, vertically, or about an axis. An object having one shape is transformed into a different shape. Horizontal shifts, vertical shifts, and reflections do not change the basic shape of a graph. Graphs remain rigid and proportionally the same when they undergo these transformations. How can we shrink and stretch graphs, thereby altering their basic shapes?

Look at the three graphs in **Figure 2.47**. The black graph in the middle is the graph of the standard quadratic function, $f(x) = x^2$. Now, look at the blue graph on the top. The equation of this graph is $g(x) = 2x^2$, or $g(x) = 2f(x)$. Thus, for each x, the y-coordinate of g is two times as large as the corresponding y-coordinate on the graph of f. The result is a narrower graph because the values of y are rising faster. We say that the graph of g is obtained by vertically *stretching* the graph of f. Now, look at the red graph on the bottom. The equation of this graph is $h(x) = \frac{1}{2}x^2$, or $h(x) = \frac{1}{2}f(x)$. Thus, for each x, the y-coordinate of h is one-half as large as the corresponding y-coordinate on the graph of f. The result is a wider graph because the values of y are rising more slowly. We say that the graph of h is obtained by vertically *shrinking* the graph of f.

These observations can be summarized as follows:

Vertically Stretching and Shrinking Graphs

Let f be a function and c a positive real number.

- If $c > 1$, the graph of $y = cf(x)$ is the graph of $y = f(x)$ vertically stretched by multiplying each of its y-coordinates by c.
- If $0 < c < 1$, the graph of $y = cf(x)$ is the graph of $y = f(x)$ vertically shrunk by multiplying each of its y-coordinates by c.

Stretching : $c > 1$ Shrinking : $0 < c < 1$

$y = cf(x)$ $y = f(x)$

$y = f(x)$ $y = cf(x)$

EXAMPLE 6   Vertically Shrinking a Graph

Use the graph of $f(x) = x^3$ to obtain the graph of $h(x) = \frac{1}{2}x^3$.

SOLUTION

The graph of $h(x) = \frac{1}{2}x^3$ is obtained by vertically shrinking the graph of $f(x) = x^3$.

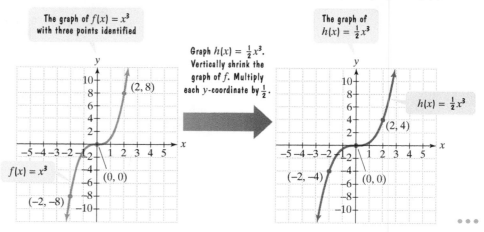

The graph of $f(x) = x^3$ with three points identified

Graph $h(x) = \frac{1}{2}x^3$. Vertically shrink the graph of f. Multiply each y-coordinate by $\frac{1}{2}$.

The graph of $h(x) = \frac{1}{2}x^3$

$(2, 8)$

$f(x) = x^3$

$(0, 0)$

$(-2, -8)$

$h(x) = \frac{1}{2}x^3$

$(2, 4)$

$(-2, -4)$ $(0, 0)$

● ● ●

⬭ Check Point **6** Use the graph of $f(x) = |x|$ to obtain the graph of $g(x) = 2|x|$.

⑥ Use horizontal stretching and shrinking to graph functions.

Horizontal Stretching and Shrinking

It is also possible to stretch and shrink graphs horizontally.

GREAT QUESTION!

How does horizontal shrinking or stretching change a graph's shape?

A horizontal shrink compresses a function's graph toward the y-axis. A horizontal stretch moves a function's graph away from the y-axis.

Horizontally Stretching and Shrinking Graphs

Let f be a function and c a positive real number.

- If $c > 1$, the graph of $y = f(cx)$ is the graph of $y = f(x)$ horizontally shrunk by dividing each of its x-coordinates by c.
- If $0 < c < 1$, the graph of $y = f(cx)$ is the graph of $y = f(x)$ horizontally stretched by dividing each of its x-coordinates by c.

EXAMPLE 7 Horizontally Stretching and Shrinking a Graph

Use the graph of $y = f(x)$ in **Figure 2.48** to obtain each of the following graphs:

a. $g(x) = f(2x)$ **b.** $h(x) = f\left(\frac{1}{2}x\right)$.

SOLUTION

a. The graph of $g(x) = f(2x)$ is obtained by horizontally shrinking the graph of $y = f(x)$.

FIGURE 2.48

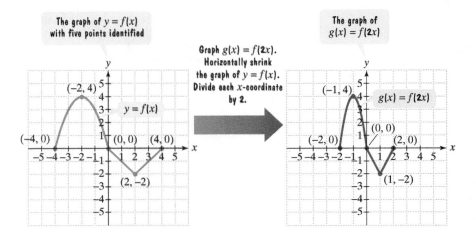

b. The graph of $h(x) = f\left(\frac{1}{2}x\right)$ is obtained by horizontally stretching the graph of $y = f(x)$.

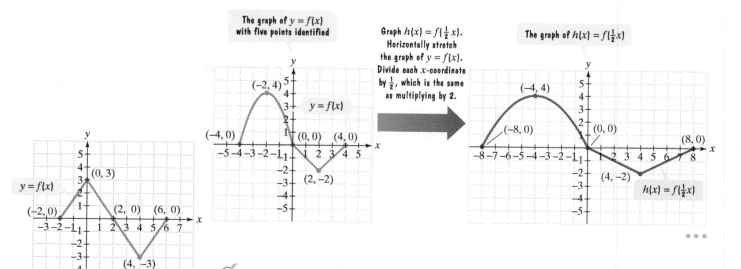

FIGURE 2.49

✓ Check Point **7** Use the graph of $y = f(x)$ in **Figure 2.49** to obtain each of the following graphs:

a. $g(x) = f(2x)$ **b.** $h(x) = f\left(\frac{1}{2}x\right)$.

⑦ Graph functions involving a sequence of transformations.

Sequences of Transformations

Table 2.4 summarizes the procedures for transforming the graph of $y = f(x)$.

Table 2.4   Summary of Transformations

In each case, c represents a positive real number.

To Graph:	Draw the Graph of f and:	Changes in the Equation of $y = f(x)$
Vertical shifts		
$y = f(x) + c$	Raise the graph of f by c units.	c is added to $f(x)$.
$y = f(x) - c$	Lower the graph of f by c units.	c is subtracted from $f(x)$.
Horizontal shifts		
$y = f(x + c)$	Shift the graph of f to the left c units.	x is replaced with $x + c$.
$y = f(x - c)$	Shift the graph of f to the right c units.	x is replaced with $x - c$.
Reflection about the x-axis	Reflect the graph of f about the x-axis.	$f(x)$ is multiplied by -1.
$y = -f(x)$		
Reflection about the y-axis	Reflect the graph of f about the y-axis.	x is replaced with $-x$.
$y = f(-x)$		
Vertical stretching or shrinking		
$y = cf(x), c > 1$	Multiply each y-coordinate of $y = f(x)$ by c, vertically stretching the graph of f.	$f(x)$ is multiplied by $c, c > 1$.
$y = cf(x), 0 < c < 1$	Multiply each y-coordinate of $y = f(x)$ by c, vertically shrinking the graph of f.	$f(x)$ is multiplied by $c, 0 < c < 1$.
Horizontal stretching or shrinking		
$y = f(cx), c > 1$	Divide each x-coordinate of $y = f(x)$ by c, horizontally shrinking the graph of f.	x is replaced with $cx, c > 1$.
$y = f(cx), 0 < c < 1$	Divide each x-coordinate of $y = f(x)$ by c, horizontally stretching the graph of f.	x is replaced with $cx, 0 < c < 1$.

A function involving more than one transformation can be graphed by performing transformations in the following order:

1. Horizontal shifting   **2.** Stretching or shrinking

3. Reflecting   **4.** Vertical shifting

EXAMPLE 8   Graphing Using a Sequence of Transformations

Use the graph of $y = f(x)$ given in **Figure 2.48** of Example 7 on page 278, and repeated below, to graph $y = -\frac{1}{2}f(x - 1) + 3$.

SOLUTION

Our graphs will evolve in the following order:

1. Horizontal shifting: Graph $y = f(x - 1)$ by shifting the graph of $y = f(x)$ 1 unit to the right.

2. Shrinking: Graph $y = \frac{1}{2}f(x - 1)$ by shrinking the previous graph by a factor of $\frac{1}{2}$.

3. Reflecting: Graph $y = -\frac{1}{2}f(x - 1)$ by reflecting the previous graph about the x-axis.

4. Vertical shifting: Graph $y = -\frac{1}{2}f(x - 1) + 3$ by shifting the previous graph up 3 units.

✓ Check Point **8** Use the graph of $y = f(x)$ given in **Figure 2.49** of Check Point 7 on page 279 to graph $y = -\frac{1}{3}f(x + 1) - 2$.

EXAMPLE 9 Graphing Using a Sequence of Transformations

Use the graph of $f(x) = x^2$ to graph $g(x) = 2(x + 3)^2 - 1$.

SOLUTION

Our graphs will evolve in the following order:

1. **Horizontal shifting:** Graph $y = (x + 3)^2$ by shifting the graph of $f(x) = x^2$ three units to the left.

2. **Stretching:** Graph $y = 2(x + 3)^2$ by stretching the previous graph by a factor of 2.

3. **Vertical shifting:** Graph $g(x) = 2(x + 3)^2 - 1$ by shifting the previous graph down 1 unit.

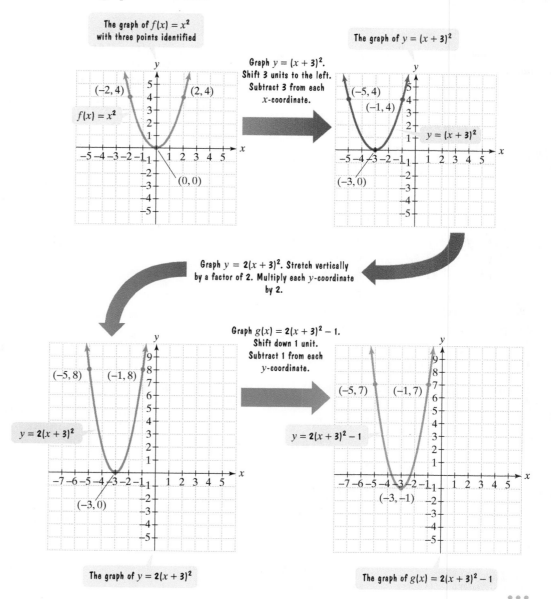

✓ Check Point **9** Use the graph of $f(x) = x^2$ to graph $g(x) = 2(x - 1)^2 + 3$.

CONCEPT AND VOCABULARY CHECK

Fill in each blank so that the resulting statement is true.

1. The graph of $y = f(x) - 5$ is obtained by a/an _____ shift of the graph of $y = f(x)$ _____ a distance of 5 units.

2. The graph of $y = f(x - 5)$ is obtained by a/an _____ shift of the graph of $y = f(x)$ _____ a distance of 5 units.

3. The graph of $y = -f(x)$ is the graph of $y = f(x)$ reflected about the _____.

4. The graph of $y = f(-x)$ is the graph of $y = f(x)$ reflected about the _____.

5. The graph of $y = 5f(x)$ is obtained by a/an _____ stretch of the graph of $y = f(x)$ by multiplying each of its ___-coordinates by 5.

6. The graph of $y = f\left(\frac{1}{5}x\right)$ is obtained by a/an _____ stretch of the graph of $y = f(x)$ by multiplying each of its ___-coordinates by 5.

7. True or false: The graph of $g(x) = \sqrt{x + 4}$ is the graph of $f(x) = \sqrt{x}$ shifted horizontally to the right by 4 units. _____

EXERCISE SET 2.5

Practice Exercises

In Exercises 1–16, use the graph of $y = f(x)$ to graph each function g.

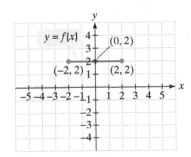

1. $g(x) = f(x) + 1$ **2.** $g(x) = f(x) - 1$
3. $g(x) = f(x + 1)$ **4.** $g(x) = f(x - 1)$
5. $g(x) = f(x - 1) - 2$ **6.** $g(x) = f(x + 1) + 2$
7. $g(x) = f(-x)$ **8.** $g(x) = -f(x)$
9. $g(x) = -f(x) + 3$ **10.** $g(x) = f(-x) + 3$
11. $g(x) = \frac{1}{2}f(x)$ **12.** $g(x) = 2f(x)$
13. $g(x) = f\left(\frac{1}{2}x\right)$ **14.** $g(x) = f(2x)$
15. $g(x) = -f\left(\frac{1}{2}x\right) + 1$ **16.** $g(x) = -f(2x) - 1$

In Exercises 17–32, use the graph of $y = f(x)$ to graph each function g.

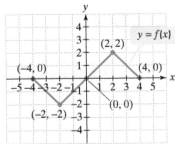

17. $g(x) = f(x) - 1$ **18.** $g(x) = f(x) + 1$
19. $g(x) = f(x - 1)$ **20.** $g(x) = f(x + 1)$
21. $g(x) = f(x - 1) + 2$ **22.** $g(x) = f(x + 1) - 2$
23. $g(x) = -f(x)$ **24.** $g(x) = f(-x)$

25. $g(x) = f(-x) + 1$ **26.** $g(x) = -f(x) + 1$
27. $g(x) = 2f(x)$ **28.** $g(x) = \frac{1}{2}f(x)$
29. $g(x) = f(2x)$ **30.** $g(x) = f\left(\frac{1}{2}x\right)$
31. $g(x) = 2f(x + 2) + 1$ **32.** $g(x) = 2f(x + 2) - 1$

In Exercises 33–44, use the graph of $y = f(x)$ to graph each function g.

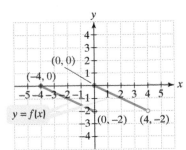

33. $g(x) = f(x) + 2$ **34.** $g(x) = f(x) - 2$
35. $g(x) = f(x + 2)$ **36.** $g(x) = f(x - 2)$
37. $g(x) = -f(x + 2)$ **38.** $g(x) = -f(x - 2)$
39. $g(x) = -\frac{1}{2}f(x + 2)$ **40.** $g(x) = -\frac{1}{2}f(x - 2)$
41. $g(x) = -\frac{1}{2}f(x + 2) - 2$ **42.** $g(x) = -\frac{1}{2}f(x - 2) + 2$
43. $g(x) = \frac{1}{2}f(2x)$ **44.** $g(x) = 2f\left(\frac{1}{2}x\right)$

In Exercises 45–52, use the graph of $y = f(x)$ to graph each function g.

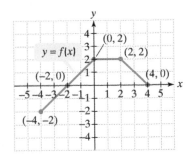

45. $g(x) = f(x - 1) - 1$ **46.** $g(x) = f(x + 1) + 1$
47. $g(x) = -f(x - 1) + 1$ **48.** $g(x) = -f(x + 1) - 1$

49. $g(x) = 2f\left(\frac{1}{2}x\right)$

50. $g(x) = \frac{1}{2}f(2x)$

51. $g(x) = \frac{1}{2}f(x + 1)$

52. $g(x) = 2f(x - 1)$

In Exercises 53–66, begin by graphing the standard quadratic function, $f(x) = x^2$. Then use transformations of this graph to graph the given function.

53. $g(x) = x^2 - 2$

54. $g(x) = x^2 - 1$

55. $g(x) = (x - 2)^2$

56. $g(x) = (x - 1)^2$

57. $h(x) = -(x - 2)^2$

58. $h(x) = -(x - 1)^2$

59. $h(x) = (x - 2)^2 + 1$

60. $h(x) = (x - 1)^2 + 2$

61. $g(x) = 2(x - 2)^2$

62. $g(x) = \frac{1}{2}(x - 1)^2$

63. $h(x) = 2(x - 2)^2 - 1$

64. $h(x) = \frac{1}{2}(x - 1)^2 - 1$

65. $h(x) = -2(x + 1)^2 + 1$

66. $h(x) = -2(x + 2)^2 + 1$

In Exercises 67–80, begin by graphing the square root function, $f(x) = \sqrt{x}$. Then use transformations of this graph to graph the given function.

67. $g(x) = \sqrt{x} + 2$

68. $g(x) = \sqrt{x} + 1$

69. $g(x) = \sqrt{x + 2}$

70. $g(x) = \sqrt{x + 1}$

71. $h(x) = -\sqrt{x + 2}$

72. $h(x) = -\sqrt{x + 1}$

73. $h(x) = \sqrt{-x + 2}$

74. $h(x) = \sqrt{-x + 1}$

75. $g(x) = \frac{1}{2}\sqrt{x + 2}$

76. $g(x) = 2\sqrt{x + 1}$

77. $h(x) = \sqrt{x + 2} - 2$

78. $h(x) = \sqrt{x + 1} - 1$

79. $g(x) = 2\sqrt{x + 2} - 2$

80. $g(x) = 2\sqrt{x + 1} - 1$

In Exercises 81–94, begin by graphing the absolute value function, $f(x) = |x|$. Then use transformations of this graph to graph the given function.

81. $g(x) = |x| + 4$

82. $g(x) = |x| + 3$

83. $g(x) = |x + 4|$

84. $g(x) = |x + 3|$

85. $h(x) = |x + 4| - 2$

86. $h(x) = |x + 3| - 2$

87. $h(x) = -|x + 4|$

88. $h(x) = -|x + 3|$

89. $g(x) = -|x + 4| + 1$

90. $g(x) = -|x + 4| + 2$

91. $h(x) = 2|x + 4|$

92. $h(x) = 2|x + 3|$

93. $g(x) = -2|x + 4| + 1$

94. $g(x) = -2|x + 3| + 2$

In Exercises 95–106, begin by graphing the standard cubic function, $f(x) = x^3$. Then use transformations of this graph to graph the given function.

95. $g(x) = x^3 - 3$

96. $g(x) = x^3 - 2$

97. $g(x) = (x - 3)^3$

98. $g(x) = (x - 2)^3$

99. $h(x) = -x^3$

100. $h(x) = -(x - 2)^3$

101. $h(x) = \frac{1}{2}x^3$

102. $h(x) = \frac{1}{4}x^3$

103. $r(x) = (x - 3)^3 + 2$

104. $r(x) = (x - 2)^3 + 1$

105. $h(x) = \frac{1}{2}(x - 3)^3 - 2$

106. $h(x) = \frac{1}{2}(x - 2)^3 - 1$

In Exercises 107–118, begin by graphing the cube root function, $f(x) = \sqrt[3]{x}$. Then use transformations of this graph to graph the given function.

107. $g(x) = \sqrt[3]{x} + 2$

108. $g(x) = \sqrt[3]{x} - 2$

109. $g(x) = \sqrt[3]{x + 2}$

110. $g(x) = \sqrt[3]{x - 2}$

111. $h(x) = \frac{1}{2}\sqrt[3]{x + 2}$

112. $h(x) = \frac{1}{2}\sqrt[3]{x - 2}$

113. $r(x) = \frac{1}{2}\sqrt[3]{x + 2} - 2$

114. $r(x) = \frac{1}{2}\sqrt[3]{x - 2} + 2$

115. $h(x) = -\sqrt[3]{x + 2}$

116. $h(x) = -\sqrt[3]{x - 2}$

117. $g(x) = \sqrt[3]{-x - 2}$

118. $g(x) = \sqrt[3]{-x + 2}$

Practice Plus

*In Exercises 119–122, use transformations of the graph of the greatest integer function, $f(x) = \text{int}(x)$, to graph each function. (The graph of $f(x) = \text{int}(x)$ is shown in **Figure 2.23** on page 236.)*

119. $g(x) = 2 \text{ int } (x + 1)$

120. $g(x) = 3 \text{ int } (x - 1)$

121. $h(x) = \text{int}(-x) + 1$

122. $h(x) = \text{int}(-x) - 1$

In Exercises 123–126, write a possible equation for the function whose graph is shown. Each graph shows a transformation of a common function.

123.

[−2, 8, 1] by [−1, 4, 1]

124.

[−3, 3, 1] by [−6, 6, 1]

125.

[−5, 3, 1] by [−5, 10, 1]

126.

[−1, 9, 1] by [−1, 5, 1]

Application Exercises

127. The function $f(x) = 2.9\sqrt{x} + 20.1$ models the median height, $f(x)$, in inches, of boys who are x months of age. The graph of f is shown.

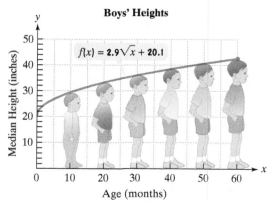

Boys' Heights

$f(x) = 2.9\sqrt{x} + 20.1$

Median Height (inches)

Age (months)

Source: Laura Walther Nathanson, *The Portable Pediatrician for Parents*

a. Describe how the graph can be obtained using transformations of the square root function $f(x) = \sqrt{x}$.

b. According to the model, what is the median height of boys who are 48 months, or four years, old? Use a calculator and round to the nearest tenth of an inch. The actual median height for boys at 48 months is 40.8 inches. How well does the model describe the actual height?

(This exercise continues on the next page.)

c. Use the model to find the average rate of change, in inches per month, between birth and 10 months. Round to the nearest tenth.

d. Use the model to find the average rate of change, in inches per month, between 50 and 60 months. Round to the nearest tenth. How does this compare with your answer in part (c)? How is this difference shown by the graph?

128. The function $f(x) = 3.1\sqrt{x} + 19$ models the median height, $f(x)$, in inches, of girls who are x months of age. The graph of f is shown.

Girls' Heights

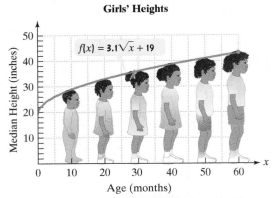

Source: Laura Walther Nathanson, *The Portable Pediatrician for Parents*

a. Describe how the graph can be obtained using transformations of the square root function $f(x) = \sqrt{x}$.

b. According to the model, what is the median height of girls who are 48 months, or 4 years, old? Use a calculator and round to the nearest tenth of an inch. The actual median height for girls at 48 months is 40.2 inches. How well does the model describe the actual height?

c. Use the model to find the average rate of change, in inches per month, between birth and 10 months. Round to the nearest tenth.

d. Use the model to find the average rate of change, in inches per month, between 50 and 60 months. Round to the nearest tenth. How does this compare with your answer in part (c)? How is this difference shown by the graph?

Writing in Mathematics

129. What must be done to a function's equation so that its graph is shifted vertically upward?

130. What must be done to a function's equation so that its graph is shifted horizontally to the right?

131. What must be done to a function's equation so that its graph is reflected about the x-axis?

132. What must be done to a function's equation so that its graph is reflected about the y-axis?

133. What must be done to a function's equation so that its graph is stretched vertically?

134. What must be done to a function's equation so that its graph is shrunk horizontally?

Technology Exercises

135. a. Use a graphing utility to graph $f(x) = x^2 + 1$.

b. Graph $f(x) = x^2 + 1$, $g(x) = f(2x)$, $h(x) = f(3x)$, and $k(x) = f(4x)$ in the same viewing rectangle.

c. Describe the relationship among the graphs of f, g, h, and k, with emphasis on different values of x for points on all four graphs that give the same y-coordinate.

d. Generalize by describing the relationship between the graph of f and the graph of g, where $g(x) = f(cx)$ for $c > 1$.

e. Try out your generalization by sketching the graphs of $f(cx)$ for $c = 1, c = 2, c = 3$, and $c = 4$ for a function of your choice.

136. a. Use a graphing utility to graph $f(x) = x^2 + 1$.

b. Graph $f(x) = x^2 + 1$, $g(x) = f\left(\frac{1}{2}x\right)$, and $h(x) = f\left(\frac{1}{4}x\right)$ in the same viewing rectangle.

c. Describe the relationship among the graphs of f, g, and h, with emphasis on different values of x for points on all three graphs that give the same y-coordinate.

d. Generalize by describing the relationship between the graph of f and the graph of g, where $g(x) = f(cx)$ for $0 < c < 1$.

e. Try out your generalization by sketching the graphs of $f(cx)$ for $c = 1$, and $c = \frac{1}{2}$, and $c = \frac{1}{4}$ for a function of your choice.

Critical Thinking Exercises

Make Sense? *During the winter, you program your home thermostat so that at midnight, the temperature is 55°. This temperature is maintained until 6 A.M. Then the house begins to warm up so that by 9 A.M. the temperature is 65°. At 6 P.M. the house begins to cool. By 9 P.M., the temperature is again 55°. The graph illustrates home temperature, $f(t)$, as a function of hours after midnight, t.*

In Exercises 137–140, determine whether each statement makes sense or does not make sense, and explain your reasoning. If the statement makes sense, graph the new function on the domain [0, 24]. *If the statement does not make sense, correct the function in the statement and graph the corrected function on the domain* [0, 24].

137. I decided to keep the house 5° warmer than before, so I reprogrammed the thermostat to $y = f(t) + 5$.

138. I decided to keep the house 5° cooler than before, so I reprogrammed the thermostat to $y = f(t) - 5$.

139. I decided to change the heating schedule to start one hour earlier than before, so I reprogrammed the thermostat to $y = f(t - 1)$.

140. I decided to change the heating schedule to start one hour later than before, so I reprogrammed the thermostat to $y = f(t + 1)$.

In Exercises 141–144, determine whether each statement is true or false. If the statement is false, make the necessary change(s) to produce a true statement.

141. If $f(x) = |x|$ and $g(x) = |x + 3| + 3$, then the graph of g is a translation of the graph of f three units to the right and three units upward.

142. If $f(x) = -\sqrt{x}$ and $g(x) = \sqrt{-x}$, then f and g have identical graphs.

143. If $f(x) = x^2$ and $g(x) = 5(x^2 - 2)$, then the graph of g can be obtained from the graph of f by stretching f five units followed by a downward shift of two units.

144. If $f(x) = x^3$ and $g(x) = -(x - 3)^3 - 4$, then the graph of g can be obtained from the graph of f by moving f three units to the right, reflecting about the x-axis, and then moving the resulting graph down four units.

In Exercises 145–148, functions f and g are graphed in the same rectangular coordinate system. If g is obtained from f through a sequence of transformations, find an equation for g.

145.

146.

147.

148.

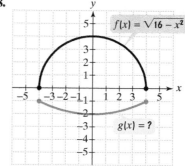

For Exercises 149–152, assume that (a, b) is a point on the graph of f. What is the corresponding point on the graph of each of the following functions?

149. $y = f(-x)$

150. $y = 2f(x)$

151. $y = f(x - 3)$

152. $y = f(x) - 3$

Preview Exercises

Exercises 153–155 will help you prepare for the material covered in the next section.

In Exercises 153–154, perform the indicated operation or operations.

153. $(2x - 1)(x^2 + x - 2)$

154. $(f(x))^2 - 2f(x) + 6$, where $f(x) = 3x - 4$

155. Simplify: $\dfrac{2}{\dfrac{3}{x} - 1}$.

SECTION 2.6   Combinations of Functions; Composite Functions

Objectives

1. Find the domain of a function.
2. Combine functions using the algebra of functions, specifying domains.
3. Form composite functions.
4. Determine domains for composite functions.
5. Write functions as compositions.

We're born. We die. **Figure 2.50** quantifies these statements by showing the number of births and deaths in the United States from 2000 through 2009.

Number of Births and Deaths in the United States

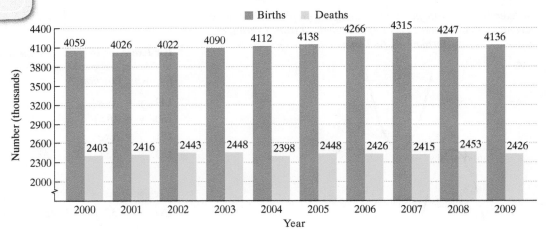

FIGURE 2.50
Source: U.S. Department of Health and Human Services

In this section, we look at these data from the perspective of functions. By considering the yearly change in the U.S. population, you will see that functions can be subtracted using procedures that will remind you of combining algebraic expressions.

1. Find the domain of a function.

The Domain of a Function

We begin with two functions that model the data in **Figure 2.50**.

$$B(x) = -2.6x^2 + 49x + 3994 \qquad D(x) = -0.6x^2 + 7x + 2412$$

Number of births, $B(x)$, in thousands, x years after **2000**

Number of deaths, $D(x)$, in thousands, x years after **2000**

The years in **Figure 2.50** extend from 2000 through 2009. Because x represents the number of years after 2000,

$$\text{Domain of } B = \{0, 1, 2, 3, \ldots, 9\}$$

and

$$\text{Domain of } D = \{0, 1, 2, 3, \ldots, 9\}.$$

Functions that model data often have their domains explicitly given with the function's equation. However, for most functions, only an equation is given and the domain is not specified. In cases like this, the domain of a function f is the largest set of real numbers for which the value of $f(x)$ is a real number. For example, consider the function

$$f(x) = \frac{1}{x - 3}.$$

Because division by 0 is undefined, the denominator, $x - 3$, cannot be 0. Thus, x cannot equal 3. The domain of the function consists of all real numbers other than 3, represented by

Domain of $f = \{x \mid x$ is a real number and $x \neq 3\}$.

Using interval notation,

Domain of $f = (-\infty, 3) \cup (3, \infty)$.

| All real numbers less than 3 | or | All real numbers greater than 3 |

Now consider a function involving a square root:

$$g(x) = \sqrt{x - 3}.$$

Because only nonnegative numbers have square roots that are real numbers, the expression under the square root sign, $x - 3$, must be nonnegative. We can use inspection to see that $x - 3 \geq 0$ if $x \geq 3$. The domain of g consists of all real numbers that are greater than or equal to 3:

Domain of $g = \{x \mid x \geq 3\}$ or $[3, \infty)$.

Finding a Function's Domain

If a function f does not model data or verbal conditions, its domain is the largest set of real numbers for which the value of $f(x)$ is a real number. Exclude from a function's domain real numbers that cause division by zero and real numbers that result in an even root, such as a square root, of a negative number.

EXAMPLE 1   Finding the Domain of a Function

Find the domain of each function:

a. $f(x) = x^2 - 7x$ **b.** $g(x) = \dfrac{3x + 2}{x^2 - 2x - 3}$

c. $h(x) = \sqrt{3x + 12}$ **d.** $j(x) = \dfrac{3x + 2}{\sqrt{14 - 2x}}$.

SOLUTION

The domain is the set of all real numbers, $(-\infty, \infty)$, unless x appears in a denominator or in an even root, such as a square root.

a. The function $f(x) = x^2 - 7x$ contains neither division nor a square root. For every real number, x, the algebraic expression $x^2 - 7x$ represents a real number. Thus, the domain of f is the set of all real numbers.

Domain of $f = (-\infty, \infty)$

b. The function $g(x) = \dfrac{3x + 2}{x^2 - 2x - 3}$ contains division. Because division by 0 is undefined, we must exclude from the domain the values of x that cause the denominator, $x^2 - 2x - 3$, to be 0. We can identify these values by setting $x^2 - 2x - 3$ equal to 0.

GREAT QUESTION!

Despite the voice balloons, the notation for the domain of f on the right is a mouthful! Will you be using set operations with interval notation in this section? What should I already know?

Yes, you'll be seeing the intersection and the union of sets that are expressed in interval notation. Recall that the intersection of sets A and B, written $A \cap B$, is the set of elements common to both set A and set B. When sets A and B are in interval notation, to find the intersection, graph each interval and take the portion of the number line that the two graphs have in common. We will also be using notation involving the union of sets A and B, $A \cup B$, meaning the set of elements in A or in B or in both. For more detail, see Section P.1, pages 5–6 and Section 1.7, pages 184–185.

$$x^2 - 2x - 3 = 0 \qquad \text{Set the function's denominator equal to 0.}$$
$$(x + 1)(x - 3) = 0 \qquad \text{Factor.}$$
$$x + 1 = 0 \quad \text{or} \quad x - 3 = 0 \qquad \text{Set each factor equal to 0.}$$
$$x = -1 \qquad\qquad x = 3 \qquad \text{Solve the resulting equations.}$$

We must exclude -1 and 3 from the domain of $g(x) = \dfrac{3x + 2}{x^2 - 2x - 3}$.

$$\text{Domain of } g = (-\infty, -1) \cup (-1, 3) \cup (3, \infty)$$

GREAT QUESTION!

When finding the domain of a function, when do I have to factor?

In parts (a) and (b), observe when to factor and when not to factor a polynomial.

- $f(x) = x^2 - 7x$

- $g(x) = \dfrac{3x + 2}{x^2 - 2x - 3}$

| **Do not** factor $x^2 - 7x$ and set it equal to zero. No values of x need be excluded from the domain. | **Do** factor $x^2 - 2x - 3$ and set it equal to zero. We must exclude values of x that cause this denominator to be zero. |

c. The function $h(x) = \sqrt{3x + 12}$ contains an even root. Because only nonnegative numbers have real square roots, the quantity under the radical sign, $3x + 12$, must be greater than or equal to 0.

$$3x + 12 \geq 0 \qquad \text{Set the function's radicand greater than or equal to 0.}$$
$$3x \geq -12 \qquad \text{Subtract 12 from both sides.}$$
$$x \geq -4 \qquad \text{Divide both sides by 3. Division by a positive number preserves the sense of the inequality.}$$

The domain of h consists of all real numbers greater than or equal to -4.

$$\text{Domain of } h = [-4, \infty)$$

The domain is highlighted on the x-axis in **Figure 2.51**.

$[-10, 10, 1]$ by $[-10, 10, 1]$

FIGURE 2.51

d. The function $j(x) = \dfrac{3x + 2}{\sqrt{14 - 2x}}$ contains both an even root and division. Because only nonnegative numbers have real square roots, the quantity under the radical sign, $14 - 2x$, must be greater than or equal to 0. But wait, there's more! Because division by 0 is undefined, $14 - 2x$ cannot equal 0. Thus, $14 - 2x$ must be strictly greater than 0.

$$14 - 2x > 0 \qquad \text{Set the function's radicand greater than 0.}$$
$$-2x > -14 \qquad \text{Subtract 14 from both sides.}$$
$$x < 7 \qquad \text{Divide both sides by } -2. \text{ Division by a negative number reverses the direction of the inequality.}$$

The domain of j consists of all real numbers less than 7.

$$\text{Domain of } j = (-\infty, 7) \qquad\qquad \bullet\bullet\bullet$$

☑ Check Point **1** Find the domain of each function:

a. $f(x) = x^2 + 3x - 17$ **b.** $g(x) = \dfrac{5x}{x^2 - 49}$

c. $h(x) = \sqrt{9x - 27}$ **d.** $j(x) = \dfrac{5x}{\sqrt{24 - 3x}}$.

② Combine functions using the algebra of functions, specifying domains.

The Algebra of Functions

We can combine functions using addition, subtraction, multiplication, and division by performing operations with the algebraic expressions that appear on the right side of the equations. For example, the functions $f(x) = 2x$ and $g(x) = x - 1$ can be combined to form the sum, difference, product, and quotient of f and g. Here's how it's done:

Sum: $f + g$

$$(f + g)(x) = f(x) + g(x)$$
$$= 2x + (x - 1) = 3x - 1$$

Difference: $f - g$

$$(f - g)(x) = f(x) - g(x)$$
$$= 2x - (x - 1) = 2x - x + 1 = x + 1$$

For each function,
$f(x) = 2x$ and
$g(x) = x - 1$.

Product: fg

$$(fg)(x) = f(x) \cdot g(x)$$
$$= 2x(x - 1) = 2x^2 - 2x$$

Quotient: $\dfrac{f}{g}$

$$\left(\frac{f}{g}\right)(x) = \frac{f(x)}{g(x)} = \frac{2x}{x - 1}, x \neq 1.$$

The domain for each of these functions consists of all real numbers that are common to the domains of f and g. Using D_f to represent the domain of f and D_g to represent the domain of g, the domain for each function is $D_f \cap D_g$. In the case of the quotient function $\dfrac{f(x)}{g(x)}$, we must remember not to divide by 0, so we add the further restriction that $g(x) \neq 0$.

The Algebra of Functions: Sum, Difference, Product, and Quotient of Functions

Let f and g be two functions. The **sum** $f + g$, the **difference** $f - g$, the **product** fg, and the **quotient** $\dfrac{f}{g}$ are functions whose domains are the set of all real numbers common to the domains of f and g ($D_f \cap D_g$), defined as follows:

1. Sum: $\qquad (f + g)(x) = f(x) + g(x)$
2. Difference: $\quad (f - g)(x) = f(x) - g(x)$
3. Product: $\qquad (fg)(x) = f(x) \cdot g(x)$

4. Quotient: $\qquad \left(\dfrac{f}{g}\right)(x) = \dfrac{f(x)}{g(x)},$ provided $g(x) \neq 0$.

EXAMPLE 2   Combining Functions

Let $f(x) = 2x - 1$ and $g(x) = x^2 + x - 2$. Find each of the following functions:

   a. $(f + g)(x)$ **b.** $(f - g)(x)$ **c.** $(fg)(x)$ **d.** $\left(\dfrac{f}{g}\right)(x).$

Determine the domain for each function.

SOLUTION

   a. $(f + g)(x) = f(x) + g(x)$ This is the definition of the sum $f + g$.

$\qquad\qquad\qquad = (2x - 1) + (x^2 + x - 2)$ Substitute the given functions.

$\qquad\qquad\qquad = x^2 + 3x - 3$ Remove parentheses and combine like terms.

   b. $(f - g)(x) = f(x) - g(x)$ This is the definition of the difference $f - g$.

$\qquad\qquad\qquad = (2x - 1) - (x^2 + x - 2)$ Substitute the given functions.

$\qquad\qquad\qquad = 2x - 1 - x^2 - x + 2$ Remove parentheses and change the sign of each term in the second set of parentheses.

$\qquad\qquad\qquad = -x^2 + x + 1$ Combine like terms and arrange terms in descending powers of x.

c. $(fg)(x) = f(x) \cdot g(x)$ This is the definition of the product fg.

$= (2x - 1)(x^2 + x - 2)$ Substitute the given functions.

$= 2x(x^2 + x - 2) - 1(x^2 + x - 2)$ Multiply each term in the second factor by 2x and −1, respectively.

$= 2x^3 + 2x^2 - 4x - x^2 - x + 2$ Use the distributive property.

$= 2x^3 + (2x^2 - x^2) + (-4x - x) + 2$ Rearrange terms so that like terms are adjacent.

$= 2x^3 + x^2 - 5x + 2$ Combine like terms.

d. $\left(\dfrac{f}{g}\right)(x) = \dfrac{f(x)}{g(x)}$ This is the definition of the quotient $\dfrac{f}{g}$.

$= \dfrac{2x - 1}{x^2 + x - 2}$ Substitute the given functions. This rational expression cannot be simplified.

GREAT QUESTION!

Should I simplify a quotient function before finding its domain?

No. If the function $\dfrac{f}{g}$ can be simplified, determine the domain *before* simplifying. All values of x for which $g(x) = 0$ must be excluded from the domain.

Example:

$f(x) = x^2 - 4$ and
$g(x) = x - 2$

$\left(\dfrac{f}{g}\right)(x) = \dfrac{x^2 - 4}{x - 2}$

> $x \neq 2$. The domain of $\dfrac{f}{g}$ is $(-\infty, 2) \cup (2, \infty)$.

$= \dfrac{\overset{1}{\cancel{(x + 2)}}(x - 2)}{\underset{1}{\cancel{(x - 2)}}} = x + 2$

Because the equations for f and g do not involve division or contain even roots, the domain of both f and g is the set of all real numbers. Thus, the domain of $f + g, f - g$, and fg is the set of all real numbers, $(-\infty, \infty)$.

The function $\dfrac{f}{g}$ contains division. We must exclude from its domain values of x that cause the denominator, $x^2 + x - 2$, to be 0. Let's identify these values.

$x^2 + x - 2 = 0$ Set the denominator of $\frac{f}{g}$ equal to 0.

$(x + 2)(x - 1) = 0$ Factor.

$x + 2 = 0$ or $x - 1 = 0$ Set each factor equal to 0.

$x = -2$ $x = 1$ Solve the resulting equations.

We must exclude -2 and 1 from the domain of $\dfrac{f}{g}$.

Domain of $\dfrac{f}{g} = (-\infty, -2) \cup (-2, 1) \cup (1, \infty)$ • • •

⊘ **Check Point 2** Let $f(x) = x - 5$ and $g(x) = x^2 - 1$. Find each of the following functions:

a. $(f + g)(x)$ **b.** $(f - g)(x)$ **c.** $(fg)(x)$ **d.** $\left(\dfrac{f}{g}\right)(x)$.

Determine the domain for each function.

> **EXAMPLE 3**   Adding Functions and Determining the Domain

Let $f(x) = \sqrt{x + 3}$ and $g(x) = \sqrt{x - 2}$. Find each of the following:
   a. $(f + g)(x)$ **b.** the domain of $f + g$.

SOLUTION

a. $(f + g)(x) = f(x) + g(x) = \sqrt{x + 3} + \sqrt{x - 2}$

b. The domain of $f + g$ is the set of all real numbers that are common to the domain of f and the domain of g. Thus, we must find the domains of f and g before finding their intersection.

• $f(x) = \sqrt{x + 3}$ • $g(x) = \sqrt{x - 2}$

> $x + 3$ must be nonnegative: $x + 3 \geq 0$. $D_f = [-3, \infty)$

> $x - 2$ must be nonnegative: $x - 2 \geq 0$. $D_g = [2, \infty)$

FIGURE 2.52 Finding the domain of the sum $f + g$

Now, we can use a number line to determine $D_f \cap D_g$, the domain of $f + g$. **Figure 2.52** shows the domain of f in blue and the domain of g in red. Can you see that all real numbers greater than or equal to 2 are common to both domains? This is shown in purple on the number line. Thus, the domain of $f + g$ is $[2, \infty)$.

• • •

TECHNOLOGY

Graphic Connections

The graph on the left is the graph of

$$y = \sqrt{x + 3} + \sqrt{x - 2}$$

in a $[-3, 10, 1]$ by $[0, 8, 1]$ viewing rectangle. The graph reveals what we discovered algebraically in Example 3(b). The domain of this function is $[2, \infty)$.

Domain: $[2, \infty)$

 Check Point 3 Let $f(x) = \sqrt{x - 3}$ and $g(x) = \sqrt{x + 1}$. Find each of the following:

a. $(f + g)(x)$ **b.** the domain of $f + g$.

EXAMPLE 4   Applying the Algebra of Functions

We opened the section with functions that model the number of births and deaths in the United States from 2000 through 2009:

$$B(x) = -2.6x^2 + 49x + 3994 \qquad D(x) = -0.6x^2 + 7x + 2412.$$

Number of births, $B(x)$, in thousands, x years after **2000**

Number of deaths, $D(x)$, in thousands, x years after **2000**

a. Write a function that models the change in U.S. population for the years from 2000 through 2009.

b. Use the function from part (a) to find the change in U.S. population in 2008.

c. Does the result in part (b) overestimate or underestimate the actual population change in 2008 obtained from the data in **Figure 2.50** on page 286? By how much?

SOLUTION

a. The change in population is the number of births minus the number of deaths. Thus, we will find the difference function, $B - D$.

$(B - D)(x)$

$= B(x) - D(x)$

$= (-2.6x^2 + 49x + 3994) - (-0.6x^2 + 7x + 2412)$ Substitute the given functions.

$= -2.6x^2 + 49x + 3994 + 0.6x^2 - 7x - 2412$ Remove parentheses and change the sign of each term in the second set of parentheses.

$= (-2.6x^2 + 0.6x^2) + (49x - 7x) + (3994 - 2412)$ Group like terms.

$= -2x^2 + 42x + 1582$ Combine like terms.

The function

$$(B - D)(x) = -2x^2 + 42x + 1582$$

models the change in U.S. population, in thousands, x years after 2000.

b. Because 2008 is 8 years after 2000, we substitute 8 for x in the difference function $(B - D)(x)$.

$$(B - D)(x) = -2x^2 + 42x + 1582 \qquad \text{Use the difference function } B - D.$$

$$(B - D)(8) = -2(8)^2 + 42(8) + 1582 \qquad \text{Substitute 8 for } x.$$

$$= -2(64) + 42(8) + 1582 \qquad \text{Evaluate the exponential expression: } 8^2 = 64.$$

$$= -128 + 336 + 1582 \qquad \text{Perform the multiplications.}$$

$$= 1790 \qquad \text{Add from left to right.}$$

We see that $(B - D)(8) = 1790$. The model indicates that there was a population increase of 1790 thousand, or approximately 1,790,000 people, in 2008.

c. The data for 2008 in **Figure 2.50** on page 286 show 4247 thousand births and 2453 thousand deaths.

$$\text{population change} = \text{births} - \text{deaths}$$

$$= 4247 - 2453 = 1794$$

The actual population increase was 1794 thousand, or 1,794,000. Our model gave us an increase of 1790 thousand. Thus, the model underestimates the actual increase by $1794 - 1790$, or 4 thousand people. • • •

⊘ Check Point **4** Use the birth and death models from Example 4.

a. Write a function that models the total number of births and deaths in the United States for the years from 2000 through 2009.

b. Use the function from part (a) to find the total number of births and deaths in the United States in 2003.

c. Does the result in part (b) overestimate or underestimate the actual number of total births and deaths in 2003 obtained from the data in **Figure 2.50** on page 286? By how much?

③ Form composite functions.

Composite Functions

There is another way of combining two functions. To help understand this new combination, suppose that your local computer store is having a sale. The models that are on sale cost either $300 less than the regular price or 85% of the regular price. If x represents the computer's regular price, the discounts can be modeled with the following functions:

$$f(x) = x - 300 \qquad g(x) = 0.85x.$$

The computer is on sale for $300 less than its regular price.

The computer is on sale for 85% of its regular price.

At the store, you bargain with the salesperson. Eventually, she makes an offer you can't refuse. The sale price will be 85% of the regular price followed by a $300 reduction:

$$0.85x - 300.$$

85% of the regular price

followed by a $300 reduction

In terms of the functions f and g, this offer can be obtained by taking the output of $g(x) = 0.85x$, namely, $0.85x$, and using it as the input of f:

$$f(x) = x - 300$$

Replace x with $0.85x$, the output of $g(x) = 0.85x$.

$$f(0.85x) = 0.85x - 300.$$

Because $0.85x$ is $g(x)$, we can write this last equation as

$$f(g(x)) = 0.85x - 300.$$

We read this equation as "f of g of x is equal to $0.85x - 300$." We call $f(g(x))$ the **composition of the function f with g**, or a **composite function**. This composite function is written $f \circ g$. Thus,

$$(f \circ g)(x) = f(g(x)) = 0.85x - 300.$$

This can be read "f of g of x" or "f composed with g of x."

Like all functions, we can evaluate $f \circ g$ for a specified value of x in the function's domain. For example, here's how to find the value of the composite function describing the offer you cannot refuse at 1400:

$$(f \circ g)(x) = 0.85x - 300$$

Replace x with 1400.

$$(f \circ g)(1400) = 0.85(1400) - 300 = 1190 - 300 = 890.$$

This means that a computer that regularly sells for $1400 is on sale for $890 subject to both discounts. We can use a partial table of coordinates for each of the discount functions, g and f, to verify this result numerically.

Computer's regular price	85% of the regular price		85% of the regular price	$300 reduction
x	$g(x) = 0.85x$		x	$f(x) = x - 300$
1200	1020		1020	720
1300	1105		1105	805
1400	1190		1190	890

Using these tables, we can find $(f \circ g)(1400)$:

$$(f \circ g)(1400) = f(g(1400)) = f(1190) = 890.$$

The table for g shows that $g(1400) = 1190$. The table for f shows that $f(1190) = 890$.

This verifies that a computer that regularly sells for $1400 is on sale for $890 subject to both discounts.

Before you run out to buy a computer, let's generalize our discussion of the computer's double discount and define the composition of any two functions.

The Composition of Functions

The **composition of the function f with g** is denoted by $f \circ g$ and is defined by the equation

$$(f \circ g)(x) = f(g(x)).$$

The **domain of the composite function $f \circ g$** is the set of all x such that

1. x is in the domain of g and
2. $g(x)$ is in the domain of f.

The composition of f with g, $f \circ g$, is illustrated in **Figure 2.53**.

Step 1 Input x into g.

Step 2 Input $g(x)$ into f.

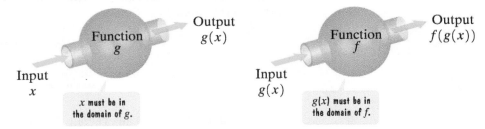

FIGURE 2.53

The figure reinforces the fact that the inside function g in $f(g(x))$ is done first.

EXAMPLE 5   Forming Composite Functions

Given $f(x) = 3x - 4$ and $g(x) = x^2 - 2x + 6$, find each of the following:

a. $(f \circ g)(x)$ **b.** $(g \circ f)(x)$ **c.** $(g \circ f)(1)$.

SOLUTION

a. We begin with $(f \circ g)(x)$, the composition of f with g. Because $(f \circ g)(x)$ means $f(g(x))$, we must replace each occurrence of x in the equation for f with $g(x)$.

$$f(x) = 3x - 4 \qquad \text{This is the given equation for f.}$$

Replace x with $g(x)$.

$$
\begin{aligned}
(f \circ g)(x) = f(g(x)) = {}& 3g(x) - 4 \\
= {}& 3(x^2 - 2x + 6) - 4 && \text{Because } g(x) = x^2 - 2x + 6, \\
&&& \text{replace } g(x) \text{ with } x^2 - 2x + 6. \\
= {}& 3x^2 - 6x + 18 - 4 && \text{Use the distributive property.} \\
= {}& 3x^2 - 6x + 14 && \text{Simplify.}
\end{aligned}
$$

Thus, $(f \circ g)(x) = 3x^2 - 6x + 14$.

b. Next, we find $(g \circ f)(x)$, the composition of g with f. Because $(g \circ f)(x)$ means $g(f(x))$, we must replace each occurrence of x in the equation for g with $f(x)$.

$$g(x) = x^2 - 2x + 6 \qquad \text{This is the equation for g.}$$

Replace x with $f(x)$.

$$
\begin{aligned}
(g \circ f)(x) = g(f(x)) = {}& (f(x))^2 - 2f(x) + 6 \\
= {}& (3x - 4)^2 - 2(3x - 4) + 6 && \text{Because } f(x) = 3x - 4, \\
&&& \text{replace } f(x) \text{ with } 3x - 4.
\end{aligned}
$$

$$= 9x^2 - 24x + 16 - 6x + 8 + 6 \qquad \text{Use } (A - B)^2 =$$

$$A^2 - 2AB + B^2$$

to square $3x - 4$.

$$= 9x^2 - 30x + 30 \qquad \text{Simplify:}$$

$$-24x - 6x = -30x$$

and $16 + 8 + 6 = 30$.

Thus, $(g \circ f)(x) = 9x^2 - 30x + 30$. **Notice that $(f \circ g)(x)$ is not the same function as $(g \circ f)(x)$.**

c. We can use $(g \circ f)(x)$ to find $(g \circ f)(1)$.

$$(g \circ f)(x) = 9x^2 - 30x + 30$$

> Replace x with 1.

$$(g \circ f)(1) = 9 \cdot 1^2 - 30 \cdot 1 + 30 = 9 - 30 + 30 = 9$$

It is also possible to find $(g \circ f)(1)$ without determining $(g \circ f)(x)$.

$$(g \circ f)(1) = g(f(1)) = g(-1) = 9$$

> First find $f(1)$.
> $f(x) = 3x - 4$, so
> $f(1) = 3 \cdot 1 - 4 = -1$.

> Next find $g(-1)$.
> $g(x) = x^2 - 2x + 6$, so
> $g(-1) = (-1)^2 - 2(-1) + 6$
> $= 1 + 2 + 6 = 9$.

● ● ●

✓ **Check Point 5** Given $f(x) = 5x + 6$ and $g(x) = 2x^2 - x - 1$, find each of the following:

a. $(f \circ g)(x)$ **b.** $(g \circ f)(x)$ **c.** $(f \circ g)(-1)$.

④ Determine domains for composite functions.

We need to be careful in determining the domain for a composite function.

Excluding Values from the Domain of $(f \circ g)(x) = f(g(x))$

The following values must be excluded from the input x:

- If x is not in the domain of g, it must not be in the domain of $f \circ g$.
- Any x for which $g(x)$ is not in the domain of f must not be in the domain of $f \circ g$.

EXAMPLE 6   Forming a Composite Function and Finding Its Domain

GREAT QUESTION!

Can you remind me of how you simplified the complex fraction on the right?

One method for simplifying complex fractions is to find the least common denominator of all the rational expressions in the numerator and the denominator. Then multiply each term in the numerator and denominator by this least common denominator. The procedures for simplifying complex fractions can be found in Section P.6, pages 83–85.

Given $f(x) = \dfrac{2}{x - 1}$ and $g(x) = \dfrac{3}{x}$, find each of the following:

a. $(f \circ g)(x)$ **b.** the domain of $f \circ g$.

SOLUTION

a. Because $(f \circ g)(x)$ means $f(g(x))$, we must replace x in $f(x) = \dfrac{2}{x - 1}$ with $g(x)$.

$$(f \circ g)(x) = f(g(x)) = \frac{2}{g(x) - 1} = \frac{2}{\frac{3}{x} - 1} = \frac{2}{\frac{3}{x} - 1} \cdot \frac{x}{x} = \frac{2x}{3 - x}$$

> $g(x) = \frac{3}{x}$

> Simplify the complex fraction by multiplying by $\frac{x}{x}$, or 1.

Thus, $(f \circ g)(x) = \dfrac{2x}{3 - x}$.

b. We determine values to exclude from the domain of $(f \circ g)(x)$ in two steps.

Rules for Excluding Numbers from the Domain of $(f \circ g)(x) = f(g(x))$	**Applying the Rules to** $f(x) = \dfrac{2}{x-1}$ and $g(x) = \dfrac{3}{x}$
If x is not in the domain of g, it must not be in the domain of $f \circ g$.	Because $g(x) = \dfrac{3}{x}$, 0 is not in the domain of g. Thus, 0 must be excluded from the domain of $f \circ g$.
Any x for which $g(x)$ is not in the domain of f must not be in the domain of $f \circ g$.	Because $f(g(x)) = \dfrac{2}{g(x) - 1}$, we must exclude from the domain of $f \circ g$ any x for which $g(x) = 1$. $$\frac{3}{x} = 1 \quad \text{Set } g(x) \text{ equal to 1.}$$ $$3 = x \quad \text{Multiply both sides by } x.$$ 3 must be excluded from the domain of $f \circ g$.

We see that 0 and 3 must be excluded from the domain of $f \circ g$. The domain of $f \circ g$ is

$$(-\infty, 0) \cup (0, 3) \cup (3, \infty).$$ • • •

 Check Point **6** Given $f(x) = \dfrac{4}{x+2}$ and $g(x) = \dfrac{1}{x}$, find each of the following:

a. $(f \circ g)(x)$ **b.** the domain of $f \circ g$.

⑤ Write functions as compositions.

Decomposing Functions

When you form a composite function, you "compose" two functions to form a new function. It is also possible to reverse this process. That is, you can "decompose" a given function and express it as a composition of two functions. Although there is more than one way to do this, there is often a "natural" selection that comes to mind first. For example, consider the function h defined by

$$h(x) = (3x^2 - 4x + 1)^5.$$

The function h takes $3x^2 - 4x + 1$ and raises it to the power 5. A natural way to write h as a composition of two functions is to raise the function $g(x) = 3x^2 - 4x + 1$ to the power 5. Thus, if we let

$$f(x) = x^5 \text{ and } g(x) = 3x^2 - 4x + 1, \text{ then}$$
$$(f \circ g)(x) = f(g(x)) = f(3x^2 - 4x + 1) = (3x^2 - 4x + 1)^5.$$

GREAT QUESTION!

Is there a procedure I can use to write a function as a composition?

Yes. Suppose the form of function h is
$h(x) = (\text{algebraic expression})^{\text{power}}$.
Function h can be expressed as a composition, $f \circ g$, using

$f(x) = x^{\text{power}}$

$g(x) = \text{algebraic expression}$.

EXAMPLE 7 Writing a Function as a Composition

Express $h(x)$ as a composition of two functions:

$$h(x) = \sqrt[3]{x^2 + 1}.$$

SOLUTION

The function h takes $x^2 + 1$ and takes its cube root. A natural way to write h as a composition of two functions is to take the cube root of the function $g(x) = x^2 + 1$. Thus, we let

$$f(x) = \sqrt[3]{x} \text{ and } g(x) = x^2 + 1.$$

We can check this composition by finding $(f \circ g)(x)$. This should give the original function, namely, $h(x) = \sqrt[3]{x^2 + 1}$.

$$(f \circ g)(x) = f(g(x)) = f(x^2 + 1) = \sqrt[3]{x^2 + 1} = h(x)$$ ...

✓ **Check Point 7** Express $h(x)$ as a composition of two functions:
$$h(x) = \sqrt{x^2 + 5}.$$

CONCEPT AND VOCABULARY CHECK

Fill in each blank so that the resulting statement is true.

1. We exclude from a function's domain real numbers that cause division by _____.
2. We exclude from a function's domain real numbers that result in a square root of a/an _____ number.
3. $(f + g)(x) = $ _____
4. $(f - g)(x) = $ _____
5. $(fg)(x) = $ _____
6. $\dfrac{f}{g}(x) = $ _____, provided _____ $\neq 0$
7. The domain of $f(x) = 5x + 7$ consists of all real numbers, represented in interval notation as _____.
8. The domain of $g(x) = \dfrac{3}{x - 2}$ consists of all real numbers except 2, represented in interval notations as $(-\infty, 2) \cup$ _____.

9. The domain of $h(x) = \dfrac{1}{x} + \dfrac{7}{x - 3}$ consists of all real numbers except 0 and 3, represented in interval notation as $(-\infty, 0) \cup$ _____ $\cup$ _____.
10. The notation $f \circ g$, called the _____ of the function f with g, is defined by $(f \circ g)(x) = $ _____.
11. I find $(f \circ g)(x)$ by replacing each occurrence of x in the equation for ____ with _____.
12. The notation $g \circ f$, called the _____ of the function g with f, is defined by $(g \circ f)(x) = $ _____.
13. I find $(g \circ f)(x)$ by replacing each occurrence of x in the equation for ____ with _____.
14. True or false: $f \circ g$ is the same function as $g \circ f$. _____
15. True or false: $f(g(x)) = f(x) \cdot g(x)$ _____
16. If $f(g(x)) = \dfrac{3}{g(x) - 4}$ and $g(x) = \dfrac{8}{x}$, then 0 and ____ must be excluded from the domain of $f \circ g$.

EXERCISE SET 2.6

Practice Exercises

In Exercises 1–30, find the domain of each function.

1. $f(x) = 3(x - 4)$
2. $f(x) = 2(x + 5)$
3. $g(x) = \dfrac{3}{x - 4}$
4. $g(x) = \dfrac{2}{x + 5}$
5. $f(x) = x^2 - 2x - 15$
6. $f(x) = x^2 + x - 12$
7. $g(x) = \dfrac{3}{x^2 - 2x - 15}$
8. $g(x) = \dfrac{2}{x^2 + x - 12}$
9. $f(x) = \dfrac{1}{x + 7} + \dfrac{3}{x - 9}$
10. $f(x) = \dfrac{1}{x + 8} + \dfrac{3}{x - 10}$
11. $g(x) = \dfrac{1}{x^2 + 1} - \dfrac{1}{x^2 - 1}$
12. $g(x) = \dfrac{1}{x^2 + 4} - \dfrac{1}{x^2 - 4}$
13. $h(x) = \dfrac{4}{\dfrac{3}{x} - 1}$
14. $h(x) = \dfrac{5}{\dfrac{4}{x} - 1}$
15. $f(x) = \dfrac{1}{\dfrac{4}{x - 1} - 2}$
16. $f(x) = \dfrac{1}{\dfrac{4}{x - 2} - 3}$
17. $f(x) = \sqrt{x - 3}$
18. $f(x) = \sqrt{x + 2}$

19. $g(x) = \dfrac{1}{\sqrt{x - 3}}$
20. $g(x) = \dfrac{1}{\sqrt{x + 2}}$
21. $g(x) = \sqrt{5x + 35}$
22. $g(x) = \sqrt{7x - 70}$
23. $f(x) = \sqrt{24 - 2x}$
24. $f(x) = \sqrt{84 - 6x}$
25. $h(x) = \sqrt{x - 2} + \sqrt{x + 3}$
26. $h(x) = \sqrt{x - 3} + \sqrt{x + 4}$
27. $g(x) = \dfrac{\sqrt{x - 2}}{x - 5}$
28. $g(x) = \dfrac{\sqrt{x - 3}}{x - 6}$
29. $f(x) = \dfrac{2x + 7}{x^3 - 5x^2 - 4x + 20}$
30. $f(x) = \dfrac{7x + 2}{x^3 - 2x^2 - 9x + 18}$

In Exercises 31–50, find $f + g$, $f - g$, fg, and $\dfrac{f}{g}$. Determine the domain for each function.

31. $f(x) = 2x + 3$, $g(x) = x - 1$
32. $f(x) = 3x - 4$, $g(x) = x + 2$
33. $f(x) = x - 5$, $g(x) = 3x^2$
34. $f(x) = x - 6$, $g(x) = 5x^2$
35. $f(x) = 2x^2 - x - 3$, $g(x) = x + 1$
36. $f(x) = 6x^2 - x - 1$, $g(x) = x - 1$

37. $f(x) = 3 - x^2, g(x) = x^2 + 2x - 15$
38. $f(x) = 5 - x^2, g(x) = x^2 + 4x - 12$
39. $f(x) = \sqrt{x}, g(x) = x - 4$
40. $f(x) = \sqrt{x}, g(x) = x - 5$
41. $f(x) = 2 + \dfrac{1}{x}, g(x) = \dfrac{1}{x}$
42. $f(x) = 6 - \dfrac{1}{x}, g(x) = \dfrac{1}{x}$
43. $f(x) = \dfrac{5x + 1}{x^2 - 9}, g(x) = \dfrac{4x - 2}{x^2 - 9}$
44. $f(x) = \dfrac{3x + 1}{x^2 - 25}, g(x) = \dfrac{2x - 4}{x^2 - 25}$
45. $f(x) = \dfrac{8x}{x - 2}, g(x) = \dfrac{6}{x + 3}$
46. $f(x) = \dfrac{9x}{x - 4}, g(x) = \dfrac{7}{x + 8}$
47. $f(x) = \sqrt{x + 4}, g(x) = \sqrt{x - 1}$
48. $f(x) = \sqrt{x + 6}, g(x) = \sqrt{x - 3}$
49. $f(x) = \sqrt{x - 2}, g(x) = \sqrt{2 - x}$
50. $f(x) = \sqrt{x - 5}, g(x) = \sqrt{5 - x}$

In Exercises 51–66, find

    a. $(f \circ g)(x)$ **b.** $(g \circ f)(x)$ **c.** $(f \circ g)(2)$ **d.** $(g \circ f)(2)$.

51. $f(x) = 2x, g(x) = x + 7$
52. $f(x) = 3x, g(x) = x - 5$
53. $f(x) = x + 4, g(x) = 2x + 1$
54. $f(x) = 5x + 2, g(x) = 3x - 4$
55. $f(x) = 4x - 3, g(x) = 5x^2 - 2$
56. $f(x) = 7x + 1, g(x) = 2x^2 - 9$
57. $f(x) = x^2 + 2, g(x) = x^2 - 2$
58. $f(x) = x^2 + 1, g(x) = x^2 - 3$
59. $f(x) = 4 - x, g(x) = 2x^2 + x + 5$
60. $f(x) = 5x - 2, g(x) = -x^2 + 4x - 1$
61. $f(x) = \sqrt{x}, g(x) = x - 1$
62. $f(x) = \sqrt{x}, g(x) = x + 2$
63. $f(x) = 2x - 3, g(x) = \dfrac{x + 3}{2}$
64. $f(x) = 6x - 3, g(x) = \dfrac{x + 3}{6}$
65. $f(x) = \dfrac{1}{x}, g(x) = \dfrac{1}{x}$
66. $f(x) = \dfrac{2}{x}, g(x) = \dfrac{2}{x}$

In Exercises 67–74, find

    a. $(f \circ g)(x)$ **b.** *the domain of* $f \circ g$.

67. $f(x) = \dfrac{2}{x + 3}, g(x) = \dfrac{1}{x}$
68. $f(x) = \dfrac{5}{x + 4}, g(x) = \dfrac{1}{x}$
69. $f(x) = \dfrac{x}{x + 1}, g(x) = \dfrac{4}{x}$
70. $f(x) = \dfrac{x}{x + 5}, g(x) = \dfrac{6}{x}$
71. $f(x) = \sqrt{x}, g(x) = x - 2$

72. $f(x) = \sqrt{x}, g(x) = x - 3$
73. $f(x) = x^2 + 4, g(x) = \sqrt{1 - x}$
74. $f(x) = x^2 + 1, g(x) = \sqrt{2 - x}$

In Exercises 75–82, express the given function h as a composition of two functions f and g so that $h(x) = (f \circ g)(x)$.

75. $h(x) = (3x - 1)^4$
76. $h(x) = (2x - 5)^3$
77. $h(x) = \sqrt[3]{x^2 - 9}$
78. $h(x) = \sqrt{5x^2 + 3}$
79. $h(x) = |2x - 5|$
80. $h(x) = |3x - 4|$
81. $h(x) = \dfrac{1}{2x - 3}$
82. $h(x) = \dfrac{1}{4x + 5}$

Practice Plus

Use the graphs of f and g to solve Exercises 83–90.

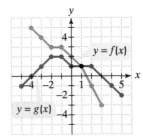

83. Find $(f + g)(-3)$.
84. Find $(g - f)(-2)$.
85. Find $(fg)(2)$.
86. Find $\left(\dfrac{g}{f}\right)(3)$.
87. Find the domain of $f + g$.
88. Find the domain of $\dfrac{f}{g}$.
89. Graph $f + g$.
90. Graph $f - g$.

In Exercises 91–94, use the graphs of f and g to evaluate each composite function.

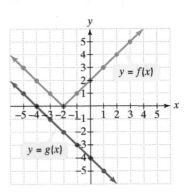

91. $(f \circ g)(-1)$
92. $(f \circ g)(1)$
93. $(g \circ f)(0)$
94. $(g \circ f)(-1)$

In Exercises 95–96, find all values of x satisfying the given conditions.

95. $f(x) = 2x - 5, g(x) = x^2 - 3x + 8$, and $(f \circ g)(x) = 7$.
96. $f(x) = 1 - 2x, g(x) = 3x^2 + x - 1$, and $(f \circ g)(x) = -5$.

Application Exercises

The bar graph shows the population of the United States, in millions, for six selected years.

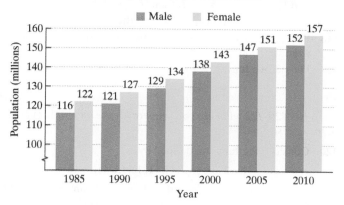

Population of the United States

Source: U.S. Census Bureau

Here are two functions that model the data:

$$M(x) = 1.53x + 114.8$$

Male U.S. population, $M(x)$, in millions, x years after 1985

$$F(x) = 1.46x + 120.7.$$

Female U.S. population, $F(x)$, in millions, x years after 1985

Use the functions to solve Exercises 97–98.

97. a. Write a function that models the total U.S. population for the years shown in the bar graph.

    b. Use the function from part (a) to find the total U.S. population in 2005.

    c. Does the result in part (b) overestimate or underestimate the actual total U.S. population in 2005 shown by the bar graph? By how much?

98. a. Write a function that models the difference between the female U.S. population and the male U.S. population for the years shown in the bar graph.

    b. Use the function from part (a) to find how many more women than men there were in the U.S. population in 2005.

    c. Does the result in part (b) overestimate or underestimate the actual difference between the female and male population in 2005 shown by the bar graph? By how much?

99. A company that sells radios has yearly fixed costs of \$600,000. It costs the company \$45 to produce each radio. Each radio will sell for \$65. The company's costs and revenue are modeled by the following functions, where x represents the number of radios produced and sold:

$$C(x) = 600,000 + 45x$$ This function models the company's costs.

$$R(x) = 65x.$$ This function models the company's revenue.

Find and interpret $(R - C)(20,000), (R - C)(30,000)$, and $(R - C)(40,000)$.

100. A department store has two locations in a city. From 2008 through 2012, the profits for each of the store's two branches are modeled by the functions $f(x) = -0.44x + 13.62$ and $g(x) = 0.51x + 11.14$. In each model, x represents the number of years after 2008, and f and g represent the profit, in millions of dollars.

    a. What is the slope of f? Describe what this means.

    b. What is the slope of g? Describe what this means.

    c. Find $f + g$. What is the slope of this function? What does this mean?

101. The regular price of a computer is x dollars. Let $f(x) = x - 400$ and $g(x) = 0.75x$.

    a. Describe what the functions f and g model in terms of the price of the computer.

    b. Find $(f \circ g)(x)$ and describe what this models in terms of the price of the computer.

    c. Repeat part (b) for $(g \circ f)(x)$.

    d. Which composite function models the greater discount on the computer, $f \circ g$ or $g \circ f$? Explain.

102. The regular price of a pair of jeans is x dollars. Let $f(x) = x - 5$ and $g(x) = 0.6x$.

    a. Describe what functions f and g model in terms of the price of the jeans.

    b. Find $(f \circ g)(x)$ and describe what this models in terms of the price of the jeans.

    c. Repeat part (b) for $(g \circ f)(x)$.

    d. Which composite function models the greater discount on the jeans, $f \circ g$ or $g \circ f$? Explain.

Writing in Mathematics

103. If a function is defined by an equation, explain how to find its domain.

104. If equations for f and g are given, explain how to find $f - g$.

105. If equations for two functions are given, explain how to obtain the quotient function and its domain.

106. Describe a procedure for finding $(f \circ g)(x)$. What is the name of this function?

107. Describe the values of x that must be excluded from the domain of $(f \circ g)(x)$.

Technology Exercises

108. Graph $y_1 = x^2 - 2x, y_2 = x$, and $y_3 = y_1 \div y_2$ in the same $[-10, 10, 1]$ by $[-10, 10, 1]$ viewing rectangle. Then use the TRACE feature to trace along y_3. What happens at $x = 0$? Explain why this occurs.

109. Graph $y_1 = \sqrt{2 - x}, y_2 = \sqrt{x}$, and $y_3 = \sqrt{2 - y_2}$ in the same $[-4, 4, 1]$ by $[0, 2, 1]$ viewing rectangle. If y_1 represents f and y_2 represents g, use the graph of y_3 to find the domain of $f \circ g$. Then verify your observation algebraically.

Critical Thinking Exercises

Make Sense? *In Exercises 110–113, determine whether each statement makes sense or does not make sense, and explain your reasoning.*

110. I used a function to model data from 1980 through 2005. The independent variable in my model represented the number of years after 1980, so the function's domain was $\{x \mid x = 0, 1, 2, 3, \ldots, 25\}$.

111. I have two functions. Function f models total world population x years after 2000 and function g models population of the world's more-developed regions x years after 2000. I can use $f - g$ to determine the population of the world's less-developed regions for the years in both function's domains.

112. I must have made a mistake in finding the composite functions $f \circ g$ and $g \circ f$, because I notice that $f \circ g$ is not the same function as $g \circ f$.

113. This diagram illustrates that $f(g(x)) = x^2 + 4$.

In Exercises 114–119, determine whether each statement is true or false. If the statement is false, make the necessary change(s) to produce a true statement.

114. If $f(x) = x^2 - 4$ and $g(x) = \sqrt{x^2 - 4}$, then $(f \circ g)(x) = -x^2$ and $(f \circ g)(5) = -25$.

115. There can never be two functions f and g, where $f \neq g$, for which $(f \circ g)(x) = (g \circ f)(x)$.

116. If $f(7) = 5$ and $g(4) = 7$, then $(f \circ g)(4) = 35$.

117. If $f(x) = \sqrt{x}$ and $g(x) = 2x - 1$, then $(f \circ g)(5) = g(2)$.

118. Prove that if f and g are even functions, then fg is also an even function.

119. Define two functions f and g so that $f \circ g = g \circ f$.

Preview Exercises

Exercises 120–122 will help you prepare for the material covered in the next section.

120. Consider the function defined by
$$\{(-2, 4), (-1, 1), (1, 1), (2, 4)\}.$$
Reverse the components of each ordered pair and write the resulting relation. Is this relation a function?

121. Solve for y: $x = \dfrac{5}{y} + 4$.

122. Solve for y: $x = y^2 - 1, y \geq 0$.

SECTION 2.7   Inverse Functions

Objectives

1. Verify inverse functions.
2. Find the inverse of a function.
3. Use the horizontal line test to determine if a function has an inverse function.
4. Use the graph of a one-to-one function to graph its inverse function.
5. Find the inverse of a function and graph both functions on the same axes.

Based on Shakespeare's *Romeo and Juliet*, the film *West Side Story* swept the 1961 Academy Awards with ten Oscars. The top four movies to win the most Oscars are shown in **Table 2.5**.

Table 2.5   Films Winning the Most Oscars

Movie	Year	Number of Academy Awards
Ben-Hur	1960	11
Titanic	1998	11
The Lord of the Rings: The Return of the King	2003	11
West Side Story	1961	10

Source: Russell Ash, *The Top 10 of Everything, 2011*

We can use the information in **Table 2.5** to define a function. Let the domain of the function be the set of four movies shown in the table. Let the range be the number of Academy Awards for each of the respective films. The function can be written as follows:

f: {(*Ben-Hur*, 11), (*Titanic*, 11), (*The Lord of the Rings*, 11), (*West Side Story*, 10)}.

Now let's "undo" f by interchanging the first and second components in each of the ordered pairs. Switching the inputs and outputs of f, we obtain the following relation:

Same first component

Undoing f: {(11, *Ben-Hur*), (11, *Titanic*), (11, *The Lord of the Rings*), (10, *West Side Story*)}.

Different second components

Can you see that this relation is not a function? Three of its ordered pairs have the same first component and different second components. This violates the definition of a function.

If a function f is a set of ordered pairs, (x, y), then the changes produced by f can be "undone" by reversing the components of all the ordered pairs. The resulting relation, (y, x), may or may not be a function. In this section, we will develop these ideas by studying functions whose compositions have a special "undoing" relationship.

Inverse Functions

Here are two functions that describe situations related to the price of a computer, x:

$$f(x) = x - 300 \qquad g(x) = x + 300.$$

Function f subtracts \$300 from the computer's price and function g adds \$300 to the computer's price. Let's see what $f(g(x))$ does. Put $g(x)$ into f:

$$f(x) = x - 300 \qquad \text{This is the given equation for f.}$$

Replace x with $g(x)$.

$$f(g(x)) = g(x) - 300$$
$$= x + 300 - 300 \qquad \text{Because } g(x) = x + 300,$$
$$= x. \qquad \text{replace } g(x) \text{ with } x + 300.$$

This is the computer's original price.

Using $f(x) = x - 300$ and $g(x) = x + 300$, we see that $f(g(x)) = x$. By putting $g(x)$ into f and finding $f(g(x))$, the computer's price, x, went through two changes: the first, an increase; the second, a decrease:

$$x + 300 - 300.$$

The final price of the computer, x, is identical to its starting price, x.

In general, if the changes made to x by a function g are undone by the changes made by a function f, then

$$f(g(x)) = x.$$

Assume, also, that this "undoing" takes place in the other direction:

$$g(f(x)) = x.$$

Under these conditions, we say that each function is the *inverse function* of the other. The fact that g is the inverse of f is expressed by renaming g as f^{-1}, read "f-inverse." For example, the inverse functions

$$f(x) = x - 300 \qquad g(x) = x + 300$$

are usually named as follows:

$$f(x) = x - 300 \qquad f^{-1}(x) = x + 300.$$

We can use partial tables of coordinates for f and f^{-1} to gain numerical insight into the relationship between a function and its inverse function.

Computer's regular price	$300 reduction		Price with $300 reduction	$300 price increase
x	$f(x) = x - 300$		x	$f^{-1}(x) = x + 300$
1200	900		900	1200
1300	1000		1000	1300
1400	1100		1100	1400

Ordered pairs for f:
(1200, 900), (1300, 1000), (1400, 1100)

Ordered pairs for f^{-1}:
(900, 1200), (1000, 1300), (1100, 1400)

The tables illustrate that if a function f is the set of ordered pairs (x, y), then its inverse, f^{-1}, is the set of ordered pairs (y, x). Using these tables, we can see how one function's changes to x are undone by the other function:

$$(f^{-1} \circ f)(1300) = f^{-1}(f(1300)) = f^{-1}(1000) = 1300.$$

The table for f shows that $f(1300) = 1000$.

The table for f^{-1} shows that $f^{-1}(1000) = 1300$.

The final price of the computer, $1300, is identical to its starting price, $1300.

With these ideas in mind, we present the formal definition of the inverse of a function:

Verify inverse functions.

Definition of the Inverse of a Function

Let f and g be two functions such that

$$f(g(x)) = x \qquad \text{for every } x \text{ in the domain of } g$$

and

$$g(f(x)) = x \qquad \text{for every } x \text{ in the domain of } f.$$

The function g is the **inverse of the function f** and is denoted by f^{-1} (read "f-inverse"). Thus, $f(f^{-1}(x)) = x$ and $f^{-1}(f(x)) = x$. The domain of f is equal to the range of f^{-1}, and vice versa.

EXAMPLE 1 Verifying Inverse Functions

Show that each function is the inverse of the other:

$$f(x) = 3x + 2 \quad \text{and} \quad g(x) = \frac{x - 2}{3}.$$

SOLUTION

To show that f and g are inverses of each other, we must show that $f(g(x)) = x$ and $g(f(x)) = x$. We begin with $f(g(x))$.

$$f(x) = 3x + 2 \qquad \text{This is the equation for } f.$$

Replace x with $g(x)$.

$$f(g(x)) = 3g(x) + 2 = 3\left(\frac{x-2}{3}\right) + 2 = x - 2 + 2 = x$$

$$g(x) = \frac{x-2}{3}$$

Next, we find $g(f(x))$.

$$g(x) = \frac{x-2}{3} \qquad \text{This is the equation for } g.$$

Replace x with $f(x)$.

$$g(f(x)) = \frac{f(x) - 2}{3} = \frac{(3x+2) - 2}{3} = \frac{3x}{3} = x$$

$$f(x) = 3x + 2$$

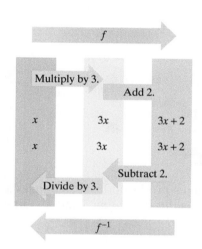

FIGURE 2.54 f^{-1} undoes the changes produced by f.

Because g is the inverse of f (and vice versa), we can use inverse notation and write

$$f(x) = 3x + 2 \quad \text{and} \quad f^{-1}(x) = \frac{x-2}{3}.$$

Notice how f^{-1} undoes the changes produced by f: f changes x by *multiplying* by 3 and *adding* 2, and f^{-1} undoes this by *subtracting* 2 and *dividing* by 3. This "undoing" process is illustrated in **Figure 2.54**. • • •

✓ Check Point **1** Show that each function is the inverse of the other:

$$f(x) = 4x - 7 \quad \text{and} \quad g(x) = \frac{x+7}{4}.$$

② Find the inverse of a function.

Finding the Inverse of a Function

The definition of the inverse of a function tells us that the domain of f is equal to the range of f^{-1}, and vice versa. This means that if the function f is the set of ordered pairs (x, y), then the inverse of f is the set of ordered pairs (y, x). If a function is defined by an equation, we can obtain the equation for f^{-1}, the inverse of f, by interchanging the role of x and y in the equation for the function f.

Finding the Inverse of a Function

The equation for the inverse of a function f can be found as follows:

1. Replace $f(x)$ with y in the equation for $f(x)$.
2. Interchange x and y.
3. Solve for y. If this equation does not define y as a function of x, the function f does not have an inverse function and this procedure ends. If this equation does define y as a function of x, the function f has an inverse function.
4. If f has an inverse function, replace y in step 3 by $f^{-1}(x)$. We can verify our result by showing that $f(f^{-1}(x)) = x$ and $f^{-1}(f(x)) = x$.

The procedure for finding a function's inverse uses a *switch-and-solve* strategy. Switch x and y, and then solve for y.

EXAMPLE 2 Finding the Inverse of a Function

Find the inverse of $f(x) = 7x - 5$.

SOLUTION

Step 1 Replace $f(x)$ with y:

$$y = 7x - 5.$$

Step 2 Interchange x and y:

$$x = 7y - 5. \quad \text{This is the inverse function.}$$

Step 3 Solve for y:

$$x + 5 = 7y \qquad \text{Add 5 to both sides.}$$

$$\frac{x + 5}{7} = y. \qquad \text{Divide both sides by 7.}$$

DISCOVERY

In Example 2, we found that if $f(x) = 7x - 5$, then

$$f^{-1}(x) = \frac{x + 5}{7}.$$

Verify this result by showing that

$$f(f^{-1}(x)) = x$$

and

$$f^{-1}(f(x)) = x.$$

Step 4 Replace y with $f^{-1}(x)$:

$$f^{-1}(x) = \frac{x + 5}{7}. \quad \begin{array}{l}\text{The equation is written} \\ \text{with } f^{-1} \text{ on the left.}\end{array}$$

Thus, the inverse of $f(x) = 7x - 5$ is $f^{-1}(x) = \dfrac{x + 5}{7}$.

The inverse function, f^{-1}, undoes the changes produced by f. f changes x by multiplying by 7 and subtracting 5. f^{-1} undoes this by adding 5 and dividing by 7. ● ● ●

☑ Check Point **2** Find the inverse of $f(x) = 2x + 7$.

EXAMPLE 3 Finding the Inverse of a Function

Find the inverse of $f(x) = x^3 + 1$.

SOLUTION

Step 1 Replace $f(x)$ with y: $y = x^3 + 1$.

Step 2 Interchange x and y: $x = y^3 + 1$.

Step 3 Solve for y:

> Our goal is to isolate y. Because $\sqrt[3]{y^3} = y$, we will take the cube root of both sides of the equation.

$$x - 1 = y^3 \qquad \text{Subtract 1 from both sides.}$$

$$\sqrt[3]{x - 1} = \sqrt[3]{y^3} \qquad \text{Take the cube root on both sides.}$$

$$\sqrt[3]{x - 1} = y. \qquad \text{Simplify.}$$

Step 4 Replace y with $f^{-1}(x)$: $f^{-1}(x) = \sqrt[3]{x - 1}$.

Thus, the inverse of $f(x) = x^3 + 1$ is $f^{-1}(x) = \sqrt[3]{x - 1}$. ● ● ●

☑ Check Point **3** Find the inverse of $f(x) = 4x^3 - 1$.

EXAMPLE 4   Finding the Inverse of a Function

Find the inverse of $f(x) = \dfrac{5}{x} + 4$.

SOLUTION

Step 1   Replace $f(x)$ with y:

$$y = \frac{5}{x} + 4.$$

Step 2   Interchange x and y:

$$x = \frac{5}{y} + 4.$$

> Our goal is to isolate y. To get y out of the denominator, we will multiply both sides of the equation by y, $y \neq 0$.

Step 3   Solve for y:

$x = \dfrac{5}{y} + 4$	This is the equation from step 2.
$xy = \left(\dfrac{5}{y} + 4\right)y$	Multiply both sides by y, $y \neq 0$.
$xy = \dfrac{5}{y} \cdot y + 4y$	Use the distributive property.
$xy = 5 + 4y$	Simplify: $\dfrac{5}{y} \cdot y = 5$.
$xy - 4y = 5$	Subtract $4y$ from both sides.
$y(x - 4) = 5$	Factor out y from $xy - 4y$ to obtain a single occurrence of y.
$\dfrac{y(x - 4)}{x - 4} = \dfrac{5}{x - 4}$	Divide both sides by $x - 4$, $x \neq 4$.
$y = \dfrac{5}{x - 4}.$	Simplify.

Step 4   Replace y with $f^{-1}(x)$:

$$f^{-1}(x) = \frac{5}{x - 4}.$$

Thus, the inverse of $f(x) = \dfrac{5}{x} + 4$ is $f^{-1}(x) = \dfrac{5}{x - 4}$.   • • •

✓ Check Point **4** Find the inverse of $f(x) = \dfrac{3}{x} - 1$.

❸ Use the horizontal line test to determine if a function has an inverse function.

The Horizontal Line Test and One-to-One Functions

Let's see what happens if we try to find the inverse of the standard quadratic function, $f(x) = x^2$.

Step 1   Replace $f(x)$ with y: $y = x^2$.

Step 2   Interchange x and y: $x = y^2$.

Step 3   Solve for y: We apply the square root property to solve $y^2 = x$ for y. We obtain

$$y = \pm\sqrt{x}.$$

The $\pm$ in $y = \pm\sqrt{x}$ shows that for certain values of x (all positive real numbers), there are two values of y. Because this equation does not represent y as a function of x, the standard quadratic function $f(x) = x^2$ does not have an inverse function.

We can use a few of the solutions of $y = x^2$ to illustrate numerically that this function does not have an inverse:

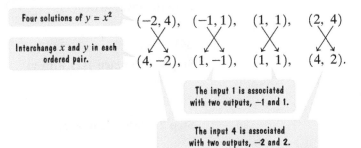

A function provides exactly one output for each input. Thus, the ordered pairs in the bottom row do not define a function.

Can we look at the graph of a function and tell if it represents a function with an inverse? Yes. The graph of the standard quadratic function $f(x) = x^2$ is shown in **Figure 2.55**. Four units above the x-axis, a horizontal line is drawn. This line intersects the graph at two of its points, $(-2, 4)$ and $(2, 4)$. Inverse functions have ordered pairs with the coordinates reversed. We just saw what happened when we interchanged x and y. We obtained $(4, -2)$ and $(4, 2)$, and these ordered pairs do not define a function.

If any horizontal line, such as the one in **Figure 2.55**, intersects a graph at two or more points, the set of these points will not define a function when their coordinates are reversed. This suggests the **horizontal line test** for inverse functions.

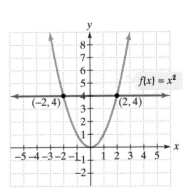

FIGURE 2.55 The horizontal line intersects the graph twice.

DISCOVERY

How might you restrict the domain of $f(x) = x^2$, graphed in **Figure 2.55**, so that the remaining portion of the graph passes the horizontal line test?

The Horizontal Line Test for Inverse Functions

A function f has an inverse that is a function, f^{-1}, if there is no horizontal line that intersects the graph of the function f at more than one point.

EXAMPLE 5   Applying the Horizontal Line Test

Which of the following graphs represent functions that have inverse functions?

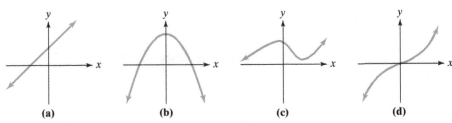

SOLUTION

Notice that horizontal lines can be drawn in graphs **(b)** and **(c)** that intersect the graphs more than once. These graphs do not pass the horizontal line test. These are not the graphs of functions with inverse functions. By contrast, no horizontal line can be drawn in graphs **(a)** and **(d)** that intersects the graphs more than once. These graphs pass the horizontal line test. Thus, the graphs in parts **(a)** and **(d)** represent functions that have inverse functions.

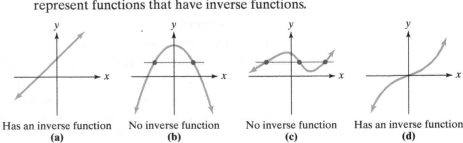

⊘ Check Point **5** Which of the following graphs represent functions that have inverse functions?

(a)   (b)   (c)

A function passes the horizontal line test when no two different ordered pairs have the same second component. This means that if $x_1 \neq x_2$, then $f(x_1) \neq f(x_2)$. Such a function is called a **one-to-one function**. Thus, **a one-to-one function is a function in which no two different ordered pairs have the same second component. Only one-to-one functions have inverse functions.** Any function that passes the horizontal line test is a one-to-one function. Any one-to-one function has a graph that passes the horizontal line test.

4 Use the graph of a one-to-one function to graph its inverse function.

Graphs of *f* and *f*⁻¹

There is a relationship between the graph of a one-to-one function, f, and its inverse, f^{-1}. Because inverse functions have ordered pairs with the coordinates interchanged, if the point (a, b) is on the graph of f, then the point (b, a) is on the graph of f^{-1}. The points (a, b) and (b, a) are symmetric with respect to the line $y = x$. Thus, **the graph of f^{-1} is a reflection of the graph of f about the line $y = x$.** This is illustrated in **Figure 2.56**.

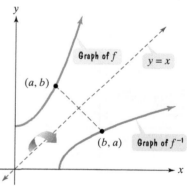

FIGURE 2.56 The graph of f^{-1} is a reflection of the graph of f about $y = x$.

EXAMPLE 6 Graphing the Inverse Function

Use the graph of f in **Figure 2.57** to draw the graph of its inverse function.

FIGURE 2.57

SOLUTION

We begin by noting that no horizontal line intersects the graph of f at more than one point, so f does have an inverse function. Because the points $(-3, -2)$, $(-1, 0)$, and $(4, 2)$ are on the graph of f, the graph of the inverse function, f^{-1}, has points with these ordered pairs reversed. Thus, $(-2, -3)$, $(0, -1)$, and $(2, 4)$ are on the graph of f^{-1}. We can use these points to graph f^{-1}. The graph of f^{-1} is shown in green in **Figure 2.58**. Note that the green graph of f^{-1} is the reflection of the blue graph of f about the line $y = x$.

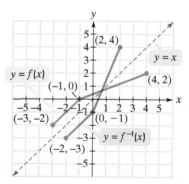

FIGURE 2.58 The graphs of f and f^{-1}

⊘ Check Point **6** The graph of function f consists of two line segments, one segment from $(-2, -2)$ to $(-1, 0)$ and a second segment from $(-1, 0)$ to $(1, 2)$. Graph f and use the graph to draw the graph of its inverse function.

⑤ Find the inverse of a function and graph both functions on the same axes.

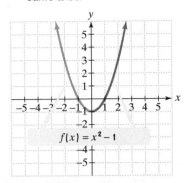

FIGURE 2.59

In our final example, we will first find f^{-1}. Then we will graph f and f^{-1} in the same rectangular coordinate system.

EXAMPLE 7   Finding the Inverse of a Domain-Restricted Function

Find the inverse of $f(x) = x^2 - 1$ if $x \geq 0$. Graph f and f^{-1} in the same rectangular coordinate system.

SOLUTION

The graph of $f(x) = x^2 - 1$ is the graph of the standard quadratic function shifted vertically down 1 unit. **Figure 2.59** shows the function's graph. This graph fails the horizontal line test, so the function $f(x) = x^2 - 1$ does not have an inverse function. By restricting the domain to $x \geq 0$, as given, we obtain a new function whose graph is shown in red in **Figure 2.59**. This red portion of the graph is increasing on the interval $(0, \infty)$ and passes the horizontal line test. This tells us that $f(x) = x^2 - 1$ has an inverse function if we restrict its domain to $x \geq 0$. We use our four-step procedure to find this inverse function. Begin with $f(x) = x^2 - 1, x \geq 0$.

Step 1   Replace $f(x)$ with y: $y = x^2 - 1, x \geq 0$.

Step 2   Interchange x and y: $x = y^2 - 1, y \geq 0$.

Step 3   Solve for y:

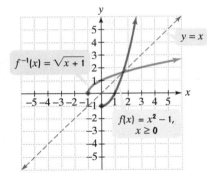

FIGURE 2.60

$$x = y^2 - 1, y \geq 0 \quad \text{This is the equation from step 2.}$$

$$x + 1 = y^2 \quad \text{Add 1 to both sides.}$$

$$\sqrt{x + 1} = y \quad \text{Apply the square root property.}$$

Because $y \geq 0$, take only the principal square root and not the negative square root.

Step 4   Replace y with $f^{-1}(x)$: $f^{-1}(x) = \sqrt{x + 1}$.

Thus, the inverse of $f(x) = x^2 - 1, x \geq 0$, is $f^{-1}(x) = \sqrt{x + 1}$. The graphs of f and f^{-1} are shown in **Figure 2.60**. We obtained the graph of $f^{-1}(x) = \sqrt{x + 1}$ by shifting the graph of the square root function, $y = \sqrt{x}$, horizontally to the left 1 unit. Note that the green graph of f^{-1} is the reflection of the red graph of f about the line $y = x$.   ● ● ●

⊘ Check Point **7** Find the inverse of $f(x) = x^2 + 1$ if $x \geq 0$. Graph f and f^{-1} in the same rectangular coordinate system.

CONCEPT AND VOCABULARY CHECK

Fill in each blank so that the resulting statement is true.

1. The notation f^{-1} means the _____ of the function f.

2. If the function g is the inverse of the function f, then
$f(g(x)) = $ ____ and $g(f(x)) = $ ____.

3. A function f has an inverse that is a function if there is no _____ line that intersects the graph of f at more than one point. Such a function is called a/an _____ function.

4. The graph of f^{-1} is a reflection of the graph of f about the line whose equation is _____.

EXERCISE SET 2.7

Practice Exercises

In Exercises 1–10, find f(g(x)) and g(f(x)) and determine whether each pair of functions f and g are inverses of each other.

1. $f(x) = 4x$ and $g(x) = \dfrac{x}{4}$

2. $f(x) = 6x$ and $g(x) = \dfrac{x}{6}$

3. $f(x) = 3x + 8$ and $g(x) = \dfrac{x - 8}{3}$

4. $f(x) = 4x + 9$ and $g(x) = \dfrac{x - 9}{4}$

5. $f(x) = 5x - 9$ and $g(x) = \dfrac{x + 5}{9}$

6. $f(x) = 3x - 7$ and $g(x) = \dfrac{x + 3}{7}$

7. $f(x) = \dfrac{3}{x - 4}$ and $g(x) = \dfrac{3}{x} + 4$

8. $f(x) = \dfrac{2}{x - 5}$ and $g(x) = \dfrac{2}{x} + 5$

9. $f(x) = -x$ and $g(x) = -x$

10. $f(x) = \sqrt[3]{x - 4}$ and $g(x) = x^3 + 4$

The functions in Exercises 11–28 are all one-to-one. For each function,

   a. Find an equation for $f^{-1}(x)$, the inverse function.

   b. Verify that your equation is correct by showing that $f(f^{-1}(x)) = x$ and $f^{-1}(f(x)) = x$.

11. $f(x) = x + 3$ **12.** $f(x) = x + 5$

13. $f(x) = 2x$ **14.** $f(x) = 4x$

15. $f(x) = 2x + 3$ **16.** $f(x) = 3x - 1$

17. $f(x) = x^3 + 2$ **18.** $f(x) = x^3 - 1$

19. $f(x) = (x + 2)^3$ **20.** $f(x) = (x - 1)^3$

21. $f(x) = \dfrac{1}{x}$ **22.** $f(x) = \dfrac{2}{x}$

23. $f(x) = \sqrt{x}$ **24.** $f(x) = \sqrt[3]{x}$

25. $f(x) = \dfrac{7}{x} - 3$ **26.** $f(x) = \dfrac{4}{x} + 9$

27. $f(x) = \dfrac{2x + 1}{x - 3}$ **28.** $f(x) = \dfrac{2x - 3}{x + 1}$

Which graphs in Exercises 29–34 represent functions that have inverse functions?

29.

30.

31.

32.

33.

34.

In Exercises 35–38, use the graph of f to draw the graph of its inverse function.

35.

36.

37.

38.

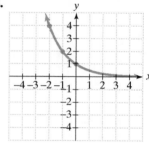

In Exercises 39–52,

   a. Find an equation for $f^{-1}(x)$.

   b. Graph f and f^{-1} in the same rectangular coordinate system.

   c. Use interval notation to give the domain and the range of f and f^{-1}.

39. $f(x) = 2x - 1$ **40.** $f(x) = 2x - 3$

41. $f(x) = x^2 - 4, x \geq 0$ **42.** $f(x) = x^2 - 1, x \leq 0$

43. $f(x) = (x - 1)^2, x \leq 1$ **44.** $f(x) = (x - 1)^2, x \geq 1$

45. $f(x) = x^3 - 1$ **46.** $f(x) = x^3 + 1$

47. $f(x) = (x + 2)^3$ **48.** $f(x) = (x - 2)^3$

(Hint for Exercises 49–52: To solve for a variable involving an nth root, raise both sides of the equation to the nth power: $(\sqrt[n]{y})^n = y$.)

49. $f(x) = \sqrt{x - 1}$ **50.** $f(x) = \sqrt{x} + 2$

51. $f(x) = \sqrt[3]{x} + 1$ **52.** $f(x) = \sqrt[3]{x - 1}$

Practice Plus

In Exercises 53–58, f and g are defined by the following tables. Use the tables to evaluate each composite function.

x	f(x)
−1	1
0	4
1	5
2	−1

x	g(x)
−1	0
1	1
4	2
10	−1

53. $f(g(1))$

54. $f(g(4))$

55. $(g \circ f)(-1)$

56. $(g \circ f)(0)$

57. $f^{-1}(g(10))$

58. $f^{-1}(g(1))$

In Exercises 59–64, let

$$f(x) = 2x - 5$$

$$g(x) = 4x - 1$$

$$h(x) = x^2 + x + 2.$$

Evaluate the indicated function without finding an equation for the function.

59. $(f \circ g)(0)$ **60.** $(g \circ f)(0)$ **61.** $f^{-1}(1)$

62. $g^{-1}(7)$ **63.** $g(f[h(1)])$ **64.** $f(g[h(1)])$

Application Exercises

In most societies, women say they prefer to marry men who are older than themselves, whereas men say they prefer women who are younger. The bar graph shows the preferred age difference in a mate in five selected countries. Use this information to solve Exercises 65–66.

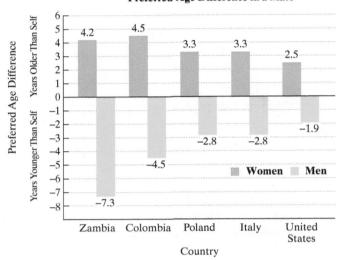

Preferred Age Difference in a Mate

Source: Carole Wade and Carol Tavris, *Psychology,* 6th Edition, Prentice Hall, 2000.

65. a. Consider a function, *f*, whose domain is the set of the five countries shown in the graph. Let the range be the set of the average number of years women in each of the respective countries prefer men who are older than themselves. Write the function *f* as a set of ordered pairs.

b. Write the relation that is the inverse of *f* as a set of ordered pairs. Based on these ordered pairs, is *f* a one-to-one function? Explain your answer.

66. a. Consider a function, *g*, whose domain is the set of the five countries shown in the graph. Let the range be the set of negative numbers representing the average number of years men in each of the respective countries prefer women who are younger than themselves. Write the function *g* as a set of ordered pairs.

b. Write the relation that is the inverse of *g* as a set of ordered pairs. Based on these ordered pairs, is *g* a one-to-one function? Explain your answer.

67. The graph represents the probability of two people in the same room sharing a birthday as a function of the number of people in the room. Call the function *f*.

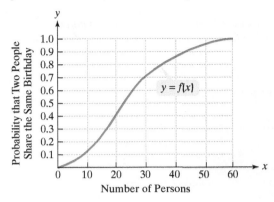

a. Explain why *f* has an inverse that is a function.

b. Describe in practical terms the meaning of $f^{-1}(0.25), f^{-1}(0.5),$ and $f^{-1}(0.7).$

68. A study of 900 working women in Texas showed that their feelings changed throughout the day. As the graph indicates, the women felt better as time passed, except for a blip (that's slang for relative maximum) at lunchtime.

Average Level of Happiness at Different Times of Day

Source: D. Kahneman et al., "A Survey Method for Characterizing Daily Life Experience," *Science.*

a. Does the graph have an inverse that is a function? Explain your answer.

b. Identify two or more times of day when the average happiness level is 3. Express your answers as ordered pairs.

c. Do the ordered pairs in part (b) indicate that the graph represents a one-to-one function? Explain your answer.

69. The formula

$$y = f(x) = \frac{9}{5}x + 32$$

is used to convert from *x* degrees Celsius to *y* degrees Fahrenheit. The formula

$$y = g(x) = \frac{5}{9}(x - 32)$$

is used to convert from *x* degrees Fahrenheit to *y* degrees Celsius. Show that *f* and *g* are inverse functions.

Writing in Mathematics

70. Explain how to determine if two functions are inverses of each other.

71. Describe how to find the inverse of a one-to-one function.

72. What is the horizontal line test and what does it indicate?

73. Describe how to use the graph of a one-to-one function to draw the graph of its inverse function.

74. How can a graphing utility be used to visually determine if two functions are inverses of each other?

75. What explanations can you offer for the trends shown by the graph in Exercise 68?

Technology Exercises

In Exercises 76–83, use a graphing utility to graph the function. Use the graph to determine whether the function has an inverse that is a function (that is, whether the function is one-to-one).

76. $f(x) = x^2 - 1$

77. $f(x) = \sqrt[3]{2 - x}$

78. $f(x) = \dfrac{x^3}{2}$

79. $f(x) = \dfrac{x^4}{4}$

80. $f(x) = \text{int}(x - 2)$

81. $f(x) = |x - 2|$

82. $f(x) = (x - 1)^3$

83. $f(x) = -\sqrt{16 - x^2}$

In Exercises 84–86, use a graphing utility to graph f and g in the same viewing rectangle. In addition, graph the line $y = x$ and visually determine if f and g are inverses.

84. $f(x) = 4x + 4, g(x) = 0.25x - 1$

85. $f(x) = \dfrac{1}{x} + 2, g(x) = \dfrac{1}{x - 2}$

86. $f(x) = \sqrt[3]{x} - 2, g(x) = (x + 2)^3$

Critical Thinking Exercises

Make Sense? *In Exercises 87–90, determine whether each statement makes sense or does not make sense, and explain your reasoning.*

87. I found the inverse of $f(x) = 5x - 4$ in my head: The reverse of multiplying by 5 and subtracting 4 is adding 4 and dividing by 5, so $f^{-1}(x) = \dfrac{x + 4}{5}$.

88. I'm working with the linear function $f(x) = 3x + 5$ and I do not need to find f^{-1} in order to determine the value of $(f \circ f^{-1})(17)$.

Exercises 89–90 are based on the following cartoon.

89. Assuming that there is no such thing as metric crickets, I modeled the information in the first frame of the cartoon with the function

$$T(n) = \dfrac{n}{4} + 40,$$

where $T(n)$ is the temperature, in degrees Fahrenheit, and n is the number of cricket chirps per minute.

90. I used the function in Exercise 89 and found an equation for T^{-1}, which expresses the number of cricket chirps per minute as a function of Fahrenheit temperature.

In Exercises 91–94, determine whether each statement is true or false. If the statement is false, make the necessary change(s) to produce a true statement.

91. The inverse of $\{(1, 4), (2, 7)\}$ is $\{(2, 7), (1, 4)\}$.

92. The function $f(x) = 5$ is one-to-one.

93. If $f(x) = 3x$, then $f^{-1}(x) = \dfrac{1}{3x}$.

94. The domain of f is the same as the range of f^{-1}.

95. If $f(x) = 3x$ and $g(x) = x + 5$, find $(f \circ g)^{-1}(x)$ and $(g^{-1} \circ f^{-1})(x)$.

96. Show that

$$f(x) = \dfrac{3x - 2}{5x - 3}$$

is its own inverse.

97. *Freedom 7* was the spacecraft that carried the first American into space in 1961. Total flight time was 15 minutes and the spacecraft reached a maximum height of 116 miles. Consider a function, s, that expresses *Freedom 7*'s height, $s(t)$, in miles, after t minutes. Is s a one-to-one function? Explain your answer.

98. If $f(2) = 6$, and f is one-to-one, find x satisfying $8 + f^{-1}(x - 1) = 10$.

Group Exercise

99. In Tom Stoppard's play *Arcadia*, the characters dream and talk about mathematics, including ideas involving graphing, composite functions, symmetry, and lack of symmetry in things that are tangled, mysterious, and unpredictable. Group members should read the play. Present a report on the ideas discussed by the characters that are related to concepts that we studied in this chapter. Bring in a copy of the play and read appropriate excerpts.

Preview Exercises

Exercises 100–102 will help you prepare for the material covered in the next section.

100. Let $(x_1, y_1) = (7, 2)$ and $(x_2, y_2) = (1, -1)$. Find $\sqrt{(x_2 - x_1)^2 + (y_2 - y_1)^2}$. Express the answer in simplified radical form.

101. Use a rectangular coordinate system to graph the circle with center $(1, -1)$ and radius 1.

102. Solve by completing the square: $y^2 - 6y - 4 = 0$.

SECTION 2.8

Distance and Midpoint Formulas; Circles

Objectives

1. Find the distance between two points.
2. Find the midpoint of a line segment.
3. Write the standard form of a circle's equation.
4. Give the center and radius of a circle whose equation is in standard form.
5. Convert the general form of a circle's equation to standard form.

It's a good idea to know your way around a circle. Clocks, angles, maps, and compasses are based on circles. Circles occur everywhere in nature: in ripples on water, patterns on a butterfly's wings, and cross sections of trees. Some consider the circle to be the most pleasing of all shapes.

The rectangular coordinate system gives us a unique way of knowing a circle. It enables us to translate a circle's geometric definition into an algebraic equation. To do this, we must first develop a formula for the distance between any two points in rectangular coordinates.

① Find the distance between two points.

FIGURE 2.61

The Distance Formula

Using the Pythagorean Theorem, we can find the distance between the two points $P_1(x_1, y_1)$ and $P_2(x_2, y_2)$ in the rectangular coordinate system. The two points are illustrated in **Figure 2.61**.

The distance that we need to find is represented by d and shown in blue. Notice that the distance between the two points on the dashed horizontal line is the absolute value of the difference between the x-coordinates of the points. This distance, $|x_2 - x_1|$, is shown in pink. Similarly, the distance between the two points on the dashed vertical line is the absolute value of the difference between the y-coordinates of the points. This distance, $|y_2 - y_1|$, is also shown in pink.

Because the dashed lines are horizontal and vertical, a right triangle is formed. Thus, we can use the Pythagorean Theorem to find the distance d. Squaring the lengths of the triangle's sides results in positive numbers, so absolute value notation is not necessary.

$$d^2 = (x_2 - x_1)^2 + (y_2 - y_1)^2$$ Apply the Pythagorean Theorem to the right triangle in Figure 2.61.

$$d = \pm\sqrt{(x_2 - x_1)^2 + (y_2 - y_1)^2}$$ Apply the square root property.

$$d = \sqrt{(x_2 - x_1)^2 + (y_2 - y_1)^2}$$ Because distance is nonnegative, write only the principal square root.

This result is called the **distance formula**.

The Distance Formula

The distance, d, between the points (x_1, y_1) and (x_2, y_2) in the rectangular coordinate system is

$$d = \sqrt{(x_2 - x_1)^2 + (y_2 - y_1)^2}.$$

To compute the distance between two points, find the square of the difference between the x-coordinates plus the square of the difference between the y-coordinates. The principal square root of this sum is the distance.

When using the distance formula, it does not matter which point you call (x_1, y_1) and which you call (x_2, y_2).

EXAMPLE 1　Using the Distance Formula

Find the distance between $(-1, 4)$ and $(3, -2)$. Express the answer in simplified radical form and then round to two decimal places.

SOLUTION

We will let $(x_1, y_1) = (-1, 4)$ and $(x_2, y_2) = (3, -2)$.

$$d = \sqrt{(x_2 - x_1)^2 + (y_2 - y_1)^2}$$ 　Use the distance formula.

$$= \sqrt{[3 - (-1)]^2 + (-2 - 4)^2}$$ 　Substitute the given values.

$$= \sqrt{4^2 + (-6)^2}$$
Perform operations inside grouping symbols: $3 - (-1) = 3 + 1 = 4$ and $-2 - 4 = -6$.

$$= \sqrt{16 + 36}$$ 　Caution: This does not equal $\sqrt{16} + \sqrt{36}$.　Square 4 and -6.

$$= \sqrt{52}$$ 　Add.

$$= \sqrt{4 \cdot 13} = 2\sqrt{13} \approx 7.21$$ 　$\sqrt{52} = \sqrt{4 \cdot 13} = \sqrt{4}\sqrt{13} = 2\sqrt{13}$

The distance between the given points is $2\sqrt{13}$ units, or approximately 7.21 units. The situation is illustrated in **Figure 2.62**. ●●●

FIGURE 2.62 Finding the distance between two points

Distance is $2\sqrt{13}$ units.

$\varnothing$ Check Point **1** Find the distance between $(-1, -3)$ and $(2, 3)$. Express the answer in simplified radical form and then round to two decimal places.

② Find the midpoint of a line segment.

The Midpoint Formula

The distance formula can be used to derive a formula for finding the midpoint of a line segment between two given points. The formula is given as follows:

The Midpoint Formula

Consider a line segment whose endpoints are (x_1, y_1) and (x_2, y_2). The coordinates of the segment's midpoint are

$$\left(\frac{x_1 + x_2}{2}, \frac{y_1 + y_2}{2}\right).$$

To find the midpoint, take the average of the two x-coordinates and the average of the two y-coordinates.

GREAT QUESTION!

Do I add or subtract coordinates when applying the midpoint and distance formulas?

The midpoint formula requires finding the *sum* of coordinates. By contrast, the distance formula requires finding the *difference* of coordinates:

Midpoint: Sum of coordinates
$$\left(\frac{x_1 + x_2}{2}, \frac{y_1 + y_2}{2}\right)$$

Distance: Difference of coordinates
$$\sqrt{(x_2 - x_1)^2 + (y_2 - y_1)^2}$$

It's easy to confuse the two formulas. Be sure to use addition, not subtraction, when applying the midpoint formula.

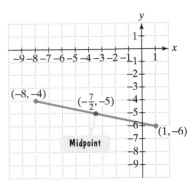

FIGURE 2.63 Finding a line segment's midpoint

EXAMPLE 2   Using the Midpoint Formula

Find the midpoint of the line segment with endpoints $(1, -6)$ and $(-8, -4)$.

SOLUTION

To find the coordinates of the midpoint, we average the coordinates of the endpoints.

$$\text{Midpoint} = \left(\frac{1 + (-8)}{2}, \frac{-6 + (-4)}{2} \right) = \left(\frac{-7}{2}, \frac{-10}{2} \right) = \left(-\frac{7}{2}, -5 \right)$$

Average the x-coordinates.   Average the y-coordinates.

Figure 2.63 illustrates that the point $\left(-\frac{7}{2}, -5 \right)$ is midway between the points $(1, -6)$ and $(-8, -4)$.   • • •

◎ **Check Point 2** Find the midpoint of the line segment with endpoints $(1, 2)$ and $(7, -3)$.

Circles

Our goal is to translate a circle's geometric definition into an equation. We begin with this geometric definition.

Definition of a Circle

A **circle** is the set of all points in a plane that are equidistant from a fixed point, called the **center**. The fixed distance from the circle's center to any point on the circle is called the **radius**.

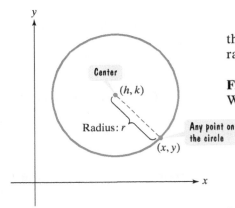

FIGURE 2.64 A circle centered at (h, k) with radius r

Figure 2.64 is our starting point for obtaining a circle's equation. We've placed the circle into a rectangular coordinate system. The circle's center is (h, k) and its radius is r. We let (x, y) represent the coordinates of any point on the circle.

What does the geometric definition of a circle tell us about the point (x, y) in **Figure 2.64**? The point is on the circle if and only if its distance from the center is r. We can use the distance formula to express this idea algebraically:

The distance between (x, y) and (h, k) is always r.

$$\sqrt{(x - h)^2 + (y - k)^2} = r.$$

Squaring both sides of $\sqrt{(x - h)^2 + (y - k)^2} = r$ yields the *standard form of the equation of a circle.*

③ Write the standard form of a circle's equation.

The Standard Form of the Equation of a Circle

The **standard form of the equation of a circle** with center (h, k) and radius r is

$$(x - h)^2 + (y - k)^2 = r^2.$$

EXAMPLE 3   Finding the Standard Form of a Circle's Equation

Write the standard form of the equation of the circle with center $(0, 0)$ and radius 2. Graph the circle.

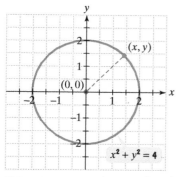

FIGURE 2.65 The graph of $x^2 + y^2 = 4$

SOLUTION

The center is (0, 0). Because the center is represented as (h, k) in the standard form of the equation, $h = 0$ and $k = 0$. The radius is 2, so we will let $r = 2$ in the equation.

$$(x - h)^2 + (y - k)^2 = r^2 \quad \text{This is the standard form of a circle's equation.}$$
$$(x - 0)^2 + (y - 0)^2 = 2^2 \quad \text{Substitute 0 for } h, \text{ 0 for } k, \text{ and 2 for } r.$$
$$x^2 + y^2 = 4 \quad \text{Simplify.}$$

The standard form of the equation of the circle is $x^2 + y^2 = 4$. **Figure 2.65** shows the graph. • • •

⊘ Check Point **3** Write the standard form of the equation of the circle with center $(0, 0)$ and radius 4.

TECHNOLOGY

To graph a circle with a graphing utility, first solve the equation for y.

$$x^2 + y^2 = 4$$
$$y^2 = 4 - x^2$$
$$y = \pm\sqrt{4 - x^2} \quad \boxed{\begin{array}{c} y \text{ is not a} \\ \text{function of } x. \end{array}}$$

Graph the two equations

$$y_1 = \sqrt{4 - x^2} \quad \text{and} \quad y_2 = -\sqrt{4 - x^2}$$

in the same viewing rectangle. The graph of $y_1 = \sqrt{4 - x^2}$ is the top semicircle because y is always positive. The graph of $y_2 = -\sqrt{4 - x^2}$ is the bottom semicircle because y is always negative. Use a $\boxed{\text{ZOOM SQUARE}}$ setting so that the circle looks like a circle. (Many graphing utilities have problems connecting the two semicircles because the segments directly to the left and to the right of the center become nearly vertical.)

Example 3 and Check Point 3 involved circles centered at the origin. The standard form of the equation of all such circles is $x^2 + y^2 = r^2$, where r is the circle's radius. Now, let's consider a circle whose center is not at the origin.

EXAMPLE 4 Finding the Standard Form of a Circle's Equation

Write the standard form of the equation of the circle with center $(-2, 3)$ and radius 4.

SOLUTION

The center is $(-2, 3)$. Because the center is represented as (h, k) in the standard form of the equation, $h = -2$ and $k = 3$. The radius is 4, so we will let $r = 4$ in the equation.

$$(x - h)^2 + (y - k)^2 = r^2 \quad \text{This is the standard form of a circle's equation.}$$
$$[x - (-2)]^2 + (y - 3)^2 = 4^2 \quad \text{Substitute } -2 \text{ for } h, \text{ 3 for } k, \text{ and 4 for } r.$$
$$(x + 2)^2 + (y - 3)^2 = 16 \quad \text{Simplify.}$$

The standard form of the equation of the circle is $(x + 2)^2 + (y - 3)^2 = 16$. • • •

⊘ Check Point **4** Write the standard form of the equation of the circle with center $(0, -6)$ and radius 10.

④ Give the center and radius of a circle whose equation is in standard form.

EXAMPLE 5   Using the Standard Form of a Circle's Equation to Graph the Circle

a. Find the center and radius of the circle whose equation is

$$(x - 2)^2 + (y + 4)^2 = 9.$$

b. Graph the equation.

c. Use the graph to identify the relation's domain and range.

SOLUTION

a. We begin by finding the circle's center, (h, k), and its radius, r. We can find the values for h, k, and r by comparing the given equation to the standard form of the equation of a circle, $(x - h)^2 + (y - k)^2 = r^2$.

$$(x - 2)^2 + (y + 4)^2 = 9$$

$$(x - 2)^2 + (y - (-4))^2 = 3^2$$

> This is $(x - h)^2$, with $h = 2$.   This is $(y - k)^2$, with $k = -4$.   This is r^2, with $r = 3$.

We see that $h = 2$, $k = -4$, and $r = 3$. Thus, the circle has center $(h, k) = (2, -4)$ and a radius of 3 units.

b. To graph this circle, first locate the center $(2, -4)$. Because the radius is 3, you can locate at least four points on the circle by going out three units to the right, to the left, up, and down from the center.

  The points three units to the right and to the left of $(2, -4)$ are $(5, -4)$ and $(-1, -4)$, respectively. The points three units up and down from $(2, -4)$ are $(2, -1)$ and $(2, -7)$, respectively.

  Using these points, we obtain the graph in **Figure 2.66**.

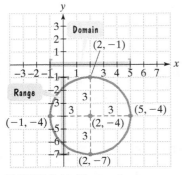

FIGURE 2.66 The graph of $(x - 2)^2 + (y + 4)^2 = 9$

c. The four points that we located on the circle can be used to determine the relation's domain and range. The points $(-1, -4)$ and $(5, -4)$ show that values of x extend from -1 to 5, inclusive:

$$\text{Domain} = [-1, 5].$$

The points $(2, -7)$ and $(2, -1)$ show that values of y extend from -7 to -1, inclusive:

$$\text{Range} = [-7, -1].$$

• • •

GREAT QUESTION!

What's the bottom line when identifying h and k in the standard form of a circle's equation?

It's easy to make sign errors when finding h and k, the coordinates of a circle's center, (h, k). Keep in mind that h and k are the numbers that *follow the subtraction signs* in a circle's equation:

$$(x - 2)^2 + (y + 4)^2 = 9$$
$$(x - 2)^2 + (y - (-4))^2 = 9.$$

> The number *after* the subtraction is **2**: $h = 2$.   The number *after* the subtraction is -4: $k = -4$.

☑ Check Point **5**

a. Find the center and radius of the circle whose equation is

$$(x + 3)^2 + (y - 1)^2 = 4.$$

b. Graph the equation.

c. Use the graph to identify the relation's domain and range.

If we square $x - 2$ and $y + 4$ in the standard form of the equation in Example 5, we obtain another form for the circle's equation.

$$(x - 2)^2 + (y + 4)^2 = 9 \qquad \text{This is the standard form of the equation in Example 5.}$$

$$x^2 - 4x + 4 + y^2 + 8y + 16 = 9 \qquad \text{Square } x - 2 \text{ and } y + 4.$$

$$x^2 + y^2 - 4x + 8y + 20 = 9 \qquad \text{Combine constants and rearrange terms.}$$

$$x^2 + y^2 - 4x + 8y + 11 = 0 \qquad \text{Subtract 9 from both sides.}$$

This result suggests that an equation in the form $x^2 + y^2 + Dx + Ey + F = 0$ can represent a circle. This is called the *general form of the equation of a circle*.

The General Form of the Equation of a Circle

The **general form of the equation of a circle** is

$$x^2 + y^2 + Dx + Ey + F = 0,$$

where D, E, and F are real numbers.

⑤ Convert the general form of a circle's equation to standard form.

We can convert the general form of the equation of a circle to the standard form $(x - h)^2 + (y - k)^2 = r^2$. We do so by completing the square on x and y. Let's see how this is done.

GREAT QUESTION!

Egad! I forgot how to complete the square. Any suggestions?

To complete the square, on $x^2 + bx$, take half the coefficient of x. Then square this number. By adding the square of half the coefficient of x, a perfect square trinomial will result. For more detail, see Section 1.5, pages 148–149.

EXAMPLE 6 Converting the General Form of a Circle's Equation to Standard Form and Graphing the Circle

Write in standard form and graph: $x^2 + y^2 + 4x - 6y - 23 = 0$.

SOLUTION

Because we plan to complete the square on both x and y, let's rearrange the terms so that x-terms are arranged in descending order, y-terms are arranged in descending order, and the constant term appears on the right.

$$x^2 + y^2 + 4x - 6y - 23 = 0 \qquad \text{This is the given equation.}$$

$$(x^2 + 4x \quad) + (y^2 - 6y \quad) = 23 \qquad \text{Rewrite in anticipation of completing the square.}$$

$$(x^2 + 4x + 4) + (y^2 - 6y + 9) = 23 + 4 + 9 \qquad \text{Complete the square on } x: \frac{1}{2} \cdot 4 = 2 \text{ and } 2^2 = 4, \text{ so add 4 to both sides. Complete the square on } y: \frac{1}{2}(-6) = -3 \text{ and } (-3)^2 = 9, \text{ so add 9 to both sides.}$$

> Remember that numbers added on the left side must also be added on the right side.

$$(x + 2)^2 + (y - 3)^2 = 36 \qquad \text{Factor on the left and add on the right.}$$

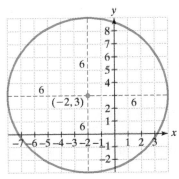

FIGURE 2.67 The graph of $(x + 2)^2 + (y - 3)^2 = 36$

This last equation, $(x + 2)^2 + (y - 3)^2 = 36$, is in standard form. We can identify the circle's center and radius by comparing this equation to the standard form of the equation of a circle, $(x - h)^2 + (y - k)^2 = r^2$.

$$(x + 2)^2 + (y - 3)^2 = 36$$
$$(x - (-2))^2 + (y - 3)^2 = 6^2$$

| This is $(x-h)^2$, with $h = -2$. | This is $(y-k)^2$, with $k = 3$. | This is r^2, with $r = 6$. |

We use the center, $(h, k) = (-2, 3)$, and the radius, $r = 6$, to graph the circle. The graph is shown in **Figure 2.67**. ● ● ●

TECHNOLOGY

To graph $x^2 + y^2 + 4x - 6y - 23 = 0$, the general form of the circle's equation given in Example 6, rewrite the equation as a quadratic equation in y.

$$y^2 - 6y + (x^2 + 4x - 23) = 0$$

Now solve for y using the quadratic formula, with $a = 1$, $b = -6$, and $c = x^2 + 4x - 23$.

$$y = \frac{-b \pm \sqrt{b^2 - 4ac}}{2a} = \frac{-(-6) \pm \sqrt{(-6)^2 - 4 \cdot 1(x^2 + 4x - 23)}}{2 \cdot 1} = \frac{6 \pm \sqrt{36 - 4(x^2 + 4x - 23)}}{2}$$

Because we will enter these equations, there is no need to simplify. Enter

$$y_1 = \frac{6 + \sqrt{36 - 4(x^2 + 4x - 23)}}{2}$$

and

$$y_2 = \frac{6 - \sqrt{36 - 4(x^2 + 4x - 23)}}{2}.$$

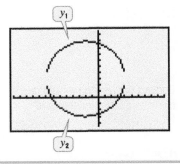

Use a ZOOM SQUARE setting. The graph is shown on the right.

 Check Point **6** Write in standard form and graph:

$$x^2 + y^2 + 4x - 4y - 1 = 0.$$

CONCEPT AND VOCABULARY CHECK

Fill in each blank so that the resulting statement is true.

1. The distance, d, between the points (x_1, y_1) and (x_2, y_2) in the rectangular coordinate system is

   $d =$ _____.

2. The midpoint of a line segment whose endpoints are

   (x_1, y_1) and (x_2, y_2) is (_____, _____).

3. The set of all points in a plane that are equidistant from a fixed point is a/an _____. The fixed point is called the _____. The distance from this fixed point to any point on the geometric figure is called the _____.

4. The standard form of the equation of a circle with center (h, k) and radius r is _____.

5. The equation $x^2 + y^2 + Dx + Ey + F = 0$ is called the _____ form of the equation of a circle.

6. In the equation $(x^2 + 4x \quad) + (y^2 - 8y \quad) = 5$, we complete the square on x by adding ____ to both sides. We complete the square on y by adding ____ to both sides.

EXERCISE SET 2.8

Practice Exercises

In Exercises 1–18, find the distance between each pair of points. If necessary, round answers to two decimals places.

1. $(2, 3)$ and $(14, 8)$
2. $(5, 1)$ and $(8, 5)$
3. $(4, -1)$ and $(-6, 3)$
4. $(2, -3)$ and $(-1, 5)$
5. $(0, 0)$ and $(-3, 4)$
6. $(0, 0)$ and $(3, -4)$
7. $(-2, -6)$ and $(3, -4)$
8. $(-4, -1)$ and $(2, -3)$
9. $(0, -3)$ and $(4, 1)$
10. $(0, -2)$ and $(4, 3)$
11. $(3.5, 8.2)$ and $(-0.5, 6.2)$
12. $(2.6, 1.3)$ and $(1.6, -5.7)$
13. $\left(0, -\sqrt{3}\right)$ and $\left(\sqrt{5}, 0\right)$
14. $\left(0, -\sqrt{2}\right)$ and $\left(\sqrt{7}, 0\right)$
15. $\left(3\sqrt{3}, \sqrt{5}\right)$ and $\left(-\sqrt{3}, 4\sqrt{5}\right)$
16. $\left(2\sqrt{3}, \sqrt{6}\right)$ and $\left(-\sqrt{3}, 5\sqrt{6}\right)$
17. $\left(\dfrac{7}{3}, \dfrac{1}{5}\right)$ and $\left(\dfrac{1}{3}, \dfrac{6}{5}\right)$
18. $\left(-\dfrac{1}{4}, -\dfrac{1}{7}\right)$ and $\left(\dfrac{3}{4}, \dfrac{6}{7}\right)$

In Exercises 19–30, find the midpoint of each line segment with the given endpoints.

19. $(6, 8)$ and $(2, 4)$
20. $(10, 4)$ and $(2, 6)$
21. $(-2, -8)$ and $(-6, -2)$
22. $(-4, -7)$ and $(-1, -3)$
23. $(-3, -4)$ and $(6, -8)$
24. $(-2, -1)$ and $(-8, 6)$
25. $\left(-\dfrac{7}{2}, \dfrac{3}{2}\right)$ and $\left(-\dfrac{5}{2}, -\dfrac{11}{2}\right)$
26. $\left(-\dfrac{2}{5}, \dfrac{7}{15}\right)$ and $\left(-\dfrac{2}{5}, -\dfrac{4}{15}\right)$
27. $(8, 3\sqrt{5})$ and $(-6, 7\sqrt{5})$
28. $(7\sqrt{3}, -6)$ and $(3\sqrt{3}, -2)$
29. $\left(\sqrt{18}, -4\right)$ and $\left(\sqrt{2}, 4\right)$
30. $\left(\sqrt{50}, -6\right)$ and $\left(\sqrt{2}, 6\right)$

In Exercises 31–40, write the standard form of the equation of the circle with the given center and radius.

31. Center $(0, 0), r = 7$
32. Center $(0, 0), r = 8$
33. Center $(3, 2), r = 5$
34. Center $(2, -1), r = 4$
35. Center $(-1, 4), r = 2$
36. Center $(-3, 5), r = 3$
37. Center $(-3, -1), r = \sqrt{3}$
38. Center $(-5, -3), r = \sqrt{5}$
39. Center $(-4, 0), r = 10$
40. Center $(-2, 0), r = 6$

In Exercises 41–52, give the center and radius of the circle described by the equation and graph each equation. Use the graph to identify the relation's domain and range.

41. $x^2 + y^2 = 16$
42. $x^2 + y^2 = 49$
43. $(x - 3)^2 + (y - 1)^2 = 36$
44. $(x - 2)^2 + (y - 3)^2 = 16$
45. $(x + 3)^2 + (y - 2)^2 = 4$
46. $(x + 1)^2 + (y - 4)^2 = 25$
47. $(x + 2)^2 + (y + 2)^2 = 4$
48. $(x + 4)^2 + (y + 5)^2 = 36$
49. $x^2 + (y - 1)^2 = 1$
50. $x^2 + (y - 2)^2 = 4$
51. $(x + 1)^2 + y^2 = 25$
52. $(x + 2)^2 + y^2 = 16$

In Exercises 53–64, complete the square and write the equation in standard form. Then give the center and radius of each circle and graph the equation.

53. $x^2 + y^2 + 6x + 2y + 6 = 0$
54. $x^2 + y^2 + 8x + 4y + 16 = 0$
55. $x^2 + y^2 - 10x - 6y - 30 = 0$
56. $x^2 + y^2 - 4x - 12y - 9 = 0$
57. $x^2 + y^2 + 8x - 2y - 8 = 0$
58. $x^2 + y^2 + 12x - 6y - 4 = 0$
59. $x^2 - 2x + y^2 - 15 = 0$
60. $x^2 + y^2 - 6y - 7 = 0$
61. $x^2 + y^2 - x + 2y + 1 = 0$
62. $x^2 + y^2 + x + y - \frac{1}{2} = 0$
63. $x^2 + y^2 + 3x - 2y - 1 = 0$
64. $x^2 + y^2 + 3x + 5y + \frac{9}{4} = 0$

Practice Plus

In Exercises 65–66, a line segment through the center of each circle intersects the circle at the points shown.

   a. Find the coordinates of the circle's center.
   b. Find the radius of the circle.
   c. Use your answers from parts (a) and (b) to write the standard form of the circle's equation.

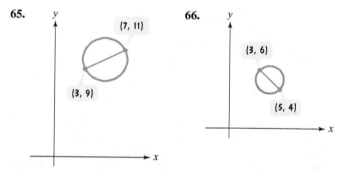

65. **66.**

In Exercises 67–70, graph both equations in the same rectangular coordinate system and find all points of intersection. Then show that these ordered pairs satisfy the equations.

67. $x^2 + y^2 = 16$
$x - y = 4$
68. $x^2 + y^2 = 9$
$x - y = 3$
69. $(x - 2)^2 + (y + 3)^2 = 4$
$y = x - 3$
70. $(x - 3)^2 + (y + 1)^2 = 9$
$y = x - 1$

Application Exercises

The cellphone screen shows coordinates of six cities from a rectangular coordinate system placed on North America by long-distance telephone companies. Each unit in this system represents $\sqrt{0.1}$ mile.

In Exercises 71–72, use this information to find the distance, to the nearest mile, between each pair of cities.

Source: Peter H. Dana

71. Boston and San Francisco

72. New Orleans and Houston

73. A rectangular coordinate system with coordinates in miles is placed with the origin at the center of Los Angeles. The figure indicates that the University of Southern California is located 2.4 miles west and 2.7 miles south of central Los Angeles. A seismograph on the campus shows that a small earthquake occurred. The quake's epicenter is estimated to be approximately 30 miles from the university. Write the standard form of the equation for the set of points that could be the epicenter of the quake.

74. The Ferris wheel in the figure has a radius of 68 feet. The clearance between the wheel and the ground is 14 feet. The rectangular coordinate system shown has its origin on the ground directly below the center of the wheel. Use the coordinate system to write the equation of the circular wheel.

Writing in Mathematics

75. In your own words, describe how to find the distance between two points in the rectangular coordinate system.

76. In your own words, describe how to find the midpoint of a line segment if its endpoints are known.

77. What is a circle? Without using variables, describe how the definition of a circle can be used to obtain a form of its equation.

78. Give an example of a circle's equation in standard form. Describe how to find the center and radius for this circle.

79. How is the standard form of a circle's equation obtained from its general form?

80. Does $(x - 3)^2 + (y - 5)^2 = 0$ represent the equation of a circle? If not, describe the graph of this equation.

81. Does $(x - 3)^2 + (y - 5)^2 = -25$ represent the equation of a circle? What sort of set is the graph of this equation?

82. Write and solve a problem about the flying time between a pair of cities shown on the cellphone screen for Exercises 71–72. Do not use the pairs in Exercise 71 or Exercise 72. Begin by determining a reasonable average speed, in miles per hour, for a jet flying between the cities.

Technology Exercises

In Exercises 83–85, use a graphing utility to graph each circle whose equation is given.

83. $x^2 + y^2 = 25$

84. $(y + 1)^2 = 36 - (x - 3)^2$

85. $x^2 + 10x + y^2 - 4y - 20 = 0$

Critical Thinking Exercises

Make Sense? *In Exercises 86–89, determine whether each statement makes sense or does not make sense, and explain your reasoning.*

86. I've noticed that in mathematics, one topic often leads logically to a new topic:

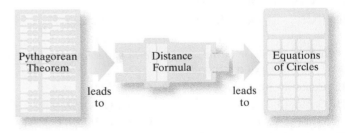

87. To avoid sign errors when finding h and k, I place parentheses around the numbers that follow the subtraction signs in a circle's equation.

88. I used the equation $(x + 1)^2 + (y - 5)^2 = -4$ to identify the circle's center and radius.

89. My graph of $(x - 2)^2 + (y + 1)^2 = 16$ is my graph of $x^2 + y^2 = 16$ translated two units right and one unit down.

In Exercises 90–93, determine whether each statement is true or false. If the statement is false, make the necessary change(s) to produce a true statement.

90. The equation of the circle whose center is at the origin with radius 16 is $x^2 + y^2 = 16$.

91. The graph of $(x - 3)^2 + (y + 5)^2 = 36$ is a circle with radius 6 centered at $(-3, 5)$.

92. The graph of $(x - 4) + (y + 6) = 25$ is a circle with radius 5 centered at $(4, -6)$.

93. The graph of $(x - 3)^2 + (y + 5)^2 = -36$ is a circle with radius 6 centered at $(3, -5)$.

94. Show that the points $A(1, 1 + d)$, $B(3, 3 + d)$, and $C(6, 6 + d)$ are collinear (lie along a straight line) by showing that the distance from A to B plus the distance from B to C equals the distance from A to C.

95. Prove the midpoint formula by using the following procedure.

  a. Show that the distance between (x_1, y_1) and $\left(\dfrac{x_1 + x_2}{2}, \dfrac{y_1 + y_2}{2}\right)$ is equal to the distance between (x_2, y_2) and $\left(\dfrac{x_1 + x_2}{2}, \dfrac{y_1 + y_2}{2}\right)$.

  b. Use the procedure from Exercise 94 and the distances from part (a) to show that the points (x_1, y_1), $\left(\dfrac{x_1 + x_2}{2}, \dfrac{y_1 + y_2}{2}\right)$, and (x_2, y_2) are collinear.

96. Find the area of the donut-shaped region bounded by the graphs of $(x - 2)^2 + (y + 3)^2 = 25$ and $(x - 2)^2 + (y + 3)^2 = 36$.

97. A **tangent line** to a circle is a line that intersects the circle at exactly one point. The tangent line is perpendicular to the radius of the circle at this point of contact. Write an equation in point-slope form for the line tangent to the circle whose equation is $x^2 + y^2 = 25$ at the point $(3, -4)$.

Preview Exercises

Exercises 98–100 will help you prepare for the material covered in the first section of the next chapter.

In Exercises 98–99, solve each quadratic equation by the method of your choice.

98. $0 = -2(x - 3)^2 + 8$

99. $-x^2 - 2x + 1 = 0$

100. Use the graph of $f(x) = x^2$ to graph $g(x) = (x + 3)^2 + 1$.

CHAPTER 2   Summary, Review, and Test

SUMMARY

DEFINITIONS AND CONCEPTS	EXAMPLES
2.1 Basics of Functions and Their Graphs	
a. A relation is any set of ordered pairs. The set of first components is the domain of the relation and the set of second components is the range.	Ex. 1, p. 211
b. A function is a correspondence from a first set, called the domain, to a second set, called the range, such that each element in the domain corresponds to exactly one element in the range. If any element in a relation's domain corresponds to more than one element in the range, the relation is not a function.	Ex. 2, p. 213
c. Functions are usually given in terms of equations involving x and y, in which x is the independent variable and y is the dependent variable. If an equation is solved for y and more than one value of y can be obtained for a given x, then the equation does not define y as a function of x. If an equation defines a function, the value of the function at x, $f(x)$, often replaces y.	Ex. 3, p. 214; Ex. 4, p. 216
d. The graph of a function is the graph of its ordered pairs.	Ex. 5, p. 217
e. The vertical line test for functions: If any vertical line intersects a graph in more than one point, the graph does not define y as a function of x.	Ex. 6, p. 218
f. The graph of a function can be used to determine the function's domain and its range. To find the domain, look for all the inputs on the x-axis that correspond to points on the graph. To find the range, look for all the outputs on the y-axis that correspond to points on the graph.	Ex. 8, p. 221
g. The zeros of a function, f, are the values of x for which $f(x) = 0$. At the real zeros, the graph of f has x-intercepts. The graph of a function can have more than one x-intercept but at most one y-intercept.	Figure 2.15, p. 223
2.2 More on Functions and Their Graphs	
a. A function is increasing on intervals where its graph rises, decreasing on intervals where it falls, and constant on intervals where it neither rises nor falls. Precise definitions are given in the box on page 230.	Ex. 1, p. 231
b. If the graph of a function is given, we can often visually locate the number(s) at which the function has a relative maximum or relative minimum. Precise definitions are given in the box on page 231.	Figure 2.17, p. 232
c. The graph of an even function in which $f(-x) = f(x)$ is symmetric with respect to the y-axis. The graph of an odd function in which $f(-x) = -f(x)$ is symmetric with respect to the origin.	Ex. 2, p. 232

DEFINITIONS AND CONCEPTS

d. Piecewise functions are defined by two (or more) equations over a specified domain. Some piecewise functions are called step functions because their graphs form discontinuous steps. An example is $f(x) = \text{int}(x)$, where $\text{int}(x)$ is the greatest integer that is less than or equal to x.

Ex. 3, p. 234;
Ex. 4, p. 235;
Figure 2.23,
p. 236

e. The difference quotient of a function f is

$$\frac{f(x+h) - f(x)}{h}, h \neq 0.$$

Ex. 5, p. 236

2.3 Linear Functions and Slope

a. The slope, m, of the line through (x_1, y_1) and (x_2, y_2) is $m = \dfrac{y_2 - y_1}{x_2 - x_1}$.

Ex. 1, p. 245

b. Equations of lines include point-slope form, $y - y_1 = m(x - x_1)$, slope-intercept form, $y = mx + b$, and general form, $Ax + By + C = 0$. The equation of a horizontal line is $y = b$; a vertical line is $x = a$. A vertical line is not a linear function.

Ex. 2, p. 247;
Ex. 3, p. 247;
Ex. 5, p. 249;
Ex. 6, p. 250

c. Linear functions in the form $f(x) = mx + b$ can be graphed using the slope, m, and the y-intercept, b. (See the box on page 248.) Linear equations in the general form $Ax + By + C = 0$ can be solved for y and graphed using the slope and the y-intercept. Intercepts can also be used to graph $Ax + By + C = 0$. (See the box on page 251.)

Ex. 4, p. 248;
Ex. 7, p. 251;
Ex. 8, p. 252

2.4 More on Slope

a. Parallel lines have equal slopes. Perpendicular lines have slopes that are negative reciprocals.

Ex. 1, p. 259;
Ex. 2, p. 261

b. The slope of a linear function is the rate of change of the dependent variable per unit change of the independent variable.

Ex. 3, p. 262

c. The average rate of change of f from x_1 to x_2 is

$$\frac{f(x_2) - f(x_1)}{x_2 - x_1}.$$

Ex. 4, p. 264;
Ex. 5, p. 265

2.5 Transformations of Functions

a. Table 2.3 on page 271 shows the graphs of the constant function, $f(x) = c$, the identity function, $f(x) = x$, the absolute value function, $f(x) = |x|$, the standard quadratic function, $f(x) = x^2$, the square root function, $f(x) = \sqrt{x}$, the standard cubic function, $f(x) = x^3$, and the cube root function, $f(x) = \sqrt[3]{x}$. The table also lists characteristics of each function.

b. Table 2.4 on page 279 summarizes how to graph a function using vertical shifts, $y = f(x) \pm c$, horizontal shifts, $y = f(x \pm c)$, reflections about the x-axis, $y = -f(x)$, reflections about the y-axis, $y = f(-x)$, vertical stretching, $y = cf(x), c > 1$, vertical shrinking, $y = cf(x), 0 < c < 1$, horizontal shrinking, $y = f(cx), c > 1$, and horizontal stretching, $y = f(cx), 0 < c < 1$.

Ex. 1, p. 272;
Ex. 2, p. 274;
Ex. 3, p. 275;
Ex. 4, p. 276;
Ex. 5, p. 276;
Ex. 6, p. 277;
Ex. 7, p. 278

c. A function involving more than one transformation can be graphed in the following order: (1) horizontal shifting; (2) stretching or shrinking; (3) reflecting; (4) vertical shifting.

Ex. 8, p. 280;
Ex. 9, p. 281

2.6 Combinations of Functions; Composite Functions

a. If a function f does not model data or verbal conditions, its domain is the largest set of real numbers for which the value of $f(x)$ is a real number. Exclude from a function's domain real numbers that cause division by zero and real numbers that result in an even root, such as a square root, of a negative number.

Ex. 1, p. 287

b. When functions are given as equations, they can be added, subtracted, multiplied, or divided by performing operations with the algebraic expressions that appear on the right side of the equations. Definitions for the sum $f + g$, the difference $f - g$, the product fg, and the quotient $\frac{f}{g}$ functions, with domains $D_f \cap D_g$, and $g(x) \neq 0$ for the quotient function, are given in the box on page 289.

Ex. 2, p. 289;
Ex. 3, p. 290;
Ex. 4, p. 291

c. The composition of functions f and g, $f \circ g$, is defined by $(f \circ g)(x) = f(g(x))$. The domain of the composite function $f \circ g$ is given in the box on page 294. This composite function is obtained by replacing each occurrence of x in the equation for f with $g(x)$.

Ex. 5, p. 294;
Ex. 6, p. 295

d. Expressing a given function as a composition of two functions is called decomposing the given function.

Ex. 7, p. 296

DEFINITIONS AND CONCEPTS

EXAMPLES

2.7 Inverse Functions

a. If $f(g(x)) = x$ and $g(f(x)) = x$, function g is the inverse of function f, denoted f^{-1} and read "f-inverse." Thus, to show that f and g are inverses of each other, one must show that $f(g(x)) = x$ and $g(f(x)) = x$.

Ex. 1, p. 302

b. The procedure for finding a function's inverse uses a switch-and-solve strategy. Switch x and y, and then solve for y. The procedure is given in the box on page 303.

Ex. 2, p. 304;
Ex. 3, p. 304;
Ex. 4, p. 305

c. The horizontal line test for inverse functions: A function f has an inverse that is a function, f^{-1}, if there is no horizontal line that intersects the graph of the function f at more than one point.

Ex. 5, p. 306

d. A one-to-one function is one in which no two different ordered pairs have the same second component. Only one-to-one functions have inverse functions.

e. If the point (a, b) is on the graph of f, then the point (b, a) is on the graph of f^{-1}. The graph of f^{-1} is a reflection of the graph of f about the line $y = x$.

Ex. 6, p. 307;
Ex. 7, p. 308

2.8 Distance and Midpoint Formulas; Circles

a. The distance, d, between the points (x_1, y_1) and (x_2, y_2) is given by $d = \sqrt{(x_2 - x_1)^2 + (y_2 - y_1)^2}$.

Ex. 1, p. 313

b. The midpoint of the line segment whose endpoints are (x_1, y_1) and (x_2, y_2) is the point with coordinates $\left(\dfrac{x_1 + x_2}{2}, \dfrac{y_1 + y_2}{2}\right)$.

Ex. 2, p. 314

c. The standard form of the equation of a circle with center (h, k) and radius r is $(x - h)^2 + (y - k)^2 = r^2$.

Ex. 3, p. 314;
Ex. 4, p. 315;
Ex. 5, p. 316

d. The general form of the equation of a circle is $x^2 + y^2 + Dx + Ey + F = 0$.

e. To convert from the general form to the standard form of a circle's equation, complete the square on x and y.

Ex. 6, p. 317

REVIEW EXERCISES

2.1 and 2.2

In Exercises 1–3, determine whether each relation is a function. Give the domain and range for each relation.

1. $\{(2, 7), (3, 7), (5, 7)\}$ **2.** $\{(1, 10), (2, 500), (13, \pi)\}$

3. $\{(12, 13), (14, 15), (12, 19)\}$

In Exercises 4–6, determine whether each equation defines y as a function of x.

4. $2x + y = 8$ **5.** $3x^2 + y = 14$

6. $2x + y^2 = 6$

In Exercises 7–10, evaluate each function at the given values of the independent variable and simplify.

7. $f(x) = 5 - 7x$
  a. $f(4)$ **b.** $f(x + 3)$ **c.** $f(-x)$

8. $g(x) = 3x^2 - 5x + 2$
  a. $g(0)$ **b.** $g(-2)$
  c. $g(x - 1)$ **d.** $g(-x)$

9. $g(x) = \begin{cases} \sqrt{x - 4} & \text{if } x \geq 4 \\ 4 - x & \text{if } x < 4 \end{cases}$
  a. $g(13)$ **b.** $g(0)$ **c.** $g(-3)$

10. $f(x) = \begin{cases} \dfrac{x^2 - 1}{x - 1} & \text{if } x \neq 1 \\ 12 & \text{if } x = 1 \end{cases}$
  a. $f(-2)$ **b.** $f(1)$ **c.** $f(2)$

In Exercises 11–16, use the vertical line test to identify graphs in which y is a function of x.

11.

12.

13.

14.

15.

16.

In Exercises 17–19, use the graph to determine **a.** *the function's domain;* **b.** *the function's range;* **c.** *the x-intercepts if any;* **d.** *the y-intercept. if there is one;* **e.** *intervals on which the function is increasing, decreasing, or constant; and* **f.** *the missing function values, indicated by question marks, below each graph.*

17.

$f(-2) = ?$ $f(3) = ?$

18.

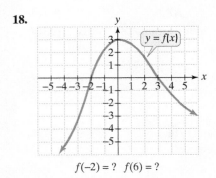

$f(-2) = ?$ $f(6) = ?$

19.

$f(-9) = ?$ $f(14) = ?$

In Exercises 20–21, find each of the following:

  a. *The numbers, if any, at which f has a relative maximum. What are these relative maxima?*

  b. *The numbers, if any, at which f has a relative minimum. What are these relative minima?*

20. Use the graph in Exercise 17.

21. Use the graph in Exercise 18.

In Exercises 22–24, determine whether each function is even, odd, or neither. State each function's symmetry. If you are using a graphing utility, graph the function and verify its possible symmetry.

22. $f(x) = x^3 - 5x$ **23.** $f(x) = x^4 - 2x^2 + 1$
24. $f(x) = 2x\sqrt{1 - x^2}$

In Exercises 25–26, the domain of each piecewise function is $(-\infty, \infty)$.

  a. *Graph each function.*

  b. *Use the graph to determine the function's range.*

25. $f(x) = \begin{cases} 5 & \text{if } x \le -1 \\ -3 & \text{if } x > -1 \end{cases}$

26. $f(x) = \begin{cases} 2x & \text{if } x < 0 \\ -x & \text{if } x \ge 0 \end{cases}$

In Exercises 27–28, find and simplify the difference quotient

$$\frac{f(x + h) - f(x)}{h}, \quad h \ne 0$$

for the given function.

27. $f(x) = 8x - 11$ **28.** $f(x) = -2x^2 + x + 10$

29. The graph shows the height, in meters, of an eagle in terms of its time, in seconds, in flight.

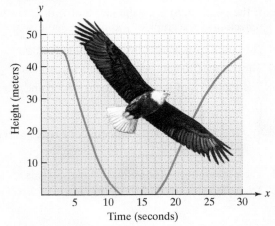

  a. Is the eagle's height a function of time? Use the graph to explain why or why not.

  b. On which interval is the function decreasing? Describe what this means in practical terms.

  c. On which intervals is the function constant? What does this mean for each of these intervals?

  d. On which interval is the function increasing? What does this mean?

30. A cargo service charges a flat fee of $5 plus $1.50 for each pound or fraction of a pound. Graph shipping cost, $C(x)$, in dollars, as a function of weight, x, in pounds, for $0 < x \le 5$.

2.3 and 2.4

In Exercises 31–34, find the slope of the line passing through each pair of points or state that the slope is undefined. Then indicate whether the line through the points rises, falls, is horizontal, or is vertical.

31. $(3, 2)$ and $(5, 1)$ **32.** $(-1, -2)$ and $(-3, -4)$
33. $\left(-3, \frac{1}{4}\right)$ and $\left(6, \frac{1}{4}\right)$ **34.** $(-2, 5)$ and $(-2, 10)$

In Exercises 35–38, use the given conditions to write an equation for each line in point-slope form and slope-intercept form.

35. Passing through $(-3, 2)$ with slope -6

36. Passing through $(1, 6)$ and $(-1, 2)$

37. Passing through $(4, -7)$ and parallel to the line whose equation is $3x + y - 9 = 0$

38. Passing through $(-3, 6)$ and perpendicular to the line whose equation is $y = \frac{1}{3}x + 4$

39. Write an equation in general form for the line passing through $(-12, -1)$ and perpendicular to the line whose equation is $6x - y - 4 = 0$.

In Exercises 40–43, give the slope and y-intercept of each line whose equation is given. Then graph the line.

40. $y = \frac{2}{5}x - 1$ **41.** $f(x) = -4x + 5$

42. $2x + 3y + 6 = 0$ **43.** $2y - 8 = 0$

44. Graph using intercepts: $2x - 5y - 10 = 0$.

45. Graph: $2x - 10 = 0$.

46. The points in the scatter plot show the number of firearms per 100 persons and the number of deaths per 100,000 persons for industrialized countries with the highest death rates.

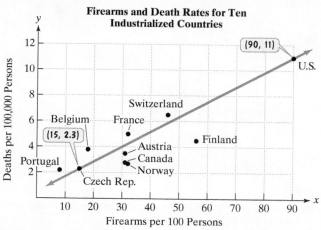

Firearms and Death Rates for Ten Industrialized Countries

Source: International Action Network on Small Arms

a. Use the two points whose coordinates are shown by the voice balloons to find an equation in point-slope form for the line that models deaths per 100,000 persons, y, as a function of firearms per 100 persons, x.

b. Write the equation in part (a) in slope-intercept form. Use function notation.

c. France has 32 firearms per 100 persons. Use the appropriate point in the scatter plot to estimate that country's deaths per 100,000 persons.

d. Use the function from part (b) to find the number of deaths per 100,000 persons for France. Round to one decimal place. Does the function underestimate or overestimate the deaths per 100,000 persons that you estimated in part (c)? How is this shown by the line in the scatter plot?

47. In a 2010 survey of more than 200,000 freshmen at 279 colleges, only 52% rated their emotional health high or above average, a drop from 64% in 1985.

Percentage of U.S. College Freshmen Rating Their Emotional Health High or Above Average

Source: UCLA Higher Education Research Institute

a. Find the slope of the line passing through the two points shown by the voice balloons.

b. Use your answer from part (a) to complete this statement:

For each year from 1985 through 2010, the percentage of U.S. college freshmen rating their emotional health high or above average decreased by ___. The rate of change was _____ per ___.

48. Find the average rate of change of $f(x) = x^2 - 4x$ from $x_1 = 5$ to $x_2 = 9$.

2.5

In Exercises 49–53, use the graph of $y = f(x)$ to graph each function g.

49. $g(x) = f(x + 2) + 3$ **50.** $g(x) = \frac{1}{2}f(x - 1)$

51. $g(x) = -f(2x)$ **52.** $g(x) = 2f\left(\frac{1}{2}x\right)$

53. $g(x) = -f(-x) - 1$

In Exercises 54–57, begin by graphing the standard quadratic function, $f(x) = x^2$. Then use transformations of this graph to graph the given function.

54. $g(x) = x^2 + 2$ **55.** $h(x) = (x + 2)^2$

56. $r(x) = -(x + 1)^2$ **57.** $y(x) = \frac{1}{2}(x - 1)^2 + 1$

In Exercises 58–60, begin by graphing the square root function, $f(x) = \sqrt{x}$. Then use transformations of this graph to graph the given function.

58. $g(x) = \sqrt{x + 3}$ **59.** $h(x) = \sqrt{3 - x}$

60. $r(x) = 2\sqrt{x + 2}$

In Exercises 61–63, begin by graphing the absolute value function, $f(x) = |x|$. Then use transformations of this graph to graph the given function.

61. $g(x) = |x + 2| - 3$ **62.** $h(x) = -|x - 1| + 1$

63. $r(x) = \frac{1}{2}|x + 2|$

In Exercises 64–66, begin by graphing the standard cubic function, $f(x) = x^3$. Then use transformations of this graph to graph the given function.

64. $g(x) = \frac{1}{2}(x - 1)^3$ **65.** $h(x) = -(x + 1)^3$

66. $r(x) = \frac{1}{4}x^3 - 1$

In Exercises 67–69, begin by graphing the cube root function, $f(x) = \sqrt[3]{x}$. Then use transformations of this graph to graph the given function.

67. $g(x) = \sqrt[3]{x + 2} - 1$ **68.** $h(x) = -\sqrt[3]{2x}$

69. $r(x) = -2\sqrt[3]{-x}$

2.6

In Exercises 70–75, find the domain of each function.

70. $f(x) = x^2 + 6x - 3$ **71.** $g(x) = \dfrac{4}{x - 7}$

72. $h(x) = \sqrt{8 - 2x}$ **73.** $f(x) = \dfrac{x}{x^2 + 4x - 21}$

74. $g(x) = \dfrac{\sqrt{x - 2}}{x - 5}$

75. $f(x) = \sqrt{x - 1} + \sqrt{x + 5}$

In Exercises 76–78, find $f + g, f - g, fg,$ and $\frac{f}{g}$. Determine the domain for each function.

76. $f(x) = 3x - 1$, $g(x) = x - 5$

77. $f(x) = x^2 + x + 1$, $g(x) = x^2 - 1$

78. $f(x) = \sqrt{x + 7}$, $g(x) = \sqrt{x - 2}$

*In Exercises 79–80, find **a.** $(f \circ g)(x)$; **b.** $(g \circ f)(x)$; **c.** $(f \circ g)(3)$.*

79. $f(x) = x^2 + 3$, $g(x) = 4x - 1$

80. $f(x) = \sqrt{x}$, $g(x) = x + 1$

*In Exercises 81–82, find **a.** $(f \circ g)(x)$; **b.** the domain of $(f \circ g)$.*

81. $f(x) = \dfrac{x + 1}{x - 2}$, $g(x) = \dfrac{1}{x}$

82. $f(x) = \sqrt{x - 1}$, $g(x) = x + 3$

In Exercises 83–84, express the given function h as a composition of two functions f and g so that $h(x) = (f \circ g)(x)$.

83. $h(x) = (x^2 + 2x - 1)^4$ **84.** $h(x) = \sqrt[3]{7x + 4}$

2.7

In Exercises 85–86, find $f(g(x))$ and $g(f(x))$ and determine whether each pair of functions f and g are inverses of each other.

85. $f(x) = \dfrac{3}{5}x + \dfrac{1}{2}$ and $g(x) = \dfrac{5}{3}x - 2$

86. $f(x) = 2 - 5x$ and $g(x) = \dfrac{2 - x}{5}$

The functions in Exercises 87–89 are all one-to-one. For each function,

    a. Find an equation for $f^{-1}(x)$, the inverse function.

    b. Verify that your equation is correct by showing that $f(f^{-1}(x)) = x$ and $f^{-1}(f(x)) = x$.

87. $f(x) = 4x - 3$

88. $f(x) = 8x^3 + 1$

89. $f(x) = \dfrac{2}{x} + 5$

Which graphs in Exercises 90–93 represent functions that have inverse functions?

90.

91.

92.

93.

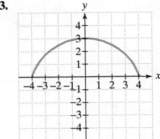

94. Use the graph of f in the figure shown to draw the graph of its inverse function.

In Exercises 95–96, find an equation for $f^{-1}(x)$. Then graph f and f^{-1} in the same rectangular coordinate system.

95. $f(x) = 1 - x^2, x \geq 0$ **96.** $f(x) = \sqrt{x} + 1$

2.8

In Exercises 97–98, find the distance between each pair of points. If necessary, round answers to two decimal places.

97. $(-2, 3)$ and $(3, -9)$ **98.** $(-4, 3)$ and $(-2, 5)$

In Exercises 99–100, find the midpoint of each line segment with the given endpoints.

99. $(2, 6)$ and $(-12, 4)$ **100.** $(4, -6)$ and $(-15, 2)$

In Exercises 101–102, write the standard form of the equation of the circle with the given center and radius.

101. Center $(0, 0), r = 3$ **102.** Center $(-2, 4), r = 6$

In Exercises 103–105, give the center and radius of each circle and graph its equation. Use the graph to identify the relation's domain and range.

103. $x^2 + y^2 = 1$ **104.** $(x + 2)^2 + (y - 3)^2 = 9$

105. $x^2 + y^2 - 4x + 2y - 4 = 0$

CHAPTER 2 TEST

1. List by letter all relations that are not functions.
  a. $\{(7,5), (8,5), (9,5)\}$
  b. $\{(5,7), (5,8), (5,9)\}$
  c.

  d. $x^2 + y^2 = 100$
  e.

2. Use the graph of $y = f(x)$ to solve this exercise.

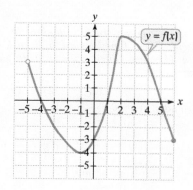

  a. What is $f(4) - f(-3)$?
  b. What is the domain of f?
  c. What is the range of f?
  d. On which interval or intervals is f increasing?
  e. On which interval or intervals is f decreasing?
  f. For what number does f have a relative maximum? What is the relative maximum?
  g. For what number does f have a relative minimum? What is the relative minimum?
  h. What are the x-intercepts?
  i. What is the y-intercept?

3. Use the graph of $y = f(x)$ to solve this exercise.

  a. What are the zeros of f?
  b. Find the value(s) of x for which $f(x) = -1$.
  c. Find the value(s) of x for which $f(x) = -2$.
  d. Is f even, odd, or neither?
  e. Does f have an inverse function?
  f. Is $f(0)$ a relative maximum, a relative minimum, or neither?
  g. Graph $g(x) = f(x + 1) - 1$.
  h. Graph $h(x) = \frac{1}{2}f\left(\frac{1}{2}x\right)$.
  i. Graph $r(x) = -f(-x) + 1$.
  j. Find the average rate of change of f from $x_1 = -2$ to $x_2 = 1$.

In Exercises 4–15, graph each equation in a rectangular coordinate system. If two functions are indicated, graph both in the same system. Then use your graphs to identify each relation's domain and range.

4. $x + y = 4$ **5.** $x^2 + y^2 = 4$
6. $f(x) = 4$ **7.** $f(x) = -\frac{1}{3}x + 2$
8. $(x + 2)^2 + (y - 1)^2 = 9$ **9.** $f(x) = \begin{cases} 2 & \text{if } x \le 0 \\ -1 & \text{if } x > 0 \end{cases}$
10. $x^2 + y^2 + 4x - 6y - 3 = 0$
11. $f(x) = |x|$ and $g(x) = \frac{1}{2}|x + 1| - 2$
12. $f(x) = x^2$ and $g(x) = -(x - 1)^2 + 4$
13. $f(x) = 2x - 4$ and f^{-1} **14.** $f(x) = x^3 - 1$ and f^{-1}
15. $f(x) = x^2 - 1, x \ge 0$, and f^{-1}

In Exercises 16–23, let $f(x) = x^2 - x - 4$ and $g(x) = 2x - 6$.

16. Find $f(x - 1)$.   **17.** Find $\dfrac{f(x + h) - f(x)}{h}$.

18. Find $(g - f)(x)$.

19. Find $\left(\dfrac{f}{g}\right)(x)$ and its domain.

20. Find $(f \circ g)(x)$.   **21.** Find $(g \circ f)(x)$.

22. Find $g(f(-1))$.

23. Find $f(-x)$. Is f even, odd, or neither?

In Exercises 24–25, use the given conditions to write an equation for each line in point-slope form and slope-intercept form.

24. Passing through $(2, 1)$ and $(-1, -8)$

25. Passing through $(-4, 6)$ and perpendicular to the line whose equation is $y = -\frac{1}{4}x + 5$

26. Write an equation in general form for the line passing through $(-7, -10)$ and parallel to the line whose equation is $4x + 2y - 5 = 0$.

27. Studies show that texting while driving is as risky as driving with a 0.08 blood alcohol level, the standard for drunk driving. The bar graph shows the number of fatalities in the United States involving distracted driving from 2004 through 2008. Although the distracted category involves such activities as talking on cellphones, conversing with passengers, and eating, experts at the National Highway Traffic Safety Administration claim that texting while driving is the clearest menace because it requires looking away from the road.

Number of Highway Fatalities in the United States Involving Distracted Driving

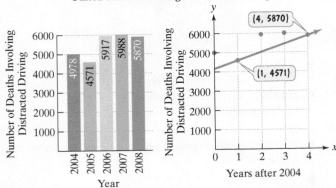

Source: National Highway Traffic Safety Administration

a. Shown to the right of the bar graph is a scatter plot with a line passing through two of the data points. Use the two points whose coordinates are shown by the voice balloons to write the point-slope form of an equation that models the number of highway fatalities involving distracted driving, y, in the United States x years after 2004.

b. Write the equation from part (a) in slope-intercept form. Use function notation.

c. In 2010, surveys showed overwhelming public support to ban texting while driving, although at that time only 19 states and Washington, D.C., outlawed the practice. Without additional laws that penalize texting drivers, use the linear function you obtained from part (b) to project the number of fatalities in the United States in 2014 involving distracted driving.

28. Find the average rate of change of $f(x) = 3x^2 - 5$ from $x_1 = 6$ to $x_2 = 10$.

29. If $g(x) = \begin{cases} \sqrt{x - 3} & \text{if } x \geq 3 \\ 3 - x & \text{if } x < 3 \end{cases}$, find $g(-1)$ and $g(7)$.

In Exercises 30–31, find the domain of each function.

30. $f(x) = \dfrac{3}{x + 5} + \dfrac{7}{x - 1}$

31. $f(x) = 3\sqrt{x + 5} + 7\sqrt{x - 1}$

32. If $f(x) = \dfrac{7}{x - 4}$ and $g(x) = \dfrac{2}{x}$, find $(f \circ g)(x)$ and the domain of $f \circ g$.

33. Express $h(x) = (2x + 3)^7$ as a composition of two functions f and g so that $h(x) = (f \circ g)(x)$.

34. Find the length and the midpoint of the line segment whose endpoints are $(2, -2)$ and $(5, 2)$.

CUMULATIVE REVIEW EXERCISES (CHAPTERS 1–2)

Use the graph of $y = f(x)$ to solve Exercises 1–5.

1. Find the domain and the range of f.

2. For what value(s) of x is $f(x) = 1$?

3. Find the relative maximum.

4. Graph $g(x) = f(x - 1) + 1$.

5. Graph $h(x) = -2f\left(\frac{1}{2}x\right)$.

In Exercises 6–10, solve each equation or inequality.

6. $(x + 3)(x - 4) = 8$

7. $3(4x - 1) = 4 - 6(x - 3)$

8. $\sqrt{x} + 2 = x$

9. $x^{\frac{2}{3}} - x^{\frac{1}{3}} - 6 = 0$

10. $\dfrac{x}{2} - 3 \leq \dfrac{x}{4} + 2$

In Exercises 11–14, graph each equation in a rectangular coordinate system. If two functions are indicated, graph both in the same system. Then use your graphs to identify each relation's domain and range.

11. $3x - 6y - 12 = 0$ **12.** $(x - 2)^2 + (y + 1)^2 = 4$

13. $f(x) = \sqrt[3]{x}$ and $g(x) = \sqrt[3]{x - 3} + 4$

14. $f(x) = \sqrt{x - 3} + 2$ and f^{-1}

In Exercises 15–16, let $f(x) = 4 - x^2$ and $g(x) = x + 5$.

15. Find $\dfrac{f(x + h) - f(x)}{h}$ and simplify.

16. Find all values of x satisfying $(f \circ g)(x) = 0$.

17. Write equations in point-slope form, slope-intercept form, and general form for the line passing through $(-2, 5)$ and perpendicular to the line whose equation is $y = -\frac{1}{4}x + \frac{1}{3}$.

18. You invested $6000 in two accounts paying 7% and 9% annual interest. At the end of the year, the total interest from these investments was $510. How much was invested at each rate?

19. For a summer sales job, you are choosing between two pay arrangements: a weekly salary of $200 plus 5% commission on sales, or a straight 15% commission. For how many dollars of sales will the earnings be the same regardless of the pay arrangement?

20. The length of a rectangular garden is 2 feet more than twice its width. If 22 feet of fencing is needed to enclose the garden, what are its dimensions?

POLYNOMIAL AND RATIONAL FUNCTIONS

We are surrounded by evidence that the world is profoundly mathematical. After turning a somersault, a diver's path can be modeled by a quadratic function, $f(x) = ax^2 + bx + c$, as can the path of a football tossed from quarterback to receiver or the path of a flipped coin. Even if you throw an object directly upward, although its path is straight and vertical, its changing height over time is described by a quadratic function. And tailgaters beware: Whether you're driving a car, a motorcycle, or a truck on dry or wet roads, an array of quadratic functions that model your required stopping distances at various speeds are available to help you become a safer driver.

HERE'S WHERE YOU'LL FIND THESE APPLICATIONS:

The quadratic functions surrounding our long history of throwing things appear throughout the chapter, including Example 5 in Section 3.1 and Example 5 in Section 3.6.

Tailgaters should pay close attention to the Section 3.6 opener, Exercises 77–78 and 92–93 in Exercise Set 3.6, and Exercise 75 in the Chapter Review Exercises.

SECTION 3.1   Quadratic Functions

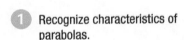

Objectives

1. Recognize characteristics of parabolas.
2. Graph parabolas.
3. Determine a quadratic function's minimum or maximum value.
4. Solve problems involving a quadratic function's minimum or maximum value.

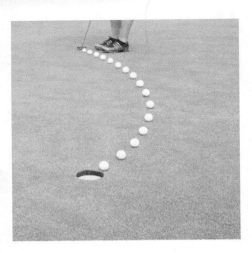

Many sports involve objects that are thrown, kicked, or hit, and then proceed with no additional force of their own. Such objects are called **projectiles**. Paths of projectiles, as well as their heights over time, can be modeled by quadratic functions. We have seen that a **quadratic function** is any function of the form

$$f(x) = ax^2 + bx + c,$$

where $a, b,$ and c are real numbers, with $a \neq 0$. A quadratic function is a polynomial function whose greatest exponent is 2. In this section, you will learn to use graphs of quadratic functions to gain a visual understanding of the algebra that describes football, baseball, basketball, the shot put, and other projectile sports.

① Recognize characteristics of parabolas.

Graphs of Quadratic Functions

The graph of any quadratic function is called a **parabola**. Parabolas are shaped like bowls or inverted bowls, as shown in **Figure 3.1**. If the coefficient of x^2 (the value of a in $ax^2 + bx + c$) is positive, the parabola opens upward. If the coefficient of x^2 is negative, the parabola opens downward. The **vertex** (or turning point) of the parabola is the lowest point on the graph when it opens upward and the highest point on the graph when it opens downward.

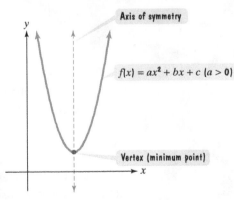

$a > 0$: Parabola opens upward.

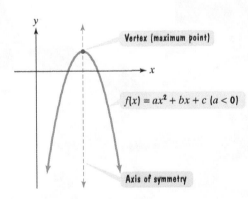

$a < 0$: Parabola opens downward.

FIGURE 3.1 Characteristics of graphs of quadratic functions

Look at the unusual image of the word *mirror* shown here. The artist, Scott Kim, has created the image so that the two halves of the whole are mirror images of each other. A parabola shares this kind of symmetry, in which a vertical line through the vertex divides the figure in half. Parabolas are symmetric with respect to this line, called the **axis of symmetry**. If a parabola is folded along its axis of symmetry, the two halves match exactly.

② Graph parabolas.

Graphing Quadratic Functions in Standard Form

In our earlier work with transformations, we applied a series of transformations to the graph of $f(x) = x^2$. The graph of this function is a parabola. The vertex for this parabola is $(0, 0)$. In **Figure 3.2(a)**, the graph of $f(x) = ax^2$ for $a > 0$ is shown in black; it opens *upward*. In **Figure 3.2(b)**, the graph of $f(x) = ax^2$ for $a < 0$ is shown in black; it opens *downward*.

Transformations of $f(x) = ax^2$

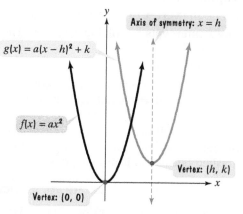

FIGURE 3.2(a) $a > 0$: Parabola opens upward.

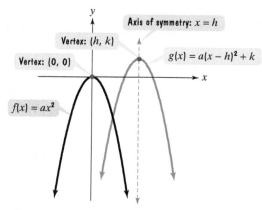

FIGURE 3.2(b) $a < 0$: Parabola opens downward.

Figure 3.2(a) and **3.2(b)** also show the graph of $g(x) = a(x - h)^2 + k$ in blue. Compare these graphs to those of $f(x) = ax^2$. Observe that h determines a horizontal shift and k determines a vertical shift of the graph of $f(x) = ax^2$:

$$g(x) = a(x - h)^2 + k.$$

> If $h > 0$, the graph of $f(x) = ax^2$ is shifted h units to the right.

> If $k > 0$, the graph of $y = a(x - h)^2$ is shifted k units up.

Consequently, the vertex $(0, 0)$ on the black graph of $f(x) = ax^2$ moves to the point (h, k) on the blue graph of $g(x) = a(x - h)^2 + k$. The axis of symmetry is the vertical line whose equation is $x = h$.

The form of the expression for g is convenient because it immediately identifies the vertex of the parabola as (h, k). This is the **standard form** of a quadratic function.

The Standard Form of a Quadratic Function

The quadratic function

$$f(x) = a(x - h)^2 + k, \quad a \neq 0$$

is in **standard form**. The graph of f is a parabola whose vertex is the point (h, k). The parabola is symmetric with respect to the line $x = h$. If $a > 0$, the parabola opens upward; if $a < 0$, the parabola opens downward.

The sign of a in $f(x) = a(x - h)^2 + k$ determines whether the parabola opens upward or downward. Furthermore, if $|a|$ is small, the parabola opens more flatly than if $|a|$ is large. Here is a general procedure for graphing parabolas whose equations are in standard form:

> ### Graphing Quadratic Functions with Equations in Standard Form
>
> To graph $f(x) = a(x - h)^2 + k$,
>
> 1. Determine whether the parabola opens upward or downward. If $a > 0$, it opens upward. If $a < 0$, it opens downward.
> 2. Determine the vertex of the parabola. The vertex is (h, k).
> 3. Find any x-intercepts by solving $f(x) = 0$. The function's real zeros are the x-intercepts.
> 4. Find the y-intercept by computing $f(0)$.
> 5. Plot the intercepts, the vertex, and additional points as necessary. Connect these points with a smooth curve that is shaped like a bowl or an inverted bowl.

In the graphs that follow, we will show each axis of symmetry as a dashed vertical line. Because this vertical line passes through the vertex, (h, k), its equation is $x = h$. The line is dashed because it is not part of the parabola.

EXAMPLE 1 Graphing a Quadratic Function in Standard Form

Graph the quadratic function $f(x) = -2(x - 3)^2 + 8$.

SOLUTION

We can graph this function by following the steps in the preceding box. We begin by identifying values for a, h, and k.

Standard form
$$f(x) = a(x - h)^2 + k$$
$$a = -2 \quad h = 3 \quad k = 8$$
Given function
$$f(x) = -2(x - 3)^2 + 8$$

Step 1 Determine how the parabola opens. Note that a, the coefficient of x^2, is -2. Thus, $a < 0$; this negative value tells us that the parabola opens downward.

Step 2 Find the vertex. The vertex of the parabola is at (h, k). Because $h = 3$ and $k = 8$, the parabola has its vertex at $(3, 8)$.

Step 3 Find the x-intercepts by solving $f(x) = 0$. Replace $f(x)$ with 0 in $f(x) = -2(x - 3)^2 + 8$.

$$0 = -2(x - 3)^2 + 8 \qquad \text{Find x-intercepts, setting f(x) equal to 0.}$$
$$2(x - 3)^2 = 8 \qquad \text{Solve for x. Add } 2(x - 3)^2 \text{ to both sides of the equation.}$$
$$(x - 3)^2 = 4 \qquad \text{Divide both sides by 2.}$$
$$x - 3 = \sqrt{4} \quad \text{or} \quad x - 3 = -\sqrt{4} \qquad \text{Apply the square root property.}$$
$$x - 3 = 2 \qquad\quad x - 3 = -2 \qquad \sqrt{4} = 2$$
$$x = 5 \qquad\qquad x = 1 \qquad \text{Add 3 to both sides in each equation.}$$

The x-intercepts are 1 and 5. The parabola passes through $(1, 0)$ and $(5, 0)$.

Step 4 Find the y-intercept by computing $f(0)$. Replace x with 0 in $f(x) = -2(x - 3)^2 + 8$.

$$f(0) = -2(0 - 3)^2 + 8 = -2(-3)^2 + 8 = -2(9) + 8 = -10$$

The y-intercept is -10. The parabola passes through $(0, -10)$.

Step 5 Graph the parabola. With a vertex at $(3, 8)$, x-intercepts at 5 and 1, and a y-intercept at -10, the graph of f is shown in **Figure 3.3**. The axis of symmetry is the vertical line whose equation is $x = 3$. ● ● ●

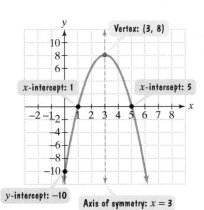

FIGURE 3.3 The graph of $f(x) = -2(x - 3)^2 + 8$

⊘ Check Point **1** Graph the quadratic function $f(x) = -(x - 1)^2 + 4$.

EXAMPLE 2   Graphing a Quadratic Function in Standard Form

Graph the quadratic function $f(x) = (x + 3)^2 + 1$.

SOLUTION

We begin by finding values for a, h, and k.

$$f(x) = a(x - h)^2 + k \quad \text{Standard form of quadratic function}$$
$$f(x) = (x + 3)^2 + 1 \quad \text{Given function}$$
$$f(x) = 1(x - (-3))^2 + 1$$

$$a = 1 \qquad h = -3 \qquad k = 1$$

Step 1   Determine how the parabola opens. Note that a, the coefficient of x^2, is 1. Thus, $a > 0$; this positive value tells us that the parabola opens upward.

Step 2   Find the vertex. The vertex of the parabola is at (h, k). Because $h = -3$ and $k = 1$, the parabola has its vertex at $(-3, 1)$.

Step 3   Find the x-intercepts by solving $f(x) = 0$. Replace $f(x)$ with 0 in $f(x) = (x + 3)^2 + 1$. Because the vertex is at $(-3, 1)$, which lies above the x-axis, and the parabola opens upward, it appears that this parabola has no x-intercepts. We can verify this observation algebraically.

$$0 = (x + 3)^2 + 1 \qquad \text{Find possible x-intercepts, setting } f(x) \text{ equal to 0.}$$
$$-1 = (x + 3)^2 \qquad \text{Solve for x. Subtract 1 from both sides.}$$
$$x + 3 = \sqrt{-1} \quad \text{or} \quad x + 3 = -\sqrt{-1} \qquad \text{Apply the square root property.}$$
$$x + 3 = i \qquad \qquad x + 3 = -i \qquad \sqrt{-1} = i$$
$$x = -3 + i \qquad \qquad x = -3 - i \qquad \text{The solutions are } -3 \pm i.$$

Because this equation has no real solutions, the parabola has no x-intercepts.

Step 4   Find the y-intercept by computing $f(0)$. Replace x with 0 in $f(x) = (x + 3)^2 + 1$.

$$f(0) = (0 + 3)^2 + 1 = 3^2 + 1 = 9 + 1 = 10$$

The y-intercept is 10. The parabola passes through $(0, 10)$.

Step 5   Graph the parabola. With a vertex at $(-3, 1)$, no x-intercepts, and a y-intercept at 10, the graph of f is shown in **Figure 3.4**. The axis of symmetry is the vertical line whose equation is $x = -3$.   ● ● ●

Axis of symmetry: $x = -3$

y-intercept: 10

Vertex: $(-3, 1)$

FIGURE 3.4 The graph of $f(x) = (x + 3)^2 + 1$

GREAT QUESTION!

I'm confused about finding h from the equation $f(x) = a(x - h)^2 + k$. Can you help me out?

It's easy to make a sign error when finding h, the x-coordinate of the vertex. In

$$f(x) = a(x - h)^2 + k,$$

h is the number that follows the subtraction sign.

- $f(x) = -2(x - 3)^2 + 8$

  The number *after* the subtraction is 3: $h = 3$.

- $f(x) = (x + 3)^2 + 1$
  $= (x - (-3))^2 + 1$

  The number *after* the subtraction is -3: $h = -3$.

⊘ Check Point **2** Graph the quadratic function $f(x) = (x - 2)^2 + 1$.

Graphing Quadratic Functions in the Form $f(x) = ax^2 + bx + c$

Quadratic functions are frequently expressed in the form $f(x) = ax^2 + bx + c$. How can we identify the vertex of a parabola whose equation is in this form? Completing the square provides the answer to this question.

$$f(x) = ax^2 + bx + c$$

$$= a\left(x^2 + \frac{b}{a}x\right) + c \qquad \text{Factor out } a \text{ from } ax^2 + bx.$$

$$= a\left(x^2 + \frac{b}{a}x + \frac{b^2}{4a^2}\right) + c - a\left(\frac{b^2}{4a^2}\right)$$

Complete the square by adding the square of half the coefficient of x.

By completing the square, we added $a \cdot \dfrac{b^2}{4a^2}$. To avoid changing the function's equation, we must subtract this term.

$$= a\left(x + \frac{b}{2a}\right)^2 + c - \frac{b^2}{4a} \qquad \begin{array}{l}\text{Write the trinomial as the}\\ \text{square of a binomial and}\\ \text{simplify the constant term.}\end{array}$$

Compare this form of the equation with a quadratic function's **standard form**.

Standard form

$$f(x) = a(x - h)^2 + k$$

$$h = -\frac{b}{2a} \qquad k = c - \frac{b^2}{4a}$$

Equation under discussion

$$f(x) = a\left(x - \left(-\frac{b}{2a}\right)\right)^2 + c - \frac{b^2}{4a}$$

The important part of this observation is that h, the x-coordinate of the vertex, is $-\dfrac{b}{2a}$. The y-coordinate can be found by evaluating the function at $-\dfrac{b}{2a}$.

The Vertex of a Parabola Whose Equation Is $f(x) = ax^2 + bx + c$

Consider the parabola defined by the quadratic function $f(x) = ax^2 + bx + c$. The parabola's vertex is $\left(-\dfrac{b}{2a}, f\left(-\dfrac{b}{2a}\right)\right)$. The x-coordinate is $-\dfrac{b}{2a}$. The y-coordinate is found by substituting the x-coordinate into the parabola's equation and evaluating the function at this value of x.

We can apply our five-step procedure to graph parabolas in the form $f(x) = ax^2 + bx + c$.

Graphing Quadratic Functions with Equations in the Form
$f(x) = ax^2 + bx + c$

To graph $f(x) = ax^2 + bx + c$,

1. Determine whether the parabola opens upward or downward. If $a > 0$, it opens upward. If $a < 0$, it opens downward.

2. Determine the vertex of the parabola. The vertex is $\left(-\dfrac{b}{2a}, f\left(-\dfrac{b}{2a}\right)\right)$.

3. Find any x-intercepts by solving $f(x) = 0$. The real solutions of $ax^2 + bx + c = 0$ are the x-intercepts.

4. Find the y-intercept by computing $f(0)$. Because $f(0) = c$ (the constant term in the function's equation), the y-intercept is c and the parabola passes through $(0, c)$.

5. Plot the intercepts, the vertex, and additional points as necessary. Connect these points with a smooth curve.

EXAMPLE 3   Graphing a Quadratic Function in the Form
$f(x) = ax^2 + bx + c$

Graph the quadratic function $f(x) = -x^2 - 2x + 1$. Use the graph to identify the function's domain and its range.

SOLUTION

Step 1   Determine how the parabola opens. Note that a, the coefficient of x^2, is -1. Thus, $a < 0$; this negative value tells us that the parabola opens downward.

Step 2   Find the vertex. We know that the x-coordinate of the vertex is $x = -\dfrac{b}{2a}$. We identify a, b, and c in $f(x) = ax^2 + bx + c$.

$$f(x) = -x^2 - 2x + 1$$

$$a = -1 \qquad b = -2 \qquad c = 1$$

Substitute the values of a and b into the equation for the x-coordinate:

$$x = -\frac{b}{2a} = -\frac{-2}{2(-1)} = -\left(\frac{-2}{-2}\right) = -1.$$

The x-coordinate of the vertex is -1. We substitute -1 for x in the equation of the function, $f(x) = -x^2 - 2x + 1$, to find the y-coordinate:

$$f(-1) = -(-1)^2 - 2(-1) + 1 = -1 + 2 + 1 = 2.$$

The vertex is at $(-1, 2)$.

Step 3   Find the x-intercepts by solving $f(x) = 0$. Replace $f(x)$ with 0 in $f(x) = -x^2 - 2x + 1$. We obtain $0 = -x^2 - 2x + 1$. This equation cannot be solved by factoring. We will use the quadratic formula to solve it.

$$-x^2 - 2x + 1 = 0$$

$$a = -1 \qquad b = -2 \qquad c = 1$$

$$x = \frac{-b \pm \sqrt{b^2 - 4ac}}{2a} = \frac{-(-2) \pm \sqrt{(-2)^2 - 4(-1)(1)}}{2(-1)} = \frac{2 \pm \sqrt{4 - (-4)}}{-2}$$

To locate the x-intercepts, we need decimal approximations. Thus, there is no need to simplify the radical form of the solutions.

$$x = \frac{2 + \sqrt{8}}{-2} \approx -2.4 \qquad \text{or} \qquad x = \frac{2 - \sqrt{8}}{-2} \approx 0.4$$

The x-intercepts are approximately -2.4 and 0.4. The parabola passes through $(-2.4, 0)$ and $(0.4, 0)$.

Step 4 Find the *y*-intercept by computing $f(0)$. Replace x with 0 in $f(x) = -x^2 - 2x + 1$.

$$f(0) = -0^2 - 2 \cdot 0 + 1 = 1$$

The *y*-intercept is 1, which is the constant term in the function's equation. The parabola passes through $(0, 1)$.

Step 5 Graph the parabola. With a vertex at $(-1, 2)$, *x*-intercepts at approximately -2.4 and 0.4, and a *y*-intercept at 1, the graph of f is shown in **Figure 3.5(a)**. The axis of symmetry is the vertical line whose equation is $x = -1$.

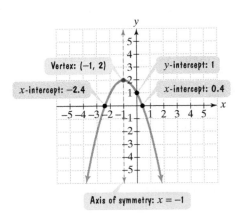

FIGURE 3.5(a) The graph of $f(x) = -x^2 - 2x + 1$

FIGURE 3.5(b) Determining the domain and range of $f(x) = -x^2 - 2x + 1$

Now we are ready to determine the domain and range of $f(x) = -x^2 - 2x + 1$. We can use the parabola, shown again in **Figure 3.5(b)**, to do so. To find the domain, look for all the inputs on the *x*-axis that correspond to points on the graph. As the graph widens and continues to fall at both ends, can you see that these inputs include all real numbers?

Domain of f is $\{x \mid x \text{ is a real number}\}$ or $(-\infty, \infty)$.

To find the range, look for all the outputs on the *y*-axis that correspond to points on the graph. **Figure 3.5(b)** shows that the parabola's vertex, $(-1, 2)$, is the highest point on the graph. Because the *y*-coordinate of the vertex is 2, outputs on the *y*-axis fall at or below 2.

Range of f is $\{y \mid y \le 2\}$ or $(-\infty, 2]$.   • • •

🖊 Check Point **3** Graph the quadratic function $f(x) = -x^2 + 4x + 1$. Use the graph to identify the function's domain and its range.

③ Determine a quadratic function's minimum or maximum value.

Minimum and Maximum Values of Quadratic Functions

Consider the quadratic function $f(x) = ax^2 + bx + c$. If $a > 0$, the parabola opens upward and the vertex is its lowest point. If $a < 0$, the parabola opens downward and the vertex is its highest point. The *x*-coordinate of the vertex is $-\dfrac{b}{2a}$. Thus, we can find the minimum or maximum value of f by evaluating the quadratic function at $x = -\dfrac{b}{2a}$.

Minimum and Maximum: Quadratic Functions

Consider the quadratic function $f(x) = ax^2 + bx + c$.

1. If $a > 0$, then f has a minimum that occurs at $x = -\dfrac{b}{2a}$. This minimum value is $f\left(-\dfrac{b}{2a}\right)$.

2. If $a < 0$, then f has a maximum that occurs at $x = -\dfrac{b}{2a}$. This maximum value is $f\left(-\dfrac{b}{2a}\right)$.

In each case, the value of x gives the location of the minimum or maximum value. The value of y, or $f\left(-\dfrac{b}{2a}\right)$, gives that minimum or maximum value.

EXAMPLE 4   Obtaining Information about a Quadratic Function from Its Equation

Consider the quadratic function $f(x) = -3x^2 + 6x - 13$.

    a. Determine, without graphing, whether the function has a minimum value or a maximum value.

    b. Find the minimum or maximum value and determine where it occurs.

    c. Identify the function's domain and its range.

SOLUTION

We begin by identifying a, b, and c in the function's equation:

$$f(x) = -3x^2 + 6x - 13.$$

$$a = -3 \qquad b = 6 \qquad c = -13$$

    a. Because $a < 0$, the function has a maximum value.

    b. The maximum value occurs at

$$x = -\frac{b}{2a} = -\frac{6}{2(-3)} = -\frac{6}{-6} = -(-1) = 1.$$

The maximum value occurs at $x = 1$ and the maximum value of $f(x) = -3x^2 + 6x - 13$ is

$$f(1) = -3 \cdot 1^2 + 6 \cdot 1 - 13 = -3 + 6 - 13 = -10.$$

We see that the maximum is -10 at $x = 1$.

    c. Like all quadratic functions, the domain is $(-\infty, \infty)$. Because the function's maximum value is -10, the range includes all real numbers at or below -10. The range is $(-\infty, -10]$.   • • •

We can use the graph of $f(x) = -3x^2 + 6x - 13$ to visualize the results of Example 4. **Figure 3.6** shows the graph in a $[-6, 6, 1]$ by $[-50, 20, 10]$ viewing rectangle. The maximum function feature verifies that the function's maximum is -10 at $x = 1$. Notice that x gives the location of the maximum and y gives the maximum value. Notice, too, that the maximum value is -10 and not the ordered pair $(1, -10)$.

    ✓ **Check Point 4** Repeat parts (a) through (c) of Example 4 using the quadratic function $f(x) = 4x^2 - 16x + 1000$.

Range is
$(-\infty, -10]$.

Maximum
X=1   Y=-10

$[-6, 6, 1]$ by $[-50, 20, 10]$

FIGURE 3.6

④ Solve problems involving a quadratic function's minimum or maximum value.

Applications of Quadratic Functions

Many applied problems involve finding the maximum or minimum value of a quadratic function, as well as where this value occurs.

EXAMPLE 5 The Parabolic Path of a Punted Football

Figure 3.7 shows that when a football is kicked, the nearest defensive player is 6 feet from the point of impact with the kicker's foot. The height of the punted football, $f(x)$, in feet, can be modeled by

$$f(x) = -0.01x^2 + 1.18x + 2,$$

where x is the ball's horizontal distance, in feet, from the point of impact with the kicker's foot.

a. What is the maximum height of the punt and how far from the point of impact does this occur?

b. How far must the nearest defensive player, who is 6 feet from the kicker's point of impact, reach to block the punt?

FIGURE 3.7

c. If the ball is not blocked by the defensive player, how far down the field will it go before hitting the ground?

d. Graph the function that models the football's parabolic path.

SOLUTION

a. We begin by identifying the numbers a, b, and c in the function's equation.

$$f(x) = -0.01x^2 + 1.18x + 2$$

$$a = -0.01 \quad b = 1.18 \quad c = 2$$

Because $a < 0$, the function has a maximum that occurs at $x = -\dfrac{b}{2a}$.

$$x = -\frac{b}{2a} = -\frac{1.18}{2(-0.01)} = -(-59) = 59$$

This means that the maximum height of the punt occurs 59 feet from the kicker's point of impact. The maximum height of the punt is

$$f(59) = -0.01(59)^2 + 1.18(59) + 2 = 36.81,$$

or 36.81 feet.

b. **Figure 3.7** shows that the defensive player is 6 feet from the kicker's point of impact. To block the punt, he must touch the football along its parabolic path. This means that we must find the height of the ball 6 feet from the kicker. Replace x with 6 in the given function, $f(x) = -0.01x^2 + 1.18x + 2$.

$$f(6) = -0.01(6)^2 + 1.18(6) + 2 = -0.36 + 7.08 + 2 = 8.72$$

The defensive player must reach 8.72 feet above the ground to block the punt.

c. Assuming that the ball is not blocked by the defensive player, we are interested in how far down the field it will go before hitting the ground. We are looking for the ball's horizontal distance, x, when its height above the ground, $f(x)$, is 0 feet. To find this x-intercept, replace $f(x)$ with 0 in $f(x) = -0.01x^2 + 1.18x + 2$. We obtain $0 = -0.01x^2 + 1.18x + 2$, or $-0.01x^2 + 1.18x + 2 = 0$. The equation cannot be solved by factoring. We will use the quadratic formula to solve it.

$$-0.01x^2 + 1.18x + 2 = 0$$

$a = -0.01$ $b = 1.18$ $c = 2$

The equation for determining the ball's maximum horizontal distance

Use a calculator to evaluate the radicand.

$$x = \frac{-b \pm \sqrt{b^2 - 4ac}}{2a} = \frac{-1.18 \pm \sqrt{(1.18)^2 - 4(-0.01)(2)}}{2(-0.01)} = \frac{-1.18 \pm \sqrt{1.4724}}{-0.02}$$

$$x = \frac{-1.18 + \sqrt{1.4724}}{-0.02} \quad \text{or} \quad x = \frac{-1.18 - \sqrt{1.4724}}{-0.02}$$

$$x \approx -1.7 \qquad\qquad\qquad x \approx 119.7$$

Use a calculator and round to the nearest tenth.

Reject this value. We are interested in the football's height corresponding to horizontal distances from its point of impact onward, or $x \geq 0$.

If the football is not blocked by the defensive player, it will go approximately 119.7 feet down the field before hitting the ground.

d. In terms of graphing the model for the football's parabolic path, $f(x) = -0.01x^2 + 1.18x + 2$, we have already determined the vertex and the approximate x-intercept.

vertex: $(59, 36.81)$

The ball's maximum height, 36.81 feet, occurs at a horizontal distance of 59 feet.

x-intercept: 119.7

The ball's maximum horizontal distance is approximately 119.7 feet.

Figure 3.7 indicates that the y-intercept is 2, meaning that the ball is kicked from a height of 2 feet. Let's verify this value by replacing x with 0 in $f(x) = -0.01x^2 + 1.18x + 2$.

$$f(0) = -0.01 \cdot 0^2 + 1.18 \cdot 0 + 2 = 0 + 0 + 2 = 2$$

Using the vertex, $(59, 36.81)$, the x-intercept, 119.7, and the y-intercept, 2, the graph of the equation that models the football's parabolic path is shown in **Figure 3.8**. The graph is shown only for $x \geq 0$, indicating horizontal distances that begin at the football's impact with the kicker's foot and end with the ball hitting the ground.

FIGURE 3.8 The parabolic path of a punted football

⊘ Check Point **5** An archer's arrow follows a parabolic path. The height of the arrow, $f(x)$, in feet, can be modeled by

$$f(x) = -0.005x^2 + 2x + 5,$$

where x is the arrow's horizontal distance, in feet.

a. What is the maximum height of the arrow and how far from its release does this occur?

b. Find the horizontal distance the arrow travels before it hits the ground. Round to the nearest foot.

c. Graph the function that models the arrow's parabolic path.

Quadratic functions can also be used to model verbal conditions. Once we have obtained a quadratic function, we can then use the x-coordinate of the vertex to determine its maximum or minimum value. Here is a step-by-step strategy for solving these kinds of problems:

> **Strategy for Solving Problems Involving Maximizing or Minimizing Quadratic Functions**
>
> **1.** Read the problem carefully and decide which quantity is to be maximized or minimized.
> **2.** Use the conditions of the problem to express the quantity as a function in one variable.
> **3.** Rewrite the function in the form $f(x) = ax^2 + bx + c$.
> **4.** Calculate $-\dfrac{b}{2a}$. If $a > 0$, f has a minimum at $x = -\dfrac{b}{2a}$. This minimum value is $f\left(-\dfrac{b}{2a}\right)$. If $a < 0$, f has a maximum at $x = -\dfrac{b}{2a}$. This maximum value is $f\left(-\dfrac{b}{2a}\right)$.
> **5.** Answer the question posed in the problem.

EXAMPLE 6   Minimizing a Product

Among all pairs of numbers whose difference is 10, find a pair whose product is as small as possible. What is the minimum product?

SOLUTION

Step 1   Decide what must be maximized or minimized. We must minimize the product of two numbers. Calling the numbers x and y, and calling the product P, we must minimize

$$P = xy.$$

Step 2   Express this quantity as a function in one variable. In the formula $P = xy$, P is expressed in terms of two variables, x and y. However, because the difference of the numbers is 10, we can write

$$x - y = 10.$$

We can solve this equation for y in terms of x (or vice versa), substitute the result into $P = xy$, and obtain P as a function of one variable.

$$-y = -x + 10 \quad \text{Subtract } x \text{ from both sides of } x - y = 10.$$
$$y = x - 10 \quad \text{Multiply both sides of the equation by } -1 \text{ and solve for } y.$$

Now we substitute $x - 10$ for y in $P = xy$.

$$P = xy = x(x - 10)$$

Because P is now a function of x, we can write

$$P(x) = x(x - 10)$$

Step 3 Write the function in the form $f(x) = ax^2 + bx + c$. We apply the distributive property to obtain

$$P(x) = x(x - 10) = x^2 - 10x.$$

Step 4 Calculate $-\dfrac{b}{2a}$. If $a > 0$, the function has a minimum at this value. The voice balloons show that $a = 1$ and $b = -10$.

$$x = -\frac{b}{2a} = -\frac{-10}{2(1)} = -(-5) = 5$$

This means that the product, P, of two numbers whose difference is 10 is a minimum when one of the numbers, x, is 5.

Step 5 Answer the question posed by the problem. The problem asks for the two numbers and the minimum product. We found that one of the numbers, x, is 5. Now we must find the second number, y.

$$y = x - 10 = 5 - 10 = -5$$

The number pair whose difference is 10 and whose product is as small as possible is $5, -5$. The minimum product is $5(-5)$, or -25. $\bullet\bullet\bullet$

⊘ Check Point **6** Among all pairs of numbers whose difference is 8, find a pair whose product is as small as possible. What is the minimum product?

EXAMPLE 7 Maximizing Area

You have 100 yards of fencing to enclose a rectangular region. Find the dimensions of the rectangle that maximize the enclosed area. What is the maximum area?

SOLUTION

Step 1 Decide what must be maximized or minimized. We must maximize area. What we do not know are the rectangle's dimensions, x and y.

Step 2 Express this quantity as a function in one variable. Because we must maximize the area of a rectangle, we have $A = xy$. We need to transform this into a function in which A is represented by one variable. Because you have 100 yards of fencing, the perimeter of the rectangle is 100 yards. This means that

$$2x + 2y = 100.$$

We can solve this equation for y in terms of x, substitute the result into $A = xy$, and obtain A as a function in one variable. We begin by solving for y.

$$2y = 100 - 2x \quad \text{Subtract 2x from both sides of 2x + 2y = 100.}$$
$$y = \frac{100 - 2x}{2} \quad \text{Divide both sides by 2.}$$
$$y = 50 - x \quad \text{Divide each term in the numerator by 2.}$$

Now we substitute $50 - x$ for y in $A = xy$.

$$A = xy = x(50 - x)$$

The rectangle and its dimensions are illustrated in **Figure 3.9**. Because A is now a function of x, we can write

$$A(x) = x(50 - x).$$

This function models the area, $A(x)$, of any rectangle whose perimeter is 100 yards in terms of one of its dimensions, x.

FIGURE 3.9 What value of x will maximize the rectangle's area?

Step 3   **Write the function in the form $f(x) = ax^2 + bx + c$.** We apply the distributive property to obtain

$$A(x) = x(50 - x) = 50x - x^2 = -x^2 + 50x.$$

$a = -1$ $b = 50$

Step 4   **Calculate $-\dfrac{b}{2a}$. If $a < 0$, the function has a maximum at this value.** The voice balloons show that $a = -1$ and $b = 50$.

$$x = -\frac{b}{2a} = -\frac{50}{2(-1)} = 25$$

This means that the area, $A(x)$, of a rectangle with perimeter 100 yards is a maximum when one of the rectangle's dimensions, x, is 25 yards.

$50 - x$ x

FIGURE 3.9 (repeated)

Step 5   **Answer the question posed by the problem.** We found that $x = 25$. **Figure 3.9** shows that the rectangle's other dimension is $50 - x = 50 - 25 = 25$. The dimensions of the rectangle that maximize the enclosed area are 25 yards by 25 yards. The rectangle that gives the maximum area is actually a square with an area of 25 yards · 25 yards, or 625 square yards.   •••

◯ Check Point **7**   You have 120 feet of fencing to enclose a rectangular region. Find the dimensions of the rectangle that maximize the enclosed area. What is the maximum area?

Blitzer Bonus ‖ Addressing Stress Parabolically

Moderate stress, high performance

High stress, low performance

Low stress, low performance

Performance

Level of Stress

Stress levels can help or hinder performance. The parabola in **Figure 3.10** serves as a model that shows people under both low stress and high stress perform worse than their moderate-stress counterparts.

FIGURE 3.10
Source: Herbert Benson, *Your Maximum Mind*, Random House, 1987.

CONCEPT AND VOCABULARY CHECK

Fill in each blank so that the resulting statement is true.

1. The quadratic function $f(x) = a(x - h)^2 + k, a \neq 0$, is in _____ form. The graph of f is called a/an _____ whose vertex is the point _____. The graph opens upward if a _____ and opens downward if a _____.

2. Consider the quadratic function $f(x) = ax^2 + bx + c, a \neq 0$. If $a > 0$, then f has a minimum that occurs at $x =$ _____. This minimum value is _____. If $a < 0$, then f has a maximum that occurs at $x =$ _____. This maximum value is _____.

3. True or false: The graph of $f(x) = (x - 2)^2 + 1$ opens upward. _____

4. True or false: The graph of $f(x) = (x + 5)^2 + 3$ has its vertex at $(5, 3)$. _____

5. True or false: The *y*-coordinate of the vertex of $f(x) = 4x^2 - 16x + 300$ is $f(2)$. _____

6. The difference between two numbers is 8. If one number is represented by *x*, the other number can be expressed as _____. The product of the numbers, $P(x)$, expressed in the form $P(x) = ax^2 + bx + c$, is $P(x) = $ _____.

7. The perimeter of a rectangle is 80 feet. If the length of the rectangle is represented by *x*, its width can be expressed as _____. The area of the rectangle, $A(x)$, expressed in the form $A(x) = ax^2 + bx + c$, is $A(x) = $ _____.

EXERCISE SET 3.1

Practice Exercises

In Exercises 1–4, the graph of a quadratic function is given. Write the function's equation, selecting from the following options.

$$f(x) = (x + 1)^2 - 1 \qquad g(x) = (x + 1)^2 + 1$$
$$h(x) = (x - 1)^2 + 1 \qquad j(x) = (x - 1)^2 - 1$$

1.

2.

3.

4.

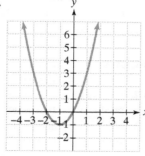

In Exercises 5–8, the graph of a quadratic function is given. Write the function's equation, selecting from the following options.

$$f(x) = x^2 + 2x + 1 \qquad g(x) = x^2 - 2x + 1$$
$$h(x) = x^2 - 1 \qquad j(x) = -x^2 - 1$$

5.

6.

7.

8.

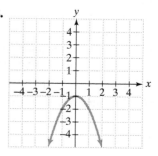

In Exercises 9–16, find the coordinates of the vertex for the parabola defined by the given quadratic function.

9. $f(x) = 2(x - 3)^2 + 1$
10. $f(x) = -3(x - 2)^2 + 12$
11. $f(x) = -2(x + 1)^2 + 5$
12. $f(x) = -2(x + 4)^2 - 8$
13. $f(x) = 2x^2 - 8x + 3$
14. $f(x) = 3x^2 - 12x + 1$
15. $f(x) = -x^2 - 2x + 8$
16. $f(x) = -2x^2 + 8x - 1$

In Exercises 17–38, use the vertex and intercepts to sketch the graph of each quadratic function. Give the equation of the parabola's axis of symmetry. Use the graph to determine the function's domain and range.

17. $f(x) = (x - 4)^2 - 1$
18. $f(x) = (x - 1)^2 - 2$
19. $f(x) = (x - 1)^2 + 2$
20. $f(x) = (x - 3)^2 + 2$
21. $y - 1 = (x - 3)^2$
22. $y - 3 = (x - 1)^2$
23. $f(x) = 2(x + 2)^2 - 1$
24. $f(x) = \frac{5}{4} - \left(x - \frac{1}{2}\right)^2$
25. $f(x) = 4 - (x - 1)^2$
26. $f(x) = 1 - (x - 3)^2$
27. $f(x) = x^2 - 2x - 3$
28. $f(x) = x^2 - 2x - 15$
29. $f(x) = x^2 + 3x - 10$
30. $f(x) = 2x^2 - 7x - 4$
31. $f(x) = 2x - x^2 + 3$
32. $f(x) = 5 - 4x - x^2$
33. $f(x) = x^2 + 6x + 3$
34. $f(x) = x^2 + 4x - 1$
35. $f(x) = 2x^2 + 4x - 3$
36. $f(x) = 3x^2 - 2x - 4$
37. $f(x) = 2x - x^2 - 2$
38. $f(x) = 6 - 4x + x^2$

In Exercises 39–44, an equation of a quadratic function is given.

   a. Determine, without graphing, whether the function has a minimum value or a maximum value.

   b. Find the minimum or maximum value and determine where it occurs.

   c. Identify the function's domain and its range.

39. $f(x) = 3x^2 - 12x - 1$
40. $f(x) = 2x^2 - 8x - 3$
41. $f(x) = -4x^2 + 8x - 3$
42. $f(x) = -2x^2 - 12x + 3$
43. $f(x) = 5x^2 - 5x$
44. $f(x) = 6x^2 - 6x$

Practice Plus

In Exercises 45–48, give the domain and the range of each quadratic function whose graph is described.

45. The vertex is $(-1, -2)$ and the parabola opens up.

46. The vertex is $(-3, -4)$ and the parabola opens down.

47. Maximum $= -6$ at $x = 10$

48. Minimum $= 18$ at $x = -6$

In Exercises 49–52, write an equation in standard form of the parabola that has the same shape as the graph of $f(x) = 2x^2$, but with the given point as the vertex.

49. $(5, 3)$ **50.** $(7, 4)$

51. $(-10, -5)$ **52.** $(-8, -6)$

In Exercises 53–56, write an equation in standard form of the parabola that has the same shape as the graph of $f(x) = 3x^2$ or $g(x) = -3x^2$, but with the given maximum or minimum.

53. Maximum $= 4$ at $x = -2$ **54.** Maximum $= -7$ at $x = 5$

55. Minimum $= 0$ at $x = 11$ **56.** Minimum $= 0$ at $x = 9$

Application Exercises

An athlete whose event is the shot put releases the shot with the same initial velocity but at different angles. The figure shows the parabolic paths for shots released at angles of 35° and 65°. Exercises 57–58 are based on the functions that model the parabolic paths.

57. When the shot whose path is shown by the blue graph is released at an angle of 35°, its height, $f(x)$, in feet, can be modeled by

$$f(x) = -0.01x^2 + 0.7x + 6.1,$$

where x is the shot's horizontal distance, in feet, from its point of release. Use this model to solve parts (a) through (c) and verify your answers using the blue graph.

  a. What is the maximum height of the shot and how far from its point of release does this occur?

  b. What is the shot's maximum horizontal distance, to the nearest tenth of a foot, or the distance of the throw?

  c. From what height was the shot released?

58. When the shot whose path is shown by the red graph in the previous column is released at an angle of 65°, its height, $g(x)$, in feet, can be modeled by

$$g(x) = -0.04x^2 + 2.1x + 6.1,$$

where x is the shot's horizontal distance, in feet, from its point of release. Use this model to solve parts (a) through (c) and verify your answers using the red graph.

  a. What is the maximum height, to the nearest tenth of a foot, of the shot and how far from its point of release does this occur?

  b. What is the shot's maximum horizontal distance, to the nearest tenth of a foot, or the distance of the throw?

  c. From what height was the shot released?

59. A ball is thrown upward and outward from a height of 6 feet. The height of the ball, $f(x)$, in feet, can be modeled by

$$f(x) = -0.8x^2 + 2.4x + 6,$$

where x is the ball's horizontal distance, in feet, from where it was thrown.

  a. What is the maximum height of the ball and how far from where it was thrown does this occur?

  b. How far does the ball travel horizontally before hitting the ground? Round to the nearest tenth of a foot.

  c. Graph the function that models the ball's parabolic path.

60. A ball is thrown upward and outward from a height of 6 feet. The height of the ball, $f(x)$, in feet, can be modeled by

$$f(x) = -0.8x^2 + 3.2x + 6,$$

where x is the ball's horizontal distance, in feet, from where it was thrown.

  a. What is the maximum height of the ball and how far from where it was thrown does this occur?

  b. How far does the ball travel horizontally before hitting the ground? Round to the nearest tenth of a foot.

  c. Graph the function that models the ball's parabolic path.

61. Among all pairs of numbers whose sum is 16, find a pair whose product is as large as possible. What is the maximum product?

62. Among all pairs of numbers whose sum is 20, find a pair whose product is as large as possible. What is the maximum product?

63. Among all pairs of numbers whose difference is 16, find a pair whose product is as small as possible. What is the minimum product?

64. Among all pairs of numbers whose difference is 24, find a pair whose product is as small as possible. What is the minimum product?

65. You have 600 feet of fencing to enclose a rectangular plot that borders on a river. If you do not fence the side along the river, find the length and width of the plot that will maximize the area. What is the largest area that can be enclosed?

66. You have 200 feet of fencing to enclose a rectangular plot that borders on a river. If you do not fence the side along the river, find the length and width of the plot that will maximize the area. What is the largest area that can be enclosed?

$200 - 2x$

67. You have 50 yards of fencing to enclose a rectangular region. Find the dimensions of the rectangle that maximize the enclosed area. What is the maximum area?

68. You have 80 yards of fencing to enclose a rectangular region. Find the dimensions of the rectangle that maximize the enclosed area. What is the maximum area?

69. A rectangular playground is to be fenced off and divided in two by another fence parallel to one side of the playground. Six hundred feet of fencing is used. Find the dimensions of the playground that maximize the total enclosed area. What is the maximum area?

70. A rectangular playground is to be fenced off and divided in two by another fence parallel to one side of the playground. Four hundred feet of fencing is used. Find the dimensions of the playground that maximize the total enclosed area. What is the maximum area?

71. A rain gutter is made from sheets of aluminum that are 20 inches wide by turning up the edges to form right angles. Determine the depth of the gutter that will maximize its cross-sectional area and allow the greatest amount of water to flow. What is the maximum cross-sectional area?

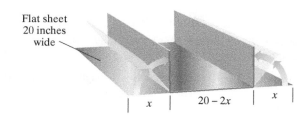

Flat sheet 20 inches wide

x $20 - 2x$ x

72. A rain gutter is made from sheets of aluminum that are 12 inches wide by turning up the edges to form right angles. Determine the depth of the gutter that will maximize its cross-sectional area and allow the greatest amount of water to flow. What is the maximum cross-sectional area?

73. Hunky Beef, a local sandwich store, has a fixed weekly cost of $525.00, and variable costs for making a roast beef sandwich are $0.55.

a. Let x represent the number of roast beef sandwiches made and sold each week. Write the weekly cost function, C, for Hunky Beef. (*Hint:* The cost function is the sum of fixed and variable costs.)

b. The function $R(x) = -0.001x^2 + 3x$ describes the money, in dollars, that Hunky Beef takes in each week from the sale of x roast beef sandwiches. Use this revenue function and the cost function from part (a) to write the store's weekly profit function, P. (*Hint:* The profit function is the difference between the revenue and cost functions.)

c. Use the store's profit function to determine the number of roast beef sandwiches it should make and sell each week to maximize profit. What is the maximum weekly profit?

Writing in Mathematics

74. What is a quadratic function?

75. What is a parabola? Describe its shape.

76. Explain how to decide whether a parabola opens upward or downward.

77. Describe how to find a parabola's vertex if its equation is expressed in standard form. Give an example.

78. Describe how to find a parabola's vertex if its equation is in the form $f(x) = ax^2 + bx + c$. Use $f(x) = x^2 - 6x + 8$ as an example.

79. A parabola that opens upward has its vertex at $(1, 2)$. Describe as much as you can about the parabola based on this information. Include in your discussion the number of x-intercepts (if any) for the parabola.

Technology Exercises

80. Use a graphing utility to verify any five of your hand-drawn graphs in Exercises 17–38.

81. a. Use a graphing utility to graph $y = 2x^2 - 82x + 720$ in a standard viewing rectangle. What do you observe?

b. Find the coordinates of the vertex for the given quadratic function.

c. The answer to part (b) is $(20.5, -120.5)$. Because the leading coefficient, 2, of the given function is positive, the vertex is a minimum point on the graph. Use this fact to help find a viewing rectangle that will give a relatively complete picture of the parabola. With an axis of symmetry at $x = 20.5$, the setting for x should extend past this, so try Xmin = 0 and Xmax = 30. The setting for y should include (and probably go below) the y-coordinate of the graph's minimum y-value, so try Ymin = -130. Experiment with Ymax until your utility shows the parabola's major features.

d. In general, explain how knowing the coordinates of a parabola's vertex can help determine a reasonable viewing rectangle on a graphing utility for obtaining a complete picture of the parabola.

In Exercises 82–85, find the vertex for each parabola. Then determine a reasonable viewing rectangle on your graphing utility and use it to graph the quadratic function.

82. $y = -0.25x^2 + 40x$

83. $y = -4x^2 + 20x + 160$

84. $y = 5x^2 + 40x + 600$

85. $y = 0.01x^2 + 0.6x + 100$

86. The bar graph shows the ratings of *American Idol* from season 1 (2002) through season 9 (2010).

American Idol: Each Season's Champion and Average Number of Viewers

Source: Nielsen

a. Let *x* represent *American Idol's* season number and let *y* represent the average number of viewers, in millions. Use a graphing utility to draw a scatter plot of the data. Explain why a quadratic function is appropriate for modeling these data.

b. Use the quadratic regression feature to find the quadratic function that best fits the data. Round all numbers to two decimal places.

c. Use the model in part (b) to determine the season in which *American Idol* had the greatest number of viewers. Round to the nearest whole number. According to the model, how many millions of viewers were there in that season? Round to one decimal place.

d. How do the results obtained from the model in part (c) compare with the data displayed by the graph?

e. Use a graphing utility to draw a scatter plot of the data and graph the quadratic function of best fit on the scatter plot. Can you see why projections based on the graph have the producers of *American Idol* looking for a shake-up?

Critical Thinking Exercises

Make Sense? *In Exercises 87–90, determine whether each statement makes sense or does not make sense, and explain your reasoning.*

87. I must have made an error when graphing this parabola because its axis of symmetry is the *y*-axis.

88. I like to think of a parabola's vertex as the point where it intersects its axis of symmetry.

89. I threw a baseball vertically upward and its path was a parabola.

90. **Figure 3.7** on page 338 shows that a linear function provides a better description of the football's path than a quadratic function.

In Exercises 91–94, determine whether each statement is true or false. If the statement is false, make the necessary change(s) to produce a true statement.

91. No quadratic functions have a range of $(-\infty, \infty)$.

92. The vertex of the parabola described by $f(x) = 2(x - 5)^2 - 1$ is at $(5, 1)$.

93. The graph of $f(x) = -2(x + 4)^2 - 8$ has one *y*-intercept and two *x*-intercepts.

94. The maximum value of *y* for the quadratic function $f(x) = -x^2 + x + 1$ is 1.

In Exercises 95–96, find the axis of symmetry for each parabola whose equation is given. Use the axis of symmetry to find a second point on the parabola whose y-coordinate is the same as the given point.

95. $f(x) = 3(x + 2)^2 - 5;$ $(-1, -2)$

96. $f(x) = (x - 3)^2 + 2;$ $(6, 11)$

In Exercises 97–98, write the equation of each parabola in standard form.

97. Vertex: $(-3, -4);$ The graph passes through the point $(1, 4)$.

98. Vertex: $(-3, -1);$ The graph passes through the point $(-2, -3)$.

99. A rancher has 1000 feet of fencing to construct six corrals, as shown in the figure. Find the dimensions that maximize the enclosed area. What is the maximum area?

100. The annual yield per lemon tree is fairly constant at 320 pounds when the number of trees per acre is 50 or fewer. For each additional tree over 50, the annual yield per tree for all trees on the acre decreases by 4 pounds due to overcrowding. Find the number of trees that should be planted on an acre to produce the maximum yield. How many pounds is the maximum yield?

Group Exercise

101. Each group member should consult an almanac, newspaper, magazine, or the Internet to find data that initially increase and then decrease, or vice versa, and therefore can be modeled by a quadratic function. Group members should select the two sets of data that are most interesting and relevant. For each data set selected,

    a. Use the quadratic regression feature of a graphing utility to find the quadratic function that best fits the data.

    b. Use the equation of the quadratic function to make a prediction from the data. What circumstances might affect the accuracy of your prediction?

    c. Use the equation of the quadratic function to write and solve a problem involving maximizing or minimizing the function.

Preview Exercises

Exercises 102–104 will help you prepare for the material covered in the next section.

102. Factor: $x^3 + 3x^2 - x - 3$.

103. If $f(x) = x^3 - 2x - 5$, find $f(2)$ and $f(3)$. Then explain why the continuous graph of f must cross the x-axis between 2 and 3.

104. Determine whether $f(x) = x^4 - 2x^2 + 1$ is even, odd, or neither. Describe the symmetry, if any, for the graph of f.

SECTION 3.2

Polynomial Functions and Their Graphs

Objectives

1. Identify polynomial functions.
2. Recognize characteristics of graphs of polynomial functions.
3. Determine end behavior.
4. Use factoring to find zeros of polynomial functions.
5. Identify zeros and their multiplicities.
6. Use the Intermediate Value Theorem.
7. Understand the relationship between degree and turning points.
8. Graph polynomial functions.

In 1980, U.S. doctors diagnosed 41 cases of a rare form of cancer, Kaposi's sarcoma, that involved skin lesions, pneumonia, and severe immunological deficiencies. All cases involved gay men ranging in age from 26 to 51. By the end of 2008, approximately 1.1 million Americans, straight and gay, male and female, old and young, were infected with the HIV virus.

Modeling AIDS-related data and making predictions about the epidemic's havoc is serious business. **Figure 3.11** on the next page shows the number of AIDS cases diagnosed in the United States from 1983 through 2008.

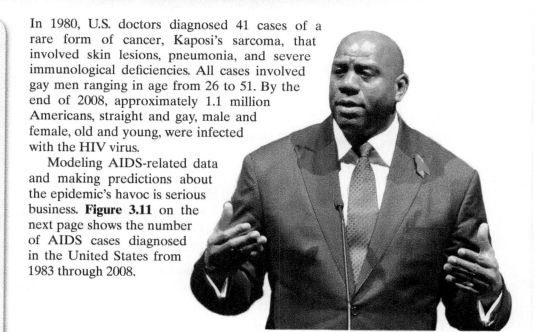

Basketball player Magic Johnson (1959–   ) tested positive for HIV in 1991.

AIDS Cases Diagnosed in the United States, 1983–2008

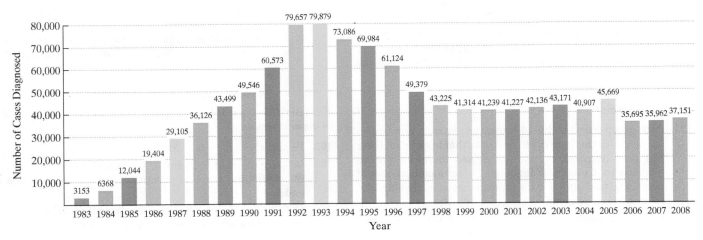

FIGURE 3.11
Source: Department of Health and Human Services

① Identify polynomial functions.

Changing circumstances and unforeseen events can result in models for AIDS-related data that are not particularly useful over long periods of time. For example, the function

$$f(x) = -49x^3 + 806x^2 + 3776x + 2503$$

models the number of AIDS cases diagnosed in the United States x years after 1983. The model was obtained using a portion of the data shown in **Figure 3.11**, namely cases diagnosed from 1983 through 1991, inclusive. **Figure 3.12** shows the graph of f from 1983 through 1991. This function is an example of a *polynomial function of degree 3*.

$f(x) = -49x^3 + 806x^2 + 3776x + 2503$

Years after 1983
$[0, 8, 1]$ by $[0, 60,000, 5000]$

FIGURE 3.12 The graph of a function modeling the number of AIDS diagnoses from 1983 through 1991

Definition of a Polynomial Function

Let n be a nonnegative integer and let $a_n, a_{n-1}, \ldots, a_2, a_1, a_0$ be real numbers, with $a_n \neq 0$. The function defined by

$$f(x) = a_n x^n + a_{n-1} x^{n-1} + \cdots + a_2 x^2 + a_1 x + a_0$$

is called a **polynomial function of degree n**. The number a_n, the coefficient of the variable to the highest power, is called the **leading coefficient**.

Polynomial Functions

$$f(x) = -3x^5 + \sqrt{2}x^2 + 5$$

Polynomial function of degree 5

$$g(x) = -3x^4(x - 2)(x + 3)$$
$$= -3x^4(x^2 + x - 6)$$
$$= -3x^6 - 3x^5 + 18x^4$$

Polynomial function of degree 6

Not Polynomial Functions

$$F(x) = -3\sqrt{x} + \sqrt{2}x^2 + 5$$
$$= -3x^{\frac{1}{2}} + \sqrt{2}x^2 + 5$$

The exponent on the variable is not an integer.

$$G(x) = -\frac{3}{x^2} + \sqrt{2}x^2 + 5$$
$$= -3x^{-2} + \sqrt{2}x^2 + 5$$

The exponent on the variable is not a nonnegative integer.

A constant function $f(x) = c$, where $c \neq 0$, is a polynomial function of degree 0. A linear function $f(x) = mx + b$, where $m \neq 0$, is a polynomial function of degree 1. A quadratic function $f(x) = ax^2 + bx + c$, where $a \neq 0$, is a polynomial function of degree 2. In this section, we focus on polynomial functions of degree 3 or higher.

② Recognize characteristics of graphs of polynomial functions.

Smooth, Continuous Graphs

Polynomial functions of degree 2 or higher have graphs that are *smooth* and *continuous*. By **smooth**, we mean that the graphs contain only rounded curves with no sharp corners. By **continuous**, we mean that the graphs have no breaks and can be drawn without lifting your pencil from the rectangular coordinate system. These ideas are illustrated in **Figure 3.13**.

Graphs of Polynomial Functions

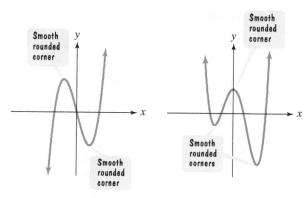

Not Graphs of Polynomial Functions

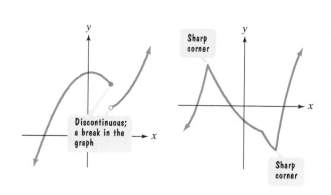

FIGURE 3.13 Recognizing graphs of polynomial functions

③ Determine end behavior.

Years after 1983

$[0, 22, 1]$ by $[-10{,}000, 85{,}000, 5000]$

FIGURE 3.14 By extending the viewing rectangle, we see that y is eventually negative and the function no longer models the number of AIDS cases.

End Behavior of Polynomial Functions

Figure 3.14 shows the graph of the function

$$f(x) = -49x^3 + 806x^2 + 3776x + 2503,$$

which models the number of U.S. AIDS diagnoses from 1983 through 1991. Look what happens to the graph when we extend the year up through 2005. By year 21 (2004), the values of y are negative and the function no longer models AIDS diagnoses. We've added an arrow to the graph at the far right to emphasize that it continues to decrease without bound. It is this far-right *end behavior* of the graph that makes it inappropriate for modeling AIDS cases into the future.

The behavior of the graph of a function to the far left or the far right is called its **end behavior**. Although the graph of a polynomial function may have intervals where it increases or decreases, the graph will eventually rise or fall without bound as it moves far to the left or far to the right.

How can you determine whether the graph of a polynomial function goes up or down at each end? The end behavior of a polynomial function

$$f(x) = a_n x^n + a_{n-1} x^{n-1} + \cdots + a_1 x + a_0$$

depends upon the leading term $a_n x^n$, because when $|x|$ is large, the other terms are relatively insignificant in size. In particular, the sign of the leading coefficient, a_n, and the degree, n, of the polynomial function reveal its end behavior. In terms of end behavior, only the term of highest degree counts, as summarized by the **Leading Coefficient Test**.

The Leading Coefficient Test

As x increases or decreases without bound, the graph of the polynomial function

$$f(x) = a_n x^n + a_{n-1} x^{n-1} + a_{n-2} x^{n-2} + \cdots + a_1 x + a_0 \quad (a_n \neq 0)$$

eventually rises or falls. In particular,

1. For n odd:

If the leading coefficient is positive, the graph falls to the left and rises to the right. ($\swarrow$, $\nearrow$)

$a_n > 0$

Rises right

Falls left

Odd degree; positive leading coefficient

If the leading coefficient is negative, the graph rises to the left and falls to the right. ($\nwarrow$, $\searrow$)

$a_n < 0$

Rises left

Falls right

Odd degree; negative leading coefficient

2. For n even:

If the leading coefficient is positive, the graph rises to the left and rises to the right. ($\nwarrow$, $\nearrow$)

$a_n > 0$

Rises right

Rises left

Even degree; positive leading coefficient

If the leading coefficient is negative, the graph falls to the left and falls to the right. ($\swarrow$, $\searrow$)

$a_n < 0$

Falls left

Falls right

Even degree; negative leading coefficient

DISCOVERY

Verify each of the four cases of the Leading Coefficient Test by using a graphing utility to graph $f(x) = x^3$, $f(x) = -x^3$, $f(x) = x^2$, and $f(x) = -x^2$.

GREAT QUESTION!

What's the bottom line on the Leading Coefficient Test?

Odd-degree polynomial functions have graphs with opposite behavior at each end. Even-degree polynomial functions have graphs with the same behavior at each end. Here's a table to help you remember the details:

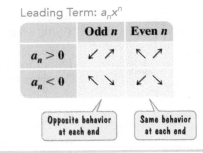

Leading Term: $a_n x^n$

	Odd n	Even n
$a_n > 0$	$\swarrow \nearrow$	$\nwarrow \nearrow$
$a_n < 0$	$\nwarrow \searrow$	$\swarrow \searrow$

Opposite behavior at each end   Same behavior at each end

EXAMPLE 1   Using the Leading Coefficient Test

Use the Leading Coefficient Test to determine the end behavior of the graph of

$$f(x) = x^3 + 3x^2 - x - 3.$$

SOLUTION

We begin by identifying the sign of the leading coefficient and the degree of the polynomial.

$$f(x) = x^3 + 3x^2 - x - 3$$

The leading coefficient, 1, is positive.   The degree of the polynomial, 3, is odd.

FIGURE 3.15 The graph of $f(x) = x^3 + 3x^2 - x - 3$

The degree of the function f is 3, which is odd. Odd-degree polynomial functions have graphs with opposite behavior at each end. The leading coefficient, 1, is positive. Thus, the graph falls to the left and rises to the right ($\swarrow$, $\nearrow$). The graph of f is shown in **Figure 3.15**.　• • •

Check Point 1 Use the Leading Coefficient Test to determine the end behavior of the graph of $f(x) = x^4 - 4x^2$.

EXAMPLE 2　Using the Leading Coefficient Test

Use the Leading Coefficient Test to determine the end behavior of the graph of

$$f(x) = -4x^3(x - 1)^2(x + 5).$$

SOLUTION

Although the equation for f is in factored form, it is not necessary to multiply to determine the degree of the function.

$$f(x) = -4x^3(x - 1)^2(x + 5)$$

Degree of this factor is **3**.　Degree of this factor is **2**.　Degree of this factor is **1**.

When multiplying exponential expressions with the same base, we add the exponents. This means that the degree of f is $3 + 2 + 1$, or 6, which is even. Even-degree polynomial functions have graphs with the same behavior at each end. Without multiplying out, you can see that the leading coefficient is -4, which is negative. Thus, the graph of f falls to the left and falls to the right ($\swarrow$, $\searrow$).　• • •

Check Point 2 Use the Leading Coefficient Test to determine the end behavior of the graph of $f(x) = 2x^3(x - 1)(x + 5)$.

EXAMPLE 3　Using the Leading Coefficient Test

Use end behavior to explain why

$$f(x) = -49x^3 + 806x^2 + 3776x + 2503$$

is only an appropriate model for AIDS diagnoses for a limited time period.

SOLUTION

We begin by identifying the sign of the leading coefficient and the degree of the polynomial.

$$f(x) = -49x^3 + 806x^2 + 3776x + 2503$$

The leading coefficient, -49, is negative.　The degree of the polynomial, **3**, is odd.

The degree of f is 3, which is odd. Odd-degree polynomial functions have graphs with opposite behavior at each end. The leading coefficient, -49, is negative. Thus, the graph rises to the left and falls to the right ($\nwarrow$, $\searrow$). The fact that the graph falls to the right indicates that at some point the number of AIDS diagnoses will be negative, an impossibility. If a function has a graph that decreases without bound over time, it will not be capable of modeling nonnegative phenomena over long time periods. Model breakdown will eventually occur.　• • •

⌀ Check Point **3** The polynomial function

$$f(x) = -0.27x^3 + 9.2x^2 - 102.9x + 400$$

models the ratio of students to computers in U.S. public schools x years after 1980. Use end behavior to determine whether this function could be an appropriate model for computers in the classroom well into the twenty-first century. Explain your answer.

If you use a graphing utility to graph a polynomial function, it is important to select a viewing rectangle that accurately reveals the graph's end behavior. If the viewing rectangle, or window, is too small, it may not accurately show a complete graph with the appropriate end behavior.

EXAMPLE 4   Using the Leading Coefficient Test

The graph of $f(x) = -x^4 + 8x^3 + 4x^2 + 2$ was obtained with a graphing utility using a $[-8, 8, 1]$ by $[-10, 10, 1]$ viewing rectangle. The graph is shown in **Figure 3.16**. Is this a complete graph that shows the end behavior of the function?

SOLUTION

We begin by identifying the sign of the leading coefficient and the degree of the polynomial.

$$f(x) = -x^4 + 8x^3 + 4x^2 + 2$$

The leading coefficient, −1, is negative.   The degree of the polynomial, 4, is even.

The degree of f is 4, which is even. Even-degree polynomial functions have graphs with the same behavior at each end. The leading coefficient, −1, is negative. Thus, the graph should fall to the left and fall to the right ($\swarrow$, $\searrow$). The graph in **Figure 3.16** is falling to the left, but it is not falling to the right. Therefore, the graph is not complete enough to show end behavior. A more complete graph of the function is shown in a larger viewing rectangle in **Figure 3.17**.   ● ● ●

⌀ Check Point **4** The graph of $f(x) = x^3 + 13x^2 + 10x - 4$ is shown in a standard viewing rectangle in **Figure 3.18**. Use the Leading Coefficient Test to determine whether this is a complete graph that shows the end behavior of the function. Explain your answer.

$[-8, 8, 1]$ by $[-10, 10, 1]$

FIGURE 3.16

$[-10, 10, 1]$ by $[-1000, 750, 250]$

FIGURE 3.17

$[-8, 8, 1]$ by $[-10, 10, 1]$

FIGURE 3.18

④ Use factoring to find zeros of polynomial functions.

Zeros of Polynomial Functions

If f is a polynomial function, then the values of x for which $f(x)$ is equal to 0 are called the **zeros** of f. These values of x are the **roots**, or **solutions**, of the polynomial equation $f(x) = 0$. Each real root of the polynomial equation appears as an x-intercept of the graph of the polynomial function.

EXAMPLE 5   Finding Zeros of a Polynomial Function

Find all zeros of $f(x) = x^3 + 3x^2 - x - 3$.

SOLUTION

By definition, the zeros are the values of x for which $f(x)$ is equal to 0. Thus, we set $f(x)$ equal to 0:

$$f(x) = x^3 + 3x^2 - x - 3 = 0.$$

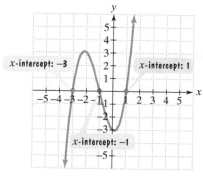

FIGURE 3.19

We solve the polynomial equation $x^3 + 3x^2 - x - 3 = 0$ for x as follows:

$$x^3 + 3x^2 - x - 3 = 0 \qquad \text{This is the equation needed to find the function's zeros.}$$

$$x^2(x + 3) - 1(x + 3) = 0 \qquad \text{Factor } x^2 \text{ from the first two terms and } -1 \text{ from the last two terms.}$$

$$(x + 3)(x^2 - 1) = 0 \qquad \text{A common factor of } x + 3 \text{ is factored from the expression.}$$

$$x + 3 = 0 \quad \text{or} \quad x^2 - 1 = 0 \qquad \text{Set each factor equal to 0.}$$

$$x = -3 \qquad\qquad x^2 = 1 \qquad \text{Solve for } x.$$

$$x = \pm 1 \qquad \text{Remember that if } x^2 = d, \text{ then } x = \pm\sqrt{d}.$$

The zeros of f are -3, -1, and 1. The graph of f in **Figure 3.19** shows that each zero is an x-intercept. The graph passes through the points $(-3, 0)$, $(-1, 0)$, and $(1, 0)$. • • •

TECHNOLOGY

Graphic and Numeric Connections

A graphing utility can be used to verify that -3, -1, and 1 are the three real zeros of $f(x) = x^3 + 3x^2 - x - 3$.

Numeric Check

Display a table for the function.

Graphic Check

Display a graph for the function. The x-intercepts indicate that -3, -1, and 1 are the real zeros.

$[-6, 6, 1]$ by $[-6, 6, 1]$

The utility's $\boxed{\text{ZERO}}$ feature on the graph of f also verifies that -3, -1, and 1 are the function's real zeros.

$\oslash$ Check Point **5** Find all zeros of $f(x) = x^3 + 2x^2 - 4x - 8$.

EXAMPLE 6 Finding Zeros of a Polynomial Function

Find all zeros of $f(x) = -x^4 + 4x^3 - 4x^2$.

SOLUTION

We find the zeros of f by setting $f(x)$ equal to 0 and solving the resulting equation.

$$-x^4 + 4x^3 - 4x^2 = 0 \qquad \text{We now have a polynomial equation.}$$

$$x^4 - 4x^3 + 4x^2 = 0 \qquad \text{Multiply both sides by } -1. \text{ This step is optional.}$$

$$x^2(x^2 - 4x + 4) = 0 \qquad \text{Factor out } x^2.$$

$$x^2(x - 2)^2 = 0 \qquad \text{Factor completely.}$$

$$x^2 = 0 \quad \text{or} \quad (x - 2)^2 = 0 \qquad \text{Set each factor equal to 0.}$$

$$x = 0 \qquad\qquad x = 2 \qquad \text{Solve for } x.$$

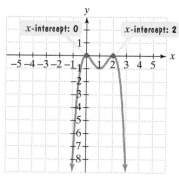

FIGURE 3.20 The zeros of $f(x) = -x^4 + 4x^3 - 4x^2$, namely 0 and 2, are the x-intercepts for the graph of f.

The zeros of $f(x) = -x^4 + 4x^3 - 4x^2$ are 0 and 2. The graph of f, shown in **Figure 3.20**, has x-intercepts at 0 and 2. The graph passes through the points $(0, 0)$ and $(2, 0)$. • • •

⌀ Check Point **6** Find all zeros of $f(x) = x^4 - 4x^2$.

GREAT QUESTION!

Can zeros of polynomial functions always be found using one or more of the factoring techniques that were reviewed in Section P.5?

No. You'll be learning additional strategies for finding zeros of polynomial functions in the next two sections of this chapter.

⑤ Identify zeros and their multiplicities.

Multiplicities of Zeros

We can use the results of factoring to express a polynomial as a product of factors. For instance, in Example 6, we can use our factoring to express the function's equation as follows:

$$f(x) = -x^4 + 4x^3 - 4x^2 = -(x^4 - 4x^3 + 4x^2) = -x^2(x - 2)^2.$$

The factor x occurs twice: $x^2 = x \cdot x.$

The factor $(x - 2)$ occurs twice: $(x - 2)^2 = (x - 2)(x - 2).$

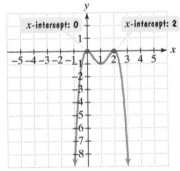

FIGURE 3.20 (repeated) The graph of $f(x) = -x^4 + 4x^3 - 4x^2$

Notice that each factor occurs twice. In factoring the equation for the polynomial function f, if the same factor $x - r$ occurs k times, but not $k + 1$ times, we call r a **zero with multiplicity k**. For the polynomial function

$$f(x) = -x^2(x - 2)^2,$$

0 and 2 are both zeros with multiplicity 2.

Multiplicity provides another connection between zeros and graphs. The multiplicity of a zero tells us whether the graph of a polynomial function touches the x-axis at the zero and turns around or if the graph crosses the x-axis at the zero. For example, look again at the graph of $f(x) = -x^4 + 4x^3 - 4x^2$ in **Figure 3.20**. Each zero, 0 and 2, is a zero with multiplicity 2. The graph of f touches, but does not cross, the x-axis at each of these zeros of even multiplicity. By contrast, a graph crosses the x-axis at zeros of odd multiplicity.

Multiplicity and x-Intercepts

If r is a zero of **even multiplicity**, then the graph **touches** the x-axis **and turns around** at r. If r is a zero of **odd multiplicity**, then the graph **crosses** the x-axis at r. Regardless of whether the multiplicity of a zero is even or odd, graphs tend to flatten out near zeros with multiplicity greater than one.

GREAT QUESTION!

If r is a zero of even multiplicity, how come the graph of f doesn't just cross the x-axis at r?

Because r is a zero of even multiplicity, the sign of $f(x)$ does not change from one side of r to the other side of r. This means that the graph must turn around at r. On the other hand, if r is a zero of odd multiplicity, the sign of $f(x)$ changes from one side of r to the other side. That's why the graph crosses the x-axis at r.

If a polynomial function's equation is expressed as a product of linear factors, we can quickly identify zeros and their multiplicities.

EXAMPLE 7 Finding Zeros and Their Multiplicities

Find the zeros of $f(x) = \frac{1}{2}(x + 1)(2x - 3)^2$ and give the multiplicity of each zero. State whether the graph crosses the x-axis or touches the x-axis and turns around at each zero.

SOLUTION

We find the zeros of f by setting $f(x)$ equal to 0:

$$\tfrac{1}{2}(x + 1)(2x - 3)^2 = 0.$$

Set each variable factor equal to 0.

$$x + 1 = 0 \qquad 2x - 3 = 0$$
$$x = -1 \qquad x = \frac{3}{2}$$

$$\frac{1}{2}(x + 1)^1(2x - 3)^2 = 0$$

This exponent is 1. Thus, the multiplicity of −1 is 1.

This exponent is 2. Thus, the multiplicity of $\frac{3}{2}$ is 2.

−1 is a zero of odd multiplicity. Graph crosses x-axis.

$\frac{3}{2}$ is a zero of even multiplicity. Graph touches x-axis, flattens, and turns around.

$[-3, 3, 1]$ by $[-10, 10, 1]$

FIGURE 3.21 The graph of $f(x) = \frac{1}{2}(x + 1)(2x - 3)^2$

The zeros of $f(x) = \frac{1}{2}(x + 1)(2x - 3)^2$ are −1, with multiplicity 1, and $\frac{3}{2}$, with multiplicity 2. Because the multiplicity of −1 is odd, the graph crosses the x-axis at this zero. Because the multiplicity of $\frac{3}{2}$ is even, the graph touches the x-axis and turns around at this zero. These relationships are illustrated by the graph of f in **Figure 3.21**.

• • •

Check Point **7** Find the zeros of $f(x) = -4\left(x + \frac{1}{2}\right)^2(x - 5)^3$ and give the multiplicity of each zero. State whether the graph crosses the x-axis or touches the x-axis and turns around at each zero.

⑥ Use the Intermediate Value Theorem.

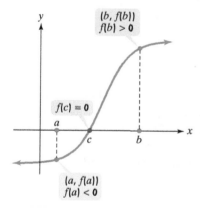

FIGURE 3.22 The graph must cross the x-axis at some value between a and b.

The Intermediate Value Theorem

The *Intermediate Value Theorem* tells us of the existence of real zeros. The idea behind the theorem is illustrated in **Figure 3.22**. The figure shows that if $(a, f(a))$ lies below the x-axis and $(b, f(b))$ lies above the x-axis, the smooth, continuous graph of the polynomial function f must cross the x-axis at some value c between a and b. This value is a real zero for the function.

These observations are summarized in the **Intermediate Value Theorem**.

The Intermediate Value Theorem for Polynomial Functions

Let f be a polynomial function with real coefficients. If $f(a)$ and $f(b)$ have opposite signs, then there is at least one value of c between a and b for which $f(c) = 0$. Equivalently, the equation $f(x) = 0$ has at least one real root between a and b.

EXAMPLE 8 Using the Intermediate Value Theorem

Show that the polynomial function $f(x) = x^3 - 2x - 5$ has a real zero between 2 and 3.

SOLUTION

Let us evaluate f at 2 and at 3. If $f(2)$ and $f(3)$ have opposite signs, then there is at least one real zero between 2 and 3. Using $f(x) = x^3 - 2x - 5$, we obtain

$$f(2) = 2^3 - 2 \cdot 2 - 5 = 8 - 4 - 5 = -1$$

$f(2)$ is negative.

and

$$f(3) = 3^3 - 2 \cdot 3 - 5 = 27 - 6 - 5 = 16.$$

$f(3)$ is positive.

$y = x^3 - 2x - 5$

Zero
X=2.0945515 Y=0

$[-3, 3, 1]$ by $[-10, 10, 1]$

FIGURE 3.23

Because $f(2) = -1$ and $f(3) = 16$, the sign change shows that the polynomial function has a real zero between 2 and 3. This zero is actually irrational and is approximated using a graphing utility's ZERO feature as 2.0945515 in **Figure 3.23**.

• • •

⏀ Check Point **8** Show that the polynomial function $f(x) = 3x^3 - 10x + 9$ has a real zero between -3 and -2.

⑦ Understand the relationship between degree and turning points.

FIGURE 3.24 Graph with four turning points

⑧ Graph polynomial functions.

Turning Points of Polynomial Functions

The graph of $f(x) = x^5 - 6x^3 + 8x + 1$ is shown in **Figure 3.24**. The graph has four smooth **turning points**.

At each turning point in **Figure 3.24**, the graph changes direction from increasing to decreasing or vice versa. The given equation has 5 as its greatest exponent and is therefore a polynomial function of degree 5. Notice that the graph has four turning points. In general, **if f is a polynomial function of degree n, then the graph of f has at most $n - 1$ turning points.**

Figure 3.24 illustrates that the y-coordinate of each turning point is either a relative maximum or a relative minimum of f. Without the aid of a graphing utility or a knowledge of calculus, it is difficult and often impossible to locate turning points of polynomial functions with degrees greater than 2. If necessary, test values can be taken between the x-intercepts to get a general idea of how high the graph rises or how low the graph falls. For the purpose of graphing in this section, a general estimate is sometimes appropriate and necessary.

A Strategy for Graphing Polynomial Functions

Here's a general strategy for graphing a polynomial function. A graphing utility is a valuable complement, but not a necessary component, to this strategy. If you are using a graphing utility, some of the steps listed in the following box will help you to select a viewing rectangle that shows the important parts of the graph.

Graphing a Polynomial Function
$$f(x) = a_n x^n + a_{n-1} x^{n-1} + a_{n-2} x^{n-2} + \cdots + a_1 x + a_0, a_n \neq 0$$

1. Use the Leading Coefficient Test to determine the graph's end behavior.
2. Find x-intercepts by setting $f(x) = 0$ and solving the resulting polynomial equation. If there is an x-intercept at r as a result of $(x - r)^k$ in the complete factorization of $f(x)$, then
   a. If k is even, the graph touches the x-axis at r and turns around.
   b. If k is odd, the graph crosses the x-axis at r.
   c. If $k > 1$, the graph flattens out near $(r, 0)$.
3. Find the y-intercept by computing $f(0)$.
4. Use symmetry, if applicable, to help draw the graph:
   a. y-axis symmetry: $f(-x) = f(x)$
   b. Origin symmetry: $f(-x) = -f(x)$.
5. Use the fact that the maximum number of turning points of the graph is $n - 1$, where n is the degree of the polynomial function, to check whether it is drawn correctly.

GREAT QUESTION!

When graphing a polynomial function, how do I determine the location of its turning points?

Without calculus, it is often impossible to give the exact location of turning points. However, you can obtain additional points satisfying the function to estimate how high the graph rises or how low it falls. To obtain these points, use values of x between (and to the left and right of) the x-intercepts.

EXAMPLE 9 Graphing a Polynomial Function

Graph: $f(x) = x^4 - 2x^2 + 1$.

SOLUTION

Step 1   Determine end behavior. Identify the sign of a_n, the leading coefficient, and the degree, n, of the polynomial function.

Rises left   Rises right

$$f(x) = x^4 - 2x^2 + 1$$

The leading coefficient, 1, is positive.   The degree of the polynomial function, 4, is even.

Because the degree, 4, is even, the graph has the same behavior at each end. The leading coefficient, 1, is positive. Thus, the graph rises to the left and rises to the right.

Step 2   Find *x*-intercepts (zeros of the function) by setting *f*(*x*) = 0.

$$
\begin{aligned}
x^4 - 2x^2 + 1 &= 0 & &\text{Set } f(x) \text{ equal to 0.} \\
(x^2 - 1)(x^2 - 1) &= 0 & &\text{Factor.} \\
(x + 1)(x - 1)(x + 1)(x - 1) &= 0 & &\text{Factor completely.} \\
(x + 1)^2(x - 1)^2 &= 0 & &\text{Express the factorization in a more} \\
& & &\text{compact form.} \\
(x + 1)^2 = 0 \quad \text{or} \quad (x - 1)^2 &= 0 & &\text{Set each factorization equal to 0.} \\
x = -1 \qquad\qquad x &= 1 & &\text{Solve for x.}
\end{aligned}
$$

We see that -1 and 1 are both repeated zeros with multiplicity 2. Because of the even multiplicity, the graph touches the *x*-axis at -1 and 1 and turns around. Furthermore, the graph tends to flatten out near these zeros with multiplicity greater than one.

Rises left   Rises right
-1 1

Step 3   Find the *y*-intercept by computing *f*(0). We use $f(x) = x^4 - 2x^2 + 1$ and compute $f(0)$.

$$f(0) = 0^4 - 2 \cdot 0^2 + 1 = 1$$

There is a *y*-intercept at 1, so the graph passes through $(0, 1)$.

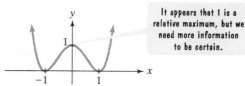

It appears that 1 is a relative maximum, but we need more information to be certain.

-1 1

Step 4   Use possible symmetry to help draw the graph. Our partial graph suggests *y*-axis symmetry. Let's verify this by finding $f(-x)$.

$$f(x) = x^4 - 2x^2 + 1$$

Replace *x* with $-x$.

$$f(-x) = (-x)^4 - 2(-x)^2 + 1 = x^4 - 2x^2 + 1$$

FIGURE 3.25 The graph of
$f(x) = x^4 - 2x^2 + 1$

Because $f(-x) = f(x)$, the graph of f is symmetric with respect to the *y*-axis. **Figure 3.25** shows the graph of $f(x) = x^4 - 2x^2 + 1$.

Step 5   Use the fact that the maximum number of turning points of the graph is *n* − 1 to check whether it is drawn correctly. Because $n = 4$, the maximum number of turning points is $4 - 1$, or 3. Because the graph in **Figure 3.25** has three turning points, we have not violated the maximum number possible. Can you see how this verifies that 1 is indeed a relative maximum and $(0, 1)$ is a turning point? If the graph rose above 1 on either side of $x = 0$, it would have to rise above 1 on the other side as well because of symmetry. This would require additional turning points to smoothly curve back to the *x*-intercepts. The graph already has three turning points, which is the maximum number for a fourth-degree polynomial function.

● ● ●

☑ Check Point **9** Use the five-step strategy to graph $f(x) = x^3 - 3x^2$.

EXAMPLE 10 Graphing a Polynomial Function

Graph: $f(x) = -2(x - 1)^2(x + 2)$.

SOLUTION

Step 1 Determine end behavior. Identify the sign of a_n, the leading coefficient, and the degree, n, of the polynomial function.

$$f(x) = \underbrace{-2(x - 1)^2(x + 2)}$$

The leading term is $-2x^2 \cdot x$, or $-2x^3$.

| The leading coefficient, −2, is negative. | The degree of the polynomial function, 3, is odd. |

Because the degree, 3, is odd, the graph has opposite behavior at each end. The leading coefficient, −2, is negative. Thus, the graph rises to the left and falls to the right.

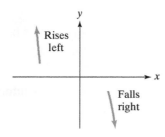

Step 2 Find x-intercepts (zeros of the function) by setting $f(x) = 0$.

$-2(x - 1)^2(x + 2) = 0$	Set $f(x)$ equal to 0.
$(x - 1)^2 = 0$ or $x + 2 = 0$	Set each variable factor equal to 0.
$x = 1$ $x = -2$	Solve for x.

We see that the zeros are 1 and −2. The multiplicity of 1 is even, so the graph touches the x-axis at 1, flattens, and turns around. The multiplicity of −2 is odd, so the graph crosses the x-axis at −2.

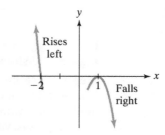

Step 3 Find the y-intercept by computing $f(0)$. We use $f(x) = -2(x - 1)^2(x + 2)$ and compute $f(0)$.

$$f(0) = -2(0 - 1)^2(0 + 2) = -2(1)(2) = -4$$

There is a *y*-intercept at −4, so the graph passes through (0, −4).

We're not sure about the graph's behavior for x between −2 and 0 or between 0 and 1. Additional points will be helpful. Furthermore, we may need to rescale the y-axis.

Based on the note in the voice balloon, let's evaluate the function at −1.5, −1, −0.5, and 0.5, as well as at −3, 2, and 3.

x	−3	−1.5	−1	−0.5	0.5	2	3
$f(x) = -2(x - 1)^2(x + 2)$	32	−6.25	−8	−6.75	−1.25	−8	−40

In order to accommodate these points, we'll scale the *y*-axis from −50 to 50, with each tick mark representing 10 units.

Step 4 Use possible symmetry to help draw the graph. Our partial graph illustrates that we have neither *y*-axis symmetry nor origin symmetry. Using end behavior, intercepts, and the points from our table, **Figure 3.26** shows the graph of $f(x) = -2(x - 1)^2(x + 2)$.

We cannot be sure about the exact location of this turning point. (Yes, your author is certain there's a relative minimum at −1: He took calculus!)

FIGURE 3.26 The graph of $f(x) = -2(x - 1)^2(x + 2)$

Step 5 Use the fact that the maximum number of turning points of the graph is *n* − 1 to check whether it is drawn correctly. The leading term is $-2x^3$, so $n = 3$. The maximum number of turning points is $3 - 1$, or 2. Because the graph in **Figure 3.26** has two turning points, we have not violated the maximum number possible.   • • •

⬯ Check Point **10** Use the five-step strategy to graph
$f(x) = 2(x + 2)^2(x - 3)$.

CONCEPT AND VOCABULARY CHECK

Fill in each blank so that the resulting statement is true.

1. The degree of the polynomial function $f(x) = -2x^3(x - 1)(x + 5)$ is _____. The leading coefficient is _____.

2. True or false: Some polynomial functions of degree 2 or higher have breaks in their graphs. _____

3. The behavior of the graph of a polynomial function to the far left or the far right is called its _____ behavior, which depends upon the _____ term.

4. The graph of $f(x) = x^3$ _____ to the left and _____ to the right.

5. The graph of $f(x) = -x^3$ _____ to the left and _____ to the right.

6. The graph of $f(x) = x^2$ _____ to the left and _____ to the right.

7. The graph of $f(x) = -x^2$ _____ to the left and _____ to the right.

8. True or false: Odd-degree polynomial functions have graphs with opposite behavior at each end. _____

9. True or false: Even-degree polynomial functions have graphs with the same behavior at each end. _____

10. Every real zero of a polynomial function appears as a/an _____ of the graph.

11. If r is a zero of even multiplicity, then the graph touches the x-axis and _____ at r. If r is a zero of odd multiplicity, then the graph _____ the x-axis at r.

12. If f is a polynomial function and $f(a)$ and $f(b)$ have opposite signs, then there must be at least one value of c between a and b for which $f(c) =$ _____. This result is called the _____ Theorem.

13. If f is a polynomial function of degree n, then the graph of f has at most _____ turning points.

EXERCISE SET 3.2

Practice Exercises

In Exercises 1–10, determine which functions are polynomial functions. For those that are, identify the degree.

1. $f(x) = 5x^2 + 6x^3$

2. $f(x) = 7x^2 + 9x^4$

3. $g(x) = 7x^5 - \pi x^3 + \frac{1}{5}x$

4. $g(x) = 6x^7 + \pi x^5 + \frac{2}{3}x$

5. $h(x) = 7x^3 + 2x^2 + \frac{1}{x}$

6. $h(x) = 8x^3 - x^2 + \frac{2}{x}$

7. $f(x) = x^{\frac{1}{2}} - 3x^2 + 5$

8. $f(x) = x^{\frac{1}{3}} - 4x^2 + 7$

9. $f(x) = \dfrac{x^2 + 7}{x^3}$

10. $f(x) = \dfrac{x^2 + 7}{3}$

In Exercises 11–14, identify which graphs are not those of polynomial functions.

11.

12.

13.

14.

In Exercises 15–18, use the Leading Coefficient Test to determine the end behavior of the graph of the given polynomial function. Then use this end behavior to match the polynomial function with its graph. [The graphs are labeled (a) through (d).]

15. $f(x) = -x^4 + x^2$

16. $f(x) = x^3 - 4x^2$

17. $f(x) = (x - 3)^2$

18. $f(x) = -x^3 - x^2 + 5x - 3$

a.

b.

c.

d.

In Exercises 19–24, use the Leading Coefficient Test to determine the end behavior of the graph of the polynomial function.

19. $f(x) = 5x^3 + 7x^2 - x + 9$

20. $f(x) = 11x^3 - 6x^2 + x + 3$

21. $f(x) = 5x^4 + 7x^2 - x + 9$

22. $f(x) = 11x^4 - 6x^2 + x + 3$

23. $f(x) = -5x^4 + 7x^2 - x + 9$

24. $f(x) = -11x^4 - 6x^2 + x + 3$

In Exercises 25–32, find the zeros for each polynomial function and give the multiplicity for each zero. State whether the graph crosses the x-axis, or touches the x-axis and turns around, at each zero.

25. $f(x) = 2(x - 5)(x + 4)^2$

26. $f(x) = 3(x + 5)(x + 2)^2$

27. $f(x) = 4(x - 3)(x + 6)^3$

28. $f(x) = -3\left(x + \frac{1}{2}\right)(x - 4)^3$

29. $f(x) = x^3 - 2x^2 + x$

30. $f(x) = x^3 + 4x^2 + 4x$

31. $f(x) = x^3 + 7x^2 - 4x - 28$

32. $f(x) = x^3 + 5x^2 - 9x - 45$

In Exercises 33–40, use the Intermediate Value Theorem to show that each polynomial has a real zero between the given integers.

33. $f(x) = x^3 - x - 1$; between 1 and 2

34. $f(x) = x^3 - 4x^2 + 2$; between 0 and 1

35. $f(x) = 2x^4 - 4x^2 + 1$; between −1 and 0

36. $f(x) = x^4 + 6x^3 - 18x^2$; between 2 and 3

37. $f(x) = x^3 + x^2 - 2x + 1$; between −3 and −2

38. $f(x) = x^5 - x^3 - 1$; between 1 and 2

39. $f(x) = 3x^3 - 10x + 9$; between −3 and −2

40. $f(x) = 3x^3 - 8x^2 + x + 2$; between 2 and 3

In Exercises 41–64,

a. *Use the Leading Coefficient Test to determine the graph's end behavior.*

b. *Find the x-intercepts. State whether the graph crosses the x-axis, or touches the x-axis and turns around, at each intercept.*

c. *Find the y-intercept.*

d. *Determine whether the graph has y-axis symmetry, origin symmetry, or neither.*

e. *If necessary, find a few additional points and graph the function. Use the maximum number of turning points to check whether it is drawn correctly.*

41. $f(x) = x^3 + 2x^2 - x - 2$

42. $f(x) = x^3 + x^2 - 4x - 4$

43. $f(x) = x^4 - 9x^2$

44. $f(x) = x^4 - x^2$

45. $f(x) = -x^4 + 16x^2$

46. $f(x) = -x^4 + 4x^2$

47. $f(x) = x^4 - 2x^3 + x^2$

48. $f(x) = x^4 - 6x^3 + 9x^2$

49. $f(x) = -2x^4 + 4x^3$

50. $f(x) = -2x^4 + 2x^3$

51. $f(x) = 6x^3 - 9x - x^5$

52. $f(x) = 6x - x^3 - x^5$

53. $f(x) = 3x^2 - x^3$

54. $f(x) = \frac{1}{2} - \frac{1}{2}x^4$

55. $f(x) = -3(x - 1)^2(x^2 - 4)$

56. $f(x) = -2(x - 4)^2(x^2 - 25)$

57. $f(x) = x^2(x - 1)^3(x + 2)$

58. $f(x) = x^3(x + 2)^2(x + 1)$

59. $f(x) = -x^2(x - 1)(x + 3)$

60. $f(x) = -x^2(x + 2)(x - 2)$

61. $f(x) = -2x^3(x - 1)^2(x + 5)$

62. $f(x) = -3x^3(x - 1)^2(x + 3)$

63. $f(x) = (x - 2)^2(x + 4)(x - 1)$

64. $f(x) = (x + 3)(x + 1)^3(x + 4)$

Practice Plus

In Exercises 65–72, complete graphs of polynomial functions whose zeros are integers are shown.

a. *Find the zeros and state whether the multiplicity of each zero is even or odd.*

b. *Write an equation, expressed as the product of factors, of a polynomial function that might have each graph. Use a leading coefficient of 1 or −1, and make the degree of f as small as possible.*

c. *Use both the equation in part (b) and the graph to find the y-intercept.*

65.

$[-5, 5, 1]$ by $[-12, 12, 1]$

66.

$[-6, 6, 1]$ by $[-40, 40, 10]$

67.

$[-3, 6, 1]$ by $[-10, 10, 1]$

68.

$[-3, 3, 1]$ by $[-10, 10, 1]$

69.

$[-4, 4, 1]$ by $[-40, 4, 4]$

70.

$[-2, 5, 1]$ by $[-40, 4, 4]$

71.

$[-3, 3, 1]$ by $[-5, 10, 1]$

72.

$[-3, 3, 1]$ by $[-5, 10, 1]$

Application Exercises

Experts fear that without conservation efforts, tigers could disappear from the wild by 2022. Just one hundred years ago, there were at least 100,000 wild tigers. By 2010, the estimated world tiger population was 3200. The bar graph shows the estimated world tiger population for selected years from 1970 through 2010. Also shown is a polynomial function, with its graph, that models the data. Use this information to solve Exercises 73–74.

Vanishing Tigers

Estimated World Tiger Population

Source: World Wildlife Fund

Graph of a Polynomial Model for the Data

$$f(x) = 0.76x^3 - 30x^2 - 882x + 37,807$$

Years after 1970

73. a. Find and interpret $f(40)$. Identify this information as a point on the graph of f.

   b. Does $f(40)$ overestimate or underestimate the actual data shown by the bar graph? By how much?

   c. Use the Leading Coefficient Test to determine the end behavior to the right for the graph of f. Will this function be useful in modeling the world tiger population if conservation efforts to save wild tigers fail? Explain your answer.

74. a. Find and interpret $f(10)$. Identify this information as a point on the graph of f.

   d. Does $f(10)$ overestimate or underestimate the actual data shown by the bar graph? By how much?

   c. Use the Leading Coefficient Test to determine the end behavior to the right for the graph of f. Might this function be useful in modeling the world tiger population if conservation efforts to save wild tigers are successful? Explain your answer.

75. During a diagnostic evaluation, a 33-year-old woman experienced a panic attack a few minutes after she had been asked to relax her whole body. The graph shows the rapid increase in heart rate during the panic attack.

a. For which time periods during the diagnostic evaluation was the woman's heart rate increasing?

b. For which time periods during the diagnostic evaluation was the woman's heart rate decreasing?

c. How many turning points (from increasing to decreasing or from decreasing to increasing) occurred for the woman's heart rate during the first 12 minutes of the diagnostic evaluation?

d. Suppose that a polynomial function is used to model the data displayed by the graph using

     (time during the evaluation, heart rate).

Use the number of turning points to determine the degree of the polynomial function of best fit.

e. For the model in part (d), should the leading coefficient of the polynomial function be positive or negative? Explain your answer.

f. Use the graph to estimate the woman's maximum heart rate during the first 12 minutes of the diagnostic evaluation. After how many minutes did this occur?

g. Use the graph to estimate the woman's minimum heart rate during the first 12 minutes of the diagnostic evaluation. After how many minutes did this occur?

76. Volatility at the Pump The graph shows the average price per gallon of gasoline in the United States in January for the period from 2005 through 2011.

Heart Rate before and during a Panic Attack

Source: Davis and Palladino, *Psychology,* Fifth Edition, Prentice Hall, 2007.

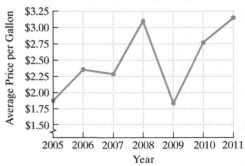

Average January Gasoline Price in the United States

Source: U.S. Energy Information Administration

a. For which years was the average price per gallon in January increasing?

b. For which years was the average price per gallon in January decreasing?

c. How many turning points (from increasing to decreasing or from decreasing to increasing) does the graph have for the period shown?

d. Suppose that a polynomial function is used to model the data displayed by the graph using

(number of years after 2005, average January price per gallon).

Use the number of turning points to determine the degree of the polynomial function of best fit.

e. For the model in part (d), should the leading coefficient of the polynomial function be positive or negative? Explain your answer.

f. Use the graph to estimate the maximum average January price per gallon. In which year did this occur?

g. Use the graph to estimate the minimum average January price per gallon. In which year did this occur?

Writing in Mathematics

77. What is a polynomial function?

78. What do we mean when we describe the graph of a polynomial function as smooth and continuous?

79. What is meant by the end behavior of a polynomial function?

80. Explain how to use the Leading Coefficient Test to determine the end behavior of a polynomial function.

81. Why is a third-degree polynomial function with a negative leading coefficient not appropriate for modeling nonnegative real-world phenomena over a long period of time?

82. What are the zeros of a polynomial function and how are they found?

83. Explain the relationship between the multiplicity of a zero and whether or not the graph crosses or touches the x-axis at that zero.

84. If f is a polynomial function, and $f(a)$ and $f(b)$ have opposite signs, what must occur between a and b? If $f(a)$ and $f(b)$ have the same sign, does it necessarily mean that this will not occur? Explain your answer.

85. Explain the relationship between the degree of a polynomial function and the number of turning points on its graph.

86. Can the graph of a polynomial function have no x-intercepts? Explain.

87. Can the graph of a polynomial function have no y-intercept? Explain.

88. Describe a strategy for graphing a polynomial function. In your description, mention intercepts, the polynomial's degree, and turning points.

Technology Exercises

89. Use a graphing utility to verify any five of the graphs that you drew by hand in Exercises 41–64.

Write a polynomial function that imitates the end behavior of each graph in Exercises 90–93. The dashed portions of the graphs indicate that you should focus only on imitating the left and right behavior of the graph and can be flexible about what occurs between the left and right ends. Then use your graphing utility to graph the polynomial function and verify that you imitated the end behavior shown in the given graph.

90.

91.

92.

93.

In Exercises 94–97, use a graphing utility with a viewing rectangle large enough to show end behavior to graph each polynomial function.

94. $f(x) = x^3 + 13x^2 + 10x - 4$

95. $f(x) = -2x^3 + 6x^2 + 3x - 1$

96. $f(x) = -x^4 + 8x^3 + 4x^2 + 2$

97. $f(x) = -x^5 + 5x^4 - 6x^3 + 2x + 20$

In Exercises 98–99, use a graphing utility to graph f and g in the same viewing rectangle. Then use the ZOOM OUT *feature to show that f and g have identical end behavior.*

98. $f(x) = x^3 - 6x + 1$, $g(x) = x^3$

99. $f(x) = -x^4 + 2x^3 - 6x$, $g(x) = -x^4$

Critical Thinking Exercises

Make Sense? *In Exercises 100–103, determine whether each statement makes sense or does not make sense, and explain your reasoning.*

100. When I'm trying to determine end behavior, it's the coefficient of the leading term of a polynomial function that I should inspect.

101. I graphed $f(x) = (x + 2)^3(x - 4)^2$, and the graph touched the x-axis and turned around at -2.

102. I'm graphing a fourth-degree polynomial function with four turning points.

103. Although I have not yet learned techniques for finding the x-intercepts of $f(x) = x^3 + 2x^2 - 5x - 6$, I can easily determine the y-intercept.

In Exercises 104–107, determine whether each statement is true or false. If the statement is false, make the necessary change(s) to produce a true statement.

104. If $f(x) = -x^3 + 4x$, then the graph of f falls to the left and falls to the right.

105. A mathematical model that is a polynomial of degree n whose leading term is $a_n x^n$, n odd and $a_n < 0$, is ideally suited to describe phenomena that have positive values over unlimited periods of time.

106. There is more than one third-degree polynomial function with the same three x-intercepts.

107. The graph of a function with origin symmetry can rise to the left and rise to the right.

Use the descriptions in Exercises 108–109 to write an equation of a polynomial function with the given characteristics. Use a graphing utility to graph your function to see if you are correct. If not, modify the function's equation and repeat this process.

108. Crosses the x-axis at $-4, 0,$ and 3; lies above the x-axis between -4 and 0; lies below the x-axis between 0 and 3

109. Touches the x-axis at 0 and crosses the x-axis at 2; lies below the x-axis between 0 and 2

Preview Exercises

Exercises 110–112 will help you prepare for the material covered in the next section.

110. Divide 737 by 21 without using a calculator. Write the answer as

$$\text{quotient} + \frac{\text{remainder}}{\text{divisor}}.$$

111. Rewrite $4 - 5x - x^2 + 6x^3$ in descending powers of x.

112. Use

$$\frac{2x^3 - 3x^2 - 11x + 6}{x - 3} = 2x^2 + 3x - 2$$

to factor $2x^3 - 3x^2 - 11x + 6$ completely.

SECTION 3.3

Dividing Polynomials; Remainder and Factor Theorems

Objectives

① Use long division to divide polynomials.

② Use synthetic division to divide polynomials.

③ Evaluate a polynomial using the Remainder Theorem.

④ Use the Factor Theorem to solve a polynomial equation.

A moth has moved into your closet. She appeared in your bedroom at night, but somehow her relatively stout body escaped your clutches. Within a few weeks, swarms of moths in your tattered wardrobe suggest that Mama Moth was in the family way. There must be at least 200 critters nesting in every crevice of your clothing.

Two hundred plus moth-tykes from one female moth—is this possible? Indeed it is. The number of eggs, $f(x)$, in a female moth is a function of her abdominal width, x, in millimeters, modeled by

$$f(x) = 14x^3 - 17x^2 - 16x + 34, \quad 1.5 \le x \le 3.5.$$

Because there are 200 moths feasting on your favorite sweaters, Mama's abdominal width can be estimated by finding the solutions of the polynomial equation

$$14x^3 - 17x^2 - 16x + 34 = 200.$$

How can we solve such an equation? You might begin by subtracting 200 from both sides to obtain zero on one side. But then what? The factoring that we used in the previous section will not work in this situation.

In Section 3.4, we will present techniques for solving certain kinds of polynomial equations. These techniques will further enhance your ability to manipulate algebraically the polynomial functions that model your world. Because these techniques are based on understanding polynomial division, in this section we look at two methods for dividing polynomials. (We'll return to Mama Moth's abdominal width in the Exercise Set.)

Long Division of Polynomials and the Division Algorithm

① Use long division to divide polynomials.

We begin by looking at division by a polynomial containing more than one term, such as

$$x + 3 \overline{\smash{)}x^2 + 10x + 21}.$$

| Divisor has two terms and is a binomial. | The polynomial dividend has three terms and is a trinomial. |

When a divisor has more than one term, the four steps used to divide whole numbers—**divide, multiply, subtract, bring down the next term**—form the repetitive procedure for polynomial long division.

EXAMPLE 1 Long Division of Polynomials

Divide $x^2 + 10x + 21$ by $x + 3$.

SOLUTION

The following steps illustrate how polynomial division is very similar to numerical division.

$$x + 3\overline{)x^2 + 10x + 21}$$

Arrange the terms of the dividend $(x^2 + 10x + 21)$ and the divisor $(x + 3)$ in descending powers of x.

$$\begin{array}{r} x \\ x + 3\overline{)x^2 + 10x + 21} \end{array}$$

Divide x^2 (the first term in the dividend) by x (the first term in the divisor): $\dfrac{x^2}{x} = x$. Align like terms.

$$x(x+3) = x^2 + 3x \qquad \begin{array}{r} x \\ x + 3\overline{)x^2 + 10x + 21} \\ \underline{x^2 + 3x} \end{array}$$

Multiply each term in the divisor $(x + 3)$ by x, aligning terms of the product under like terms in the dividend.

$$\begin{array}{r} x \\ x + 3\overline{)x^2 + 10x + 21} \\ \underline{\ominus x^2 \ominus 3x} \\ 7x \end{array}$$

Subtract $x^2 + 3x$ from $x^2 + 10x$ by changing the sign of each term in the lower expression and adding.

Change signs of the polynomial being subtracted.

$$\begin{array}{r} x \\ x + 3\overline{)x^2 + 10x + 21} \\ \underline{x^2 + 3x} \downarrow \\ 7x + 21 \end{array}$$

Bring down 21 from the original dividend and add algebraically to form a new dividend.

$$\begin{array}{r} x + 7 \\ x + 3\overline{)x^2 + 10x + 21} \\ \underline{x^2 + 3x} \\ 7x + 21 \end{array}$$

Find the second term of the quotient. Divide the first term of $7x + 21$ by x, the first term of the divisor: $\dfrac{7x}{x} = 7$.

$$7(x+3) = 7x + 21 \qquad \begin{array}{r} x + 7 \\ x + 3\overline{)x^2 + 10x + 21} \\ \underline{x^2 + 3x} \\ 7x + 21 \\ \underline{\ominus 7x \ominus 21} \\ 0 \end{array}$$

Multiply the divisor $(x + 3)$ by 7, aligning under like terms in the new dividend. Then subtract to obtain the remainder of 0.

Remainder

The quotient is $x + 7$. Because the remainder is 0, we can conclude that $x + 3$ is a factor of $x^2 + 10x + 21$ and

$$\frac{x^2 + 10x + 21}{x + 3} = x + 7.$$

• • •

⫾ Check Point **1** Divide $x^2 + 14x + 45$ by $x + 9$.

Before considering additional examples, let's summarize the general procedure for dividing one polynomial by another.

Long Division of Polynomials

1. **Arrange** the terms of both the dividend and the divisor in descending powers of any variable.
2. **Divide** the first term in the dividend by the first term in the divisor. The result is the first term of the quotient.
3. **Multiply** every term in the divisor by the first term in the quotient. Write the resulting product beneath the dividend with like terms lined up.
4. **Subtract** the product from the dividend.
5. **Bring down** the next term in the original dividend and write it next to the remainder to form a new dividend.
6. Use this new expression as the dividend and repeat this process until the remainder can no longer be divided. This will occur when the degree of the remainder (the highest exponent on a variable in the remainder) is less than the degree of the divisor.

In our next long division, we will obtain a nonzero remainder.

EXAMPLE 2   Long Division of Polynomials

Divide $4 - 5x - x^2 + 6x^3$ by $3x - 2$.

SOLUTION

We begin by writing the dividend in descending powers of x.

$$4 - 5x - x^2 + 6x^3 = 6x^3 - x^2 - 5x + 4$$

$2x^2(3x - 2) = 6x^3 - 4x^2$

$$
\begin{array}{r}
2x^2 \phantom{{}- x^2 - 5x + 4} \\
3x - 2 \overline{)6x^3 - x^2 - 5x + 4} \\
6x^3 \oplus 4x^2 \phantom{{}- 5x + 4} \\
\hline
3x^2 - 5x \phantom{{}+ 4}
\end{array}
$$

Change signs of the polynomial being subtracted.

Divide: $\dfrac{6x^3}{3x} = 2x^2$.

Multiply: $2x^2(3x - 2) = 6x^3 - 4x^2$.

Subtract $6x^3 - 4x^2$ from $6x^3 - x^2$ and bring down $-5x$.

Now we divide $3x^2$ by $3x$ to obtain x, multiply x and the divisor, and subtract.

$x(3x - 2) = 3x^2 - 2x$

$$
\begin{array}{r}
2x^2 + x \phantom{{}+ 4} \\
3x - 2 \overline{)6x^3 - x^2 - 5x + 4} \\
6x^3 - 4x^2 \phantom{{}- 5x + 4} \\
\hline
3x^2 - 5x \phantom{{}+ 4} \\
3x^2 \oplus 2x \phantom{{}+ 4} \\
\hline
-3x + 4
\end{array}
$$

Change signs of the polynomial being subtracted.

Divide: $\dfrac{3x^2}{3x} = x$.

Multiply: $x(3x - 2) = 3x^2 - 2x$.

Subtract $3x^2 - 2x$ from $3x^2 - 5x$ and bring down 4.

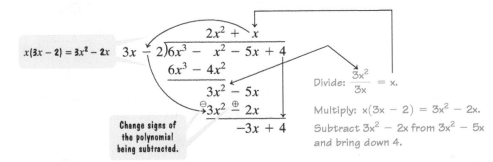

Now we divide $-3x$ by $3x$ to obtain -1, multiply -1 and the divisor, and subtract.

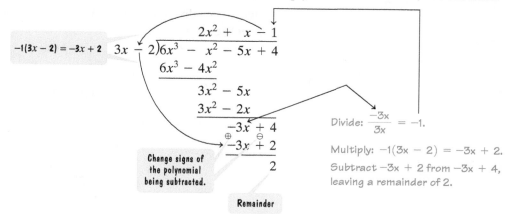

$-1(3x - 2) = -3x + 2$

$$
\begin{array}{r}
2x^2 + x - 1 \\
3x - 2 \overline{)6x^3 - x^2 - 5x + 4} \\
6x^3 - 4x^2 \\
\hline
3x^2 - 5x \\
3x^2 - 2x \\
\hline
-3x + 4 \\
-3x + 2 \\
\hline
2
\end{array}
$$

Change signs of the polynomial being subtracted.

Divide: $\dfrac{-3x}{3x} = -1.$

Multiply: $-1(3x - 2) = -3x + 2.$

Subtract $-3x + 2$ from $-3x + 4$, leaving a remainder of 2.

Remainder

The quotient is $2x^2 + x - 1$ and the remainder is 2. When there is a nonzero remainder, as in this example, list the quotient, plus the remainder above the divisor. Thus,

$$
\frac{6x^3 - x^2 - 5x + 4}{3x - 2} = \underbrace{2x^2 + x - 1}_{\text{Quotient}} + \underbrace{\frac{2}{3x - 2}}_{\substack{\text{Remainder} \\ \text{above divisor}}}.
$$

An important property of division can be illustrated by clearing fractions in the equation that concluded Example 2. Multiplying both sides of this equation by $3x - 2$ results in the following equation:

$$
\underset{\text{Dividend}}{6x^3 - x^2 - 5x + 4} = \underset{\text{Divisor}}{(3x - 2)} \underset{\text{Quotient}}{(2x^2 + x - 1)} + \underset{\text{Remainder}}{2}.
$$

Polynomial long division is checked by multiplying the divisor with the quotient and then adding the remainder. This should give the dividend. The process illustrates the **Division Algorithm**.

The Division Algorithm

If $f(x)$ and $d(x)$ are polynomials, with $d(x) \neq 0$, and the degree of $d(x)$ is less than or equal to the degree of $f(x)$, then there exist unique polynomials $q(x)$ and $r(x)$ such that

$$
\underset{\text{Dividend}}{f(x)} = \underset{\text{Divisor}}{d(x)} \cdot \underset{\text{Quotient}}{q(x)} + \underset{\text{Remainder}}{r(x)}.
$$

The remainder, $r(x)$, equals 0 or it is of degree less than the degree of $d(x)$. If $r(x) = 0$, we say that $d(x)$ **divides evenly** into $f(x)$ and that $d(x)$ and $q(x)$ are **factors** of $f(x)$.

⊘ Check Point **2** Divide $7 - 11x - 3x^2 + 2x^3$ by $x - 3$. Express the result in the form quotient, plus remainder divided by divisor.

If a power of x is missing in either a dividend or a divisor, add that power of x with a coefficient of 0 and then divide. In this way, like terms will be aligned as you carry out the long division.

EXAMPLE 3   Long Division of Polynomials

Divide $6x^4 + 5x^3 + 3x - 5$ by $3x^2 - 2x$.

SOLUTION

We write the dividend, $6x^4 + 5x^3 + 3x - 5$, as $6x^4 + 5x^3 + 0x^2 + 3x - 5$ to keep all like terms aligned.

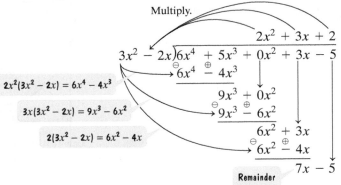

The division process is finished because the degree of $7x - 5$, which is 1, is less than the degree of the divisor $3x^2 - 2x$, which is 2. The answer is

$$\frac{6x^4 + 5x^3 + 3x - 5}{3x^2 - 2x} = 2x^2 + 3x + 2 + \frac{7x - 5}{3x^2 - 2x}.$$

• • •

⬟ Check Point **3** Divide $2x^4 + 3x^3 - 7x - 10$ by $x^2 - 2x$.

② Use synthetic division to divide polynomials.

Dividing Polynomials Using Synthetic Division

We can use **synthetic division** to divide polynomials if the divisor is of the form $x - c$. This method provides a quotient more quickly than long division. Let's compare the two methods showing $x^3 + 4x^2 - 5x + 5$ divided by $x - 3$.

Long Division   **Synthetic Division**

$$
\begin{array}{r}
x^2 + 7x + 16 \\
x - 3\overline{\smash{)}x^3 + 4x^2 - 5x + 5} \\
\underline{x^3 - 3x^2} \\
7x^2 - 5x \\
\underline{7x^2 - 21x} \\
16x + 5 \\
\underline{16x - 48} \\
53
\end{array}
$$

Divisor
$x - c$;
$c = 3$

Quotient

Dividend

Remainder

$$
\begin{array}{r|rrrr}
3 & 1 & 4 & -5 & 5 \\
& & 3 & 21 & 48 \\
\hline
& 1 & 7 & 16 & 53
\end{array}
$$

Notice the relationship between the polynomials in the long division process and the numbers that appear in synthetic division.

The divisor is $x - 3$.
This is 3, or c, in $x - c$.

These are the coefficients of the dividend $x^3 + 4x^2 - 5x + 5$.

$$
\begin{array}{r|rrrr}
3 & 1 & 4 & -5 & 5 \\
& & 3 & 21 & 48 \\
\hline
& 1 & 7 & 16 & 53
\end{array}
$$

These are the coefficients of the quotient $x^2 + 7x + 16$.

This is the remainder.

Now let's look at the steps involved in synthetic division.

Synthetic Division

To divide a polynomial by $x - c$:

Example

1. Arrange the polynomial in descending powers, with a 0 coefficient for any missing term.

$$x - 3\overline{\smash{\big)}x^3 + 4x^2 - 5x + 5}$$

2. Write c for the divisor, $x - c$. To the right, write the coefficients of the dividend.

$$\underline{3}\quad 1 \quad 4 \quad -5 \quad 5$$

3. Write the leading coefficient of the dividend on the bottom row.

$$\begin{array}{c|cccc} \underline{3} & 1 & 4 & -5 & 5 \\ & \downarrow & \multicolumn{3}{l}{\text{Bring down 1.}} \\ \hline & 1 \end{array}$$

4. Multiply c (in this case, 3) times the value just written on the bottom row. Write the product in the next column in the second row.

$$\begin{array}{c|cccc} \underline{3} & 1 & 4 & -5 & 5 \\ & & 3 \\ \hline & 1 \end{array}$$

Multiply by 3: $3 \cdot 1 = 3$.

5. Add the values in this new column, writing the sum in the bottom row.

$$\begin{array}{c|cccc} \underline{3} & 1 & 4 & -5 & 5 \\ & & 3 & & \text{Add.} \\ \hline & 1 & 7 \end{array}$$

6. Repeat this series of multiplications and additions until all columns are filled in.

$$\begin{array}{c|cccc} \underline{3} & 1 & 4 & -5 & 5 \\ & & 3 & 21 & \text{Add.} \\ \hline & 1 & 7 & 16 \end{array}$$

Multiply by 3: $3 \cdot 7 = 21$.

$$\begin{array}{c|cccc} \underline{3} & 1 & 4 & -5 & 5 \\ & & 3 & 21 & 48 & \text{Add.} \\ \hline & 1 & 7 & 16 & 53 \end{array}$$

Multiply by 3: $3 \cdot 16 = 48$.

7. Use the numbers in the last row to write the quotient, plus the remainder above the divisor. **The degree of the first term of the quotient is one less than the degree of the first term of the dividend.** The final value in this row is the remainder.

Written from
1 7 16 53
the last row of the synthetic division

$$1x^2 + 7x + 16 + \frac{53}{x - 3}$$

$$x - 3\overline{\smash{\big)}x^3 + 4x^2 - 5x + 5}$$

EXAMPLE 4   Using Synthetic Division

Use synthetic division to divide $5x^3 + 6x + 8$ by $x + 2$.

SOLUTION

The divisor must be in the form $x - c$. Thus, we write $x + 2$ as $x - (-2)$. This means that $c = -2$. Writing a 0 coefficient for the missing x^2-term in the dividend, we can express the division as follows:

$$x - (-2)\overline{\smash{\big)}5x^3 + 0x^2 + 6x + 8}.$$

Now we are ready to set up the problem so that we can use synthetic division.

> Use the coefficients of the dividend
> $5x^3 + 0x^2 + 6x + 8$ in descending powers of x.

$$x - (-2)\overline{)5x^3 + 0x^2 + 6x + 8}$$

The given division problem (repeated)

> This is c in $x - (-2)$.

$$-2\,\big|\ 5\quad 0\quad 6\quad 8$$

We begin the synthetic division process by bringing down 5. This is followed by a series of multiplications and additions.

1. Bring down 5.

$$-2\,\big|\ 5\quad 0\quad 6\quad 8$$
$$\downarrow$$
$$5$$

2. Multiply: $-2(5) = -10$.

$$-2\,\big|\ 5\quad 0\quad 6\quad 8$$
$$-10$$
$$5$$

Multiply 5 by −2.

3. Add: $0 + (-10) = -10$.

$$-2\,\big|\ 5\quad\ 0\quad 6\quad 8$$
$$-10\downarrow\ \text{Add.}$$
$$5\quad -10$$

4. Multiply: $-2(-10) = 20$.

$$-2\,\big|\ 5\quad\ 0\quad 6\quad 8$$
$$-10\ \ 20$$
$$5\ \ -10$$

Multiply −10 by −2.

5. Add: $6 + 20 = 26$.

$$-2\,\big|\ 5\quad\ 0\quad 6\quad\ 8$$
$$-10\ \ 20\downarrow\ \text{Add.}$$
$$5\ \ -10\ \ 26$$

6. Multiply: $-2(26) = -52$.

$$-2\,\big|\ 5\quad\ 0\quad 6\quad\ 8$$
$$-10\ \ 20\ \ -52$$
$$5\ \ -10\ \ 26$$

Multiply 26 by −2.

7. Add: $8 + (-52) = -44$.

$$-2\,\big|\ 5\quad\ 0\quad 6\quad\ 8$$
$$-10\ \ 20\ \ -52\downarrow\ \text{Add.}$$
$$5\ \ -10\ \ 26\ \ -44$$

The numbers in the last row represent the coefficients of the quotient and the remainder. The degree of the first term of the quotient is one less than that of the dividend. Because the degree of the dividend, $5x^3 + 6x + 8$, is 3, the degree of the quotient is 2. This means that the 5 in the last row represents $5x^2$.

$$-2\,\big|\ 5\quad\ 0\quad 6\quad\ 8$$
$$-10\ \ 20\ \ -52$$
$$5\ \ -10\ \ 26\ \ -44$$

> The quotient is $5x^2 - 10x + 26$.

> The remainder is −44.

Thus,

$$x + 2\overline{)5x^3 + 6x + 8}\ \begin{array}{c}5x^2 - 10x + 26 - \dfrac{44}{x + 2}\end{array}.$$

• • •

○ Check Point **4** Use synthetic division to divide $x^3 - 7x - 6$ by $x + 2$.

③ Evaluate a polynomial using the Remainder Theorem.

The Remainder Theorem

Let's consider the Division Algorithm when the dividend, $f(x)$, is divided by $x - c$. In this case, the remainder must be a constant because its degree is less than one, the degree of $x - c$.

$$f(x)\quad =\quad (x - c)q(x)\quad +\quad r$$

> Dividend · · · · Divisor · · · · Quotient · · · · The remainder, r, is a constant when dividing by $x - c$.

Now let's evaluate f at c.

$$f(c) = (c - c)q(c) + r \qquad \text{Find } f(c) \text{ by letting } x = c \text{ in } f(x) = (x - c)q(x) + r.$$
This will give an expression for r.

$$f(c) = 0 \cdot q(c) + r \qquad c - c = 0$$

$$f(c) = r \qquad 0 \cdot q(c) = 0 \text{ and } 0 + r = r.$$

What does this last equation mean? If a polynomial is divided by $x - c$, the remainder is the value of the polynomial at c. This result is called the **Remainder Theorem**.

> ### The Remainder Theorem
>
> If the polynomial $f(x)$ is divided by $x - c$, then the remainder is $f(c)$.

Example 5 shows how we can use the Remainder Theorem to evaluate a polynomial function at 2. Rather than substituting 2 for x, we divide the function by $x - 2$. The remainder is $f(2)$.

EXAMPLE 5 Using the Remainder Theorem to Evaluate a Polynomial Function

Given $f(x) = x^3 - 4x^2 + 5x + 3$, use the Remainder Theorem to find $f(2)$.

SOLUTION

By the Remainder Theorem, if $f(x)$ is divided by $x - 2$, then the remainder is $f(2)$. We'll use synthetic division to divide.

$$
\begin{array}{r|rrrr}
2 & 1 & -4 & 5 & 3 \\
  &   & 2 & -4 & 2 \\
\hline
  & 1 & -2 & 1 & 5
\end{array}
\quad \text{Remainder}
$$

The remainder, 5, is the value of $f(2)$. Thus, $f(2) = 5$. We can verify that this is correct by evaluating $f(2)$ directly. Using $f(x) = x^3 - 4x^2 + 5x + 3$, we obtain

$$f(2) = 2^3 - 4 \cdot 2^2 + 5 \cdot 2 + 3 = 8 - 16 + 10 + 3 = 5. \qquad \bullet \bullet \bullet$$

☑ **Check Point 5** Given $f(x) = 3x^3 + 4x^2 - 5x + 3$, use the Remainder Theorem to find $f(-4)$.

④ Use the Factor Theorem to solve a polynomial equation.

The Factor Theorem

Let's look again at the Division Algorithm when the divisor is of the form $x - c$.

$$
\underbrace{f(x)}_{\text{Dividend}} = \underbrace{(x - c)}_{\text{Divisor}}\underbrace{q(x)}_{\text{Quotient}} + \underbrace{r}_{\text{Constant remainder}}
$$

By the Remainder Theorem, the remainder r is $f(c)$, so we can substitute $f(c)$ for r:

$$f(x) = (x - c)q(x) + f(c).$$

Notice that if $f(c) = 0$, then

$$f(x) = (x - c)q(x)$$

so that $x - c$ is a factor of $f(x)$. This means that for the polynomial function $f(x)$, if $f(c) = 0$, then $x - c$ is a factor of $f(x)$.

Let's reverse directions and see what happens if $x - c$ is a factor of $f(x)$. This means that

$$f(x) = (x - c)q(x).$$

If we replace x in $f(x) = (x - c)q(x)$ with c, we obtain

$$f(c) = (c - c)q(c) = 0 \cdot q(c) = 0.$$

Thus, if $x - c$ is a factor of $f(x)$, then $f(c) = 0$.

We have proved a result known as the **Factor Theorem**.

The Factor Theorem

Let $f(x)$ be a polynomial.

a. If $f(c) = 0$, then $x - c$ is a factor of $f(x)$.

b. If $x - c$ is a factor of $f(x)$, then $f(c) = 0$.

The example that follows shows how the Factor Theorem can be used to solve a polynomial equation.

EXAMPLE 6   Using the Factor Theorem

Solve the equation $2x^3 - 3x^2 - 11x + 6 = 0$ given that 3 is a zero of $f(x) = 2x^3 - 3x^2 - 11x + 6$.

SOLUTION

We are given that 3 is a zero of $f(x) = 2x^3 - 3x^2 - 11x + 6$. This means that $f(3) = 0$. Because $f(3) = 0$, the Factor Theorem tells us that $x - 3$ is a factor of $f(x)$. We'll use synthetic division to divide $f(x)$ by $x - 3$.

TECHNOLOGY

Graphic Connections

Because the solution set of

$$2x^3 - 3x^2 - 11x + 6 = 0$$

is $\left\{-2, \frac{1}{2}, 3\right\}$, this implies that the polynomial function

$$f(x) = 2x^3 - 3x^2 - 11x + 6$$

has x-intercepts (or zeros) at $-2, \frac{1}{2},$ and 3. This is verified by the graph of f.

$[-10, 10, 1]$ by $[-15, 15, 1]$

$$\begin{array}{r|rrrr} 3 & 2 & -3 & -11 & 6 \\ & & 6 & 9 & -6 \\ \hline & 2 & 3 & -2 & 0 \end{array}$$

The remainder, 0, verifies that $x - 3$ is a factor of $2x^3 - 3x^2 - 11x + 6.$

$$\begin{array}{r} 2x^2 + 3x - 2 \\ x - 3 \overline{) 2x^3 - 3x^2 - 11x + 6} \end{array}$$

Equivalently,

$$2x^3 - 3x^2 - 11x + 6 = (x - 3)(2x^2 + 3x - 2).$$

Now we can solve the polynomial equation.

$2x^3 - 3x^2 - 11x + 6 = 0$ This is the given equation.

$(x - 3)(2x^2 + 3x - 2) = 0$ Factor using the result from the synthetic division.

$(x - 3)(2x - 1)(x + 2) = 0$ Factor the trinomial.

$x - 3 = 0$ or $2x - 1 = 0$ or $x + 2 = 0$ Set each factor equal to 0.

$x = 3$ $x = \frac{1}{2}$ $x = -2$ Solve for x.

The solution set is $\left\{-2, \frac{1}{2}, 3\right\}$. $\bullet\bullet\bullet$

Based on the Factor Theorem, the following statements are useful in solving polynomial equations:

1. If $f(x)$ is divided by $x - c$ and the remainder is zero, then c is a zero of f and c is a root of the polynomial equation $f(x) = 0$.
2. If $f(x)$ is divided by $x - c$ and the remainder is zero, then $x - c$ is a factor of $f(x)$.

✓ Check Point **6** Solve the equation $15x^3 + 14x^2 - 3x - 2 = 0$ given that -1 is a zero of $f(x) = 15x^3 + 14x^2 - 3x - 2$.

CONCEPT AND VOCABULARY CHECK

Fill in each blank so that the resulting statement is true.

1. Consider the following long division problem:

$$x + 4 \overline{)6x - 4 + 2x^3}.$$

We begin the division process by rewriting the dividend as _____.

2. Consider the following long division problem:

$$3x - 1\overline{)6x^3 + 7x^2 + 12x - 5}.$$

We begin the division process by dividing _____ by _____. We obtain _____. We write this result above _____ in the dividend.

3. In the following long division problem, the first step has been completed:

$$5x - 2 \overline{)\overset{\displaystyle 2x^2}{10x^3 + 6x^2 - 9x + 10}}.$$

The next step is to multiply _____ and _____. We obtain _____. We write this result below _____.

4. In the following long division problem, the first two steps have been completed:

$$3x - 5 \overline{)\overset{\displaystyle 2x}{\underset{6x^2 - 10x}{6x^2 + 8x - 4}}}.$$

The next step is to subtract _____ from _____. We obtain _____. Then we bring down _____ and form the new dividend _____.

5. In the following long division problem, most of the steps have been completed:

$$2x + 1 \overline{)\overset{\displaystyle 3x - 5}{6x^2 - 7x + 4}}$$
$$\underline{6x^2 + 3x}$$
$$-10x + 4$$
$$\underline{-10x - 5}$$
$$?$$

Completing the step designated by the question mark, we obtain _____. Thus, the quotient is _____ and the remainder is _____. The answer to this long division problem is _____.

6. After performing polynomial long division, the answer may be checked by multiplying the _____ by the _____, and then adding the _____. You should obtain the _____.

7. To divide $x^3 + 5x^2 - 7x + 1$ by $x - 4$ using synthetic division, the first step is to write

$$\underline{}\big| \underline{} \ \underline{} \ \underline{} \ \underline{}.$$

8. To divide $4x^3 - 8x - 2$ by $x + 5$ using synthetic division, the first step is to write

$$\underline{}\big| \underline{} \ \underline{} \ \underline{} \ \underline{}.$$

9. True or false:

$$\begin{array}{r|rrrr} -1 & 3 & -4 & 2 & -1 \\ & & -3 & 7 & -9 \\ \hline & 3 & -7 & 9 & -10 \end{array} \text{ means}$$

$$\frac{3x^3 - 4x^2 + 2x - 1}{x + 1} = 3x^2 - 7x + 9 - \frac{10}{x + 1}. \underline{}$$

10. The Remainder Theorem states that if the polynomial $f(x)$ is divided by $x - c$, then the remainder is _____.
11. The Factor Theorem states that if f is a polynomial function and $f(c) = 0$, then _____ is a factor of $f(x)$.

EXERCISE SET 3.3

Practice Exercises

In Exercises 1–16, divide using long division. State the quotient, $q(x)$, and the remainder, $r(x)$.

1. $(x^2 + 8x + 15) \div (x + 5)$
2. $(x^2 + 3x - 10) \div (x - 2)$
3. $(x^3 + 5x^2 + 7x + 2) \div (x + 2)$
4. $(x^3 - 2x^2 - 5x + 6) \div (x - 3)$
5. $(6x^3 + 7x^2 + 12x - 5) \div (3x - 1)$
6. $(6x^3 + 17x^2 + 27x + 20) \div (3x + 4)$
7. $(12x^2 + x - 4) \div (3x - 2)$
8. $(4x^2 - 8x + 6) \div (2x - 1)$

9. $\dfrac{2x^3 + 7x^2 + 9x - 20}{x + 3}$

10. $\dfrac{3x^2 - 2x + 5}{x - 3}$

11. $\dfrac{4x^4 - 4x^2 + 6x}{x - 4}$

12. $\dfrac{x^4 - 81}{x - 3}$

13. $\dfrac{6x^3 + 13x^2 - 11x - 15}{3x^2 - x - 3}$

14. $\dfrac{x^4 + 2x^3 - 4x^2 - 5x - 6}{x^2 + x - 2}$

15. $\dfrac{18x^4 + 9x^3 + 3x^2}{3x^2 + 1}$

16. $\dfrac{2x^5 - 8x^4 + 2x^3 + x^2}{2x^3 + 1}$

In Exercises 17–32, divide using synthetic division.

17. $(2x^2 + x - 10) \div (x - 2)$ **18.** $(x^2 + x - 2) \div (x - 1)$

19. $(3x^2 + 7x - 20) \div (x + 5)$

20. $(5x^2 - 12x - 8) \div (x + 3)$

21. $(4x^3 - 3x^2 + 3x - 1) \div (x - 1)$

22. $(5x^3 - 6x^2 + 3x + 11) \div (x - 2)$

23. $(6x^5 - 2x^3 + 4x^2 - 3x + 1) \div (x - 2)$

24. $(x^5 + 4x^4 - 3x^2 + 2x + 3) \div (x - 3)$

25. $(x^2 - 5x - 5x^3 + x^4) \div (5 + x)$

26. $(x^2 - 6x - 6x^3 + x^4) \div (6 + x)$

27. $\dfrac{x^5 + x^3 - 2}{x - 1}$

28. $\dfrac{x^7 + x^5 - 10x^3 + 12}{x + 2}$

29. $\dfrac{x^4 - 256}{x - 4}$

30. $\dfrac{x^7 - 128}{x - 2}$

31. $\dfrac{2x^5 - 3x^4 + x^3 - x^2 + 2x - 1}{x + 2}$

32. $\dfrac{x^5 - 2x^4 - x^3 + 3x^2 - x + 1}{x - 2}$

In Exercises 33–40, use synthetic division and the Remainder Theorem to find the indicated function value.

33. $f(x) = 2x^3 - 11x^2 + 7x - 5;\quad f(4)$

34. $f(x) = x^3 - 7x^2 + 5x - 6;\quad f(3)$

35. $f(x) = 3x^3 - 7x^2 - 2x + 5;\quad f(-3)$

36. $f(x) = 4x^3 + 5x^2 - 6x - 4;\quad f(-2)$

37. $f(x) = x^4 + 5x^3 + 5x^2 - 5x - 6;\quad f(3)$

38. $f(x) = x^4 - 5x^3 + 5x^2 + 5x - 6;\quad f(2)$

39. $f(x) = 2x^4 - 5x^3 - x^2 + 3x + 2;\quad f\left(-\dfrac{1}{2}\right)$

40. $f(x) = 6x^4 + 10x^3 + 5x^2 + x + 1;\quad f\left(-\dfrac{2}{3}\right)$

41. Use synthetic division to divide
$$f(x) = x^3 - 4x^2 + x + 6 \text{ by } x + 1.$$
Use the result to find all zeros of f.

42. Use synthetic division to divide
$$f(x) = x^3 - 2x^2 - x + 2 \text{ by } x + 1.$$
Use the result to find all zeros of f.

43. Solve the equation $2x^3 - 5x^2 + x + 2 = 0$ given that 2 is a zero of $f(x) = 2x^3 - 5x^2 + x + 2$.

44. Solve the equation $2x^3 - 3x^2 - 11x + 6 = 0$ given that -2 is a zero of $f(x) = 2x^3 - 3x^2 - 11x + 6$.

45. Solve the equation $12x^3 + 16x^2 - 5x - 3 = 0$ given that $-\frac{3}{2}$ is a root.

46. Solve the equation $3x^3 + 7x^2 - 22x - 8 = 0$ given that $-\frac{1}{3}$ is a root.

Practice Plus

In Exercises 47–50, use the graph or the table to determine a solution of each equation. Use synthetic division to verify that this number is a solution of the equation. Then solve the polynomial equation.

47. $x^3 + 2x^2 - 5x - 6 = 0$

[0, 4, 1] by [−25, 25, 5]

48. $2x^3 + x^2 - 13x + 6 = 0$

[−4, 0, 1] by [−25, 25, 5]

49. $6x^3 - 11x^2 + 6x - 1 = 0$

50. $2x^3 + 11x^2 - 7x - 6 = 0$

Application Exercises

51. a. Use synthetic division to show that 3 is a solution of the polynomial equation
$$14x^3 - 17x^2 - 16x - 177 = 0.$$

b. Use the solution from part (a) to solve this problem. The number of eggs, $f(x)$, in a female moth is a function of her abdominal width, x, in millimeters, modeled by

$$f(x) = 14x^3 - 17x^2 - 16x + 34.$$

What is the abdominal width when there are 211 eggs?

52. a. Use synthetic division to show that 2 is a solution of the polynomial equation

$$2h^3 + 14h^2 - 72 = 0.$$

b. Use the solution from part (a) to solve this problem. The width of a rectangular box is twice the height and the length is 7 inches more than the height. If the volume is 72 cubic inches, find the dimensions of the box.

In Exercises 53–54, write a polynomial that represents the length of each rectangle.

53.

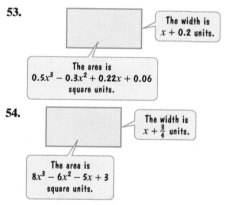

The width is $x + 0.2$ units.

The area is $0.5x^3 - 0.3x^2 + 0.22x + 0.06$ square units.

54.

The width is $x + \frac{3}{4}$ units.

The area is $8x^3 - 6x^2 - 5x + 3$ square units.

During the 1980s, the controversial economist Arthur Laffer promoted the idea that tax increases lead to a reduction in government revenue. Called supply-side economics, the theory uses functions such as

$$f(x) = \frac{80x - 8000}{x - 110}, 30 \le x \le 100.$$

This function models the government tax revenue, $f(x)$, in tens of billions of dollars, in terms of the tax rate, x. The graph of the function is shown. It illustrates tax revenue decreasing quite dramatically as the tax rate increases. At a tax rate of (gasp) 100%, the government takes all our money and no one has an incentive to work. With no income earned, zero dollars in tax revenue is generated.

Use function f and its graph to solve Exercises 55–56.

55. a. Find and interpret $f(30)$. Identify the solution as a point on the graph of the function.

b. Rewrite the function by using long division to perform

$$(80x - 8000) \div (x - 110).$$

Then use this new form of the function to find $f(30)$. Do you obtain the same answer as you did in part (a)?

c. Is f a polynomial function? Explain your answer.

56. a. Find and interpret $f(40)$. Identify the solution as a point on the graph of the function.

b. Rewrite the function by using long division to perform

$$(80x - 8000) \div (x - 110).$$

Then use this new form of the function to find $f(40)$. Do you obtain the same answer as you did in part (a)?

c. Is f a polynomial function? Explain your answer.

Writing in Mathematics

57. Explain how to perform long division of polynomials. Use $2x^3 - 3x^2 - 11x + 7$ divided by $x - 3$ in your explanation.

58. In your own words, state the Division Algorithm.

59. How can the Division Algorithm be used to check the quotient and remainder in a long division problem?

60. Explain how to perform synthetic division. Use the division problem in Exercise 57 to support your explanation.

61. State the Remainder Theorem.

62. Explain how the Remainder Theorem can be used to find $f(-6)$ if $f(x) = x^4 + 7x^3 + 8x^2 + 11x + 5$. What advantage is there to using the Remainder Theorem in this situation rather than evaluating $f(-6)$ directly?

63. How can the Factor Theorem be used to determine if $x - 1$ is a factor of $x^3 - 2x^2 - 11x + 12$?

64. If you know that -2 is a zero of

$$f(x) = x^3 + 7x^2 + 4x - 12,$$

explain how to solve the equation

$$x^3 + 7x^2 + 4x - 12 = 0.$$

Technology Exercise

65. For each equation that you solved in Exercises 43–46, use a graphing utility to graph the polynomial function defined by the left side of the equation. Use end behavior to obtain a complete graph. Then use the graph's x-intercepts to verify your solutions.

Critical Thinking Exercises

Make Sense? *In Exercises 66–69, determine whether each statement makes sense or does not make sense, and explain your reasoning.*

66. When performing the division $(x^5 + 1) \div (x + 1)$, there's no need for me to follow all the steps involved in polynomial long division because I can work the problem in my head and see that the quotient must be $x^4 + 1$.

67. Every time I divide polynomials using synthetic division, I am using a highly condensed form of the long division procedure where omitting the variables and exponents does not involve the loss of any essential data.

68. The only nongraphic method that I have for evaluating a function at a given value is to substitute that value into the function's equation.

69. I found the zeros of function f, but I still need to find the solutions of the equation $f(x) = 0$.

In Exercises 70–73, determine whether each statement is true or false. If the statement is false, make the necessary change(s) to produce a true statement.

70. If a trinomial in x of degree 6 is divided by a trinomial in x of degree 3, the degree of the quotient is 2.

71. Synthetic division can be used to find the quotient of $10x^3 - 6x^2 + 4x - 1$ and $x - \frac{1}{2}$.

72. Any problem that can be done by synthetic division can also be done by the method for long division of polynomials.

73. If a polynomial long-division problem results in a remainder that is a whole number, then the divisor is a factor of the dividend.

74. Find k so that $4x + 3$ is a factor of
$$20x^3 + 23x^2 - 10x + k.$$

75. When $2x^2 - 7x + 9$ is divided by a polynomial, the quotient is $2x - 3$ and the remainder is 3. Find the polynomial.

76. Find the quotient of $x^{3n} + 1$ and $x^n + 1$.

77. Synthetic division is a process for dividing a polynomial by $x - c$. The coefficient of x in the divisor is 1. How might synthetic division be used if you are dividing by $2x - 4$?

78. Use synthetic division to show that 5 is a solution of
$$x^4 - 4x^3 - 9x^2 + 16x + 20 = 0.$$
Then solve the polynomial equation.

Preview Exercises

Exercises 79–81 will help you prepare for the material covered in the next section.

79. Solve: $x^2 + 4x - 1 = 0$.

80. Solve: $x^2 + 4x + 6 = 0$.

81. Let $f(x) = a_n(x^4 - 3x^2 - 4)$. If $f(3) = -150$, determine the value of a_n. _____

SECTION 3.4   Zeros of Polynomial Functions

Objectives

1. Use the Rational Zero Theorem to find possible rational zeros.
2. Find zeros of a polynomial function.
3. Solve polynomial equations.
4. Use the Linear Factorization Theorem to find polynomials with given zeros.
5. Use Descartes's Rule of Signs.

HIERONYMVS CARDANVS.

You stole my formula!

Tartaglia's Secret Formula for One Solution of
$x^3 + mx = n$

$$x = \sqrt[3]{\sqrt{\left(\frac{n}{2}\right)^2 + \left(\frac{m}{3}\right)^3} + \frac{n}{2}}$$
$$- \sqrt[3]{\sqrt{\left(\frac{n}{2}\right)^2 + \left(\frac{m}{3}\right)^3} - \frac{n}{2}}$$

Popularizers of mathematics are sharing bizarre stories that are giving math a secure place in popular culture. One episode, able to compete with the wildest fare served up by television talk shows and the tabloids, involves three Italian mathematicians and, of all things, zeros of polynomial functions.

Tartaglia (1499–1557), poor and starving, has found a formula that gives a root for a third-degree polynomial equation. Cardano (1501–1576) begs Tartaglia to reveal the secret formula, wheedling it from him with the promise he will find the impoverished Tartaglia a patron. Then Cardano publishes his famous work *Ars Magna*, in which he presents Tartaglia's formula as his own. Cardano uses his most talented student, Ferrari (1522–1565), who derived a formula for a root of a fourth-degree polynomial equation, to falsely accuse Tartaglia of plagiarism. The dispute becomes violent and Tartaglia is fortunate to escape alive.

The noise from this "You Stole My Formula" episode is quieted by the work of French mathematician Evariste Galois (1811–1832). Galois proved that there is no general formula for finding roots of polynomial equations of degree 5 or higher. There are, however, methods for finding roots. In this section, we study methods for finding zeros of polynomial functions. We begin with a theorem that plays an important role in this process.

GREAT QUESTION!

When finding zeros of polynomial functions, what kinds of numbers can I get?

Here's a quick example that involves all possible kinds of zeros:

$$f(x) = \underbrace{(x + 3)}\underbrace{(2x - 1)}\underbrace{(x + \sqrt{2})}\underbrace{(x - \sqrt{2})}\underbrace{(x - 4 + 5i)}\underbrace{(x - 4 - 5i)}.$$

Zeros: $-3,$ $\dfrac{1}{2},$ $-\sqrt{2},$ $\sqrt{2},$ $4 - 5i,$ $4 + 5i$

Rational zeros   Irrational zeros   Complex imaginary zeros

Real zeros   Nonreal zeros

---

① Use the Rational Zero Theorem to find possible rational zeros.

The Rational Zero Theorem

The *Rational Zero Theorem* provides us with a tool that we can use to make a list of all possible rational zeros of a polynomial function. Equivalently, the theorem gives all possible rational roots of a polynomial equation. Not every number in the list will be a zero of the function, but every rational zero of the polynomial function will appear somewhere in the list.

> **The Rational Zero Theorem**
>
> If $f(x) = a_n x^n + a_{n-1} x^{n-1} + \cdots + a_1 x + a_0$ has *integer* coefficients and $\dfrac{p}{q}$ (where $\dfrac{p}{q}$ is reduced to lowest terms) is a rational zero of f , then p is a factor of the constant term, a_0 , and q is a factor of the leading coefficient, a_n .

You can explore the "why" behind the Rational Zero Theorem in Exercise 92 of Exercise Set 3.4. For now, let's see if we can figure out what the theorem tells us about possible rational zeros. To use the theorem, list all the integers that are factors of the constant term, a_0 . Then list all the integers that are factors of the leading coefficient, a_n . Finally, list all possible rational zeros:

$$\text{Possible rational zeros} = \frac{\text{Factors of the constant term}}{\text{Factors of the leading coefficient}}.$$

EXAMPLE 1 Using the Rational Zero Theorem

List all possible rational zeros of $f(x) = -x^4 + 3x^2 + 4$.

SOLUTION

The constant term is 4. We list all of its factors: $\pm 1, \pm 2, \pm 4$. The leading coefficient is -1 . Its factors are ± 1 .

Factors of the constant term, 4: $\pm 1,\quad \pm 2,\quad \pm 4$

Factors of the leading coefficient, -1 : ± 1

Because

$$\text{Possible rational zeros} = \frac{\text{Factors of the constant term}}{\text{Factors of the leading coefficient}},$$

we must take each number in the first row, $\pm 1,\ \pm 2,\ \pm 4$, and divide by each number in the second row, ± 1.

$$\text{Possible rational zeros} = \frac{\text{Factors of } 4}{\text{Factors of } -1} = \frac{\pm 1, \pm 2, \pm 4}{\pm 1} = \pm 1, \quad \pm 2, \quad \pm 4$$

| Divide ±1 by ±1. | Divide ±2 by ±1. | Divide ±4 by ±1. |

There are six possible rational zeros. The graph of $f(x) = -x^4 + 3x^2 + 4$ is shown in **Figure 3.27**. The x-intercepts are -2 and 2. Thus, -2 and 2 are the actual rational zeros.   • • •

−2 is a rational zero.   2 is a rational zero.

FIGURE 3.27 The graph of $f(x) = -x^4 + 3x^2 + 4$ shows that -2 and 2 are rational zeros.

⊘ Check Point **1** List all possible rational zeros of
$$f(x) = x^3 + 2x^2 - 5x - 6.$$

EXAMPLE 2   Using the Rational Zero Theorem

List all possible rational zeros of $f(x) = 15x^3 + 14x^2 - 3x - 2$.

SOLUTION

The constant term is -2 and the leading coefficient is 15.

$$\text{Possible rational zeros} = \frac{\text{Factors of the constant term, } -2}{\text{Factors of the leading coefficient, } 15} = \frac{\pm 1, \pm 2}{\pm 1, \pm 3, \pm 5, \pm 15}$$

$$= \pm 1, \quad \pm 2, \quad \pm\frac{1}{3}, \quad \pm\frac{2}{3}, \quad \pm\frac{1}{5}, \quad \pm\frac{2}{5}, \quad \pm\frac{1}{15}, \quad \pm\frac{2}{15}$$

| Divide ±1 and ±2 by ±1. | Divide ±1 and ±2 by ±3. | Divide ±1 and ±2 by ±5. | Divide ±1 and ±2 by ±15. |

There are 16 possible rational zeros. The actual solution set of
$$15x^3 + 14x^2 - 3x - 2 = 0$$
is $\left\{-1, -\frac{1}{3}, \frac{2}{5}\right\}$, which contains three of the 16 possible zeros.   • • •

⊘ Check Point **2** List all possible rational zeros of
$$f(x) = 4x^5 + 12x^4 - x - 3.$$

② Find zeros of a polynomial function.

How do we determine which (if any) of the possible rational zeros are rational zeros of the polynomial function? To find the first rational zero, we can use a trial-and-error process involving synthetic division: If $f(x)$ is divided by $x - c$ and the remainder is zero, then c is a zero of f. After we identify the first rational zero, we use the result of the synthetic division to factor the original polynomial. Then we set each factor equal to zero to identify any additional rational zeros.

EXAMPLE 3   Finding Zeros of a Polynomial Function

Find all zeros of $f(x) = x^3 + 2x^2 - 5x - 6$.

SOLUTION

We begin by listing all possible rational zeros.

Possible rational zeros

$$= \frac{\text{Factors of the constant term, } -6}{\text{Factors of the leading coefficient, } 1} = \frac{\pm1, \pm2, \pm3, \pm6}{\pm1} = \pm1, \pm2, \pm3, \pm6$$

Divide the eight numbers in the numerator by ±1.

Now we will use synthetic division to see if we can find a rational zero among the possible rational zeros $\pm1, \pm2, \pm3, \pm6$. Keep in mind that if $f(x)$ is divided by $x - c$ and the remainder is zero, then c is a zero of f. Let's start by testing 1. If 1 is not a rational zero, then we will test other possible rational zeros.

Test 1.

Coefficients of
$f(x) = x^3 + 2x^2 - 5x - 6$

Possible rational zero $\quad \underline{1|} \quad 1 \quad 2 \quad -5 \quad -6$

$\qquad\qquad\qquad\qquad\quad 1 \quad 3 \quad -2$

$\qquad\qquad\qquad\quad \overline{1 \quad 3 \quad -2 \quad -8}$

The nonzero remainder
shows that 1 is not a zero.

Test 2.

Coefficients of
$f(x) = x^3 + 2x^2 - 5x - 6$

Possible rational zero $\quad \underline{2|} \quad 1 \quad 2 \quad -5 \quad -6$

$\qquad\qquad\qquad\qquad\quad 2 \quad 8 \quad 6$

$\qquad\qquad\qquad\quad \overline{1 \quad 4 \quad 3 \quad 0}$

The zero remainder
shows that 2 is a zero.

The zero remainder tells us that 2 is a zero of the polynomial function $f(x) = x^3 + 2x^2 - 5x - 6$. Equivalently, 2 is a solution, or root, of the polynomial equation $x^3 + 2x^2 - 5x - 6 = 0$. Thus, $x - 2$ is a factor of the polynomial. The first three numbers in the bottom row of the synthetic division on the right, 1, 4, and 3, give the coefficients of the other factor. This factor is $x^2 + 4x + 3$.

$x^3 + 2x^2 - 5x - 6 = 0$ Finding the zeros of $f(x) = x^3 + 2x^2 - 5x - 6$ is the same as finding the roots of this equation.

$(x - 2)(x^2 + 4x + 3) = 0$ Factor using the result from the synthetic division.

$(x - 2)(x + 3)(x + 1) = 0$ Factor completely.

$x - 2 = 0 \quad \text{or} \quad x + 3 = 0 \quad \text{or} \quad x + 1 = 0$ Set each factor equal to zero.

$\quad x = 2 \qquad\qquad\quad x = -3 \qquad\qquad x = -1$ Solve for x.

The solution set is $\{-3, -1, 2\}$. The zeros of f are $-3, -1$, and 2.   • • •

 Check Point **3** Find all zeros of
$$f(x) = x^3 + 8x^2 + 11x - 20.$$

Our work in Example 3 involved finding zeros of a third-degree polynomial function. The Rational Zero Theorem is a tool that allows us to rewrite such functions as products of two factors, one linear and one quadratic. Zeros of the quadratic factor are found by factoring, the quadratic formula, or the square root property.

EXAMPLE 4   Finding Zeros of a Polynomial Function

Find all zeros of $f(x) = x^3 + 7x^2 + 11x - 3$.

SOLUTION

We begin by listing all possible rational zeros.

Possible rational zeros $= \dfrac{\text{Factors of the constant term, } -3}{\text{Factors of the leading coefficient, } 1} = \dfrac{\pm1, \pm3}{\pm1} = \pm1, \pm3$

Now we will use synthetic division to see if we can find a rational zero among the four possible rational zeros, $\pm 1, \pm 3$, of $f(x) = x^3 + 7x^2 + 11x - 3$.

Test 1.	Test −1.	Test 3.	Test −3.

$\underline{1|}$	1	7	11	−3
		1	8	19
	1	8	19	16

$\underline{-1|}$	1	7	11	−3
		−1	−6	−5
	1	6	5	−8

$\underline{3|}$	1	7	11	−3
		3	30	123
	1	10	41	120

$\underline{-3|}$	1	7	11	−3
		−3	−12	3
	1	4	−1	0

The zero remainder when testing −3 tells us that −3 is a zero of the polynomial function $f(x) = x^3 + 7x^2 + 11x - 3$. To find all zeros of f, we proceed as follows:

$$x^3 + 7x^2 + 11x - 3 = 0 \qquad \text{Finding the zeros of } f \text{ is the same thing as finding the roots of } f(x) = 0.$$

$$(x + 3)(x^2 + 4x - 1) = 0 \qquad \text{This result is from the last synthetic division, shown above. The first three numbers in the bottom row, 1, 4, and −1, give the coefficients of the second factor.}$$

$$x + 3 = 0 \quad \text{or} \quad x^2 + 4x - 1 = 0 \qquad \text{Set each factor equal to 0.}$$
$$x = -3. \qquad \qquad\qquad\qquad\qquad \text{Solve the linear equation.}$$

We can use the quadratic formula to solve $x^2 + 4x - 1 = 0$.

$$x = \frac{-b \pm \sqrt{b^2 - 4ac}}{2a} \qquad \text{We use the quadratic formula because } x^2 + 4x - 1 \text{ cannot be factored.}$$

$$= \frac{-4 \pm \sqrt{4^2 - 4(1)(-1)}}{2(1)} \qquad \text{Let } a = 1, b = 4, \text{ and } c = -1.$$

$$= \frac{-4 \pm \sqrt{20}}{2} \qquad \text{Multiply and subtract under the radical:}$$
$$\qquad\qquad\qquad\qquad 4^2 - 4(1)(-1) = 16 - (-4) = 16 + 4 = 20.$$

$$= \frac{-4 \pm 2\sqrt{5}}{2} \qquad \sqrt{20} = \sqrt{4 \cdot 5} = 2\sqrt{5}$$

$$= -2 \pm \sqrt{5} \qquad \text{Divide the numerator and the denominator by 2.}$$

The solution set is $\{-3, -2 - \sqrt{5}, -2 + \sqrt{5}\}$. The zeros of $f(x) = x^3 + 7x^2 + 11x - 3$ are $-3, -2 - \sqrt{5},$ and $-2 + \sqrt{5}$. Among these three real zeros, one zero is rational and two are irrational. $\quad \bullet\bullet\bullet$

📝 **Check Point 4** Find all zeros of $f(x) = x^3 + x^2 - 5x - 2$.

If the degree of a polynomial function or equation is 4 or higher, it is often necessary to find more than one linear factor by synthetic division.

One way to speed up the process of finding the first zero is to graph the function. Any x-intercept is a zero.

③ Solve polynomial equations.

EXAMPLE 5 Solving a Polynomial Equation

Solve: $x^4 - 6x^2 - 8x + 24 = 0$.

SOLUTION

Recall that we refer to the *zeros* of a polynomial function and the *roots* of a polynomial equation. Because we are given an equation, we will use the word "roots," rather than "zeros," in the solution process. We begin by listing all possible rational roots.

$$\text{Possible rational roots} = \frac{\text{Factors of the constant term, } 24}{\text{Factors of the leading coefficient, } 1}$$

$$= \frac{\pm 1, \ \pm 2, \ \pm 3, \ \pm 4, \ \pm 6, \ \pm 8, \ \pm 12, \ \pm 24}{\pm 1}$$

$$= \pm 1, \ \pm 2, \ \pm 3, \ \pm 4, \ \pm 6, \ \pm 8, \ \pm 12, \ \pm 24$$

FIGURE 3.28 The graph of $f(x) = x^4 - 6x^2 - 8x + 24$ in a $[-1, 5, 1]$ by $[-2, 10, 1]$ viewing rectangle

Part of the graph of $f(x) = x^4 - 6x^2 - 8x + 24$ is shown in **Figure 3.28**. Because the x-intercept is 2, we will test 2 by synthetic division and show that it is a root of the given equation. Without the graph, the procedure would be to start the trial-and-error synthetic division with 1 and proceed until a zero remainder is found, as we did in Example 4.

Careful!
$x^4 - 6x^2 - 8x + 24 = x^4 + 0x^3 - 6x^2 - 8x + 24$

The zero remainder indicates that **2** is a root of
$x^4 - 6x^2 - 8x + 24 = 0.$

Now we can rewrite the given equation in factored form.

$$x^4 - 6x^2 - 8x + 24 = 0 \qquad \text{This is the given equation.}$$

$$(x - 2)(x^3 + 2x^2 - 2x - 12) = 0 \qquad \text{This is the result obtained from the synthetic division. The first four numbers in the bottom row, 1, 2, −2, and −12, give the coefficients of the second factor.}$$

$$x - 2 = 0 \quad \text{or} \quad x^3 + 2x^2 - 2x - 12 = 0 \qquad \text{Set each factor equal to 0.}$$

We can use the same approach to look for rational roots of the polynomial equation $x^3 + 2x^2 - 2x - 12 = 0$, listing all possible rational roots. Without the graph in **Figure 3.28**, the procedure would be to start testing possible rational roots by trial-and-error synthetic division. However, take a second look at the graph in **Figure 3.28**. Because the graph turns around at 2, this means that 2 is a root of even multiplicity. Thus, 2 must also be a root of $x^3 + 2x^2 - 2x - 12 = 0$, confirmed by the following synthetic division.

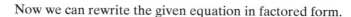

These are the coefficients of
$x^3 + 2x^2 - 2x - 12 = 0.$

The zero remainder indicates that **2** is a
root of $x^3 + 2x^2 - 2x - 12 = 0.$

Now we can solve the original equation as follows:

$$x^4 - 6x^2 - 8x + 24 = 0 \qquad \text{This is the given equation.}$$

$$(x - 2)(x^3 + 2x^2 - 2x - 12) = 0 \qquad \text{This factorization was obtained from the first synthetic division.}$$

$$(x - 2)(x - 2)(x^2 + 4x + 6) = 0 \qquad \text{This factorization was obtained from the second synthetic division. The first three numbers in the bottom row, 1, 4, and 6, give the coefficients of the third factor.}$$

$$x - 2 = 0 \quad \text{or} \quad x - 2 = 0 \quad \text{or} \quad x^2 + 4x + 6 = 0 \qquad \text{Set each factor equal to 0.}$$

$$x = 2 \qquad\qquad x = 2. \qquad\qquad\qquad \text{Solve the linear equations.}$$

We can use the quadratic formula to solve $x^2 + 4x + 6 = 0$.

$$x = \frac{-b \pm \sqrt{b^2 - 4ac}}{2a}$$ We use the quadratic formula because $x^2 + 4x + 6$ cannot be factored.

$$= \frac{-4 \pm \sqrt{4^2 - 4(1)(6)}}{2(1)}$$ Let $a = 1$, $b = 4$, and $c = 6$.

$$= \frac{-4 \pm \sqrt{-8}}{2}$$ Multiply and subtract under the radical: $4^2 - 4(1)(6) = 16 - 24 = -8$.

$$= \frac{-4 \pm 2i\sqrt{2}}{2}$$ $\sqrt{-8} = \sqrt{4(2)(-1)} = 2i\sqrt{2}$

$$= -2 \pm i\sqrt{2}$$ Simplify.

FIGURE 3.28 (repeated) The graph of $f(x) = x^4 - 6x^2 - 8x + 24$ in a $[-1, 5, 1]$ by $[-2, 10, 1]$ viewing rectangle

The solution set of the original equation, $x^4 - 6x^2 - 8x + 24 = 0$, is $\{2, -2 - i\sqrt{2}, -2 + i\sqrt{2}\}$. **Figure 3.28**, repeated in the margin, shows that a graphing utility does not reveal the two imaginary roots. • • •

In Example 5, 2 is a repeated root of the equation with multiplicity 2. Counting this multiple root separately, the fourth-degree equation $x^4 - 6x^2 - 8x + 24 = 0$ has four roots: 2, 2, $-2 + i\sqrt{2}$, and $-2 - i\sqrt{2}$. The equation and its roots illustrate two general properties:

Properties of Roots of Polynomial Equations

1. If a polynomial equation is of degree n, then counting multiple roots separately, the equation has n roots.
2. If $a + bi$ is a root of a polynomial equation with real coefficients ($b \neq 0$), then the imaginary number $a - bi$ is also a root. Imaginary roots, if they exist, occur in conjugate pairs.

☑ Check Point **5** Solve: $x^4 - 6x^3 + 22x^2 - 30x + 13 = 0$.

The Fundamental Theorem of Algebra

The fact that a polynomial equation of degree n has n roots is a consequence of a theorem proved in 1799 by a 22-year-old student named Carl Friedrich Gauss in his doctoral dissertation. His result is called the **Fundamental Theorem of Algebra**.

The Fundamental Theorem of Algebra

If $f(x)$ is a polynomial of degree n, where $n \geq 1$, then the equation $f(x) = 0$ has at least one complex root.

Suppose, for example, that $f(x) = 0$ represents a polynomial equation of degree n. By the Fundamental Theorem of Algebra, we know that this equation has at least one complex root; we'll call it c_1. By the Factor Theorem, we know that $x - c_1$ is a factor of $f(x)$. Therefore, we obtain

$$(x - c_1)q_1(x) = 0$$ The degree of the polynomial $q_1(x)$ is $n - 1$.

$$x - c_1 = 0 \quad \text{or} \quad q_1(x) = 0.$$ Set each factor equal to 0.

If the degree of $q_1(x)$ is at least 1, by the Fundamental Theorem of Algebra, the equation $q_1(x) = 0$ has at least one complex root. We'll call it c_2. The Factor Theorem gives us

$$q_1(x) = 0$$ The degree of $q_1(x)$ is $n - 1$.

$$(x - c_2)q_2(x) = 0$$ The degree of $q_2(x)$ is $n - 2$.

$$x - c_2 = 0 \quad \text{or} \quad q_2(x) = 0.$$ Set each factor equal to 0.

Let's see what we have up to this point and then continue the process.

$$f(x) = 0 \qquad \text{This is the original polynomial equation of degree } n.$$
$$(x - c_1)q_1(x) = 0 \qquad \text{This is the result from our first application of the Fundamental Theorem.}$$
$$(x - c_1)(x - c_2)q_2(x) = 0 \qquad \text{This is the result from our second application of the Fundamental Theorem.}$$

By continuing this process, we will obtain the product of n linear factors. Setting each of these linear factors equal to zero results in n complex roots. Thus, if $f(x)$ is a polynomial of degree n, where $n \geq 1$, then $f(x) = 0$ has exactly n roots, where roots are counted according to their multiplicity.

Use the Linear Factorization Theorem to find polynomials with given zeros.

The Linear Factorization Theorem

In Example 5, we found that $x^4 - 6x^2 - 8x + 24 = 0$ has $\{2, -2 \pm i\sqrt{2}\}$ as a solution set, where 2 is a repeated root with multiplicity 2. The polynomial can be factored over the complex nonreal numbers as follows:

$$f(x) = x^4 - 6x^2 - 8x + 24 \qquad \text{These are the four zeros.}$$

$$= \underbrace{[x - (-2 + i\sqrt{2})]}\underbrace{[x - (-2 - i\sqrt{2})]}\underbrace{(x - 2)}\underbrace{(x - 2)}.$$

These are the linear factors.

This fourth-degree polynomial has four linear factors. Just as an nth-degree polynomial equation has n roots, an nth-degree polynomial has n linear factors. This is formally stated as the **Linear Factorization Theorem**.

The Linear Factorization Theorem

If $f(x) = a_n x^n + a_{n-1} x^{n-1} + \cdots + a_1 x + a_0$, where $n \geq 1$ and $a_n \neq 0$, then

$$f(x) = a_n(x - c_1)(x - c_2) \cdots (x - c_n),$$

where $c_1, c_2, \ldots, c_n$ are complex numbers (possibly real and not necessarily distinct). In words: An nth-degree polynomial can be expressed as the product of a nonzero constant and n linear factors, where each linear factor has a leading coefficient of 1.

Many of our problems involving polynomial functions and polynomial equations dealt with the process of finding zeros and roots. The Linear Factorization Theorem enables us to reverse this process, finding a polynomial function when the zeros are given.

EXAMPLE 6   Finding a Polynomial Function with Given Zeros

Find a fourth-degree polynomial function $f(x)$ with real coefficients that has $-2, 2$, and i as zeros and such that $f(3) = -150$.

SOLUTION

Because i is a zero and the polynomial has real coefficients, the conjugate, $-i$, must also be a zero. We can now use the Linear Factorization Theorem.

$$f(x) = a_n(x - c_1)(x - c_2)(x - c_3)(x - c_4) \qquad \text{This is the linear factorization for a fourth-degree polynomial.}$$

$$= a_n(x + 2)(x - 2)(x - i)(x + i) \qquad \text{Use the given zeros:}$$
$$c_1 = -2, c_2 = 2, c_3 = i, \text{ and, from above,}$$
$$c_4 = -i.$$

$$= a_n(x^2 - 4)(x^2 + 1) \qquad \text{Multiply: } (x - i)(x + i) = x^2 - i^2 = x^2 - (-1) = x^2 + 1.$$

TECHNOLOGY

Graphic Connections

The graph of
$f(x) = -3x^4 + 9x^2 + 12$, shown
in a $[-3, 3, 1]$ by $[-200, 20, 20]$
viewing rectangle, verifies that -2
and 2 are real zeros. By tracing
along the curve, we can check that
$f(3) = -150$.

$$f(x) = a_n(x^4 - 3x^2 - 4)$$

Complete the multiplication for
$f(x) = a_n(x^2 - 4)(x^2 + 1)$.

$$f(3) = a_n(3^4 - 3 \cdot 3^2 - 4) = -150$$

To find a_n, use the fact that $f(3) = -150$.

$$a_n(81 - 27 - 4) = -150$$

Solve for a_n.

$$50a_n = -150$$

Simplify: $81 - 27 - 4 = 50$.

$$a_n = -3$$

Divide both sides by 50.

Substituting -3 for a_n in the formula for $f(x)$, we obtain

$$f(x) = -3(x^4 - 3x^2 - 4).$$

Equivalently,

$$f(x) = -3x^4 + 9x^2 + 12.$$

• • •

✍ **Check Point 6** Find a third-degree polynomial function $f(x)$ with real coefficients that has -3 and i as zeros and such that $f(1) = 8$.

⑤ Use Descartes's Rule of Signs.

"An equation can have as many true [positive] roots as it contains changes of sign, from plus to minus or from minus to plus." René Descartes (1596–1650) in *La Géométrie* (1637)

GREAT QUESTION!

Does Descartes's Rule of Signs include both rational and irrational zeros?

Yes. The number of real zeros given by Descartes's Rule of Signs includes rational zeros from a list of possible rational zeros, as well as irrational zeros not on the list. It does not include any imaginary zeros.

Descartes's Rule of Signs

Because an nth-degree polynomial equation might have roots that are imaginary numbers, we should note that such an equation can have *at most n* real roots. **Descartes's Rule of Signs** provides even more specific information about the number of real zeros that a polynomial can have. The rule is based on considering *variations in sign* between consecutive coefficients. For example, the function $f(x) = 3x^7 - 2x^5 - x^4 + 7x^2 + x - 3$ has three sign changes:

$$f(x) = 3x^7 - 2x^5 - x^4 + 7x^2 + x - 3.$$

sign change   sign change   sign change

Descartes's Rule of Signs

Let $f(x) = a_n x^n + a_{n-1}x^{n-1} + \cdots + a_2 x^2 + a_1 x + a_0$ be a polynomial with real coefficients.

1. The number of *positive real zeros* of f is either
   a. the same as the number of sign changes of $f(x)$

      or

   b. less than the number of sign changes of $f(x)$ by a positive even integer. If $f(x)$ has only one variation in sign, then f has exactly one positive real zero.

2. The number of *negative real zeros* of f is either
   a. the same as the number of sign changes of $f(-x)$

      or

   b. less than the number of sign changes of $f(-x)$ by a positive even integer. If $f(-x)$ has only one variation in sign, then f has exactly one negative real zero.

GREAT QUESTION!

Does a polynomial function have to be written in descending powers of x when counting sign changes?

Yes. Be sure that the function's equation is in this form before using Descartes's Rule of signs.

Table 3.1 illustrates what Descartes's Rule of Signs tells us about the positive real zeros of various polynomial functions.

Table 3.1   Descartes's Rule of Signs and Positive Real Zeros

Polynomial Function	Sign Changes	Conclusion
$f(x) = 3x^7 - 2x^5 - x^4 + 7x^2 + x - 3$ sign change sign change sign change	3	There are 3 positive real zeros. or There is $3 - 2 = 1$ positive real zero.
$f(x) = 4x^5 + 2x^4 - 3x^2 + x + 5$ sign change sign change	2	There are 2 positive real zeros. or There are $2 - 2 = 0$ positive real zeros.
$f(x) = -7x^6 - 5x^4 + x + 9$ sign change	1	There is 1 positive real zero.

EXAMPLE 7   Using Descartes's Rule of Signs

Determine the possible numbers of positive and negative real zeros of $f(x) = x^3 + 2x^2 + 5x + 4$.

SOLUTION

1. To find possibilities for positive real zeros, count the number of sign changes in the equation for $f(x)$. Because all the coefficients are positive, there are no variations in sign. Thus, there are no positive real zeros.

2. To find possibilities for negative real zeros, count the number of sign changes in the equation for $f(-x)$. We obtain this equation by replacing x with $-x$ in the given function.

$$f(x) = x^3 + 2x^2 + 5x + 4$$

Replace x with $-x$.

$$f(-x) = (-x)^3 + 2(-x)^2 + 5(-x) + 4$$
$$= -x^3 + 2x^2 - 5x + 4$$

Now count the sign changes.

$$f(-x) = -x^3 + 2x^2 - 5x + 4$$

sign change   sign change   sign change

There are three variations in sign. The number of negative real zeros of f is either equal to the number of sign changes, 3, or is less than this number by an even integer. This means that either there are 3 negative real zeros or there is $3 - 2 = 1$ negative real zero.   ● ● ●

What do the results of Example 7 mean in terms of solving

$$x^3 + 2x^2 + 5x + 4 = 0?$$

Without using Descartes's Rule of Signs, we list the possible rational roots as follows:

Possible rational roots

$$= \frac{\text{Factors of the constant term, } 4}{\text{Factors of the leading coefficient, } 1} = \frac{\pm 1, \pm 2, \pm 4}{\pm 1} = \pm 1, \pm 2, \pm 4.$$

We see that the possible rational roots of $x^3 + 2x^2 + 5x + 4 = 0$ are ± 1, ± 2, and ± 4. However, Descartes's Rule of Signs informed us that $f(x) = x^3 + 2x^2 + 5x + 4$ has no positive real zeros. Thus, the polynomial equation $x^3 + 2x^2 + 5x + 4 = 0$ has no positive real roots. This means that we can eliminate the positive numbers 1, 2, and 4 from our list of possible rational roots. Possible rational roots include only $-1, -2,$ and -4. We can use synthetic division and test the first of these three possible rational roots of $x^3 + 2x^2 + 5x + 4 = 0$ as follows:

Test
-1. $\underline{-1}\begin{vmatrix} 1 & 2 & 5 & 4 \end{vmatrix}$
$\phantom{-1\begin{vmatrix} 1 & 2 \end{vmatrix}} -1 \; -1 \; -4$
$\overline{\; 1 \quad 1 \quad 4 \quad 0.}$

The zero remainder shows
that -1 is a root.

By solving the equation $x^3 + 2x^2 + 5x + 4 = 0$, you will find that this equation of degree 3 has three roots. One root is -1 and the other two roots are imaginary numbers in a conjugate pair. Verify this by completing the solution process.

 Check Point **7** Determine the possible numbers of positive and negative real zeros of $f(x) = x^4 - 14x^3 + 71x^2 - 154x + 120$.

CONCEPT AND VOCABULARY CHECK

Fill in each blank so that the resulting statement is true.

1. Consider the polynomial function with integer coefficients

$f(x) = a_n x^n + a_{n-1} x^{n-1} + \cdots + a_1 x + a_0, a_n \neq 0.$

The Rational Zero Theorem states that if $\dfrac{p}{q}$ is a rational zero of f (where $\dfrac{p}{q}$ is reduced to lowest terms), then p is a factor of _____ and q is a factor of _____.

2. True or false: $\dfrac{3}{2}$ is a possible rational zero of $f(x) = 2x^3 + 11x^2 - 7x - 6.$ _____

3. True or false: $\dfrac{1}{2}$ is a possible rational zero of $f(x) = 3x^4 - 3x^3 + x^2 - x + 1.$ _____

4. If a polynomial equation is of degree n, then counting multiple roots separately, the equation has ____ roots.

5. If $a + bi$ is a root of a polynomial equation with real coefficients, $b \neq 0$, then _____ is also a root of the equation.

6. Consider solving $2x^3 + 11x^2 - 7x - 6 = 0$. The synthetic division shown below indicates that _____ is a root.

$\underline{-6}\begin{vmatrix} 2 & 11 & -7 & -6 \end{vmatrix}$
$\phantom{-6\begin{vmatrix} 2 \end{vmatrix}} -12 \quad 6 \quad 6$
$\overline{\; 2 \quad -1 \quad -1 \quad 0}$

Based on the synthetic division, $2x^3 + 11x^2 - 7x - 6 = 0$ can be written in factored form as _____.

7. The Linear Factorization Theorem states that an nth-degree polynomial can be expressed as the product of a nonzero constant and ____ linear factors, where each linear factor has a leading coefficient of ____.

Use Descartes's Rule of Signs to determine whether each statement is true of false.

8. A polynomial function with four sign changes must have four positive real zeros. _____

9. A polynomial function with one sign change must have one positive real zero. _____

10. A polynomial function with seven sign changes can have one, three, five, or seven positive real zeros. _____

Practice Exercises

In Exercises 1–8, use the Rational Zero Theorem to list all possible rational zeros for each given function.

1. $f(x) = x^3 + x^2 - 4x - 4$

2. $f(x) = x^3 + 3x^2 - 6x - 8$

3. $f(x) = 3x^4 - 11x^3 - x^2 + 19x + 6$

4. $f(x) = 2x^4 + 3x^3 - 11x^2 - 9x + 15$

5. $f(x) = 4x^4 - x^3 + 5x^2 - 2x - 6$

6. $f(x) = 3x^4 - 11x^3 - 3x^2 - 6x + 8$

7. $f(x) = x^5 - x^4 - 7x^3 + 7x^2 - 12x - 12$

8. $f(x) = 4x^5 - 8x^4 - x + 2$

In Exercises 9–16,

   a. *List all possible rational zeros.*

   b. *Use synthetic division to test the possible rational zeros and find an actual zero.*

   c. *Use the quotient from part (b) to find the remaining zeros of the polynomial function.*

9. $f(x) = x^3 + x^2 - 4x - 4$

10. $f(x) = x^3 - 2x^2 - 11x + 12$

11. $f(x) = 2x^3 - 3x^2 - 11x + 6$

12. $f(x) = 2x^4 - 5x^2 + x + 2$

13. $f(x) = x^3 + 4x^2 - 3x - 6$

14. $f(x) = 2x^3 + x^2 - 3x + 1$

15. $f(x) = 2x^3 + 6x^2 + 5x + 2$

16. $f(x) = x^3 - 4x^2 + 8x - 5$

In Exercises 17–24,

   a. *List all possible rational roots.*

   b. *Use synthetic division to test the possible rational roots and find an actual root.*

   c. *Use the quotient from part (b) to find the remaining roots and solve the equation.*

17. $x^3 - 2x^2 - 11x + 12 = 0$

18. $x^3 - 2x^2 - 7x - 4 = 0$

19. $x^3 - 10x - 12 = 0$

20. $x^3 - 5x^2 + 17x - 13 = 0$

21. $6x^3 + 25x^2 - 24x + 5 = 0$

22. $2x^3 - 5x^2 - 6x + 4 = 0$

23. $x^4 - 2x^3 - 5x^2 + 8x + 4 = 0$

24. $x^4 - 2x^2 - 16x - 15 = 0$

In Exercises 25–32, find an nth-degree polynomial function with real coefficients satisfying the given conditions. If you are using a graphing utility, use it to graph the function and verify the real zeros and the given function value.

25. $n = 3$; 1 and $5i$ are zeros; $f(-1) = -104$

26. $n = 3$; 4 and $2i$ are zeros; $f(-1) = -50$

27. $n = 3$; -5 and $4 + 3i$ are zeros; $f(2) = 91$

28. $n = 3$; 6 and $-5 + 2i$ are zeros; $f(2) = -636$

29. $n = 4$; i and $3i$ are zeros; $f(-1) = 20$

30. $n = 4$; $-2, -\frac{1}{2}$, and i are zeros; $f(1) = 18$

31. $n = 4$; $-2, 5$, and $3 + 2i$ are zeros; $f(1) = -96$

32. $n = 4$; $-4, \frac{1}{3}$, and $2 + 3i$ are zeros; $f(1) = 100$

In Exercises 33–38, use Descartes's Rule of Signs to determine the possible number of positive and negative real zeros for each given function.

33. $f(x) = x^3 + 2x^2 + 5x + 4$

34. $f(x) = x^3 + 7x^2 + x + 7$

35. $f(x) = 5x^3 - 3x^2 + 3x - 1$

36. $f(x) = -2x^3 + x^2 - x + 7$

37. $f(x) = 2x^4 - 5x^3 - x^2 - 6x + 4$

38. $f(x) = 4x^4 - x^3 + 5x^2 - 2x - 6$

In Exercises 39–52, find all zeros of the polynomial function or solve the given polynomial equation. Use the Rational Zero Theorem, Descartes's Rule of Signs, and possibly the graph of the polynomial function shown by a graphing utility as an aid in obtaining the first zero or the first root.

39. $f(x) = x^3 - 4x^2 - 7x + 10$

40. $f(x) = x^3 + 12x^2 + 21x + 10$

41. $2x^3 - x^2 - 9x - 4 = 0$

42. $3x^3 - 8x^2 - 8x + 8 = 0$

43. $f(x) = x^4 - 2x^3 + x^2 + 12x + 8$

44. $f(x) = x^4 - 4x^3 - x^2 + 14x + 10$

45. $x^4 - 3x^3 - 20x^2 - 24x - 8 = 0$

46. $x^4 - x^3 + 2x^2 - 4x - 8 = 0$

47. $f(x) = 3x^4 - 11x^3 - x^2 + 19x + 6$

48. $f(x) = 2x^4 + 3x^3 - 11x^2 - 9x + 15$

49. $4x^4 - x^3 + 5x^2 - 2x - 6 = 0$

50. $3x^4 - 11x^3 - 3x^2 - 6x + 8 = 0$

51. $2x^5 + 7x^4 - 18x^2 - 8x + 8 = 0$

52. $4x^5 + 12x^4 - 41x^3 - 99x^2 + 10x + 24 = 0$

Practice Plus

Exercises 53–60 show incomplete graphs of given polynomial functions.

   a. *Find all the zeros of each function.*

   b. *Without using a graphing utility, draw a complete graph of the function.*

53. $f(x) = -x^3 + x^2 + 16x - 16$

$[-5, 0, 1]$ by $[-40, 25, 5]$

54. $f(x) = -x^3 + 3x^2 - 4$

$[-2, 0, 1]$ by $[-10, 10, 1]$

55. $f(x) = 4x^3 - 8x^2 - 3x + 9$

$[-2, 0, 1]$ by $[-10, 10, 1]$

56. $f(x) = 3x^3 + 2x^2 + 2x - 1$

$[0, 2, \frac{1}{6}]$ by $[-3, 15, 1]$

57. $f(x) = 2x^4 - 3x^3 - 7x^2 - 8x + 6$

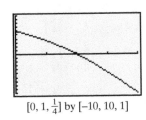

$[0, 1, \frac{1}{4}]$ by $[-10, 10, 1]$

58. $f(x) = 2x^4 + 2x^3 - 22x^2 - 18x + 36$

$[0, 4, 1]$ by $[-50, 50, 10]$

59. $f(x) = 3x^5 + 2x^4 - 15x^3 - 10x^2 + 12x + 8$

$[0, 4, 1]$ by $[-20, 25, 5]$

60. $f(x) = -5x^4 + 4x^3 - 19x^2 + 16x + 4$

$[0, 2, 1]$ by $[-10, 10, 1]$

Application Exercises

A popular model of carry-on luggage has a length that is 10 inches greater than its depth. Airline regulations require that the sum of the length, width, and depth cannot exceed 40 inches. These conditions, with the assumption that this sum is 40 inches, can be modeled by a function that gives the volume of the luggage, V, in cubic inches, in terms of its depth, x, in inches.

Volume	=	depth	·	length	·	width: 40 − (depth + length)

$$V(x) = x \cdot (x + 10) \cdot [40 - (x + x + 10)]$$
$$V(x) = x(x + 10)(30 - 2x)$$

Use function V to solve Exercises 61–62.

61. If the volume of the carry-on luggage is 2000 cubic inches, determine two possibilities for its depth. Where necessary, round to the nearest tenth of an inch.

62. If the volume of the carry-on luggage is 1500 cubic inches, determine two possibilities for its depth. Where necessary, round to the nearest tenth of an inch.

Use the graph of the function modeling the volume of the carry-on luggage to solve Exercises 63–64.

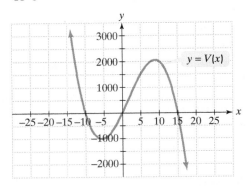

63. a. Identify your answers from Exercise 61 as points on the graph.

b. Use the graph to describe a realistic domain, x, for the volume function, where x represents the depth of the carry-on luggage.

64. a. Identify your answers from Exercise 62 as points on the graph.

b. Use the graph to describe a realistic domain, x, for the volume function, where x represents the depth of the carry-on luggage.

Writing in Mathematics

65. Describe how to find the possible rational zeros of a polynomial function.

66. How does the linear factorization of $f(x)$, that is,

$$f(x) = a_n(x - c_1)(x - c_2) \cdots (x - c_n),$$

show that a polynomial equation of degree n has n roots?

67. Describe how to use Descartes's Rule of Signs to determine the possible number of positive real zeros of a polynomial function.

68. Describe how to use Descartes's Rule of Signs to determine the possible number of negative roots of a polynomial equation.

69. Why must every polynomial equation with real coefficients of degree 3 have at least one real root?

70. Explain why the equation $x^4 + 6x^2 + 2 = 0$ has no rational roots.

71. Suppose $\frac{3}{4}$ is a root of a polynomial equation. What does this tell us about the leading coefficient and the constant term in the equation?

The equations in Exercises 72–75 have real roots that are rational. Use the Rational Zero Theorem to list all possible rational roots. Then graph the polynomial function in the given viewing rectangle to determine which possible rational roots are actual roots of the equation.

72. $2x^3 - 15x^2 + 22x + 15 = 0$; $[-1, 6, 1]$ by $[-50, 50, 10]$

73. $6x^3 - 19x^2 + 16x - 4 = 0$; $[0, 2, 1]$ by $[-3, 2, 1]$

74. $2x^4 + 7x^3 - 4x^2 - 27x - 18 = 0$; $[-4, 3, 1]$ by $[-45, 45, 15]$

75. $4x^4 + 4x^3 + 7x^2 - x - 2 = 0$; $[-2, 2, 1]$ by $[-5, 5, 1]$

76. Use Descartes's Rule of Signs to determine the possible number of positive and negative real zeros of $f(x) = 3x^4 + 5x^2 + 2$. What does this mean in terms of the graph of f? Verify your result by using a graphing utility to graph f.

77. Use Descartes's Rule of Signs to determine the possible number of positive and negative real zeros of $f(x) = x^5 - x^4 + x^3 - x^2 + x - 8$. Verify your result by using a graphing utility to graph f.

78. Write equations for several polynomial functions of odd degree and graph each function. Is it possible for the graph to have no real zeros? Explain. Try doing the same thing for polynomial functions of even degree. Now is it possible to have no real zeros?

Use a graphing utility to obtain a complete graph for each polynomial function in Exercises 79–82. Then determine the number of real zeros and the number of imaginary zeros for each function.

79. $f(x) = x^3 - 6x - 9$

80. $f(x) = 3x^5 - 2x^4 + 6x^3 - 4x^2 - 24x + 16$

81. $f(x) = 3x^4 + 4x^3 - 7x^2 - 2x - 3$

82. $f(x) = x^6 - 64$

Make Sense? *In Exercises 83–86, determine whether each statement makes sense or does not make sense, and explain your reasoning.*

83. I've noticed that $f(-x)$ is used to explore the number of negative real zeros of a polynomial function, as well as to determine whether a function is even, odd, or neither.

84. By using the quadratic formula, I do not need to bother with synthetic division when solving polynomial equations of degree 3 or higher.

85. I'm working with a fourth-degree polynomial function with integer coefficients and zeros at 1 and $3 + \sqrt{5}$. I'm certain that $3 + \sqrt{2}$ cannot also be a zero of this function.

86. I'm working with the polynomial function $f(x) = x^4 + 3x^2 + 2$ that has four possible rational zeros but no actual rational zeros.

In Exercises 87–90, determine whether each statement is true or false. If the statement is false, make the necessary change(s) to produce a true statement.

87. The equation $x^3 + 5x^2 + 6x + 1 = 0$ has one positive real root.

88. Descartes's Rule of Signs gives the exact number of positive and negative real roots for a polynomial equation.

89. Every polynomial equation of degree 3 with integer coefficients has at least one rational root.

90. Every polynomial equation of degree n has n distinct solutions.

91. If the volume of the solid shown in the figure is 208 cubic inches, find the value of x.

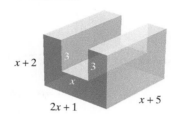

92. In this exercise, we lead you through the steps involved in the proof of the Rational Zero Theorem. Consider the polynomial equation

$$a_n x^n + a_{n-1}x^{n-1} + a_{n-2}x^{n-2} + \cdots + a_1 x + a_0 = 0,$$

and let $\dfrac{p}{q}$ be a rational root reduced to lowest terms.

a. Substitute $\dfrac{p}{q}$ for x in the equation and show that the equation can be written as

$$a_n p^n + a_{n-1}p^{n-1}q + a_{n-2}p^{n-2}q^2 + \cdots + a_1 pq^{n-1} = -a_0 q^n.$$

b. Why is p a factor of the left side of the equation?

c. Because p divides the left side, it must also divide the right side. However, because $\dfrac{p}{q}$ is reduced to lowest terms, p and q have no common factors other than -1 and 1. Because p does divide the right side and has no factors in common with q^n, what can you conclude?

d. Rewrite the equation from part (a) with all terms containing q on the left and the term that does not have a factor of q on the right. Use an argument that parallels parts (b) and (c) to conclude that q is a factor of a_n.

In Exercises 93–96, the graph of a polynomial function is given. What is the smallest degree that each polynomial could have?

93.

94.

95.

96.

97. Explain why a polynomial function of degree 20 cannot cross the x-axis exactly once.

Exercises 98–100 will help you prepare for the material covered in the next section. Use the graph of function f to solve each exercise.

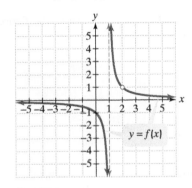

98. For what values of x is the function undefined?

99. Write the equation of the vertical asymptote, or the vertical line that the graph of f approaches but does not touch.

100. Write the equation of the horizontal asymptote, or the horizontal line that the graph of f approaches but does not touch.

CHAPTER 3   Mid-Chapter Check Point

WHAT YOU KNOW: We graphed quadratic functions using vertices, intercepts, and additional points, as necessary. We learned that the vertex of $f(x) = a(x - h)^2 + k$ is (h, k) and the vertex of $f(x) = ax^2 + bx + c$ is $\left(-\frac{b}{2a}, f\left(-\frac{b}{2a}\right)\right)$. We used the vertex to solve problems that involved minimizing or maximizing quadratic functions. We learned a number of techniques for finding the zeros of a polynomial function f of degree 3 or higher or, equivalently, finding the roots, or solutions, of the equation $f(x) = 0$. For some functions, the zeros were found by factoring $f(x)$. For other functions, we listed possible rational zeros and used synthetic division and the Factor Theorem to determine the zeros. We saw that graphs cross the x-axis at zeros of odd multiplicity and touch the x-axis and turn around at zeros of even multiplicity. We learned to graph polynomial functions using zeros, the Leading Coefficient Test, intercepts, and symmetry. We checked graphs using the fact that a polynomial function of degree n has a graph with at most $n - 1$ turning points. After finding zeros of polynomial functions, we reversed directions by using the Linear Factorization Theorem to find functions with given zeros.

In Exercises 1–4, graph the given quadratic function. Give each function's domain and range.

1. $f(x) = (x - 3)^2 - 4$
2. $f(x) = 5 - (x + 2)^2$
3. $f(x) = -x^2 - 4x + 5$
4. $f(x) = 3x^2 - 6x + 1$

In Exercises 5–13, find all zeros of each polynomial function. Then graph the function.

5. $f(x) = (x - 2)^2(x + 1)^3$
6. $f(x) = -(x - 2)^2(x + 1)^2$
7. $f(x) = x^3 - x^2 - 4x + 4$
8. $f(x) = x^4 - 5x^2 + 4$
9. $f(x) = -(x + 1)^6$
10. $f(x) = -6x^3 + 7x^2 - 1$

11. $f(x) = 2x^3 - 2x$
12. $f(x) = x^3 - 2x^2 + 26x$
13. $f(x) = -x^3 + 5x^2 - 5x - 3$

In Exercises 14–19, solve each polynomial equation.

14. $x^3 - 3x + 2 = 0$
15. $6x^3 - 11x^2 + 6x - 1 = 0$
16. $(2x + 1)(3x - 2)^3(2x - 7) = 0$
17. $2x^3 + 5x^2 - 200x - 500 = 0$
18. $x^4 - x^3 - 11x^2 = x + 12$
19. $2x^4 + x^3 - 17x^2 - 4x + 6 = 0$

20. A company manufactures and sells bath cabinets. The function
$$P(x) = -x^2 + 150x - 4425$$
models the company's daily profit, $P(x)$, when x cabinets are manufactured and sold per day. How many cabinets should be manufactured and sold per day to maximize the company's profit? What is the maximum daily profit?

21. Among all pairs of numbers whose sum is -18, find a pair whose product is as large as possible. What is the maximum product?

22. The base of a triangle measures 40 inches minus twice the measure of its height. For what measure of the height does the triangle have a maximum area? What is the maximum area?

In Exercises 23–24, divide, using synthetic division if possible.

23. $(6x^4 - 3x^3 - 11x^2 + 2x + 4) \div (3x^2 - 1)$
24. $(2x^4 - 13x^3 + 17x^2 + 18x - 24) \div (x - 4)$

In Exercises 25–26, find an nth-degree polynomial function with real coefficients satisfying the given conditions.

25. $n = 3$; 1 and i are zeros; $f(-1) = 8$
26. $n = 4$; 2 (with multiplicity 2) and $3i$ are zeros; $f(0) = 36$
27. Does $f(x) = x^3 - x - 5$ have a real zero between 1 and 2?

SECTION 3.5 Rational Functions and Their Graphs

Objectives

1. Find the domains of rational functions.
2. Use arrow notation.
3. Identify vertical asymptotes.
4. Identify horizontal asymptotes.
5. Use transformations to graph rational functions.
6. Graph rational functions.
7. Identify slant asymptotes.
8. Solve applied problems involving rational functions.

Your grandmother appears to be slowing down. Enter ... Mechanical-Grandma! Japanese researchers have developed the robotic exoskeleton shown here to help the elderly and disabled walk and even lift heavy objects like the three 22-pound bags of rice in the photo. It's called the Hybrid Assistive Limb, or HAL. (The inventor has obviously never seen *2001: A Space Odyssey*.) HAL's brain is a computer housed in a backpack that learns to mimic the wearer's gait and posture. Bioelectric sensors pick up signals transmitted from the brain to the muscles, so it can anticipate movements the moment the wearer thinks of them. A commercial version is available at a hefty cost ranging between $14,000 and $20,000. (*Source:* sanlab. kz.tsukuba.ac.jp)

The cost of manufacturing robotic exoskeletons can be modeled by rational functions. In this section, you will see that high production levels of HAL can eventually make this amazing invention more affordable for the elderly and people with disabilities.

Rational Functions

1 Find the domains of rational functions.

Rational functions are quotients of polynomial functions. This means that rational functions can be expressed as

$$f(x) = \frac{p(x)}{q(x)},$$

where p and q are polynomial functions and $q(x) \neq 0$. The **domain** of a rational function is the set of all real numbers except the x-values that make the denominator zero. For example, the domain of the rational function

$$f(x) = \frac{x^2 + 7x + 9}{x(x - 2)(x + 5)}$$

This is $p(x)$.

This is $q(x)$.

is the set of all real numbers except $0, 2,$ and -5.

EXAMPLE 1 Finding the Domain of a Rational Function

Find the domain of each rational function:

a. $f(x) = \dfrac{x^2 - 9}{x - 3}$ **b.** $g(x) = \dfrac{x}{x^2 - 9}$ **c.** $h(x) = \dfrac{x + 3}{x^2 + 9}.$

SOLUTION

Rational functions contain division. Because division by 0 is undefined, we must exclude from the domain of each function values of x that cause the polynomial function in the denominator to be 0.

a. The denominator of $f(x) = \dfrac{x^2 - 9}{x - 3}$ is 0 if $x = 3$. Thus, x cannot equal 3.

The domain of f consists of all real numbers except 3. We can express the domain in set-builder or interval notation:

$$\text{Domain of } f = \{x \mid x \neq 3\}$$
$$\text{Domain of } f = (-\infty, 3) \cup (3, \infty).$$

b. The denominator of $g(x) = \dfrac{x}{x^2 - 9}$ is 0 if $x = -3$ or $x = 3$. Thus, the domain of g consists of all real numbers except -3 and 3. We can express the domain in set-builder or interval notation:

$$\text{Domain of } g = \{x \mid x \neq -3, x \neq 3\}$$
$$\text{Domain of } g = (-\infty, -3) \cup (-3, 3) \cup (3, \infty).$$

c. No real numbers cause the denominator of $h(x) = \dfrac{x + 3}{x^2 + 9}$ to equal 0. The domain of h consists of all real numbers.

$$\text{Domain of } h = (-\infty, \infty)$$

• • •

 Check Point **1** Find the domain of each rational function:

a. $f(x) = \dfrac{x^2 - 25}{x - 5}$ **b.** $g(x) = \dfrac{x}{x^2 - 25}$ **c.** $h(x) = \dfrac{x + 5}{x^2 + 25}$.

② Use arrow notation.

The most basic rational function is the **reciprocal function**, defined by $f(x) = \dfrac{1}{x}$. The denominator of the reciprocal function is zero when $x = 0$, so the domain of f is the set of all real numbers except 0.

Let's look at the behavior of f near the excluded value 0. We start by evaluating $f(x)$ to the left of 0.

x approaches 0 from the left.

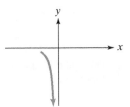

x	-1	-0.5	-0.1	-0.01	-0.001
$f(x) = \dfrac{1}{x}$	-1	-2	-10	-100	-1000

Mathematically, we say that "x approaches 0 from the left." From the table and the accompanying graph, it appears that as x approaches 0 from the left, the function values, $f(x)$, decrease without bound. We say that "$f(x)$ approaches negative infinity." We use a special arrow notation to describe this situation symbolically:

As $x \to 0^-$, $f(x) \to -\infty$.

> As x approaches 0 from the left, $f(x)$ approaches negative infinity (that is, the graph falls).

Observe that the minus $(-)$ superscript on the 0 $(x \to 0^-)$ is read "from the left." Next, we evaluate $f(x)$ to the right of 0.

x approaches 0 from the right.

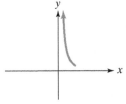

x	0.001	0.01	0.1	0.5	1
$f(x) = \dfrac{1}{x}$	1000	100	10	2	1

Mathematically, we say that "x approaches 0 from the right." From the table and the accompanying graph, it appears that as x approaches 0 from the right, the function values, $f(x)$, increase without bound. We say that "$f(x)$ approaches infinity." We again use a special arrow notation to describe this situation symbolically:

As $x \to 0^+$, $f(x) \to \infty$.

> As x approaches 0 from the right, $f(x)$ approaches infinity (that is, the graph rises).

Observe that the plus $(+)$ superscript on the 0 $(x \to 0^+)$ is read "from the right."

Now let's see what happens to the function values of $f(x) = \dfrac{1}{x}$ as x gets farther away from the origin. The following tables suggest what happens to $f(x)$ as x increases or decreases without bound.

x increases without bound:				
x	1	10	100	1000
$f(x) = \dfrac{1}{x}$	1	0.1	0.01	0.001

x decreases without bound:				
x	−1	−10	−100	−1000
$f(x) = \dfrac{1}{x}$	−1	−0.1	−0.01	−0.001

It appears that as x increases or decreases without bound, the function values, $f(x)$, are getting progressively closer to 0.

Figure 3.29 illustrates the end behavior of $f(x) = \dfrac{1}{x}$ as x increases or decreases without bound. The graph shows that the function values, $f(x)$, are approaching 0. This means that as x increases or decreases without bound, the graph of f is approaching the horizontal line $y = 0$ (that is, the x-axis). We use arrow notation to describe this situation:

$$\text{As } x \to \infty,\ f(x) \to 0 \qquad \text{and} \qquad \text{as } x \to -\infty,\ f(x) \to 0.$$

As x approaches infinity (that is, increases without bound), $f(x)$ approaches 0.

As x approaches negative infinity (that is, decreases without bound), $f(x)$ approaches 0.

Thus, as x approaches infinity ($x \to \infty$) or as x approaches negative infinity ($x \to -\infty$), the function values are approaching zero: $f(x) \to 0$.

The graph of the reciprocal function $f(x) = \dfrac{1}{x}$ is shown in **Figure 3.30**. Unlike the graph of a polynomial function, the graph of the reciprocal function has a break and is composed of two branches.

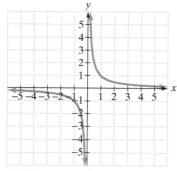

FIGURE 3.29 $f(x)$ approaches 0 as x increases or decreases without bound.

FIGURE 3.30 The graph of the reciprocal function $f(x) = \dfrac{1}{x}$

GREAT QUESTION!

What is the relationship between x and $\dfrac{1}{x}$ when x is far from 0? What happens if x is close to 0?

If x is far from 0, then $\dfrac{1}{x}$ is close to 0. By contrast, if x is close to 0, then $\dfrac{1}{x}$ is far from 0.

Blitzer Bonus || The Reciprocal Function as a Knuckle Tattoo

"I got the tattoo because I like the idea of math not being well behaved. That sounds lame and I really don't mean that in some kind of anarchy-type way. I just think that it's kind of nice that something as perfectly functional as math can kink up around the edges."

Kink up around the edges? On the next page, we'll describe the graphic behavior of the reciprocal function using *asymptotes* rather than kink. Asymptotes are lines that graphs approach but never touch. *Asymptote* comes from the Greek word *asymptotos*, meaning "not meeting."

The arrow notation used throughout our discussion of the reciprocal function is summarized in the following box:

Arrow Notation

Symbol	Meaning
$x \to a^+$	x approaches a from the right.
$x \to a^-$	x approaches a from the left.
$x \to \infty$	x approaches infinity; that is, x increases without bound.
$x \to -\infty$	x approaches negative infinity; that is, x decreases without bound.

Another basic rational function is $f(x) = \dfrac{1}{x^2}$. The graph of this even function, with y-axis symmetry and positive function values, is shown in **Figure 3.31**. Like the reciprocal function, the graph has a break and is composed of two distinct branches.

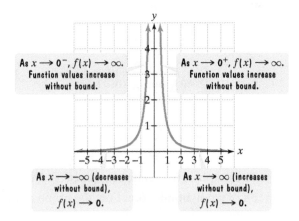

As $x \to 0^-$, $f(x) \to \infty$.
Function values increase without bound.

As $x \to 0^+$, $f(x) \to \infty$.
Function values increase without bound.

As $x \to -\infty$ (decreases without bound), $f(x) \to 0$.

As $x \to \infty$ (increases without bound), $f(x) \to 0$.

FIGURE 3.31 The graph of $f(x) = \dfrac{1}{x^2}$

③ Identify vertical asymptotes.

Vertical Asymptotes of Rational Functions

Look again at the graph of $f(x) = \dfrac{1}{x^2}$ in **Figure 3.31**. The curve approaches, but does not touch, the y-axis. The y-axis, or $x = 0$, is said to be a *vertical asymptote* of the graph. A rational function may have no vertical asymptotes, one vertical asymptote, or several vertical asymptotes. The graph of a rational function never intersects a vertical asymptote. We will use dashed lines to show asymptotes.

Definition of a Vertical Asymptote

The line $x = a$ is a **vertical asymptote** of the graph of a function f if $f(x)$ increases or decreases without bound as x approaches a.

As $x \to a^+$, $f(x) \to \infty$.

As $x \to a^-$, $f(x) \to \infty$.

As $x \to a^+$, $f(x) \to -\infty$.

As $x \to a^-$, $f(x) \to -\infty$.

Thus, as x approaches a from either the left or the right, $f(x) \to \infty$ or $f(x) \to -\infty$.

If the graph of a rational function has vertical asymptotes, they can be located using the following theorem:

> **Locating Vertical Asymptotes**
>
> If $f(x) = \dfrac{p(x)}{q(x)}$ is a rational function in which $p(x)$ and $q(x)$ have no common factors and a is a zero of $q(x)$, the denominator, then $x = a$ is a vertical asymptote of the graph of f.

EXAMPLE 2   Finding the Vertical Asymptotes of a Rational Function

Find the vertical asymptotes, if any, of the graph of each rational function:

a. $f(x) = \dfrac{x}{x^2 - 9}$ **b.** $g(x) = \dfrac{x + 3}{x^2 - 9}$ **c.** $h(x) = \dfrac{x + 3}{x^2 + 9}$.

SOLUTION

Factoring is usually helpful in identifying zeros of denominators and any common factors in the numerators and denominators.

a. $f(x) = \dfrac{x}{x^2 - 9} = \dfrac{x}{(x + 3)(x - 3)}$

This factor is 0 if $x = -3$.   This factor is 0 if $x = 3$.

There are no common factors in the numerator and the denominator. The zeros of the denominator are -3 and 3. Thus, the lines $x = -3$ and $x = 3$ are the vertical asymptotes for the graph of f. [See **Figure 3.32(a)**.]

b. We will use factoring to see if there are common factors.

$$g(x) = \dfrac{x + 3}{x^2 - 9} = \dfrac{(x + 3)}{(x + 3)(x - 3)} = \dfrac{1}{x - 3}, \text{ provided } x \neq -3$$

There is a common factor, $x + 3$, so simplify.   This denominator is 0 if $x = 3$.

The only zero of the denominator of $g(x)$ in simplified form is 3. Thus, the line $x = 3$ is the only vertical asymptote of the graph of g. [See **Figure 3.32(b)**.]

c. We cannot factor the denominator of $h(x)$ over the real numbers.

$$h(x) = \dfrac{x + 3}{x^2 + 9}$$

No real numbers make this denominator 0.

The denominator has no real zeros. Thus, the graph of h has no vertical asymptotes. [See **Figure 3.32(c)**.]

FIGURE 3.32(a) The graph of $f(x) = \dfrac{x}{x^2 - 9}$ has two vertical asymptotes.

Vertical asymptote: $x = -3$ Vertical asymptote: $x = 3$

FIGURE 3.32(b) The graph of $g(x) = \dfrac{x + 3}{x^2 - 9}$ has one vertical asymptote.

There is a hole in the graph corresponding to $x = -3$.

Vertical asymptote: $x = 3$

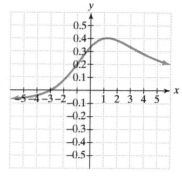

FIGURE 3.32(c) The graph of $h(x) = \dfrac{x + 3}{x^2 + 9}$ has no vertical asymptotes.

✓ Check Point **2** Find the vertical asymptotes, if any, of the graph of each rational function:

a. $f(x) = \dfrac{x}{x^2 - 1}$ **b.** $g(x) = \dfrac{x - 1}{x^2 - 1}$ **c.** $h(x) = \dfrac{x - 1}{x^2 + 1}$.

TECHNOLOGY

The graph of the rational function $f(x) = \dfrac{x}{x^2 - 9}$, drawn by hand in **Figure 3.32(a)** on the previous page, is graphed below in a $[-5, 5, 1]$ by $[-4, 4, 1]$ viewing rectangle. The graph is shown in connected mode and in dot mode. In connected mode, the graphing utility plots many points and connects the points with curves. In dot mode, the utility plots the same points but does not connect them.

Connected Mode

Dot Mode

This might appear to be the vertical asymptote $x = -3$, but it is neither vertical nor an asymptote.

This might appear to be the vertical asymptote $x = 3$, but it is neither vertical nor an asymptote.

The steep lines that may appear on some graphing utilities in connected mode and seem to be the vertical asymptotes $x = -3$ and $x = 3$ are not part of the graph and do not represent the vertical asymptotes. The graphing utility has incorrectly connected the last point to the left of $x = -3$ with the first point to the right of $x = -3$. It has also incorrectly connected the last point to the left of $x = 3$ with the first point to the right of $x = 3$. The effect is to create two near-vertical segments that look like asymptotes. This erroneous effect does not appear using dot mode.

GREAT QUESTION!

Do I have to factor to identify a rational function's possible vertical asymptotes or holes?

Yes. It is essential to factor the numerator and the denominator of the rational function.

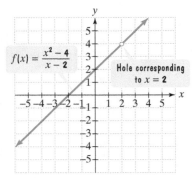

FIGURE 3.33 A graph with a hole corresponding to the denominator's zero

A value where the denominator of a rational function is zero does not necessarily result in a vertical asymptote. There is a hole corresponding to $x = a$, and not a vertical asymptote, in the graph of a rational function under the following conditions: The value a causes the denominator to be zero, but there is a reduced form of the function's equation in which a does not cause the denominator to be zero.

Consider, for example, the function

$$f(x) = \frac{x^2 - 4}{x - 2}.$$

Because the denominator is zero when $x = 2$, the function's domain is all real numbers except 2. However, there is a reduced form of the equation in which 2 does not cause the denominator to be zero:

$$f(x) = \frac{x^2 - 4}{x - 2} = \frac{(x + 2)(x - 2)}{x - 2} = x + 2, \; x \neq 2.$$

Denominator is zero at $x = 2$.

In this reduced form, 2 does not result in a zero denominator.

Figure 3.33 shows that the graph has a hole corresponding to $x = 2$. Graphing utilities do not show this feature of the graph.

④ Identify horizontal asymptotes.

Horizontal Asymptotes of Rational Functions

Figure 3.30, repeated in the margin at the top of the next page, shows the graph of the reciprocal function $f(x) = \dfrac{1}{x}$. As $x \to \infty$ and as $x \to -\infty$, the function values are approaching 0: $f(x) \to 0$. The line $y = 0$ (that is, the x-axis) is a *horizontal asymptote* of the graph. Many, but not all, rational functions have horizontal asymptotes.

FIGURE 3.30 The graph of
$f(x) = \dfrac{1}{x}$ (repeated)

Definition of a Horizontal Asymptote

The line $y = b$ is a **horizontal asymptote** of the graph of a function f if $f(x)$ approaches b as x increases or decreases without bound.

As $x \to \infty, f(x) \to b$. As $x \to \infty, f(x) \to b$. As $x \to \infty, f(x) \to b$.

Recall that a rational function may have several vertical asymptotes. By contrast, it can have at most one horizontal asymptote. Although a graph can never intersect a vertical asymptote, it may cross its horizontal asymptote.

If the graph of a rational function has a horizontal asymptote, it can be located using the following theorem:

Locating Horizontal Asymptotes

Let f be the rational function given by

$$f(x) = \frac{a_n x^n + a_{n-1} x^{n-1} + \cdots + a_1 x + a_0}{b_m x^m + b_{m-1} x^{m-1} + \cdots + b_1 x + b_0}, \quad a_n \neq 0, b_m \neq 0.$$

The degree of the numerator is n. The degree of the denominator is m.

1. If $n < m$, the x-axis, or $y = 0$, is the horizontal asymptote of the graph of f.

2. If $n = m$, the line $y = \dfrac{a_n}{b_m}$ is the horizontal asymptote of the graph of f.

3. If $n > m$, the graph of f has no horizontal asymptote.

GREAT QUESTION!

Do I have to factor to identify a rational function's possible horizontal asymptote?

No. Unlike identifying possible vertical asymptotes or holes, we do not use factoring to determine a possible horizontal asymptote.

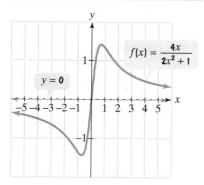

FIGURE 3.34(a) The horizontal asymptote of the graph is $y = 0$.

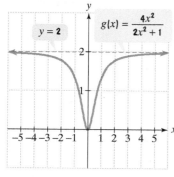

FIGURE 3.34(b) The horizontal asymptote of the graph is $y = 2$.

EXAMPLE 3   Finding the Horizontal Asymptote of a Rational Function

Find the horizontal asymptote, if there is one, of the graph of each rational function:

a. $f(x) = \dfrac{4x}{2x^2 + 1}$ **b.** $g(x) = \dfrac{4x^2}{2x^2 + 1}$ **c.** $h(x) = \dfrac{4x^3}{2x^2 + 1}.$

SOLUTION

a. $f(x) = \dfrac{4x}{2x^2 + 1}$

The degree of the numerator, 1, is less than the degree of the denominator, 2. Thus, the graph of f has the x-axis as a horizontal asymptote. [See **Figure 3.34(a)**.] The equation of the horizontal asymptote is $y = 0$.

b. $g(x) = \dfrac{4x^2}{2x^2 + 1}$

The degree of the numerator, 2, is equal to the degree of the denominator, 2. The leading coefficients of the numerator and denominator, 4 and 2, are used to obtain the equation of the horizontal asymptote. The equation of the horizontal asymptote is $y = \frac{4}{2}$ or $y = 2$. [See **Figure 3.34(b)**.]

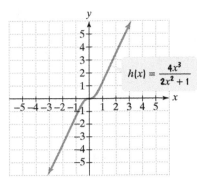

FIGURE 3.34(c) The graph has no horizontal asymptote.

⑤ Use transformations to graph rational functions.

c. $h(x) = \dfrac{4x^3}{2x^2 + 1}$

The degree of the numerator, 3, is greater than the degree of the denominator, 2. Thus, the graph of h has no horizontal asymptote. [See **Figure 3.34(c)**.] • • •

⊘ Check Point **3** Find the horizontal asymptote, if there is one, of the graph of each rational function:

a. $f(x) = \dfrac{9x^2}{3x^2 + 1}$ **b.** $g(x) = \dfrac{9x}{3x^2 + 1}$ **c.** $h(x) = \dfrac{9x^3}{3x^2 + 1}$.

Using Transformations to Graph Rational Functions

Table 3.2 shows the graphs of two rational functions, $f(x) = \dfrac{1}{x}$ and $f(x) = \dfrac{1}{x^2}$. The dashed green lines indicate the asymptotes.

Table 3.2   Graphs of Common Rational Functions

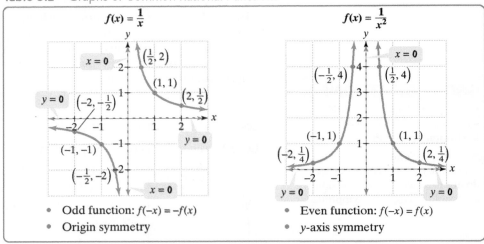

- Odd function: $f(-x) = -f(x)$
- Origin symmetry
- Even function: $f(-x) = f(x)$
- y-axis symmetry

Some rational functions can be graphed using transformations (horizontal shifting, stretching or shrinking, reflecting, vertical shifting) of these two common graphs.

EXAMPLE 4   Using Transformations to Graph a Rational Function

Use the graph of $f(x) = \dfrac{1}{x^2}$ to graph $g(x) = \dfrac{1}{(x-2)^2} + 1$.

SOLUTION

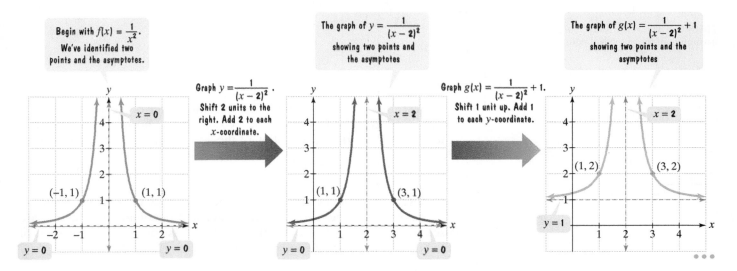

• • •

⊘ Check Point **4** Use the graph of $f(x) = \dfrac{1}{x}$ to graph $g(x) = \dfrac{1}{x+2} - 1$.

⑥ Graph rational functions.

Graphing Rational Functions

Rational functions that are not transformations of $f(x) = \dfrac{1}{x}$ or $f(x) = \dfrac{1}{x^2}$ can be graphed using the following procedure:

Strategy for Graphing a Rational Function

The following strategy can be used to graph

$$f(x) = \frac{p(x)}{q(x)},$$

where p and q are polynomial functions with no common factors.

1. Determine whether the graph of f has symmetry.

$$f(-x) = f(x): \qquad y\text{-axis symmetry}$$
$$f(-x) = -f(x): \qquad \text{origin symmetry}$$

2. Find the y-intercept (if there is one) by evaluating $f(0)$.

3. Find the x-intercepts (if there are any) by solving the equation $p(x) = 0$.

4. Find any vertical asymptote(s) by solving the equation $q(x) = 0$.

5. Find the horizontal asymptote (if there is one) using the rule for determining the horizontal asymptote of a rational function.

6. Plot at least one point between and beyond each x-intercept and vertical asymptote.

7. Use the information obtained previously to graph the function between and beyond the vertical asymptotes.

EXAMPLE 5   Graphing a Rational Function

Graph: $f(x) = \dfrac{2x - 1}{x - 1}$.

SOLUTION

Step 1   Determine symmetry.

$$f(-x) = \frac{2(-x) - 1}{-x - 1} = \frac{-2x - 1}{-x - 1} = \frac{2x + 1}{x + 1}$$

Because $f(-x)$ does not equal either $f(x)$ or $-f(x)$, the graph has neither y-axis symmetry nor origin symmetry.

Step 2   Find the y-intercept.   Evaluate $f(0)$.

$$f(0) = \frac{2 \cdot 0 - 1}{0 - 1} = \frac{-1}{-1} = 1$$

The y-intercept is 1, so the graph passes through $(0, 1)$.

Step 3   Find x-intercept(s).   This is done by solving $p(x) = 0$, where $p(x)$ is the numerator of $f(x)$.

$$2x - 1 = 0 \qquad \text{Set the numerator equal to 0.}$$
$$2x = 1 \qquad \text{Add 1 to both sides.}$$
$$x = \frac{1}{2} \qquad \text{Divide both sides by 2.}$$

The x-intercept is $\frac{1}{2}$, so the graph passes through $\left(\frac{1}{2}, 0\right)$.

Step 4 Find the vertical asymptote(s). Solve $q(x) = 0$, where $q(x)$ is the denominator of $f(x)$, thereby finding zeros of the denominator. (Note that the numerator and denominator of $f(x) = \dfrac{2x - 1}{x - 1}$ have no common factors.)

$$x - 1 = 0 \qquad \text{Set the denominator equal to 0.}$$
$$x = 1 \qquad \text{Add 1 to both sides.}$$

The equation of the vertical asymptote is $x = 1$.

Step 5 Find the horizontal asymptote. Because the numerator and denominator of $f(x) = \dfrac{2x - 1}{x - 1}$ have the same degree, 1, the leading coefficients of the numerator and denominator, 2 and 1, respectively, are used to obtain the equation of the horizontal asymptote. The equation is

$$y = \frac{2}{1} = 2.$$

The equation of the horizontal asymptote is $y = 2$.

Step 6 Plot points between and beyond each x-intercept and vertical asymptote. With an x-intercept at $\frac{1}{2}$ and a vertical asymptote at $x = 1$, we evaluate the function at $-2, -1, \dfrac{3}{4}, 2$, and 4.

x				-2	-1	$\dfrac{3}{4}$	2	4
$f(x) = \dfrac{2x - 1}{x - 1}$				$\dfrac{5}{3}$	$\dfrac{3}{2}$	-2	3	$\dfrac{7}{3}$

Figure 3.35 shows these points, the y-intercept, the x-intercept, and the asymptotes.

Step 7 Graph the function. The graph of $f(x) = \dfrac{2x - 1}{x - 1}$ is shown in **Figure 3.36**.

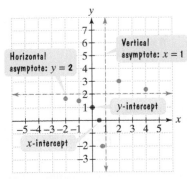

FIGURE 3.35 Preparing to graph the rational function $f(x) = \dfrac{2x - 1}{x - 1}$

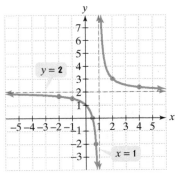

FIGURE 3.36 The graph of $f(x) = \dfrac{2x - 1}{x - 1}$

· · ·

✓ Check Point **5** Graph: $f(x) = \dfrac{3x - 3}{x - 2}$.

EXAMPLE 6 Graphing a Rational Function

Graph: $f(x) = \dfrac{3x^2}{x^2 - 4}$.

SOLUTION

Step 1 Determine symmetry. $f(-x) = \dfrac{3(-x)^2}{(-x)^2 - 4} = \dfrac{3x^2}{x^2 - 4} = f(x)$: The graph of f is symmetric with respect to the y-axis.

Step 2   Find the y-intercept. $f(0) = \dfrac{3 \cdot 0^2}{0^2 - 4} = \dfrac{0}{-4} = 0$: The y-intercept is 0, so the graph passes through the origin.

Step 3   Find the x-intercept(s). $3x^2 = 0$, so $x = 0$: The x-intercept is 0, verifying that the graph passes through the origin.

Step 4   Find the vertical asymptote(s). Set $q(x) = 0$. (Note that the numerator and denominator of $f(x) = \dfrac{3x^2}{x^2 - 4}$ have no common factors.)

$$\begin{aligned} x^2 - 4 &= 0 &&\text{\textit{Set the denominator equal to 0.}} \\ x^2 &= 4 &&\text{\textit{Add 4 to both sides.}} \\ x &= \pm 2 &&\text{\textit{Use the square root property.}} \end{aligned}$$

The vertical asymptotes are $x = -2$ and $x = 2$.

Step 5   Find the horizontal asymptote. Because the numerator and denominator of $f(x) = \dfrac{3x^2}{x^2 - 4}$ have the same degree, 2, their leading coefficients, 3 and 1, are used to determine the equation of the horizontal asymptote. The equation is $y = \frac{3}{1} = 3$.

Step 6   Plot points between and beyond each x-intercept and vertical asymptote. With an x-intercept at 0 and vertical asymptotes at $x = -2$ and $x = 2$, we evaluate the function at $-3, -1, 1, 3,$ and 4.

x		-3	-1	1	3	4
$f(x) =$	$\dfrac{3x^2}{x^2 - 4}$	$\dfrac{27}{5}$	-1	-1	$\dfrac{27}{5}$	4

Figure 3.37 shows the points $\left(-3, \dfrac{27}{5}\right), (-1, -1), (1, -1), \left(3, \dfrac{27}{5}\right),$ and $(4, 4),$ the y-intercept, the x-intercept, and the asymptotes.

Step 7   Graph the function. The graph of $f(x) = \dfrac{3x^2}{x^2 - 4}$ is shown in **Figure 3.38**. The y-axis symmetry is now obvious.

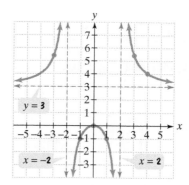

FIGURE 3.37 Preparing to graph $f(x) = \dfrac{3x^2}{x^2 - 4}$

FIGURE 3.38 The graph of $f(x) = \dfrac{3x^2}{x^2 - 4}$

● ● ●

GREAT QUESTION!

Do I have to evaluate $f(x)$ at all five of the values shown in the table for Step 6?

No. Because the graph has y-axis symmetry, it is not necessary to evaluate the even function at -3 and again at 3.

$$f(-3) = f(3) = \tfrac{27}{5}$$

This also applies to evaluation at -1 and 1.

TECHNOLOGY

The graph of $y = \dfrac{3x^2}{x^2 - 4}$, generated by a graphing utility, verifies that our hand-drawn graph is correct.

$[-6, 6, 1]$ by $[-6, 6, 1]$

⊘ Check Point **6** Graph: $f(x) = \dfrac{2x^2}{x^2 - 9}$.

Example 7 illustrates that not every rational function has vertical and horizontal asymptotes.

EXAMPLE 7 Graphing a Rational Function

Graph: $f(x) = \dfrac{x^4}{x^2 + 1}$.

SOLUTION

Step 1 Determine symmetry. $f(-x) = \dfrac{(-x)^4}{(-x)^2 + 1} = \dfrac{x^4}{x^2 + 1} = f(x)$

The graph of f is symmetric with respect to the y-axis.

Step 2 Find the y-intercept. $f(0) = \dfrac{0^4}{0^2 + 1} = \dfrac{0}{1} = 0$: The y-intercept is 0.

Step 3 Find the x-intercept(s). $x^4 = 0$, so $x = 0$: The x-intercept is 0.

Step 4 Find the vertical asymptote(s). Set $q(x) = 0$.

$$x^2 + 1 = 0 \quad \text{Set the denominator equal to 0.}$$
$$x^2 = -1 \quad \text{Subtract 1 from both sides.}$$

Although this equation has imaginary roots ($x = \pm i$), there are no real roots. Thus, the graph of f has no vertical asymptotes.

Step 5 Find the horizontal asymptote. Because the degree of the numerator, 4, is greater than the degree of the denominator, 2, there is no horizontal asymptote.

Step 6 Plot points between and beyond each x-intercept and vertical asymptote. With an x-intercept at 0 and no vertical asymptotes, let's look at function values at $-2, -1, 1$, and 2. You can evaluate the function at 1 and 2. Use y-axis symmetry to obtain function values at -1 and -2:

$$f(-1) = f(1) \text{ and } f(-2) = f(2).$$

x	-2	-1	1	2
$f(x) = \dfrac{x^4}{x^2 + 1}$	$\dfrac{16}{5}$	$\dfrac{1}{2}$	$\dfrac{1}{2}$	$\dfrac{16}{5}$

Step 7 Graph the function. Figure 3.39 shows the graph of f using the points obtained from the table and y-axis symmetry. Notice that as x approaches infinity or negative infinity ($x \to \infty$ or $x \to -\infty$), the function values, $f(x)$, are getting larger without bound $[f(x) \to \infty]$. • • •

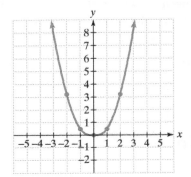

FIGURE 3.39 The graph of $f(x) = \dfrac{x^4}{x^2 + 1}$

$\oslash$ **Check Point 7** Graph: $f(x) = \dfrac{x^4}{x^2 + 2}$.

⑦ Identify slant asymptotes.

Slant Asymptotes

Examine the graph of

$$f(x) = \dfrac{x^2 + 1}{x - 1},$$

shown in **Figure 3.40**. Note that the degree of the numerator, 2, is greater than the degree of the denominator, 1. Thus, the graph of this function has no horizontal asymptote. However, the graph has a **slant asymptote,** $y = x + 1$.

The graph of a rational function has a slant asymptote if the degree of the numerator is one more than the degree of the denominator. The equation of the slant asymptote can be found by division. For example, to find the slant asymptote for the graph of $f(x) = \dfrac{x^2 + 1}{x - 1}$, divide $x - 1$ into $x^2 + 1$:

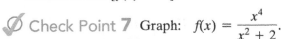

$$\underline{1}\underline{|}\quad 1 \quad 0 \quad 1$$
$$ 1 \quad 1$$
$$\overline{ 1 \quad 1 \quad 2}$$

$$1x + 1 + \dfrac{2}{x - 1}.$$
$$x - 1\overline{)x^2 + 0x + 1}$$

Remainder

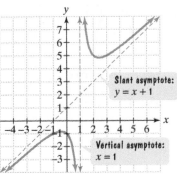

FIGURE 3.40 The graph of $f(x) = \dfrac{x^2 + 1}{x - 1}$ with a slant asymptote

Slant asymptote: $y = x + 1$

Vertical asymptote: $x = 1$

Observe that

$$f(x) = \frac{x^2 + 1}{x - 1} = \underbrace{x + 1}_{} + \frac{2}{x - 1}.$$

The equation of the slant asymptote is $y = x + 1$.

As $|x| \to \infty$, the value of $\dfrac{2}{x - 1}$ is approximately 0. Thus, when $|x|$ is large, the function is very close to $y = x + 1 + 0$. This means that as $x \to \infty$ or as $x \to -\infty$, the graph of f gets closer and closer to the line whose equation is $y = x + 1$. The line $y = x + 1$ is a slant asymptote of the graph.

In general, if $f(x) = \dfrac{p(x)}{q(x)}$, p and q have no common factors, and the degree of p is one greater than the degree of q, find the slant asymptote by dividing $q(x)$ into $p(x)$. The division will take the form

$$\frac{p(x)}{q(x)} = mx + b + \frac{\text{remainder}}{q(x)}.$$

Slant asymptote:
$y = mx + b$

The equation of the slant asymptote is obtained by dropping the term with the remainder. Thus, the equation of the slant asymptote is $y = mx + b$.

EXAMPLE 8 Finding the Slant Asymptote of a Rational Function

Find the slant asymptote of $f(x) = \dfrac{x^2 - 4x - 5}{x - 3}$.

SOLUTION

Because the degree of the numerator, 2, is exactly one more than the degree of the denominator, 1, and $x - 3$ is not a factor of $x^2 - 4x - 5$, the graph of f has a slant asymptote. To find the equation of the slant asymptote, divide $x - 3$ into $x^2 - 4x - 5$:

Slant asymptote:
$y = x - 1$

Vertical asymptote:
$x = 3$

FIGURE 3.41 The graph of
$f(x) = \dfrac{x^2 - 4x - 5}{x - 3}$

$$\underline{3|}\ \ 1\ \ -4\ \ -5$$
$$\ \ \ \ \ \ \ \ \ \underline{3\ \ -3}\ \ \ \ \text{Remainder}$$
$$\ \ \ \ \ 1\ \ -1\ \ -8$$

$$x - 3\overline{)x^2 - 4x - 5}\ \ \ \ 1x - 1 - \frac{8}{x - 3}$$

Drop the remainder term and you'll have the equation of the slant asymptote.

The equation of the slant asymptote is $y = x - 1$. Using our strategy for graphing rational functions, the graph of $f(x) = \dfrac{x^2 - 4x - 5}{x - 3}$ is shown in **Figure 3.41**. • • •

⊘ Check Point **8** Find the slant asymptote of $f(x) = \dfrac{2x^2 - 5x + 7}{x - 2}$.

8 Solve applied problems involving rational functions.

Applications

There are numerous examples of asymptotic behavior in functions that model real-world phenomena. Let's consider an example from the business world. The **cost function**, C, for a business is the sum of its fixed and variable costs:

$$C(x) = (\text{fixed cost}) + cx.$$

Cost per unit times the number of units produced, x

The **average cost** per unit for a company to produce x units is the sum of its fixed and variable costs divided by the number of units produced. The **average cost function** is a rational function that is denoted by $\overline{C}$. Thus,

Cost of producing x units: fixed plus variable costs

$$\overline{C}(x) = \frac{(\text{fixed cost}) + cx}{x}.$$

Number of units produced

EXAMPLE 9   Average Cost for a Business

We return to the robotic exoskeleton described in the section opener. Suppose a company that manufactures this invention has a fixed monthly cost of $1,000,000 and that it costs $5000 to produce each robotic system.

   a. Write the cost function, C, of producing x robotic systems.
   b. Write the average cost function, $\overline{C}$, of producing x robotic systems.
   c. Find and interpret $\overline{C}(1000)$, $\overline{C}(10,000)$, and $\overline{C}(100,000)$.
   d. What is the horizontal asymptote for the graph of the average cost function, $\overline{C}$? Describe what this represents for the company.

SOLUTION

   a. The cost function, C, is the sum of the fixed cost and the variable costs.

$$C(x) = 1,000,000 + 5000x$$

Fixed cost is $1,000,000.

Variable cost: $5000 for each robotic system produced

   b. The average cost function, $\overline{C}$, is the sum of fixed and variable costs divided by the number of robotic systems produced.

$$\overline{C}(x) = \frac{1,000,000 + 5000x}{x} \quad \text{or} \quad \overline{C}(x) = \frac{5000x + 1,000,000}{x}$$

   c. We evaluate $\overline{C}$ at 1000, 10,000, and 100,000, interpreting the results.

$$\overline{C}(1000) = \frac{5000(1000) + 1,000,000}{1000} = 6000$$

The average cost per robotic system of producing 1000 systems per month is $6000.

$$\overline{C}(10,000) = \frac{5000(10,000) + 1,000,000}{10,000} = 5100$$

The average cost per robotic system of producing 10,000 systems per month is $5100.

$$\overline{C}(100,000) = \frac{5000(100,000) + 1,000,000}{100,000} = 5010$$

The average cost per robotic system of producing 100,000 systems per month is \$5010. Notice that with higher production levels, the cost of producing each robotic exoskeleton decreases.

d. We developed the average cost function

$$\overline{C}(x) = \frac{5000x + 1,000,000}{x}$$

in which the degree of the numerator, 1, is equal to the degree of the denominator, 1. The leading coefficients of the numerator and denominator, 5000 and 1, are used to obtain the equation of the horizontal asymptote. The equation of the horizontal asymptote is

$$y = \frac{5000}{1} \quad \text{or} \quad y = 5000.$$

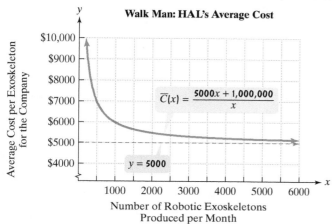

Walk Man: HAL's Average Cost

$\overline{C}(x) = \frac{5000x + 1,000,000}{x}$

y = 5000

Number of Robotic Exoskeletons Produced per Month

FIGURE 3.42

The horizontal asymptote is shown in **Figure 3.42**. This means that the more robotic systems produced each month, the closer the average cost per system for the company comes to \$5000. The least possible cost per robotic exoskeleton is approaching \$5000. Competitively low prices take place with high production levels, posing a major problem for small businesses.   ● ● ●

⊘ Check Point **9**   A company is planning to manufacture wheelchairs that are light, fast, and beautiful. The fixed monthly cost will be \$500,000 and it will cost \$400 to produce each radically innovative chair.

a. Write the cost function, C, of producing x wheelchairs.

b. Write the average cost function, $\overline{C}$, of producing x wheelchairs.

c. Find and interpret $\overline{C}(1000)$, $\overline{C}(10,000)$, and $\overline{C}(100,000)$.

d. What is the horizontal asymptote for the graph of the average cost function, $\overline{C}$? Describe what this represents for the company.

CONCEPT AND VOCABULARY CHECK

Fill in each blank so that the resulting statement is true.

1. All rational functions can be expressed as

$$f(x) = \frac{p(x)}{q(x)},$$

where p and q are _____ functions and $q(x) \neq 0$.

2. True or false: The domain of every rational function is the set of all real numbers. _____

3. True or false: The graph of the reciprocal function $f(x) = \dfrac{1}{x}$ has a break and is composed of two distinct branches. _____

4. If the graph of a function f increases or decreases without bound as x approaches a, then the line $x = a$ is a/an _____ of the graph of f. The equation of such a line for the graph of $f(x) = \dfrac{2}{x + 5}$ is _____.

5. If the graph of a function f approaches b as x increases or decreases without bound, then the line $y = b$ is a/an _____ of the graph of f. The equation of such a line for the graph of $y = \dfrac{x - 10}{3x^2 + x + 1}$ is _____. The equation of such a line for the graph of $y = \dfrac{x^2 - 10}{3x^2 + x + 1}$ is _____.

6. True or false: If the degree of the numerator of a rational function equals the degree of the denominator, then setting y equal to the ratio of the leading coefficients gives the equation of the horizontal asymptote. _____

7. Compared with the graph of $f(x) = \dfrac{1}{x}$, the graph of

$g(x) = \dfrac{1}{x+2} - 1$ is shifted 2 units _____ and 1 unit _____.

8. The graph of a rational function has a slant asymptote if the degree of the numerator is _____ the degree of the denominator.

9. Based on the synthetic division shown below, the equation of the slant asymptote of

$f(x) = \dfrac{3x^2 - 7x + 5}{x - 4}$ is _____.

$$
\begin{array}{r|rrr}
4 & 3 & -7 & 5 \\
  &   & 12 & 20 \\
\hline
  & 3 & 5 & 25
\end{array}
$$

EXERCISE SET 3.5

Practice Exercises

In Exercises 1–8, find the domain of each rational function.

1. $f(x) = \dfrac{5x}{x - 4}$

2. $f(x) = \dfrac{7x}{x - 8}$

3. $g(x) = \dfrac{3x^2}{(x - 5)(x + 4)}$

4. $g(x) = \dfrac{2x^2}{(x - 2)(x + 6)}$

5. $h(x) = \dfrac{x + 7}{x^2 - 49}$

6. $h(x) = \dfrac{x + 8}{x^2 - 64}$

7. $f(x) = \dfrac{x + 7}{x^2 + 49}$

8. $f(x) = \dfrac{x + 8}{x^2 + 64}$

Use the graph of the rational function in the figure shown to complete each statement in Exercises 9–14.

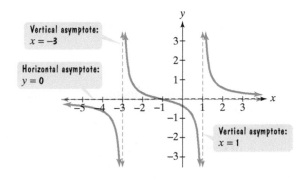

9. As $x \to -3^-$, $f(x) \to$ _____.

10. As $x \to -3^+$, $f(x) \to$ _____.

11. As $x \to 1^-$, $f(x) \to$ _____.

12. As $x \to 1^+$, $f(x) \to$ _____.

13. As $x \to -\infty$, $f(x) \to$ _____.

14. As $x \to \infty$, $f(x) \to$ _____.

Use the graph of the rational function in the figure shown to complete each statement in Exercises 15–20.

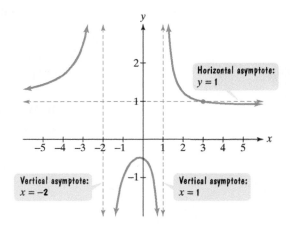

15. As $x \to 1^+$, $f(x) \to$ _____.

16. As $x \to 1^-$, $f(x) \to$ _____.

17. As $x \to -2^+$, $f(x) \to$ _____.

18. As $x \to -2^-$, $f(x) \to$ _____.

19. As $x \to \infty$, $f(x) \to$ _____.

20. As $x \to -\infty$, $f(x) \to$ _____.

In Exercises 21–36, find the vertical asymptotes, if any, and the values of x corresponding to holes, if any, of the graph of each rational function.

21. $f(x) = \dfrac{x}{x + 4}$

22. $f(x) = \dfrac{x}{x - 3}$

23. $g(x) = \dfrac{x + 3}{x(x + 4)}$

24. $g(x) = \dfrac{x + 3}{x(x - 3)}$

25. $h(x) = \dfrac{x}{x(x + 4)}$

26. $h(x) = \dfrac{x}{x(x - 3)}$

27. $r(x) = \dfrac{x}{x^2 + 4}$

28. $r(x) = \dfrac{x}{x^2 + 3}$

29. $f(x) = \dfrac{x^2 - 9}{x - 3}$

30. $f(x) = \dfrac{x^2 - 25}{x - 5}$

31. $g(x) = \dfrac{x - 3}{x^2 - 9}$

32. $g(x) = \dfrac{x - 5}{x^2 - 25}$

33. $h(x) = \dfrac{x + 7}{x^2 + 4x - 21}$

34. $h(x) = \dfrac{x + 6}{x^2 + 2x - 24}$

35. $r(x) = \dfrac{x^2 + 4x - 21}{x + 7}$

36. $r(x) = \dfrac{x^2 + 2x - 24}{x + 6}$

In Exercises 37–44, find the horizontal asymptote, if there is one, of the graph of each rational function.

37. $f(x) = \dfrac{12x}{3x^2 + 1}$

38. $f(x) = \dfrac{15x}{3x^2 + 1}$

39. $g(x) = \dfrac{12x^2}{3x^2 + 1}$

40. $g(x) = \dfrac{15x^2}{3x^2 + 1}$

41. $h(x) = \dfrac{12x^3}{3x^2 + 1}$

42. $h(x) = \dfrac{15x^3}{3x^2 + 1}$

43. $f(x) = \dfrac{-2x + 1}{3x + 5}$

44. $f(x) = \dfrac{-3x + 7}{5x - 2}$

In Exercises 45–56, use transformations of $f(x) = \dfrac{1}{x}$ or $f(x) = \dfrac{1}{x^2}$ to graph each rational function.

45. $g(x) = \dfrac{1}{x - 1}$

46. $g(x) = \dfrac{1}{x - 2}$

47. $h(x) = \dfrac{1}{x} + 2$

48. $h(x) = \dfrac{1}{x} + 1$

49. $g(x) = \dfrac{1}{x + 1} - 2$

50. $g(x) = \dfrac{1}{x + 2} - 2$

51. $g(x) = \dfrac{1}{(x + 2)^2}$

52. $g(x) = \dfrac{1}{(x + 1)^2}$

53. $h(x) = \dfrac{1}{x^2} - 4$

54. $h(x) = \dfrac{1}{x^2} - 3$

55. $h(x) = \dfrac{1}{(x - 3)^2} + 1$

56. $h(x) = \dfrac{1}{(x - 3)^2} + 2$

In Exercises 57–80, follow the seven steps on page 399 to graph each rational function.

57. $f(x) = \dfrac{4x}{x - 2}$

58. $f(x) = \dfrac{3x}{x - 1}$

59. $f(x) = \dfrac{2x}{x^2 - 4}$

60. $f(x) = \dfrac{4x}{x^2 - 1}$

61. $f(x) = \dfrac{2x^2}{x^2 - 1}$

62. $f(x) = \dfrac{4x^2}{x^2 - 9}$

63. $f(x) = \dfrac{-x}{x + 1}$

64. $f(x) = \dfrac{-3x}{x + 2}$

65. $f(x) = -\dfrac{1}{x^2 - 4}$

66. $f(x) = -\dfrac{2}{x^2 - 1}$

67. $f(x) = \dfrac{2}{x^2 + x - 2}$

68. $f(x) = \dfrac{-2}{x^2 - x - 2}$

69. $f(x) = \dfrac{2x^2}{x^2 + 4}$

70. $f(x) = \dfrac{4x^2}{x^2 + 1}$

71. $f(x) = \dfrac{x + 2}{x^2 + x - 6}$

72. $f(x) = \dfrac{x - 4}{x^2 - x - 6}$

73. $f(x) = \dfrac{x - 2}{x^2 - 4}$

74. $f(x) = \dfrac{x - 3}{x^2 - 9}$

75. $f(x) = \dfrac{x^4}{x^2 + 2}$

76. $f(x) = \dfrac{2x^4}{x^2 + 1}$

77. $f(x) = \dfrac{x^2 + x - 12}{x^2 - 4}$

78. $f(x) = \dfrac{x^2}{x^2 + x - 6}$

79. $f(x) = \dfrac{3x^2 + x - 4}{2x^2 - 5x}$

80. $f(x) = \dfrac{x^2 - 4x + 3}{(x + 1)^2}$

*In Exercises 81–88, **a.** Find the slant asymptote of the graph of each rational function and **b.** Follow the seven-step strategy and use the slant asymptote to graph each rational function.*

81. $f(x) = \dfrac{x^2 - 1}{x}$

82. $f(x) = \dfrac{x^2 - 4}{x}$

83. $f(x) = \dfrac{x^2 + 1}{x}$

84. $f(x) = \dfrac{x^2 + 4}{x}$

85. $f(x) = \dfrac{x^2 + x - 6}{x - 3}$

86. $f(x) = \dfrac{x^2 - x + 1}{x - 1}$

87. $f(x) = \dfrac{x^3 + 1}{x^2 + 2x}$

88. $f(x) = \dfrac{x^3 - 1}{x^2 - 9}$

Practice Plus

In Exercises 89–94, the equation for f is given by the simplified expression that results after performing the indicated operation. Write the equation for f and then graph the function.

89. $\dfrac{5x^2}{x^2 - 4} \cdot \dfrac{x^2 + 4x + 4}{10x^3}$

90. $\dfrac{x - 5}{10x - 2} \div \dfrac{x^2 - 10x + 25}{25x^2 - 1}$

91. $\dfrac{x}{2x + 6} - \dfrac{9}{x^2 - 9}$

92. $\dfrac{2}{x^2 + 3x + 2} - \dfrac{4}{x^2 + 4x + 3}$

93. $\dfrac{1 - \dfrac{3}{x + 2}}{1 + \dfrac{1}{x - 2}}$

94. $\dfrac{x - \dfrac{1}{x}}{x + \dfrac{1}{x}}$

In Exercises 95–98, use long division to rewrite the equation for g in the form

$$quotient + \frac{remainder}{divisor}.$$

Then use this form of the function's equation and transformations of $f(x) = \dfrac{1}{x}$ to graph g.

95. $g(x) = \dfrac{2x + 7}{x + 3}$

96. $g(x) = \dfrac{3x + 7}{x + 2}$

97. $g(x) = \dfrac{3x - 7}{x - 2}$

98. $g(x) = \dfrac{2x - 9}{x - 4}$

Application Exercises

99. A company is planning to manufacture mountain bikes. The fixed monthly cost will be $100,000 and it will cost $100 to produce each bicycle.

 a. Write the cost function, C, of producing x mountain bikes.

 b. Write the average cost function, $\overline{C}$, of producing x mountain bikes.

 c. Find and interpret $\overline{C}(500)$, $\overline{C}(1000)$, $\overline{C}(2000)$, and $\overline{C}(4000)$.

 d. What is the horizontal asymptote for the graph of the average cost function, $\overline{C}$? Describe what this means in practical terms.

100. A company that manufactures running shoes has a fixed monthly cost of $300,000. It costs $30 to produce each pair of shoes.

   a. Write the cost function, C, of producing x pairs of shoes.

   b. Write the average cost function, $\overline{C}$, of producing x pairs of shoes.

   c. Find and interpret $\overline{C}(1000)$, $\overline{C}(10,000)$, and $\overline{C}(100,000)$.

   d. What is the horizontal asymptote for the graph of the average cost function, $\overline{C}$? Describe what this represents for the company.

101. The function

$$f(x) = \frac{6.5x^2 - 20.4x + 234}{x^2 + 36}$$

models the pH level, $f(x)$, of the human mouth x minutes after a person eats food containing sugar. The graph of this function is shown in the figure.

Number of Minutes after
Eating Food Containing Sugar

   a. Use the graph to obtain a reasonable estimate, to the nearest tenth, of the pH level of the human mouth 42 minutes after a person eats food containing sugar.

   b. After eating sugar, when is the pH level the lowest? Use the function's equation to determine the pH level, to the nearest tenth, at this time.

   c. According to the graph, what is the normal pH level of the human mouth?

   d. What is the equation of the horizontal asymptote associated with this function? Describe what this means in terms of the mouth's pH level over time.

   e. Use the graph to describe what happens to the pH level during the first hour.

102. A drug is injected into a patient and the concentration of the drug in the bloodstream is monitored. The drug's concentration, $C(t)$, in milligrams per liter, after t hours is modeled by

$$C(t) = \frac{5t}{t^2 + 1}.$$

The graph of this rational function, obtained with a graphing utility, is shown in the figure.

$[0, 10, 1]$ by $[0, 3, 1]$

   a. Use the preceding graph to obtain a reasonable estimate of the drug's concentration after 3 hours.

   b. Use the function's equation displayed in the voice balloon by the graph to determine the drug's concentration after 3 hours.

   c. Use the function's equation to find the horizontal asymptote for the graph. Describe what this means about the drug's concentration in the patient's bloodstream as time increases.

*Among all deaths from a particular disease, the percentage that is smoking related (21–39 cigarettes per day) is a function of the disease's **incidence ratio**. The incidence ratio describes the number of times more likely smokers are than nonsmokers to die from the disease. The following table shows the incidence ratios for heart disease and lung cancer for two age groups.*

Incidence Ratios		
	Heart Disease	**Lung Cancer**
Ages 55–64	1.9	10
Ages 65–74	1.7	9

Source: Alexander M. Walker, *Observations and Inference*, Epidemiology Resources Inc., 1991.

For example, the incidence ratio of 9 in the table means that smokers between the ages of 65 and 74 are 9 times more likely than nonsmokers in the same age group to die from lung cancer. The rational function

$$P(x) = \frac{100(x - 1)}{x}$$

models the percentage of smoking-related deaths among all deaths from a disease, $P(x)$, in terms of the disease's incidence ratio, x. The graph of the rational function is shown. Use this function to solve Exercises 103–106.

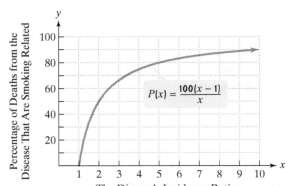

The Disease's Incidence Ratio:
The number of times more likely smokers are
than nonsmokers to die from the disease

103. Find $P(10)$. Describe what this means in terms of the incidence ratio, 10, given in the table. Identify your solution as a point on the graph.

104. Find $P(9)$. Round to the nearest percent. Describe what this means in terms of the incidence ratio, 9, given in the table. Identify your solution as a point on the graph.

105. What is the horizontal asymptote of the graph? Describe what this means about the percentage of deaths caused by smoking with increasing incidence ratios.

106. According to the model and its graph, is there a disease for which all deaths are caused by smoking? Explain your answer.

107. The bar graph shows the amount, in billions of dollars, that the United States government spent on human resources and total budget outlays for six selected years. (Human resources include education, health, Medicare, Social Security, and veterans benefits and services.)

Federal Budget Expenditures on Human Resources

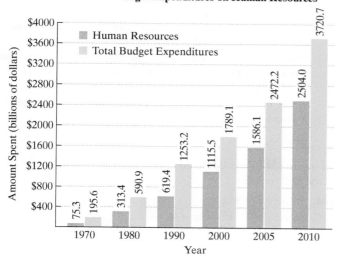

Source: Office of Management and Budget

The function $p(x) = 1.75x^2 - 15.9x + 160$ models the amount, $p(x)$, in billions of dollars, that the United States government spent on human resources x years after 1970. The function $q(x) = 2.1x^2 - 3.5x + 296$ models total budget expenditures, $q(x)$, in billions of dollars, x years after 1970.

a. Use p and q to write a rational function that models the fraction of total budget outlays spent on human resources x years after 1970.

b. Use the data displayed by the bar graph to find the percentage of federal expenditures spent on human resources in 2010. Round to the nearest percent.

c. Use the rational function from part (a) to find the percentage of federal expenditures spent on human resources in 2010. Round to the nearest percent. Does this underestimate or overestimate the actual percent that you found in part (b)? By how much?

d. What is the equation of the horizontal asymptote associated with the rational function in part (a)? If trends modeled by the function continue, what percentage of the federal budget will be spent on human resources over time? Round to the nearest percent.

Writing in Mathematics

108. What is a rational function?

109. Use everyday language to describe the graph of a rational function f such that as $x \to -\infty$, $f(x) \to 3$.

110. Use everyday language to describe the behavior of a graph near its vertical asymptote if $f(x) \to \infty$ as $x \to -2^-$ and $f(x) \to -\infty$ as $x \to -2^+$.

111. If you are given the equation of a rational function, explain how to find the vertical asymptotes, if there is one, of the function's graph.

112. If you are given the equation of a rational function, explain how to find the horizontal asymptote, if any, of the function's graph.

113. Describe how to graph a rational function.

114. If you are given the equation of a rational function, how can you tell if the graph has a slant asymptote? If it does, how do you find its equation?

115. Is every rational function a polynomial function? Why or why not? Does a true statement result if the two adjectives *rational* and *polynomial* are reversed? Explain.

116. Although your friend has a family history of heart disease, he smokes, on average, 25 cigarettes per day. He sees the table showing incidence ratios for heart disease (see Exercises 103–106) and feels comfortable that they are less than 2, compared to 9 and 10 for lung cancer. He claims that all family deaths have been from heart disease and decides not to give up smoking. Use the given function and its graph to describe some additional information not given in the table that might influence his decision.

Technology Exercises

117. Use a graphing utility to verify any five of your hand-drawn graphs in Exercises 45–88.

118. Use a graphing utility to graph $y = \dfrac{1}{x}$, $y = \dfrac{1}{x^3}$, and $\dfrac{1}{x^5}$ in the same viewing rectangle. For odd values of n, how does changing n affect the graph of $y = \dfrac{1}{x^n}$?

119. Use a graphing utility to graph $y = \dfrac{1}{x^2}$, $y = \dfrac{1}{x^4}$, and $y = \dfrac{1}{x^6}$ in the same viewing rectangle. For even values of n, how does changing n affect the graph of $y = \dfrac{1}{x^n}$?

120. Use a graphing utility to graph
$$f(x) = \frac{x^2 - 4x + 3}{x - 2} \quad \text{and} \quad g(x) = \frac{x^2 - 5x + 6}{x - 2}.$$
What differences do you observe between the graph of f and the graph of g? How do you account for these differences?

121. The rational function
$$f(x) = \frac{27{,}725(x - 14)}{x^2 + 9} - 5x$$
models the number of arrests, $f(x)$, per 100,000 drivers, for driving under the influence of alcohol, as a function of a driver's age, x.

a. Graph the function in a $[0, 70, 5]$ by $[0, 400, 20]$ viewing rectangle.

b. Describe the trend shown by the graph.

c. Use the ZOOM and TRACE features or the maximum function feature of your graphing utility to find the age that corresponds to the greatest number of arrests. How many arrests, per 100,000 drivers, are there for this age group?

Critical Thinking Exercises

Make Sense? *In Exercises 122–125, determine whether each statement makes sense or does not make sense, and explain your reasoning.*

122. I've graphed a rational function that has two vertical asymptotes and two horizontal asymptotes.

123. My graph of $y = \dfrac{x - 1}{(x - 1)(x - 2)}$ has vertical asymptotes at $x = 1$ and $x = 2$.

124. The function

$$f(x) = \frac{1.96x + 3.14}{3.04x + 21.79}$$

models the fraction of nonviolent prisoners in New York State prisons x years after 1980. I can conclude from this equation that over time the percentage of nonviolent prisoners will exceed 60%.

125. As production level increases, the average cost for a company to produce each unit of its product also increases.

In Exercises 126–129, determine whether each statement is true or false. If the statement is false, make the necessary change(s) to produce a true statement.

126. The graph of a rational function cannot have both a vertical asymptote and a horizontal asymptote.

127. It is possible to have a rational function whose graph has no y-intercept.

128. The graph of a rational function can have three vertical asymptotes.

129. The graph of a rational function can never cross a vertical asymptote.

In Exercises 130–133, write the equation of a rational function $f(x) = \dfrac{p(x)}{q(x)}$ having the indicated properties, in which the degrees of p and q are as small as possible. More than one correct function may be possible. Graph your function using a graphing utility to verify that it has the required properties.

130. f has a vertical asymptote given by $x = 3$, a horizontal asymptote $y = 0$, y-intercept at -1, and no x-intercept.

131. f has vertical asymptotes given by $x = -2$ and $x = 2$, a horizontal asymptote $y = 2$, y-intercept at $\frac{9}{2}$, x-intercepts at -3 and 3, and y-axis symmetry.

132. f has a vertical asymptote given by $x = 1$, a slant asymptote whose equation is $y = x$, y-intercept at 2, and x-intercepts at -1 and 2.

133. f has no vertical, horizontal, or slant asymptotes, and no x-intercepts.

Preview Exercises

Exercises 134–136 will help you prepare for the material covered in the next section.

134. Solve: $2x^2 + x = 15$.

135. Solve: $x^3 + x^2 = 4x + 4$.

136. Simplify: $\dfrac{x + 1}{x + 3} - 2$.

SECTION 3.6 Polynomial and Rational Inequalities

Objectives

1. Solve polynomial inequalities.
2. Solve rational inequalities.
3. Solve problems modeled by polynomial or rational inequalities.

Tailgaters beware: If your car is going 35 miles per hour on dry pavement, your required stopping distance is 160 feet, or the width of a football field. At 65 miles per hour, the distance required is 410 feet, or approximately the length of one and one-tenth football fields. **Figure 3.43** at the top of the next page shows stopping distances for cars at various speeds on dry roads and on wet roads.

Stopping Distances for Cars at Selected Speeds

FIGURE 3.43

Source: National Highway Traffic Safety Administration

A car's required stopping distance, $f(x)$, in feet, on dry pavement traveling at x miles per hour can be modeled by the quadratic function

$$f(x) = 0.0875x^2 - 0.4x + 66.6.$$

How can we use this function to determine speeds on dry pavement requiring stopping distances that exceed the length of one and one-half football fields, or 540 feet? We must solve the inequality

$$0.0875x^2 - 0.4x + 66.6 > 540.$$

Required stopping distance   exceeds   540 feet.

We begin by subtracting 540 from both sides. This will give us zero on the right:

$$0.0875x^2 - 0.4x + 66.6 - 540 > 540 - 540$$
$$0.0875x^2 - 0.4x - 473.4 > 0.$$

The form of this inequality is $ax^2 + bx + c > 0$. Such a quadratic inequality is called a *polynomial inequality*.

TECHNOLOGY

We used the statistical menu of a graphing utility and the quadratic regression program to obtain the quadratic function that models stopping distance on dry pavement. After entering the appropriate data from **Figure 3.43**, namely,

$(35, 160), (45, 225), (55, 310),$
$(65, 410),$

we obtained the results shown in the screen.

Definition of a Polynomial Inequality

A polynomial inequality is any inequality that can be put into one of the forms
$$f(x) < 0, \quad f(x) > 0, \quad f(x) \le 0, \quad \text{or} \quad f(x) \ge 0,$$
where f is a polynomial function.

In this section, we establish the basic techniques for solving polynomial inequalities. We will also use these techniques to solve inequalities involving rational functions.

Solving Polynomial Inequalities

Graphs can help us visualize the solutions of polynomial inequalities. For example, the graph of $f(x) = x^2 - 7x + 10$ is shown in **Figure 3.44**. The x-intercepts, 2 and 5, are **boundary points** between where the graph lies above the x-axis, shown in blue, and where the graph lies below the x-axis, shown in red.

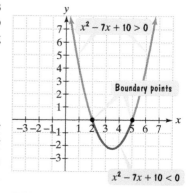

FIGURE 3.44

Locating the x-intercepts of a polynomial function, f, is an important step in finding the solution set for polynomial inequalities in the form $f(x) < 0$ or $f(x) > 0$. We use the x-intercepts of f as boundary points that divide the real number line into intervals. On each interval, the graph of f is either above the x-axis [$f(x) > 0$] or below the x-axis [$f(x) < 0$]. For this reason, x-intercepts play a fundamental role in solving polynomial inequalities. The x-intercepts are found by solving the equation $f(x) = 0$.

① Solve polynomial inequalities.

Procedure for Solving Polynomial Inequalities

1. Express the inequality in the form

$$f(x) < 0 \quad \text{or} \quad f(x) > 0,$$

   where f is a polynomial function.
2. Solve the equation $f(x) = 0$. The real solutions are the **boundary points**.
3. Locate these boundary points on a number line, thereby dividing the number line into intervals.
4. Choose one representative number, called a **test value**, within each interval and evaluate f at that number.
   a. If the value of f is positive, then $f(x) > 0$ for all numbers, x, in the interval.
   b. If the value of f is negative, then $f(x) < 0$ for all numbers, x, in the interval.
5. Write the solution set, selecting the interval or intervals that satisfy the given inequality.

This procedure is valid if $<$ is replaced by $\leq$ or $>$ is replaced by $\geq$. However, if the inequality involves $\leq$ or $\geq$, include the boundary points [the solutions of $f(x) = 0$] in the solution set.

EXAMPLE 1   Solving a Polynomial Inequality

Solve and graph the solution set on a real number line: $2x^2 + x > 15$.

SOLUTION

Step 1   Express the inequality in the form $f(x) < 0$ or $f(x) > 0$. We begin by rewriting the inequality so that 0 is on the right side.

$2x^2 + x > 15$	This is the given inequality.
$2x^2 + x - 15 > 15 - 15$	Subtract 15 from both sides.
$2x^2 + x - 15 > 0$	Simplify.

This inequality is equivalent to the one we wish to solve. It is in the form $f(x) > 0$, where $f(x) = 2x^2 + x - 15$.

Step 2   Solve the equation $f(x) = 0$. We find the x-intercepts of $f(x) = 2x^2 + x - 15$ by solving the equation $2x^2 + x - 15 = 0$.

$2x^2 + x - 15 = 0$	This polynomial equation is a quadratic equation.
$(2x - 5)(x + 3) = 0$	Factor.
$2x - 5 = 0 \quad \text{or} \quad x + 3 = 0$	Set each factor equal to 0.
$x = \frac{5}{2} \qquad\qquad x = -3$	Solve for x.

The x-intercepts of f are -3 and $\frac{5}{2}$. We will use these x-intercepts as boundary points on a number line.

Step 3   Locate the boundary points on a number line and separate the line into intervals. The number line with the boundary points is shown as follows:

The boundary points divide the number line into three intervals:

$$(-\infty, -3) \quad \left(-3, \tfrac{5}{2}\right) \quad \left(\tfrac{5}{2}, \infty\right).$$

Step 4 Choose one test value within each interval and evaluate f at that number.

Interval	Test Value	Substitute into $f(x) = 2x^2 + x - 15$	Conclusion
$(-\infty, -3)$	-4	$f(-4) = 2(-4)^2 + (-4) - 15$ $= 13$, positive	$f(x) > 0$ for all x in $(-\infty, -3)$.
$\left(-3, \dfrac{5}{2}\right)$	0	$f(0) = 2 \cdot 0^2 + 0 - 15$ $= -15$, negative	$f(x) < 0$ for all x in $\left(-3, \dfrac{5}{2}\right)$.
$\left(\dfrac{5}{2}, \infty\right)$	3	$f(3) = 2 \cdot 3^2 + 3 - 15$ $= 6$, positive	$f(x) > 0$ for all x in $\left(\dfrac{5}{2}, \infty\right)$.

TECHNOLOGY

Graphic Connections

The solution set for

$$2x^2 + x > 15$$

or, equivalently,

$$2x^2 + x - 15 > 0$$

can be verified with a graphing utility. The graph of $f(x) = 2x^2 + x - 15$ was obtained using a $[-10, 10, 1]$ by $[-16, 6, 1]$ viewing rectangle. The graph lies above the x-axis, representing $>$, for all x in $(-\infty, -3)$ or $\left(\frac{5}{2}, \infty\right)$.

Step 5 Write the solution set, selecting the interval or intervals that satisfy the given inequality. We are interested in solving $f(x) > 0$, where $f(x) = 2x^2 + x - 15$. Based on our work in step 4, we see that $f(x) > 0$ for all x in $(-\infty, -3)$ or $\left(\frac{5}{2}, \infty\right)$. Thus, the solution set of the given inequality, $2x^2 + x > 15$, or, equivalently, $2x^2 + x - 15 > 0$, is

$$(-\infty, -3) \cup \left(\tfrac{5}{2}, \infty\right) \text{ or } \left\{x \,\middle|\, x < -3 \text{ or } x > \tfrac{5}{2}\right\}.$$

The graph of the solution set on a number line is shown as follows:

✓ Check Point **1** Solve and graph the solution set: $x^2 - x > 20$.

EXAMPLE 2 Solving a Polynomial Inequality

Solve and graph the solution set on a real number line: $4x^2 \leq 1 - 2x$.

SOLUTION

Step 1 Express the inequality in the form $f(x) \leq 0$ or $f(x) \geq 0$. We begin by rewriting the inequality so that 0 is on the right side.

$$4x^2 \leq 1 - 2x \qquad \text{This is the given inequality.}$$
$$4x^2 + 2x - 1 \leq 1 - 2x + 2x - 1 \qquad \text{Add 2x and subtract 1 on both sides.}$$
$$4x^2 + 2x - 1 \leq 0 \qquad \text{Simplify.}$$

This inequality is equivalent to the one we wish to solve. It is in the form $f(x) \leq 0$, where $f(x) = 4x^2 + 2x - 1$.

Step 2 Solve the equation $f(x) = 0$. We will find the x-intercepts of $f(x) = 4x^2 + 2x - 1$ by solving the equation $4x^2 + 2x - 1 = 0$. This equation cannot be solved by factoring. We will use the quadratic formula to solve it.

$$4x^2 + 2x - 1 = 0$$

$$a = 4 \quad b = 2 \quad c = -1$$

$$x = \frac{-b \pm \sqrt{b^2 - 4ac}}{2a} = \frac{-2 \pm \sqrt{2^2 - 4 \cdot 4(-1)}}{2 \cdot 4} = \frac{-2 \pm \sqrt{4 - (-16)}}{8}$$

$$= \frac{-2 \pm \sqrt{20}}{8} = \frac{-2 \pm \sqrt{4}\sqrt{5}}{8} = \frac{-2 \pm 2\sqrt{5}}{8} = \frac{2(-1 \pm \sqrt{5})}{8} = \frac{-1 \pm \sqrt{5}}{4}$$

$$x = \frac{-1 + \sqrt{5}}{4} \approx 0.3 \qquad\qquad x = \frac{-1 - \sqrt{5}}{4} \approx -0.8$$

The x-intercepts of f are $\dfrac{-1 + \sqrt{5}}{4}$ (approximately 0.3) and $\dfrac{-1 - \sqrt{5}}{4}$ (approximately -0.8). We will use these x-intercepts as boundary points on a number line.

Step 3   Locate the boundary points on a number line and separate the line into intervals. The number line with the boundary points is shown as follows:

$$\frac{-1 - \sqrt{5}}{4} \approx -0.8 \qquad \frac{-1 + \sqrt{5}}{4} \approx 0.3$$

The boundary points divide the number line into three intervals:

$$\left(-\infty, \frac{-1 - \sqrt{5}}{4}\right) \quad \left(\frac{-1 - \sqrt{5}}{4}, \frac{-1 + \sqrt{5}}{4}\right) \quad \left(\frac{-1 + \sqrt{5}}{4}, \infty\right).$$

Step 4   Choose one test value within each interval and evaluate f at that number.

Interval	Test Value	Substitute into $f(x) = 4x^2 + 2x - 1$	Conclusion
$\left(-\infty, \dfrac{-1 - \sqrt{5}}{4}\right)$	-1	$f(-1) = 4(-1)^2 + 2(-1) - 1$ $= 1$, positive	$f(x) > 0$ for all x in $\left(-\infty, \dfrac{-1 - \sqrt{5}}{4}\right)$.
$\left(\dfrac{-1 - \sqrt{5}}{4}, \dfrac{-1 + \sqrt{5}}{4}\right)$	0	$f(0) = 4 \cdot 0^2 + 2 \cdot 0 - 1$ $= -1$, negative	$f(x) < 0$ for all x in $\left(\dfrac{-1 - \sqrt{5}}{4}, \dfrac{-1 + \sqrt{5}}{4}\right)$.
$\left(\dfrac{-1 + \sqrt{5}}{4}, \infty\right)$	1	$f(1) = 4 \cdot 1^2 + 2 \cdot 1 - 1$ $= 5$, positive	$f(x) > 0$ for all x in $\left(\dfrac{-1 + \sqrt{5}}{4}, \infty\right)$.

TECHNOLOGY

Graphic Connections

The solution set for

$$4x^2 \le 1 - 2x$$

or, equivalently,

$$4x^2 + 2x - 1 \le 0$$

can be verified with a graphing utility. The graph of $f(x) = 4x^2 + 2x - 1$ was obtained using a $[-2, 2, 1]$ by $[-10, 10, 1]$ viewing rectangle. The graph lies on or below the x-axis, representing $\le$, for all x in

$$\left[\frac{-1 - \sqrt{5}}{4}, \frac{-1 + \sqrt{5}}{4}\right]$$

$$\approx [-0.8, 0.3].$$

$[-2, 2, 1]$ by $[-10, 10, 1]$

Step 5   Write the solution set, selecting the interval or intervals that satisfy the given inequality. We are interested in solving $f(x) \le 0$, where $f(x) = 4x^2 + 2x - 1$. Based on our work in step 4, we see that $f(x) < 0$ for all x in $\left(\dfrac{-1 - \sqrt{5}}{4}, \dfrac{-1 + \sqrt{5}}{4}\right)$. However, because the inequality involves $\le$ (less than or *equal to*), we must also include the solutions of $4x^2 + 2x - 1 = 0$, namely, $\dfrac{-1 - \sqrt{5}}{4}$ and $\dfrac{-1 + \sqrt{5}}{4}$, in the solution set. Thus, the solution set of the given inequality $4x^2 \le 1 - 2x$, or, equivalently, $4x^2 + 2x - 1 \le 0$, is

$$\left[\frac{-1 - \sqrt{5}}{4}, \frac{-1 + \sqrt{5}}{4}\right] \text{ or } \left\{x \,\middle|\, \frac{-1 - \sqrt{5}}{4} \le x \le \frac{-1 + \sqrt{5}}{4}\right\}.$$

The graph of the solution set on a number line is shown as follows:

⌀ Check Point **2** Solve and graph the solution set on a real number line: $2x^2 \le -6x - 1$.

EXAMPLE 3   Solving a Polynomial Inequality

Solve and graph the solution set on a real number line: $x^3 + x^2 \le 4x + 4$.

SOLUTION

Step 1   Express the inequality in the form $f(x) \le 0$ or $f(x) \ge 0$. We begin by rewriting the inequality so that 0 is on the right side.

$$x^3 + x^2 \le 4x + 4 \qquad \text{This is the given inequality.}$$
$$x^3 + x^2 - 4x - 4 \le 4x + 4 - 4x - 4 \qquad \text{Subtract } 4x + 4 \text{ from both sides.}$$
$$x^3 + x^2 - 4x - 4 \le 0 \qquad \text{Simplify.}$$

This inequality is equivalent to the one we wish to solve. It is in the form $f(x) \le 0$, where $f(x) = x^3 + x^2 - 4x - 4$.

Step 2 Solve the equation $f(x) = 0$. We find the x-intercepts of $f(x) = x^3 + x^2 - 4x - 4$ by solving the equation $x^3 + x^2 - 4x - 4 = 0$.

$$x^3 + x^2 - 4x - 4 = 0 \quad \text{This polynomial equation is of degree 3.}$$

$$x^2(x + 1) - 4(x + 1) = 0 \quad \text{Factor } x^2 \text{ from the first two terms and}$$
$$\text{−4 from the last two terms.}$$

$$(x + 1)(x^2 - 4) = 0 \quad \text{A common factor of } x + 1 \text{ is factored}$$
$$\text{from the expression.}$$

$$(x + 1)(x + 2)(x - 2) = 0 \quad \text{Factor completely.}$$

$$x + 1 = 0 \quad \text{or} \quad x + 2 = 0 \quad \text{or} \quad x - 2 = 0 \quad \text{Set each factor equal to 0.}$$
$$x = -1 \qquad\qquad x = -2 \qquad\qquad x = 2 \quad \text{Solve for x.}$$

The x-intercepts of f are $-2, -1$, and 2. We will use these x-intercepts as boundary points on a number line.

Step 3 Locate the boundary points on a number line and separate the line into intervals. The number line with the boundary points is shown as follows:

$$\begin{array}{c} -2 \quad -1 \qquad\quad 2 \\ \xrightarrow{\quad\quad\quad\quad\quad\quad\quad\quad\quad\quad\quad\quad\quad\quad} x \\ -5 \;-4 \;-3 \;-2 \;-1 \;\; 0 \;\; 1 \;\; 2 \;\; 3 \;\; 4 \;\; 5 \end{array}$$

The boundary points divide the number line into four intervals:

$$(-\infty, -2) \quad (-2, -1) \quad (-1, 2) \quad (2, \infty).$$

Step 4 Choose one test value within each interval and evaluate f at that number.

Interval	Test Value	Substitute into $f(x) = x^3 + x^2 - 4x - 4$	Conclusion
$(-\infty, -2)$	-3	$f(-3) = (-3)^3 + (-3)^2 - 4(-3) - 4$ $= -10$, negative	$f(x) < 0$ for all x in $(-\infty, -2)$.
$(-2, -1)$	-1.5	$f(-1.5) = (-1.5)^3 + (-1.5)^2 - 4(-1.5) - 4$ $= 0.875$, positive	$f(x) > 0$ for all x in $(-2, -1)$.
$(-1, 2)$	0	$f(0) = 0^3 + 0^2 - 4 \cdot 0 - 4$ $= -4$, negative	$f(x) < 0$ for all x in $(-1, 2)$.
$(2, \infty)$	3	$f(3) = 3^3 + 3^2 - 4 \cdot 3 - 4$ $= 20$, positive	$f(x) > 0$ for all x in $(2, \infty)$.

TECHNOLOGY

Graphic Connections

The solution set for

$$x^3 + x^2 \le 4x + 4$$

or, equivalently,

$$x^3 + x^2 - 4x - 4 \le 0$$

can be verified with a graphing utility. The graph of $f(x) = x^3 + x^2 - 4x - 4$ lies on or below the x-axis, representing $\le$, for all x in $(-\infty, -2]$ or $[-1, 2]$.

$[-4, 4, 1]$ by $[-7, 3, 1]$

Step 5 Write the solution set, selecting the interval or intervals that satisfy the given inequality. We are interested in solving $f(x) \le 0$, where $f(x) = x^3 + x^2 - 4x - 4$. Based on our work in step 4, we see that $f(x) < 0$ for all x in $(-\infty, -2)$ or $(-1, 2)$. However, because the inequality involves $\le$ (less than or *equal to*), we must also include the solutions of $x^3 + x^2 - 4x - 4 = 0$, namely $-2, -1$, and 2, in the solution set. Thus, the solution set of the given inequality, $x^3 + x^2 \le 4x + 4$, or, equivalently, $x^3 + x^2 - 4x - 4 \le 0$, is

$$(-\infty, -2] \cup [-1, 2]$$

$$\text{or} \quad \{x \,|\, x \le -2 \text{ or } -1 \le x \le 2\}.$$

The graph of the solution set on a number line is shown as follows:

✓ Check Point **3** Solve and graph the solution set on a real number line: $x^3 + 3x^2 \le x + 3$.

② Solve rational inequalities.

Solving Rational Inequalities

A **rational inequality** is any inequality that can be put into one of the forms

$$f(x) < 0, \quad f(x) > 0, \quad f(x) \le 0, \quad \text{or} \quad f(x) \ge 0,$$

where f is a rational function. An example of a rational inequality is

$$\frac{3x + 3}{2x + 4} > 0.$$

This inequality is in the form $f(x) > 0$, where f is the rational function given by

$$f(x) = \frac{3x + 3}{2x + 4}.$$

The graph of f is shown in **Figure 3.45**.

We can find the x-intercept of f by setting the numerator equal to 0:

$$3x + 3 = 0$$
$$3x = -3$$
$$x = -1. \quad \boxed{\text{f has an x-intercept at -1 and passes through $(-1, 0)$.}}$$

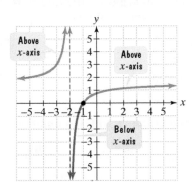

FIGURE 3.45 The graph of
$$f(x) = \frac{3x + 3}{2x + 4}$$

We can determine where f is undefined by setting the denominator equal to 0:

$$2x + 4 = 0$$
$$2x = -4$$
$$x = -2. \quad \boxed{\text{f is undefined at -2. \textbf{Figure 3.45} shows that the function's vertical asymptote is $x = -2$.}}$$

By setting both the numerator and the denominator of f equal to 0, we obtained -2 and -1. These numbers separate the x-axis into three intervals: $(-\infty, -2), (-2, -1)$, and $(-1, \infty)$. On each interval, the graph of f is either above the x-axis $[f(x) > 0]$ or below the x-axis $[f(x) < 0]$.

Examine the graph in **Figure 3.45** carefully. Can you see that it is above the x-axis for all x in $(-\infty, -2)$ or $(-1, \infty)$, shown in blue? Thus, the solution set of $\frac{3x + 3}{2x + 4} > 0$ is $(-\infty, -2) \cup (-1, \infty)$. By contrast, the graph of f lies below the x-axis for all x in $(-2, -1)$, shown in red. Thus, the solution set of $\frac{3x + 3}{2x + 4} < 0$ is $(-2, -1)$.

The first step in solving a rational inequality is to bring all terms to one side, obtaining zero on the other side. Then express the rational function on the nonzero side as a single quotient. The second step is to set the numerator and the denominator of the rational function f equal to zero. The solutions of these equations serve as boundary points that separate the real number line into intervals. At this point, the procedure is the same as the one we used for solving polynomial inequalities.

GREAT QUESTION!

Can I begin solving

$$\frac{x + 1}{x + 3} \ge 2$$

by multiplying both sides by $x + 3$?

No. We do not know if $x + 3$ is positive or negative. Thus, we do not know whether or not to change the sense of the inequality.

EXAMPLE 4 Solving a Rational Inequality

Solve and graph the solution set:

SOLUTION

Step 1   Express the inequality so that one side is zero and the other side is a single quotient. We subtract 2 from both sides to obtain zero on the right.

$$\frac{x + 1}{x + 3} \geq 2 \quad \text{This is the given inequality.}$$

$$\frac{x + 1}{x + 3} - 2 \geq 0 \quad \text{Subtract 2 from both sides, obtaining 0 on the right.}$$

$$\frac{x + 1}{x + 3} - \frac{2(x + 3)}{x + 3} \geq 0 \quad \text{The least common denominator is } x + 3. \text{ Express 2 in terms of this denominator.}$$

$$\frac{x + 1 - 2(x + 3)}{x + 3} \geq 0 \quad \text{Subtract rational expressions.}$$

$$\frac{x + 1 - 2x - 6}{x + 3} \geq 0 \quad \text{Apply the distributive property.}$$

$$\frac{-x - 5}{x + 3} \geq 0 \quad \text{Simplify.}$$

This inequality is equivalent to the one we wish to solve. It is in the form $f(x) \geq 0$, where $f(x) = \dfrac{-x - 5}{x + 3}$.

Step 2   Set the numerator and the denominator of f equal to zero. The real solutions are the boundary points.

$$-x - 5 = 0 \qquad x + 3 = 0 \quad \text{Set the numerator and denominator equal to 0. These are the values that make the previous quotient zero or undefined.}$$

$$x = -5 \qquad x = -3 \quad \text{Solve for } x.$$

We will use these solutions as boundary points on a number line.

Step 3   Locate the boundary points on a number line and separate the line into intervals. The number line with the boundary points is shown as follows:

The boundary points divide the number line into three intervals:

$$(-\infty, -5) \quad (-5, -3) \quad (-3, \infty).$$

Step 4   Choose one test value within each interval and evaluate f at that number.

Interval	Test Value	Substitute into $f(x) = \dfrac{-x - 5}{x + 3}$	Conclusion
$(-\infty, -5)$	-6	$f(-6) = \dfrac{-(-6) - 5}{-6 + 3}$ $= -\frac{1}{3}$, negative	$f(x) < 0$ for all x in $(-\infty, -5)$.
$(-5, -3)$	-4	$f(-4) = \dfrac{-(-4) - 5}{-4 + 3}$ $= 1$, positive	$f(x) > 0$ for all x in $(-5, -3)$.
$(-3, \infty)$	0	$f(0) = \dfrac{-0 - 5}{0 + 3}$ $= -\frac{5}{3}$, negative	$f(x) < 0$ for all x in $(-3, \infty)$.

GREAT QUESTION!

Which boundary points must I always exclude from the solution set of a rational inequality?

Never include values that cause a rational function's denominator to equal zero. Division by zero is undefined.

Step 5   Write the solution set, selecting the interval or intervals that satisfy the given inequality. We are interested in solving $f(x) \geq 0$, where $f(x) = \dfrac{-x - 5}{x + 3}$.

Based on our work in step 4, we see that $f(x) > 0$ for all x in $(-5, -3)$. However, because the inequality involves $\geq$ (greater than or *equal to*), we must also include the solution of $f(x) = 0$, namely, the value that we obtained when we set the

TECHNOLOGY

Graphic Connections

The solution set for

$$\frac{x+1}{x+3} \geq 2$$

or, equivalently,

$$\frac{-x-5}{x+3} \geq 0$$

can be verified with a graphing utility. The graph of $f(x) = \dfrac{-x-5}{x+3}$ lies on or above the x-axis, representing $\geq$, for all x in $[-5, -3)$.

$[-8, 8, 1]$ by $[-3, 3, 1]$

③ Solve problems modeled by polynomial or rational inequalities.

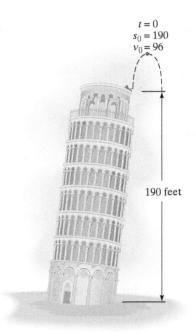

$t = 0$
$s_0 = 190$
$v_0 = 96$

190 feet

FIGURE 3.46 Throwing a ball from 190 feet with a velocity of 96 feet per second

---

numerator of f equal to zero. Thus, we must include -5 in the solution set. The solution set of the given inequality is

$$[-5, -3) \text{ or } \{x \mid -5 \leq x < -3\}.$$

> -3 causes the denominator of f to equal zero. It must be excluded from the solution set.

The graph of the solution set on a number line is shown as follows:

⊘ Check Point **4** Solve and graph the solution set: $\dfrac{2x}{x+1} \geq 1$.

Applications

If you throw an object directly upward, although its path is straight and vertical, its changing height over time can be described by a quadratic function.

The Position Function for a Free-Falling Object Near Earth's Surface

An object that is falling or vertically projected into the air has its height above the ground, $s(t)$, in feet, given by

$$s(t) = -16t^2 + v_0 t + s_0,$$

where v_0 is the original velocity (initial velocity) of the object, in feet per second, t is the time that the object is in motion, in seconds, and s_0 is the original height (initial height) of the object, in feet.

In Example 5, we solve a polynomial inequality in a problem about the position of a free-falling object.

EXAMPLE 5   Using the Position Function

A ball is thrown vertically upward from the top of the Leaning Tower of Pisa (190 feet high) with an initial velocity of 96 feet per second (**Figure 3.46**). During which time period will the ball's height exceed that of the tower?

SOLUTION

$s(t) = -16t^2 + v_0 t + s_0$ This is the position function for a free-falling object.

$s(t) = -16t^2 + 96t + 190$ Because v_0 (initial velocity) $= 96$ and s_0 (initial position) $= 190$, substitute these values into the formula.

> When will $s(t)$, the ball's height,   exceed that   of the tower?

$$-16t^2 + 96t + 190 > 190$$

$-16t^2 + 96t + 190 > 190$ This is the inequality that models the problem's question. We must find t.

$-16t^2 + 96t > 0$ Subtract 190 from both sides. This inequality is in the form $f(t) > 0$, where $f(t) = -16t^2 + 96t$.

$-16t^2 + 96t = 0$ Solve the equation $f(t) = 0$.

$-16t(t - 6) = 0$ Factor.

$-16t = 0$ or $t - 6 = 0$ Set each factor equal to 0.

$t = 0$ $t = 6$ Solve for t. The boundary points are 0 and 6. Locate these values on a number line.

The intervals are $(-\infty, 0)$, $(0, 6)$, and $(6, \infty)$. For our purposes, the mathematical model is useful only from $t = 0$ until the ball hits the ground. (By setting $-16t^2 + 96t + 190$ equal to zero, we find $t \approx 7.57$; the ball hits the ground after approximately 7.57 seconds.) Thus, we use $(0, 6)$ and $(6, 7.57)$ for our intervals.

Interval	Test Value	Substitute into $f(t) = -16t^2 + 96t$	Conclusion
$(0, 6)$	1	$f(1) = -16 \cdot 1^2 + 96 \cdot 1$ $= 80$, positive	$f(t) > 0$ for all t in $(0, 6)$.
$(6, 7.57)$	7	$f(7) = -16 \cdot 7^2 + 96 \cdot 7$ $= -112$, negative	$f(t) < 0$ for all t in $(6, 7.57)$.

We are interested in solving $f(t) > 0$, where $f(t) = -16t^2 + 96t$. We see that $f(t) > 0$ for all t in $(0, 6)$. This means that the ball's height exceeds that of the tower between 0 and 6 seconds. • • •

TECHNOLOGY

Graphic Connections

The graphs of

$$y_1 = -16x^2 + 96x + 190$$

and

$$y_2 = 190$$

are shown in a

$[0, 8, 1]$ by $[0, 360, 36]$

seconds in motion

height, in feet

$[0, 8, 1]$ by $[0, 360, 36]$

viewing rectangle. The graphs show that the ball's height exceeds that of the tower between 0 and 6 seconds.

⊘ Check Point **5** An object is propelled straight up from ground level with an initial velocity of 80 feet per second. Its height at time t is modeled by

$$s(t) = -16t^2 + 80t,$$

where the height, $s(t)$, is measured in feet and the time, t, is measured in seconds. In which time interval will the object be more than 64 feet above the ground?

CONCEPT AND VOCABULARY CHECK

Fill in each blank so that the resulting statement is true.

1. We solve the polynomial inequality $x^2 + 8x + 15 > 0$ by first solving the equation _____. The real solutions of this equation, -5 and -3, shown on the number line, are called _____ points.

2. The points at -5 and -3 shown in Exercise 1 divide the number line into three intervals:

_____ , _____ , _____ .

3. True or false: A test value for the leftmost interval on the number line shown in Exercise 1 could be -10. _____

4. True or false: A test value for the rightmost interval on the number line shown in Exercise 1 could be 0. _____

5. Consider the rational inequality

$$\frac{x - 1}{x + 2} \geq 0.$$

Setting the numerator and the denominator of $\frac{x - 1}{x + 2}$ equal to zero, we obtain $x = 1$ and $x = -2$. These values are shown as points on the number line. Also shown is information about three test values.

Based on the information shown above, the solution set of $\frac{x - 1}{x + 2} \geq 0$ is _____.

EXERCISE SET 3.6

Practice Exercises

Solve each polynomial inequality in Exercises 1–42 and graph the solution set on a real number line. Express each solution set in interval notation.

1. $(x - 4)(x + 2) > 0$
2. $(x + 3)(x - 5) > 0$
3. $(x - 7)(x + 3) \leq 0$
4. $(x + 1)(x - 7) \leq 0$
5. $x^2 - 5x + 4 > 0$
6. $x^2 - 4x + 3 < 0$
7. $x^2 + 5x + 4 > 0$
8. $x^2 + x - 6 > 0$
9. $x^2 - 6x + 9 < 0$
10. $x^2 - 2x + 1 > 0$
11. $3x^2 + 10x - 8 \leq 0$
12. $9x^2 + 3x - 2 \geq 0$
13. $2x^2 + x < 15$
14. $6x^2 + x > 1$
15. $4x^2 + 7x < -3$
16. $3x^2 + 16x < -5$
17. $5x \leq 2 - 3x^2$
18. $4x^2 + 1 \geq 4x$
19. $x^2 - 4x \geq 0$
20. $x^2 + 2x < 0$
21. $2x^2 + 3x > 0$
22. $3x^2 - 5x \leq 0$
23. $-x^2 + x \geq 0$
24. $-x^2 + 2x \geq 0$
25. $x^2 \leq 4x - 2$
26. $x^2 \leq 2x + 2$
27. $9x^2 - 6x + 1 < 0$
28. $4x^2 - 4x + 1 \geq 0$
29. $(x - 1)(x - 2)(x - 3) \geq 0$
30. $(x + 1)(x + 2)(x + 3) \geq 0$
31. $x(3 - x)(x - 5) \leq 0$
32. $x(4 - x)(x - 6) \leq 0$
33. $(2 - x)^2 \left(x - \frac{7}{2} \right) < 0$
34. $(5 - x)^2 \left(x - \frac{13}{2} \right) < 0$
35. $x^3 + 2x^2 - x - 2 \geq 0$
36. $x^3 + 2x^2 - 4x - 8 \geq 0$
37. $x^3 - 3x^2 - 9x + 27 < 0$
38. $x^3 + 7x^2 - x - 7 < 0$
39. $x^3 + x^2 + 4x + 4 > 0$
40. $x^3 - x^2 + 9x - 9 > 0$
41. $x^3 \geq 9x^2$
42. $x^3 \leq 4x^2$

Solve each rational inequality in Exercises 43–60 and graph the solution set on a real number line. Express each solution set in interval notation.

43. $\dfrac{x - 4}{x + 3} > 0$
44. $\dfrac{x + 5}{x - 2} > 0$
45. $\dfrac{x + 3}{x + 4} < 0$
46. $\dfrac{x + 5}{x + 2} < 0$
47. $\dfrac{-x + 2}{x - 4} \geq 0$
48. $\dfrac{-x - 3}{x + 2} \leq 0$
49. $\dfrac{4 - 2x}{3x + 4} \leq 0$
50. $\dfrac{3x + 5}{6 - 2x} \geq 0$
51. $\dfrac{x}{x - 3} > 0$
52. $\dfrac{x + 4}{x} > 0$
53. $\dfrac{(x + 4)(x - 1)}{x + 2} \leq 0$
54. $\dfrac{(x + 3)(x - 2)}{x + 1} \leq 0$
55. $\dfrac{x + 1}{x + 3} < 2$
56. $\dfrac{x}{x - 1} > 2$

57. $\dfrac{x + 4}{2x - 1} \leq 3$
58. $\dfrac{1}{x - 3} < 1$
59. $\dfrac{x - 2}{x + 2} \leq 2$
60. $\dfrac{x}{x + 2} \geq 2$

Practice Plus

In Exercises 61–64, find the domain of each function.

61. $f(x) = \sqrt{2x^2 - 5x + 2}$
62. $f(x) = \dfrac{1}{\sqrt{4x^2 - 9x + 2}}$
63. $f(x) = \sqrt{\dfrac{2x}{x + 1} - 1}$
64. $f(x) = \sqrt{\dfrac{x}{2x - 1} - 1}$

Solve each inequality in Exercises 65–70 and graph the solution set on a real number line.

65. $|x^2 + 2x - 36| > 12$
66. $|x^2 + 6x + 1| > 8$
67. $\dfrac{3}{x + 3} > \dfrac{3}{x - 2}$
68. $\dfrac{1}{x + 1} > \dfrac{2}{x - 1}$
69. $\dfrac{x^2 - x - 2}{x^2 - 4x + 3} > 0$
70. $\dfrac{x^2 - 3x + 2}{x^2 - 2x - 3} > 0$

In Exercises 71–72, use the graph of the polynomial function to solve each inequality.

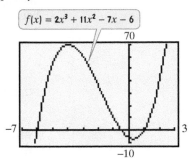

71. $2x^3 + 11x^2 \geq 7x + 6$
72. $2x^3 + 11x^2 < 7x + 6$

In Exercises 73–74, use the graph of the rational function to solve each inequality.

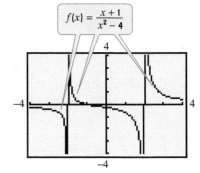

73. $\dfrac{1}{4(x + 2)} \leq -\dfrac{3}{4(x - 2)}$
74. $\dfrac{1}{4(x + 2)} > -\dfrac{3}{4(x - 2)}$

Application Exercises

Use the position function

$$s(t) = -16t^2 + v_0 t + s_0$$

(v_0 = initial velocity, s_0 = initial position, t = time)

to answer Exercises 75–76.

75. Divers in Acapulco, Mexico, dive headfirst at 8 feet per second from the top of a cliff 87 feet above the Pacific Ocean. During which time period will a diver's height exceed that of the cliff?

76. You throw a ball straight up from a rooftop 160 feet high with an initial velocity of 48 feet per second. During which time period will the ball's height exceed that of the rooftop?

The functions

$$f(x) = 0.0875x^2 - 0.4x + 66.6$$

Dry pavement

and   Wet pavement

$$g(x) = 0.0875x^2 + 1.9x + 11.6$$

model a car's stopping distance, f(x) or g(x), in feet, traveling at x miles per hour. Function f models stopping distance on dry pavement and function g models stopping distance on wet pavement. The graphs of these functions are shown for $\{x \mid x \geq 30\}$. Notice that the figure does not specify which graph is the model for dry roads and which is the model for wet roads. Use this information to solve Exercises 77–78.

Graphs of Models for Stopping Distances

77. a. Use the given functions to find the stopping distance on dry pavement and the stopping distance on wet pavement for a car traveling at 35 miles per hour. Round to the nearest foot.

   b. Based on your answers to part (a), which rectangular coordinate graph shows stopping distances on dry pavement and which shows stopping distances on wet pavement?

   c. How well do your answers to part (a) model the actual stopping distances shown in **Figure 3.43** on page 411?

   d. Determine speeds on dry pavement requiring stopping distances that exceed the length of one and one-half football fields, or 540 feet. Round to the nearest mile per hour. How is this shown on the appropriate graph of the models?

78. a. Use the given functions to find the stopping distance on dry pavement and the stopping distance on wet pavement for a car traveling at 55 miles per hour. Round to the nearest foot.

   b. Based on your answers to part (a), which rectangular coordinate graph shows stopping distances on dry pavement and which shows stopping distances on wet pavement?

   c. How well do your answers to part (a) model the actual stopping distances shown in **Figure 3.43** on page 411?

   d. Determine speeds on wet pavement requiring stopping distances that exceed the length of one and one-half football fields, or 540 feet. Round to the nearest mile per hour. How is this shown on the appropriate graph of the models?

79. The perimeter of a rectangle is 50 feet. Describe the possible lengths of a side if the area of the rectangle is not to exceed 114 square feet.

80. The perimeter of a rectangle is 180 feet. Describe the possible lengths of a side if the area of the rectangle is not to exceed 800 square feet.

Writing in Mathematics

81. What is a polynomial inequality?

82. What is a rational inequality?

83. If f is a polynomial or rational function, explain how the graph of f can be used to visualize the solution set of the inequality $f(x) < 0$.

Technology Exercises

84. Use a graphing utility to verify your solution sets to any three of the polynomial inequalities that you solved algebraically in Exercises 1–42.

85. Use a graphing utility to verify your solution sets to any three of the rational inequalities that you solved algebraically in Exercises 43–60.

Solve each inequality in Exercises 86–91 using a graphing utility.

86. $x^2 + 3x - 10 > 0$ 87. $2x^2 + 5x - 3 \leq 0$

88. $x^3 + x^2 - 4x - 4 > 0$ 89. $\dfrac{x-4}{x-1} \leq 0$

90. $\dfrac{x+2}{x-3} \leq 2$ 91. $\dfrac{1}{x+1} \leq \dfrac{2}{x+4}$

The graph shows stopping distances for trucks at various speeds on dry roads and on wet roads. Use this information to solve Exercises 92–93.

Stopping Distances for Trucks at Selected Speeds

Source: National Highway Traffic Safety Administration

(In Exercises 92–93, be sure to refer to the graph at the bottom of the previous page.)

92. a. Use the statistical menu of your graphing utility and the quadratic regression program to obtain the quadratic function that models a truck's stopping distance, $f(x)$, in feet, on dry pavement traveling at x miles per hour. Round the x-coefficient and the constant term to one decimal place.

    b. Use the function from part (a) to determine speeds on dry pavement requiring stopping distances that exceed 455 feet. Round to the nearest mile per hour.

93. a. Use the statistical menu of your graphing utility and the quadratic regression program to obtain the quadratic function that models a truck's stopping distance, $f(x)$, in feet, on wet pavement traveling at x miles per hour. Round the x-coefficient and the constant term to one decimal place.

    b. Use the function from part (a) to determine speeds on wet pavement requiring stopping distances that exceed 446 feet.

Critical Thinking Exercises

Make Sense? *In Exercises 94–97, determine whether each statement makes sense or does not make sense, and explain your reasoning.*

94. When solving $f(x) > 0$, where f is a polynomial function, I only pay attention to the sign of f at each test value and not the actual function value.

95. I'm solving a polynomial inequality that has a value for which the polynomial function is undefined.

96. Because it takes me longer to come to a stop on a wet road than on a dry road, graph (a) for Exercises 77–78 is the model for stopping distances on wet pavement and graph (b) is the model for stopping distances on dry pavement.

97. I began the solution of the rational inequality $\dfrac{x + 1}{x + 3} \geq 2$ by setting both $x + 1$ and $x + 3$ equal to zero.

In Exercises 98–101, determine whether each statement is true or false. If the statement is false, make the necessary change(s) to produce a true statement.

98. The solution set of $x^2 > 25$ is $(5, \infty)$.

99. The inequality $\dfrac{x - 2}{x + 3} < 2$ can be solved by multiplying both sides by $x + 3$, resulting in the equivalent inequality $x - 2 < 2(x + 3)$.

100. $(x + 3)(x - 1) \geq 0$ and $\dfrac{x + 3}{x - 1} \geq 0$ have the same solution set.

101. The inequality $\dfrac{x - 2}{x + 3} < 2$ can be solved by multiplying both sides by $(x + 3)^2, x \neq -3$, resulting in the equivalent inequality $(x - 2)(x + 3) < 2(x + 3)^2$.

102. Write a polynomial inequality whose solution set is $[-3, 5]$.

103. Write a rational inequality whose solution set is $(-\infty, -4) \cup [3, \infty)$.

In Exercises 104–107, use inspection to describe each inequality's solution set. Do not solve any of the inequalities.

104. $(x - 2)^2 > 0$

105. $(x - 2)^2 \leq 0$

106. $(x - 2)^2 < -1$

107. $\dfrac{1}{(x - 2)^2} > 0$

108. The graphing utility screen shows the graph of $y = 4x^2 - 8x + 7$.

$[-2, 6, 1]$ by $[-2, 8, 1]$

    a. Use the graph to describe the solution set of $4x^2 - 8x + 7 > 0$.

    b. Use the graph to describe the solution set of $4x^2 - 8x + 7 < 0$.

    c. Use an algebraic approach to verify each of your descriptions in parts (a) and (b).

109. The graphing utility screen shows the graph of $y = \sqrt{27 - 3x^2}$. Write and solve a quadratic inequality that explains why the graph only appears for $-3 \leq x \leq 3$.

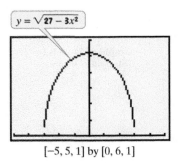

$[-5, 5, 1]$ by $[0, 6, 1]$

Preview Exercises

Exercises 110–112 will help you prepare for the material covered in the next section.

110. a. If $y = kx^2$, find the value of k using $x = 2$ and $y = 64$.

    b. Substitute the value for k into $y = kx^2$ and write the resulting equation.

    c. Use the equation from part (b) to find y when $x = 5$.

111. a. If $y = \dfrac{k}{x}$, find the value of k using $x = 8$ and $y = 12$.

    b. Substitute the value for k into $y = \dfrac{k}{x}$ and write the resulting equation.

    c. Use the equation from part (b) to find y when $x = 3$.

112. If $S = \dfrac{kA}{P}$, find the value of k using $A = 60,000, P = 40$, and $S = 12,000$.

SECTION 3.7 Modeling Using Variation

Objectives

1. Solve direct variation problems.
2. Solve inverse variation problems.
3. Solve combined variation problems.
4. Solve problems involving joint variation.

Have you ever wondered how telecommunication companies estimate the number of phone calls expected per day between two cities? The formula

$$C = \frac{0.02 P_1 P_2}{d^2}$$

shows that the daily number of phone calls, C, increases as the populations of the cities, P_1 and P_2, in thousands, increase and decreases as the distance, d, between the cities increases.

Certain formulas occur so frequently in applied situations that they are given special names. Variation formulas show how one quantity changes in relation to other quantities. Quantities can vary *directly, inversely*, or *jointly*. In this section, we look at situations that can be modeled by each of these kinds of variation.

① Solve direct variation problems.

Direct Variation

When you swim underwater, the pressure in your ears depends on the depth at which you are swimming. The formula

$$p = 0.43d$$

describes the water pressure, p, in pounds per square inch, at a depth of d feet. We can use this linear function to determine the pressure in your ears at various depths:

If $d = 20$, $p = 0.43(20) = 8.6$.   At a depth of 20 feet, water pressure is 8.6 pounds per square inch.

Doubling the depth doubles the pressure.

If $d = 40$, $p = 0.43(40) = 17.2$.   At a depth of 40 feet, water pressure is 17.2 pounds per square inch.

Doubling the depth doubles the pressure.

If $d = 80$, $p = 0.43(80) = 34.4$.   At a depth of 80 feet, water pressure is 34.4 pounds per square inch.

The formula $p = 0.43d$ illustrates that water pressure is a constant multiple of your underwater depth. If your depth is doubled, the pressure is doubled; if your depth is tripled, the pressure is tripled; and so on. Because of this, the pressure in your ears is said to **vary directly** as your underwater depth. The **equation of variation** is

$$p = 0.43d.$$

Generalizing our discussion of pressure and depth, we obtain the following statement:

Direct Variation

If a situation is described by an equation in the form

$$y = kx,$$

where k is a nonzero constant, we say that **y varies directly as x** or **y is directly proportional to x**. The number k is called the **constant of variation** or the **constant of proportionality**.

Can you see that **the direct variation equation, $y = kx$, is a special case of the linear function $y = mx + b$?** When $m = k$ and $b = 0$, $y = mx + b$ becomes $y = kx$. Thus, the slope of a direct variation equation is k, the constant of variation. Because b, the y-intercept, is 0, the graph of a variation equation is a line passing through the origin. This is illustrated in **Figure 3.47**, which shows the graph of $p = 0.43d$: Water pressure varies directly as depth.

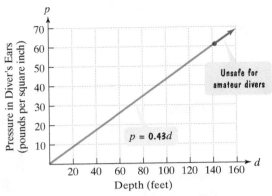

FIGURE 3.47 Water pressure at various depths

Problems involving direct variation can be solved using the following procedure. This procedure applies to direct variation problems, as well as to the other kinds of variation problems that we will discuss.

Solving Variation Problems

1. Write an equation that models the given English statement.
2. Substitute the given pair of values into the equation in step 1 and find the value of k, the constant of variation.
3. Substitute the value of k into the equation in step 1.
4. Use the equation from step 3 to answer the problem's question.

EXAMPLE 1 Solving a Direct Variation Problem

The volume of blood, B, in a person's body varies directly as body weight, W. A person who weighs 160 pounds has approximately 5 quarts of blood. Estimate the number of quarts of blood in a person who weighs 200 pounds.

SOLUTION

Step 1 Write an equation. We know that *y varies directly as x* is expressed as

$$y = kx.$$

By changing letters, we can write an equation that models the following English statement: The volume of blood, B, varies directly as body weight, W.

$$B = kW$$

Step 2 Use the given values to find k. A person who weighs 160 pounds has approximately 5 quarts of blood. Substitute 160 for W and 5 for B in the direct variation equation. Then solve for k.

$$B = kW$$ The volume of blood varies directly as body weight.
$$5 = k \cdot 160$$ Substitute 160 for W and 5 for B.
$$\frac{5}{160} = \frac{k \cdot 160}{160}$$ Divide both sides by 160.
$$0.03125 = k$$ Express $\frac{5}{160}$, or $\frac{1}{32}$, in decimal form.

Step 3 Substitute the value of k into the equation.

$$B = kW$$ Use the equation from step 1.
$$B = 0.03125W$$ Replace k, the constant of variation, with 0.03125.

Step 4   Answer the problem's question. We are interested in estimating the number of quarts of blood in a person who weighs 200 pounds. Substitute 200 for W in $B = 0.03125W$ and solve for B.

$$B = 0.03125W \qquad \text{This is the equation from step 3.}$$
$$B = 0.03125(200) \qquad \text{Substitute 200 for } W.$$
$$= 6.25 \qquad \text{Multiply.}$$

A person who weighs 200 pounds has approximately 6.25 quarts of blood.   • • •

⌀ Check Point **1** The number of gallons of water, W, used when taking a shower varies directly as the time, t, in minutes, in the shower. A shower lasting 5 minutes uses 30 gallons of water. How much water is used in a shower lasting 11 minutes?

The direct variation equation $y = kx$ is a linear function. If $k > 0$, then the slope of the line is positive. Consequently, as x increases, y also increases.
   A direct variation situation can involve variables to higher powers. For example, y can vary directly as $x^2 (y = kx^2)$ or as $x^3 (y = kx^3)$.

Direct Variation with Powers

y **varies directly as the nth power of *x*** if there exists some nonzero constant k such that

$$y = kx^n.$$

We also say that *y* **is directly proportional to the nth power of *x*.**

Direct variation with whole number powers is modeled by polynomial functions. In our next example, the graph of the variation equation is the familiar parabola.

EXAMPLE 2   Solving a Direct Variation Problem

The distance, s, that a body falls from rest varies directly as the square of the time, t, of the fall. If skydivers fall 64 feet in 2 seconds, how far will they fall in 4.5 seconds?

SOLUTION

Step 1   Write an equation. We know that *y varies directly as the square of x* is expressed as

$$y = kx^2.$$

By changing letters, we can write an equation that models the following English statement: Distance, s, varies directly as the square of time, t, of the fall.

$$s = kt^2$$

Step 2   Use the given values to find k. Skydivers fall 64 feet in 2 seconds. Substitute 64 for s and 2 for t in the direct variation equation. Then solve for k.

$$s = kt^2 \qquad \text{Distance varies directly as the square of time.}$$
$$64 = k \cdot 2^2 \qquad \text{Skydivers fall 64 feet in 2 seconds.}$$
$$64 = 4k \qquad \text{Simplify: } 2^2 = 4.$$
$$\frac{64}{4} = \frac{4k}{4} \qquad \text{Divide both sides by 4.}$$
$$16 = k \qquad \text{Simplify.}$$

Distance Fallen by Skydivers over Time

FIGURE 3.48 The graph of $s(t) = 16t^2$

Step 3 Substitute the value of k into the equation.

$$s = kt^2 \qquad \text{Use the equation from step 1.}$$
$$s = 16t^2 \qquad \text{Replace } k \text{, the constant of variation, with 16.}$$

Step 4 Answer the problem's question. How far will the skydivers fall in 4.5 seconds? Substitute 4.5 for t in $s = 16t^2$ and solve for s.

$$s = 16(4.5)^2 = 16(20.25) = 324$$

Thus, in 4.5 seconds, the skydivers will fall 324 feet. • • •

We can express the variation equation from Example 2 in function notation, writing

$$s(t) = 16t^2.$$

The distance that a body falls from rest is a function of the time, t, of the fall. The parabola that is the graph of this quadratic function is shown in **Figure 3.48**. The graph increases rapidly from left to right, showing the effects of the acceleration of gravity.

⊘ Check Point **2** The weight of a great white shark varies directly as the cube of its length. A great white shark caught off Catalina Island, California, was 15 feet long and weighed 2025 pounds. What was the weight of the 25-foot-long shark in the novel *Jaws*?

2 Solve inverse variation problems.

FIGURE 3.49

Inverse Variation

The distance from San Francisco to Los Angeles is 420 miles. The time that it takes to drive from San Francisco to Los Angeles depends on the rate at which one drives and is given by

$$\text{Time} = \frac{420}{\text{Rate}}.$$

For example, if you average 30 miles per hour, the time for the drive is

$$\text{Time} = \frac{420}{30} = 14,$$

or 14 hours. If you average 50 miles per hour, the time for the drive is

$$\text{Time} = \frac{420}{50} = 8.4,$$

or 8.4 hours. As your rate (or speed) increases, the time for the trip decreases and vice versa. This is illustrated by the graph in **Figure 3.49**.

We can express the time for the San Francisco–Los Angeles trip using t for time and r for rate:

$$t = \frac{420}{r}.$$

This equation is an example of an **inverse variation** equation. Time, t, **varies inversely** as rate, r. When two quantities vary inversely, one quantity increases as the other decreases and vice versa.

Generalizing, we obtain the following statement:

Inverse Variation

If a situation is described by an equation in the form

$$y = \frac{k}{x},$$

where k is a nonzero constant, we say that **y varies inversely as x** or **y is inversely proportional to x.** The number k is called the **constant of variation**.

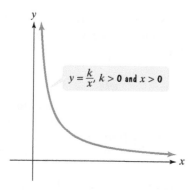

$y = \dfrac{k}{x}, k > 0 \text{ and } x > 0$

FIGURE 3.50 The graph of the inverse variation equation

Doubling the pressure halves the volume.

Notice that the **inverse variation equation**

$$y = \frac{k}{x}, \quad \text{or} \quad f(x) = \frac{k}{x},$$

is a rational function. For $k > 0$ and $x > 0$, the graph of the function takes on the shape shown in **Figure 3.50**.

We use the same procedure to solve inverse variation problems as we did to solve direct variation problems. Example 3 illustrates this procedure.

EXAMPLE 3   Solving an Inverse Variation Problem

When you use a spray can and press the valve at the top, you decrease the pressure of the gas in the can. This decrease of pressure causes the volume of the gas in the can to increase. Because the gas needs more room than is provided in the can, it expands in spray form through the small hole near the valve. In general, if the temperature is constant, the pressure, P, of a gas in a container varies inversely as the volume, V, of the container. The pressure of a gas sample in a container whose volume is 8 cubic inches is 12 pounds per square inch. If the sample expands to a volume of 22 cubic inches, what is the new pressure of the gas?

SOLUTION

Step 1   Write an equation. We know that y *varies inversely as* x is expressed as

$$y = \frac{k}{x}.$$

By changing letters, we can write an equation that models the following English statement: The pressure, P, of a gas in a container varies inversely as the volume, V.

$$P = \frac{k}{V}$$

Step 2   Use the given values to find k. The pressure of a gas sample in a container whose volume is 8 cubic inches is 12 pounds per square inch. Substitute 12 for P and 8 for V in the inverse variation equation. Then solve for k.

$$P = \frac{k}{V} \qquad \text{Pressure varies inversely as volume.}$$

$$12 = \frac{k}{8} \qquad \text{The pressure in an 8 cubic-inch container is 12 pounds per square inch.}$$

$$12 \cdot 8 = \frac{k}{8} \cdot 8 \qquad \text{Multiply both sides by 8.}$$

$$96 = k \qquad \text{Simplify.}$$

Step 3   Substitute the value of k into the equation.

$$P = \frac{k}{V} \qquad \text{Use the equation from step 1.}$$

$$P = \frac{96}{V} \qquad \text{Replace } k, \text{ the constant of variation, with 96.}$$

Step 4   Answer the problem's question. We need to find the pressure when the volume expands to 22 cubic inches. Substitute 22 for V and solve for P.

$$P = \frac{96}{V} = \frac{96}{22} = \frac{48}{11} = 4\frac{4}{11}$$

When the volume is 22 cubic inches, the pressure of the gas is $4\frac{4}{11}$ pounds per square inch.

● ● ●

☑ Check Point **3** The length of a violin string varies inversely as the frequency of its vibrations. A violin string 8 inches long vibrates at a frequency of 640 cycles per second. What is the frequency of a 10-inch string?

③ Solve combined variation problems.

Combined Variation

In **combined variation**, direct variation and inverse variation occur at the same time. For example, as the advertising budget, A, of a company increases, its monthly sales, S, also increase. Monthly sales vary directly as the advertising budget:

$$S = kA.$$

By contrast, as the price of the company's product, P, increases, its monthly sales, S, decrease. Monthly sales vary inversely as the price of the product:

$$S = \frac{k}{P}.$$

We can combine these two variation equations into one combined equation:

$$S = \frac{kA}{P}.$$

> Monthly sales, S, vary directly as the advertising budget, A, and inversely as the price of the product, P.

The following example illustrates an application of combined variation.

EXAMPLE 4 Solving a Combined Variation Problem

The owners of Rollerblades Plus determine that the monthly sales, S, of their skates vary directly as their advertising budget, A, and inversely as the price of the skates, P. When \$60,000 is spent on advertising and the price of the skates is \$40, the monthly sales are 12,000 pairs of rollerblades.

a. Write an equation of variation that describes this situation.

b. Determine monthly sales if the amount of the advertising budget is increased to \$70,000.

SOLUTION

a. Write an equation.

$$S = \frac{kA}{P}$$

> Translate "sales vary directly as the advertising budget and inversely as the skates' price."

Use the given values to find k.

$$12,000 = \frac{k(60,000)}{40}$$

> When \$60,000 is spent on advertising ($A = 60,000$) and the price is \$40 ($P = 40$), monthly sales are 12,000 units ($S = 12,000$).

$$12,000 = k \cdot 1500$$

> Divide 60,000 by 40.

$$\frac{12,000}{1500} = \frac{k \cdot 1500}{1500}$$

> Divide both sides of the equation by 1500.

$$8 = k$$

> Simplify.

Therefore, the equation of variation that models monthly sales is

$$S = \frac{8A}{P}.$$

> Substitute 8 for k in $S = \frac{kA}{P}$.

b. The advertising budget is increased to $70,000, so $A = 70,000$. The skates' price is still $40, so $P = 40$.

$$S = \frac{8A}{P} \qquad \text{This is the equation from part (a).}$$

$$S = \frac{8(70,000)}{40} \qquad \text{Substitute 70,000 for A and 40 for P.}$$

$$S = 14,000 \qquad \text{Simplify.}$$

With a $70,000 advertising budget and $40 price, the company can expect to sell 14,000 pairs of rollerblades in a month (up from 12,000). • • •

✓ Check Point **4** The number of minutes needed to solve an Exercise Set of variation problems varies directly as the number of problems and inversely as the number of people working to solve the problems. It takes 4 people 32 minutes to solve 16 problems. How many minutes will it take 8 people to solve 24 problems?

④ Solve problems involving joint variation.

Joint Variation

Joint variation is a variation in which a variable varies directly as the product of two or more other variables. Thus, the equation $y = kxz$ is read "y varies jointly as x and z."

Joint variation plays a critical role in Isaac Newton's formula for gravitation:

$$F = G\frac{m_1 m_2}{d^2}.$$

The formula states that the force of gravitation, F, between two bodies varies jointly as the product of their masses, m_1 and m_2, and inversely as the square of the distance between them, d. (G is the gravitational constant.) The formula indicates that gravitational force exists between any two objects in the universe, increasing as the distance between the bodies decreases. One practical result is that the pull of the moon on the oceans is greater on the side of Earth closer to the moon. This gravitational imbalance is what produces tides.

EXAMPLE 5   Modeling Centrifugal Force

The centrifugal force, C, of a body moving in a circle varies jointly with the radius of the circular path, r, and the body's mass, m, and inversely with the square of the time, t, it takes to move about one full circle. A 6-gram body moving in a circle with radius 100 centimeters at a rate of 1 revolution in 2 seconds has a centrifugal force of 6000 dynes. Find the centrifugal force of an 18-gram body moving in a circle with radius 100 centimeters at a rate of 1 revolution in 3 seconds.

SOLUTION

$$C = \frac{krm}{t^2} \qquad \text{Translate "Centrifugal force, C, varies jointly with radius, r, and mass, m, and inversely with the square of time, t."}$$

$$6000 = \frac{k(100)(6)}{2^2} \qquad \text{A 6-gram body (m = 6) moving in a circle with radius 100 centimeters (r = 100) at 1 revolution in 2 seconds (t = 2) has a centrifugal force of 6000 dynes (C = 6000).}$$

$$6000 = 150k \qquad \text{Simplify.}$$

$$40 = k \qquad \text{Divide both sides by 150 and solve for k.}$$

$$C = \frac{40rm}{t^2} \qquad \text{Substitute 40 for k in the model for centrifugal force.}$$

$$C = \frac{40(100)(18)}{3^2}$$ Find centrifugal force, C, of an 18-gram body $(m = 18)$ moving in a circle with·radius 100 centimeters $(r = 100)$ at 1 revolution in 3 seconds $(t = 3)$.

$$= 8000$$ Simplify.

The centrifugal force is 8000 dynes.   • • •

 Check Point **5** The volume of a cone, V, varies jointly as its height, h, and the square of its radius, r. A cone with a radius measuring 6 feet and a height measuring 10 feet has a volume of 120π cubic feet. Find the volume of a cone having a radius of 12 feet and a height of 2 feet.

CONCEPT AND VOCABULARY CHECK

Fill in each blank so that the resulting statement is true.

1. y varies directly as x can be modeled by the equation _____, where k is called the _____.

2. y varies directly as the nth power of x can be modeled by the equation _____.

3. y varies inversely as x can be modeled by the equation _____.

4. y varies directly as x and inversely as z can be modeled by the equation _____.

5. y varies jointly as x and z can be modeled by the equation _____.

6. In the equation $S = \dfrac{8A}{P}$, S varies _____ as A and _____ as P.

7. In the equation $C = \dfrac{0.02P_1P_2}{d^2}$, C varies _____ as P_1 and P_2 and _____ as the square of d.

EXERCISE SET 3.7

Practice Exercises

Use the four-step procedure for solving variation problems given on page 424 to solve Exercises 1–10.

1. y varies directly as x. $y = 65$ when $x = 5$. Find y when $x = 12$.

2. y varies directly as x. $y = 45$ when $x = 5$. Find y when $x = 13$.

3. y varies inversely as x. $y = 12$ when $x = 5$. Find y when $x = 2$.

4. y varies inversely as x. $y = 6$ when $x = 3$. Find y when $x = 9$.

5. y varies directly as x and inversely as the square of z. $y = 20$ when $x = 50$ and $z = 5$. Find y when $x = 3$ and $z = 6$.

6. a varies directly as b and inversely as the square of c. $a = 7$ when $b = 9$ and $c = 6$. Find a when $b = 4$ and $c = 8$.

7. y varies jointly as x and z. $y = 25$ when $x = 2$ and $z = 5$. Find y when $x = 8$ and $z = 12$.

8. C varies jointly as A and T. $C = 175$ when $A = 2100$ and $T = 4$. Find C when $A = 2400$ and $T = 6$.

9. y varies jointly as a and b and inversely as the square root of c. $y = 12$ when $a = 3$, $b = 2$, and $c = 25$. Find y when $a = 5$, $b = 3$, and $c = 9$.

10. y varies jointly as m and the square of n and inversely as p. $y = 15$ when $m = 2, n = 1$, and $p = 6$. Find y when $m = 3, n = 4$, and $p = 10$.

Practice Plus

In Exercises 11–20, write an equation that expresses each relationship. Then solve the equation for y.

11. x varies jointly as y and z.

12. x varies jointly as y and the square of z.

13. x varies directly as the cube of z and inversely as y.

14. x varies directly as the cube root of z and inversely as y.

15. x varies jointly as y and z and inversely as the square root of w.

16. x varies jointly as y and z and inversely as the square of w.

17. x varies jointly as z and the sum of y and w.

18. x varies jointly as z and the difference between y and w.

19. x varies directly as z and inversely as the difference between y and w.

20. x varies directly as z and inversely as the sum of y and w.

Application Exercises

Use the four-step procedure for solving variation problems given on page 424 to solve Exercises 21–36.

21. An alligator's tail length, *T*, varies directly as its body length, *B*. An alligator with a body length of 4 feet has a tail length of 3.6 feet. What is the tail length of an alligator whose body length is 6 feet?

|←——— Body length, *B* ———→|←——— Tail length, *T* ———→|

22. An object's weight on the moon, *M*, varies directly as its weight on Earth, *E*. Neil Armstrong, the first person to step on the moon on July 20, 1969, weighed 360 pounds on Earth (with all of his equipment on) and 60 pounds on the moon. What is the moon weight of a person who weighs 186 pounds on Earth?

23. The height that a ball bounces varies directly as the height from which it was dropped. A tennis ball dropped from 12 inches bounces 8.4 inches. From what height was the tennis ball dropped if it bounces 56 inches?

24. The distance that a spring will stretch varies directly as the force applied to the spring. A force of 12 pounds is needed to stretch a spring 9 inches. What force is required to stretch the spring 15 inches?

25. If all men had identical body types, their weight would vary directly as the cube of their height. Shown below is Robert Wadlow, who reached a record height of 8 feet 11 inches (107 inches) before his death at age 22. If a man who is 5 feet 10 inches tall (70 inches) with the same body type as Mr. Wadlow weighs 170 pounds, what was Robert Wadlow's weight shortly before his death?

26. The number of houses that can be served by a water pipe varies directly as the square of the diameter of the pipe. A water pipe that has a 10-centimeter diameter can supply 50 houses.
   a. How many houses can be served by a water pipe that has a 30-centimeter diameter?
   b. What size water pipe is needed for a new subdivision of 1250 houses?

27. The figure shows that a bicyclist tips the cycle when making a turn. The angle *B*, formed by the vertical direction and the bicycle, is called the banking angle. The banking angle varies inversely as the cycle's turning radius. When the turning radius is 4 feet, the banking angle is 28°. What is the banking angle when the turning radius is 3.5 feet?

28. The water temperature of the Pacific Ocean varies inversely as the water's depth. At a depth of 1000 meters, the water temperature is 4.4° Celsius. What is the water temperature at a depth of 5000 meters?

29. Radiation machines, used to treat tumors, produce an intensity of radiation that varies inversely as the square of the distance from the machine. At 3 meters, the radiation intensity is 62.5 milliroentgens per hour. What is the intensity at a distance of 2.5 meters?

30. The illumination provided by a car's headlight varies inversely as the square of the distance from the headlight. A car's headlight produces an illumination of 3.75 foot-candles at a distance of 40 feet. What is the illumination when the distance is 50 feet?

31. Body-mass index, or BMI, takes both weight and height into account when assessing whether an individual is underweight or overweight. BMI varies directly as one's weight, in pounds, and inversely as the square of one's height, in inches. In adults, normal values for the BMI are between 20 and 25, inclusive. Values below 20 indicate that an individual is underweight and values above 30 indicate that an individual is obese. A person who weighs 180 pounds and is 5 feet, or 60 inches, tall has a BMI of 35.15. What is the BMI, to the nearest tenth, for a 170-pound person who is 5 feet 10 inches tall? Is this person overweight?

32. One's intelligence quotient, or IQ, varies directly as a person's mental age and inversely as that person's chronological age. A person with a mental age of 25 and a chronological age of 20 has an IQ of 125. What is the chronological age of a person with a mental age of 40 and an IQ of 80?

33. The heat loss of a glass window varies jointly as the window's area and the difference between the outside and inside temperatures. A window 3 feet wide by 6 feet long loses 1200 Btu per hour when the temperature outside is 20° colder than the temperature inside. Find the heat loss through a glass window that is 6 feet wide by 9 feet long when the temperature outside is 10° colder than the temperature inside.

34. Kinetic energy varies jointly as the mass and the square of the velocity. A mass of 8 grams and velocity of 3 centimeters per second has a kinetic energy of 36 ergs. Find the kinetic energy for a mass of 4 grams and velocity of 6 centimeters per second.

35. Sound intensity varies inversely as the square of the distance from the sound source. If you are in a movie theater and you change your seat to one that is twice as far from the speakers, how does the new sound intensity compare to that of your original seat?

36. Many people claim that as they get older, time seems to pass more quickly. Suppose that the perceived length of a period of time is inversely proportional to your age. How long will a year seem to be when you are three times as old as you are now?

37. The average number of daily phone calls, C, between two cities varies jointly as the product of their populations, P_1 and P_2, and inversely as the square of the distance, d, between them.

   a. Write an equation that expresses this relationship.

   b. The distance between San Francisco (population: 777,000) and Los Angeles (population: 3,695,000) is 420 miles. If the average number of daily phone calls between the cities is 326,000, find the value of k to two decimal places and write the equation of variation.

   c. Memphis (population: 650,000) is 400 miles from New Orleans (population: 490,000). Find the average number of daily phone calls, to the nearest whole number, between these cities.

38. The force of wind blowing on a window positioned at a right angle to the direction of the wind varies jointly as the area of the window and the square of the wind's speed. It is known that a wind of 30 miles per hour blowing on a window measuring 4 feet by 5 feet exerts a force of 150 pounds. During a storm with winds of 60 miles per hour, should hurricane shutters be placed on a window that measures 3 feet by 4 feet and is capable of withstanding 300 pounds of force?

39. The table shows the values for the current, I, in an electric circuit and the resistance, R, of the circuit.

I (amperes)	0.5	1.0	1.5	2.0	2.5	3.0	4.0	5.0
R (ohms)	12.0	6.0	4.0	3.0	2.4	2.0	1.5	1.2

   a. Graph the ordered pairs in the table of values, with values of I along the x-axis and values of R along the y-axis. Connect the eight points with a smooth curve.

   b. Does current vary directly or inversely as resistance? Use your graph and explain how you arrived at your answer.

   c. Write an equation of variation for I and R, using one of the ordered pairs in the table to find the constant of variation. Then use your variation equation to verify the other seven ordered pairs in the table.

Writing in Mathematics

40. What does it mean if two quantities vary directly?

41. In your own words, explain how to solve a variation problem.

42. What does it mean if two quantities vary inversely?

43. Explain what is meant by combined variation. Give an example with your explanation.

44. Explain what is meant by joint variation. Give an example with your explanation.

In Exercises 45–46, describe in words the variation shown by the given equation.

45. $z = \dfrac{k\sqrt{x}}{y^2}$ 46. $z = kx^2\sqrt{y}$

47. We have seen that the daily number of phone calls between two cities varies jointly as their populations and inversely as the square of the distance between them. This model, used by telecommunication companies to estimate the line capacities needed among various cities, is called the *gravity model*. Compare the model to Newton's formula for gravitation on page 429 and describe why the name *gravity model* is appropriate.

Technology Exercise

48. Use a graphing utility to graph any three of the variation equations in Exercises 21–30. Then TRACE along each curve and identify the point that corresponds to the problem's solution.

Critical Thinking Exercises

Make Sense? *In Exercises 49–52, determine whether each statement makes sense or does not make sense, and explain your reasoning.*

49. I'm using an inverse variation equation and I need to determine the value of the dependent variable when the independent variable is zero.

50. The graph of this direct variation equation that has a positive constant of variation shows one variable increasing as the other variable decreases.

51. When all is said and done, it seems to me that direct variation equations are special kinds of linear functions and inverse variation equations are special kinds of rational functions.

52. Using the language of variation, I can now state the formula for the area of a trapezoid, $A = \frac{1}{2}h(b_1 + b_2)$, as, "A trapezoid's area varies jointly with its height and the sum of its bases."

53. In a hurricane, the wind pressure varies directly as the square of the wind velocity. If wind pressure is a measure of a hurricane's destructive capacity, what happens to this destructive power when the wind speed doubles?

54. The illumination from a light source varies inversely as the square of the distance from the light source. If you raise a lamp from 15 inches to 30 inches over your desk, what happens to the illumination?

55. The heat generated by a stove element varies directly as the square of the voltage and inversely as the resistance. If the voltage remains constant, what needs to be done to triple the amount of heat generated?

56. Galileo's telescope brought about revolutionary changes in astronomy. A comparable leap in our ability to observe the universe took place as a result of the Hubble Space Telescope. The space telescope was able to see stars and galaxies whose brightness is $\frac{1}{50}$ of the faintest objects observable using ground-based telescopes. Use the fact that the brightness of a point source, such as a star, varies inversely as the square of its distance from an observer to show that the space telescope was able to see about seven times farther than a ground-based telescope.

Group Exercise

57. Begin by deciding on a product that interests the group because you are now in charge of advertising this product. Members were told that the demand for the product varies directly as the amount spent on advertising and inversely as the price of the product. However, as more money is spent on advertising, the price of your product rises. Under what conditions would members recommend an increased expense in advertising? Once you've determined what your product is, write formulas for the given conditions and experiment with hypothetical numbers. What other factors might you take into consideration in terms of your recommendation? How do these factors affect the demand for your product?

Preview Exercises

Exercises 58–60 will help you prepare for the material covered in the first section of the next chapter.

58. Use point plotting to graph $f(x) = 2^x$. Begin by setting up a partial table of coordinates, selecting integers from -3 to 3, inclusive, for x. Because $y = 0$ is a horizontal asymptote, your graph should approach, but never touch, the negative portion of the x-axis.

In Exercises 59–60, use transformations of your graph from Exercise 58 to graph each function.

59. $g(x) = f(-x) = 2^{-x}$ **60.** $h(x) = f(x) + 1 = 2^x + 1$

CHAPTER 3 Summary, Review, and Test

SUMMARY

DEFINITIONS AND CONCEPTS

EXAMPLES

3.1 Quadratic Functions

a. A quadratic function is of the form $f(x) = ax^2 + bx + c, a \neq 0$.

b. The standard form of a quadratic function is $f(x) = a(x - h)^2 + k, a \neq 0$.

c. The graph of a quadratic function is a parabola. The vertex is (h, k) or $\left(-\frac{b}{2a}, f\left(-\frac{b}{2a}\right)\right)$. A procedure for graphing a quadratic function in standard form is given in the box on page 332. A procedure for graphing a quadratic function in the form $f(x) = ax^2 + bx + c$ is given in the box on page 335.
Ex. 1, p. 332; Ex. 2, p. 333; Ex. 3, p. 335

d. See the box on page 337 for minimum or maximum values of quadratic functions.
Ex. 4, p. 337; Ex. 5, p. 338

e. A strategy for solving problems involving maximizing or minimizing quadratic functions is given in the box on page 340.
Ex. 6, p. 340; Ex. 7, p. 341

3.2 Polynomial Functions and Their Graphs

a. Polynomial Function of Degree n: $f(x) = a_nx^n + a_{n-1}x^{n-1} + \cdots + a_2x^2 + a_1x + a_0, a_n \neq 0$

b. The graphs of polynomial functions are smooth and continuous.
Fig. 3.13, p. 349

c. The end behavior of the graph of a polynomial function depends on the leading term, given by the Leading Coefficient Test in the box on page 350. Odd-degree polynomial functions have graphs with opposite behavior at each end. Even-degree polynomial functions have graphs with the same behavior at each end.
Ex. 1, p. 350; Ex. 2, p. 351; Ex. 3, p. 351; Ex. 4, p. 352

d. The values of x for which $f(x)$ is equal to 0 are the zeros of the polynomial function f. These values are the roots, or solutions, of the polynomial equation $f(x) = 0$.
Ex. 5, p. 352; Ex. 6, p. 353

e. If $x - r$ occurs k times in a polynomial function's factorization, r is a repeated zero with multiplicity k. If k is even, the graph touches the x-axis and turns around at r. If k is odd, the graph crosses the x-axis at r.
Ex. 7, p. 354

f. The Intermediate Value Theorem: If f is a polynomial function and $f(a)$ and $f(b)$ have opposite signs, there is at least one value of c between a and b for which $f(c) = 0$.
Ex. 8, p. 355

DEFINITIONS AND CONCEPTS	EXAMPLES

g. If f is a polynomial of degree n, the graph of f has at most $n - 1$ turning points.

Fig. 3.24, p. 356

h. A strategy for graphing a polynomial function is given in the box on page 356.

Ex. 9, p. 356;
Ex. 10, p. 358

3.3 Dividing Polynomials; Remainder and Factor Theorems

a. Long division of polynomials is performed by dividing, multiplying, subtracting, bringing down the next term, and repeating this process until the degree of the remainder is less than the degree of the divisor. The details are given in the box on page 366.

Ex. 1, p. 365;
Ex. 2, p 366;
Ex. 3, p. 367

b. The Division Algorithm: $f(x) = d(x)q(x) + r(x)$. The dividend is the product of the divisor and the quotient plus the remainder.

c. Synthetic division is used to divide a polynomial by $x - c$. The details are given in the box on page 369.

Ex. 4, p. 369

d. The Remainder Theorem: If a polynomial $f(x)$ is divided by $x - c$, then the remainder is $f(c)$.

Ex. 5, p. 371

e. The Factor Theorem: If $x - c$ is a factor of a polynomial function $f(x)$, then c is a zero of f and a root of $f(x) = 0$. If c is a zero of f or a root of $f(x) = 0$, then $x - c$ is a factor of $f(x)$.

Ex. 6, p. 372

3.4 Zeros of Polynomial Functions

a. The Rational Zero Theorem states that the possible rational zeros of a polynomial
function $= \dfrac{\text{Factors of the constant term}}{\text{Factors of the leading coefficient}}$. The theorem is stated in the box on page 377.

Ex. 1, p. 377;
Ex. 2, p. 378;
Ex. 3, p. 378;
Ex. 4, p. 379;
Ex. 5, p. 380

b. Number of roots: If $f(x)$ is a polynomial of degree $n \geq 1$, then, counting multiple roots separately, the equation $f(x) = 0$ has n roots.

c. If $a + bi$ is a root of $f(x) = 0$ with real coefficients, then $a - bi$ is also a root.

d. The Linear Factorization Theorem: An nth-degree polynomial can be expressed as the product of n linear factors. Thus, $f(x) = a_n(x - c_1)(x - c_2) \cdots (x - c_n)$.

Ex. 6, p. 383

e. Descartes's Rule of Signs: The number of positive real zeros of f equals the number of sign changes of $f(x)$ or is less than that number by an even integer. The number of negative real zeros of f applies a similar statement to $f(-x)$.

Table 3.1, p. 385;
Ex. 7, p. 385

3.5 Rational Functions and Their Graphs

a. Rational function: $f(x) = \dfrac{p(x)}{q(x)}$; p and q are polynomial functions and $q(x) \neq 0$. The domain of f is the set of all real numbers excluding values of x that make $q(x)$ zero.

Ex. 1, p. 391

b. Arrow notation is summarized in the box on page 394.

c. The line $x = a$ is a vertical asymptote of the graph of f if $f(x)$ increases or decreases without bound as x approaches a. Vertical asymptotes are located using the theorem in the box on page 395.

Ex. 2, p. 395

d. The line $y = b$ is a horizontal asymptote of the graph of f if $f(x)$ approaches b as x increases or decreases without bound. Horizontal asymptotes are located using the theorem in the box on page 397.

Ex. 3, p. 397

e. Table 3.2 on page 398 shows the graphs of $f(x) = \dfrac{1}{x}$ and $f(x) = \dfrac{1}{x^2}$. Some rational functions can be graphed using transformations of these common graphs.

Ex. 4, p. 398

f. A strategy for graphing rational functions is given in the box on page 399.

Ex. 5, p. 399;
Ex. 6, p. 400;
Ex. 7, p. 402

g. The graph of a rational function has a slant asymptote when the degree of the numerator is one more than the degree of the denominator. The equation of the slant asymptote is found using division and dropping the remainder term.

Ex. 8, p. 403

3.6 Polynomial and Rational Inequalities

a. A polynomial inequality can be expressed as $f(x) < 0, f(x) > 0, f(x) \leq 0$, or $f(x) \geq 0$, where f is a polynomial function. A procedure for solving polynomial inequalities is given in the box on page 412.

Ex. 1, p. 412;
Ex. 2, p. 413;
Ex. 3, p. 414

DEFINITIONS AND CONCEPTS

EXAMPLES

b. A rational inequality can be expressed as $f(x) < 0, f(x) > 0, f(x) \le 0$, or $f(x) \ge 0$, where f is a rational function. The procedure for solving such inequalities begins with expressing them so that one side is zero and the other side is a single quotient. Find boundary points by setting the numerator and denominator equal to zero. Then follow a procedure similar to that for solving polynomial inequalities.

Ex. 4, p. 416

3.7 Modeling Using Variation

a. A procedure for solving variation problems is given in the box on page 424.

b. English Statement

English Statement	Equation	
y varies directly as x. y is directly proportional to x.	$y = kx$	Ex. 1, p. 424
y varies directly as x^n. y is directly proportional to x^n.	$y = kx^n$	Ex. 2, p. 425
y varies inversely as x. y is inversely proportional to x.	$y = \dfrac{k}{x}$	Ex. 3, p. 427; Ex. 4, p. 428
y varies inversely as x^n. y is inversely proportional to x^n.	$y = \dfrac{k}{x^n}$	
y varies jointly as x and z.	$y = kxz$	Ex. 5, p. 429

REVIEW EXERCISES

3.1

In Exercises 1–4, use the vertex and intercepts to sketch the graph of each quadratic function. Give the equation for the parabola's axis of symmetry. Use the graph to determine the function's domain and range.

1. $f(x) = -(x + 1)^2 + 4$ **2.** $f(x) = (x + 4)^2 - 2$

3. $f(x) = -x^2 + 2x + 3$ **4.** $f(x) = 2x^2 - 4x - 6$

In Exercises 5–6, use the function's equation, and not its graph, to find

  a. *the minimum or maximum value and where it occurs.*

  b. *the function's domain and its range.*

5. $f(x) = -x^2 + 14x - 106$ **6.** $f(x) = 2x^2 + 12x + 703$

7. A quarterback tosses a football to a receiver 40 yards downfield. The height of the football, $f(x)$, in feet, can be modeled by

$$f(x) = -0.025x^2 + x + 6,$$

where x is the ball's horizontal distance, in yards, from the quarterback.

  a. What is the ball's maximum height and how far from the quarterback does this occur?

  b. From what height did the quarterback toss the football?

  c. If the football is not blocked by a defensive player nor caught by the receiver, how far down the field will it go before hitting the ground? Round to the nearest tenth of a yard.

  d. Graph the function that models the football's parabolic path.

8. A field bordering a straight stream is to be enclosed. The side bordering the stream is not to be fenced. If 1000 yards of fencing material is to be used, what are the dimensions of the largest rectangular field that can be fenced? What is the maximum area?

$1000 - 2x$

9. Among all pairs of numbers whose difference is 14, find a pair whose product is as small as possible. What is the minimum product?

3.2

In Exercises 10–13, use the Leading Coefficient Test to determine the end behavior of the graph of the given polynomial function. Then use this end behavior to match the polynomial function with its graph. [The graphs are labeled (a) through (d).]

10. $f(x) = -x^3 + x^2 + 2x$ **11.** $f(x) = x^6 - 6x^4 + 9x^2$

12. $f(x) = x^5 - 5x^3 + 4x$ **13.** $f(x) = -x^4 + 1$

a.

b.

c.

d.

14. The Brazilian Amazon rain forest is the world's largest tropical rain forest, with some of the greatest biodiversity of any region. In 2009, the number of trees cut down in the Amazon dropped to its lowest level in 20 years. The line graph shows the number of square kilometers cleared from 2001 through 2009.

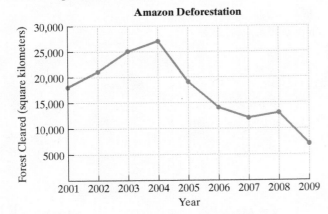

Amazon Deforestation

Source: Brazil's National Institute for Space Research

The data in the line graph can be modeled by the following third- and fourth-degree polynomial functions:

$$f(x) = 158x^3 - 2845x^2 + 12{,}926x + 7175$$
$$g(x) = -17x^4 + 508x^3 - 5180x^2 + 18{,}795x + 2889.$$

Amazon deforestation, in square kilometers, x years after 2000

a. Use the Leading Coefficient Test to determine the end behavior to the right for the graph of f.

b. Assume that the rate at which the Amazon rain forest is being cut down continues to decline. Based on your answer to part (a), will f be useful in modeling Amazon deforestation over an extended period of time? Explain your answer.

c. Use the Leading Coefficient Test to determine the end behavior to the right for the graph of g

d. Assume that the rate at which the Amazon rain forest is being cut down continues to decline. Based on your answer to part (c), will g be useful in modeling Amazon deforestation over an extended period of time? Explain your answer.

15. The polynomial function

$$f(x) = -0.87x^3 + 0.35x^2 + 81.62x + 7684.94$$

model the number of thefts, $f(x)$, in thousands in the United States x years after 1987. Will this function be useful in modeling the number of thefts over an extended period of time? Explain your answer.

In Exercises 16–17, find the zeros for each polynomial function and give the multiplicity of each zero. State whether the graph crosses the x-axis, or touches the x-axis and turns around, at each zero.

16. $f(x) = -2(x - 1)(x + 2)^2(x + 5)^3$

17. $f(x) = x^3 - 5x^2 - 25x + 125$

18. Show that $f(x) = x^3 - 2x - 1$ has a real zero between 1 and 2.

In Exercises 19–24,

   a. *Use the Leading Coefficient Test to determine the graph's end behavior.*

   b. *Determine whether the graph has y-axis symmetry, origin symmetry, or neither.*

   c. *Graph the function.*

19. $f(x) = x^3 - x^2 - 9x + 9$ **20.** $f(x) = 4x - x^3$

21. $f(x) = 2x^3 + 3x^2 - 8x - 12$ **22.** $f(x) = -x^4 + 25x^2$

23. $f(x) = -x^4 + 6x^3 - 9x^2$ **24.** $f(x) = 3x^4 - 15x^3$

In Exercises 25–26, graph each polynomial function.

25. $f(x) = 2x^2(x - 1)^3(x + 2)$

26. $f(x) = -x^3(x + 4)^2(x - 1)$

3.3

In Exercises 27–29, divide using long division.

27. $(4x^3 - 3x^2 - 2x + 1) \div (x + 1)$

28. $(10x^3 - 26x^2 + 17x - 13) \div (5x - 3)$

29. $(4x^4 + 6x^3 + 3x - 1) \div (2x^2 + 1)$

In Exercises 30–31, divide using synthetic division.

30. $(3x^4 + 11x^3 - 20x^2 + 7x + 35) \div (x + 5)$

31. $(3x^4 - 2x^2 - 10x) \div (x - 2)$

32. Given $f(x) = 2x^3 - 7x^2 + 9x - 3$, use the Remainder Theorem to find $f(-13)$.

33. Use synthetic division to divide $f(x) = 2x^3 + x^2 - 13x + 6$ by $x - 2$. Use the result to find all zeros of f.

34. Solve the equation $x^3 - 17x + 4 = 0$ given that 4 is a root.

3.4

In Exercises 35–36, use the Rational Zero Theorem to list all possible rational zeros for each given function.

35. $f(x) = x^4 - 6x^3 + 14x^2 - 14x + 5$

36. $f(x) = 3x^5 - 2x^4 - 15x^3 + 10x^2 + 12x - 8$

In Exercises 37–38, use Descartes's Rule of Signs to determine the possible number of positive and negative real zeros for each given function.

37. $f(x) = 3x^4 - 2x^3 - 8x + 5$

38. $f(x) = 2x^5 - 3x^3 - 5x^2 + 3x - 1$

39. Use Descartes's Rule of Signs to explain why $2x^4 + 6x^2 + 8 = 0$ has no real roots.

For Exercises 40–46,

   a. *List all possible rational roots or rational zeros.*

   b. *Use Descartes's Rule of Signs to determine the possible number of positive and negative real roots or real zeros.*

   c. *Use synthetic division to test the possible rational roots or zeros and find an actual root or zero.*

   d. *Use the quotient from part (c) to find all the remaining roots or zeros.*

40. $f(x) = x^3 + 3x^2 - 4$

41. $f(x) = 6x^3 + x^2 - 4x + 1$

42. $8x^3 - 36x^2 + 46x - 15 = 0$

43. $2x^3 + 9x^2 - 7x + 1 = 0$

44. $x^4 - x^3 - 7x^2 + x + 6 = 0$

45. $4x^4 + 7x^2 - 2 = 0$

46. $f(x) = 2x^4 + x^3 - 9x^2 - 4x + 4$

In Exercises 47–48, find an nth-degree polynomial function with real coefficients satisfying the given conditions. If you are using a graphing utility, graph the function and verify the real zeros and the given function value.

47. $n = 3$; 2 and $2 - 3i$ are zeros; $f(1) = -10$

48. $n = 4$; i is a zero; -3 is a zero of multiplicity 2; $f(-1) = 16$

In Exercises 49–50, find all the zeros of each polynomial function and write the polynomial as a product of linear factors.

49. $f(x) = 2x^4 + 3x^3 + 3x - 2$

50. $g(x) = x^4 - 6x^3 + x^2 + 24x + 16$

In Exercises 51–54, graphs of fifth-degree polynomial functions are shown. In each case, specify the number of real zeros and the number of imaginary zeros. Indicate whether there are any real zeros with multiplicity other than 1.

51.

52.

53.

54.

3.5

In Exercises 55–56, use transformations of $f(x) = \dfrac{1}{x}$ or $f(x) = \dfrac{1}{x^2}$ to graph each rational function.

55. $g(x) = \dfrac{1}{(x + 2)^2} - 1$ **56.** $h(x) = \dfrac{1}{x - 1} + 3$

In Exercises 57–64, find the vertical asymptotes, if any, the horizontal asymptote, if one exists, and the slant asymptote, if there is one, of the graph of each rational function. Then graph the rational function.

57. $f(x) = \dfrac{2x}{x^2 - 9}$ **58.** $g(x) = \dfrac{2x - 4}{x + 3}$

59. $h(x) = \dfrac{x^2 - 3x - 4}{x^2 - x - 6}$ **60.** $r(x) = \dfrac{x^2 + 4x + 3}{(x + 2)^2}$

61. $y = \dfrac{x^2}{x + 1}$ **62.** $y = \dfrac{x^2 + 2x - 3}{x - 3}$

63. $f(x) = \dfrac{-2x^3}{x^2 + 1}$ **64.** $g(x) = \dfrac{4x^2 - 16x + 16}{2x - 3}$

65. A company is planning to manufacture affordable graphing calculators. The fixed monthly cost will be \$50,000 and it will cost \$25 to produce each calculator.

  a. Write the cost function, C, of producing x graphing calculators.

  b. Write the average cost function, $\overline{C}$, of producing x graphing calculators.

  c. Find and interpret $\overline{C}(50)$, $\overline{C}(100)$, $\overline{C}(1000)$, and $\overline{C}(100,000)$.

  d. What is the horizontal asymptote for the graph of this function and what does it represent?

Exercises 66–67 involve rational functions that model the given situations. In each case, find the horizontal asymptote as $x \to \infty$ and then describe what this means in practical terms.

66. $f(x) = \dfrac{150x + 120}{0.05x + 1}$; the number of bass, $f(x)$, after x months in a lake that was stocked with 120 bass

67. $P(x) = \dfrac{72,900}{100x^2 + 729}$; the percentage, $P(x)$, of people in the United States with x years of education who are unemployed

68. The bar graph shows the population of the United States, in millions, for six selected years.

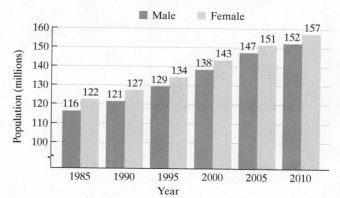

Population of the United States

Source: U.S. Census Bureau

Here are two functions that model the data:

$M(x) = 1.53x + 114.8$ — Male U.S. population, $M(x)$, in millions, x years after 1985

$F(x) = 1.46x + 120.7$ — Female U.S. population, $F(x)$, in millions, x years after 1985

  a. Write a function that models the total U.S. population, $P(x)$, in millions, x years after 1985.

  b. Write a rational function that models the fraction of men in the U.S. population, $R(x)$, x years after 1985.

  c. What is the equation of the horizontal asymptote associated with the function in part (b)? Round to two decimal places. What does this mean about the percentage of men in the U.S. population over time?

3.6

In Exercises 69–74, solve each inequality and graph the solution set on a real number line.

69. $2x^2 + 5x - 3 < 0$

70. $2x^2 + 9x + 4 \geq 0$

71. $x^3 + 2x^2 > 3x$

72. $\dfrac{x - 6}{x + 2} > 0$

73. $\dfrac{(x + 1)(x - 2)}{x - 1} \geq 0$

74. $\dfrac{x + 3}{x - 4} \leq 5$

75. The graph shows stopping distances for motorcycles at various speeds on dry roads and on wet roads.

Stopping Distances for Motorcycles at Selected Speeds

Source: National Highway Traffic Safety Administration

The functions

$$f(x) = 0.125x^2 - 0.8x + 99 \quad \text{Dry pavement}$$

and

$$g(x) = 0.125x^2 + 2.3x + 27 \quad \text{Wet pavement}$$

model a motorcycle's stopping distance, $f(x)$ or $g(x)$, in feet, traveling at x miles per hour. Function f models stopping distance on dry pavement and function g models stopping distance on wet pavement.

a. Use function g to find the stopping distance on wet pavement for a motorcycle traveling at 35 miles per hour. Round to the nearest foot. Does your rounded answer overestimate or underestimate the stopping distance shown by the graph? By how many feet?

b. Use function f to determine speeds on dry pavement requiring stopping distances that exceed 267 feet.

76. Use the position function

$$s(t) = -16t^2 + v_0 t + s_0$$

to solve this problem. A projectile is fired vertically upward from ground level with an initial velocity of 48 feet per second. During which time period will the projectile's height exceed 32 feet?

3.7

Solve the variation problems in Exercises 77–82.

77. Many areas of Northern California depend on the snowpack of the Sierra Nevada mountain range for their water supply. The volume of water produced from melting snow varies directly as the volume of snow. Meteorologists have determined that 250 cubic centimeters of snow will melt to 28 cubic centimeters of water. How much water does 1200 cubic centimeters of melting snow produce?

78. The distance that a body falls from rest is directly proportional to the square of the time of the fall. If skydivers fall 144 feet in 3 seconds, how far will they fall in 10 seconds?

79. The pitch of a musical tone varies inversely as its wavelength. A tone has a pitch of 660 vibrations per second and a wavelength of 1.6 feet. What is the pitch of a tone that has a wavelength of 2.4 feet?

80. The loudness of a stereo speaker, measured in decibels, varies inversely as the square of your distance from the speaker. When you are 8 feet from the speaker, the loudness is 28 decibels. What is the loudness when you are 4 feet from the speaker?

81. The time required to assemble computers varies directly as the number of computers assembled and inversely as the number of workers. If 30 computers can be assembled by 6 workers in 10 hours, how long would it take 5 workers to assemble 40 computers?

82. The volume of a pyramid varies jointly as its height and the area of its base. A pyramid with a height of 15 feet and a base with an area of 35 square feet has a volume of 175 cubic feet. Find the volume of a pyramid with a height of 20 feet and a base with an area of 120 square feet.

83. Heart rates and life spans of most mammals can be modeled using inverse variation. The bar graph shows the average heart rate and the average life span of five mammals.

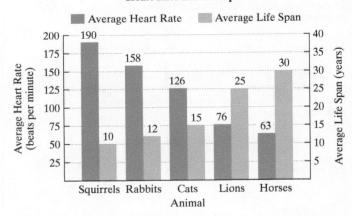

Heart Rate and Life Span

Source: *The Handy Science Answer Book,* Visible Ink Press, 2003.

a. A mammal's average life span, L, in years, varies inversely as its average heart rate, R, in beats per minute. Use the data shown for horses to write the equation that models this relationship.

b. Is the inverse variation equation in part (a) an exact model or an approximate model for the data shown for lions?

c. Elephants have an average heart rate of 27 beats per minute. Determine their average life span.

CHAPTER 3 TEST

In Exercises 1–2, use the vertex and intercepts to sketch the graph of each quadratic function. Give the equation for the parabola's axis of symmetry. Use the graph to determine the function's domain and range.

1. $f(x) = (x + 1)^2 + 4$

2. $f(x) = x^2 - 2x - 3$

3. Determine, without graphing, whether the quadratic function $f(x) = -2x^2 + 12x - 16$ has a minimum value or a maximum value. Then find

   a. the minimum or maximum value and where it occurs.

   b. the function's domain and its range.

4. The function $f(x) = -x^2 + 46x - 360$ models the daily profit, $f(x)$, in hundreds of dollars, for a company that manufactures x computers daily. How many computers should be manufactured each day to maximize profit? What is the maximum daily profit?

5. Among all pairs of numbers whose sum is 14, find a pair whose product is as large as possible. What is the maximum product?

6. Consider the function $f(x) = x^3 - 5x^2 - 4x + 20$.

   a. Use factoring to find all zeros of f.

   b. Use the Leading Coefficient Test and the zeros of f to graph the function.

7. Use end behavior to explain why the following graph cannot be the graph of $f(x) = x^5 - x$. Then use intercepts to explain why the graph cannot represent $f(x) = x^5 - x$.

8. The graph of $f(x) = 6x^3 - 19x^2 + 16x - 4$ is shown in the figure.

$f(x) = 6x^3 - 19x^2 + 16x - 4$

   a. Based on the graph of f, find the root of the equation $6x^3 - 19x^2 + 16x - 4 = 0$ that is an integer.

   b. Use synthetic division to find the other two roots of $6x^3 - 19x^2 + 16x - 4 = 0$.

9. Use the Rational Zero Theorem to list all possible rational zeros of $f(x) = 2x^3 + 11x^2 - 7x - 6$.

10. Use Descartes's Rule of Signs to determine the possible number of positive and negative real zeros of

$$f(x) = 3x^5 - 2x^4 - 2x^2 + x - 1.$$

11. Solve: $x^3 + 9x^2 + 16x - 6 = 0$.

12. Consider the function whose equation is given by $f(x) = 2x^4 - x^3 - 13x^2 + 5x + 15$.

   a. List all possible rational zeros.

   b. Use the graph of f in the figure shown and synthetic division to find all zeros of the function.

$f(x) = 2x^4 - x^3 - 13x^2 + 5x + 15$

13. Use the graph of $f(x) = x^3 + 3x^2 - 4$ in the figure shown to factor $x^3 + 3x^2 - 4$.

$f(x) = x^3 + 3x^2 - 4$

14. Find a fourth-degree polynomial function $f(x)$ with real coefficients that has $-1, 1$, and i as zeros and such that $f(3) = 160$.

15. The figure shows an incomplete graph of $f(x) = -3x^3 - 4x^2 + x + 2$. Find all the zeros of the function. Then draw a complete graph.

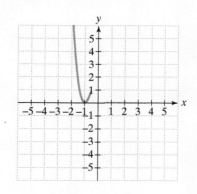

In Exercises 16–21, find the domain of each rational function and graph the function.

16. $f(x) = \dfrac{1}{(x + 3)^2}$

17. $f(x) = \dfrac{1}{x - 1} + 2$

18. $f(x) = \dfrac{x}{x^2 - 16}$

19. $f(x) = \dfrac{x^2 - 9}{x - 2}$

20. $f(x) = \dfrac{x + 1}{x^2 + 2x - 3}$

21. $f(x) = \dfrac{4x^2}{x^2 + 3}$

22. A company is planning to manufacture portable satellite radio players. The fixed monthly cost will be \$300,000 and it will cost \$10 to produce each player.

    a. Write the average cost function, $\overline{C}$, of producing x players.

    b. What is the horizontal asymptote for the graph of this function and what does it represent?

Solve each inequality in Exercises 23–24 and graph the solution set on a real number line. Express each solution set in interval notation.

23. $x^2 < x + 12$

24. $\dfrac{2x + 1}{x - 3} \le 3$

25. The intensity of light received at a source varies inversely as the square of the distance from the source. A particular light has an intensity of 20 foot-candles at 15 feet. What is the light's intensity at 10 feet?

CUMULATIVE REVIEW EXERCISES (CHAPTERS 1–3)

Use the graph of $y = f(x)$ to solve Exercises 1–6.

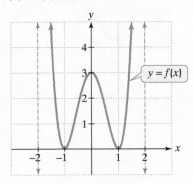

1. Find the domain and the range of f.

2. Find the zeros and the least possible multiplicity of each zero.

3. Where does the relative maximum occur?

4. Find $(f \circ f)(-1)$.

5. Use arrow notation to complete this statement: $f(x) \to \infty$ as _____ or as _____ .

6. Graph $g(x) = f(x + 2) + 1$.

In Exercises 7–12, solve each equation or inequality.

7. $|2x - 1| = 3$

8. $3x^2 - 5x + 1 = 0$

9. $9 + \dfrac{3}{x} = \dfrac{2}{x^2}$

10. $x^3 + 2x^2 - 5x - 6 = 0$

11. $|2x - 5| > 3$

12. $3x^2 > 2x + 5$

In Exercises 13–18, graph each equation in a rectangular coordinate system. If two functions are given, graph both in the same system.

13. $f(x) = x^3 - 4x^2 - x + 4$

14. $f(x) = x^2 + 2x - 8$

15. $f(x) = x^2(x - 3)$

16. $f(x) = \dfrac{x - 1}{x - 2}$

17. $f(x) = |x|$ and $g(x) = -|x| - 1$

18. $x^2 + y^2 - 2x + 4y - 4 = 0$

In Exercises 19–20, let $f(x) = 2x^2 - x - 1$ and $g(x) = 4x - 1$.

19. Find $(f \circ g)(x)$.

20. Find $\dfrac{f(x + h) - f(x)}{h}$.

EXPONENTIAL AND LOGARITHMIC FUNCTIONS

CHAPTER

4

Can I put aside $25,000 when I'm 20 and wind up sitting on half a million dollars by my early fifties? Will population growth lead to a future without comfort or individual choice? Why did I feel I was walking too slowly on my visit to New York City? Are Californians at greater risk from drunk drivers than from earthquakes? What is the difference between earthquakes measuring 6 and 7 on the Richter scale? Can I live forever? And what can possibly be causing merchants at our local shopping mall to grin from ear to ear as they watch the browsers?

The functions that you will be learning about in this chapter will provide you with the mathematics for answering these questions. You will see how these remarkable functions enable us to predict the future and rediscover the past.

HERE'S WHERE YOU'LL FIND THESE APPLICATIONS:

- You'll be sitting on $500,000 in Example 10 of Section 4.4.
- World population growth: Section 4.5, Example 5
- Population and walking speed: Section 4.5, Check Point 4
- Alcohol and risk of a car accident: Section 4.4, Example 9
- Earthquake intensity: Section 4.2, Example 9
- Immortality: Blitzer Bonus, page 446

We open the chapter with those grinning merchants and the sound of ka-ching!

SECTION 4.1   Exponential Functions

Objectives

1. Evaluate exponential functions.
2. Graph exponential functions.
3. Evaluate functions with base e.
4. Use compound interest formulas.

Just browsing? Take your time. Researchers know, to the dollar, the average amount the typical consumer spends per minute at the shopping mall. And the longer you stay, the more you spend. So if you say you're just browsing, that's just fine with the mall merchants. Browsing is time and, as shown in **Figure 4.1**, time is money.

The data in **Figure 4.1** can be modeled by the function

$$f(x) = 42.2(1.56)^x,$$

where $f(x)$ is the average amount spent, in dollars, at a shopping mall after x hours. Can you see how this function is different from a polynomial function? The variable x is in the exponent. Functions whose equations contain a variable in the exponent are called **exponential functions**. Many real-life situations, including population growth, growth of epidemics, radioactive decay, and other changes that involve rapid increase or decrease, can be described using exponential functions.

Mall Browsing Time and Average Amount Spent

FIGURE 4.1
Source: International Council of Shopping Centers Research, 2006

Definition of the Exponential Function

The **exponential function f with base b** is defined by

$$f(x) = b^x \quad \text{or} \quad y = b^x,$$

where b is a positive constant other than 1 ($b > 0$ and $b \neq 1$) and x is any real number.

Here are some examples of exponential functions:

$$f(x) = 2^x \qquad g(x) = 10^x \qquad h(x) = 3^{x+1} \qquad j(x) = \left(\frac{1}{2}\right)^{x-1}.$$

Base is 2.   Base is 10.   Base is 3.   Base is $\frac{1}{2}$.

Each of these functions has a constant base and a variable exponent.

By contrast, the following functions are not exponential functions:

$$F(x) = x^2 \qquad G(x) = 1^x \qquad H(x) = (-1)^x \qquad J(x) = x^x.$$

Variable is the base and not the exponent.   The base of an exponential function must be a positive constant other than 1.   The base of an exponential function must be positive.   Variable is both the base and the exponent.

Why is $G(x) = 1^x$ not classified as an exponential function? The number 1 raised to any power is 1. Thus, the function G can be written as $G(x) = 1$, which is a constant function.

Why is $H(x) = (-1)^x$ not an exponential function? The base of an exponential function must be positive to avoid having to exclude many values of x from the domain that result in nonreal numbers in the range:

$$H(x) = (-1)^x \qquad H\left(\frac{1}{2}\right) = (-1)^{\frac{1}{2}} = \sqrt{-1} = i.$$

Not an exponential function

All values of x resulting in even roots of negative numbers produce nonreal numbers.

① Evaluate exponential functions.

You will need a calculator to evaluate exponential expressions. Most scientific calculators have a $\boxed{y^x}$ key. Graphing calculators have a $\boxed{\wedge}$ key. To evaluate expressions of the form b^x, enter the base b, press $\boxed{y^x}$ or $\boxed{\wedge}$, enter the exponent x, and finally press $\boxed{=}$ or $\boxed{\text{ENTER}}$.

EXAMPLE 1   Evaluating an Exponential Function

The exponential function $f(x) = 42.2(1.56)^x$ models the average amount spent, $f(x)$, in dollars, at a shopping mall after x hours. What is the average amount spent, to the nearest dollar, after four hours?

SOLUTION

Because we are interested in the amount spent after four hours, substitute 4 for x and evaluate the function.

$$f(x) = 42.2(1.56)^x \quad \text{This is the given function.}$$
$$f(4) = 42.2(1.56)^4 \quad \text{Substitute 4 for x.}$$

Use a scientific or graphing calculator to evaluate $f(4)$. Press the following keys on your calculator to do this:

Scientific calculator: 42.2 $\boxed{\times}$ 1.56 $\boxed{y^x}$ 4 $\boxed{=}$

Graphing calculator: 42.2 $\boxed{\times}$ 1.56 $\boxed{\wedge}$ 4 $\boxed{\text{ENTER}}$.

The display should be approximately 249.92566.

$$f(4) = 42.2(1.56)^4 \approx 249.92566 \approx 250$$

Thus, the average amount spent after four hours at a mall is $250.   ● ● ●

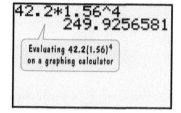

42.2*1.56^4
      249.9256581

Evaluating $42.2(1.56)^4$ on a graphing calculator

$\oslash$ Check Point **1** Use the exponential function in Example 1 to find the average amount spent, to the nearest dollar, after three hours at a shopping mall. Does this rounded function value underestimate or overestimate the amount shown in **Figure 4.1**? By how much?

② Graph exponential functions.

Graphing Exponential Functions

We are familiar with expressions involving b^x, where x is a rational number. For example,

$$b^{1.7} = b^{\frac{17}{10}} = \sqrt[10]{b^{17}} \quad \text{and} \quad b^{1.73} = b^{\frac{173}{100}} = \sqrt[100]{b^{173}}.$$

However, note that the definition of $f(x) = b^x$ includes all real numbers for the domain x. You may wonder what b^x means when x is an irrational number, such as $b^{\sqrt{3}}$ or b^{π}. Using closer and closer approximations for $\sqrt{3}$ ($\sqrt{3} \approx 1.73205$), we can think of $b^{\sqrt{3}}$ as the value that has the successively closer approximations

$$b^{1.7}, b^{1.73}, b^{1.732}, b^{1.73205}, \ldots.$$

In this way, we can graph exponential functions with no holes, or points of discontinuity, at the irrational domain values.

EXAMPLE 2 Graphing an Exponential Function

Graph: $f(x) = 2^x$.

SOLUTION

We begin by setting up a table of coordinates.

> We selected integers from −3 to 3, inclusive, to include three negative numbers, 0, and three positive numbers. We also wanted to keep the resulting computations for y relatively simple.

x	$f(x) = 2^x$
−3	$f(-3) = 2^{-3} = \dfrac{1}{8}$
−2	$f(-2) = 2^{-2} = \dfrac{1}{4}$
−1	$f(-1) = 2^{-1} = \dfrac{1}{2}$
0	$f(0) = 2^0 = 1$
1	$f(1) = 2^1 = 2$
2	$f(2) = 2^2 = 4$
3	$f(3) = 2^3 = 8$

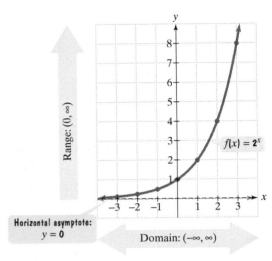

FIGURE 4.2 The graph of $f(x) = 2^x$

We plot these points, connecting them with a continuous curve. **Figure 4.2** shows the graph of $f(x) = 2^x$. Observe that the graph approaches, but never touches, the negative portion of the x-axis. Thus, the x-axis, or $y = 0$, is a horizontal asymptote. The range is the set of all positive real numbers. Although we used integers for x in our table of coordinates, you can use a calculator to find additional points. For example, $f(0.3) = 2^{0.3} \approx 1.231$ and $f(0.95) = 2^{0.95} \approx 1.932$. The points $(0.3, 1.231)$ and $(0.95, 1.932)$ approximately fit the graph. • • •

✓ Check Point **2** Graph: $f(x) = 3^x$.

EXAMPLE 3 Graphing an Exponential Function

Graph: $g(x) = \left(\dfrac{1}{2}\right)^x$.

SOLUTION

We begin by setting up a table of coordinates. We compute the function values by noting that

$$g(x) = \left(\frac{1}{2}\right)^x = (2^{-1})^x = 2^{-x}.$$

x	$g(x) = \left(\dfrac{1}{2}\right)^x$ or 2^{-x}
−3	$g(-3) = 2^{-(-3)} = 2^3 = 8$
−2	$g(-2) = 2^{-(-2)} = 2^2 = 4$
−1	$g(-1) = 2^{-(-1)} = 2^1 = 2$
0	$g(0) = 2^{-0} = 1$
1	$g(1) = 2^{-1} = \dfrac{1}{2^1} = \dfrac{1}{2}$
2	$g(2) = 2^{-2} = \dfrac{1}{2^2} = \dfrac{1}{4}$
3	$g(3) = 2^{-3} = \dfrac{1}{2^3} = \dfrac{1}{8}$

We plot these points, connecting them with a continuous curve. **Figure 4.3** shows the graph of $g(x) = \left(\frac{1}{2}\right)^x$. This time the graph approaches, but never touches, the *positive* portion of the x-axis. Once again, the x-axis, or $y = 0$, is a horizontal asymptote. The range consists of all positive real numbers.

FIGURE 4.3 The graph of $g(x) = \left(\dfrac{1}{2}\right)^x$ • • •

Do you notice a relationship between the graphs of $f(x) = 2^x$ and $g(x) = \left(\frac{1}{2}\right)^x$ in **Figures 4.2** and **4.3**? The graph of $g(x) = \left(\frac{1}{2}\right)^x$ is the graph of $f(x) = 2^x$ reflected about the y-axis:

$$g(x) = \left(\frac{1}{2}\right)^x = 2^{-x} = f(-x).$$

Recall that the graph of $y = f(-x)$ is the graph of $y = f(x)$ reflected about the y-axis.

⊘ Check Point **3** Graph: $f(x) = \left(\frac{1}{3}\right)^x$. Note that $f(x) = \left(\frac{1}{3}\right)^x = (3^{-1})^x = 3^{-x}$.

Four exponential functions have been graphed in **Figure 4.4**. Compare the black and green graphs, where $b > 1$, to those in blue and red, where $b < 1$. When $b > 1$, the value of y increases as the value of x increases. When $b < 1$, the value of y decreases as the value of x increases. Notice that all four graphs pass through $(0, 1)$.

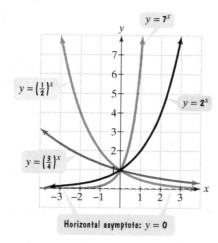

FIGURE 4.4 Graphs of four exponential functions

These graphs illustrate the following general characteristics of exponential functions:

Characteristics of Exponential Functions of the Form $f(x) = b^x$

1. The domain of $f(x) = b^x$ consists of all real numbers: $(-\infty, \infty)$. The range of $f(x) = b^x$ consists of all positive real numbers: $(0, \infty)$.
2. The graphs of all exponential functions of the form $f(x) = b^x$ pass through the point $(0, 1)$ because $f(0) = b^0 = 1(b \neq 0)$. The y-intercept is 1. There is no x-intercept.
3. If $b > 1, f(x) = b^x$ has a graph that goes up to the right and is an increasing function. The greater the value of b, the steeper the increase.
4. If $0 < b < 1, f(x) = b^x$ has a graph that goes down to the right and is a decreasing function. The smaller the value of b, the steeper the decrease.
5. $f(x) = b^x$ is one-to-one and has an inverse that is a function.
6. The graph of $f(x) = b^x$ approaches, but does not touch, the x-axis. The x-axis, or $y = 0$, is a horizontal asymptote.

Blitzer Bonus ‖ Exponential Growth: The Year Humans Become Immortal

In 2011, *Jeopardy!* aired a three-night match between a personable computer named Watson and the show's two most successful players. The winner: Watson. In the time it took each human contestant to respond to one trivia question, Watson was able to scan the content of one million books. It was also trained to understand the puns and twists of phrases unique to *Jeopardy!* clues.

Watson's remarkable accomplishments can be thought of as a single data point on an exponential curve that models growth in computing power. According to inventor, author, and computer scientist Ray Kurzweil (1948–   ), computer technology is progressing exponentially, doubling in power each year. What does this mean in terms of the accelerating pace of the graph of $y = 2^x$ that starts slowly and then rockets skyward toward infinity? According to Kurzweil, by 2023, a supercomputer will surpass the brainpower of a human. As progress accelerates exponentially and every hour brings a century's worth of scientific breakthroughs, by 2045, computers will surpass the brainpower equivalent to that of all human brains combined. Here's where it gets exponentially weird: In that year (says Kurzweil), we will be able to scan our consciousness into computers and enter a virtual existence, or swap our bodies for immortal robots. Indefinite life extension will become a reality and people will die only if they choose to.

Transformations of Exponential Functions

The graphs of exponential functions can be translated vertically or horizontally, reflected, stretched, or shrunk. These transformations are summarized in **Table 4.1**.

Table 4.1 Transformations Involving Exponential Functions

In each case, c represents a positive real number.

Transformation	Equation	Description
Vertical translation	$g(x) = b^x + c$	• Shifts the graph of $f(x) = b^x$ upward c units.
	$g(x) = b^x - c$	• Shifts the graph of $f(x) = b^x$ downward c units.
Horizontal translation	$g(x) = b^{x+c}$	• Shifts the graph of $f(x) = b^x$ to the left c units.
	$g(x) = b^{x-c}$	• Shifts the graph of $f(x) = b^x$ to the right c units.
Reflection	$g(x) = -b^x$	• Reflects the graph of $f(x) = b^x$ about the x-axis.
	$g(x) = b^{-x}$	• Reflects the graph of $f(x) = b^x$ about the y-axis.
Vertical stretching or shrinking	$g(x) = cb^x$	• Vertically stretches the graph of $f(x) = b^x$ if $c > 1$.
		• Vertically shrinks the graph of $f(x) = b^x$ if $0 < c < 1$.
Horizontal stretching or shrinking	$g(x) = b^{cx}$	• Horizontally shrinks the graph of $f(x) = b^x$ if $c > 1$.
		• Horizontally stretches the graph of $f(x) = b^x$ if $0 < c < 1$.

EXAMPLE 4   Transformations Involving Exponential Functions

Use the graph of $f(x) = 3^x$ to obtain the graph of $g(x) = 3^{x+1}$.

SOLUTION

The graph of $g(x) = 3^{x+1}$ is the graph of $f(x) = 3^x$ shifted 1 unit to the left.

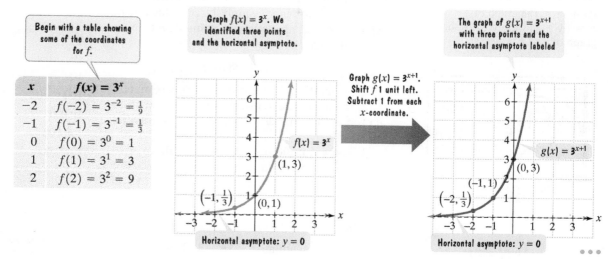

Begin with a table showing some of the coordinates for f.

x	$f(x) = 3^x$
−2	$f(-2) = 3^{-2} = \frac{1}{9}$
−1	$f(-1) = 3^{-1} = \frac{1}{3}$
0	$f(0) = 3^0 = 1$
1	$f(1) = 3^1 = 3$
2	$f(2) = 3^2 = 9$

Graph $f(x) = 3^x$. We identified three points and the horizontal asymptote.

Graph $g(x) = 3^{x+1}$. Shift f 1 unit left. Subtract 1 from each x-coordinate.

The graph of $g(x) = 3^{x+1}$ with three points and the horizontal asymptote labeled

Check Point 4 Use the graph of $f(x) = 3^x$ to obtain the graph of $g(x) = 3^{x-1}$.

If an exponential function is translated upward or downward, the horizontal asymptote is shifted by the amount of the vertical shift.

EXAMPLE 5   Transformations Involving Exponential Functions

Use the graph of $f(x) = 2^x$ to obtain the graph of $g(x) = 2^x - 3$.

SOLUTION

The graph of $g(x) = 2^x - 3$ is the graph of $f(x) = 2^x$ shifted down 3 units.

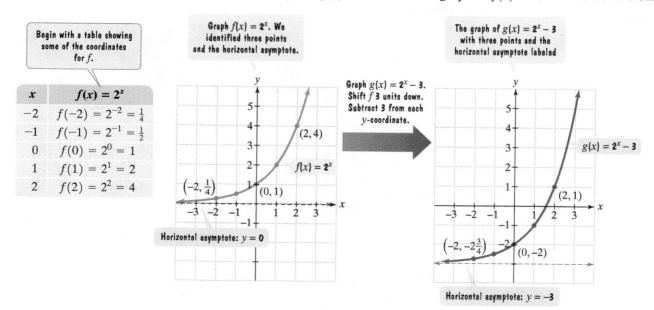

Begin with a table showing some of the coordinates for f.

x	$f(x) = 2^x$
−2	$f(-2) = 2^{-2} = \frac{1}{4}$
−1	$f(-1) = 2^{-1} = \frac{1}{2}$
0	$f(0) = 2^0 = 1$
1	$f(1) = 2^1 = 2$
2	$f(2) = 2^2 = 4$

Graph $f(x) = 2^x$. We identified three points and the horizontal asymptote.

Graph $g(x) = 2^x - 3$. Shift f 3 units down. Subtract 3 from each y-coordinate.

The graph of $g(x) = 2^x - 3$ with three points and the horizontal asymptote labeled

Check Point 5 Use the graph of $f(x) = 2^x$ to obtain the graph of $g(x) = 2^x + 1$.

③ Evaluate functions with base *e*.

TECHNOLOGY

Graphic Connections

As $n \to \infty$, the graph of $y = \left(1 + \frac{1}{n}\right)^n$ approaches the graph of $y = e$.

$[0, 15, 1]$ by $[0, 3, 1]$

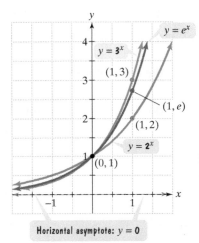

Horizontal asymptote: $y = 0$

FIGURE 4.5 Graphs of three exponential functions

The Natural Base *e*

An irrational number, symbolized by the letter *e*, appears as the base in many applied exponential functions. The number *e* is defined as the value that $\left(1 + \frac{1}{n}\right)^n$ approaches as *n* gets larger and larger. **Table 4.2** shows values of $\left(1 + \frac{1}{n}\right)^n$ for increasingly large values of *n*. As $n \to \infty$, the approximate value of *e* to nine decimal places is

$$e \approx 2.718281827.$$

The irrational number *e*, approximately 2.72, is called the **natural base**. The function $f(x) = e^x$ is called the **natural exponential function**.

Use a scientific or graphing calculator with an $\boxed{e^x}$ key to evaluate *e* to various powers. For example, to find e^2, press the following keys on most calculators:

Scientific calculator: $2 \; \boxed{e^x}$

Graphing calculator: $\boxed{e^x} \; 2 \; \boxed{\text{ENTER}}$.

The display should be approximately 7.389.

$$e^2 \approx 7.389$$

The number *e* lies between 2 and 3. Because $2^2 = 4$ and $3^2 = 9$, it makes sense that e^2, approximately 7.389, lies between 4 and 9.

Because $2 < e < 3$, the graph of $y = e^x$ is between the graphs of $y = 2^x$ and $y = 3^x$, shown in **Figure 4.5**.

Table 4.2

n	$\left(1 + \frac{1}{n}\right)^n$
1	2
2	2.25
5	2.48832
10	2.59374246
100	2.704813829
1000	2.716923932
10,000	2.718145927
100,000	2.718268237
1,000,000	2.718280469
1,000,000,000	2.718281827

As $n \to \infty$, $\left(1 + \frac{1}{n}\right)^n \to e$.

In calculus, this is expressed as
$$\lim_{n \to \infty} \left(1 + \frac{1}{n}\right)^n = e.$$

EXAMPLE 6 Gray Wolf Population

Insatiable killer. That's the reputation the gray wolf acquired in the United States in the nineteenth and early twentieth centuries. Although the label was undeserved, an estimated two million wolves were shot, trapped, or poisoned. By 1960, the population was reduced to 800 wolves. **Figure 4.6** shows the rebounding population in two recovery areas after the gray wolf was declared an endangered species and received federal protection.

The exponential function

$$f(x) = 1.26e^{0.247x}$$

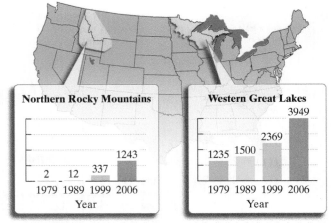

Gray Wolf Population in Two Recovery Areas for Selected Years

FIGURE 4.6
Source: U.S. Fish and Wildlife Service

models the gray wolf population of the Northern Rocky Mountains, $f(x)$, x years after 1978. If the wolf is not removed from the endangered species list and trends shown in **Figure 4.6** continue, project its population in the recovery area in 2010.

SOLUTION

Because 2010 is 32 years after 1978, we substitute 32 for x in the given function.

$$f(x) = 1.26e^{0.247x} \quad \text{This is the given function.}$$

$$f(32) = 1.26e^{0.247(32)} \quad \text{Substitute 32 for x.}$$

Perform this computation on your calculator.

Scientific calculator: 1.26 $\boxed{\times}$ $\boxed{(}$ .247 $\boxed{\times}$ 32 $\boxed{)}$ $\boxed{e^x}$ $\boxed{=}$

Graphing calculator: 1.26 $\boxed{\times}$ $\boxed{e^x}$ $\boxed{(}$ .247 $\boxed{\times}$ 32 $\boxed{)}$ $\boxed{\text{ENTER}}$

The display should be approximately 3412.1973.

Thus, $f(32) = 1.26e^{0.247(32)} \approx 3412.$

> This parenthesis is given on some calculators.

This indicates that the gray wolf population of the Northern Rocky Mountains in the year 2010 is projected to have been 3412.   • • •

✓ **Check Point 6** The exponential function $f(x) = 1066e^{0.042x}$ models the gray wolf population of the Western Great Lakes, $f(x)$, x years after 1978. If trends shown in **Figure 4.6** continue, project the gray wolf's population in the recovery area in 2012.

In 2008, using exponential functions and projections like those in Example 6 and Check Point 6, the U.S. Fish and Wildlife Service removed the gray wolf from the endangered species list, a ruling environmentalists vowed to appeal.

④ Use compound interest formulas.

Compound Interest

We all want a wonderful life with fulfilling work, good health, and loving relationships. And let's be honest: Financial security wouldn't hurt! Achieving this goal depends on understanding how money in savings accounts grows in remarkable ways as a result of *compound interest*. **Compound interest** is interest computed on your original investment as well as on any accumulated interest.

Suppose a sum of money, called the **principal**, P, is invested at an annual percentage rate r, in decimal form, compounded once per year. Because the interest is added to the principal at year's end, the accumulated value, A, is

$$A = P + Pr = P(1 + r).$$

The accumulated amount of money follows this pattern of multiplying the previous principal by $(1 + r)$ for each successive year, as indicated in **Table 4.3**.

Table 4.3

Time in Years	Accumulated Value after Each Compounding
0	$A = P$
1	$A = P(1 + r)$
2	$A = P(1 + r)(1 + r) = P(1 + r)^2$
3	$A = P(1 + r)^2(1 + r) = P(1 + r)^3$
4	$A = P(1 + r)^3(1 + r) = P(1 + r)^4$
⋮	⋮
t	$A = P(1 + r)^t$

> This formula gives the balance, A, that a principal, P, is worth after t years at interest rate r, compounded once a year.

Most savings institutions have plans in which interest is paid more than once a year. If compound interest is paid twice a year, the compounding period is six months. We say that the interest is **compounded semiannually**. When compound interest is paid four times a year, the compounding period is three months and the interest is said to be **compounded quarterly**. Some plans allow for monthly compounding or daily compounding.

In general, when compound interest is paid n times a year, we say that there are n **compounding periods per year. Table 4.4** shows the three most frequently used plans in which interest is paid more than once a year.

Table 4.4   Interest Plans

Name	Number of Compounding Periods per Year	Length of Each Compounding Period
Semiannual Compounding	$n = 2$	6 months
Quarterly Compounding	$n = 4$	3 months
Monthly Compounding	$n = 12$	1 month

The formula $A = P(1 + r)^t$ can be adjusted to take into account the number of compounding periods in a year. If there are n compounding periods per year, in each time period the interest rate is $\frac{r}{n}$ and there are nt time periods in t years. This results in the following formula for the balance, A, after t years:

$$A = P\left(1 + \frac{r}{n}\right)^{nt}.$$

Some banks use **continuous compounding**, where the number of compounding periods increases infinitely (compounding interest every trillionth of a second, every quadrillionth of a second, etc.). Let's see what happens to the balance, A, as $n \to \infty$.

$$\frac{n}{r} \cdot rt = nt$$

$$A = P\left(1 + \frac{r}{n}\right)^{nt} = P\left[\left(1 + \frac{1}{\frac{n}{r}}\right)^{\frac{n}{r}}\right]^{rt} = P\left[\left(1 + \frac{1}{h}\right)^{h}\right]^{rt} = Pe^{rt}$$

Let $h = \frac{n}{r}$.
As $n \to \infty$, $h \to \infty$.

As $h \to \infty$, by definition
$\left(1 + \frac{1}{h}\right)^{h} \to e$.

We see that the formula for continuous compounding is $A = Pe^{rt}$. Although continuous compounding sounds terrific, it yields only a fraction of a percent more interest over a year than daily compounding.

Formulas for Compound Interest

After t years, the balance, A, in an account with principal P and annual interest rate r (in decimal form) is given by the following formulas:

1. For n compounding periods per year: $A = P\left(1 + \frac{r}{n}\right)^{nt}$

2. For continuous compounding: $A = Pe^{rt}$.

EXAMPLE 7   Choosing between Investments

You decide to invest $8000 for 6 years and you have a choice between two accounts. The first pays 7% per year, compounded monthly. The second pays 6.85% per year, compounded continuously. Which is the better investment?

SOLUTION

The better investment is the one with the greater balance in the account after 6 years. Let's begin with the account with monthly compounding. We use the compound interest model with $P = 8000, r = 7\% = 0.07, n = 12$ (monthly compounding means 12 compoundings per year), and $t = 6$.

$$A = P\left(1 + \frac{r}{n}\right)^{nt} = 8000\left(1 + \frac{0.07}{12}\right)^{12\cdot6} \approx 12{,}160.84$$

The balance in this account after 6 years is $12,160.84.

For the second investment option, we use the model for continuous compounding with $P = 8000, r = 6.85\% = 0.0685$, and $t = 6$.

$$A = Pe^{rt} = 8000e^{0.0685(6)} \approx 12{,}066.60$$

The balance in this account after 6 years is $12,066.60, slightly less than the previous amount. Thus, the better investment is the 7% monthly compounding option. • • •

 Check Point **7** A sum of $10,000 is invested at an annual rate of 8%. Find the balance in the account after 5 years subject to **a.** quarterly compounding and **b.** continuous compounding.

CONCEPT AND VOCABULARY CHECK

Fill in each blank so that the resulting statement is true.

1. The exponential function f with base b is defined by $f(x) = $ _____, $b > 0$ and $b \neq 1$. Using interval notation, the domain of this function is _____ and the range is _____.

2. The graph of the exponential function f with base b approaches, but does not touch, the _____-axis. This axis, whose equation is _____, is a/an _____ asymptote.

3. The value that $\left(1 + \dfrac{1}{n}\right)^n$ approaches as n gets larger and larger is the irrational number _____, called the _____ base. This irrational number is approximately equal to _____.

4. Consider the compound interest formula

$$A = P\left(1 + \frac{r}{n}\right)^{nt}.$$

This formula gives the balance, _____, in an account with principal _____ and annual interest rate _____, in decimal form, subject to compound interest paid _____ times per year.

5. If compound interest is paid twice a year, we say that the interest is compounded _____. If compound interest is paid four times a year, we say that the interest is compounded _____. If the number of compounding periods increases infinitely, we call this _____ compounding.

EXERCISE SET 4.1

Practice Exercises

In Exercises 1–10, approximate each number using a calculator. Round your answer to three decimal places.

1. $2^{3.4}$ **2.** $3^{2.4}$ **3.** $3^{\sqrt{5}}$ **4.** $5^{\sqrt{3}}$ **5.** $4^{-1.5}$

6. $6^{-1.2}$ **7.** $e^{2.3}$ **8.** $e^{3.4}$ **9.** $e^{-0.95}$ **10.** $e^{-0.75}$

In Exercises 11–18, graph each function by making a table of coordinates. If applicable, use a graphing utility to confirm your hand-drawn graph.

11. $f(x) = 4^x$

12. $f(x) = 5^x$

13. $g(x) = \left(\frac{3}{2}\right)^x$

14. $g(x) = \left(\frac{4}{3}\right)^x$

15. $h(x) = \left(\frac{1}{2}\right)^x$

16. $h(x) = \left(\frac{1}{3}\right)^x$

17. $f(x) = (0.6)^x$

18. $f(x) = (0.8)^x$

In Exercises 19–24, the graph of an exponential function is given. Select the function for each graph from the following options:

$$f(x) = 3^x, g(x) = 3^{x-1}, h(x) = 3^x - 1,$$
$$F(x) = -3^x, G(x) = 3^{-x}, H(x) = -3^{-x}.$$

19.

20.

21.

22.

23.

24.

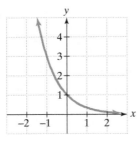

In Exercises 25–34, begin by graphing f(x) = 2^x. Then use transformations of this graph to graph the given function. Be sure to graph and give equations of the asymptotes. Use the graphs to determine each function's domain and range. If applicable, use a graphing utility to confirm your hand-drawn graphs.

25. $g(x) = 2^{x+1}$ **26.** $g(x) = 2^{x+2}$

27. $g(x) = 2^x - 1$ **28.** $g(x) = 2^x + 2$

29. $h(x) = 2^{x+1} - 1$ **30.** $h(x) = 2^{x+2} - 1$

31. $g(x) = -2^x$ **32.** $g(x) = 2^{-x}$

33. $g(x) = 2 \cdot 2^x$ **34.** $g(x) = \frac{1}{2} \cdot 2^x$

The figure shows the graph of f(x) = e^x. In Exercises 35–46, use transformations of this graph to graph each function. Be sure to give equations of the asymptotes. Use the graphs to determine each function's domain and range. If applicable, use a graphing utility to confirm your hand-drawn graphs.

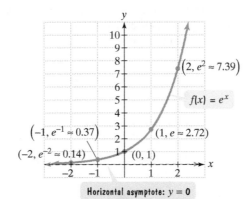

35. $g(x) = e^{x-1}$ **36.** $g(x) = e^{x+1}$

37. $g(x) = e^x + 2$ **38.** $g(x) = e^x - 1$

39. $h(x) = e^{x-1} + 2$ **40.** $h(x) = e^{x+1} - 1$

41. $h(x) = e^{-x}$ **42.** $h(x) = -e^x$

43. $g(x) = 2e^x$ **44.** $g(x) = \frac{1}{2}e^x$

45. $h(x) = e^{2x} + 1$ **46.** $h(x) = e^{\frac{x}{2}} + 2$

In Exercises 47–52, graph functions f and g in the same rectangular coordinate system. Graph and give equations of all asymptotes. If applicable, use a graphing utility to confirm your hand-drawn graphs.

47. $f(x) = 3^x$ and $g(x) = 3^{-x}$

48. $f(x) = 3^x$ and $g(x) = -3^x$

49. $f(x) = 3^x$ and $g(x) = \frac{1}{3} \cdot 3^x$

50. $f(x) = 3^x$ and $g(x) = 3 \cdot 3^x$

51. $f(x) = \left(\frac{1}{2}\right)^x$ and $g(x) = \left(\frac{1}{2}\right)^{x-1} + 1$

52. $f(x) = \left(\frac{1}{2}\right)^x$ and $g(x) = \left(\frac{1}{2}\right)^{x-1} + 2$

Use the compound interest formulas $A = P\left(1 + \dfrac{r}{n}\right)^{nt}$ and $A = Pe^{rt}$ to solve Exercises 53–56. Round answers to the nearest cent.

53. Find the accumulated value of an investment of $10,000 for 5 years at an interest rate of 5.5% if the money is **a.** compounded semiannually; **b.** compounded quarterly; **c.** compounded monthly; **d.** compounded continuously.

54. Find the accumulated value of an investment of $5000 for 10 years at an interest rate of 6.5% if the money is **a.** compounded semiannually; **b.** compounded quarterly; **c.** compounded monthly; **d.** compounded continuously.

55. Suppose that you have $12,000 to invest. Which investment yields the greater return over 3 years: 7% compounded monthly or 6.85% compounded continuously?

56. Suppose that you have $6000 to invest. Which investment yields the greater return over 4 years: 8.25% compounded quarterly or 8.3% compounded semiannually?

Practice Plus

In Exercises 57–58, graph f and g in the same rectangular coordinate system. Then find the point of intersection of the two graphs.

57. $f(x) = 2^x, g(x) = 2^{-x}$

58. $f(x) = 2^{x+1}, g(x) = 2^{-x+1}$

59. Graph $y = 2^x$ and $x = 2^y$ in the same rectangular coordinate system.

60. Graph $y = 3^x$ and $x = 3^y$ in the same rectangular coordinate system.

In Exercises 61–64, give the equation of each exponential function whose graph is shown.

61.

62.

63.

64.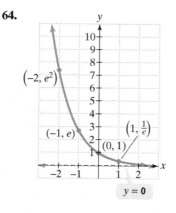

Application Exercises

Use a calculator with a $\boxed{y^x}$ *key or a* $\boxed{\wedge}$ *key to solve Exercises 65–70.*

65. India is currently one of the world's fastest-growing countries. By 2040, the population of India will be larger than the population of China; by 2050, nearly one-third of the world's population will live in these two countries alone. The exponential function $f(x) = 574(1.026)^x$ models the population of India, $f(x)$, in millions, x years after 1974.

  a. Substitute 0 for x and, without using a calculator, find India's population in 1974.

  b. Substitute 27 for x and use your calculator to find India's population, to the nearest million, in the year 2001 as modeled by this function.

  c. Find India's population, to the nearest million, in the year 2028 as predicted by this function.

  d. Find India's population, to the nearest million, in the year 2055 as predicted by this function.

  e. What appears to be happening to India's population every 27 years?

66. The 1986 explosion at the Chernobyl nuclear power plant in the former Soviet Union sent about 1000 kilograms of radioactive cesium-137 into the atmosphere. The function $f(x) = 1000(0.5)^{\frac{x}{30}}$ describes the amount, $f(x)$, in kilograms, of cesium-137 remaining in Chernobyl x years after 1986. If even 100 kilograms of cesium-137 remain in Chernobyl's atmosphere, the area is considered unsafe for human habitation. Find $f(80)$ and determine if Chernobyl will be safe for human habitation by 2066.

The formula $S = C(1 + r)^t$ models inflation, where $C =$ the value today, $r =$ the annual inflation rate, and $S =$ the inflated value t years from now. Use this formula to solve Exercises 67–68. Round answers to the nearest dollar.

67. If the inflation rate is 6%, how much will a house now worth $465,000 be worth in 10 years?

68. If the inflation rate is 3%, how much will a house now worth $510,000 be worth in 5 years?

69. A decimal approximation for $\sqrt{3}$ is 1.7320508. Use a calculator to find $2^{1.7}$, $2^{1.73}$, $2^{1.732}$, $2^{1.73205}$, and $2^{1.7320508}$. Now find $2^{\sqrt{3}}$. What do you observe?

70. A decimal approximation for π is 3.141593. Use a calculator to find 2^3, $2^{3.1}$, $2^{3.14}$, $2^{3.141}$, $2^{3.1415}$, $2^{3.14159}$, and $2^{3.141593}$. Now find 2^{π}. What do you observe?

Use a calculator with an $\boxed{e^x}$ *key to solve Exercises 71–76.*

Average annual premiums for employer-sponsored family health insurance policies more than doubled over 11 years. The bar graph shows the average cost of a family health insurance plan in the United States for six selected years from 2000 through 2011.

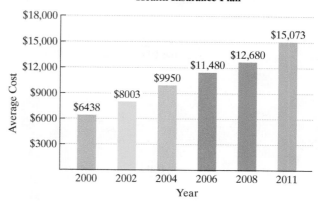

Source: Kaiser Family Foundation

The data can be modeled by

$$f(x) = 782x + 6564 \quad \text{and} \quad g(x) = 6875e^{0.077x},$$

in which $f(x)$ and $g(x)$ represent the average cost of a family health insurance plan x years after 2000. Use these functions to solve Exercises 71–72. Where necessary, round answers to the nearest whole dollar.

71. a. According to the linear model, what was the average cost of a family health insurance plan in 2011?

  b. According to the exponential model, what was the average cost of a family health insurance plan in 2011?

  c. Which function is a better model for the data in 2011?

72. a. According to the linear model, what was the average cost of a family health insurance plan in 2008?

  b. According to the exponential model, what was the average cost of a family health insurance plan in 2008?

  c. Which function is a better model for the data in 2008?

73. In college, we study large volumes of information— information that, unfortunately, we do not often retain for very long. The function

$$f(x) = 80e^{-0.5x} + 20$$

describes the percentage of information, $f(x)$, that a particular person remembers x weeks after learning the information.

  a. Substitute 0 for x and, without using a calculator, find the percentage of information remembered at the moment it is first learned.

  b. Substitute 1 for x and find the percentage of information that is remembered after 1 week.

  c. Find the percentage of information that is remembered after 4 weeks.

  d. Find the percentage of information that is remembered after one year (52 weeks).

74. In 1626, Peter Minuit convinced the Wappinger Indians to sell him Manhattan Island for $24. If the Native Americans had put the $24 into a bank account paying 5% interest, how much would the investment have been worth in the year 2010 if interest were compounded

a. monthly? **b.** continuously?

The bar graph shows the percentage of people 25 years of age and older who were college graduates in the United States for seven selected years.

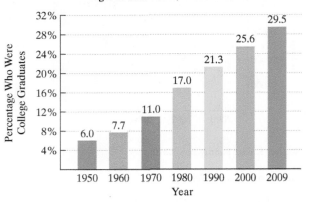

Percentage of College Graduates, Among People Ages 25 and Older, in the United States

Source: U.S. Census Bureau

The functions

$$f(x) = 6.25(1.029)^x \quad \text{and} \quad g(x) = \frac{38.8}{1 + 6.3e^{-0.051x}}$$

model the percentage of college graduates, among people ages 25 and older, $f(x)$ or $g(x)$, x years after 1950. Use these functions to solve Exercises 75–76.

75. Which function is a better model for the percentage who were college graduates in 2009?

76. Which function is a better model for the percentage who were college graduates in 1990?

Writing in Mathematics

77. What is an exponential function?

78. What is the natural exponential function?

79. Use a calculator to evaluate $\left(1 + \dfrac{1}{x}\right)^x$ for $x = 10, 100, 1000,$ 10,000, 100,000, and 1,000,000. Describe what happens to the expression as x increases.

80. Describe how you could use the graph of $f(x) = 2^x$ to obtain a decimal approximation for $\sqrt{2}$.

Technology Exercises

81. You have $10,000 to invest. One bank pays 5% interest compounded quarterly and a second bank pays 4.5% interest compounded monthly.

a. Use the formula for compound interest to write a function for the balance in each bank at any time t.

b. Use a graphing utility to graph both functions in an appropriate viewing rectangle. Based on the graphs, which bank offers the better return on your money?

82. a. Graph $y = e^x$ and $y = 1 + x + \dfrac{x^2}{2}$ in the same viewing rectangle.

b. Graph $y = e^x$ and $y = 1 + x + \dfrac{x^2}{2} + \dfrac{x^3}{6}$ in the same viewing rectangle.

c. Graph $y = e^x$ and $y = 1 + x + \dfrac{x^2}{2} + \dfrac{x^3}{6} + \dfrac{x^4}{24}$ in the same viewing rectangle.

d. Describe what you observe in parts (a)–(c). Try generalizing this observation.

Critical Thinking Exercises

Make Sense? *In Exercises 83–86, determine whether each statement makes sense or does not make sense, and explain your reasoning.*

83. My graph of $f(x) = 3 \cdot 2^x$ shows that the horizontal asymptote for f is $x = 3$.

84. I'm using a photocopier to reduce an image over and over by 50%, so the exponential function $f(x) = \left(\frac{1}{2}\right)^x$ models the new image size, where x is the number of reductions.

85. I'm looking at data that show the number of new college programs in green studies, and a linear function appears to be a better choice than an exponential function for modeling the number of new college programs from 2005 through 2009.

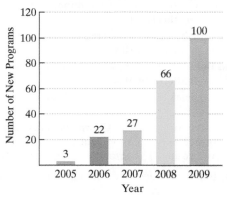

Number of New Programs in Green Studies at U.S. Colleges

Source: Association for the Advancement of Sustainability in Higher Education

86. I use the natural base e when determining how much money I'd have in a bank account that earns compound interest subject to continuous compounding.

In Exercises 87–90, determine whether each statement is true or false. If the statement is false, make the necessary change(s) to produce a true statement.

87. As the number of compounding periods increases on a fixed investment, the amount of money in the account over a fixed interval of time will increase without bound.

88. The functions $f(x) = 3^{-x}$ and $g(x) = -3^x$ have the same graph.

89. If $f(x) = 2^x$, then $f(a + b) = f(a) + f(b)$.

90. The functions $f(x) = \left(\frac{1}{3}\right)^x$ and $g(x) = 3^{-x}$ have the same graph.

91. The graphs labeled (a)–(d) in the figure represent $y = 3^x$, $y = 5^x$, $y = \left(\frac{1}{3}\right)^x$, and $y = \left(\frac{1}{5}\right)^x$, but not necessarily in that order. Which is which? Describe the process that enables you to make this decision.

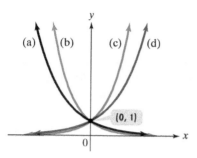

92. Graph $f(x) = 2^x$ and its inverse function in the same rectangular coordinate system.

93. The *hyperbolic cosine* and *hyperbolic sine* functions are defined by

$$\cosh x = \frac{e^x + e^{-x}}{2} \quad \text{and} \quad \sinh x = \frac{e^x - e^{-x}}{2}.$$

a. Show that cosh x is an even function.
b. Show that sinh x is an odd function.
c. Prove that $(\cosh x)^2 - (\sinh x)^2 = 1$.

Preview Exercises

Exercises 94–96 will help you prepare for the material covered in the next section.

94. What problem do you encounter when using the switch-and-solve strategy to find the inverse of $f(x) = 2^x$? (The switch-and-solve strategy is described in the box on page 303.)

95. 25 to what power gives 5? ($25^? = 5$)

96. Solve: $(x - 3)^2 > 0$.

SECTION 4.2 Logarithmic Functions

Objectives

① Change from logarithmic to exponential form.
② Change from exponential to logarithmic form.
③ Evaluate logarithms.
④ Use basic logarithmic properties.
⑤ Graph logarithmic functions.
⑥ Find the domain of a logarithmic function.
⑦ Use common logarithms.
⑧ Use natural logarithms.

The earthquake that ripped through northern California on October 17, 1989, measured 7.1 on the Richter scale, killed more than 60 people, and injured more than 2400. Shown here is San Francisco's Marina district, where shock waves tossed houses off their foundations and into the street.

A higher measure on the Richter scale is more devastating than it seems because for each increase in one unit on the scale, there is a tenfold increase in the intensity of an earthquake. In this section, our focus is on the inverse of the exponential function, called the logarithmic function. The logarithmic function will help you to understand diverse phenomena, including earthquake intensity, human memory, and the pace of life in large cities.

GREAT QUESTION!

You mentioned that the inverse of the exponential function is called the logarithmic function. We haven't discussed inverses of functions since Section 2.7. What should I already know about functions and their inverses?

Here's a brief summary:

1. Only one-to-one functions have inverses that are functions. A function, f, has an inverse function, f^{-1}, if there is no horizontal line that intersects the graph of f at more than one point.
2. If a function is one-to-one, its inverse function can be found by interchanging x and y in the function's equation and solving for y.
3. If $f(a) = b$, then $f^{-1}(b) = a$. The domain of f is the range of f^{-1}. The range of f is the domain of f^{-1}.
4. $f(f^{-1}(x)) = x$ and $f^{-1}(f(x)) = x$.
5. The graph of f^{-1} is the reflection of the graph of f about the line $y = x$.

The Definition of Logarithmic Functions

No horizontal line can be drawn that intersects the graph of an exponential function at more than one point. This means that the exponential function is one-to-one and has an inverse. Let's use our switch-and-solve strategy from Section 2.7 to find the inverse.

All exponential functions have
inverse functions.

$$f(x) = b^x$$

Step 1   Replace $f(x)$ with y: $y = b^x$.

Step 2   Interchange x and y: $x = b^y$.

Step 3   Solve for y: ?

The question mark indicates that we do not have a method for solving $b^y = x$ for y. To isolate the exponent y, a new notation, called *logarithmic notation*, is needed. This notation gives us a way to name the inverse of $f(x) = b^x$. **The inverse function of the exponential function with base b is called the *logarithmic function with base b*.**

Definition of the Logarithmic Function

For $x > 0$ and $b > 0, b \neq 1,$

$$y = \log_b x \text{ is equivalent to } b^y = x.$$

The function $f(x) = \log_b x$ is the **logarithmic function with base b.**

The equations

$$y = \log_b x \quad \text{and} \quad b^y = x$$

are different ways of expressing the same thing. The first equation is in **logarithmic form** and the second equivalent equation is in **exponential form**.

Notice that a **logarithm, y, is an exponent.** You should learn the location of the base and exponent in each form.

Location of Base and Exponent in Exponential and Logarithmic Forms

Exponent

Exponent

Logarithmic Form: $y = \log_b x$ Exponential Form: $b^y = x$

Base

Base

① Change from logarithmic
to exponential form.

EXAMPLE 1   Changing from Logarithmic to Exponential Form

Write each equation in its equivalent exponential form:

a. $2 = \log_5 x$ **b.** $3 = \log_b 64$ **c.** $\log_3 7 = y$.

SOLUTION

We use the fact that $y = \log_b x$ means $b^y = x$.

a. $2 = \log_5 x$ means $5^2 = x$.   **b.** $3 = \log_b 64$ means $b^3 = 64$.

Logarithms are exponents.

Logarithms are exponents.

c. $\log_3 7 = y$ or $y = \log_3 7$ means $3^y = 7$.   • • •

GREAT QUESTION!

Much of what you've discussed so far involves changing from logarithmic form to the more familiar exponential form. Is there a pattern I can use to help me remember how to do this?

Yes. To change from logarithmic form to exponential form, use this pattern:

$$y = \log_b x \text{ means } b^y = x.$$

⊘ Check Point **1**   Write each equation in its equivalent exponential form:

a. $3 = \log_7 x$ **b.** $2 = \log_b 25$ **c.** $\log_4 26 = y$.

② Change from exponential to logarithmic form.

EXAMPLE 2 Changing from Exponential to Logarithmic Form

Write each equation in its equivalent logarithmic form:

a. $12^2 = x$ **b.** $b^3 = 8$ **c.** $e^y = 9$.

SOLUTION

We use the fact that $b^y = x$ means $y = \log_b x$.

a. $12^2 = x$ means $2 = \log_{12} x$. **b.** $b^3 = 8$ means $3 = \log_b 8$.

Exponents are logarithms.

Exponents are logarithms.

c. $e^y = 9$ means $y = \log_e 9$.

● ● ●

✓ Check Point **2** Write each equation in its equivalent logarithmic form:

a. $2^5 = x$ **b.** $b^3 = 27$ **c.** $e^y = 33$.

③ Evaluate logarithms.

Remembering that logarithms are exponents makes it possible to evaluate some logarithms by inspection. The logarithm of x with base b, $\log_b x$, is the exponent to which b must be raised to get x. For example, suppose we want to evaluate $\log_2 32$. We ask, 2 to what power gives 32? Because $2^5 = 32$, $\log_2 32 = 5$.

EXAMPLE 3 Evaluating Logarithms

Evaluate:

a. $\log_2 16$ **b.** $\log_7 \frac{1}{49}$ **c.** $\log_{25} 5$ **d.** $\log_2 \sqrt[5]{2}$.

SOLUTION

Logarithmic Expression	Question Needed for Evaluation	Logarithmic Expression Evaluated
a. $\log_2 16$	2 to what power gives 16? $2^? = 16$	$\log_2 16 = 4$ because $2^4 = 16$.
b. $\log_7 \frac{1}{49}$	7 to what power gives $\frac{1}{49}$? $7^? = \frac{1}{49}$	$\log_7 \frac{1}{49} = -2$ because $7^{-2} = \frac{1}{7^2} = \frac{1}{49}$.
c. $\log_{25} 5$	25 to what power gives 5? $25^? = 5$	$\log_{25} 5 = \frac{1}{2}$ because $25^{\frac{1}{2}} = \sqrt{25} = 5$.
d. $\log_2 \sqrt[5]{2}$	2 to what power gives $\sqrt[5]{2}$, or $2^{\frac{1}{5}}$? $2^? = \sqrt[5]{2}$	$\log_2 \sqrt[5]{2} = \frac{1}{5}$ because $2^{\frac{1}{5}} = \sqrt[5]{2}$.

● ● ●

✓ Check Point **3** Evaluate:

a. $\log_{10} 100$ **b.** $\log_5 \frac{1}{125}$ **c.** $\log_{36} 6$ **d.** $\log_3 \sqrt[7]{3}$.

④ Use basic logarithmic properties.

Basic Logarithmic Properties

Because logarithms are exponents, they have properties that can be verified using properties of exponents.

Basic Logarithmic Properties Involving One

1. $\log_b b = 1$ because 1 is the exponent to which b must be raised to obtain b. ($b^1 = b$)

2. $\log_b 1 = 0$ because 0 is the exponent to which b must be raised to obtain 1. ($b^0 = 1$)

EXAMPLE 4 Using Properties of Logarithms

Evaluate:

    a. $\log_7 7$ **b.** $\log_5 1$.

SOLUTION

    a. Because $\log_b b = 1$, we conclude $\log_7 7 = 1$.   This means that $7^1 = 7$.
    b. Because $\log_b 1 = 0$, we conclude $\log_5 1 = 0$.   This means that $5^0 = 1$.

    ● ● ●

⊘ Check Point **4** Evaluate:

    a. $\log_9 9$ **b.** $\log_8 1$.

Now that we are familiar with logarithmic notation, let's resume and finish the switch-and-solve strategy for finding the inverse of $f(x) = b^x$.

Step 1 **Replace $f(x)$ with y:** $y = b^x$.
Step 2 **Interchange x and y:** $x = b^y$.
Step 3 **Solve for y:** $y = \log_b x$.
Step 4 **Replace y with $f^{-1}(x)$:** $f^{-1}(x) = \log_b x$.

The completed switch-and-solve strategy illustrates that if $f(x) = b^x$, then $f^{-1}(x) = \log_b x$. The inverse of an exponential function is the logarithmic function with the same base.

In Section 2.7, we saw how inverse functions "undo" one another. In particular,

$$f(f^{-1}(x)) = x \quad \text{and} \quad f^{-1}(f(x)) = x.$$

Applying these relationships to exponential and logarithmic functions, we obtain the following **inverse properties of logarithms**:

Inverse Properties of Logarithms

For $b > 0$ and $b \neq 1$,

$\log_b b^x = x$ The logarithm with base b of b raised to a power equals that power.

$b^{\log_b x} = x$. b raised to the logarithm with base b of a number equals that number.

EXAMPLE 5 Using Inverse Properties of Logarithms

Evaluate:

    a. $\log_4 4^5$ **b.** $6^{\log_6 9}$.

SOLUTION

    a. Because $\log_b b^x = x$, we conclude $\log_4 4^5 = 5$.
    b. Because $b^{\log_b x} = x$, we conclude $6^{\log_6 9} = 9$.

    ● ● ●

⊘ Check Point **5** Evaluate:

    a. $\log_7 7^8$ **b.** $3^{\log_3 17}$.

⑤ Graph logarithmic functions.

Graphs of Logarithmic Functions

How do we graph logarithmic functions? We use the fact that a logarithmic function is the inverse of an exponential function. This means that the logarithmic function reverses the coordinates of the exponential function. It also means that the graph of the logarithmic function is a reflection of the graph of the exponential function about the line $y = x$.

EXAMPLE 6   Graphs of Exponential and Logarithmic Functions

Graph $f(x) = 2^x$ and $g(x) = \log_2 x$ in the same rectangular coordinate system.

SOLUTION

We first set up a table of coordinates for $f(x) = 2^x$. Reversing these coordinates gives the coordinates for the inverse function $g(x) = \log_2 x$.

x	-2	-1	0	1	2	3
$f(x) = 2^x$	$\frac{1}{4}$	$\frac{1}{2}$	1	2	4	8

Reverse coordinates.

x	$\frac{1}{4}$	$\frac{1}{2}$	1	2	4	8
$g(x) = \log_2 x$	-2	-1	0	1	2	3

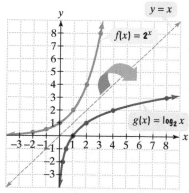

FIGURE 4.7 The graphs of $f(x) = 2^x$ and its inverse function

We now plot the ordered pairs from each table, connecting them with smooth curves. **Figure 4.7** shows the graphs of $f(x) = 2^x$ and its inverse function $g(x) = \log_2 x$. The graph of the inverse can also be drawn by reflecting the graph of $f(x) = 2^x$ about the line $y = x$.

• • •

GREAT QUESTION!

You found the coordinates of $g(x) = \log_2 x$ by reversing the coordinates of $f(x) = 2^x$. Do I have to do it that way?

Not necessarily. You can obtain a partial table of coordinates for $g(x) = \log_2 x$ without having to obtain and reverse coordinates for $f(x) = 2^x$. Because $g(x) = \log_2 x$ means $2^{g(x)} = x$, we begin with values for $g(x)$ and compute corresponding values for x:

Use $x = 2^{g(x)}$ to compute x. For example, if $g(x) = -2$, $x = 2^{-2} = \frac{1}{2^2} = \frac{1}{4}$.

Start with values for $g(x)$.

x	$\frac{1}{4}$	$\frac{1}{2}$	1	2	4	8
$g(x) = \log_2 x$	-2	-1	0	1	2	3

⊘ **Check Point 6**   Graph $f(x) = 3^x$ and $g(x) = \log_3 x$ in the same rectangular coordinate system.

Figure 4.8 illustrates the relationship between the graph of an exponential function, shown in blue, and its inverse, a logarithmic function, shown in red, for bases greater than 1 and for bases between 0 and 1. Also shown and labeled are the exponential function's horizontal asymptote ($y = 0$) and the logarithmic function's vertical asymptote ($x = 0$).

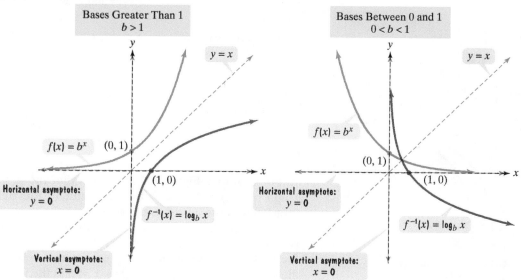

FIGURE 4.8 Graphs of exponential and logarithmic functions

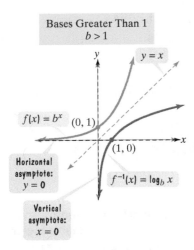

Bases Greater Than 1
$b > 1$

$y = x$

$f(x) = b^x$ $(0, 1)$

$(1, 0)$

$f^{-1}(x) = \log_b x$

Horizontal asymptote: $y = 0$

Vertical asymptote: $x = 0$

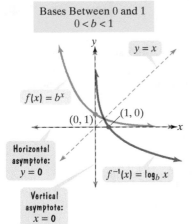

Bases Between 0 and 1
$0 < b < 1$

$y = x$

$f(x) = b^x$

$(0, 1)$ $(1, 0)$

Horizontal asymptote: $y = 0$

$f^{-1}(x) = \log_b x$

Vertical asymptote: $x = 0$

FIGURE 4.8 (repeated)

The red graphs in **Figure 4.8** illustrate the following general characteristics of logarithmic functions:

Characteristics of Logarithmic Functions of the Form $f(x) = \log_b x$

1. The domain of $f(x) = \log_b x$ consists of all positive real numbers: $(0, \infty)$. The range of $f(x) = \log_b x$ consists of all real numbers: $(-\infty, \infty)$.
2. The graphs of all logarithmic functions of the form $f(x) = \log_b x$ pass through the point $(1, 0)$ because $f(1) = \log_b 1 = 0$. The x-intercept is 1. There is no y-intercept.
3. If $b > 1$, $f(x) = \log_b x$ has a graph that goes up to the right and is an increasing function.
4. If $0 < b < 1$, $f(x) = \log_b x$ has a graph that goes down to the right and is a decreasing function.
5. The graph of $f(x) = \log_b x$ approaches, but does not touch, the y-axis. The y-axis, or $x = 0$, is a vertical asymptote.

The graphs of logarithmic functions can be translated vertically or horizontally, reflected, stretched, or shrunk. These transformations are summarized in **Table 4.5**.

Table 4.5 Transformations Involving Logarithmic Functions

In each case, c represents a positive real number.

Transformation	Equation	Description
Vertical translation	$g(x) = \log_b x + c$	• Shifts the graph of $f(x) = \log_b x$ upward c units.
	$g(x) = \log_b x - c$	• Shifts the graph of $f(x) = \log_b x$ downward c units.
Horizontal translation	$g(x) = \log_b(x + c)$	• Shifts the graph of $f(x) = \log_b x$ to the left c units. Vertical asymptote: $x = -c$
	$g(x) = \log_b(x - c)$	• Shifts the graph of $f(x) = \log_b x$ to the right c units. Vertical asymptote: $x = c$
Reflection	$g(x) = -\log_b x$	• Reflects the graph of $f(x) = \log_b x$ about the x-axis.
	$g(x) = \log_b(-x)$	• Reflects the graph of $f(x) = \log_b x$ about the y-axis.
Vertical stretching or shrinking	$g(x) = c \log_b x$	• Vertically stretches the graph of $f(x) = \log_b x$ if $c > 1$. • Vertically shrinks the graph of $f(x) = \log_b x$ if $0 < c < 1$.
Horizontal stretching or shrinking	$g(x) = \log_b(cx)$	• Horizontally shrinks the graph of $f(x) = \log_b x$ if $c > 1$. • Horizontally stretches the graph of $f(x) = \log_b x$ if $0 < c < 1$.

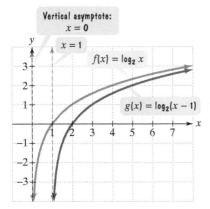

Vertical asymptote: $x = 0$

$x = 1$

$f(x) = \log_2 x$

$g(x) = \log_2(x - 1)$

FIGURE 4.9 Shifting $f(x) = \log_2 x$ one unit to the right

For example, **Figure 4.9** illustrates that the graph of $g(x) = \log_2(x - 1)$ is the graph of $f(x) = \log_2 x$ shifted one unit to the right. If a logarithmic function is translated to the left or to the right, both the x-intercept and the vertical asymptote are shifted by the amount of the horizontal shift. In **Figure 4.9**, the x-intercept of f is 1. Because g is shifted one unit to the right, its x-intercept is 2. Also observe that the vertical asymptote for f, the y-axis, or $x = 0$, is shifted one unit to the right for the vertical asymptote for g. Thus, $x = 1$ is the vertical asymptote for g.

Here are some other examples of transformations of graphs of logarithmic functions:

- The graph of $g(x) = 3 + \log_4 x$ is the graph of $f(x) = \log_4 x$ shifted up three units, shown in **Figure 4.10**.
- The graph of $h(x) = -\log_2 x$ is the graph of $f(x) = \log_2 x$ reflected about the x-axis, shown in **Figure 4.11**.
- The graph of $r(x) = \log_2(-x)$ is the graph of $f(x) = \log_2 x$ reflected about the y-axis, shown in **Figure 4.12**.

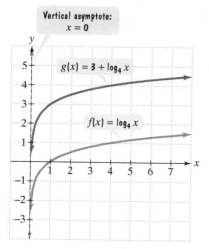

FIGURE 4.10 Shifting vertically up three units

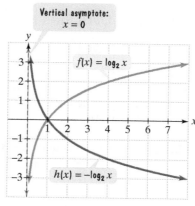

FIGURE 4.11 Reflection about the x-axis

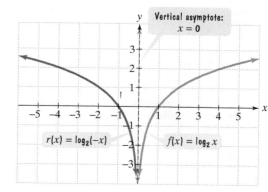

FIGURE 4.12 Reflection about the y-axis

⑥ Find the domain of a logarithmic function.

The Domain of a Logarithmic Function

In Section 4.1, we learned that the domain of an exponential function of the form $f(x) = b^x$ includes all real numbers and its range is the set of positive real numbers. Because the logarithmic function reverses the domain and the range of the exponential function, the **domain of a logarithmic function of the form $f(x) = \log_b x$ is the set of all positive real numbers**. Thus, $\log_2 8$ is defined because the value of x in the logarithmic expression, 8, is greater than zero and therefore is included in the domain of the logarithmic function $f(x) = \log_2 x$. However, $\log_2 0$ and $\log_2(-8)$ are not defined because 0 and -8 are not positive real numbers and therefore are excluded from the domain of the logarithmic function $f(x) = \log_2 x$. In general, **the domain of $f(x) = \log_b g(x)$ consists of all x for which $g(x) > 0$.**

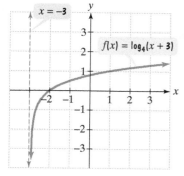

FIGURE 4.13 The domain of $f(x) = \log_4(x + 3)$ is $(-3, \infty)$.

EXAMPLE 7 Finding the Domain of a Logarithmic Function

Find the domain of $f(x) = \log_4(x + 3)$.

SOLUTION

The domain of f consists of all x for which $x + 3 > 0$. Solving this inequality for x, we obtain $x > -3$. Thus, the domain of f is $(-3, \infty)$. This is illustrated in **Figure 4.13**. The vertical asymptote is $x = -3$ and all points on the graph of f have x-coordinates that are greater than -3.   ● ● ●

⊘ Check Point **7** Find the domain of $f(x) = \log_4(x - 5)$.

7 Use common logarithms.

Common Logarithms

The logarithmic function with base 10 is called the **common logarithmic function**. The function $f(x) = \log_{10} x$ is usually expressed as $f(x) = \log x$. A calculator with a $\boxed{\text{LOG}}$ key can be used to evaluate common logarithms. Here are some examples:

Logarithm	Most Scientific Calculator Keystrokes	Most Graphing Calculator Keystrokes	Display (or Approximate Display)
log 1000	1000 $\boxed{\text{LOG}}$	$\boxed{\text{LOG}}$ 1000 $\boxed{\text{ENTER}}$	3
$\log\dfrac{5}{2}$	$\boxed{(}$ 5 $\boxed{\div}$ 2 $\boxed{)}$ $\boxed{\text{LOG}}$	$\boxed{\text{LOG}}$ $\boxed{(}$ 5 $\boxed{\div}$ 2 $\boxed{)}$ $\boxed{\text{ENTER}}$	0.39794
$\dfrac{\log 5}{\log 2}$	5 $\boxed{\text{LOG}}$ $\boxed{\div}$ 2 $\boxed{\text{LOG}}$ $\boxed{=}$	$\boxed{\text{LOG}}$ 5 $\boxed{\div}$ $\boxed{\text{LOG}}$ 2 $\boxed{\text{ENTER}}$	2.32193
$\log(-3)$	3 $\boxed{+/-}$ $\boxed{\text{LOG}}$	$\boxed{\text{LOG}}$ $\boxed{(-)}$ 3 $\boxed{\text{ENTER}}$	$\boxed{\text{ERROR}}$

> Some graphing calculators display an open parenthesis when the $\boxed{\text{LOG}}$ key is pressed. In this case, remember to close the set of parentheses after entering the function's domain value: $\boxed{\text{LOG}}$ 5 $\boxed{)}$ $\boxed{\div}$ $\boxed{\text{LOG}}$ 2 $\boxed{)}$ $\boxed{\text{ENTER}}$.

The error message or $\boxed{\text{NONREAL ANS}}$ given by many calculators for $\log(-3)$ is a reminder that the domain of the common logarithmic function, $f(x) = \log x$, is the set of positive real numbers. In general, the domain of $f(x) = \log g(x)$ consists of all x for which $g(x) > 0$.

Many real-life phenomena start with rapid growth and then the growth begins to level off. This type of behavior can be modeled by logarithmic functions.

EXAMPLE 8 Modeling Height of Children

The percentage of adult height attained by a boy who is x years old can be modeled by

$$f(x) = 29 + 48.8 \log(x + 1),$$

where x represents the boy's age (from 5 to 15) and $f(x)$ represents the percentage of his adult height. Approximately what percentage of his adult height has a boy attained at age eight?

SOLUTION

We substitute the boy's age, 8, for x and evaluate the function.

$$f(x) = 29 + 48.8 \log(x + 1) \qquad \text{This is the given function.}$$
$$f(8) = 29 + 48.8 \log(8 + 1) \qquad \text{Substitute 8 for x.}$$
$$= 29 + 48.8 \log 9 \qquad \text{Graphing calculator keystrokes:}$$
$$\qquad\qquad\qquad 29 \boxed{+} 48.8 \boxed{\text{LOG}} 9 \boxed{\text{ENTER}}$$
$$\approx 76$$

Thus, an 8-year-old boy has attained approximately 76% of his adult height. • • •

✓ Check Point **8** Use the function in Example 8 to answer this question: Approximately what percentage of his adult height has a boy attained at age ten?

The basic properties of logarithms that were listed earlier in this section can be applied to common logarithms.

Properties of Common Logarithms

General Properties	Common Logarithms
1. $\log_b 1 = 0$	**1.** $\log 1 = 0$
2. $\log_b b = 1$	**2.** $\log 10 = 1$
3. $\log_b b^x = x$ — Inverse properties	**3.** $\log 10^x = x$
4. $b^{\log_b x} = x$ —	**4.** $10^{\log x} = x$

The property $\log 10^x = x$ can be used to evaluate common logarithms involving powers of 10. For example,

$$\log 100 = \log 10^2 = 2, \quad \log 1000 = \log 10^3 = 3, \quad \text{and} \quad \log 10^{7.1} = 7.1.$$

EXAMPLE 9 Earthquake Intensity

The magnitude, R, on the Richter scale of an earthquake of intensity I is given by

$$R = \log \frac{I}{I_0},$$

where I_0 is the intensity of a barely felt zero-level earthquake. The earthquake that destroyed San Francisco in 1906 was $10^{8.3}$ times as intense as a zero-level earthquake. What was its magnitude on the Richter scale?

SOLUTION

Because the earthquake was $10^{8.3}$ times as intense as a zero-level earthquake, the intensity, I, is $10^{8.3}I_0$.

$$R = \log \frac{I}{I_0} \qquad \text{This is the formula for magnitude on the Richter scale.}$$

$$R = \log \frac{10^{8.3}I_0}{I_0} \qquad \text{Substitute } 10^{8.3}I_0 \text{ for } I.$$

$$= \log 10^{8.3} \qquad \text{Simplify.}$$

$$= 8.3 \qquad \text{Use the property } \log 10^x = x.$$

San Francisco's 1906 earthquake registered 8.3 on the Richter scale. • • •

⊘ Check Point **9** Use the formula in Example 9 to solve this problem. If an earthquake is 10,000 times as intense as a zero-level quake ($I = 10,000I_0$), what is its magnitude on the Richter scale?

⑧ Use natural logarithms.

Natural Logarithms

The logarithmic function with base e is called the **natural logarithmic function**. The function $f(x) = \log_e x$ is usually expressed as $f(x) = \ln x$, read "el en of x." A calculator with an $\boxed{\text{LN}}$ key can be used to evaluate natural logarithms. Keystrokes are identical to those shown for common logarithmic evaluations on page 462.

Like the domain of all logarithmic functions, the domain of the natural logarithmic function $f(x) = \ln x$ is the set of all positive real numbers. Thus, the domain of $f(x) = \ln g(x)$ consists of all x for which $g(x) > 0$.

[−10, 10, 1] by [−10, 10, 1]

FIGURE 4.14 The domain of $f(x) = \ln(3 − x)$ is $(-\infty, 3)$.

EXAMPLE 10 Finding Domains of Natural Logarithmic Functions

Find the domain of each function:

a. $f(x) = \ln(3 − x)$ **b.** $h(x) = \ln(x − 3)^2$.

SOLUTION

a. The domain of f consists of all x for which $3 − x > 0$. Solving this inequality for x, we obtain $x < 3$. Thus, the domain of f is $\{x \,|\, x < 3\}$ or $(-\infty, 3)$. This is verified by the graph in **Figure 4.14**.

b. The domain of h consists of all x for which $(x − 3)^2 > 0$. It follows that the domain of h is all real numbers except 3. Thus, the domain of h is $\{x \,|\, x \neq 3\}$ or $(-\infty, 3) \cup (3, \infty)$. This is shown by the graph in **Figure 4.15**. To make it more obvious that 3 is excluded from the domain, we used a $\boxed{\text{DOT}}$ format. • • •

[−10, 10, 1] by [−10, 10, 1]

FIGURE 4.15 3 is excluded from the domain of $h(x) = \ln(x − 3)^2$.

⊘ Check Point **10** Find the domain of each function:

a. $f(x) = \ln(4 − x)$ **b.** $h(x) = \ln x^2$.

The basic properties of logarithms that were listed earlier in this section can be applied to natural logarithms.

Properties of Natural Logarithms

General Properties	**Natural Logarithms**
1. $\log_b 1 = 0$	**1.** $\ln 1 = 0$
2. $\log_b b = 1$	**2.** $\ln e = 1$
3. $\log_b b^x = x$ ⟵ Inverse ⟶	**3.** $\ln e^x = x$
4. $b^{\log_b x} = x$ ⟵ properties ⟶	**4.** $e^{\ln x} = x$

Examine the inverse properties, $\ln e^x = x$ and $e^{\ln x} = x$. Can you see how ln and e "undo" one another? For example,

$$\ln e^2 = 2, \quad \ln e^{7x^2} = 7x^2, \quad e^{\ln 2} = 2, \quad \text{and} \quad e^{\ln 7x^2} = 7x^2.$$

EXAMPLE 11   Dangerous Heat: Temperature in an Enclosed Vehicle

When the outside air temperature is anywhere from 72° to 96° Fahrenheit, the temperature in an enclosed vehicle climbs by 43° in the first hour. The bar graph in **Figure 4.16** shows the temperature increase throughout the hour. The function

$$f(x) = 13.4 \ln x - 11.6$$

models the temperature increase, $f(x)$, in degrees Fahrenheit, after x minutes. Use the function to find the temperature increase, to the nearest degree, after 50 minutes. How well does the function model the actual increase shown in **Figure 4.16**?

Temperature Increase in an Enclosed Vehicle

FIGURE 4.16
Source: Professor Jan Null, San Francisco State University

SOLUTION

We find the temperature increase after 50 minutes by substituting 50 for x and evaluating the function at 50.

$$f(x) = 13.4 \ln x - 11.6 \qquad \text{This is the given function.}$$
$$f(50) = 13.4 \ln 50 - 11.6 \qquad \text{Substitute 50 for x.}$$
$$\approx 41 \qquad \text{Graphing calculator keystrokes:}$$

13.4 |ln| 50 |−| 11.6 |ENTER|. On some calculators, a parenthesis is needed after 50.

According to the function, the temperature will increase by approximately 41° after 50 minutes. Because the increase shown in **Figure 4.16** is 41°, the function models the actual increase extremely well. • • •

✓ Check Point **11** Use the function in Example 11 to find the temperature increase, to the nearest degree, after 30 minutes. How well does the function model the actual increase shown in **Figure 4.16**?

Blitzer Bonus ‖ The Curious Number e

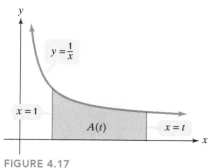

FIGURE 4.17

You will learn more about each curiosity mentioned below if you take calculus.

- The number e was named by the Swiss mathematician Leonhard Euler (1707–1783), who proved that it is the limit as $n \to \infty$ of $\left(1 + \dfrac{1}{n}\right)^n$.
- e features in Euler's remarkable relationship $e^{i\pi} = -1$, in which $i = \sqrt{-1}$.
- The first few decimal places of e are fairly easy to remember:
  $e = 2.7\ 1828\ 1828\ 45\ 90\ 45\ldots.$
- The best approximation of e using numbers less than 1000 is also easy to remember:
  $e \approx \dfrac{878}{323} \approx 2.71826\ldots.$
- Isaac Newton (1642–1727), one of the cofounders of calculus, showed that
  $e^x = 1 + x + \dfrac{x^2}{2!} + \dfrac{x^3}{3!} + \dfrac{x^4}{4!} + \cdots,$ from which we obtain $e = 1 + 1 + \dfrac{1}{2!} + \dfrac{1}{3!} + \dfrac{1}{4!} + \cdots,$ an infinite sum suitable for calculation because its terms decrease so rapidly. (*Note: n!* (*n* factorial) is the product of all the consecutive integers from *n* down to 1: $n! = n(n-1)(n-2)(n-3)\cdot \cdots \cdot 3\cdot 2\cdot 1$.)
- The area of the region bounded by $y = \dfrac{1}{x}$, the *x*-axis, $x = 1$, and $x = t$ (shaded in **Figure 4.17**) is a function of t, designated by $A(t)$. Grégoire de Saint-Vincent, a Belgian Jesuit (1584–1667), spent his entire professional life attempting to find a formula for $A(t)$. With his student, he showed that $A(t) = \ln t$, becoming one of the first mathematicians to make use of the logarithmic function for something other than a computational device.

CONCEPT AND VOCABULARY CHECK

Fill in each blank so that the resulting statement is true.

1. $y = \log_b x$ is equivalent to the exponential form _____, $x > 0, b > 0, b \neq 1$.
2. The function $f(x) = \log_b x$ is the _____ function with base _____.
3. $\log_b b =$ _____
4. $\log_b 1 =$ _____
5. $\log_b b^x =$ _____
6. $b^{\log_b x} =$ _____
7. Using interval notation, the domain of $f(x) = \log_b x$ is _____ and the range is _____.
8. The graph of $f(x) = \log_b x$ approaches, but does not touch, the _____-axis. This axis, whose equation is _____, is a/an _____ asymptote.
9. The graph of $g(x) = 5 + \log_2 x$ is the graph of $f(x) = \log_2 x$ shifted _____.

10. The graph of $g(x) = \log_3(x + 5)$ is the graph of $f(x) = \log_3 x$ shifted _____.
11. The graph of $g(x) = -\log_4 x$ is the graph of $f(x) = \log_4 x$ reflected about the _____.
12. The graph of $g(x) = \log_5(-x)$ is the graph of $f(x) = \log_5 x$ reflected about the _____.
13. The domain of $g(x) = \log_2(5 - x)$ can be found by solving the inequality _____.
14. The logarithmic function with base 10 is called the _____ logarithmic function. The function $f(x) = \log_{10} x$ is usually expressed as $f(x) =$ _____.
15. The logarithmic function with base e is called the _____ logarithmic function. The function $f(x) = \log_e x$ is usually expressed as $f(x) =$ _____.

EXERCISE SET 4.2

Practice Exercises

In Exercises 1–8, write each equation in its equivalent exponential form.

1. $4 = \log_2 16$
2. $6 = \log_2 64$
3. $2 = \log_3 x$
4. $2 = \log_9 x$
5. $5 = \log_b 32$
6. $3 = \log_b 27$
7. $\log_6 216 = y$
8. $\log_5 125 = y$

In Exercises 9–20, write each equation in its equivalent logarithmic form.

9. $2^3 = 8$
10. $5^4 = 625$
11. $2^{-4} = \frac{1}{16}$
12. $5^{-3} = \frac{1}{125}$
13. $\sqrt[3]{8} = 2$
14. $\sqrt[3]{64} = 4$
15. $13^2 = x$
16. $15^2 = x$
17. $b^3 = 1000$
18. $b^3 = 343$
19. $7^y = 200$
20. $8^y = 300$

In Exercises 21–42, evaluate each expression without using a calculator.

21. $\log_4 16$ **22.** $\log_7 49$ **23.** $\log_2 64$ **24.** $\log_3 27$

25. $\log_5 \frac{1}{5}$ **26.** $\log_6 \frac{1}{6}$ **27.** $\log_2 \frac{1}{8}$ **28.** $\log_3 \frac{1}{9}$

29. $\log_7 \sqrt{7}$ **30.** $\log_6 \sqrt{6}$ **31.** $\log_2 \frac{1}{\sqrt{2}}$ **32.** $\log_3 \frac{1}{\sqrt{3}}$

33. $\log_{64} 8$ **34.** $\log_{81} 9$ **35.** $\log_5 5$ **36.** $\log_{11} 11$

37. $\log_4 1$ **38.** $\log_6 1$ **39.** $\log_5 5^7$ **40.** $\log_4 4^6$

41. $8^{\log_8 19}$ **42.** $7^{\log_7 23}$

43. Graph $f(x) = 4^x$ and $g(x) = \log_4 x$ in the same rectangular coordinate system.

44. Graph $f(x) = 5^x$ and $g(x) = \log_5 x$ in the same rectangular coordinate system.

45. Graph $f(x) = \left(\frac{1}{2}\right)^x$ and $g(x) = \log_{\frac{1}{2}} x$ in the same rectangular coordinate system.

46. Graph $f(x) = \left(\frac{1}{4}\right)^x$ and $g(x) = \log_{\frac{1}{4}} x$ in the same rectangular coordinate system.

In Exercises 47–52, the graph of a logarithmic function is given. Select the function for each graph from the following options:

$$f(x) = \log_3 x, g(x) = \log_3(x - 1), h(x) = \log_3 x - 1,$$
$$F(x) = -\log_3 x, G(x) = \log_3(-x), H(x) = 1 - \log_3 x.$$

47.

48.

49.

50.

51.

52.
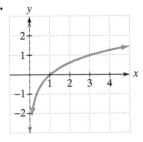

In Exercises 53–58, begin by graphing $f(x) = \log_2 x$. Then use transformations of this graph to graph the given function. What is the vertical asymptote? Use the graphs to determine each function's domain and range.

53. $g(x) = \log_2(x + 1)$ **54.** $g(x) = \log_2(x + 2)$

55. $h(x) = 1 + \log_2 x$ **56.** $h(x) = 2 + \log_2 x$

57. $g(x) = \frac{1}{2}\log_2 x$ **58.** $g(x) = -2\log_2 x$

The figure shows the graph of $f(x) = \log x$. In Exercises 59–64, use transformations of this graph to graph each function. Graph and give equations of the asymptotes. Use the graphs to determine each function's domain and range.

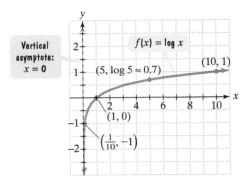

59. $g(x) = \log(x - 1)$ **60.** $g(x) = \log(x - 2)$

61. $h(x) = \log x - 1$ **62.** $h(x) = \log x - 2$

63. $g(x) = 1 - \log x$ **64.** $g(x) = 2 - \log x$

The figure shows the graph of $f(x) = \ln x$. In Exercises 65–74, use transformations of this graph to graph each function. Graph and give equations of the asymptotes. Use the graphs to determine each function's domain and range.

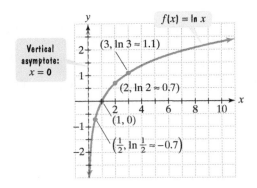

65. $g(x) = \ln(x + 2)$ **66.** $g(x) = \ln(x + 1)$

67. $h(x) = \ln(2x)$ **68.** $h(x) = \ln\left(\frac{1}{2}x\right)$

69. $g(x) = 2\ln x$ **70.** $g(x) = \frac{1}{2}\ln x$

71. $h(x) = -\ln x$ **72.** $h(x) = \ln(-x)$

73. $g(x) = 2 - \ln x$ **74.** $g(x) = 1 - \ln x$

In Exercises 75–80, find the domain of each logarithmic function.

75. $f(x) = \log_5(x + 4)$ **76.** $f(x) = \log_5(x + 6)$

77. $f(x) = \log(2 - x)$ **78.** $f(x) = \log(7 - x)$

79. $f(x) = \ln(x - 2)^2$ **80.** $f(x) = \ln(x - 7)^2$

In Exercises 81–100, evaluate or simplify each expression without using a calculator.

81. $\log 100$ **82.** $\log 1000$ **83.** $\log 10^7$ **84.** $\log 10^8$

85. $10^{\log 33}$ **86.** $10^{\log 53}$ **87.** $\ln 1$ **88.** $\ln e$

89. $\ln e^6$ **90.** $\ln e^7$ **91.** $\ln \frac{1}{e^6}$ **92.** $\ln \frac{1}{e^7}$

93. $e^{\ln 125}$ **94.** $e^{\ln 300}$ **95.** $\ln e^{9x}$ **96.** $\ln e^{13x}$

97. $e^{\ln 5x^2}$ **98.** $e^{\ln 7x^2}$ **99.** $10^{\log \sqrt{x}}$ **100.** $10^{\log \sqrt[3]{x}}$

Practice Plus

In Exercises 101–104, write each equation in its equivalent exponential form. Then solve for x.

101. $\log_3(x - 1) = 2$

102. $\log_5(x + 4) = 2$

103. $\log_4 x = -3$

104. $\log_{64} x = \dfrac{2}{3}$

In Exercises 105–108, evaluate each expression without using a calculator.

105. $\log_3(\log_7 7)$

106. $\log_5(\log_2 32)$

107. $\log_2(\log_3 81)$

108. $\log(\ln e)$

In Exercises 109–112, find the domain of each logarithmic function.

109. $f(x) = \ln(x^2 - x - 2)$

110. $f(x) = \ln(x^2 - 4x - 12)$

111. $f(x) = \log\left(\dfrac{x + 1}{x - 5}\right)$

112. $f(x) = \log\left(\dfrac{x - 2}{x + 5}\right)$

Application Exercises

The percentage of adult height attained by a girl who is x years old can be modeled by

$$f(x) = 62 + 35 \log(x - 4),$$

where x represents the girl's age (from 5 to 15) and f(x) represents the percentage of her adult height. Use the function to solve Exercises 113–114. Round answers to the nearest tenth of a percent.

113. Approximately what percentage of her adult height has a girl attained at age 13?

114. Approximately what percentage of her adult height has a girl attained at age ten?

The bar graph indicates that the percentage of first-year college students expressing antifeminist views declined after 1970. Use this information to solve Exercises 115–116.

Opposition to Feminism among First-Year United States College Students, 1970–2008

Statement: "The activities of married women are best confined to the home and family."

Source: John Macionis, *Sociology, Thirteenth Edition*, Prentice Hall, 2010.

115. The function

$$f(x) = -7.52 \ln x + 53$$

models the percentage of first-year college men, $f(x)$, expressing antifeminist views (by agreeing with the statement) x years after 1969.

a. Use the function to find the percentage of first-year college men expressing antifeminist views in 2008. Round to one decimal place. Does this function value overestimate or underestimate the percentage displayed by the graph? By how much?

b. Use the function to project the percentage of first-year college men who will express antifeminist views in 2015. Round to one decimal place.

116. The function

$$f(x) = -4.82 \ln x + 32.5$$

models the percentage of first-year college women, $f(x)$, expressing antifeminist views (by agreeing with the statement) x years after 1969.

a. Use the function to find the percentage of first-year college women expressing antifeminist views in 2008. Round to one decimal place. Does this function value overestimate or underestimate the percentage displayed by the graph? By how much?

b. Use the function to project the percentage of first-year college women who will express antifeminist views in 2015. Round to one decimal place.

The loudness level of a sound, D, in decibels, is given by the formula

$$D = 10 \log(10^{12} I),$$

where I is the intensity of the sound, in watts per meter². Decibel levels range from 0, a barely audible sound, to 160, a sound resulting in a ruptured eardrum. (Any exposure to sounds of 130 decibels or higher puts a person at immediate risk for hearing damage.) Use the formula to solve Exercises 117–118.

117. The sound of a blue whale can be heard 500 miles away, reaching an intensity of 6.3×10^6 watts per meter². Determine the decibel level of this sound. At close range, can the sound of a blue whale rupture the human eardrum?

118. What is the decibel level of a normal conversation, 3.2×10^{-6} watt per meter²?

119. Students in a psychology class took a final examination. As part of an experiment to see how much of the course content they remembered over time, they took equivalent forms of the exam in monthly intervals thereafter. The average score for the group, $f(t)$, after t months was modeled by the function

$$f(t) = 88 - 15 \ln(t + 1), \qquad 0 \le t \le 12.$$

a. What was the average score on the original exam?

b. What was the average score after 2 months? 4 months? 6 months? 8 months? 10 months? one year?

c. Sketch the graph of f (either by hand or with a graphing utility). Describe what the graph indicates in terms of the material retained by the students.

Writing in Mathematics

120. Describe the relationship between an equation in logarithmic form and an equivalent equation in exponential form.

121. What question can be asked to help evaluate $\log_3 81$?

122. Explain why the logarithm of 1 with base b is 0.

123. Describe the following property using words: $\log_b b^x = x$.

124. Explain how to use the graph of $f(x) = 2^x$ to obtain the graph of $g(x) = \log_2 x$.

125. Explain how to find the domain of a logarithmic function.

126. Logarithmic models are well suited to phenomena in which growth is initially rapid but then begins to level off. Describe something that is changing over time that can be modeled using a logarithmic function.

127. Suppose that a girl is 4 feet 6 inches at age 10. Explain how to use the function in Exercises 113–114 to determine how tall she can expect to be as an adult.

Technology Exercises

In Exercises 128–131, graph f and g in the same viewing rectangle. Then describe the relationship of the graph of g to the graph of f.

128. $f(x) = \ln x, g(x) = \ln(x + 3)$

129. $f(x) = \ln x, g(x) = \ln x + 3$

130. $f(x) = \log x, g(x) = -\log x$

131. $f(x) = \log x, g(x) = \log(x - 2) + 1$

132. Students in a mathematics class took a final examination. They took equivalent forms of the exam in monthly intervals thereafter. The average score, $f(t)$, for the group after t months was modeled by the human memory function $f(t) = 75 - 10\log(t + 1)$, where $0 \le t \le 12$. Use a graphing utility to graph the function. Then determine how many months elapsed before the average score fell below 65.

133. In parts (a)–(c), graph f and g in the same viewing rectangle.

    a. $f(x) = \ln(3x), g(x) = \ln 3 + \ln x$

    b. $f(x) = \log(5x^2), g(x) = \log 5 + \log x^2$

    c. $f(x) = \ln(2x^3), g(x) = \ln 2 + \ln x^3$

    d. Describe what you observe in parts (a)–(c). Generalize this observation by writing an equivalent expression for $\log_b(MN)$, where $M > 0$ and $N > 0$.

    e. Complete this statement: The logarithm of a product is equal to _____.

134. Graph each of the following functions in the same viewing rectangle and then place the functions in order from the one that increases most slowly to the one that increases most rapidly.

$$y = x, y = \sqrt{x}, y = e^x, y = \ln x, y = x^x, y = x^2$$

Critical Thinking Exercises

Make Sense? *In Exercises 135–138, determine whether each statement makes sense or does not make sense, and explain your reasoning.*

135. I've noticed that exponential functions and logarithmic functions exhibit inverse, or opposite, behavior in many ways. For example, a vertical translation shifts an exponential function's horizontal asymptote and a horizontal translation shifts a logarithmic function's vertical asymptote.

136. I estimate that $\log_8 16$ lies between 1 and 2 because $8^1 = 8$ and $8^2 = 64$.

137. I can evaluate some common logarithms without having to use a calculator.

138. An earthquake of magnitude 8 on the Richter scale is twice as intense as an earthquake of magnitude 4.

In Exercises 139–142, determine whether each statement is true or false. If the statement is false, make the necessary change(s) to produce a true statement.

139. $\dfrac{\log_2 8}{\log_2 4} = \dfrac{8}{4}$

140. $\log(-100) = -2$

141. The domain of $f(x) = \log_2 x$ is $(-\infty, \infty)$.

142. $\log_b x$ is the exponent to which b must be raised to obtain x.

143. Without using a calculator, find the exact value of

$$\frac{\log_3 81 - \log_\pi 1}{\log_{2\sqrt{2}} 8 - \log 0.001}.$$

144. Without using a calculator, find the exact value of $\log_4[\log_3(\log_2 8)]$.

145. Without using a calculator, determine which is the greater number: $\log_4 60$ or $\log_3 40$.

Group Exercise

146. This group exercise involves exploring the way we grow. Group members should create a graph for the function that models the percentage of adult height attained by a boy who is x years old, $f(x) = 29 + 48.8\log(x + 1)$. Let $x = 5, 6, 7, \ldots, 15$, find function values, and connect the resulting points with a smooth curve. Then create a graph for the function that models the percentage of adult height attained by a girl who is x years old, $g(x) = 62 + 35\log(x - 4)$. Let $x = 5, 6, 7, \ldots, 15$, find function values, and connect the resulting points with a smooth curve. Group members should then discuss similarities and differences in the growth patterns for boys and girls based on the graphs.

Preview Exercises

Exercises 147–149 will help you prepare for the material covered in the next section. In each exercise, evaluate the indicated logarithmic expressions without using a calculator.

147. a. Evaluate: $\log_2 32$.

    b. Evaluate: $\log_2 8 + \log_2 4$.

    c. What can you conclude about $\log_2 32$, or $\log_2(8 \cdot 4)$?

148. a. Evaluate: $\log_2 16$.

    b. Evaluate: $\log_2 32 - \log_2 2$.

    c. What can you conclude about

$$\log_2 16, \text{ or } \log_2\left(\frac{32}{2}\right)?$$

149. a. Evaluate: $\log_3 81$.

    b. Evaluate: $2\log_3 9$.

    c. What can you conclude about

$$\log_3 81, \text{ or } \log_3 9^2?$$

SECTION 4.3   Properties of Logarithms

Objectives

1. Use the product rule.
2. Use the quotient rule.
3. Use the power rule.
4. Expand logarithmic expressions.
5. Condense logarithmic expressions.
6. Use the change-of-base property.

We all learn new things in different ways. In this section, we consider important properties of logarithms. What would be the most effective way for you to learn these properties? Would it be helpful to use your graphing utility and discover one of these properties for yourself? To do so, work Exercise 133 in Exercise Set 4.2 before continuing. Would it be helpful to evaluate certain logarithmic expressions that suggest three of the properties? If this is the case, work Preview Exercises 147–149 in Exercise Set 4.2 before continuing. Would the properties become more meaningful if you could see exactly where they come from? If so, you will find details of the proofs of many of these properties in the appendix. The remainder of our work in this chapter will be based on the properties of logarithms that you learn in this section.

1. Use the product rule.

DISCOVERY

We know that log 100,000 = 5. Show that you get the same result by writing 100,000 as $1000 \cdot 100$ and then using the product rule. Then verify the product rule by using other numbers whose logarithms are easy to find.

The Product Rule

Properties of exponents correspond to properties of logarithms. For example, when we multiply with the same base, we add exponents:

$$b^m \cdot b^n = b^{m+n}.$$

This property of exponents, coupled with an awareness that a logarithm is an exponent, suggests the following property, called the **product rule:**

You can find the proof of the product rule in the appendix.

The Product Rule

Let b, M, and N be positive real numbers with $b \neq 1$.

$$\log_b(MN) = \log_b M + \log_b N$$

The logarithm of a product is the sum of the logarithms.

When we use the product rule to write a single logarithm as the sum of two logarithms, we say that we are **expanding a logarithmic expression**. For example, we can use the product rule to expand $\ln(7x)$:

$$\ln(7x) \;=\; \ln 7 \,+\, \ln x.$$

The logarithm of a product   is   the sum of the logarithms.

EXAMPLE 1   Using the Product Rule

Use the product rule to expand each logarithmic expression:

a. $\log_4(7 \cdot 5)$ **b.** $\log(10x)$.

SOLUTION

a. $\log_4(7 \cdot 5) = \log_4 7 + \log_4 5$ *The logarithm of a product is the sum of the logarithms.*

b. $\log(10x) = \log 10 + \log x$ *The logarithm of a product is the sum of the logarithms. These are common logarithms with base 10 understood.*

$= 1 + \log x$ *Because $\log_b b = 1$, then $\log 10 = 1$.*   • • •

 Check Point **1** Use the product rule to expand each logarithmic expression:
a. $\log_6(7 \cdot 11)$ **b.** $\log(100x)$.

2 Use the quotient rule.

The Quotient Rule

When we divide with the same base, we subtract exponents:

$$\frac{b^m}{b^n} = b^{m-n}.$$

This property suggests the following property of logarithms, called the **quotient rule**:

The Quotient Rule

Let b, M, and N be positive real numbers with $b \neq 1$.

$$\log_b\left(\frac{M}{N}\right) = \log_b M - \log_b N$$

The logarithm of a quotient is the difference of the logarithms.

When we use the quotient rule to write a single logarithm as the difference of two logarithms, we say that we are **expanding a logarithmic expression**. For example, we can use the quotient rule to expand $\log \dfrac{x}{2}$:

$$\log\left(\frac{x}{2}\right) = \log x - \log 2.$$

The logarithm of a quotient   is   the difference of the logarithms.

EXAMPLE 2   Using the Quotient Rule

Use the quotient rule to expand each logarithmic expression:

a. $\log_7\left(\dfrac{19}{x}\right)$ **b.** $\ln\left(\dfrac{e^3}{7}\right)$.

SOLUTION

a. $\log_7\left(\dfrac{19}{x}\right) = \log_7 19 - \log_7 x$ *The logarithm of a quotient is the difference of the logarithms.*

b. $\ln\left(\dfrac{e^3}{7}\right) = \ln e^3 - \ln 7$ *The logarithm of a quotient is the difference of the logarithms. These are natural logarithms with base e understood.*

$= 3 - \ln 7$ *Because $\ln e^x = x$, then $\ln e^3 = 3$.*   • • •

⊘ Check Point **2** Use the quotient rule to expand each logarithmic expression:

a. $\log_8\left(\dfrac{23}{x}\right)$ **b.** $\ln\left(\dfrac{e^5}{11}\right)$.

③ Use the power rule.

The Power Rule

When an exponential expression is raised to a power, we multiply exponents:

$$(b^m)^n = b^{mn}.$$

This property suggests the following property of logarithms, called the **power rule**:

> ### The Power Rule
>
> Let b and M be positive real numbers with $b \neq 1$, and let p be any real number.
>
> $$\log_b M^p = p \log_b M$$
>
> The logarithm of a number with an exponent is the product of the exponent and the logarithm of that number.

When we use the power rule to "pull the exponent to the front," we say that we are **expanding a logarithmic expression**. For example, we can use the power rule to expand $\ln x^2$:

$$\ln x^2 = 2 \ln x.$$

| The logarithm of a number with an exponent | is | the product of the exponent and the logarithm of that number. |

Figure 4.18 shows the graphs of $y = \ln x^2$ and $y = 2 \ln x$ in $[-5, 5, 1]$ by $[-5, 5, 1]$ viewing rectangles. Are $\ln x^2$ and $2 \ln x$ the same? The graphs illustrate that $y = \ln x^2$ and $y = 2 \ln x$ have different domains. The graphs are only the same if $x > 0$. Thus, we should write

$$\ln x^2 = 2 \ln x \text{ for } x > 0.$$

Domain: $(-\infty, 0) \cup (0, \infty)$ Domain: $(0, \infty)$

FIGURE 4.18 $\ln x^2$ and $2 \ln x$ have different domains.

When expanding a logarithmic expression, you might want to determine whether the rewriting has changed the domain of the expression. For the rest of this section, assume that all variables and variable expressions represent positive numbers.

EXAMPLE 3 Using the Power Rule

Use the power rule to expand each logarithmic expression:

a. $\log_5 7^4$ **b.** $\ln \sqrt{x}$ **c.** $\log(4x)^5$.

SOLUTION

a. $\log_5 7^4 = 4 \log_5 7$ The logarithm of a number with an exponent is the exponent times the logarithm of the number.

b. $\ln \sqrt{x} = \ln x^{\frac{1}{2}}$ Rewrite the radical using a rational exponent.

$= \frac{1}{2} \ln x$ Use the power rule to bring the exponent to the front.

c. $\log(4x)^5 = 5 \log(4x)$ We immediately apply the power rule because the entire variable expression, 4x, is raised to the 5th power. • • •

⬭ Check Point **3** Use the power rule to expand each logarithmic expression:

a. $\log_6 3^9$ **b.** $\ln \sqrt[3]{x}$ **c.** $\log(x + 4)^2$.

④ Expand logarithmic expressions.

Expanding Logarithmic Expressions

It is sometimes necessary to use more than one property of logarithms when you expand a logarithmic expression. Properties for expanding logarithmic expressions are as follows:

Properties for Expanding Logarithmic Expressions

For $M > 0$ and $N > 0$:

1. $\log_b (MN) = \log_b M + \log_b N$ Product rule

2. $\log_b \left(\dfrac{M}{N} \right) = \log_b M - \log_b N$ Quotient rule

3. $\log_b M^p = p \log_b M$ Power rule

GREAT QUESTION!

Are there some common screw-ups that I can avoid when using properties of logarithms?

The graphs show that

$$\ln(x + 3) \ne \ln x + \ln 3.$$

> $y = \ln x$ shifted 3 units left $y = \ln x$ shifted ln 3 units up

In general,

$$\log_b(M + N) \ne \log_b M + \log_b N.$$

[−4, 5, 1] by [−3, 3, 1]

Try to avoid the following errors:

Incorrect!

$$\log_b (M + N) = \log_b M + \log_b N$$

$$\log_b (M - N) = \log_b M - \log_b N$$

$$\log_b (M \cdot N) = \log_b M \cdot \log_b N$$

$$\log_b \left(\frac{M}{N} \right) = \frac{\log_b M}{\log_b N}$$

$$\frac{\log_b M}{\log_b N} = \log_b M - \log_b N$$

$$\log_b (MN^p) = p \log_b (MN)$$

EXAMPLE 4   Expanding Logarithmic Expressions

Use logarithmic properties to expand each expression as much as possible:

a. $\log_b(x^2 \sqrt{y})$ **b.** $\log_6 \left(\dfrac{\sqrt[3]{x}}{36y^4} \right)$.

SOLUTION

We will have to use two or more of the properties for expanding logarithms in each part of this example.

a. $\log_b (x^2\sqrt{y}) = \log_b \left(x^2 y^{\frac{1}{2}}\right)$ Use exponential notation.

$$= \log_b x^2 + \log_b y^{\frac{1}{2}}$$ Use the product rule.

$$= 2\log_b x + \frac{1}{2}\log_b y$$ Use the power rule.

b. $\log_6 \left(\dfrac{\sqrt[3]{x}}{36y^4}\right) = \log_6 \left(\dfrac{x^{\frac{1}{3}}}{36y^4}\right)$ Use exponential notation.

$$= \log_6 x^{\frac{1}{3}} - \log_6 (36y^4)$$ Use the quotient rule.

$$= \log_6 x^{\frac{1}{3}} - (\log_6 36 + \log_6 y^4)$$ Use the product rule on $\log_6 (36y^4)$.

$$= \frac{1}{3}\log_6 x - (\log_6 36 + 4\log_6 y)$$ Use the power rule.

$$= \frac{1}{3}\log_6 x - \log_6 36 - 4\log_6 y$$ Apply the distributive property.

$$= \frac{1}{3}\log_6 x - 2 - 4\log_6 y$$ $\log_6 36 = 2$ because 2 is the power to which we must raise 6 to get 36. ($6^2 = 36$) • • •

✐ **Check Point 4** Use logarithmic properties to expand each expression as much as possible:

a. $\log_b \left(x^4 \sqrt[3]{y}\right)$ **b.** $\log_5 \left(\dfrac{\sqrt{x}}{25y^3}\right)$.

⑤ Condense logarithmic expressions.

Condensing Logarithmic Expressions

To **condense a logarithmic expression**, we write the sum or difference of two or more logarithmic expressions as a single logarithmic expression. We use the properties of logarithms to do so.

GREAT QUESTION!

Are the properties listed on the right the same as those in the box on page 472?

Yes. The only difference is that we've reversed the sides in each property from the previous box.

Properties for Condensing Logarithmic Expressions

For $M > 0$ and $N > 0$:

1. $\log_b M + \log_b N = \log_b (MN)$ Product rule

2. $\log_b M - \log_b N = \log_b \left(\dfrac{M}{N}\right)$ Quotient rule

3. $p \log_b M = \log_b M^p$ Power rule

EXAMPLE 5 Condensing Logarithmic Expressions

Write as a single logarithm:

a. $\log_4 2 + \log_4 32$ **b.** $\log(4x - 3) - \log x$.

SOLUTION

a. $\log_4 2 + \log_4 32 = \log_4(2 \cdot 32)$ Use the product rule.

$$= \log_4 64$$ We now have a single logarithm. However, we can simplify.

$$= 3$$ $\log_4 64 = 3$ because $4^3 = 64$.

b. $\log(4x - 3) - \log x = \log\left(\dfrac{4x - 3}{x}\right)$ Use the quotient rule. • • •

⌀ Check Point **5** Write as a single logarithm:

a. $\log 25 + \log 4$ **b.** $\log (7x + 6) - \log x$.

Coefficients of logarithms must be 1 before you can condense them using the product and quotient rules. For example, to condense

$$2 \ln x + \ln(x + 1),$$

the coefficient of the first term must be 1. We use the power rule to rewrite the coefficient as an exponent:

> 1. Use the power rule to make the number in front an exponent.

$$2 \ln x + \ln(x + 1) = \ln x^2 + \ln(x + 1) = \ln[x^2(x + 1)].$$

> 2. Use the product rule. The sum of logarithms with coefficients of 1 is the logarithm of the product.

EXAMPLE 6   Condensing Logarithmic Expressions

Write as a single logarithm:

a. $\frac{1}{2} \log x + 4 \log (x - 1)$ **b.** $3 \ln (x + 7) - \ln x$

c. $4 \log_b x - 2 \log_b 6 - \frac{1}{2} \log_b y$.

SOLUTION

a. $\frac{1}{2} \log x + 4 \log (x - 1)$

$= \log x^{\frac{1}{2}} + \log (x - 1)^4$ Use the power rule so that all coefficients are 1.

$= \log\left[x^{\frac{1}{2}}(x - 1)^4\right]$ Use the product rule. The condensed form can be expressed as $\log[\sqrt{x}\,(x - 1)^4]$.

b. $3 \ln(x + 7) - \ln x$

$= \ln(x + 7)^3 - \ln x$ Use the power rule so that all coefficients are 1.

$= \ln\left[\dfrac{(x + 7)^3}{x}\right]$ Use the quotient rule.

c. $4 \log_b x - 2 \log_b 6 - \frac{1}{2} \log_b y$

$= \log_b x^4 - \log_b 6^2 - \log_b y^{\frac{1}{2}}$ Use the power rule so that all coefficients are 1.

$= \log_b x^4 - \left(\log_b 36 + \log_b y^{\frac{1}{2}}\right)$ Rewrite as a single subtraction.

$= \log_b x^4 - \log_b\left(36 y^{\frac{1}{2}}\right)$ Use the product rule.

$= \log_b\left(\dfrac{x^4}{36y^{\frac{1}{2}}}\right)$ or $\log_b\left(\dfrac{x^4}{36\sqrt{y}}\right)$ Use the quotient rule.   • • •

⌀ Check Point **6** Write as a single logarithm:

a. $2 \ln x + \frac{1}{3} \ln (x + 5)$ **b.** $2 \log (x - 3) - \log x$

c. $\frac{1}{4} \log_b x - 2 \log_b 5 - 10 \log_b y$.

⑥ Use the change-of-base property.

The Change-of-Base Property

We have seen that calculators give the values of both common logarithms (base 10) and natural logarithms (base e). To find a logarithm with any other base, we can use the following change-of-base property:

The Change-of-Base Property

For any logarithmic bases a and b, and any positive number M,

$$\log_b M = \frac{\log_a M}{\log_a b}.$$

The logarithm of M with base b is equal to the logarithm of M with any new base divided by the logarithm of b with that new base.

In the change-of-base property, base b is the base of the original logarithm. Base a is a new base that we introduce. Thus, the change-of-base property allows us to change from base b to *any* new base a, as long as the newly introduced base is a positive number not equal to 1.

The change-of-base property is used to write a logarithm in terms of quantities that can be evaluated with a calculator. Because calculators contain keys for common (base 10) and natural (base e) logarithms, we will frequently introduce base 10 or base e.

Change-of-Base Property	Introducing Common Logarithms	Introducing Natural Logarithms
$\log_b M = \dfrac{\log_a M}{\log_a b}$	$\log_b M = \dfrac{\log_{10} M}{\log_{10} b}$	$\log_b M = \dfrac{\log_e M}{\log_e b}$
a is the new introduced base.	10 is the new introduced base.	e is the new introduced base.

Using the notations for common logarithms and natural logarithms, we have the following results:

The Change-of-Base Property: Introducing Common and Natural Logarithms

Introducing Common Logarithms

$$\log_b M = \frac{\log M}{\log b}$$

Introducing Natural Logarithms

$$\log_b M = \frac{\ln M}{\ln b}$$

EXAMPLE 7   Changing Base to Common Logarithms

Use common logarithms to evaluate $\log_5 140$.

SOLUTION

Because $\log_b M = \dfrac{\log M}{\log b}$,

$$\log_5 140 = \frac{\log 140}{\log 5}$$

$$\approx 3.07.$$ Use a calculator: 140 [LOG] [÷] 5 [LOG] [=]
or [LOG] 140 [÷] [LOG] 5 [ENTER]. On some calculators, parentheses are needed after 140 and 5.

This means that $\log_5 140 \approx 3.07$.

• • •

Check Point **7** Use common logarithms to evaluate $\log_7 2506$.

EXAMPLE 8   Changing Base to Natural Logarithms

Use natural logarithms to evaluate $\log_5 140$.

SOLUTION

Because $\log_b M = \dfrac{\ln M}{\ln b}$,

$$\log_5 140 = \frac{\ln 140}{\ln 5}$$

$$\approx 3.07.$$ Use a calculator: 140 $\boxed{\text{LN}}$ $\boxed{\div}$ 5 $\boxed{\text{LN}}$ $\boxed{=}$
or $\boxed{\text{LN}}$ 140 $\boxed{\div}$ $\boxed{\text{LN}}$ 5 $\boxed{\text{ENTER}}$. On some calculators, parentheses are needed after 140 and 5.

We have again shown that $\log_5 140 \approx 3.07$.   • • •

Check Point **8**   Use natural logarithms to evaluate $\log_7 2506$.

TECHNOLOGY

We can use the change-of-base property to graph logarithmic functions with bases other than 10 or e on a graphing utility. For example, **Figure 4.19** shows the graphs of

$$y = \log_2 x \quad \text{and} \quad y = \log_{20} x$$

in a $[0, 10, 1]$ by $[-3, 3, 1]$ viewing rectangle. Because $\log_2 x = \dfrac{\ln x}{\ln 2}$ and $\log_{20} x = \dfrac{\ln x}{\ln 20}$, the functions are entered as

$$y_1 = \boxed{\text{LN}}x \boxed{\div}\boxed{\text{LN}}2$$
$$\text{and} \quad y_2 = \boxed{\text{LN}}x \boxed{\div}\boxed{\text{LN}}20.$$

On some calculators, parentheses are needed after x, **2**, and **20**.

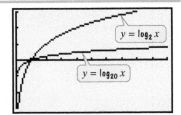

FIGURE 4.19 Using the change-of-base property to graph logarithmic functions

CONCEPT AND VOCABULARY CHECK

Fill in each blank so that the resulting statement is true.

1. The product rule for logarithms states that $\log_b(MN) =$ _____. The logarithm of a product is the _____ of the logarithms.

2. The quotient rule for logarithms states that $\log_b\left(\dfrac{M}{N}\right) =$ _____. The logarithm of a quotient is the _____ of the logarithms.

3. The power rule for logarithms states that $\log_b M^p =$ _____. The logarithm of a number with an exponent is the _____ of the exponent and the logarithm of that number.

4. The change-of-base property for logarithms allows us to write logarithms with base b in terms of a new base a. Introducing base a, the property states that

$$\log_b M = \frac{\rule{1.5cm}{0.4pt}}{\rule{1cm}{0.4pt}}.$$

EXERCISE SET 4.3

Practice Exercises

In Exercises 1–40, use properties of logarithms to expand each logarithmic expression as much as possible. Where possible, evaluate logarithmic expressions without using a calculator.

1. $\log_5(7 \cdot 3)$ **2.** $\log_8(13 \cdot 7)$ **3.** $\log_7(7x)$

4. $\log_9(9x)$ **5.** $\log(1000x)$ **6.** $\log(10{,}000x)$

7. $\log_7\left(\dfrac{7}{x}\right)$ **8.** $\log_9\left(\dfrac{9}{x}\right)$ **9.** $\log\left(\dfrac{x}{100}\right)$

10. $\log\left(\dfrac{x}{1000}\right)$ **11.** $\log_4\left(\dfrac{64}{y}\right)$ **12.** $\log_5\left(\dfrac{125}{y}\right)$

13. $\ln\left(\dfrac{e^2}{5}\right)$ **14.** $\ln\left(\dfrac{e^4}{8}\right)$ **15.** $\log_b x^3$

16. $\log_b x^7$ **17.** $\log N^{-6}$ **18.** $\log M^{-8}$

19. $\ln\sqrt[5]{x}$ **20.** $\ln\sqrt[7]{x}$ **21.** $\log_b(x^2 y)$

22. $\log_b(xy^3)$ **23.** $\log_4\left(\dfrac{\sqrt{x}}{64}\right)$ **24.** $\log_5\left(\dfrac{\sqrt{x}}{25}\right)$

25. $\log_6\left(\dfrac{36}{\sqrt{x+1}}\right)$ **26.** $\log_8\left(\dfrac{64}{\sqrt{x+1}}\right)$ **27.** $\log_b\left(\dfrac{x^2 y}{z^2}\right)$

28. $\log_b\left(\dfrac{x^3 y}{z^2}\right)$ **29.** $\log\sqrt{100x}$ **30.** $\ln\sqrt{ex}$

31. $\log\sqrt[3]{\dfrac{x}{y}}$ **32.** $\log\sqrt[5]{\dfrac{x}{y}}$ **33.** $\log_b\left(\dfrac{\sqrt{x}\,y^3}{z^3}\right)$

34. $\log_b\left(\dfrac{\sqrt[3]{x}\,y^4}{z^5}\right)$ **35.** $\log_5\sqrt[3]{\dfrac{x^2 y}{25}}$ **36.** $\log_2\sqrt[5]{\dfrac{xy^4}{16}}$

37. $\ln\left[\dfrac{x^3\sqrt{x^2+1}}{(x+1)^4}\right]$ **38.** $\ln\left[\dfrac{x^4\sqrt{x^2+3}}{(x+3)^5}\right]$

39. $\log\left[\dfrac{10x^2\sqrt[3]{1-x}}{7(x+1)^2}\right]$ **40.** $\log\left[\dfrac{100x^3\sqrt[3]{5-x}}{3(x+7)^2}\right]$

In Exercises 41–70, use properties of logarithms to condense each logarithmic expression. Write the expression as a single logarithm whose coefficient is 1. Where possible, evaluate logarithmic expressions without using a calculator.

41. $\log 5 + \log 2$ **42.** $\log 250 + \log 4$

43. $\ln x + \ln 7$ **44.** $\ln x + \ln 3$

45. $\log_2 96 - \log_2 3$ **46.** $\log_3 405 - \log_3 5$

47. $\log(2x+5) - \log x$ **48.** $\log(3x+7) - \log x$

49. $\log x + 3\log y$ **50.** $\log x + 7\log y$

51. $\frac{1}{2}\ln x + \ln y$ **52.** $\frac{1}{3}\ln x + \ln y$

53. $2\log_b x + 3\log_b y$ **54.** $5\log_b x + 6\log_b y$

55. $5\ln x - 2\ln y$ **56.** $7\ln x - 3\ln y$

57. $3\ln x - \frac{1}{3}\ln y$ **58.** $2\ln x - \frac{1}{2}\ln y$

59. $4\ln(x+6) - 3\ln x$ **60.** $8\ln(x+9) - 4\ln x$

61. $3\ln x + 5\ln y - 6\ln z$ **62.** $4\ln x + 7\ln y - 3\ln z$

63. $\frac{1}{2}(\log x + \log y)$ **64.** $\frac{1}{3}(\log_4 x - \log_4 y)$

65. $\frac{1}{2}(\log_5 x + \log_5 y) - 2\log_5(x+1)$

66. $\frac{1}{3}(\log_4 x - \log_4 y) + 2\log_4(x+1)$

67. $\frac{1}{3}[2\ln(x+5) - \ln x - \ln(x^2-4)]$

68. $\frac{1}{3}[5\ln(x+6) - \ln x - \ln(x^2-25)]$

69. $\log x + \log(x^2-1) - \log 7 - \log(x+1)$

70. $\log x + \log(x^2-4) - \log 15 - \log(x+2)$

In Exercises 71–78, use common logarithms or natural logarithms and a calculator to evaluate to four decimal places.

71. $\log_5 13$ **72.** $\log_6 17$ **73.** $\log_{14} 87.5$

74. $\log_{16} 57.2$ **75.** $\log_{0.1} 17$ **76.** $\log_{0.3} 19$

77. $\log_\pi 63$ **78.** $\log_\pi 400$

In Exercises 79–82, use a graphing utility and the change-of-base property to graph each function.

79. $y = \log_3 x$ **80.** $y = \log_{15} x$

81. $y = \log_2(x+2)$ **82.** $y = \log_3(x-2)$

Practice Plus

In Exercises 83–88, let $\log_b 2 = A$ and $\log_b 3 = C$. Write each expression in terms of A and C.

83. $\log_b \frac{3}{2}$ **84.** $\log_b 6$ **85.** $\log_b 8$

86. $\log_b 81$ **87.** $\log_b\sqrt{\dfrac{2}{27}}$ **88.** $\log_b\sqrt{\dfrac{3}{16}}$

In Exercises 89–102, determine whether each equation is true or false. Where possible, show work to support your conclusion. If the statement is false, make the necessary change(s) to produce a true statement.

89. $\ln e = 0$ **90.** $\ln 0 = e$

91. $\log_4(2x^3) = 3\log_4(2x)$ **92.** $\ln(8x^3) = 3\ln(2x)$

93. $x\log 10^x = x^2$ **94.** $\ln(x+1) = \ln x + \ln 1$

95. $\ln(5x) + \ln 1 = \ln(5x)$ **96.** $\ln x + \ln(2x) = \ln(3x)$

97. $\log(x+3) - \log(2x) = \dfrac{\log(x+3)}{\log(2x)}$

98. $\dfrac{\log(x+2)}{\log(x-1)} = \log(x+2) - \log(x-1)$

99. $\log_6\left(\dfrac{x-1}{x^2+4}\right) = \log_6(x-1) - \log_6(x^2+4)$

100. $\log_6[4(x+1)] = \log_6 4 + \log_6(x+1)$

101. $\log_3 7 = \dfrac{1}{\log_7 3}$ **102.** $e^x = \dfrac{1}{\ln x}$

Application Exercises

103. The loudness level of a sound can be expressed by comparing the sound's intensity to the intensity of a sound barely audible to the human ear. The formula

$$D = 10(\log I - \log I_0)$$

describes the loudness level of a sound, D, in decibels, where I is the intensity of the sound, in watts per meter^2, and I_0 is the intensity of a sound barely audible to the human ear.

a. Express the formula so that the expression in parentheses is written as a single logarithm.

b. Use the form of the formula from part (a) to answer this question: If a sound has an intensity 100 times the intensity of a softer sound, how much larger on the decibel scale is the loudness level of the more intense sound?

104. The formula

$$t = \frac{1}{c}[\ln A - \ln(A - N)]$$

describes the time, t, in weeks, that it takes to achieve mastery of a portion of a task, where A is the maximum learning possible, N is the portion of the learning that is to be achieved, and c is a constant used to measure an individual's learning style.

a. Express the formula so that the expression in brackets is written as a single logarithm.

b. The formula is also used to determine how long it will take chimpanzees and apes to master a task. For example, a typical chimpanzee learning sign language can master a maximum of 65 signs. Use the form of the formula from part (a) to answer this question: How many weeks will it take a chimpanzee to master 30 signs if c for that chimp is 0.03?

Writing in Mathematics

105. Describe the product rule for logarithms and give an example.

106. Describe the quotient rule for logarithms and give an example.

107. Describe the power rule for logarithms and give an example.

108. Without showing the details, explain how to condense $\ln x - 2\ln(x + 1)$.

109. Describe the change-of-base property and give an example.

110. Explain how to use your calculator to find $\log_{14} 283$.

111. You overhear a student talking about a property of logarithms in which division becomes subtraction. Explain what the student means by this.

112. Find $\ln 2$ using a calculator. Then calculate each of the following: $1 - \frac{1}{2}$; $1 - \frac{1}{2} + \frac{1}{3}$; $1 - \frac{1}{2} + \frac{1}{3} - \frac{1}{4}$; $1 - \frac{1}{2} + \frac{1}{3} - \frac{1}{4} + \frac{1}{5}$; .... Describe what you observe.

Technology Exercises

113. a. Use a graphing utility (and the change-of-base property) to graph $y = \log_3 x$.

b. Graph $y = 2 + \log_3 x$, $y = \log_3(x + 2)$, and $y = -\log_3 x$ in the same viewing rectangle as $y = \log_3 x$. Then describe the change or changes that need to be made to the graph of $y = \log_3 x$ to obtain each of these three graphs.

114. Graph $y = \log x$, $y = \log(10x)$, and $y = \log(0.1x)$ in the same viewing rectangle. Describe the relationship among the three graphs. What logarithmic property accounts for this relationship?

115. Use a graphing utility and the change-of-base property to graph $y = \log_3 x$, $y = \log_{25} x$, and $y = \log_{100} x$ in the same viewing rectangle.

a. Which graph is on the top in the interval $(0, 1)$? Which is on the bottom?

b. Which graph is on the top in the interval $(1, \infty)$? Which is on the bottom?

c. Generalize by writing a statement about which graph is on top, which is on the bottom, and in which intervals, using $y = \log_b x$ where $b > 1$.

Disprove each statement in Exercises 116–120 by

a. *letting y equal a positive constant of your choice, and*

b. *using a graphing utility to graph the function on each side of the equal sign. The two functions should have different graphs, showing that the equation is not true in general.*

116. $\log(x + y) = \log x + \log y$

117. $\log\left(\dfrac{x}{y}\right) = \dfrac{\log x}{\log y}$

118. $\ln(x - y) = \ln x - \ln y$

119. $\ln(xy) = (\ln x)(\ln y)$

120. $\dfrac{\ln x}{\ln y} = \ln x - \ln y$

Critical Thinking Exercises

Make Sense? *In Exercises 121–124, determine whether each statement makes sense or does not make sense, and explain your reasoning.*

121. Because I cannot simplify the expression $b^m + b^n$ by adding exponents, there is no property for the logarithm of a sum.

122. Because logarithms are exponents, the product, quotient, and power rules remind me of properties for operations with exponents.

123. I can use any positive number other than 1 in the change-of-base property, but the only practical bases are 10 and e because my calculator gives logarithms for these two bases.

124. I expanded $\log_4 \sqrt{\dfrac{x}{y}}$ by writing the radical using a rational exponent and then applying the quotient rule, obtaining $\dfrac{1}{2}\log_4 x - \log_4 y$.

In Exercises 125–128, determine whether each statement is true or false. If the statement is false, make the necessary change(s) to produce a true statement.

125. $\ln\sqrt{2} = \dfrac{\ln 2}{2}$

126. $\dfrac{\log_7 49}{\log_7 7} = \log_7 49 - \log_7 7$

127. $\log_b(x^3 + y^3) = 3\log_b x + 3\log_b y$

128. $\log_b(xy)^5 = (\log_b x + \log_b y)^5$

129. Use the change-of-base property to prove that

$$\log e = \frac{1}{\ln 10}.$$

130. If $\log 3 = A$ and $\log 7 = B$, find $\log_7 9$ in terms of A and B.

131. Write as a single term that does not contain a logarithm:

$$e^{\ln 8x^5 - \ln 2x^2}.$$

132. If $f(x) = \log_b x$, show that

$$\frac{f(x + h) - f(x)}{h} = \log_b\left(1 + \frac{h}{x}\right)^{\frac{1}{h}}, h \neq 0.$$

133. Use the proof of the product rule on page 795 of the appendix to prove the quotient rule.

Preview Exercises

Exercises 134–136 will help you prepare for the material covered in the next section.

134. Solve for x: $a(x - 2) = b(2x + 3)$.

135. Solve: $x(x - 7) = 3$.

136. Solve: $\dfrac{x + 2}{4x + 3} = \dfrac{1}{x}$.

CHAPTER 4 Mid-Chapter Check Point

WHAT YOU KNOW: We evaluated and graphed exponential functions $[f(x) = b^x, b > 0$ and $b \neq 1]$, including the natural exponential function $[f(x) = e^x, e \approx 2.718]$. A function has an inverse that is a function if there is no horizontal line that intersects the function's graph more than once. The exponential function passes this horizontal line test and we called the inverse of the exponential function with base b the logarithmic function with base b. We learned that $y = \log_b x$ is equivalent to $b^y = x$. We evaluated and graphed logarithmic functions, including the common logarithmic function $[f(x) = \log_{10} x$ or $f(x) = \log x]$ and the natural logarithmic function $[f(x) = \log_e x$ or $f(x) = \ln x]$. We learned to use transformations to graph exponential and logarithmic functions. Finally, we used properties of logarithms to expand and condense logarithmic expressions.

In Exercises 1–5, graph f and g in the same rectangular coordinate system. Graph and give equations of all asymptotes. Give each function's domain and range.

1. $f(x) = 2^x$ and $g(x) = 2^x - 3$
2. $f(x) = \left(\frac{1}{2}\right)^x$ and $g(x) = \left(\frac{1}{2}\right)^{x-1}$
3. $f(x) = e^x$ and $g(x) = \ln x$
4. $f(x) = \log_2 x$ and $g(x) = \log_2(x - 1) + 1$
5. $f(x) = \log_{\frac{1}{2}} x$ and $g(x) = -2 \log_{\frac{1}{2}} x$

In Exercises 6–9, find the domain of each function.

6. $f(x) = \log_3(x + 6)$
7. $g(x) = \log_3 x + 6$
8. $h(x) = \log_3(x + 6)^2$
9. $f(x) = 3^{x+6}$

In Exercises 10–20, evaluate each expression without using a calculator. If evaluation is not possible, state the reason.

10. $\log_2 8 + \log_5 25$
11. $\log_3 \frac{1}{9}$
12. $\log_{100} 10$
13. $\log \sqrt[3]{10}$
14. $\log_2(\log_3 81)$
15. $\log_3\left(\log_2 \frac{1}{8}\right)$
16. $6^{\log_6 5}$
17. $\ln e^{\sqrt{7}}$
18. $10^{\log 13}$
19. $\log_{100} 0.1$
20. $\log_\pi \pi^{\sqrt{\pi}}$

In Exercises 21–22, expand and evaluate numerical terms.

21. $\log\left(\dfrac{\sqrt{xy}}{1000}\right)$
22. $\ln(e^{19}x^{20})$

In Exercises 23–25, write each expression as a single logarithm.

23. $8 \log_7 x - \dfrac{1}{3}\log_7 y$
24. $7 \log_5 x + 2 \log_5 x$
25. $\dfrac{1}{2}\ln x - 3 \ln y - \ln(z - 2)$

26. Use the formulas

$$A = P\left(1 + \frac{r}{n}\right)^{nt} \quad \text{and} \quad A = Pe^{rt}$$

to solve this exercise. You decide to invest \$8000 for 3 years at an annual rate of 8%. How much more is the return if the interest is compounded continuously than if it is compounded monthly? Round to the nearest dollar.

SECTION 4.4 Exponential and Logarithmic Equations

Objectives

1. Use like bases to solve exponential equations.
2. Use logarithms to solve exponential equations.
3. Use the definition of a logarithm to solve logarithmic equations.
4. Use the one-to-one property of logarithms to solve logarithmic equations.
5. Solve applied problems involving exponential and logarithmic equations.

At age 20, you inherit \$30,000. You'd like to put aside \$25,000 and eventually have over half a million dollars for early retirement. Is this possible? In Example 10 in this section, you will see how techniques for solving equations with variable exponents provide an answer to this question.

Exponential Equations

An **exponential equation** is an equation containing a variable in an exponent. Examples of exponential equations include

$$2^{3x-8} = 16, \quad 4^x = 15, \quad \text{and} \quad 40e^{0.6x} = 240.$$

Some exponential equations can be solved by expressing each side of the equation as a power of the same base. All exponential functions are one-to-one—that is, no two different ordered pairs have the same second component. Thus, if b is a positive number other than 1 and $b^M = b^N$, then $M = N$.

① Use like bases to solve exponential equations.

Solving Exponential Equations by Expressing Each Side as a Power of the Same Base

$$\text{If } b^M = b^N, \text{ then } M = N.$$

Express each side as a power of the same base.　　Set the exponents equal to each other.

1. Rewrite the equation in the form $b^M = b^N$.
2. Set $M = N$.
3. Solve for the variable.

TECHNOLOGY

Graphic Connections

The graphs of
$$y_1 = 2^{3x-8}$$
and $y_2 = 16$
have an intersection point whose x-coordinate is 4. This verifies that {4} is the solution set of $2^{3x-8} = 16$.

$[-1, 5, 1]$ by $[0, 20, 1]$

EXAMPLE 1　Solving Exponential Equations

Solve:
    a. $2^{3x-8} = 16$　　**b.** $27^{x+3} = 9^{x-1}$.

SOLUTION

In each equation, express both sides as a power of the same base. Then set the exponents equal to each other and solve for the variable.

    a. Because 16 is 2^4, we express each side of $2^{3x-8} = 16$ in terms of base 2.

$$
\begin{aligned}
2^{3x-8} &= 16 &&\text{This is the given equation.}\\
2^{3x-8} &= 2^4 &&\text{Write each side as a power of the same base.}\\
3x - 8 &= 4 &&\text{If } b^M = b^N, b > 0 \text{ and } b \neq 1, \text{ then } M = N.\\
3x &= 12 &&\text{Add 8 to both sides.}\\
x &= 4 &&\text{Divide both sides by 3.}
\end{aligned}
$$

Substituting 4 for x into the original equation produces the true statement $16 = 16$. The solution set is {4}.

    b. Because $27 = 3^3$ and $9 = 3^2$, we can express both sides of $27^{x+3} = 9^{x-1}$ in terms of base 3.

$$
\begin{aligned}
27^{x+3} &= 9^{x-1} &&\text{This is the given equation.}\\
(3^3)^{x+3} &= (3^2)^{x-1} &&\text{Write each side as a power of the same base.}\\
3^{3(x+3)} &= 3^{2(x-1)} &&\text{When an exponential expression is raised to a power,}\\
&&&\text{multiply exponents.}\\
3(x + 3) &= 2(x - 1) &&\text{If two powers of the same base are equal,}\\
&&&\text{then the exponents are equal.}\\
3x + 9 &= 2x - 2 &&\text{Apply the distributive property.}\\
x + 9 &= -2 &&\text{Subtract 2x from both sides.}\\
x &= -11 &&\text{Subtract 9 from both sides.}
\end{aligned}
$$

Substituting -11 for x into the original equation produces $27^{-8} = 9^{-12}$, which simplifies to the true statement $3^{-24} = 3^{-24}$. The solution set is {−11}.   ● ● ●

 Check Point 1　Solve:
    a. $5^{3x-6} = 125$　　**b.** $8^{x+2} = 4^{x-3}$.

② Use logarithms to solve exponential equations.

Most exponential equations cannot be rewritten so that each side has the same base. Here are two examples:

$$4^x = 15 \qquad\qquad 10^x = 120{,}000.$$

We cannot rewrite both sides in terms of base 2 or base 4.

We cannot rewrite both sides in terms of base 10.

Logarithms are extremely useful in solving these equations. The solution begins with isolating the exponential expression. Notice that the exponential expression is already isolated in both $4^x = 15$ and $10^x = 120,000$. Then we take the logarithm on both sides. Why can we do this? All logarithmic relations are functions. Thus, if M and N are positive real numbers and $M = N$, then $\log_b M = \log_b N$.

The base that is used when taking the logarithm on both sides of an equation can be any base at all. If the exponential equation involves base 10, as in $10^x = 120,000$, we'll take the common logarithm on both sides. If the exponential equation involves any other base, as in $4^x = 15$, we'll take the natural logarithm on both sides.

Using Logarithms to Solve Exponential Equations

1. Isolate the exponential expression.
2. Take the common logarithm on both sides of the equation for base 10. Take the natural logarithm on both sides of the equation for bases other than 10.
3. Simplify using one of the following properties:

$$\ln b^x = x \ln b \quad \text{or} \quad \ln e^x = x \quad \text{or} \quad \log 10^x = x.$$

4. Solve for the variable.

EXAMPLE 2　Solving Exponential Equations

Solve:

a. $4^x = 15$　　**b.** $10^x = 120,000.$

SOLUTION

We will use the natural logarithmic function to solve $4^x = 15$ and the common logarithmic function to solve $10^x = 120,000$.

a. Because the exponential expression, 4^x, is already isolated on the left side of $4^x = 15$, we begin by taking the natural logarithm on both sides of the equation.

$$4^x = 15 \qquad \text{This is the given equation.}$$
$$\ln 4^x = \ln 15 \qquad \text{Take the natural logarithm on both sides.}$$
$$x \ln 4 = \ln 15 \qquad \text{Use the power rule and bring the variable exponent to the front: } \ln b^x = x \ln b.$$
$$x = \frac{\ln 15}{\ln 4} \qquad \text{Solve for x by dividing both sides by ln 4. Equivalently, } x = \log_4 15.$$

We now have an exact value for x. We use the exact value for x in the equation's solution set. Thus, the equation's solution is $\dfrac{\ln 15}{\ln 4}$ and the solution set is $\left\{ \dfrac{\ln 15}{\ln 4} \right\}$. We can obtain a decimal approximation by using a calculator: $x \approx 1.95$. Because $4^2 = 16$, it seems reasonable that the solution to $4^x = 15$ is approximately 1.95.

b. Because the exponential expression, 10^x, is already isolated on the left side of $10^x = 120,000$, we begin by taking the common logarithm on both sides of the equation.

$$10^x = 120,000 \qquad \text{This is the given equation.}$$
$$\log 10^x = \log 120,000 \qquad \text{Take the common logarithm on both sides.}$$
$$x = \log 120,000 \qquad \text{Use the inverse property } \log 10^x = x \text{ on the left.}$$

The equation's solution is $\log 120,000$ and the solution set is $\{\log 120,000\}$. We can obtain a decimal approximation by using a calculator: $x \approx 5.08$. Because $10^5 = 100,000$, it seems reasonable that the solution to $10^x = 120,000$ is approximately 5.08.　　• • •

DISCOVERY

Keep in mind that the base used when taking the logarithm on both sides of an equation can be any base at all. Solve $4^x = 15$ by taking the common logarithm on both sides. Solve again, this time taking the logarithm with base 4 on both sides. Use the change-of-base property to show that the solutions are the same as the one obtained in Example 2(a).

⌀ Check Point **2** Solve:

a. $5^x = 134$ **b.** $10^x = 8000$.

Find each solution set and then use a calculator to obtain a decimal approximation to two decimal places for the solution.

EXAMPLE 3   Solving an Exponential Equation

Solve: $40e^{0.6x} - 3 = 237$.

SOLUTION

We begin by adding 3 to both sides and dividing both sides by 40 to isolate the exponential expression, $e^{0.6x}$. Then we take the natural logarithm on both sides of the equation.

$$40e^{0.6x} - 3 = 237$$ This is the given equation.

$$40e^{0.6x} = 240$$ Add 3 to both sides.

$$e^{0.6x} = 6$$ Isolate the exponential factor by dividing both sides by 40.

$$\ln e^{0.6x} = \ln 6$$ Take the natural logarithm on both sides.

$$0.6x = \ln 6$$ Use the inverse property $\ln e^x = x$ on the left.

$$x = \frac{\ln 6}{0.6} \approx 2.99$$ Divide both sides by 0.6 and solve for x.

Thus, the solution of the equation is $\dfrac{\ln 6}{0.6} \approx 2.99$. Try checking this approximate solution in the original equation to verify that $\left\{\dfrac{\ln 6}{0.6}\right\}$ is the solution set.   • • •

⌀ Check Point **3** Solve: $7e^{2x} - 5 = 58$. Find the solution set and then use a calculator to obtain a decimal approximation to two decimal places for the solution.

EXAMPLE 4   Solving an Exponential Equation

Solve: $5^{x-2} = 4^{2x+3}$.

SOLUTION

Because each exponential expression is isolated on one side of the equation, we begin by taking the natural logarithm on both sides.

$$5^{x-2} = 4^{2x+3}$$ This is the given equation.

$$\ln 5^{x-2} = \ln 4^{2x+3}$$ Take the natural logarithm on both sides.

Be sure to insert parentheses around the binomials.

$$(x - 2)\ln 5 = (2x + 3)\ln 4$$ Use the power rule and bring the variable exponents to the front: $\ln b^x = x \ln b$.

Remember that ln 5 and ln 4 are constants, not variables.

$$x \ln 5 - 2\ln 5 = 2x \ln 4 + 3 \ln 4$$ Use the distributive property to distribute ln 5 and ln 4 to both terms in parentheses.

$$x \ln 5 - 2x \ln 4 = 2 \ln 5 + 3 \ln 4$$ Collect variable terms involving x on the left by subtracting 2x ln 4 and adding 2 ln 5 on both sides.

$$x(\ln 5 - 2\ln 4) = 2\ln 5 + 3\ln 4 \qquad \text{Factor out } x \text{ from the two terms on the left.}$$

$$x = \frac{2\ln 5 + 3\ln 4}{\ln 5 - 2\ln 4} \qquad \text{Isolate } x \text{ by dividing both sides by } \ln 5 - 2\ln 4.$$

The solution set is $\left\{\dfrac{2\ln 5 + 3\ln 4}{\ln 5 - 2\ln 4}\right\}$. The solution is approximately -6.34. $\bullet\bullet\bullet$

📐 Check Point **4** Solve: $3^{2x-1} = 7^{x+1}$. Find the solution set and then use a calculator to obtain a decimal approximation to two decimal places for the solution.

EXAMPLE 5 Solving an Exponential Equation

Solve: $e^{2x} - 4e^x + 3 = 0$.

SOLUTION

The given equation is quadratic in form. If $u = e^x$, the equation can be expressed as $u^2 - 4u + 3 = 0$. Because this equation can be solved by factoring, we factor to isolate the exponential term.

$$e^{2x} - 4e^x + 3 = 0 \qquad \text{This is the given equation.}$$

$$(e^x - 3)(e^x - 1) = 0 \qquad \text{Factor on the left. Notice that if } u = e^x, u^2 - 4u + 3 = (u - 3)(u - 1).$$

$$\begin{array}{ll} e^x - 3 = 0 \quad\text{or}\quad e^x - 1 = 0 & \text{Set each factor equal to 0.} \\ e^x = 3 \qquad\qquad e^x = 1 & \text{Solve for } e^x. \\ \ln e^x = \ln 3 \qquad\qquad x = 0 & \text{Take the natural logarithm on both sides of the first equation. The equation on the right can be solved by inspection.} \\ x = \ln 3 & \ln e^x = x \end{array}$$

The solution set is $\{0, \ln 3\}$. The solutions are 0 and $\ln 3$, which is approximately 1.10. $\bullet\bullet\bullet$

📐 Check Point **5** Solve: $e^{2x} - 8e^x + 7 = 0$. Find the solution set and then use a calculator to obtain a decimal approximation to two decimal places, if necessary, for the solutions.

③ Use the definition of a logarithm to solve logarithmic equations.

Logarithmic Equations

A **logarithmic equation** is an equation containing a variable in a logarithmic expression. Examples of logarithmic equations include

$$\log_4(x + 3) = 2 \quad \text{and} \quad \ln(x + 2) - \ln(4x + 3) = \ln\left(\frac{1}{x}\right).$$

Some logarithmic equations can be expressed in the form $\log_b M = c$. We can solve such equations by rewriting them in exponential form.

Using the Definition of a Logarithm to Solve Logarithmic Equations

1. Express the equation in the form $\log_b M = c$.

2. Use the definition of a logarithm to rewrite the equation in exponential form:

$$\log_b M = c \quad \text{means} \quad b^c = M.$$

Logarithms are exponents.

3. Solve for the variable.

4. Check proposed solutions in the original equation. Include in the solution set only values for which $M > 0$.

EXAMPLE 6 Solving Logarithmic Equations

Solve:

a. $\log_4(x + 3) = 2$ **b.** $3 \ln(2x) = 12$.

SOLUTION

The form $\log_b M = c$ involves a single logarithm whose coefficient is 1 on one side and a constant on the other side. Equation (a) is already in this form. We will need to divide both sides of equation (b) by 3 to obtain this form.

a.	$\log_4(x + 3) = 2$	This is the given equation.
	$4^2 = x + 3$	Rewrite in exponential form: $\log_b M = c$ means $b^c = M$.
	$16 = x + 3$	Square 4.
	$13 = x$	Subtract 3 from both sides.

Check 13:

$\log_4(x + 3) = 2$	This is the given logarithmic equation.
$\log_4(13 + 3) \stackrel{?}{=} 2$	Substitute 13 for x.
$\log_4 16 \stackrel{?}{=} 2$	
$2 = 2$, true	$\log_4 16 = 2$ because $4^2 = 16$.

This true statement indicates that the solution set is {13}.

b.	$3 \ln(2x) = 12$	This is the given equation.
	$\ln(2x) = 4$	Divide both sides by 3.
	$\log_e(2x) = 4$	Rewrite the natural logarithm showing base e. This step is optional.
	$e^4 = 2x$	Rewrite in exponential form: $\log_b M = c$ means $b^c = M$.
	$\dfrac{e^4}{2} = x$	Divide both sides by 2.

Check $\dfrac{e^4}{2}$:

$3 \ln(2x) = 12$	This is the given logarithmic equation.
$3 \ln\left[2\left(\dfrac{e^4}{2}\right) \right] \stackrel{?}{=} 12$	Substitute $\dfrac{e^4}{2}$ for x.
$3 \ln e^4 \stackrel{?}{=} 12$	Simplify: $\dfrac{2}{1} \cdot \dfrac{e^4}{2} = e^4$.
$3 \cdot 4 \stackrel{?}{=} 12$	Because $\ln e^x = x$, we conclude $\ln e^4 = 4$.
$12 = 12$, true	

This true statement indicates that the solution set is $\left\{ \dfrac{e^4}{2} \right\}$. • • •

 Check Point **6** Solve:

a. $\log_2(x - 4) = 3$ **b.** $4 \ln(3x) = 8$.

Logarithmic expressions are defined only for logarithms of positive real numbers. **Always check proposed solutions of a logarithmic equation in the original equation. Exclude from the solution set any proposed solution that produces the logarithm of a negative number or the logarithm of 0.**

GREAT QUESTION!

Can a negative number belong to the solution set of a logarithmic equation?

Yes. Here's an example.

$$\log_2(x + 20) = 3 \qquad \text{Solve this equation.}$$
$$2^3 = x + 20 \qquad \text{Rewrite in exponential form.}$$
$$8 = x + 20 \qquad \text{Cube 2.}$$
$$-12 = x \qquad \text{Subtract 20 from both sides.}$$

Check -12**:**

$$\log_2(-12 + 20) \stackrel{?}{=} 3 \qquad \text{Substitute } -12 \text{ for } x.$$
$$\log_2 8 \stackrel{?}{=} 3$$
$$3 = 3, \text{ true} \qquad \log_2 8 = 3 \text{ because } 2^3 = 8.$$

The solution set is $\{-12\}$. Although -12 is negative, it does not produce the logarithm of a negative number in $\log_2(x + 20) = 3$, the given equation. Note that the domain of the expression $\log_2(x + 20)$ is $(-20, \infty)$, which includes negative numbers such as -12.

To rewrite the logarithmic equation $\log_b M = c$ in the equivalent exponential form $b^c = M$, we need a single logarithm whose coefficient is one. It is sometimes necessary to use properties of logarithms to condense logarithms into a single logarithm. In the next example, we use the product rule for logarithms to obtain a single logarithmic expression on the left side.

EXAMPLE 7   Solving a Logarithmic Equation

Solve: $\log_2 x + \log_2(x - 7) = 3$.

SOLUTION

$$\log_2 x + \log_2(x - 7) = 3 \qquad \text{This is the given equation.}$$
$$\log_2[x(x - 7)] = 3 \qquad \begin{array}{l}\text{Use the product rule to obtain a single} \\ \text{logarithm: } \log_b M + \log_b N = \log_b(MN).\end{array}$$
$$2^3 = x(x - 7) \qquad \begin{array}{l}\text{Rewrite in exponential form: } \log_b M = c \\ \text{means } b^c = M.\end{array}$$
$$8 = x^2 - 7x \qquad \begin{array}{l}\text{Evaluate } 2^3 \text{ on the left and apply the} \\ \text{distributive property on the right.}\end{array}$$
$$0 = x^2 - 7x - 8 \qquad \text{Set the equation equal to 0.}$$
$$0 = (x - 8)(x + 1) \qquad \text{Factor.}$$
$$x - 8 = 0 \quad \text{or} \quad x + 1 = 0 \qquad \text{Set each factor equal to 0.}$$
$$x = 8 \qquad \qquad x = -1 \qquad \text{Solve for } x.$$

Check 8**:**	**Check** -1**:**
$\log_2 x + \log_2(x - 7) = 3$	$\log_2 x + \log_2(x - 7) = 3$
$\log_2 8 + \log_2(8 - 7) \stackrel{?}{=} 3$	$\log_2(-1) + \log_2(-1 - 7) \stackrel{?}{=} 3$
$\log_2 8 + \log_2 1 \stackrel{?}{=} 3$	The number -1 does not check.
$3 + 0 \stackrel{?}{=} 3$	The domain of a logarithmic function consists of positive numbers.
$3 = 3, \text{ true}$	

The solution set is $\{8\}$.   •••

⊘ Check Point **7** Solve: $\log x + \log(x - 3) = 1$.

4 Use the one-to-one property of logarithms to solve logarithmic equations.

Some logarithmic equations can be expressed in the form $\log_b M = \log_b N$, where the bases on both sides of the equation are the same. Because all logarithmic functions are one-to-one, we can conclude that $M = N$.

Using the One-to-One Property of Logarithms to Solve Logarithmic Equations

1. Express the equation in the form $\log_b M = \log_b N$. This form involves a single logarithm whose coefficient is 1 on each side of the equation.
2. Use the one-to-one property to rewrite the equation without logarithms: If $\log_b M = \log_b N$, then $M = N$.
3. Solve for the variable.
4. Check proposed solutions in the original equation. Include in the solution set only values for which $M > 0$ and $N > 0$.

EXAMPLE 8   Solving a Logarithmic Equation

Solve: $\ln(x + 2) - \ln(4x + 3) = \ln\left(\dfrac{1}{x}\right).$

SOLUTION

In order to apply the one-to-one property of logarithms, we need a single logarithm whose coefficient is 1 on each side of the equation. The right side is already in this form. We can obtain a single logarithm on the left side by applying the quotient rule.

$$\ln(x + 2) - \ln(4x + 3) = \ln\left(\frac{1}{x}\right)$$ This is the given equation.

$$\ln\left(\frac{x + 2}{4x + 3}\right) = \ln\left(\frac{1}{x}\right)$$ Use the quotient rule to obtain a single logarithm on the left side: $\log_b M - \log_b N = \log_b\left(\frac{M}{N}\right).$

$$\frac{x + 2}{4x + 3} = \frac{1}{x}$$ Use the one-to-one property: If $\log_b M = \log_b N$, then $M = N$.

$$x(4x + 3)\left(\frac{x + 2}{4x + 3}\right) = x(4x + 3)\left(\frac{1}{x}\right)$$ Multiply both sides by $x(4x + 3)$, the LCD.

$$x(x + 2) = 4x + 3$$ Simplify.

$$x^2 + 2x = 4x + 3$$ Apply the distributive property.

$$x^2 - 2x - 3 = 0$$ Subtract $4x + 3$ from both sides and set the equation equal to 0.

$$(x - 3)(x + 1) = 0$$ Factor.

$$x - 3 = 0 \quad \text{or} \quad x + 1 = 0$$ Set each factor equal to 0.

$$x = 3 \qquad\qquad x = -1$$ Solve for x.

Substituting 3 for x into $\ln(x + 2) - \ln(4x + 3) = \ln\left(\frac{1}{x}\right)$ produces the true statement $\ln\left(\frac{1}{3}\right) = \ln\left(\frac{1}{3}\right)$. However, substituting -1 produces logarithms of negative numbers. Thus, -1 is not a solution. The solution set is $\{3\}$.   •••

⌀ **Check Point 8** Solve: $\ln(x - 3) = \ln(7x - 23) - \ln(x + 1).$

TECHNOLOGY

Numeric Connections

A graphing utility's [TABLE] feature can be used to verify that $\{3\}$ is the solution set of

$$\ln(x + 2) - \ln(4x + 3) = \ln\left(\frac{1}{x}\right).$$

| $y_1 = \ln(x + 2) - \ln(4x + 3)$ | $y_2 = \ln\left(\frac{1}{x}\right)$ |

X	Y1	Y2
-2	ERROR	ERROR
-1	ERROR	ERROR
0	-.4055	ERROR
1	-.8473	0
2	-1.012	-.6931
3	-1.099	-1.099
4	-1.153	-1.386

X=-2

y_1 and y_2 are equal when $x = 3$.

5 Solve applied problems involving exponential and logarithmic equations.

Applications

Our first applied example provides a mathematical perspective on the old slogan "Alcohol and driving don't mix." In California, where 38% of fatal traffic crashes involve drinking drivers, it is illegal to drive with a blood alcohol concentration of 0.08 or higher. At these levels, drivers may be arrested and charged with driving under the influence.

A blood alcohol concentration of 0.22 corresponds to near certainty, or a 100% probability, of a car accident.

FIGURE 4.20

EXAMPLE 9 Alcohol and Risk of a Car Accident

Medical research indicates that the risk of having a car accident increases exponentially as the concentration of alcohol in the blood increases. The risk is modeled by

$$R = 6e^{12.77x},$$

where x is the blood alcohol concentration and R, given as a percent, is the risk of having a car accident. What blood alcohol concentration corresponds to a 17% risk of a car accident? How is this shown on the graph of R in **Figure 4.20**?

SOLUTION

For a risk of 17%, we let $R = 17$ in the equation and solve for x, the blood alcohol concentration.

$R = 6e^{12.77x}$ This is the given equation.

$6e^{12.77x} = 17$ Substitute 17 for R and (optional) reverse the two sides of the equation.

$e^{12.77x} = \dfrac{17}{6}$ Isolate the exponential factor by dividing both sides by 6.

$\ln e^{12.77x} = \ln\left(\dfrac{17}{6}\right)$ Take the natural logarithm on both sides.

$12.77x = \ln\left(\dfrac{17}{6}\right)$ Use the inverse property $\ln e^x = x$ on the left side.

$x = \dfrac{\ln\left(\dfrac{17}{6}\right)}{12.77} \approx 0.08$ Divide both sides by 12.77.

For a blood alcohol concentration of 0.08, the risk of a car accident is 17%. This is shown on the graph of R in **Figure 4.20** by the point (0.08, 17) that lies on the blue curve. Take a moment to locate this point on the curve. In many states, it is illegal to drive with a blood alcohol concentration of 0.08. • • •

✓ **Check Point 9** Use the formula in Example 9 to answer this question: What blood alcohol concentration corresponds to a 7% risk of a car accident? (In many states, drivers under the age of 21 can lose their licenses for driving at this level.)

Suppose that you inherit $30,000 at age 20. Is it possible to invest $25,000 and have over half a million dollars for early retirement? Our next example illustrates the power of compound interest.

EXAMPLE 10 Revisiting the Formula for Compound Interest

The formula

$$A = P\left(1 + \frac{r}{n}\right)^{nt}$$

describes the accumulated value, A, of a sum of money, P, the principal, after t years at annual percentage rate r (in decimal form) compounded n times a year. How long will it take $25,000 to grow to $500,000 at 9% annual interest compounded monthly?

SOLUTION

$$A = P\left(1 + \frac{r}{n}\right)^{nt}$$

This is the given formula.

$$500{,}000 = 25{,}000\left(1 + \frac{0.09}{12}\right)^{12t}$$

A(the desired accumulated value) = $500,000,
P(the principal) = $25,000,
r(the interest rate) = 9% = 0.09, and n = 12
(monthly compounding).

Because of the exponent, 12t, do not distribute 25,000 over the terms in parentheses.

Our goal is to solve the equation for t. Let's reverse the two sides of the equation and then simplify within parentheses.

$$25{,}000\left(1 + \frac{0.09}{12}\right)^{12t} = 500{,}000$$

Reverse the two sides of the previous equation.

$$25{,}000(1 + 0.0075)^{12t} = 500{,}000$$

Divide within parentheses: $\frac{0.09}{12} = 0.0075$.

$$25{,}000(1.0075)^{12t} = 500{,}000$$

Add within parentheses.

$$(1.0075)^{12t} = 20$$

Divide both sides by 25,000.

$$\ln(1.0075)^{12t} = \ln 20$$

Take the natural logarithm on both sides.

$$12t \ln(1.0075) = \ln 20$$

Use the power rule to bring the exponent to the front: $\ln b^x = x \ln b$.

$$t = \frac{\ln 20}{12 \ln 1.0075}$$

Solve for t, dividing both sides by 12 ln 1.0075.

$$\approx 33.4$$

Use a calculator.

After approximately 33.4 years, the $25,000 will grow to an accumulated value of $500,000. If you set aside the money at age 20, you can begin enjoying a life as a half-millionaire at about age 53. ●●●

⊘ **Check Point 10** How long, to the nearest tenth of a year, will it take $1000 to grow to $3600 at 8% annual interest compounded quarterly?

EXAMPLE 11 Revisiting the Model for Height of Children

We have seen that the percentage of adult height attained by a boy who is x years old can be modeled by

$$f(x) = 29 + 48.8 \log(x + 1),$$

where x represents the boy's age (from 5 to 15) and $f(x)$ represents the percentage of his adult height. At what age, rounded to the nearest year, has a boy attained 85% of his adult height?

SOLUTION

To find at what age a boy has attained 85% of his adult height, we substitute 85 for $f(x)$ and solve for x, the boy's age.

$$f(x) = 29 + 48.8 \log(x + 1)$$

This is the given function.

$$85 = 29 + 48.8 \log(x + 1)$$

Substitute 85 for f(x).

Our goal is to isolate log(x + 1) and then rewrite the equation in exponential form.

$$56 = 48.8 \log(x + 1)$$

Subtract 29 from both sides.

$$\frac{56}{48.8} = \log(x + 1)$$

Divide both sides by 48.8.

$$\frac{56}{48.8} = \log_{10}(x + 1)$$

Rewrite the common logarithm showing base 10. This step is optional.

$$10^{\frac{56}{48.8}} = x + 1$$

Rewrite in exponential form.

$$10^{\frac{56}{48.8}} - 1 = x$$

Subtract 1 from both sides.

$$13 \approx x$$

Use a calculator:

At approximately age 13, a boy has attained 85% of his adult height. This is shown on the graph of the model in **Figure 4.21** by the point $(13, 85)$.

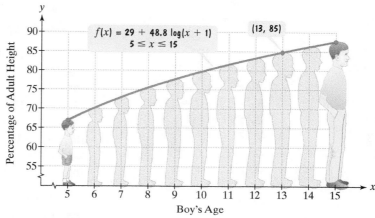

FIGURE 4.21 Graph of a model for the percentage of adult height attained by a boy   • • •

⊘ Check Point **11** The percentage of adult height attained by a girl who is x years old can be modeled by

$$f(x) = 62 + 35 \log(x - 4),$$

where x represents the girl's age (from 5 to 15) and $f(x)$ represents the percentage of her adult height. At what age has a girl attained 97% of her adult height?

CONCEPT AND VOCABULARY CHECK

Fill in each blank so that the resulting statement is true.

1. If $b^M = b^N$, then _____.

2. If $2^{4x-1} = 2^7$, then _____ $= 7$.

3. If $x \ln 9 = \ln 20$, then $x =$ _____.

4. If $e^{0.6x} = 6$, then $0.6x =$ _____.

5. If $\log_5(x + 1) = 3$, then _____ $= x + 1$.

6. If $\log_3 x + \log_3(x + 1) = 2$, then $\log_3$ _____ $= 2$.

7. If $\ln\left(\dfrac{7x - 23}{x + 1}\right) = \ln(x - 3)$, then _____ $= x - 3$.

8. True or false: $x^4 = 15$ is an exponential equation. _____

9. True or false: $4^x = 15$ is an exponential equation. _____

10. True or false: -3 is a solution of $\log_5 9 = 2 \log_5 x$. _____

11. True or false: -10 is a solution of $\log_5(x + 35) = 2$. _____

EXERCISE SET 4.4

Practice Exercises

Solve each exponential equation in Exercises 1–22 by expressing each side as a power of the same base and then equating exponents.

1. $2^x = 64$

2. $3^x = 81$

3. $5^x = 125$

4. $5^x = 625$

5. $2^{2x-1} = 32$

6. $3^{2x+1} = 27$

7. $4^{2x-1} = 64$

8. $5^{3x-1} = 125$

9. $32^x = 8$

10. $4^x = 32$

11. $9^x = 27$

12. $125^x = 625$

13. $3^{1-x} = \frac{1}{27}$

14. $5^{2-x} = \frac{1}{125}$

15. $6^{\frac{x-3}{4}} = \sqrt{6}$

16. $7^{\frac{x-2}{6}} = \sqrt{7}$

17. $4^x = \dfrac{1}{\sqrt{2}}$

18. $9^x = \dfrac{1}{\sqrt[3]{3}}$

19. $8^{x+3} = 16^{x-1}$

20. $8^{1-x} = 4^{x+2}$

21. $e^{x+1} = \dfrac{1}{e}$

22. $e^{x+4} = \dfrac{1}{e^{2x}}$

Solve each exponential equation in Exercises 23–48. Express the solution set in terms of natural logarithms or common logarithms. Then use a calculator to obtain a decimal approximation, correct to two decimal places, for the solution.

23. $10^x = 3.91$

24. $10^x = 8.07$

25. $e^x = 5.7$

26. $e^x = 0.83$

27. $5^x = 17$

28. $19^x = 143$

29. $5e^x = 23$

30. $9e^x = 107$

31. $3e^{5x} = 1977$

32. $4e^{7x} = 10{,}273$

33. $e^{1-5x} = 793$

34. $e^{1-8x} = 7957$

35. $e^{5x-3} - 2 = 10{,}476$

36. $e^{4x-5} - 7 = 11{,}243$

37. $7^{x+2} = 410$

38. $5^{x-3} = 137$

39. $7^{0.3x} = 813$

40. $3^{\frac{x}{7}} = 0.2$

41. $5^{2x+3} = 3^{x-1}$

42. $7^{2x+1} = 3^{x+2}$

43. $e^{2x} - 3e^x + 2 = 0$

44. $e^{2x} - 2e^x - 3 = 0$

45. $e^{4x} + 5e^{2x} - 24 = 0$

46. $e^{4x} - 3e^{2x} - 18 = 0$

47. $3^{2x} + 3^x - 2 = 0$

48. $2^{2x} + 2^x - 12 = 0$

Solve each logarithmic equation in Exercises 49–92. Be sure to reject any value of x that is not in the domain of the original logarithmic expressions. Give the exact answer. Then, where necessary, use a calculator to obtain a decimal approximation, correct to two decimal places, for the solution.

49. $\log_3 x = 4$

50. $\log_5 x = 3$

51. $\ln x = 2$

52. $\ln x = 3$

53. $\log_4(x + 5) = 3$

54. $\log_5(x - 7) = 2$

55. $\log_2(x + 25) = 4$

56. $\log_2(x + 50) = 5$

57. $\log_3(x + 4) = -3$

58. $\log_7(x + 2) = -2$

59. $\log_4(3x + 2) = 3$

60. $\log_2(4x + 1) = 5$

61. $5 \ln(2x) = 20$

62. $6 \ln(2x) = 30$

63. $6 + 2 \ln x = 5$

64. $7 + 3 \ln x = 6$

65. $\ln \sqrt{x + 3} = 1$

66. $\ln \sqrt{x + 4} = 1$

67. $\log_5 x + \log_5(4x - 1) = 1$

68. $\log_6(x + 5) + \log_6 x = 2$

69. $\log_3(x + 6) + \log_3(x + 4) = 1$

70. $\log_6(x + 3) + \log_6(x + 4) = 1$

71. $\log_2(x + 2) - \log_2(x - 5) = 3$

72. $\log_4(x + 2) - \log_4(x - 1) = 1$

73. $2 \log_3(x + 4) = \log_3 9 + 2$

74. $3 \log_2(x - 1) = 5 - \log_2 4$

75. $\log_2(x - 6) + \log_2(x - 4) - \log_2 x = 2$

76. $\log_2(x - 3) + \log_2 x - \log_2(x + 2) = 2$

77. $\log(x + 4) = \log x + \log 4$

78. $\log(5x + 1) = \log(2x + 3) + \log 2$

79. $\log(3x - 3) = \log(x + 1) + \log 4$

80. $\log(2x - 1) = \log(x + 3) + \log 3$

81. $2 \log x = \log 25$

82. $3 \log x = \log 125$

83. $\log(x + 4) - \log 2 = \log(5x + 1)$

84. $\log(x + 7) - \log 3 = \log(7x + 1)$

85. $2 \log x - \log 7 = \log 112$

86. $\log(x - 2) + \log 5 = \log 100$

87. $\log x + \log(x + 3) = \log 10$

88. $\log(x + 3) + \log(x - 2) = \log 14$

89. $\ln(x - 4) + \ln(x + 1) = \ln(x - 8)$

90. $\log_2(x - 1) - \log_2(x + 3) = \log_2\left(\dfrac{1}{x}\right)$

91. $\ln(x - 2) - \ln(x + 3) = \ln(x - 1) - \ln(x + 7)$

92. $\ln(x - 5) - \ln(x + 4) = \ln(x - 1) - \ln(x + 2)$

Practice Plus

In Exercises 93–102, solve each equation.

93. $5^{2x} \cdot 5^{4x} = 125$

94. $3^{x+2} \cdot 3^x = 81$

95. $2|\ln x| - 6 = 0$

96. $3|\log x| - 6 = 0$

97. $3^{x^2} = 45$

98. $5^{x^2} = 50$

99. $\ln(2x + 1) + \ln(x - 3) - 2 \ln x = 0$

100. $\ln 3 - \ln(x + 5) - \ln x = 0$

101. $5^{x^2-12} = 25^{2x}$

102. $3^{x^2-12} = 9^{2x}$

Application Exercises

103. The formula $A = 37.3e^{0.0095t}$ models the population of California, A, in millions, t years after 2010.

   a. What was the population of California in 2010?

   b. When will the population of California reach 40 million?

104. The formula $A = 25.1e^{0.0187t}$ models the population of Texas, A, in millions, t years after 2010.

   a. What was the population of Texas in 2010?

   b. When will the population of Texas reach 28 million?

The function $f(x) = 20(0.975)^x$ models the percentage of surface sunlight, $f(x)$, that reaches a depth of x feet beneath the surface of the ocean. The figure shows the graph of this function. Use this information to solve Exercises 105–106.

105. Use the function to determine at what depth, to the nearest foot, there is 1% of surface sunlight. How is this shown on the graph of f?

106. Use the function to determine at what depth, to the nearest foot, there is 3% of surface sunlight. How is this shown on the graph of f?

In Exercises 107–110, complete the table for a savings account subject to n compoundings yearly $\left[A = P\left(1 + \dfrac{r}{n}\right)^{nt}\right]$. Round answers to one decimal place.

	Amount Invested	Number of Compounding Periods	Annual Interest Rate	Accumulated Amount	Time t in Years
107.	$12,500	4	5.75%	$20,000	
108.	$7250	12	6.5%	$15,000	
109.	$1000	360	16.8%	$1400	
110.	$5000	360	14.7%	$9000	

In Exercises 111–114, complete the table for a savings account subject to continuous compounding ($A = Pe^{rt}$). Round answers to one decimal place.

	Amount Invested	Annual Interest Rate	Accumulated Amount	Time t in Years
111.	$8000	8%	Double the amount invested	
112.	$8000	20.3%	$12,000	
113.	$2350	15.7%	Triple the amount invested	
114.	$17,425	4.25%	$25,000	

By 2019, nearly $1 out of every $5 spent in the U.S. economy is projected to go for health care. The bar graph shows the percentage of the U.S. gross domestic product (GDP) going toward health care from 2007 through 2010, with projections for 2014 and 2019.

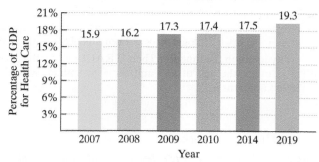

Percentage of the Gross Domestic Product in the United States Going Toward Health Care

Source: Health Affairs (healthaffairs.org)

The data can be modeled by the function $f(x) = 1.2\ln x + 15.7$, where $f(x)$ is the percentage of the U.S. gross domestic product going toward health care x years after 2006. Use this information to solve Exercises 115–116.

115. a. Use the function to determine the percentage of the U.S. gross domestic product that went toward health care in 2009. Round to the nearest tenth of a percent. Does this underestimate or overestimate the percent displayed by the graph? By how much?

   b. According to the model, when will 18.5% of the U.S. gross domestic product go toward health care? Round to the nearest year.

116. a. Use the function to determine the percentage of the U.S. gross domestic product that went toward health care in 2008. Round to the nearest tenth of a percent. Does this underestimate or overestimate the percent displayed by the graph? By how much?

   b. According to the model, when will 18.6% of the U.S. gross domestic product go toward health care? Round to the nearest year.

The function $P(x) = 95 - 30\log_2 x$ models the percentage, $P(x)$, of students who could recall the important features of a classroom lecture as a function of time, where x represents the number of days that have elapsed since the lecture was given. The figure shows the graph of the function. Use this information to solve Exercises 117–118. Round answers to one decimal place.

$P(x) = 95 - 30\log_2 x$

117. After how many days do only half the students recall the important features of the classroom lecture? (Let $P(x) = 50$ and solve for x.) Locate the point on the graph that conveys this information.

118. After how many days have all students forgotten the important features of the classroom lecture? (Let $P(x) = 0$ and solve for x.) Locate the point on the graph that conveys this information.

The pH scale is used to measure the acidity or alkalinity of a solution. The scale ranges from 0 to 14. A neutral solution, such as pure water, has a pH of 7. An acid solution has a pH less than 7 and an alkaline solution has a pH greater than 7. The lower the pH below 7, the more acidic is the solution. Each whole-number decrease in pH represents a tenfold increase in acidity.

The pH Scale

The pH of a solution is given by

$$\text{pH} = -\log x,$$

where x represents the concentration of the hydrogen ions in the solution, in moles per liter. Use the formula to solve Exercises 119–120. Express answers as powers of 10.

119. a. Normal, unpolluted rain has a pH of about 5.6. What is the hydrogen ion concentration?

 b. An environmental concern involves the destructive effects of acid rain. The most acidic rainfall ever had a pH of 2.4. What was the hydrogen ion concentration?

 c. How many times greater is the hydrogen ion concentration of the acidic rainfall in part (b) than the normal rainfall in part (a)?

120. a. The figure indicates that lemon juice has a pH of 2.3. What is the hydrogen ion concentration?

 b. Stomach acid has a pH that ranges from 1 to 3. What is the hydrogen ion concentration of the most acidic stomach?

 c. How many times greater is the hydrogen ion concentration of the acidic stomach in part (b) than the lemon juice in part (a)?

Writing in Mathematics

121. Explain how to solve an exponential equation when both sides can be written as a power of the same base.

122. Explain how to solve an exponential equation when both sides cannot be written as a power of the same base. Use $3^x = 140$ in your explanation.

123. Explain the differences between solving $\log_3(x - 1) = 4$ and $\log_3(x - 1) = \log_3 4$.

124. In many states, a 17% risk of a car accident with a blood alcohol concentration of 0.08 is the lowest level for charging a motorist with driving under the influence. Do you agree with the 17% risk as a cutoff percentage, or do you feel that the percentage should be lower or higher? Explain your answer. What blood alcohol concentration corresponds to what you believe is an appropriate percentage?

Technology Exercises

In Exercises 125–132, use your graphing utility to graph each side of the equation in the same viewing rectangle. Then use the x-coordinate of the intersection point to find the equation's solution set. Verify this value by direct substitution into the equation.

125. $2^{x+1} = 8$

126. $3^{x+1} = 9$

127. $\log_3(4x - 7) = 2$

128. $\log_3(3x - 2) = 2$

129. $\log(x + 3) + \log x = 1$

130. $\log(x - 15) + \log x = 2$

131. $3^x = 2x + 3$

132. $5^x = 3x + 4$

Hurricanes are one of nature's most destructive forces. These low-pressure areas often have diameters of over 500 miles. The function $f(x) = 0.48 \ln(x + 1) + 27$ models the barometric air pressure, $f(x)$, in inches of mercury, at a distance of x miles from the eye of a hurricane. Use this function to solve Exercises 133–134.

133. Graph the function in a [0, 500, 50] by [27, 30, 1] viewing rectangle. What does the shape of the graph indicate about barometric air pressure as the distance from the eye increases?

134. Use an equation to answer this question: How far from the eye of a hurricane is the barometric air pressure 29 inches of mercury? Use the TRACE and ZOOM features or the intersect command of your graphing utility to verify your answer.

135. The function $P(t) = 145e^{-0.092t}$ models a runner's pulse, $P(t)$, in beats per minute, t minutes after a race, where $0 \le t \le 15$. Graph the function using a graphing utility. TRACE along the graph and determine after how many minutes the runner's pulse will be 70 beats per minute. Round to the nearest tenth of a minute. Verify your observation algebraically.

136. The function $W(t) = 2600(1 - 0.51e^{-0.075t})^3$ models the weight, $W(t)$, in kilograms, of a female African elephant at age t years. (1 kilogram ≈ 2.2 pounds) Use a graphing utility to graph the function. Then TRACE along the curve to estimate the age of an adult female elephant weighing 1800 kilograms.

Critical Thinking Exercises

Make Sense? *In Exercises 137–140, determine whether each statement makes sense or does not make sense, and explain your reasoning.*

137. Because the equations $2^x = 15$ and $2^x = 16$ are similar, I solved them using the same method.

138. Because the equations

$$\log(3x + 1) = 5 \text{ and } \log(3x + 1) = \log 5$$

are similar, I solved them using the same method.

139. I can solve $4^x = 15$ by writing the equation in logarithmic form.

140. It's important for me to check that the proposed solution of an equation with logarithms gives only logarithms of positive numbers in the original equation.

In Exercises 141–144, determine whether each statement is true or false. If the statement is false, make the necessary change(s) to produce a true statement.

141. If $\log(x + 3) = 2$, then $e^2 = x + 3$.

142. If $\log(7x + 3) - \log(2x + 5) = 4$, then the equation in exponential form is $10^4 = (7x + 3) - (2x + 5)$.

143. If $x = \dfrac{1}{k} \ln y$, then $y = e^{kx}$.

144. Examples of exponential equations include $10^x = 5.71$, $e^x = 0.72$, and $x^{10} = 5.71$.

145. If $4000 is deposited into an account paying 3% interest compounded annually and at the same time $2000 is deposited into an account paying 5% interest compounded annually, after how long will the two accounts have the same balance? Round to the nearest year.

Solve each equation in Exercises 146–148. Check each proposed solution by direct substitution or with a graphing utility.

146. $(\ln x)^2 = \ln x^2$

147. $(\log x)(2 \log x + 1) = 6$

148. $\ln(\ln x) = 0$

Group Exercise

149. Research applications of logarithmic functions as mathematical models and plan a seminar based on your group's research. Each group member should research one of the following areas or any other area of interest: pH (acidity of solutions), intensity of sound (decibels), brightness of stars, human memory, progress over time in a sport, profit over time. For the area that you select, explain how logarithmic functions are used and provide examples.

Preview Exercises

Exercises 150–152 will help you prepare for the material covered in the next section.

150. The formula $A = 10e^{-0.003t}$ models the population of Hungary, A, in millions, t years after 2006.

    a. Find Hungary's population, in millions, for 2006, 2007, 2008, and 2009. Round to two decimal places.

    b. Is Hungary's population increasing or decreasing?

151. **a.** Simplify: $e^{\ln 3}$.

    b. Use your simplification from part (a) to rewrite 3^x in terms of base e.

152. U.S. soldiers fight Russian troops who have invaded New York City. Incoming missiles from Russian submarines and warships ravage the Manhattan skyline. It's just another scenario for the multi-billion-dollar video games *Call of Duty*, which have sold more than 100 million games since the franchise's birth in 2003.

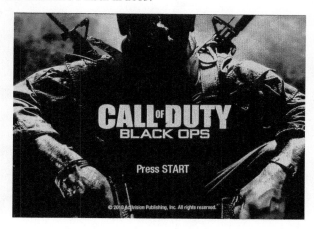

The table shows the annual retail sales for *Call of Duty* video games from 2004 through 2010. Create a scatter plot for the data. Based on the shape of the scatter plot, would a logarithmic function, an exponential function, or a linear function be the best choice for modeling the data?

Annual Retail Sales for *Call of Duty* Games

Year	Retail Sales (millions of dollars)
2004	56
2005	101
2006	196
2007	352
2008	436
2009	778
2010	980

Source: The NPD Group

SECTION 4.5   Exponential Growth and Decay; Modeling Data

Objectives

1 Model exponential growth and decay.

2 Use logistic growth models.

3 Choose an appropriate model for data.

4 Express an exponential model in base *e*.

On October 31, 2011, the world marked a major milestone: According to the United Nations, the number of people on Earth reached 7 billion—and counting. Since the dawn of humankind some 50,000 years ago, an estimated total of 108 billion people have lived on our planet, which means that about 6.5% of all humans ever born are alive today. That's a lot of bodies to feed, clothe, and shelter. Scientists, politicians, economists, and demographers have long disagreed when it comes to making predictions about the effects of the world's growing population. Debates about entities that are growing exponentially can be approached mathematically: We can create functions that model data and use these functions to make predictions. In this section, we will show you how this is done.

1   Model exponential growth and decay.

Exponential Growth and Decay

One of algebra's many applications is to predict the behavior of variables. This can be done with *exponential growth* and *decay models*. With exponential growth or decay, quantities grow or decay at a rate directly proportional to their size. Populations that are growing exponentially grow extremely rapidly as they get larger because there are more adults to have offspring. For example, world population is increasing at approximately 1.2% per year. This means that each year world population is 1.2% more than what it was in the previous year. In 2010, world population was 6.9 billion. Thus, we compute the world population in 2011 as follows:

$$6.9 \text{ billion} + 1.2\% \text{ of } 6.9 \text{ billion} = 6.9 + (0.012)(6.9) = 6.9828.$$

This computation indicates that 6.9828 billion people populated the world in 2011. The 0.0828 billion represents an increase of 82.8 million people from 2010 to 2011, the equivalent of the population of Germany. Using 1.2% as the annual rate of increase, world population for 2012 is found in a similar manner:

$$6.9828 + 1.2\% \text{ of } 6.9828 = 6.9828 + (0.012)(6.9828) \approx 7.067.$$

This computation indicates that approximately 7.1 billion people populated the world in 2012.

The explosive growth of world population may remind you of the growth of money in an account subject to compound interest. Just as the growth rate for world population is multiplied by the population plus any increase in the population, a compound interest rate is multiplied by the original investment plus any accumulated interest. The balance in an account subject to continuous compounding and world population are special cases of *exponential growth models*.

Exponential Growth and Decay Models

The mathematical model for **exponential growth** or **decay** is given by

$$f(t) = A_0e^{kt} \quad \text{or} \quad A = A_0e^{kt}.$$

- **If $k > 0$, the function models the amount, or size, of a *growing* entity.** A_0 is the original amount, or size, of the growing entity at time $t = 0$, A is the amount at time t, and k is a constant representing the growth rate.

- **If $k < 0$, the function models the amount, or size, of a *decaying* entity.** A_0 is the original amount, or size, of the decaying entity at time $t = 0$, A is the amount at time t, and k is a constant representing the decay rate.

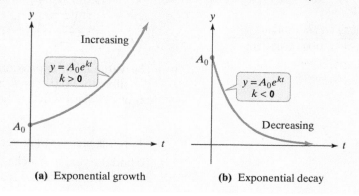

(a) Exponential growth   **(b)** Exponential decay

Sometimes we need to use given data to determine k, the rate of growth or decay. After we compute the value of k, we can use the formula $A = A_0e^{kt}$ to make predictions. This idea is illustrated in our first two examples.

EXAMPLE 1 Modeling the Growth of the U.S. Population

The graph in **Figure 4.22** shows the U.S. population, in millions, for five selected years from 1970 through 2010. In 1970, the U.S. population was 203.3 million. By 2010, it had grown to 308.7 million.

a. Find an exponential growth function that models the data for 1970 through 2010.

b. By which year will the U.S. population reach 335 million?

SOLUTION

a. We use the exponential growth model

$$A = A_0e^{kt}$$

in which t is the number of years after 1970. This means that 1970 corresponds to $t = 0$. At that time the U.S. population was 203.3 million, so we substitute 203.3 for A_0 in the growth model:

$$A = 203.3e^{kt}.$$

We are given that 308.7 million was the population in 2010. Because 2010 is 40 years after 1970, when $t = 40$ the value of A is 308.7. Substituting these numbers into the growth model will enable us to find k, the growth rate. We know that $k > 0$ because the problem involves growth.

U.S. Population, 1970–2010

Population (millions)

350	
300	308.7
250	281.4
200	248.7
150	226.5
100	203.3
50	

1970 1980 1990 2000 2010
Year

FIGURE 4.22
Source: U.S. Census Bureau

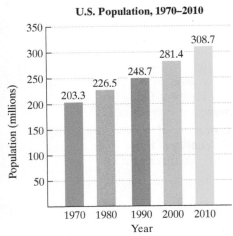

U.S. Population, 1970–2010

FIGURE 4.22 (repeated)

$$A = 203.3e^{kt}$$
$$308.7 = 203.3e^{k \cdot 40}$$

Use the growth model with $A_0 = 203.3$. When $t = 40$, $A = 308.7$. Substitute these numbers into the model.

$$e^{40k} = \frac{308.7}{203.3}$$

Isolate the exponential factor by dividing both sides by 203.3. We also reversed the sides.

$$\ln e^{40k} = \ln\left(\frac{308.7}{203.3}\right)$$

Take the natural logarithm on both sides.

$$40k = \ln\left(\frac{308.7}{203.3}\right)$$

Simplify the left side using $\ln e^x = x$.

$$k = \frac{\ln\left(\dfrac{308.7}{203.3}\right)}{40} \approx 0.01$$

Divide both sides by 40 and solve for k. Then use a calculator.

The value of k, approximately 0.01, indicates a growth rate of about 1%. We substitute 0.01 for k in the growth model, $A = 203.3e^{kt}$, to obtain an exponential growth function for the U.S. population. It is

$$A = 203.3e^{0.01t},$$

where t is measured in years after 1970.

b. To find the year in which the U.S. population will reach 335 million, substitute 335 for A in the model from part (a) and solve for t.

$$A = 203.3e^{0.01t}$$

This is the model from part (a).

$$335 = 203.3e^{0.01t}$$

Substitute 335 for A.

$$e^{0.01t} = \frac{335}{203.3}$$

Divide both sides by 203.3. We also reversed the sides.

$$\ln e^{0.01t} = \ln\left(\frac{335}{203.3}\right)$$

Take the natural logarithm on both sides.

$$0.01t = \ln\left(\frac{335}{203.3}\right)$$

Simplify on the left using $\ln e^x = x$.

$$t = \frac{\ln\left(\dfrac{335}{203.3}\right)}{0.01} \approx 50$$

Divide both sides by 0.01 and solve for t. Then use a calculator.

Because t represents the number of years after 1970, the model indicates that the U.S. population will reach 335 million by 1970 + 50, or in the year 2020. • • •

In Example 1, we used only two data values, the population for 1970 and the population for 2010, to develop a model for U.S. population growth from 1970 through 2010. By not using data for any other years, have we created a model that inaccurately describes both the existing data and future population projections given by the U.S. Census Bureau? Something else to think about: Is an exponential model the best choice for describing U.S. population growth, or might a linear model provide a better description? We return to these issues in Exercises 66–70 in the Exercise Set.

 Check Point **1** In 2000, the population of Africa was 807 million and by 2011 it had grown to 1052 million.

a. Use the exponential growth model $A = A_0e^{kt}$, in which t is the number of years after 2000, to find the exponential growth function that models the data.

b. By which year will Africa's population reach 2000 million, or two billion?

Our next example involves exponential decay and its use in determining the age of fossils and artifacts. The method is based on considering the percentage of carbon-14 remaining in the fossil or artifact. Carbon-14 decays exponentially with a *half-life* of approximately 5715 years. The **half-life** of a substance is the time required for half of a given sample to disintegrate. Thus, after 5715 years a given amount of carbon-14 will have decayed to half the original amount. Carbon dating is useful for artifacts or fossils up to 80,000 years old. Older objects do not have enough carbon-14 left to determine age accurately.

EXAMPLE 2   Carbon-14 Dating: The Dead Sea Scrolls

a. Use the fact that after 5715 years a given amount of carbon-14 will have decayed to half the original amount to find the exponential decay model for carbon-14.

b. In 1947, earthenware jars containing what are known as the Dead Sea Scrolls were found by an Arab Bedouin herdsman. Analysis indicated that the scroll wrappings contained 76% of their original carbon-14. Estimate the age of the Dead Sea Scrolls.

SOLUTION

a. We begin with the exponential decay model $A = A_0 e^{kt}$. We know that $k < 0$ because the problem involves the decay of carbon-14. After 5715 years ($t = 5715$), the amount of carbon-14 present, A, is half the original amount, A_0.

Thus, we can substitute $\dfrac{A_0}{2}$ for A in the exponential decay model. This will enable us to find k, the decay rate.

$$A = A_0 e^{kt}$$ Begin with the exponential decay model.

$$\frac{A_0}{2} = A_0 e^{k5715}$$ After 5715 years ($t = 5715$), $A = \dfrac{A_0}{2}$

(because the amount present, A, is half the original amount, A_0).

$$\frac{1}{2} = e^{5715k}$$ Divide both sides of the equation by A_0.

$$\ln\left(\frac{1}{2}\right) = \ln e^{5715k}$$ Take the natural logarithm on both sides.

$$\ln\left(\frac{1}{2}\right) = 5715k$$ Simplify the right side using $\ln e^x = x$.

$$k = \frac{\ln\left(\frac{1}{2}\right)}{5715} \approx -0.000121$$ Divide both sides by 5715 and solve for k.

Substituting -0.000121 for k in the decay model, $A = A_0 e^{kt}$, the model for carbon-14 is

$$A = A_0 e^{-0.000121t}.$$

b. In 1947, the Dead Sea Scrolls contained 76% of their original carbon-14. To find their age in 1947, substitute $0.76A_0$ for A in the model from part (a) and solve for t.

$$A = A_0 e^{-0.000121t}$$ This is the decay model for carbon-14.

$$0.76A_0 = A_0 e^{-0.000121t}$$ A, the amount present, is 76% of the original amount, so $A = 0.76A_0$.

$$0.76 = e^{-0.000121t}$$ Divide both sides of the equation by A_0.

$$\ln 0.76 = \ln e^{-0.000121t}$$ Take the natural logarithm on both sides.

$$\ln 0.76 = -0.000121t$$ Simplify the right side using $\ln e^x = x$.

$$t = \frac{\ln 0.76}{-0.000121} \approx 2268$$ Divide both sides by -0.000121 and solve for t.

The Dead Sea Scrolls are approximately 2268 years old plus the number of years between 1947 and the current year.

● ● ●

Blitzer Bonus

Carbon Dating and Artistic Development

The artistic community was electrified by the discovery in 1995 of spectacular cave paintings in a limestone cavern in France. Carbon dating of the charcoal from the site showed that the images, created by artists of remarkable talent, were 30,000 years old, making them the oldest cave paintings ever found. The artists seemed to have used the cavern's natural contours to heighten a sense of perspective. The quality of the painting suggests that the art of early humans did not mature steadily from primitive to sophisticated in any simple linear fashion.

✓ Check Point **2** Strontium-90 is a waste product from nuclear reactors. As a consequence of fallout from atmospheric nuclear tests, we all have a measurable amount of strontium-90 in our bones.

    a. The half-life of strontium-90 is 28 years, meaning that after 28 years a given amount of the substance will have decayed to half the original amount. Find the exponential decay model for strontium-90.

    b. Suppose that a nuclear accident occurs and releases 60 grams of strontium-90 into the atmosphere. How long will it take for strontium-90 to decay to a level of 10 grams?

② Use logistic growth models.

Logistic Growth Models

From population growth to the spread of an epidemic, nothing on Earth can grow exponentially indefinitely. Growth is always limited. This is shown in **Figure 4.23** by the horizontal asymptote. The *logistic growth model* is a function used to model situations of this type.

Logistic Growth Model

The mathematical model for limited logistic growth is given by

$$f(t) = \frac{c}{1 + ae^{-bt}} \quad \text{or} \quad A = \frac{c}{1 + ae^{-bt}},$$

where a, b, and c are constants, with $c > 0$ and $b > 0$.

As time increases ($t \rightarrow \infty$), the expression ae^{-bt} in the model approaches 0, and A gets closer and closer to c. This means that $y = c$ is a horizontal asymptote for the graph of the function. Thus, the value of A can never exceed c and c represents the limiting size that A can attain.

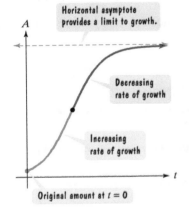

FIGURE 4.23 The logistic growth curve has a horizontal asymptote that identifies the limit of the growth of A over time.

EXAMPLE 3   Modeling the Spread of the Flu

The function

$$f(t) = \frac{30{,}000}{1 + 20e^{-1.5t}}$$

describes the number of people, $f(t)$, who have become ill with influenza t weeks after its initial outbreak in a town with 30,000 inhabitants.

    a. How many people became ill with the flu when the epidemic began?

    b. How many people were ill by the end of the fourth week?

    c. What is the limiting size of $f(t)$, the population that becomes ill?

SOLUTION

    a. The time at the beginning of the flu epidemic is $t = 0$. Thus, we can find the number of people who were ill at the beginning of the epidemic by substituting 0 for t.

$$f(t) = \frac{30{,}000}{1 + 20e^{-1.5t}} \qquad \text{This is the given logistic growth function.}$$

$$f(0) = \frac{30{,}000}{1 + 20e^{-1.5(0)}} \qquad \text{When the epidemic began, } t = 0.$$

$$= \frac{30{,}000}{1 + 20} \qquad e^{-1.5(0)} = e^0 = 1$$

$$\approx 1429$$

Approximately 1429 people were ill when the epidemic began.

The graph of the logistic growth function for the flu epidemic

$$y = \frac{30,000}{1 + 20e^{-1.5x}}$$

can be obtained using a graphing utility. We started x at 0 and ended at 10. This takes us to week 10. (In Example 3, we found that by week 4 approximately 28,583 people were ill.) We also know that 30,000 is the limiting size, so we took values of y up to 30,000. Using a $[0, 10, 1]$ by $[0, 30,000, 3000]$ viewing rectangle, the graph of the logistic growth function is shown below.

b. We find the number of people who were ill at the end of the fourth week by substituting 4 for t in the logistic growth function.

$$f(t) = \frac{30,000}{1 + 20e^{-1.5t}} \quad \text{Use the given logistic growth function.}$$

$$f(4) = \frac{30,000}{1 + 20e^{-1.5(4)}} \quad \text{To find the number of people ill by the end of week four, let } t = 4.$$

$$\approx 28,583 \quad \text{Use a calculator.}$$

Approximately 28,583 people were ill by the end of the fourth week. Compared with the number of people who were ill initially, 1429, this illustrates the virulence of the epidemic.

c. Recall that in the logistic growth model, $f(t) = \dfrac{c}{1 + ae^{-bt}}$, the constant c represents the limiting size that $f(t)$ can attain. Thus, the number in the numerator, 30,000, is the limiting size of the population that becomes ill. ●●●

⊘ Check Point **3**   In a learning theory project, psychologists discovered that

$$f(t) = \frac{0.8}{1 + e^{-0.2t}}$$

is a model for describing the proportion of correct responses, $f(t)$, after t learning trials.

a. Find the proportion of correct responses prior to learning trials taking place.

b. Find the proportion of correct responses after 10 learning trials.

c. What is the limiting size of $f(t)$, the proportion of correct responses, as continued learning trials take place?

③ Choose an appropriate model for data.

Modeling Data

Throughout this chapter, we have been working with models that were given. However, we can create functions that model data by observing patterns in scatter plots. **Figure 4.24** shows scatter plots for data that are exponential, logarithmic, and linear.

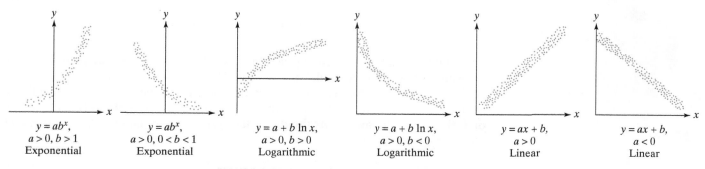

$y = ab^x$,
$a > 0, b > 1$
Exponential

$y = ab^x$,
$a > 0, 0 < b < 1$
Exponential

$y = a + b \ln x$,
$a > 0, b > 0$
Logarithmic

$y = a + b \ln x$,
$a > 0, b < 0$
Logarithmic

$y = ax + b$,
$a > 0$
Linear

$y = ax + b$,
$a < 0$
Linear

FIGURE 4.24   Scatter plots for exponential, logarithmic, and linear models

Table 4.6 Growth of the Human Brain

Age	Percentage of Adult Size Brain
1	30%
2	50%
4	78%
6	88%
8	92%
10	95%
11	99%

Source: Gerrig and Zimbardo, *Psychology and Life*, 18th Edition, Allyn and Bacon, 2008.

EXAMPLE 4 Choosing a Model for Data

The data in **Table 4.6** indicate that between the ages of 1 and 11, the human brain does not grow linearly, or steadily. A scatter plot for the data is shown in **Figure 4.25**. What type of function would be a good choice for modeling the data?

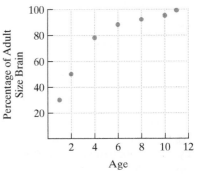

FIGURE 4.25

SOLUTION

Because the data in the scatter plot increase rapidly at first and then begin to level off a bit, the shape suggests that a logarithmic function is a good choice for modeling the data.   • • •

 Check Point **4** **Table 4.7** shows the populations of various cities, in thousands, and the average walking speed, in feet per second, of a person living in the city. Create a scatter plot for the data. Based on the scatter plot, what type of function would be a good choice for modeling the data?

Table 4.7 Population and Walking Speed

Population (thousands)	Walking Speed (feet per second)
5.5	0.6
14	1.0
71	1.6
138	1.9
342	2.2

Source: Mark H. Bornstein and Helen G. Bornstein, "The Pace of Life." *Nature*, 259, Feb. 19, 1976, pp. 557–559

Table 4.8

x, Age	y, Percentage of Adult Size Brain
1	30
2	50
4	78
6	88
8	92
10	95
11	99

```
LnReg
y=a+blnx
a=31.95404756
b=28.94733911
r²=.9806647799
r=.9902852013
```

FIGURE 4.26 A logarithmic model for the data in **Table 4.8**

How can we obtain a logarithmic function that models the data for the growth of the human brain? A graphing utility can be used to obtain a logarithmic model of the form $y = a + b \ln x$. **Because the domain of the logarithmic function is the set of positive numbers, zero must not be a value for x.** This is not a problem for the data giving the percentage of an adult size brain because the data begin at age 1. We will assign x to represent age and y to represent the percentage of an adult size brain. This gives us the data shown in **Table 4.8**. Using the logarithmic regression option, we obtain the equation in **Figure 4.26**.

From **Figure 4.26**, we see that the logarithmic model of the data, with numbers rounded to three decimal places, is

$$y = 31.954 + 28.947 \ln x.$$

The number r that appears in **Figure 4.26** is called the **correlation coefficient** and is a measure of how well the model fits the data. The value of r is such that $-1 \leq r \leq 1$. A positive r means that as the x-values increase, so do the y-values. A negative r means that as the x-values increase, the y-values decrease. **The closer that r is to -1 or 1, the better the model fits the data.** Because r is approximately 0.99, the model fits the data very well.

EXAMPLE 5 Choosing a Model for Data

Figure 4.27(a) shows world population, in billions, for seven selected years from 1950 through 2010. A scatter plot is shown in **Figure 4.27(b)**. Suggest two types of functions that would be good choices for modeling the data.

World Population, 1950–2010

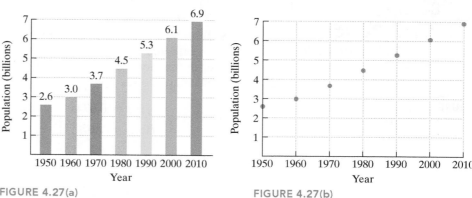

FIGURE 4.27(a)　　　　　　　　FIGURE 4.27(b)

Source: U.S. Census Bureau, International Database

Table 4.9　Percentage of U.S. Men Who Are Married or Who Have Been Married, by Age

Age	Percent
18	2
20	7
25	36
30	61
35	75

Source: National Center for Health Statistics

SOLUTION

Because the data in the scatter plot appear to increase more and more rapidly, the shape suggests that an exponential model might be a good choice. Furthermore, we can probably draw a line that passes through or near the seven points. Thus, a linear function would also be a good choice for modeling the data.　●●●

⊘ Check Point **5**　**Table 4.9** shows the percentage of U.S. men who are married or who have been married, by age. Create a scatter plot for the data. Based on the scatter plot, what type of function would be a good choice for modeling the data?

EXAMPLE 6 Comparing Linear and Exponential Models

The data for world population are shown in **Table 4.10**. Using a graphing utility's linear regression feature and exponential regression feature, we enter the data and obtain the models shown in **Figure 4.28**.

Table 4.10

> Although the domain of $y = ab^x$ is the set of all real numbers, some graphing utilities only accept positive values for x. That's why we assigned x to represent the number of years after 1949.

x, Number of Years after 1949	y, World Population (billions)
1 (1950)	2.6
11 (1960)	3.0
21 (1970)	3.7
31 (1980)	4.5
41 (1990)	5.3
51 (2000)	6.1
61 (2010)	6.9

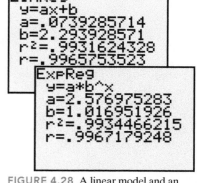

FIGURE 4.28　A linear model and an exponential model for the data in **Table 4.10**

Because *r*, the correlation coefficient, is close to 1 in each screen in **Figure 4.28**, the models fit the data very well.

a. Use **Figure 4.28** to express each model in function notation, with numbers rounded to three decimal places.

b. How well do the functions model world population in 2000?

c. By one projection, world population is expected to reach 8 billion in the year 2026. Which function serves as a better model for this prediction?

FIGURE 4.28 (repeated) A linear model and an exponential model for world population

GREAT QUESTION!

How can I use a graphing utility to see how well my models describe the data?

Once you have obtained one or more models for the data, you can use a graphing utility's TABLE feature to numerically see how well each model describes the data. Enter the models as y_1, y_2, and so on. Create a table, scroll through the table, and compare the table values given by the models to the actual data.

SOLUTION

a. Using **Figure 4.28** and rounding to three decimal places, the functions

$$f(x) = 0.074x + 2.294 \quad \text{and} \quad g(x) = 2.577(1.017)^x$$

model world population, in billions, x years after 1949. We named the linear function f and the exponential function g, although any letters can be used.

b. **Table 4.10** on the previous page shows that world population in 2000 was 6.1 billion. The year 2000 is 51 years after 1949. Thus, we substitute 51 for x in each function's equation and then evaluate the resulting expressions with a calculator to see how well the functions describe world population in 2000.

$f(x) = 0.074x + 2.294$	This is the linear model.
$f(51) = 0.074(51) + 2.294$	Substitute 51 for x.
≈ 6.1	Use a calculator.
$g(x) = 2.577(1.017)^x$	This is the exponential model.
$g(51) = 2.577(1.017)^{51}$	Substitute 51 for x.
≈ 6.1	Use a calculator: 2.577 $\times$ 1.017 y^x (or $\wedge$) 51 $=$.

Because 6.1 billion was the actual world population in 2000, both functions model world population in 2000 extremely well.

c. Let's see which model comes closer to projecting a world population of 8 billion in the year 2026. Because 2026 is 77 years after 1949 $(2026 - 1949 = 77)$, we substitute 77 for x in each function's equation.

$f(x) = 0.074x + 2.294$	This is the linear model.
$f(77) = 0.074(77) + 2.294$	Substitute 77 for x.
≈ 8.0	Use a calculator.
$g(x) = 2.577(1.017)^x$	This is the exponential model.
$g(77) = 2.577(1.017)^{77}$	Substitute 77 for x.
≈ 9.4	Use a calculator: 2.577 $\times$ 1.017 y^x (or $\wedge$) 77 $=$.

The linear function $f(x) = 0.074x + 2.294$ serves as a better model for a projected world population of 8 billion by 2026. • • •

 Check Point 6 Use the models $f(x) = 0.074x + 2.294$ and $g(x) = 2.577(1.017)^x$ to solve this problem.

a. World population in 1970 was 3.7 billion. Which function serves as a better model for this year?

b. By one projection, world population is expected to reach 9.3 billion by 2050. Which function serves as a better model for this projection?

When using a graphing utility to model data, begin with a scatter plot, drawn either by hand or with the graphing utility, to obtain a general picture for the shape of the data. It might be difficult to determine which model best fits the data—linear, logarithmic, exponential, quadratic, or something else. If necessary, use your graphing utility to fit several models to the data. The best model is the one that yields the value r, the correlation coefficient, closest to 1 or -1. Finding a proper fit for data can be almost as much art as it is mathematics. In this era of technology, the process of creating models that best fit data is one that involves more decision making than computation.

4 Express an exponential model in base e.

Expressing $y = ab^x$ in Base e

Graphing utilities display exponential models in the form $y = ab^x$. However, our discussion of exponential growth involved base e. Because of the inverse property $b = e^{\ln b}$, we can rewrite any model in the form $y = ab^x$ in terms of base e.

Expressing an Exponential Model in Base e

$$y = ab^x \quad \text{is equivalent to} \quad y = ae^{(\ln b) \cdot x}.$$

EXAMPLE 7   Rewriting the Model for World Population in Base e

We have seen that the function

$$g(x) = 2.577(1.017)^x$$

models world population, $g(x)$, in billions, x years after 1949. Rewrite the model in terms of base e.

SOLUTION

We use the two equivalent equations shown in the voice balloons to rewrite the model in terms of base e.

$$y = ab^x \qquad\qquad y = ae^{(\ln b) \cdot x}$$

$$g(x) = 2.577(1.017)^x \quad \text{is equivalent to} \quad g(x) = 2.577e^{(\ln 1.017)x}.$$

Using $\ln 1.017 \approx 0.017$, the exponential growth model for world population, $g(x)$, in billions, x years after 1949 is

$$g(x) = 2.577e^{0.017x}. \qquad \bullet\bullet\bullet$$

In Example 7, we can replace $g(x)$ with A and x with t so that the model has the same letters as those in the exponential growth model $A = A_0e^{kt}$.

$$A = \boxed{A_o} \; e^{kt} \qquad \text{This is the exponential growth model.}$$

$$A = 2.577e^{0.017t} \qquad \text{This is the model for world population.}$$

The value of k, 0.017, indicates a growth rate of 1.7%. Although this is an excellent model for the data, we must be careful about making projections about world population using this growth function. Why? World population growth rate is now 1.2%, not 1.7%, so our model will overestimate future populations.

 Check Point **7** Rewrite $y = 4(7.8)^x$ in terms of base e. Express the answer in terms of a natural logarithm and then round to three decimal places.

CONCEPT AND VOCABULARY CHECK

Fill in each blank so that the resulting statement is true.

1. Consider the model for exponential growth or decay given by
$$A = A_0e^{kt}.$$
If k _____, the function models the amount, or size, of a growing entity. If k _____, the function models the amount, or size, of a decaying entity.

2. In the model for exponential growth or decay, the amount, or size, at $t = 0$ is represented by _____. The amount, or size, at time t is represented by _____.

3. Consider the model for limited logistic growth given by
$$A = \frac{c}{1 + ae^{-bt}}.$$
The amount, or size, at time t is represented by _____. This value can never exceed _____.

For each of the scatter plots in Exercises 4–6, determine whether an exponential function, a logarithmic function, or a linear function is the best choice for modeling the data.

4.

5.

6.
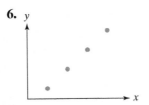

7. $y = 3(5)^x$ can be written in terms of base e as $y = 3e^{(\underline{\quad})\cdot x}$.

EXERCISE SET 4.5

Practice Exercises and Application Exercises

The exponential models describe the population of the indicated country, A, in millions, t years after 2010. Use these models to solve Exercises 1–6.

India $A = 1173.1e^{0.008t}$

Iraq $A = 31.5e^{0.019t}$

Japan $A = 127.3e^{-0.006t}$

Russia $A = 141.9e^{-0.005t}$

1. What was the population of Japan in 2010?
2. What was the population of Iraq in 2010?
3. Which country has the greatest growth rate? By what percentage is the population of that country increasing each year?
4. Which countries have a decreasing population? By what percentage is the population of these countries decreasing each year?
5. When will India's population be 1377 million?
6. When will India's population be 1491 million?

About the size of New Jersey, Israel has seen its population soar to more than 6 million since it was established. The graphs show that by 2050, Palestinians in the West Bank, Gaza Strip, and East Jerusalem will outnumber Israelis. Exercises 7–8 involve the projected growth of these two populations.

Population of Israel

Palestinian Population in West Bank, Gaza, and East Jerusalem

Source: *Newsweek*

7. a. In 2000, the population of Israel was approximately 6.04 million and by 2050 it is projected to grow to 10 million. Use the exponential growth model $A = A_0e^{kt}$, in which t is the number of years after 2000, to find an exponential growth function that models the data.
   b. In which year will Israel's population be 9 million?

8. a. In 2000, the population of the Palestinians in the West Bank, Gaza Strip, and East Jerusalem was approximately 3.2 million and by 2050 it is projected to grow to 12 million. Use the exponential growth model $A = A_0e^{kt}$, in which t is the number of years after 2000, to find the exponential growth function that models the data.
   b. In which year will the Palestinian population be 9 million?

In Exercises 9–14, complete the table. Round projected populations to one decimal place and values of k to four decimal places.

	Country	2010 Population (millions)	Projected 2050 Population (millions)	Projected Growth Rate, k
9.	Philippines	99.9		0.0095
10.	Pakistan	184.4		0.0149
11.	Colombia	44.2	62.9	
12.	Madagascar	21.3	42.7	
13.	Germany	82.3	70.5	
14.	Bulgaria	7.1	5.4	

Source: International Programs Center, U.S. Census Bureau

An artifact originally had 16 grams of carbon-14 present. The decay model $A = 16e^{-0.000121t}$ describes the amount of carbon-14 present after t years. Use this model to solve Exercises 15–16.

15. How many grams of carbon-14 will be present in 5715 years?
16. How many grams of carbon-14 will be present in 11,430 years?
17. The half-life of the radioactive element krypton-91 is 10 seconds. If 16 grams of krypton-91 are initially present, how many grams are present after 10 seconds? 20 seconds? 30 seconds? 40 seconds? 50 seconds?
18. The half-life of the radioactive element plutonium-239 is 25,000 years. If 16 grams of plutonium-239 are initially present, how many grams are present after 25,000 years? 50,000 years? 75,000 years? 100,000 years? 125,000 years?

Use the exponential decay model for carbon-14, $A = A_0 e^{-0.000121t}$, to solve Exercises 19–20.

19. Prehistoric cave paintings were discovered in a cave in France. The paint contained 15% of the original carbon-14. Estimate the age of the paintings.

20. Skeletons were found at a construction site in San Francisco in 1989. The skeletons contained 88% of the expected amount of carbon-14 found in a living person. In 1989, how old were the skeletons?

In Exercises 21–26, complete the table. Round half-lives to one decimal place and values of k to six decimal places.

	Radioactive Substance	Half-Life	Decay Rate, k
21.	Tritium		5.5% per year = −0.055
22.	Krypton-85		6.3% per year = −0.063
23.	Radium-226	1620 years	
24.	Uranium-238	4560 years	
25.	Arsenic-74	17.5 days	
26.	Calcium-47	113 hours	

27. The August 1978 issue of *National Geographic* described the 1964 find of bones of a newly discovered dinosaur weighing 170 pounds, measuring 9 feet, with a 6-inch claw on one toe of each hind foot. The age of the dinosaur was estimated using potassium-40 dating of rocks surrounding the bones.

   a. Potassium-40 decays exponentially with a half-life of approximately 1.31 billion years. Use the fact that after 1.31 billion years a given amount of potassium-40 will have decayed to half the original amount to show that the decay model for potassium-40 is given by $A = A_0 e^{-0.52912t}$, where t is in billions of years.

   b. Analysis of the rocks surrounding the dinosaur bones indicated that 94.5% of the original amount of potassium-40 was still present. Let $A = 0.945A_0$ in the model in part (a) and estimate the age of the bones of the dinosaur.

Use the exponential decay model, $A = A_0 e^{kt}$, to solve Exercises 28–31. Round answers to one decimal place.

28. The half-life of thorium-229 is 7340 years. How long will it take for a sample of this substance to decay to 20% of its original amount?

29. The half-life of lead is 22 years. How long will it take for a sample of this substance to decay to 80% of its original amount?

30. The half-life of aspirin in your bloodstream is 12 hours. How long will it take for the aspirin to decay to 70% of the original dosage?

31. Xanax is a tranquilizer used in the short-term relief of symptoms of anxiety. Its half-life in the bloodstream is 36 hours. How long will it take for Xanax to decay to 90% of the original dosage?

32. A bird species in danger of extinction has a population that is decreasing exponentially ($A = A_0 e^{kt}$). Five years ago the population was at 1400 and today only 1000 of the birds are alive. Once the population drops below 100, the situation will be irreversible. When will this happen?

33. Use the exponential growth model, $A = A_0 e^{kt}$, to show that the time it takes a population to double (to grow from A_0 to $2A_0$) is given by $t = \dfrac{\ln 2}{k}$.

34. Use the exponential growth model, $A = A_0 e^{kt}$, to show that the time it takes a population to triple (to grow from A_0 to $3A_0$) is given by $t = \dfrac{\ln 3}{k}$.

Use the formula $t = \dfrac{\ln 2}{k}$ that gives the time for a population with a growth rate k to double to solve Exercises 35–36. Express each answer to the nearest whole year.

35. The growth model $A = 4.3e^{0.01t}$ describes New Zealand's population, A, in millions, t years after 2010.

   a. What is New Zealand's growth rate?

   b. How long will it take New Zealand to double its population?

36. The growth model $A = 112.5e^{0.012t}$ describes Mexico's population, A, in millions, t years after 2010.

   a. What is Mexico's growth rate?

   b. How long will it take Mexico to double its population?

37. The logistic growth function

$$f(t) = \frac{100,000}{1 + 5000e^{-t}}$$

describes the number of people, $f(t)$, who have become ill with influenza t weeks after its initial outbreak in a particular community.

   a. How many people became ill with the flu when the epidemic began?

   b. How many people were ill by the end of the fourth week?

   c. What is the limiting size of the population that becomes ill?

Shown, again, in the following table is world population, in billions, for seven selected years from 1950 through 2010. Using a graphing utility's logistic regression option, we obtain the equation shown on the screen.

x, Number of Years after 1949	y, World Population (billions)
1 (1950)	2.6
11 (1960)	3.0
21 (1970)	3.7
31 (1980)	4.5
41 (1990)	5.3
51 (2000)	6.1
61 (2010)	6.9

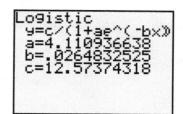

We see from the calculator screen at the bottom of the previous page that a logistic growth model for world population, $f(x)$, in billions, x years after 1949 is

$$f(x) = \frac{12.57}{1 + 4.11e^{-0.026x}}.$$

Use this function to solve Exercises 38–42.

38. How well does the function model the data showing a world population of 6.1 billion for 2000?

39. How well does the function model the data showing a world population of 6.9 billion for 2010?

40. When will world population reach 7 billion?

41. When will world population reach 8 billion?

42. According to the model, what is the limiting size of the population that Earth will eventually sustain?

The logistic growth function

$$P(x) = \frac{90}{1 + 271e^{-0.122x}}$$

models the percentage, $P(x)$, of Americans who are x years old with some coronary heart disease. Use the function to solve Exercises 43–46.

43. What percentage of 20-year-olds have some coronary heart disease?

44. What percentage of 80-year-olds have some coronary heart disease?

45. At what age is the percentage of some coronary heart disease 50%?

46. At what age is the percentage of some coronary heart disease 70%?

Exercises 47–52 present data in the form of tables. For each data set shown by the table,

   a. Create a scatter plot for the data.

   b. Use the scatter plot to determine whether an exponential function, a logarithmic function, or a linear function is the best choice for modeling the data. (If applicable, in Exercise 72, you will use your graphing utility to obtain these functions.)

47. Percent of Miscarriages, by Age

Woman's Age	Percent of Miscarriages
22	9%
27	10%
32	13%
37	20%
42	38%
47	52%

Source: *Time*

48. Savings Needed for Health-Care Expenses during Retirement

Age at Death	Savings Needed
80	$219,000
85	$307,000
90	$409,000
95	$524,000
100	$656,000

Source: Employee Benefit Research Institute

49. Intensity and Loudness Level of Various Sounds

Intensity (watts per meter^2)	Loudness Level (decibels)
0.1 (loud thunder)	110
1 (rock concert, 2 yd from speakers)	120
10 (jackhammer)	130
100 (jet takeoff, 40 yd away)	140

50. Temperature Increase in an Enclosed Vehicle

Minutes	Temperature Increase (°F)
10	19°
20	29°
30	34°
40	38°
50	41°
60	43°

51. Dads Raising Kids Alone

Year	Number of Single U.S. Fathers Heading Households with Children Younger Than 18 (millions)
1980	0.6
1990	1.2
2000	1.8
2010	2.5

Source: U.S. Census Bureau

52. Percentage of Births to Unmarried Women in the United States

Year	Percentage of Births
1960	5%
1970	11%
1980	18%
1990	28%
2000	33%
2009	41%

Source: National Center for Health Statistics

In Exercises 53–56, rewrite the equation in terms of base e. Express the answer in terms of a natural logarithm and then round to three decimal places.

53. $y = 100(4.6)^x$ **54.** $y = 1000(7.3)^x$

55. $y = 2.5(0.7)^x$ **56.** $y = 4.5(0.6)^x$

Writing in Mathematics

57. Nigeria has a growth rate of 0.025 or 2.5%. Describe what this means.

58. How can you tell whether an exponential model describes exponential growth or exponential decay?

59. Suppose that a population that is growing exponentially increases from 800,000 people in 2007 to 1,000,000 people in 2010. Without showing the details, describe how to obtain the exponential growth function that models the data.

60. What is the half-life of a substance?

61. Describe a difference between exponential growth and logistic growth.

62. Describe the shape of a scatter plot that suggests modeling the data with an exponential function.

63. You take up weightlifting and record the maximum number of pounds you can lift at the end of each week. You start off with rapid growth in terms of the weight you can lift from week to week, but then the growth begins to level off. Describe how to obtain a function that models the number of pounds you can lift at the end of each week. How can you use this function to predict what might happen if you continue the sport?

64. Would you prefer that your salary be modeled exponentially or logarithmically? Explain your answer.

65. One problem with all exponential growth models is that nothing can grow exponentially forever. Describe factors that might limit the size of a population.

Technology Exercises

In Example 1 on page 495, we used two data points and an exponential function to model the population of the United States from 1970 through 2010. The data are shown again in the table. Use all five data points to solve Exercises 66–70.

x, Number of Years after 1969	y, U.S. Population (millions)
1 (1970)	203.3
11 (1980)	226.5
21 (1990)	248.7
31 (2000)	281.4
41 (2010)	308.7

66. a. Use your graphing utility's exponential regression option to obtain a model of the form $y = ab^x$ that fits the data. How well does the correlation coefficient, r, indicate that the model fits the data?

b. Rewrite the model in terms of base e. By what percentage is the population of the United States increasing each year?

67. Use your graphing utility's logarithmic regression option to obtain a model of the form $y = a + b \ln x$ that fits the data. How well does the correlation coefficient, r, indicate that the model fits the data?

68. Use your graphing utility's linear regression option to obtain a model of the form $y = ax + b$ that fits the data. How well does the correlation coefficient, r, indicate that the model fits the data?

69. Use your graphing utility's power regression option to obtain a model of the form $y = ax^b$ that fits the data. How well does the correlation coefficient, r, indicate that the model fits the data?

70. Use the values of r in Exercises 66–69 to select the two models of best fit. Use each of these models to predict by which year the U.S. population will reach 335 million. How do these answers compare to the year we found in Example 1, namely 2020? If you obtained different years, how do you account for this difference?

71. The figure shows the number of people in the United States age 65 and over, with projected figures for the year 2020 and beyond.

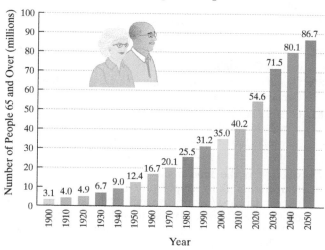

Source: U.S. Census Bureau

a. Let x represent the number of years after 1899 and let y represent the U.S. population age 65 and over, in millions. Use your graphing utility to find the model that best fits the data in the bar graph.

b. Rewrite the model in terms of base e. By what percentage is the 65 and over population increasing each year?

72. In Exercises 47–52, you determined the best choice for the kind of function that modeled the data in the table. For each of the exercises that you worked, use a graphing utility to find the actual function that best fits the data. Then use the model to make a reasonable prediction for a value that exceeds those shown in the table's first column.

Critical Thinking Exercises

Make Sense? *In Exercises 73–76, determine whether each statement makes sense or does not make sense, and explain your reasoning.*

73. I used an exponential model with a positive growth rate to describe the depreciation in my car's value over four years.

74. After 100 years, a population whose growth rate is 3% will have three times as many people as a population whose growth rate is 1%.

75. When I used an exponential function to model Russia's declining population, the growth rate k was negative.

76. Because carbon-14 decays exponentially, carbon dating can determine the ages of ancient fossils.

The exponential growth models describe the population of the indicated country, A, in millions, t years after 2006.

Canada $A = 33.1e^{0.009t}$

Uganda $A = 28.2e^{0.034t}$

In Exercises 77–80, use this information to determine whether each statement is true or false. If the statement is false, make the necessary change(s) to produce a true statement.

(In Exercises 77–80, be sure to refer to the information at the bottom of the previous page.)

77. In 2006, Canada's population exceeded Uganda's by 4.9 million.

78. By 2009, the models indicate that Canada's population will exceed Uganda's by approximately 2.8 million.

79. The models indicate that in 2013, Uganda's population will exceed Canada's.

80. Uganda's growth rate is approximately 3.8 times that of Canada's.

81. Over a period of time, a hot object cools to the temperature of the surrounding air. This is described mathematically by Newton's Law of Cooling:
$$T = C + (T_0 - C)e^{-kt},$$
where t is the time it takes for an object to cool from temperature T_0 to temperature T, C is the surrounding air temperature, and k is a positive constant that is associated with the cooling object. A cake removed from the oven has a temperature of 210°F and is left to cool in a room that has a temperature of 70°F. After 30 minutes, the temperature of the cake is 140°F. What is the temperature of the cake after 40 minutes?

Group Exercise

82. Each group member should consult an almanac, newspaper, magazine, or the Internet to find data that can be modeled by exponential or logarithmic functions. Group members should select the two sets of data that are most interesting and relevant. For each set selected, find a model that best fits the data. Each group member should make one prediction based on the model and then discuss a consequence of this prediction. What factors might change the accuracy of the prediction?

Preview Exercises

Exercises 83–85 will help you prepare for the material covered in the first section of the next chapter.

83. a. Does $(4, -1)$ satisfy $x + 2y = 2$?
  b. Does $(4, -1)$ satisfy $x - 2y = 6$?

84. Graph $x + 2y = 2$ and $x - 2y = 6$ in the same rectangular coordinate system. At what point do the graphs intersect?

85. Solve: $5(2x - 3) - 4x = 9$.

CHAPTER 4 Summary, Review, and Test

SUMMARY

DEFINITIONS AND CONCEPTS	**EXAMPLES**
4.1 Exponential Functions	
a. The exponential function with base b is defined by $f(x) = b^x$, where $b > 0$ and $b \neq 1$.	Ex. 1, p. 443
b. Characteristics of exponential functions and graphs for $0 < b < 1$ and $b > 1$ are shown in the box on page 445.	Ex. 2, p. 444; Ex. 3, p. 444
c. Transformations involving exponential functions are summarized in Table 4.1 on page 446.	Ex. 4, p. 447; Ex. 5, p. 447
d. The natural exponential function is $f(x) = e^x$. The irrational number e is called the natural base, where $e \approx 2.7183$. e is the value that $\left(1 + \frac{1}{n}\right)^n$ approaches as $n \to \infty$.	Ex. 6, p. 448
e. Formulas for compound interest: After t years, the balance, A, in an account with principal P and annual interest rate r (in decimal form) is given by one of the following formulas: **1.** For n compoundings per year: $A = P\left(1 + \frac{r}{n}\right)^{nt}$ **2.** For continuous compounding: $A = Pe^{rt}$.	Ex. 7, p. 450
4.2 Logarithmic Functions	
a. Definition of the logarithmic function: For $x > 0$ and $b > 0, b \neq 1, y = \log_b x$ is equivalent to $b^y = x$. The function $f(x) = \log_b x$ is the logarithmic function with base b. This function is the inverse function of the exponential function with base b.	Ex. 1, p. 456; Ex. 2, p. 457; Ex. 3, p. 457
b. Graphs of logarithmic functions for $b > 1$ and $0 < b < 1$ are shown in Figure 4.8 on page 459. Characteristics of the graphs are summarized in the box on page 460.	Ex. 6, p. 459
c. Transformations involving logarithmic functions are summarized in Table 4.5 on page 460.	Figures 4.9–4.12, pp. 460–461
d. The domain of a logarithmic function of the form $f(x) = \log_b x$ is the set of all positive real numbers. The domain of $f(x) = \log_b g(x)$ consists of all x for which $g(x) > 0$.	Ex. 7, p. 461; Ex. 10, p. 463

DEFINITIONS AND CONCEPTS

EXAMPLES

e. Common and natural logarithms: $f(x) = \log x$ means $f(x) = \log_{10} x$ and is the common logarithmic function. $f(x) = \ln x$ means $f(x) = \log_e x$ and is the natural logarithmic function.

Ex. 8, p. 462;
Ex. 9, p. 463;
Ex. 11, p. 464

f. Basic Logarithmic Properties

Base b ($b > 0, b \neq 1$)	Base 10 (Common Logarithms)	Base e (Natural Logarithms)
$\log_b 1 = 0$	$\log 1 = 0$	$\ln 1 = 0$
$\log_b b = 1$	$\log 10 = 1$	$\ln e = 1$
$\log_b b^x = x$	$\log 10^x = x$	$\ln e^x = x$
$b^{\log_b x} = x$	$10^{\log x} = x$	$e^{\ln x} = x$

Ex. 4, p. 458

Ex. 5, p. 458

4.3 Properties of Logarithms

a. *The Product Rule:* $\log_b(MN) = \log_b M + \log_b N$

Ex. 1, p. 469

b. *The Quotient Rule:* $\log_b\left(\dfrac{M}{N}\right) = \log_b M - \log_b N$

Ex. 2, p. 470

c. *The Power Rule:* $\log_b M^p = p \log_b M$

Ex. 3, p. 471

d. *The Change-of-Base Property:*

The General Property	Introducing Common Logarithms	Introducing Natural Logarithms
$\log_b M = \dfrac{\log_a M}{\log_a b}$	$\log_b M = \dfrac{\log M}{\log b}$	$\log_b M = \dfrac{\ln M}{\ln b}$

Ex. 7, p. 475;
Ex. 8, p. 476

e. Properties for expanding logarithmic expressions are given in the box on page 472.

Ex. 4, p. 472

f. Properties for condensing logarithmic expressions are given in the box on page 473.

Ex. 5, p. 473;
Ex. 6, p. 474

4.4 Exponential and Logarithmic Equations

a. An exponential equation is an equation containing a variable in an exponent. Some exponential equations can be solved by expressing each side as a power of the same base: If $b^M = b^N$, then $M = N$. Details are in the box on page 480.

Ex. 1, p. 480

b. The procedure for using logarithms to solve exponential equations is given in the box on page 481. The solution procedure involves isolating the exponential expression. Take the common logarithm on both sides for base 10. Take the natural logarithm on both sides for bases other than 10. Simplify using

$$\ln b^x = x \ln b \quad \text{or} \quad \ln e^x = x \quad \text{or} \quad \log 10^x = x.$$

Ex. 2, p. 481;
Ex. 3, p. 482;
Ex. 4, p. 482;
Ex. 5, p. 483

c. A logarithmic equation is an equation containing a variable in a logarithmic expression. Some logarithmic equations can be expressed in the form $\log_b M = c$. The definition of a logarithm is used to rewrite the equation in exponential form: $b^c = M$. See the box on page 483. When checking logarithmic equations, reject proposed solutions that produce the logarithm of a negative number or the logarithm of 0 in the original equation.

Ex. 6, p. 484;
Ex. 7, p. 485

d. Some logarithmic equations can be expressed in the form $\log_b M = \log_b N$. Use the one-to-one property to rewrite the equation without logarithms: $M = N$. See the box on page 486.

Ex. 8, p. 486

4.5 Exponential Growth and Decay; Modeling Data

a. Exponential growth and decay models are given by $A = A_0 e^{kt}$ in which t represents time, A_0 is the amount present at $t = 0$, and A is the amount present at time t. If $k > 0$, the model describes growth and k is the growth rate. If $k < 0$, the model describes decay and k is the decay rate.

Ex. 1, p. 495;
Ex. 2, p. 497

b. The logistic growth model, given by $A = \dfrac{c}{1 + ae^{-bt}}$, describes situations in which growth is limited. $y = c$ is a horizontal asymptote for the graph, and growth, A, can never exceed c.

Ex. 3, p. 498

c. Scatter plots for exponential, logarithmic, and linear models are shown in Figure 4.24 on page 499. When using a graphing utility to model data, the closer that the correlation coefficient, r, is to -1 or 1, the better the model fits the data.

Ex. 4, p. 500;
Ex. 5, p. 501;
Ex. 6, p. 501

d. Expressing an Exponential Model in Base e: $y = ab^x$ is equivalent to $y = ae^{(\ln b) \cdot x}$.

Ex. 7, p. 503

REVIEW EXERCISES

4.1

In Exercises 1–4, the graph of an exponential function is given. Select the function for each graph from the following options:

$$f(x) = 4^x, g(x) = 4^{-x},$$

$$h(x) = -4^{-x}, r(x) = -4^{-x} + 3.$$

1.

2.

3.

4.
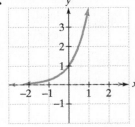

In Exercises 5–9, graph f and g in the same rectangular coordinate system. Use transformations of the graph of f to obtain the graph of g. Graph and give equations of all asymptotes. Use the graphs to determine each function's domain and range.

5. $f(x) = 2^x$ and $g(x) = 2^{x-1}$

6. $f(x) = 3^x$ and $g(x) = 3^x - 1$

7. $f(x) = 3^x$ and $g(x) = -3^x$

8. $f(x) = \left(\frac{1}{2}\right)^x$ and $g(x) = \left(\frac{1}{2}\right)^{-x}$

9. $f(x) = e^x$ and $g(x) = 2e^{\frac{x}{2}}$

Use the compound interest formulas to solve Exercises 10–11.

10. Suppose that you have $5000 to invest. Which investment yields the greater return over 5 years: 5.5% compounded semiannually or 5.25% compounded monthly?

11. Suppose that you have $14,000 to invest. Which investment yields the greater return over 10 years: 7% compounded monthly or 6.85% compounded continuously?

12. A cup of coffee is taken out of a microwave oven and placed in a room. The temperature, T, in degrees Fahrenheit, of the coffee after t minutes is modeled by the function $T = 70 + 130e^{-0.04855t}$. The graph of the function is shown in the figure.

Use the graph to answer each of the following questions.

a. What was the temperature of the coffee when it was first taken out of the microwave?

b. What is a reasonable estimate of the temperature of the coffee after 20 minutes? Use your calculator to verify this estimate.

c. What is the limit of the temperature to which the coffee will cool? What does this tell you about the temperature of the room?

4.2

In Exercises 13–15, write each equation in its equivalent exponential form.

13. $\frac{1}{2} = \log_{49} 7$ **14.** $3 = \log_4 x$ **15.** $\log_3 81 = y$

In Exercises 16–18, write each equation in its equivalent logarithmic form.

16. $6^3 = 216$ **17.** $b^4 = 625$ **18.** $13^y = 874$

In Exercises 19–29, evaluate each expression without using a calculator. If evaluation is not possible, state the reason.

19. $\log_4 64$ **20.** $\log_5 \frac{1}{25}$ **21.** $\log_3(-9)$

22. $\log_{16} 4$ **23.** $\log_{17} 17$ **24.** $\log_3 3^8$

25. $\ln e^5$ **26.** $\log_3 \frac{1}{\sqrt{3}}$ **27.** $\ln \frac{1}{e^2}$

28. $\log \frac{1}{1000}$ **29.** $\log_3(\log_8 8)$

30. Graph $f(x) = 2^x$ and $g(x) = \log_2 x$ in the same rectangular coordinate system. Use the graphs to determine each function's domain and range.

31. Graph $f(x) = \left(\frac{1}{3}\right)^x$ and $g(x) = \log_{\frac{1}{3}} x$ in the same rectangular coordinate system. Use the graphs to determine each function's domain and range.

In Exercises 32–35, the graph of a logarithmic function is given. Select the function for each graph from the following options:

$$f(x) = \log x, g(x) = \log(-x),$$
$$h(x) = \log(2 - x), r(x) = 1 + \log(2 - x).$$

32.

33.

34.

35.

In Exercises 36–38, begin by graphing $f(x) = \log_2 x$. Then use transformations of this graph to graph the given function. What is the graph's x-intercept? What is the vertical asymptote? Use the graphs to determine each function's domain and range.

36. $g(x) = \log_2(x - 2)$ **37.** $h(x) = -1 + \log_2 x$

38. $r(x) = \log_2(-x)$

In Exercises 39–40, graph f and g in the same rectangular coordinate system. Use transformations of the graph of f to obtain the graph of g. Graph and give equations of all asymptotes. Use the graphs to determine each function's domain and range.

39. $f(x) = \log x$ and $g(x) = -\log(x + 3)$

40. $f(x) = \ln x$ and $g(x) = -\ln(2x)$

In Exercises 41–43, find the domain of each logarithmic function.

41. $f(x) = \log_8(x + 5)$ **42.** $f(x) = \log(3 - x)$

43. $f(x) = \ln(x - 1)^2$

In Exercises 44–46, use inverse properties of logarithms to simplify each expression.

44. $\ln e^{6x}$ **45.** $e^{\ln \sqrt{x}}$ **46.** $10^{\log 4x^2}$

47. On the Richter scale, the magnitude, R, of an earthquake of intensity I is given by $R = \log \dfrac{I}{I_0}$, where I_0 is the intensity of a barely felt zero-level earthquake. If the intensity of an earthquake is $1000I_0$, what is its magnitude on the Richter scale?

48. Students in a psychology class took a final examination. As part of an experiment to see how much of the course content they remembered over time, they took equivalent forms of the exam in monthly intervals thereafter. The average score, $f(t)$, for the group after t months is modeled by the function $f(t) = 76 - 18 \log(t + 1)$, where $0 \le t \le 12$.

    a. What was the average score when the exam was first given?

    b. What was the average score after 2 months? 4 months? 6 months? 8 months? one year?

    c. Use the results from parts (a) and (b) to graph f. Describe what the shape of the graph indicates in terms of the material retained by the students.

49. The formula

$$t = \frac{1}{c}\ln\left(\frac{A}{A - N}\right)$$

describes the time, t, in weeks, that it takes to achieve mastery of a portion of a task. In the formula, A represents maximum learning possible, N is the portion of the learning that is to be achieved, and c is a constant used to measure an individual's learning style. A 50-year-old man decides to start running as a way to maintain good health. He feels that the maximum rate he could ever hope to achieve is 12 miles per hour. How many weeks will it take before the man can run 5 miles per hour if $c = 0.06$ for this person?

4.3

In Exercises 50–53, use properties of logarithms to expand each logarithmic expression as much as possible. Where possible, evaluate logarithmic expressions without using a calculator.

50. $\log_6(36x^3)$ **51.** $\log_4\left(\dfrac{\sqrt{x}}{64}\right)$

52. $\log_2\left(\dfrac{xy^2}{64}\right)$ **53.** $\ln \sqrt[3]{\dfrac{x}{e}}$

In Exercises 54–57, use properties of logarithms to condense each logarithmic expression. Write the expression as a single logarithm whose coefficient is 1.

54. $\log_b 7 + \log_b 3$ **55.** $\log 3 - 3 \log x$

56. $3 \ln x + 4 \ln y$ **57.** $\frac{1}{2} \ln x - \ln y$

In Exercises 58–59, use common logarithms or natural logarithms and a calculator to evaluate to four decimal places.

58. $\log_6 72{,}348$ **59.** $\log_4 0.863$

In Exercises 60–63, determine whether each equation is true or false. Where possible, show work to support your conclusion. If the statement is false, make the necessary change(s) to produce a true statement.

60. $(\ln x)(\ln 1) = 0$

61. $\log(x + 9) - \log(x + 1) = \dfrac{\log(x + 9)}{\log(x + 1)}$

62. $(\log_2 x)^4 = 4 \log_2 x$ **63.** $\ln e^x = x \ln e$

4.4

In Exercises 64–73, solve each exponential equation. Where necessary, express the solution set in terms of natural or common logarithms and use a calculator to obtain a decimal approximation, correct to two decimal places, for the solution.

64. $2^{4x-2} = 64$ **65.** $125^x = 25$

66. $10^x = 7000$ **67.** $9^{x+2} = 27^{-x}$

68. $8^x = 12{,}143$ **69.** $9e^{5x} = 1269$

70. $e^{12-5x} - 7 = 123$ **71.** $5^{4x+2} = 37{,}500$

72. $3^{x+4} = 7^{2x-1}$ **73.** $e^{2x} - e^x - 6 = 0$

In Exercises 74–79, solve each logarithmic equation.

74. $\log_4(3x - 5) = 3$

75. $3 + 4\ln(2x) = 15$

76. $\log_2(x + 3) + \log_2(x - 3) = 4$

77. $\log_3(x - 1) - \log_3(x + 2) = 2$

78. $\ln(x + 4) - \ln(x + 1) = \ln x$

79. $\log_4(2x + 1) = \log_4(x - 3) + \log_4(x + 5)$

80. The function $P(x) = 14.7e^{-0.21x}$ models the average atmospheric pressure, $P(x)$, in pounds per square inch, at an altitude of x miles above sea level. The atmospheric pressure at the peak of Mt. Everest, the world's highest mountain, is 4.6 pounds per square inch. How many miles above sea level, to the nearest tenth of a mile, is the peak of Mt. Everest?

81. The bar graph shows the number of smartphones sold in the United States from 2004 through 2010.

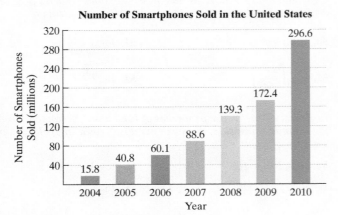

Number of Smartphones Sold in the United States

Source: *Newsweek*, April 11, 2011

The function $S(t) = 21.4(1.56)^t$ models the number of smartphones sold in the United States, $S(t)$, in millions, t years after 2004. When does this model project that 1170.9 million smartphones will be sold? Round to the nearest year.

82. Researchers have surveyed attitudes of college freshmen every year since 1969. The bar graph shows that since 1980, there has been a decline in first-year college students' opposition to homosexual relationships.

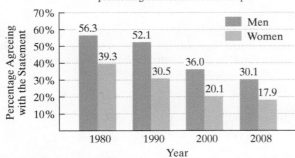

Opposition to Homosexual Relationships among First-Year United States College Students, 1980–2008

Statement: "It is important to have laws prohibiting homosexual relationships."

Source: John Macionis, *Sociology, Thirteenth Edition*, Prentice Hall, 2010.

a. The function
$$f(x) = -6.2 \ln x + 40.5$$
models the percentage of first-year college women, $f(x)$, opposed to homosexual relationships x years after 1979. If trends modeled by the function continue, when will opposition to homosexual relationships among first-year college women diminish to 16%? Round to the nearest year.

b. The function $g(x) = -7 \ln x + 59$ models the percentage of first-year college men, $g(x)$, opposed to homosexual relationships x years after 1979. According to this model, when did 40% of male freshmen oppose homosexual relationships? Round to the nearest year.

83. Use the formula for compound interest with n compoundings per year to solve this problem. How long, to the nearest tenth of a year, will it take $12,500 to grow to $20,000 at 6.5% annual interest compounded quarterly?

Use the formula for continuous compounding to solve Exercises 84–85.

84. How long, to the nearest tenth of a year, will it take $50,000 to triple in value at 7.5% annual interest compounded continuously?

85. What interest rate, to the nearest percent, is required for an investment subject to continuous compounding to triple in 5 years?

4.5

86. According to the U.S. Bureau of the Census, in 2000 there were 35.3 million residents of Hispanic origin living in the United States. By 2010, the number had increased to 50.5 million. The exponential growth function $A = 35.3e^{kt}$ describes the U.S. Hispanic population, A, in millions, t years after 2000.

a. Find k, correct to three decimal places.

b. Use the resulting model to project the Hispanic resident population in 2015.

c. In which year will the Hispanic resident population reach 70 million?

87. Use the exponential decay model, $A = A_0e^{kt}$, to solve this exercise. The half-life of polonium-210 is 140 days. How long will it take for a sample of this substance to decay to 20% of its original amount?

88. The function
$$f(t) = \frac{500,000}{1 + 2499e^{-0.92t}}$$
models the number of people, $f(t)$, in a city who have become ill with influenza t weeks after its initial outbreak.

a. How many people became ill with the flu when the epidemic began?

b. How many people were ill by the end of the sixth week?

c. What is the limiting size of $f(t)$, the population that becomes ill?

Exercises 89–91 present data in the form of tables. For each data set shown by the table,

a. *Create a scatter plot for the data.*

b. *Use the scatter plot to determine whether an exponential function, a logarithmic function, or a linear function is the best choice for modeling the data.*

89. U.S. Ice Cream Consumption

Year	Average Annual Consumption (pounds)
1968	18.5
1978	17.6
1988	17.3
1998	16.3
2008	13.9

Source: USDA, Feb. 2010

90. Percentage of Bachelor's Degrees Awarded to Women in the United States

Year	Percentage of Degrees
1975	45%
1985	51%
1995	55%
2005	57%

Source: U.S. Department of Education

91. E-Filing of Federal Taxes

Year	Percentage of E-Filed Returns
1990	4%
1995	10%
2000	28%
2005	51%
2010	69%

Source: IRS

In Exercises 92–93, rewrite the equation in terms of base e. Express the answer in terms of a natural logarithm and then round to three decimal places.

92. $y = 73(2.6)^x$

93. $y = 6.5(0.43)^x$

94. The figure shows world population projections through the year 2150. The data are from the United Nations Family Planning Program and are based on optimistic or pessimistic expectations for successful control of human population growth. Suppose that you are interested in modeling these data using exponential, logarithmic, linear, and quadratic functions. Which function would you use to model each of the projections? Explain your choices. For the choice corresponding to a quadratic model, would your formula involve one with a positive or negative leading coefficient? Explain.

Projections in World Population Growth

Source: United Nations

CHAPTER 4 TEST

1. Graph $f(x) = 2^x$ and $g(x) = 2^{x+1}$ in the same rectangular coordinate system.

2. Graph $f(x) = \log_2 x$ and $g(x) = \log_2(x - 1)$ in the same rectangular coordinate system.

3. Write in exponential form: $\log_5 125 = 3$.

4. Write in logarithmic form: $\sqrt{36} = 6$.

5. Find the domain: $f(x) = \ln(3 - x)$.

In Exercises 6–7, use properties of logarithms to expand each logarithmic expression as much as possible. Where possible, evaluate logarithmic expressions without using a calculator.

6. $\log_4(64x^5)$

7. $\log_3\left(\dfrac{\sqrt[3]{x}}{81}\right)$

In Exercises 8–9, write each expression as a single logarithm.

8. $6 \log x + 2 \log y$

9. $\ln 7 - 3 \ln x$

10. Use a calculator to evaluate $\log_{15} 71$ to four decimal places.

In Exercises 11–18, solve each equation.

11. $3^{x-2} = 9^{x+4}$

12. $5^x = 1.4$

13. $400e^{0.005x} = 1600$

14. $e^{2x} - 6e^x + 5 = 0$

15. $\log_6(4x - 1) = 3$

16. $2 \ln(3x) = 8$

17. $\log x + \log(x + 15) = 2$

18. $\ln(x - 4) - \ln(x + 1) = \ln 6$

19. On the decibel scale, the loudness of a sound, D, in decibels, is given by $D = 10 \log \dfrac{I}{I_0}$, where I is the intensity of the sound, in watts per meter^2, and I_0 is the intensity of a sound barely audible to the human ear. If the intensity of a sound is $10^{12}I_0$, what is its loudness in decibels? (Such a sound is potentially damaging to the ear.)

In Exercises 20–22, simplify each expression.

20. $\ln e^{5x}$

21. $\log_b b$

22. $\log_6 1$

Use the compound interest formulas to solve Exercises 23–25.

23. Suppose you have $3000 to invest. Which investment yields the greater return over 10 years: 6.5% compounded semiannually or 6% compounded continuously? How much more (to the nearest dollar) is yielded by the better investment?

24. How long, to the nearest tenth of a year, will it take $4000 to grow to $8000 at 5% annual interest compounded quarterly?

25. What interest rate, to the nearest tenth of a percent, is required for an investment subject to continuous compounding to double in 10 years?

26. The function

$$A = 82.3e^{-0.004t}$$

models the population of Germany, A, in millions, t years after 2010.

   a. What was the population of Germany in 2010?

   b. Is the population of Germany increasing or decreasing? Explain.

   c. In which year will the population of Germany be 79.1 million?

27. The 2010 population of Asia was 4121 million; in 2050, it is projected to be 5231 million. Write the exponential growth function that describes the population of Asia, in millions, t years after 2010.

28. Use the exponential decay model, $A = A_0e^{kt}$, to solve this exercise. The half-life of iodine-131 is 7.2 days. How long will it take for a sample of this substance to decay to 30% of its original amount? Round to one decimal place.

29. The logistic growth function

$$f(t) = \frac{140}{1 + 9e^{-0.165t}}$$

describes the population, $f(t)$, of an endangered species of elk t years after they were introduced to a nonthreatening habitat.

   a. How many elk were initially introduced to the habitat?

   b. How many elk are expected in the habitat after 10 years?

   c. What is the limiting size of the elk population that the habitat will sustain?

In Exercises 30–33, determine whether the values in each table belong to an exponential function, a logarithmic function, a linear function, or a quadratic function.

30.

x	y
0	3
1	1
2	−1
3	−3
4	−5

31.

x	y
$\frac{1}{3}$	−1
1	0
3	1
9	2
27	3

32.

x	y
0	1
1	5
2	25
3	125
4	625

33.

x	y
0	12
1	3
2	0
3	3
4	12

34. Rewrite $y = 96(0.38)^x$ in terms of base e. Express the answer in terms of a natural logarithm and then round to three decimal places.

CUMULATIVE REVIEW EXERCISES (CHAPTERS 1–4)

In Exercises 1–8, solve each equation or inequality.

1. $|3x − 4| = 2$

2. $\sqrt{2x − 5} − \sqrt{x − 3} = 1$

3. $x^4 + x^3 − 3x^2 − x + 2 = 0$

4. $e^{5x} − 32 = 96$

5. $\log_2(x + 5) + \log_2(x − 1) = 4$

6. $\ln(x + 4) + \ln(x + 1) = 2\ln(x + 3)$

7. $14 − 5x \geq −6$

8. $|2x − 4| \leq 2$

In Exercises 9–14, graph each equation in a rectangular coordinate system. If two functions are indicated, graph both in the same system.

9. $(x − 3)^2 + (y + 2)^2 = 4$

10. $f(x) = (x − 2)^2 − 1$

11. $f(x) = \dfrac{x^2 − 1}{x^2 − 4}$

12. $f(x) = (x − 2)^2(x + 1)$

13. $f(x) = 2x − 4$ and $f^{-1}(x)$

14. $f(x) = \ln x$ and $g(x) = \ln(x − 2) + 1$

15. Write the point-slope form and the slope-intercept form of the line passing through $(1, 3)$ and $(3, −3)$.

16. If $f(x) = x^2$ and $g(x) = x + 2$, find $(f \circ g)(x)$ and $(g \circ f)(x)$.

17. You discover that the number of hours you sleep each night varies inversely as the square of the number of cups of coffee consumed during the early evening. If 2 cups of coffee are consumed, you get 8 hours of sleep. If the number of cups of coffee is doubled, how many hours should you expect to sleep?

A baseball player hits a pop fly into the air. The function

$$s(t) = −16t^2 + 64t + 5$$

models the ball's height above the ground, $s(t)$, in feet, t seconds after it is hit. Use the function to solve Exercises 18–19.

18. When does the baseball reach its maximum height? What is that height?

19. After how many seconds does the baseball hit the ground? Round to the nearest tenth of a second.

20. You are paid time-and-a-half for each hour worked over 40 hours a week. Last week you worked 50 hours and earned $660. What is your normal hourly salary?

SYSTEMS OF EQUATIONS AND INEQUALITIES

Television, movies, and magazines place great emphasis on physical beauty. Our culture emphasizes physical appearance to such an extent that it is a central factor in the perception and judgment of others. The modern emphasis on thinness as the ideal body shape has been suggested as a major cause of eating disorders among adolescent women.

Cultural values of physical attractiveness change over time. During the 1950s, actress Jayne Mansfield embodied the postwar ideal: curvy, buxom, and big-hipped. Men, too, have been caught up in changes of how they "ought" to look. The 1960s ideal was the soft and scrawny hippie. Today's ideal man is tough and muscular.

Given the importance of culture in setting standards of attractiveness, how can you establish a healthy weight range for your age and height? In this chapter, we will use systems of inequalities to explore these skin-deep issues.

HERE'S WHERE YOU'LL FIND THESE APPLICATIONS:

You'll find a weight that fits you using the models (mathematical, not fashion) in Example 5 of Section 5.5 and Exercises 77–80 in Exercise Set 5.5. Exercises 85–86 use graphs and a formula for body-mass index to indicate whether you are obese, overweight, borderline overweight, normal weight, or underweight.

<table>
<tr><td>

SECTION 5.1

</td><td>

Systems of Linear Equations in Two Variables

</td></tr>
</table>

Objectives

① Decide whether an ordered pair is a solution of a linear system.

② Solve linear systems by substitution.

③ Solve linear systems by addition.

④ Identify systems that do not have exactly one ordered-pair solution.

⑤ Solve problems using systems of linear equations.

Researchers identified college students who generally were procrastinators or nonprocrastinators. The students were asked to report throughout the semester how many symptoms of physical illness they had experienced. **Figure 5.1** shows that by late in the semester, all students experienced increases in symptoms. Early in the semester, procrastinators reported fewer symptoms, but late in the semester, as work came due, they reported more symptoms than their nonprocrastinating peers.

The data in **Figure 5.1** can be analyzed using a pair of linear models in two variables. The figure shows that by week 6, both groups reported the same number of symptoms of illness, an average of approximately 3.5 symptoms per group. In this section, you will learn two algebraic methods, called *substitution* and *addition*, that will reinforce this graphic observation, verifying (6, 3.5) as the point of intersection.

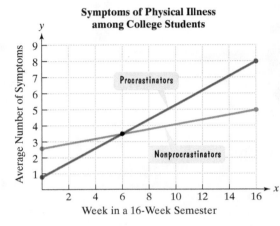

FIGURE 5.1
Source: Gerrig and Zimbardo, *Psychology and Life,* 18th Edition, Allyn and Bacon, 2008.

① Decide whether an ordered pair is a solution of a linear system.

Systems of Linear Equations and Their Solutions

All equations in the form $Ax + By = C$ are straight lines when graphed. Two such equations are called a **system of linear equations** or a **linear system. A solution to a system of linear equations in two variables** is an ordered pair that satisfies both equations in the system. For example, (3, 4) satisfies the system

$$\begin{cases} x + y = 7 & \text{(3 + 4 is, indeed, 7.)} \\ x - y = -1. & \text{(3 - 4 is, indeed, -1.)} \end{cases}$$

Thus, (3, 4) satisfies both equations and is a solution of the system. The solution can be described by saying that $x = 3$ and $y = 4$. The solution can also be described using set notation. The solution set to the system is {(3, 4)}—that is, the set consisting of the ordered pair (3, 4).

A system of linear equations can have exactly one solution, no solution, or infinitely many solutions. We begin with systems that have exactly one solution.

EXAMPLE 1 Determining Whether Ordered Pairs Are Solutions of a System

Consider the system:

$$\begin{cases} x + 2y = 2 \\ x - 2y = 6. \end{cases}$$

Determine if each ordered pair is a solution of the system:

a. $(4, -1)$ **b.** $(-4, 3)$.

SOLUTION

a. We begin by determining whether $(4, -1)$ is a solution. Because 4 is the x-coordinate and -1 is the y-coordinate of $(4, -1)$, we replace x with 4 and y with -1.

$$x + 2y = 2 \qquad\qquad x - 2y = 6$$
$$4 + 2(-1) \stackrel{?}{=} 2 \qquad\qquad 4 - 2(-1) \stackrel{?}{=} 6$$
$$4 + (-2) \stackrel{?}{=} 2 \qquad\qquad 4 - (-2) \stackrel{?}{=} 6$$
$$2 = 2, \quad \text{true} \qquad\qquad 4 + 2 \stackrel{?}{=} 6$$
$$6 = 6, \quad \text{true}$$

The pair $(4, -1)$ satisfies both equations: It makes each equation true. Thus, the ordered pair is a solution of the system.

b. To determine whether $(-4, 3)$ is a solution, we replace x with -4 and y with 3.

$$x + 2y = 2 \qquad\qquad x - 2y = 6$$
$$-4 + 2 \cdot 3 \stackrel{?}{=} 2 \qquad\qquad -4 - 2 \cdot 3 \stackrel{?}{=} 6$$
$$-4 + 6 \stackrel{?}{=} 2 \qquad\qquad -4 - 6 \stackrel{?}{=} 6$$
$$2 = 2, \quad \text{true} \qquad\qquad -10 = 6, \quad \text{false}$$

The pair $(-4, 3)$ fails to satisfy *both* equations: It does not make both equations true. Thus, the ordered pair is not a solution of the system.   • • •

GREAT QUESTION!

Can I use a rough sketch on scratch paper to solve a linear system by graphing?

No. When solving linear systems by graphing, neatly drawn graphs are essential for determining points of intersection.

- Use rectangular coordinate graph paper.
- Use a ruler or straightedge.
- Use a pencil with a sharp point.

The solution of a system of linear equations can sometimes be found by graphing both of the equations in the same rectangular coordinate system. For a system with one solution, the **coordinates of the point of intersection give the system's solution**. For example, the system in Example 1,

$$\begin{cases} x + 2y = 2 \\ x - 2y = 6, \end{cases}$$

is graphed in **Figure 5.2**. The solution of the system, $(4, -1)$, corresponds to the point of intersection of the lines.

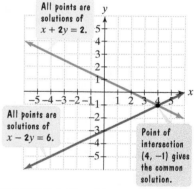

FIGURE 5.2 Visualizing a system's solution

✓ Check Point **1** Consider the system:

$$\begin{cases} 2x - 3y = -4 \\ 2x + y = 4. \end{cases}$$

Determine if each ordered pair is a solution of the system:
  a. $(1, 2)$ **b.** $(7, 6)$.

2 Solve linear systems by substitution.

Eliminating a Variable Using the Substitution Method

Finding the solution to a linear system by graphing equations may not be easy to do. For example, a solution of $\left(-\frac{2}{3}, \frac{157}{29}\right)$ would be difficult to "see" as an intersection point on a graph.

Let's consider a method that does not depend on finding a system's solution visually: the substitution method. This method involves converting the system to one equation in one variable by an appropriate substitution.

GREAT QUESTION!

In the first step of the substitution method, how do I know which variable to isolate and in which equation?

You can choose both the variable and the equation. If possible, solve for a variable whose coefficient is 1 or −1 to avoid working with fractions.

Solving Linear Systems by Substitution

1. Solve either of the equations for one variable in terms of the other. (If one of the equations is already in this form, you can skip this step.)
2. Substitute the expression found in step 1 into the *other* equation. This will result in an equation in one variable.
3. Solve the equation containing one variable.
4. Back-substitute the value found in step 3 into one of the original equations. Simplify and find the value of the remaining variable.
5. Check the proposed solution in both of the system's given equations.

EXAMPLE 2   Solving a System by Substitution

Solve by the substitution method:

$$\begin{cases} 5x - 4y = 9 \\ x - 2y = -3. \end{cases}$$

SOLUTION

Step 1   Solve either of the equations for one variable in terms of the other. We begin by isolating one of the variables in either of the equations. By solving for x in the second equation, which has a coefficient of 1, we can avoid fractions.

$$x - 2y = -3 \quad \text{This is the second equation in the given system.}$$
$$x = 2y - 3 \quad \text{Solve for x by adding 2y to both sides.}$$

Step 2   Substitute the expression from step 1 into the other equation. We substitute $2y - 3$ for x in the first equation.

$$x = \boxed{2y - 3} \qquad 5\boxed{x} - 4y = 9$$

This gives us an equation in one variable, namely

$$5(2y - 3) - 4y = 9.$$

The variable x has been eliminated.

Step 3   Solve the resulting equation containing one variable.

$$5(2y - 3) - 4y = 9 \quad \text{This is the equation containing one variable.}$$
$$10y - 15 - 4y = 9 \quad \text{Apply the distributive property.}$$
$$6y - 15 = 9 \quad \text{Combine like terms.}$$
$$6y = 24 \quad \text{Add 15 to both sides.}$$
$$y = 4 \quad \text{Divide both sides by 6.}$$

GREAT QUESTION!

When I back-substitute the value for one of the variables, which equation should I use?

The equation from step 1, in which one variable is expressed in terms of the other, is equivalent to one of the original equations. It is often easiest to back-substitute the obtained value into this equation to find the value of the other variable. After obtaining both values, get into the habit of checking the ordered-pair solution in *both* equations of the system.

Step 4   Back-substitute the obtained value into one of the original equations. Now that we have the y-coordinate of the solution, we back-substitute 4 for y into one of the original equations to find x. Let's use both equations to show that we obtain the same value for x in either case.

Using the first equation:	Using the second equation:
$5x - 4y = 9$	$x - 2y = -3$
$5x - 4(4) = 9$	$x - 2(4) = -3$
$5x - 16 = 9$	$x - 8 = -3$
$5x = 25$	$x = 5$
$x = 5$	

With $x = 5$ and $y = 4$, the proposed solution is $(5, 4)$.

Step 5   Check. Take a moment to show that $(5, 4)$ satisfies both given equations. The solution set is $\{(5, 4)\}$.   • • •

TECHNOLOGY

Graphic Connections

A graphing utility can be used to solve the system in Example 2. Solve each equation for y, graph the equations, and use the intersection feature. The utility displays the solution $(5, 4)$ as $x = 5, y = 4$.

$[-10, 10, 1]$ by $[-10, 10, 1]$

⌀ Check Point **2** Solve by the substitution method:

$$\begin{cases} 3x + 2y = 4 \\ 2x + y = 1. \end{cases}$$

③ Solve linear systems by addition.

Eliminating a Variable Using the Addition Method

The substitution method is most useful if one of the given equations has an isolated variable. A second, and frequently the easiest, method for solving a linear system is the addition method. Like the substitution method, the addition method involves eliminating a variable and ultimately solving an equation containing only one variable. However, this time we eliminate a variable by adding the equations.

For example, consider the following system of linear equations:

$$\begin{cases} 3x - 4y = 11 \\ -3x + 2y = -7. \end{cases}$$

When we add these two equations, the x-terms are eliminated. This occurs because the coefficients of the x-terms, 3 and -3, are opposites (additive inverses) of each other:

$$\begin{cases} 3x - 4y = 11 \\ \underline{-3x + 2y = -7} \end{cases}$$
$$-2y = 4$$
$$y = -2.$$

The sum is an equation in one variable.

Divide both sides by -2 and solve for y.

Now we can back-substitute -2 for y into one of the original equations to find x. It does not matter which equation you use; you will obtain the same value for x in either case. If we use either equation, we can show that $x = 1$ and the solution $(1, -2)$ satisfies both equations in the system.

When we use the addition method, we want to obtain two equations whose sum is an equation containing only one variable. The key step is to **obtain, for one of the variables, coefficients that differ only in sign**. To do this, we may need to multiply one or both equations by some nonzero number so that the coefficients of one of the variables, x or y, become opposites. Then when the two equations are added, this variable is eliminated.

GREAT QUESTION!

Isn't the addition method also called the elimination method?

Although the addition method is also known as the elimination method, variables are eliminated when using both the substitution and addition methods. The name *addition method* specifically tells us that the elimination of a variable is accomplished by adding two equations.

Solving Linear Systems by Addition

1. If necessary, rewrite both equations in the form $Ax + By = C$.
2. If necessary, multiply either equation or both equations by appropriate nonzero numbers so that the sum of the x-coefficients or the sum of the y-coefficients is 0.
3. Add the equations in step 2. The sum is an equation in one variable.
4. Solve the equation in one variable.
5. Back-substitute the value obtained in step 4 into either of the given equations and solve for the other variable.
6. Check the solution in both of the original equations.

EXAMPLE 3   Solving a System by the Addition Method

Solve by the addition method:

$$\begin{cases} 3x + 2y = 48 \\ 9x - 8y = -24. \end{cases}$$

SOLUTION

Step 1   Rewrite both equations in the form $Ax + By = C$. Both equations are already in this form. Variable terms appear on the left and constants appear on the right.

Step 2   If necessary, multiply either equation or both equations by appropriate numbers so that the sum of the x-coefficients or the sum of the y-coefficients is 0. We can eliminate x or y. Let's eliminate x. Consider the terms in x in each equation, that is, $3x$ and $9x$. To eliminate x, we can multiply each term of the first equation by -3 and then add the equations.

$$\begin{cases} 3x + 2y = 48 \quad \xrightarrow{\text{Multiply by } -3.} \\ 9x - 8y = -24 \quad \xrightarrow{\text{No change}} \end{cases} \begin{cases} -9x - 6y = -144 \\ \underline{9x - 8y = -24} \end{cases}$$

Step 3   Add the equations.   Add: $-14y = -168$

Step 4   Solve the equation in one variable. We solve $-14y = -168$ by dividing both sides by -14.

$$\frac{-14y}{-14} = \frac{-168}{-14} \quad \text{Divide both sides by } -14.$$

$$y = 12 \quad \text{Simplify.}$$

Step 5   Back-substitute and find the value for the other variable. We can back-substitute 12 for y into either one of the given equations. We'll use the first one.

$$3x + 2y = 48 \quad \text{This is the first equation in the given system.}$$
$$3x + 2(12) = 48 \quad \text{Substitute 12 for } y.$$
$$3x + 24 = 48 \quad \text{Multiply.}$$
$$3x = 24 \quad \text{Subtract 24 from both sides.}$$
$$x = 8 \quad \text{Divide both sides by 3.}$$

We found that $y = 12$ and $x = 8$. The proposed solution is $(8, 12)$.

Step 6   Check. Take a few minutes to show that $(8, 12)$ satisfies both of the original equations in the system. The solution set is $\{(8, 12)\}$.   •••

✐ Check Point **3** Solve by the addition method:

$$\begin{cases} 4x + 5y = 3 \\ 2x - 3y = 7. \end{cases}$$

Some linear systems have solutions that are not integers. If the value of one variable turns out to be a "messy" fraction, back-substitution might lead to cumbersome arithmetic. If this happens, you can return to the original system and use the addition method to find the value of the other variable.

EXAMPLE 4   Solving a System by the Addition Method

Solve by the addition method:

$$\begin{cases} 2x = 7y - 17 \\ 5y = 17 - 3x. \end{cases}$$

SOLUTION

Step 1   Rewrite both equations in the form $Ax + By = C$. We first arrange the system so that variable terms appear on the left and constants appear on the right. We obtain

$$\begin{cases} 2x - 7y = -17 & \text{Subtract } 7y \text{ from both sides of the first equation.} \\ 3x + 5y = 17. & \text{Add } 3x \text{ to both sides of the second equation.} \end{cases}$$

Step 2   If necessary, multiply either equation or both equations by appropriate numbers so that the sum of the x-coefficients or the sum of the y-coefficients is 0. We can eliminate x or y. Let's eliminate x by multiplying the first equation by 3 and the second equation by -2.

$$\begin{cases} 2x - 7y = -17 & \xrightarrow{\text{Multiply by 3.}} \\ 3x + 5y = 17 & \xrightarrow{\text{Multiply by } -2.} \end{cases} \quad \begin{cases} 6x - 21y = -51 \\ -6x - 10y = -34 \end{cases}$$

Step 3   Add the equations.   Add: $-31y = -85$

Step 4   Solve the equation in one variable. We solve $-31y = -85$ by dividing both sides by -31.

$$\frac{-31y}{-31} = \frac{-85}{-31} \quad \text{Divide both sides by } -31.$$

$$y = \frac{85}{31} \quad \text{Simplify.}$$

Step 5   Back-substitute and find the value for the other variable. Back-substitution of $\frac{85}{31}$ for y into either of the given equations results in cumbersome arithmetic. Instead, let's use the addition method on the given system in the form $Ax + By = C$ to find the value for x. Thus, we eliminate y by multiplying the first equation by 5 and the second equation by 7.

$$\begin{cases} 2x - 7y = -17 & \xrightarrow{\text{Multiply by 5.}} \\ 3x + 5y = 17 & \xrightarrow{\text{Multiply by 7.}} \end{cases} \quad \begin{cases} 10x - 35y = -85 \\ 21x + 35y = 119 \end{cases}$$

Add: $31x = 34$

$$x = \frac{34}{31} \quad \text{Divide both sides by 31.}$$

We found that $y = \dfrac{85}{31}$ and $x = \dfrac{34}{31}$. The proposed solution is $\left(\dfrac{34}{31}, \dfrac{85}{31} \right)$.

Step 6   Check. For this system, a calculator is helpful in showing that $\left(\frac{34}{31}, \frac{85}{31} \right)$ satisfies both of the original equations in the system. The solution set is $\left\{ \left(\frac{34}{31}, \frac{85}{31} \right) \right\}$.

⊘ Check Point **4** Solve by the addition method:

$$\begin{cases} 2x = 9 + 3y \\ 4y = 8 - 3x. \end{cases}$$

④ Identify systems that do not have exactly one ordered-pair solution.

Linear Systems Having No Solution or Infinitely Many Solutions

We have seen that a system of linear equations in two variables represents a pair of lines. The lines either intersect at one point, are parallel, or are identical. Thus, there are three possibilities for the number of solutions to a system of two linear equations in two variables.

The Number of Solutions to a System of Two Linear Equations

The number of solutions to a system of two linear equations in two variables is given by one of the following. (See **Figure 5.3**.)

Number of Solutions	What This Means Graphically
Exactly one ordered-pair solution	The two lines intersect at one point.
No solution	The two lines are parallel.
Infinitely many solutions	The two lines are identical.

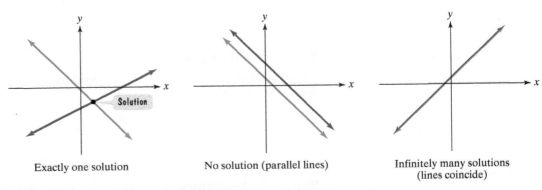

Exactly one solution   No solution (parallel lines)   Infinitely many solutions (lines coincide)

FIGURE 5.3 Possible graphs for a system of two linear equations in two variables

A linear system with no solution is called an **inconsistent system**. If you attempt to solve such a system by substitution or addition, you will eliminate both variables. A false statement, such as $0 = 12$, will be the result.

EXAMPLE 5 A System with No Solution

Solve the system:

$$\begin{cases} 4x + 6y = 12 \\ 6x + 9y = 12. \end{cases}$$

SOLUTION

Because no variable is isolated, we will use the addition method. To obtain coefficients of x that differ only in sign, we multiply the first equation by 3 and multiply the second equation by -2.

$$\begin{cases} 4x + 6y = 12 \\ 6x + 9y = 12 \end{cases} \xrightarrow[\text{Multiply by } -2.}]{\text{Multiply by 3.}} \quad \begin{cases} 12x + 18y = 36 \\ \underline{-12x - 18y = -24} \end{cases}$$

$$\text{Add:} \qquad \qquad 0 = 12$$

> There are no values of x and y for which $0 = 12$. No values of x and y satisfy $0x + 0y = 12$.

The false statement $0 = 12$ indicates that the system is inconsistent and has no solution. The solution set is the empty set, $\varnothing$. • • •

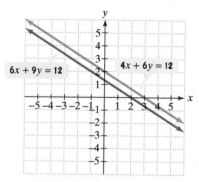

6x + 9y = 12   4x + 6y = 12

FIGURE 5.4 The graph of an inconsistent system

The lines corresponding to the two equations in Example 5 are shown in **Figure 5.4**. The lines are parallel and have no point of intersection.

DISCOVERY

Show that the graphs of $4x + 6y = 12$ and $6x + 9y = 12$ must be parallel lines by solving each equation for y. What are the slope and y-intercept for each line? What does this mean? If a linear system is inconsistent, what must be true about the slopes and y-intercepts for the system's graphs?

 Check Point **5** Solve the system:

$$\begin{cases} 5x - 2y = 4 \\ -10x + 4y = 7. \end{cases}$$

A linear system that has at least one solution is called a **consistent system**. Lines that intersect and lines that coincide both represent consistent systems. If the lines coincide, then the consistent system has infinitely many solutions, represented by every point on either line.

The equations in a linear system with infinitely many solutions are called **dependent**. If you attempt to solve such a system by substitution or addition, you will eliminate both variables. However, a true statement, such as $10 = 10$, will be the result.

EXAMPLE 6   A System with Infinitely Many Solutions

Solve the system:

$$\begin{cases} y = 3x - 2 \\ 15x - 5y = 10. \end{cases}$$

SOLUTION

Because the variable y is isolated in $y = 3x - 2$, the first equation, we can use the substitution method. We substitute the expression for y into the second equation.

$$y = \boxed{3x - 2} \qquad 15x - 5\boxed{y} = 10 \qquad \text{Substitute } 3x - 2 \text{ for } y.$$

$$15x - 5(3x - 2) = 10 \qquad \text{The substitution results in an equation in one variable.}$$

$$15x - 15x + 10 = 10 \qquad \text{Apply the distributive property.}$$

$$10 = 10 \qquad \text{Simplify.}$$

> This statement is true for all values of x and y.

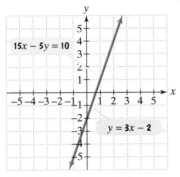

FIGURE 5.5 The graph of a system with infinitely many solutions

In our final step, both variables have been eliminated and the resulting statement, $10 = 10$, is true. This true statement indicates that the system has infinitely many solutions. The solution set consists of all points (x, y) lying on either of the coinciding lines, $y = 3x - 2$ or $15x - 5y = 10$, as shown in **Figure 5.5**.

We express the solution set for the system in one of two equivalent ways:

$$\{(x, y) \mid y = 3x - 2\} \quad \text{or} \quad \{(x, y) \mid 15x - 5y = 10\}.$$

The set of all ordered pairs (x, y) such that $y = 3x - 2$

The set of all ordered pairs (x, y) such that $15x - 5y = 10$

• • •

GREAT QUESTION!

The system in Example 6 has infinitely many solutions. Does that mean that any ordered pair of numbers is a solution?

No. Although the system in Example 6 has infinitely many solutions, this does not mean that any ordered pair of numbers you can form will be a solution. The ordered pair (x, y) must satisfy one of the system's equations, $y = 3x - 2$ or $15x - 5y = 10$, and there are infinitely many such ordered pairs. Because the graphs are coinciding lines, the ordered pairs that are solutions of one of the equations are also solutions of the other equation.

⬛ Check Point **6** Solve the system:

$$\begin{cases} x = 4y - 8 \\ 5x - 20y = -40. \end{cases}$$

⑤ Solve problems using systems of linear equations.

Functions of Business: Break-Even Analysis

Suppose that a company produces and sells x units of a product. Its *revenue* is the money generated by selling x units of the product. Its *cost* is the cost of producing x units of the product.

Revenue and Cost Functions

A company produces and sells x units of a product.

Revenue Function

$$R(x) = (\text{price per unit sold})x$$

Cost Function

$$C(x) = \text{fixed cost} + (\text{cost per unit produced})x$$

The point of intersection of the graphs of the revenue and cost functions is called the **break-even point**. The x-coordinate of the point reveals the number of units that a company must produce and sell so that money coming in, the revenue, is equal to money going out, the cost. The y-coordinate of the break-even point gives the amount of money coming in and going out. Example 7 illustrates the use of the substitution method in determining a company's break-even point.

EXAMPLE 7   Finding a Break-Even Point

Technology is now promising to bring light, fast, and beautiful wheelchairs to millions of people with disabilities. A company is planning to manufacture these radically different wheelchairs. Fixed cost will be $500,000 and it will cost $400 to produce each wheelchair. Each wheelchair will be sold for $600.

a. Write the cost function, C, of producing x wheelchairs.
b. Write the revenue function, R, from the sale of x wheelchairs.
c. Determine the break-even point. Describe what this means.

SOLUTION

a. The cost function is the sum of the fixed cost and variable cost.

> Fixed cost of $500,000   plus   Variable cost: $400 for each chair produced

$$C(x) = 500,000 + 400x$$

b. The revenue function is the money generated from the sale of x wheelchairs.

> Revenue per chair, $600, times   the number of chairs sold

$$R(x) = 600x$$

c. The break-even point occurs where the graphs of C and R intersect. Thus, we find this point by solving the system

$$\begin{cases} C(x) = 500,000 + 400x \\ R(x) = 600x \end{cases} \quad \text{or} \quad \begin{cases} y = 500,000 + 400x \\ y = 600x. \end{cases}$$

Using substitution, we can substitute $600x$ for y in the first equation:

$$600x = 500,000 + 400x \qquad \text{Substitute } 600x \text{ for } y \text{ in } y = 500,000 + 400x.$$

$$200x = 500,000 \qquad \text{Subtract } 400x \text{ from both sides.}$$

$$x = 2500. \qquad \text{Divide both sides by 200.}$$

Back-substituting 2500 for x in either of the system's equations (or functions), we obtain

$$R(2500) = 600(2500) = 1,500,000.$$

> We used $R(x) = 600x$.

The break-even point is $(2500, 1,500,000)$. This means that the company will break even if it produces and sells 2500 wheelchairs. At this level, the money coming in is equal to the money going out: $1,500,000. • • •

FIGURE 5.6

Figure 5.6 shows the graphs of the revenue and cost functions for the wheelchair business. Similar graphs and models apply no matter how small or large a business venture may be.

The intersection point confirms that the company breaks even by producing and selling 2500 wheelchairs. Can you see what happens for $x < 2500$? The red cost graph lies above the blue revenue graph. The cost is greater than the revenue and the business is losing money. Thus, if the company sells fewer than 2500 wheelchairs, the result is a *loss*. By contrast, look at what happens for $x > 2500$. The blue revenue graph lies above the red cost graph. The revenue is greater than the cost and the business is making money. Thus, if the company sells more than 2500 wheelchairs, the result is a *gain*.

⊘ Check Point **7** A company that manufactures running shoes has a fixed cost of $300,000. Additionally, it costs $30 to produce each pair of shoes. They are sold at $80 per pair.

  a. Write the cost function, C, of producing x pairs of running shoes.

  b. Write the revenue function, R, from the sale of x pairs of running shoes.

  c. Determine the break-even point. Describe what this means.

What does every entrepreneur, from a kid selling lemonade to Mark Zuckerberg, want to do? Generate profit, of course. The *profit* made is the money taken in, or the revenue, minus the money spent, or the cost. This relationship between revenue and cost allows us to define the *profit function, P(x)*.

The Profit Function

The profit, $P(x)$, generated after producing and selling x units of a product is given by the **profit function**

$$P(x) = R(x) - C(x),$$

where R and C are the revenue and cost functions, respectively.

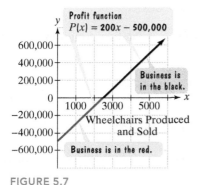

FIGURE 5.7

The profit function for the wheelchair business in Example 7 is

$$P(x) = R(x) - C(x)$$
$$= 600x - (500,000 + 400x)$$
$$= 200x - 500,000.$$

The graph of this profit function is shown in **Figure 5.7**. The red portion lies below the x-axis and shows a loss when fewer than 2500 wheelchairs are sold. The business is "in the red." The black portion lies above the x-axis and shows a gain when more than 2500 wheelchairs are sold. The wheelchair business is "in the black."

CONCEPT AND VOCABULARY CHECK

Fill in each blank so that the resulting statement is true.

1. A solution to a system of linear equations in two variables is an ordered pair that _____

_____.

2. When solving a system of linear equations by graphing, the system's solution is determined by locating _____.

3. When solving

$$\begin{cases} 3x - 2y = 5 \\ y = 3x - 3 \end{cases}$$

by the substitution method, we obtain $x = \frac{1}{3}$, so the solution set is _____.

4. When solving

$$\begin{cases} 2x + 10y = 9 \\ 8x + 5y = 7 \end{cases}$$

by the addition method, we can eliminate y by multiplying the second equation by _____ and then adding the equations.

5. When solving

$$\begin{cases} 4x - 3y = 15 \\ 3x - 2y = 10 \end{cases}$$

by the addition method, we can eliminate y by multiplying the first equation by 2 and the second equation by _____, and then adding the equations.

6. When solving

$$\begin{cases} 12x - 21y = 24 \\ 4x - 7y = 7 \end{cases}$$

by the addition method, we obtain $0 = 3$, so the solution set is _____. The linear system is a/an _____ system. If you attempt to solve such a system by graphing, you will obtain two lines that are _____.

7. When solving

$$\begin{cases} x = 3y + 2 \\ 5x - 15y = 10 \end{cases}$$

by the substitution method, we obtain $10 = 10$, so the solution set is _____.
The equations in this system are called _____. If you attempt to solve such a system by graphing, you will obtain two lines that _____.

8. A company's _____ function is the money generated by selling x units of its product. The difference between this function and the company's cost function is called its _____ function.

9. A company has a graph that shows the money it generates by selling x units of its product. It also has a graph that shows its cost of producing x units of its product. The point of intersection of these graphs is called the company's _____.

EXERCISE SET 5.1

Practice Exercises

In Exercises 1–4, determine whether the given ordered pair is a solution of the system.

1. $(2, 3)$
$$\begin{cases} x + 3y = 11 \\ x - 5y = -13 \end{cases}$$

2. $(-3, 5)$
$$\begin{cases} 9x + 7y = 8 \\ 8x - 9y = -69 \end{cases}$$

3. $(2, 5)$
$$\begin{cases} 2x + 3y = 17 \\ x + 4y = 16 \end{cases}$$

4. $(8, 5)$
$$\begin{cases} 5x - 4y = 20 \\ 3y = 2x + 1 \end{cases}$$

In Exercises 5–18, solve each system by the substitution method.

5. $\begin{cases} x + y = 4 \\ y = 3x \end{cases}$

6. $\begin{cases} x + y = 6 \\ y = 2x \end{cases}$

7. $\begin{cases} x + 3y = 8 \\ y = 2x - 9 \end{cases}$

8. $\begin{cases} 2x - 3y = -13 \\ y = 2x + 7 \end{cases}$

9. $\begin{cases} x = 4y - 2 \\ x = 6y + 8 \end{cases}$

10. $\begin{cases} x = 3y + 7 \\ x = 2y - 1 \end{cases}$

11. $\begin{cases} 5x + 2y = 0 \\ x - 3y = 0 \end{cases}$

12. $\begin{cases} 4x + 3y = 0 \\ 2x - y = 0 \end{cases}$

13. $\begin{cases} 2x + 5y = -4 \\ 3x - y = 11 \end{cases}$

14. $\begin{cases} 2x + 5y = 1 \\ -x + 6y = 8 \end{cases}$

15. $\begin{cases} 2x - 3y = 8 - 2x \\ 3x + 4y = x + 3y + 14 \end{cases}$

16. $\begin{cases} 3x - 4y = x - y + 4 \\ 2x + 6y = 5y - 4 \end{cases}$

17. $\begin{cases} y = \dfrac{1}{3}x + \dfrac{2}{3} \\ y = \dfrac{5}{7}x - 2 \end{cases}$

18. $\begin{cases} y = -\dfrac{1}{2}x + 2 \\ y = \dfrac{3}{4}x + 7 \end{cases}$

In Exercises 19–30, solve each system by the addition method.

19. $\begin{cases} x + y = 1 \\ x - y = 3 \end{cases}$

20. $\begin{cases} x + y = 6 \\ x - y = -2 \end{cases}$

21. $\begin{cases} 2x + 3y = 6 \\ 2x - 3y = 6 \end{cases}$

22. $\begin{cases} 3x + 2y = 14 \\ 3x - 2y = 10 \end{cases}$

23. $\begin{cases} x + 2y = 2 \\ -4x + 3y = 25 \end{cases}$

24. $\begin{cases} 2x - 7y = 2 \\ 3x + y = -20 \end{cases}$

25. $\begin{cases} 4x + 3y = 15 \\ 2x - 5y = 1 \end{cases}$

26. $\begin{cases} 3x - 7y = 13 \\ 6x + 5y = 7 \end{cases}$

27. $\begin{cases} 3x - 4y = 11 \\ 2x + 3y = -4 \end{cases}$

28. $\begin{cases} 2x + 3y = -16 \\ 5x - 10y = 30 \end{cases}$

29. $\begin{cases} 3x = 4y + 1 \\ 3y = 1 - 4x \end{cases}$

30. $\begin{cases} 5x = 6y + 40 \\ 2y = 8 - 3x \end{cases}$

In Exercises 31–42, solve by the method of your choice. Identify systems with no solution and systems with infinitely many solutions, using set notation to express their solution sets.

31. $\begin{cases} x = 9 - 2y \\ x + 2y = 13 \end{cases}$

32. $\begin{cases} 6x + 2y = 7 \\ y = 2 - 3x \end{cases}$

33. $\begin{cases} y = 3x - 5 \\ 21x - 35 = 7y \end{cases}$

34. $\begin{cases} 9x - 3y = 12 \\ y = 3x - 4 \end{cases}$

35. $\begin{cases} 3x - 2y = -5 \\ 4x + y = 8 \end{cases}$

36. $\begin{cases} 2x + 5y = -4 \\ 3x - y = 11 \end{cases}$

37. $\begin{cases} x + 3y = 2 \\ 3x + 9y = 6 \end{cases}$

38. $\begin{cases} 4x - 2y = 2 \\ 2x - y = 1 \end{cases}$

39. $\begin{cases} \dfrac{x}{4} - \dfrac{y}{4} = -1 \\ x + 4y = -9 \end{cases}$

40. $\begin{cases} \dfrac{x}{6} - \dfrac{y}{2} = \dfrac{1}{3} \\ x + 2y = -3 \end{cases}$

41. $\begin{cases} 2x = 3y + 4 \\ 4x = 3 - 5y \end{cases}$

42. $\begin{cases} 4x = 3y + 8 \\ 2x = -14 + 5y \end{cases}$

In Exercises 43–46, let x represent one number and let y represent the other number. Use the given conditions to write a system of equations. Solve the system and find the numbers.

43. The sum of two numbers is 7. If one number is subtracted from the other, their difference is −1. Find the numbers.

44. The sum of two numbers is 2. If one number is subtracted from the other, their difference is 8. Find the numbers.

45. Three times a first number decreased by a second number is 1. The first number increased by twice the second number is 12. Find the numbers.

46. The sum of three times a first number and twice a second number is 8. If the second number is subtracted from twice the first number, the result is 3. Find the numbers.

Practice Plus

In Exercises 47–48, solve each system by the method of your choice.

47. $\begin{cases} \dfrac{x + 2}{2} - \dfrac{y + 4}{3} = 3 \\ \dfrac{x + y}{5} = \dfrac{x - y}{2} - \dfrac{5}{2} \end{cases}$

48. $\begin{cases} \dfrac{x - y}{3} = \dfrac{x + y}{2} - \dfrac{1}{2} \\ \dfrac{x + 2}{2} - 4 = \dfrac{y + 4}{3} \end{cases}$

In Exercises 49–50, solve each system for x and y, expressing either value in terms of a or b, if necessary. Assume that $a \neq 0$ and $b \neq 0$.

49. $\begin{cases} 5ax + 4y = 17 \\ ax + 7y = 22 \end{cases}$ **50.** $\begin{cases} 4ax + by = 3 \\ 6ax + 5by = 8 \end{cases}$

51. For the linear function $f(x) = mx + b, f(-2) = 11$ and $f(3) = -9$. Find m and b.

52. For the linear function $f(x) = mx + b, f(-3) = 23$ and $f(2) = -7$. Find m and b.

Use the graphs of the linear functions to solve Exercises 53–54.

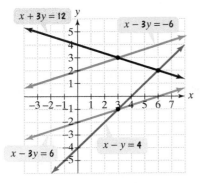

53. Write the linear system whose solution set is $\{(6, 2)\}$. Express each equation in the system in slope-intercept form.

54. Write the linear system whose solution set is $\varnothing$. Express each equation in the system in slope-intercept form.

Application Exercises

The figure shows the graphs of the cost and revenue functions for a company that manufactures and sells small radios. Use the information in the figure to solve Exercises 55–60.

Radios Produced and Sold

55. How many radios must be produced and sold for the company to break even?

56. More than how many radios must be produced and sold for the company to have a profit?

57. Use the formulas shown in the voice balloons to find $R(200) - C(200)$. Describe what this means for the company.

58. Use the formulas shown in the voice balloons to find $R(300) - C(300)$. Describe what this means for the company.

59. a. Use the formulas shown in the voice balloons to write the company's profit function, P, from producing and selling x radios.

  b. Find the company's profit if 10,000 radios are produced and sold.

60. a. Use the formulas shown in the voice balloons to write the company's profit function, P, from producing and selling x radios.

  b. Find the company's profit if 20,000 radios are produced and sold.

Exercises 61–64 describe a number of business ventures. For each exercise,

  a. *Write the cost function, C.*

  b. *Write the revenue function, R.*

  c. *Determine the break-even point. Describe what this means.*

61. A company that manufactures small canoes has a fixed cost of $18,000. It costs $20 to produce each canoe. The selling price is $80 per canoe. (In solving this exercise, let x represent the number of canoes produced and sold.)

62. A company that manufactures bicycles has a fixed cost of $100,000. It costs $100 to produce each bicycle. The selling price is $300 per bike. (In solving this exercise, let x represent the number of bicycles produced and sold.)

63. You invest in a new play. The cost includes an overhead of $30,000, plus production costs of $2500 per performance. A sold-out performance brings in $3125. (In solving this exercise, let x represent the number of sold-out performances.)

64. You invested $30,000 and started a business writing greeting cards. Supplies cost 2¢ per card and you are selling each card for 50¢. (In solving this exercise, let x represent the number of cards produced and sold.)

*An important application of systems of equations arises in connection with supply and demand. As the price of a product increases, the demand for that product decreases. However, at higher prices, suppliers are willing to produce greater quantities of the product. The price at which supply and demand are equal is called the **equilibrium price**. The quantity supplied and demanded at that price is called the **equilibrium quantity**. Exercises 65–66 involve supply and demand.*

65. The following models describe wages for low-skilled labor.

Demand Model	**Supply Model**
$p = -0.325x + 5.8$	$p = 0.375x + 3$
Price of labor (per hour) — Millions of workers employers will hire	Price of labor (per hour) — Millions of available workers

Source: O'Sullivan and Sheffrin, *Economics*, Prentice Hall, 2007.

  a. Solve the system and find the equilibrium number of workers, in millions, and the equilibrium hourly wage.

  b. Use your answer from part (a) to complete this statement:

   If workers are paid _____ per hour, there will be ____ million available workers and ____ million workers will be hired.

  c. In 2007, the federal minimum wage was set at $5.15 per hour. Substitute 5.15 for p in the demand model, $p = -0.325x + 5.8$, and determine the millions of workers employers will hire at this price.

  d. At a minimum wage of $5.15 per hour, use the supply model, $p = 0.375x + 3$, to determine the millions of available workers. Round to one decimal place.

  e. At a minimum wage of $5.15 per hour, use your answers from parts (c) and (d) to determine how many more people are looking for work than employers are willing to hire.

66. The following models describe demand and supply for three-bedroom rental apartments.

Demand Model

$p = -50x + 2000$

Monthly rental price

Number of apartments demanded, in thousands

Supply Model

$p = 50x$

Monthly rental price

Number of apartments supplied, in thousands

a. Solve the system and find the equilibrium quantity and the equilibrium price.

b. Use your answer from part (a) to complete this statement:

When rents are _____ per month, consumers will demand _____ apartments and suppliers will offer _____ apartments for rent.

67. The bar graph indicates that fewer U.S. adults are getting married.

Marital Status of U.S. Adults

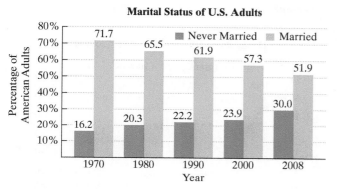

Source: U.S. Census Bureau

The data can be modeled by the following system of linear equations:

$$\begin{cases} -3x + 10y = 160 \\ x + 2y = 142. \end{cases}$$

Percentage of never-married American adults, y, x years after 1970

Percentage of married American adults, y, x years after 1970

a. Use these models to determine the year, rounded to the nearest year, when the percentage of never-married adults will be the same as the percentage of married adults. For that year, approximately what percentage of Americans, rounded to the nearest percent, will belong to each group?

b. How is your approximate solution from part (a) shown by the following graphs?

68. The bar graph shows the percentage of Americans for and against the death penalty for a person convicted of murder.

Are You in Favor of the Death Penalty for a Person Convicted of Murder?

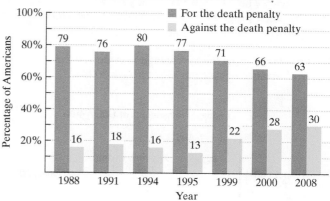

Source: *Newsweek* poll

The data can be modeled by the following system of equations:

$$\begin{cases} 13x + 12y = 992 \\ -x + y = 16. \end{cases}$$

The percent, y, in favor of the death penalty x years after 1988

The percent, y, against the death penalty x years after 1988

In which year will the percentage of Americans in favor of the death penalty be the same as the percentage of Americans who oppose it? For that year, what percent will be for the death penalty and what percent will be against it?

69. We opened this section with a study showing that late in the semester, procrastinating students reported more symptoms of physical illness than their nonprocrastinating peers.

a. At the beginning of the semester, procrastinators reported an average of 0.8 symptoms, increasing at a rate of 0.45 symptoms per week. Write a function that models the average number of symptoms after x weeks.

b. At the beginning of the semester, nonprocrastinators reported an average of 2.6 symptoms, increasing at a rate of 0.15 symptoms per week. Write a function that models the average number of symptoms after x weeks.

c. By which week in the semester did both groups report the same number of symptoms of physical illness? For that week, how many symptoms were reported by each group? How is this shown in **Figure 5.1** on page 516?

70. Although Social Security is a problem, some projections indicate that there's a much bigger time bomb ticking in the federal budget, and that's Medicare. In 2000, the cost of Social Security was 5.48% of the gross domestic product, increasing by 0.04% of the GDP per year. In 2000, the cost of Medicare was 1.84% of the gross domestic product, increasing by 0.17% of the GDP per year.

(Source: Congressional Budget Office)

(Exercise 70 continues on the next page.)

a. Write a function that models the cost of Social Security as a percentage of the GDP x years after 2000.

b. Write a function that models the cost of Medicare as a percentage of the GDP x years after 2000.

c. In which year will the cost of Medicare and Social Security be the same? For that year, what will be the cost of each program as a percentage of the GDP? Which program will have the greater cost after that year?

71. The graphs show the percentage of American adults in two living arrangements from 1960 through 2008.

Living Arrangements of U.S. Adults

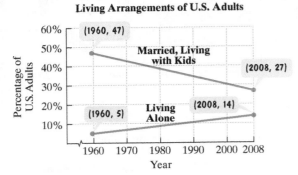

Source: U.S. Census Bureau

a. Write the slope-intercept equation of the line that models the percentage of U.S. adults living alone, y, x years after 1960. Round the value of the slope, m, to one decimal place.

b. Write the slope-intercept equation of the line that models the percentage of married U.S. adults living with kids, y, x years after 1960. Round the value of the slope, m, to one decimal place.

c. Use the models from parts (a) and (b) to project the year in which the percentage of adults living alone will be the same as the percentage of married adults living with kids. What percentage of U.S. adults will belong to each group during that year?

72. The graphs show that the U.S. public has taken a more conservative stance on gun control for the period from 1999 through 2009.

U.S. Public Opinion on Gun Control

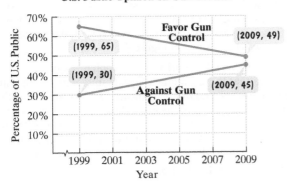

Source: pewresearch.org

a. Write the slope-intercept equation of the line that models the percentage of the U.S. public that favors gun control, y, x years after 1999.

b. Write the slope-intercept equation of the line that models the percentage of the U.S. public against gun control, y, x years after 1999.

c. Use the models from parts (a) and (b) to project the year, to the nearest whole year, during which the percentage in favor of gun control was the same as the percentage against gun control. What percentage of the U.S. public, to the nearest percent, shared each of these opinions during that year?

Use a system of linear equations to solve Exercises 73–84.

Looking for Mr. Goodbar? It's probably not a good idea if you want to look like Mr. Universe or Julia Roberts. The graph shows the four candy bars with the highest fat content, representing grams of fat and calories in each bar. Exercises 73–76 are based on the graph.

Candy Bars with the Highest Fat Content

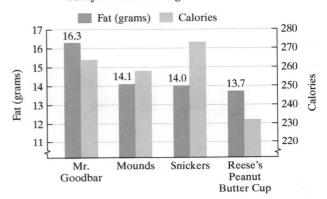

Source: Krantz and Sveum, *The World's Worsts,* HarperCollins, 2005

73. One Mr. Goodbar and two Mounds bars contain 780 calories. Two Mr. Goodbars and one Mounds bar contain 786 calories. Find the caloric content of each candy bar.

74. One Snickers bar and two Reese's Peanut Butter Cups contain 737 calories. Two Snickers bars and one Reese's Peanut Butter Cup contain 778 calories. Find the caloric content of each candy bar.

75. A collection of Halloween candy contains a total of five Mr. Goodbars and Mounds bars. Chew on this: The grams of fat in these candy bars exceed the daily maximum desirable fat intake of 70 grams by 7.1 grams. How many bars of each kind of candy are contained in the Halloween collection?

76. A collection of Halloween candy contains a total of 12 Snickers bars and Reese's Peanut Butter Cups. Chew on this: The grams of fat in these candy bars exceed twice the daily maximum desirable fat intake of 70 grams by 26.5 grams. How many bars of each kind of candy are contained in the Halloween collection?

77. A hotel has 200 rooms. Those with kitchen facilities rent for $100 per night and those without kitchen facilities rent for $80 per night. On a night when the hotel was completely occupied, revenues were $17,000. How many of each type of room does the hotel have?

78. A new restaurant is to contain two-seat tables and four-seat tables. Fire codes limit the restaurant's maximum occupancy to 56 customers. If the owners have hired enough servers to handle 17 tables of customers, how many of each kind of table should they purchase?

79. A rectangular lot whose perimeter is 360 feet is fenced along three sides. An expensive fencing along the lot's length costs $20 per foot and an inexpensive fencing along the two side widths costs only $8 per foot. The total cost of the fencing along the three sides comes to $3280. What are the lot's dimensions?

80. A rectangular lot whose perimeter is 320 feet is fenced along three sides. An expensive fencing along the lot's length costs $16 per foot and an inexpensive fencing along the two side widths costs only $5 per foot. The total cost of the fencing along the three sides comes to $2140. What are the lot's dimensions?

81. When a crew rows with the current, it travels 16 miles in 2 hours. Against the current, the crew rows 8 miles in 2 hours. Let x = the crew's rowing rate in still water and let y = the rate of the current. The following chart summarizes this information:

	Rate	×	Time	=	Distance
Rowing with current	$x + y$		2		16
Rowing against current	$x - y$		2		8

Find the rate of rowing in still water and the rate of the current.

82. When an airplane flies with the wind, it travels 800 miles in 4 hours. Against the wind, it takes 5 hours to cover the same distance. Find the plane's rate in still air and the rate of the wind.

In Exercises 83–84, an isosceles triangle containing two angles with equal measure is shown. The degree measure of each triangle's three interior angles and an exterior angle is represented with variables. Find the measure of the three interior angles.

83.

84.

Writing in Mathematics

85. What is a system of linear equations? Provide an example with your description.

86. What is the solution of a system of linear equations?

87. Explain how to solve a system of equations using the substitution method. Use $y = 3 - 3x$ and $3x + 4y = 6$ to illustrate your explanation.

88. Explain how to solve a system of equations using the addition method. Use $3x + 5y = -2$ and $2x + 3y = 0$ to illustrate your explanation.

89. When is it easier to use the addition method rather than the substitution method to solve a system of equations?

90. When using the addition or substitution method, how can you tell if a system of linear equations has infinitely many solutions? What is the relationship between the graphs of the two equations?

91. When using the addition or substitution method, how can you tell if a system of linear equations has no solution? What is the relationship between the graphs of the two equations?

92. Describe the break-even point for a business.

Technology Exercise

93. Verify your solutions to any five exercises in Exercises 5–42 by using a graphing utility to graph the two equations in the system in the same viewing rectangle. Then use the intersection feature to display the solution.

Critical Thinking Exercises

Make Sense? *In Exercises 94–97, determine whether each statement makes sense or does not make sense, and explain your reasoning.*

94. Even if a linear system has a solution set involving fractions, such as $\{(\frac{8}{11}, \frac{43}{11})\}$, I can use graphs to determine if the solution set is reasonable.

95. Each equation in a system of linear equations has infinitely many ordered-pair solutions.

96. Every linear system has infinitely many ordered-pair solutions.

97. If I know the perimeter of this rectangle and triangle, each in the same unit of measure, I can use a system of linear equations to determine values for x and y.

 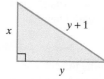

98. Write a system of equations having $\{(-2, 7)\}$ as a solution set. (More than one system is possible.)

99. Solve the system for x and y in terms of $a_1, b_1, c_1, a_2, b_2,$ and c_2:
$$\begin{cases} a_1x + b_1y = c_1 \\ a_2x + b_2y = c_2. \end{cases}$$

100. Two identical twins can only be distinguished by the characteristic that one always tells the truth and the other always lies. One twin tells you of a lucky number pair: "When I multiply my first lucky number by 3 and my second lucky number by 6, the addition of the resulting numbers produces a sum of 12. When I add my first lucky number and twice my second lucky number, the sum is 5." Which twin is talking?

101. A marching band has 52 members, and there are 24 in the pom-pom squad. They wish to form several hexagons and squares like those diagrammed below. Can it be done with no people left over?

B   B
B P B   B
B B

P   P
B
P   P

B = Band Member
P = Pom-pom Person

102. The group should write four different word problems that can be solved using a system of linear equations in two variables. All of the problems should be on different topics. The group should turn in the four problems and their algebraic solutions.

Preview Exercises

Exercises 103–105 will help you prepare for the material covered in the next section.

103. If $x = 3, y = 2,$ and $z = -3,$ does the ordered triple (x, y, z) satisfy the equation $2x - y + 4z = -8$?

104. Consider the following equations:

$$\begin{cases} 5x - 2y - 4z = \ \ 3 & \text{Equation 1} \\ 3x + 3y + 2z = -3. & \text{Equation 2} \end{cases}$$

Use this process to eliminate z: Copy Equation 1 and multiply Equation 2 by 2. Then add the equations.

105. Write an equation involving $a, b,$ and c based on the following description:

When the value of x in $y = ax^2 + bx + c$ is 4, the value of y is 1682.

SECTION 5.2   Systems of Linear Equations in Three Variables

Objectives

1. Verify the solution of a system of linear equations in three variables.

2. Solve systems of linear equations in three variables.

3. Solve problems using systems in three variables.

1. Verify the solution of a system of linear equations in three variables.

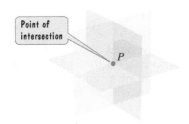

Point of intersection

P

FIGURE 5.8

All animals sleep, but the length of time they sleep varies widely: Cattle sleep for only a few minutes at a time. We humans seem to need more sleep than other animals, up to eight hours a day. Without enough sleep, we have difficulty concentrating, make mistakes in routine tasks, lose energy, and feel bad-tempered. There is a relationship between hours of sleep and death rate per year per 100,000 people. How many hours of sleep will put you in the group with the minimum death rate? In this section, we will answer this question by solving a system of linear equations with more than two variables.

Systems of Linear Equations in Three Variables and Their Solutions

An equation such as $x + 2y - 3z = 9$ is called a *linear equation in three variables*. In general, any equation of the form

$$Ax + By + Cz = D,$$

where $A, B, C,$ and D are real numbers such that $A, B,$ and C are not all 0, is a **linear equation in three variables: $x, y,$ and z.** The graph of this linear equation in three variables is a plane in three-dimensional space.

The process of solving a system of three linear equations in three variables is geometrically equivalent to finding the point of intersection (assuming that there is one) of three planes in space. (See **Figure 5.8.**) A **solution** of a system of linear equations in three variables is an ordered triple of real numbers that satisfies all equations of the system. The **solution set** of the system is the set of all its solutions.

EXAMPLE 1   Determining Whether an Ordered Triple Satisfies a System

Show that the ordered triple $(-1, 2, -2)$ is a solution of the system:

$$\begin{cases} x + 2y - 3z = 9 \\ 2x - y + 2z = -8 \\ -x + 3y - 4z = 15. \end{cases}$$

SOLUTION

Because -1 is the x-coordinate, 2 is the y-coordinate, and -2 is the z-coordinate of $(-1, 2, -2),$ we replace x with $-1, y$ with 2, and z with -2 in each of the three equations.

$$\begin{array}{rcl} x + 2y - 3z &=& 9 \\ -1 + 2(2) - 3(-2) &\overset{?}{=}& 9 \\ -1 + 4 + 6 &\overset{?}{=}& 9 \\ 9 &=& 9, \quad \text{true} \end{array}$$

$$\begin{array}{rcl} 2x - y + 2z &=& -8 \\ 2(-1) - 2 + 2(-2) &\overset{?}{=}& -8 \\ -2 - 2 - 4 &\overset{?}{=}& -8 \\ -8 &=& -8, \quad \text{true} \end{array}$$

$$\begin{array}{rcl} -x + 3y - 4z &=& 15 \\ -(-1) + 3(2) - 4(-2) &\overset{?}{=}& 15 \\ 1 + 6 + 8 &\overset{?}{=}& 15 \\ 15 &=& 15, \quad \text{true} \end{array}$$

The ordered triple $(-1, 2, -2)$ satisfies the three equations: It makes each equation true. Thus, the ordered triple is a solution of the system.

● ● ●

✓ Check Point 1 Show that the ordered triple $(-1, -4, 5)$ is a solution of the system:

$$\begin{cases} x - 2y + 3z = 22 \\ 2x - 3y - z = 5 \\ 3x + y - 5z = -32. \end{cases}$$

② Solve systems of linear equations in three variables.

Solving Systems of Linear Equations in Three Variables by Eliminating Variables

The method for solving a system of linear equations in three variables is similar to that used on systems of linear equations in two variables. We use addition to eliminate any variable, reducing the system to two equations in two variables. Once we obtain a system of two equations in two variables, we use addition or substitution to eliminate a variable. The result is a single equation in one variable. We solve this equation to get the value of the remaining variable. Other variable values are found by back-substitution.

GREAT QUESTION!

When solving a linear system in three variables, which variable should I eliminate first?

It does not matter which variable you eliminate first, as long as you eliminate the same variable in two different pairs of equations.

Solving Linear Systems in Three Variables by Eliminating Variables

1. Reduce the system to two equations in two variables. This is usually accomplished by taking two different pairs of equations and using the addition method to eliminate the same variable from both pairs.
2. Solve the resulting system of two equations in two variables using addition or substitution. The result is an equation in one variable that gives the value of that variable.
3. Back-substitute the value of the variable found in step 2 into either of the equations in two variables to find the value of the second variable.
4. Use the values of the two variables from steps 2 and 3 to find the value of the third variable by back-substituting into one of the original equations.
5. Check the proposed solution in each of the original equations.

EXAMPLE 2 Solving a System in Three Variables

Solve the system:

$$\begin{cases} 5x - 2y - 4z = 3 & \text{Equation 1} \\ 3x + 3y + 2z = -3 & \text{Equation 2} \\ -2x + 5y + 3z = 3. & \text{Equation 3} \end{cases}$$

SOLUTION

There are many ways to proceed. Because our initial goal is to reduce the system to two equations in two variables, **the central idea is to take two different pairs of equations and eliminate the same variable from both pairs.**

Step 1 Reduce the system to two equations in two variables. We choose any two equations and use the addition method to eliminate a variable. Let's eliminate z using Equations 1 and 2. We do so by multiplying Equation 2 by 2. Then we add equations.

$$\begin{array}{lll} \text{(Equation 1)} & \begin{cases} 5x - 2y - 4z = 3 \\ 3x + 3y + 2z = -3 \end{cases} & \xrightarrow{\text{No change}} \begin{cases} 5x - 2y - 4z = 3 \\ 6x + 6y + 4z = -6 \end{cases} \\ \text{(Equation 2)} & & \xrightarrow{\text{Multiply by 2.}} \end{array}$$

$$\text{Add:} \quad 11x + 4y = -3 \quad \text{Equation 4}$$

$$\begin{cases} 5x - 2y - 4z = 3 & \text{Equation 1} \\ 3x + 3y + 2z = -3 & \text{Equation 2} \\ -2x + 5y + 3z = 3 & \text{Equation 3} \end{cases}$$

The given system (repeated)

Now we must eliminate the *same* variable using another pair of equations. We can eliminate z from Equations 2 and 3. First, we multiply Equation 2 by -3. Next, we multiply Equation 3 by 2. Finally, we add equations.

(Equation 2)
(Equation 3)

$$\begin{cases} 3x + 3y + 2z = -3 \\ -2x + 5y + 3z = 3 \end{cases} \quad \xrightarrow{\text{Multiply by } -3.} \quad \begin{cases} -9x - 9y - 6z = 9 \\ -4x + 10y + 6z = 6 \end{cases}$$

Add: $\quad -13x + \quad y \quad = 15 \quad$ Equation 5

Equation 4, $11x + 4y = -3$, obtained on the previous page, and Equation 5, $-13x + y = 15$, obtained above, give us a system of two equations in two variables:

$$\begin{cases} 11x + 4y = -3 & \text{Equation 4} \\ -13x + y = 15. & \text{Equation 5} \end{cases}$$

Step 2   Solve the resulting system of two equations in two variables. We will use the addition method to solve Equations 4 and 5 for x and y. To do so, we multiply Equation 5 on both sides by -4 and add this to Equation 4.

(Equation 4)
(Equation 5)

$$\begin{cases} 11x + 4y = -3 \\ -13x + y = 15 \end{cases} \quad \xrightarrow[\text{Multiply by } -4.]{\text{No change}} \quad \begin{cases} 11x + 4y = -3 \\ 52x - 4y = -60 \end{cases}$$

Add: $\quad 63x \quad = -63$

$\quad\quad\quad x \quad\quad = -1 \quad$ Divide both sides by 63.

Step 3   Use back-substitution in one of the equations in two variables to find the value of the second variable. We back-substitute -1 for x in either Equation 4 or 5 to find the value of y.

$$\begin{aligned} -13x + y &= 15 & \text{Equation 5} \\ -13(-1) + y &= 15 & \text{Substitute } -1 \text{ for } x. \\ 13 + y &= 15 & \text{Multiply.} \\ y &= 2 & \text{Subtract 13 from both sides.} \end{aligned}$$

Step 4   Back-substitute the values found for two variables into one of the original equations to find the value of the third variable. We can now use any one of the original equations and back-substitute the values of x and y to find the value for z. We will use Equation 2.

$$\begin{aligned} 3x + 3y + 2z &= -3 & \text{Equation 2} \\ 3(-1) + 3(2) + 2z &= -3 & \text{Substitute } -1 \text{ for } x \text{ and 2 for } y. \\ 3 + 2z &= -3 & \text{Multiply and then add:} \\ & & 3(-1) + 3(2) = -3 + 6 = 3. \\ 2z &= -6 & \text{Subtract 3 from both sides.} \\ z &= -3 & \text{Divide both sides by 2.} \end{aligned}$$

With $x = -1, y = 2$, and $z = -3$, the proposed solution is the ordered triple $(-1, 2, -3)$.

Step 5   Check. Check the proposed solution, $(-1, 2, -3)$, by substituting the values for x, y, and z into each of the three original equations. These substitutions yield three true statements. Thus, the solution set is $\{(-1, 2, -3)\}$.   • • •

⊘ Check Point **2**   Solve the system:

$$\begin{cases} x + 4y - z = 20 \\ 3x + 2y + z = 8 \\ 2x - 3y + 2z = -16. \end{cases}$$

In some examples, one of the variables is already eliminated from a given equation. In this case, the missing variable should be eliminated from the other two equations, thereby making it possible to omit one of the elimination steps. We illustrate this idea in Example 3.

EXAMPLE 3 Solving a System of Equations with a Missing Term

Solve the system:

$$\begin{cases} x + z = 8 & \text{Equation 1} \\ x + y + 2z = 17 & \text{Equation 2} \\ x + 2y + z = 16. & \text{Equation 3} \end{cases}$$

DISCOVERY

Solve Equation 1 for z and then replace z with $8 - x$ in Equations 2 and 3. Solve the resulting system of two equations in two variables. Compare your solution method with the one shown on the right. Which method do you prefer?

SOLUTION

Step 1 Reduce the system to two equations in two variables. Because Equation 1 contains only x and z, we could omit one of the elimination steps by eliminating y using Equations 2 and 3. This will give us two equations in x and z. To eliminate y using Equations 2 and 3, we multiply Equation 2 by -2 and add Equation 3.

(Equation 2) $\begin{cases} x + y + 2z = 17 \end{cases}$ $\xrightarrow[]{\text{Multiply by } -2.}$ $\begin{cases} -2x - 2y - 4z = -34 \end{cases}$
(Equation 3) $\begin{cases} x + 2y + z = 16 \end{cases}$ $\xrightarrow[]{\text{No change}}$ $\underline{x + 2y + z = 16}$

Add: $ -x - 3z = -18$ Equation 4

Equation 4 and the given Equation 1 provide us with a system of two equations in two variables:

$$\begin{cases} x + z = 8 & \text{Equation 1} \\ -x - 3z = -18. & \text{Equation 4} \end{cases}$$

Step 2 Solve the resulting system of two equations in two variables. We will solve Equations 1 and 4 for x and z.

$$\begin{cases} x + z = 8 & \text{Equation 1} \\ \underline{-x - 3z = -18} & \text{Equation 4} \end{cases}$$

Add: $ -2z = -10$
$ z = 5$ Divide both sides by -2.

Step 3 Use back-substitution in one of the equations in two variables to find the value of the second variable. To find x, we back-substitute 5 for z in either Equation 1 or 4. We will use Equation 1.

$x + z = 8$ Equation 1
$x + 5 = 8$ Substitute 5 for z.
$x = 3$ Subtract 5 from both sides.

Step 4 Back-substitute the values found for two variables into one of the original equations to find the value of the third variable. To find y, we back-substitute 3 for x and 5 for z into Equation 2 or 3. We cannot use Equation 1 because y is missing in this equation. We will use Equation 2.

$x + y + 2z = 17$ Equation 2
$3 + y + 2(5) = 17$ Substitute 3 for x and 5 for z.
$y + 13 = 17$ Multiply and add.
$y = 4$ Subtract 13 from both sides.

We found that $z = 5, x = 3$, and $y = 4$. Thus, the proposed solution is the ordered triple $(3, 4, 5)$.

Step 5 Check. Substituting 3 for x, 4 for y, and 5 for z into each of the three original equations yields three true statements. Consequently, the solution set is $\{(3, 4, 5)\}$. $\bullet\bullet\bullet$

$\oslash$ Check Point **3** Solve the system:

$$\begin{cases} 2y - z = 7 \\ x + 2y + z = 17 \\ 2x - 3y + 2z = -1. \end{cases}$$

A system of linear equations in three variables represents three planes. The three planes may not always intersect at one point. The planes may have no common point of intersection and represent an inconsistent system with no solution. By contrast, the planes may coincide or intersect along a line. In these cases, the planes have infinitely many points in common and represent systems with infinitely many solutions. Systems of linear equations in three variables that are inconsistent or that contain dependent equations will be discussed in Chapter 6.

③ Solve problems using systems in three variables.

Applications

Systems of equations may allow us to find models for data without using a graphing utility. Three data points that do not lie on or near a line determine the graph of a quadratic function of the form $y = ax^2 + bx + c, a \neq 0$. Quadratic functions often model situations in which values of y are decreasing and then increasing, suggesting the bowl-like shape of a parabola.

EXAMPLE 4 Modeling Data Relating Sleep and Death Rate

In a study relating sleep and death rate, the following data were obtained. Use the function $y = ax^2 + bx + c$ to model the data.

x (Average Number of Hours of Sleep)	y (Death Rate per Year per 100,000 Males)
4	1682
7	626
9	967

SOLUTION

We need to find values for a, b, and c in $y = ax^2 + bx + c$. We can do so by solving a system of three linear equations in a, b, and c. We obtain the three equations by using the values of x and y from the data as follows:

$y = ax^2 + bx + c$ *Use the quadratic function to model the data.*

When $x = 4, y = 1682$: $\begin{cases} 1682 = a \cdot 4^2 + b \cdot 4 + c \\ 626 = a \cdot 7^2 + b \cdot 7 + c \\ 967 = a \cdot 9^2 + b \cdot 9 + c \end{cases}$ or $\begin{cases} 16a + 4b + c = 1682 \\ 49a + 7b + c = 626 \\ 81a + 9b + c = 967. \end{cases}$
When $x = 7, y = 626$:
When $x = 9, y = 967$:

The easiest way to solve this system is to eliminate c from two pairs of equations, obtaining two equations in a and b. Solving this system gives $a = 104.5$, $b = -1501.5$, and $c = 6016$. We now substitute the values for a, b, and c into $y = ax^2 + bx + c$. The function that models the given data is

$$y = 104.5x^2 - 1501.5x + 6016.$$ • • •

We can use the model that we obtained in Example 4 to find the death rate of males who average, say, 6 hours of sleep. First, write the model in function notation:

$$f(x) = 104.5x^2 - 1501.5x + 6016.$$

Substitute 6 for x:

$$f(6) = 104.5(6)^2 - 1501.5(6) + 6016 = 769.$$

According to the model, the death rate for males who average 6 hours of sleep is 769 deaths per 100,000 males.

TECHNOLOGY

The graph of

$$y = 104.5x^2 - 1501.5x + 6016$$

is displayed in a [3, 12, 1] by [500, 2000, 100] viewing rectangle. The minimum function feature shows that the lowest point on the graph, the vertex, is approximately (7.2, 622.5). Men who average 7.2 hours of sleep are in the group with the lowest death rate, approximately 622.5 deaths per 100,000 males.

Minimum
X=7.212766 Y=622.53916

⊘ **Check Point 4** Find the quadratic function $y = ax^2 + bx + c$ whose graph passes through the points $(1, 4), (2, 1)$, and $(3, 4)$.

CONCEPT AND VOCABULARY CHECK

Fill in each blank so that the resulting statement is true.

1. A solution of a system of linear equations in three variables is an ordered _____ of real numbers that satisfies all/some of the equations in the system.

Circle the correct choice.

2. Consider the following system:

$$\begin{cases} x + y - z = -1 & \text{Equation 1} \\ 2x - 2y - 5z = 7 & \text{Equation 2} \\ 4x + y - 2z = 7. & \text{Equation 3} \end{cases}$$

We can eliminate x from Equations 1 and 2 by multiplying Equation 1 by _____ and adding equations. We can eliminate x from Equations 1 and 3 by multiplying Equation 1 by _____ and adding equations.

3. Consider the following system:

$$\begin{cases} x + y + z = 2 & \text{Equation 1} \\ 2x - 3y = 3 & \text{Equation 2} \\ 10y - z = 12. & \text{Equation 3} \end{cases}$$

Equation 2 does not contain the variable ____. To obtain a second equation that does not contain this variable, we can _____.

EXERCISE SET 5.2

Practice Exercises

In Exercises 1–4, determine if the given ordered triple is a solution of the system.

1. $(2, -1, 3)$
$$\begin{cases} x + y + z = 4 \\ x - 2y - z = 1 \\ 2x - y - 2z = -1 \end{cases}$$

2. $(5, -3, -2)$
$$\begin{cases} x + y + z = 0 \\ x + 2y - 3z = 5 \\ 3x + 4y + 2z = -1 \end{cases}$$

3. $(4, 1, 2)$
$$\begin{cases} x - 2y = 2 \\ 2x + 3y = 11 \\ y - 4z = -7 \end{cases}$$

4. $(-1, 3, 2)$
$$\begin{cases} x - 2z = -5 \\ y - 3z = -3 \\ 2x - z = -4 \end{cases}$$

Solve each system in Exercises 5–18.

5. $\begin{cases} x + y + 2z = 11 \\ x + y + 3z = 14 \\ x + 2y - z = 5 \end{cases}$

6. $\begin{cases} 2x + y - 2z = -1 \\ 3x - 3y - z = 5 \\ x - 2y + 3z = 6 \end{cases}$

7. $\begin{cases} 4x - y + 2z = 11 \\ x + 2y - z = -1 \\ 2x + 2y - 3z = -1 \end{cases}$

8. $\begin{cases} x - y + 3z = 8 \\ 3x + y - 2z = -2 \\ 2x + 4y + z = 0 \end{cases}$

9. $\begin{cases} 3x + 2y - 3z = -2 \\ 2x - 5y + 2z = -2 \\ 4x - 3y + 4z = 10 \end{cases}$

10. $\begin{cases} 2x + 3y + 7z = 13 \\ 3x + 2y - 5z = -22 \\ 5x + 7y - 3z = -28 \end{cases}$

11. $\begin{cases} 2x - 4y + 3z = 17 \\ x + 2y - z = 0 \\ 4x - y - z = 6 \end{cases}$

12. $\begin{cases} x + z = 3 \\ x + 2y - z = 1 \\ 2x - y + z = 3 \end{cases}$

13. $\begin{cases} 2x + y = 2 \\ x + y - z = 4 \\ 3x + 2y + z = 0 \end{cases}$

14. $\begin{cases} x + 3y + 5z = 20 \\ y - 4z = -16 \\ 3x - 2y + 9z = 36 \end{cases}$

15. $\begin{cases} x + y = -4 \\ y - z = 1 \\ 2x + y + 3z = -21 \end{cases}$

16. $\begin{cases} x + y = 4 \\ x + z = 4 \\ y + z = 4 \end{cases}$

17. $\begin{cases} 3(2x + y) + 5z = -1 \\ 2(x - 3y + 4z) = -9 \\ 4(1 + x) = -3(z - 3y) \end{cases}$

18. $\begin{cases} 7z - 3 = 2(x - 3y) \\ 5y + 3z - 7 = 4x \\ 4 + 5z = 3(2x - y) \end{cases}$

In Exercises 19–22, find the quadratic function $y = ax^2 + bx + c$ whose graph passes through the given points.

19. $(-1, 6), (1, 4), (2, 9)$

20. $(-2, 7), (1, -2), (2, 3)$

21. $(-1, -4), (1, -2), (2, 5)$

22. $(1, 3), (3, -1), (4, 0)$

In Exercises 23–24, let x represent the first number, y the second number, and z the third number. Use the given conditions to write a system of equations. Solve the system and find the numbers.

23. The sum of three numbers is 16. The sum of twice the first number, 3 times the second number, and 4 times the third number is 46. The difference between 5 times the first number and the second number is 31. Find the three numbers.

24. The following is known about three numbers: Three times the first number plus the second number plus twice the third number is 5. If 3 times the second number is subtracted from the sum of the first number and 3 times the third number, the result is 2. If the third number is subtracted from 2 times the first number and 3 times the second number, the result is 1. Find the numbers.

Solve each system in Exercises 25–26.

25. $\begin{cases} \dfrac{x+2}{6} - \dfrac{y+4}{3} + \dfrac{z}{2} = 0 \\ \dfrac{x+1}{2} + \dfrac{y-1}{2} - \dfrac{z}{4} = \dfrac{9}{2} \\ \dfrac{x-5}{4} + \dfrac{y+1}{3} + \dfrac{z-2}{2} = \dfrac{19}{4} \end{cases}$

26. $\begin{cases} \dfrac{x+3}{2} - \dfrac{y-1}{2} + \dfrac{z+2}{4} = \dfrac{3}{2} \\ \dfrac{x-5}{2} + \dfrac{y+1}{3} - \dfrac{z}{4} = -\dfrac{25}{6} \\ \dfrac{x-3}{4} - \dfrac{y+1}{2} + \dfrac{z-3}{2} = -\dfrac{5}{2} \end{cases}$

In Exercises 27–28, find the equation of the quadratic function $y = ax^2 + bx + c$ whose graph is shown. Select three points whose coordinates appear to be integers.

27.

28.

In Exercises 29–30, solve each system for (x, y, z) in terms of the nonzero constants a, b, and c.

29. $\begin{cases} ax - by - 2cz = 21 \\ ax + by + cz = 0 \\ 2ax - by + cz = 14 \end{cases}$ **30.** $\begin{cases} ax - by + 2cz = -4 \\ ax + 3by - cz = 1 \\ 2ax + by + 3cz = 2 \end{cases}$

31. You throw a ball straight up from a rooftop. The ball misses the rooftop on its way down and eventually strikes the ground. A mathematical model can be used to describe the relationship for the ball's height above the ground, y, after x seconds. Consider the following data:

x, seconds after the ball is thrown	y, ball's height, in feet, above the ground
1	224
3	176
4	104

a. Find the quadratic function $y = ax^2 + bx + c$ whose graph passes through the given points.

b. Use the function in part (a) to find the value for y when $x = 5$. Describe what this means.

32. A mathematical model can be used to describe the relationship between the number of feet a car travels once the brakes are applied, y, and the number of seconds the car is in motion after the brakes are applied, x. A research firm collects the following data:

x, seconds in motion after brakes are applied	y, feet car travels once the brakes are applied
1	46
2	84
3	114

a. Find the quadratic function $y = ax^2 + bx + c$ whose graph passes through the given points.

b. Use the function in part (a) to find the value for y when $x = 6$. Describe what this means.

Use a system of linear equations in three variables to solve Exercises 33–41.

The bar graph shows the average annual spending per person on selected items in 1980 and 2010. All dollar amounts are adjusted for inflation. Use this display to solve Exercises 33–34.

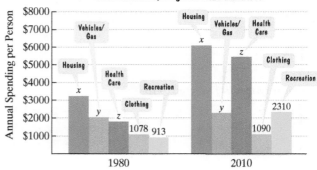

Annual Spending per Person in the United States, Adjusted for Inflation

Source: U.S. Bureau of Economic Analysis

33. In this exercise, we refer to annual spending per person in 2010. The combined spending on housing, vehicles/gas, and health care was $13,840. The difference between spending on housing and spending on vehicles/gas was $3864. The difference between spending on housing and spending on health care was $695. Find the average per-person spending on housing, vehicles/gas, and health care in 2010.

34. In this exercise, we refer to annual spending per person in 1980. The combined spending on housing, vehicles/gas, and health care was $7073. The difference between spending on housing and spending on vehicles/gas was $1247. The difference between spending on housing and spending on health care was $1466. Find the average per-person spending on housing, vehicles/gas, and health care in 1980.

35. On a recent trip to the convenience store, you picked up 2 gallons of milk, 5 bottles of water, and 6 snack-size bags of chips. Your total bill (before tax) was $19.00. If a bottle of water costs twice as much as a bag of chips, and a gallon of milk costs $2.00 more than a bottle of water, how much does each item cost?

36. On a recent trip to the convenience store, you picked up 1 gallon of milk, 7 bottles of water, and 4 snack-size bags of chips. Your total bill (before tax) was $17.00. If a bottle of water costs twice as much as a bag of chips, and a gallon of milk costs $2.00 more than a bottle of water, how much does each item cost?

37. At a college production of *A Streetcar Named Desire*, 400 tickets were sold. The ticket prices were $8, $10, and $12, and the total income from ticket sales was $3700. How many tickets of each type were sold if the combined number of $8 and $10 tickets sold was 7 times the number of $12 tickets sold?

38. A certain brand of razor blades comes in packages of 6, 12, and 24 blades, costing $2, $3, and $4 per package, respectively. A store sold 12 packages containing a total of 162 razor blades and took in $35. How many packages of each type were sold?

39. A person invested $6700 for one year, part at 8%, part at 10%, and the remainder at 12%. The total annual income from these investments was $716. The amount of money invested at 12% was $300 more than the amount invested at 8% and 10% combined. Find the amount invested at each rate.

40. A person invested $17,000 for one year, part at 10%, part at 12%, and the remainder at 15%. The total annual income from these investments was $2110. The amount of money invested at 12% was $1000 less than the amount invested at 10% and 15% combined. Find the amount invested at each rate.

41. In the following triangle, the degree measures of the three interior angles and two of the exterior angles are represented with variables. Find the measure of each interior angle.

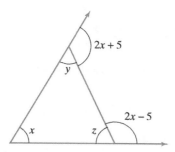

Writing in Mathematics

42. What is a system of linear equations in three variables?

43. How do you determine whether a given ordered triple is a solution of a system in three variables?

44. Describe in general terms how to solve a system in three variables.

45. AIDS is taking a deadly toll on southern Africa. Describe how to use the techniques that you learned in this section to obtain a model for African life span using projections with AIDS, shown by the red graph in the figure. Let x represent the number of years after 1985 and let y represent African life span in that year.

African Life Span

Source: United Nations

Technology Exercises

46. Does your graphing utility have a feature that allows you to solve linear systems by entering coefficients and constant terms? If so, use this feature to verify the solutions to any five exercises that you worked by hand from Exercises 5–16.

47. Verify your results in Exercises 19–22 by using a graphing utility to graph the resulting parabola. Trace along the curve and convince yourself that the three points given in the exercise lie on the parabola.

Critical Thinking Exercises

Make Sense? *In Exercises 48–51, determine whether each statement makes sense or does not make sense, and explain your reasoning.*

48. Solving a system in three variables, I found that $x = 3$ and $y = -1$. Because z represents a third variable, z cannot equal 3 or -1.

49. A system of linear equations in three variables, x, y, and z, cannot contain an equation in the form $y = mx + b$.

50. I'm solving a three-variable system in which one of the given equations has a missing term, so it will not be necessary to use any of the original equations twice when I reduce the system to two equations in two variables.

51. Because the percentage of the U.S. population that was foreign-born decreased from 1910 through 1970 and then increased after that, a quadratic function of the form $f(x) = ax^2 + bx + c$, rather than a linear function of the form $f(x) = mx + b$, should be used to model the data.

52. Describe how the system

$$\begin{cases} x + y - z - 2w = -8 \\ x - 2y + 3z + w = 18 \\ 2x + 2y + 2z - 2w = 10 \\ 2x + y - z + w = 3 \end{cases}$$

could be solved. Is it likely that in the near future a graphing utility will be available to provide a geometric solution (using intersecting graphs) to this system? Explain.

53. A modernistic painting consists of triangles, rectangles, and pentagons, all drawn so as to not overlap or share sides. Within each rectangle are drawn 2 red roses and each pentagon contains 5 carnations. How many triangles, rectangles, and pentagons appear in the painting if the painting contains a total of 40 geometric figures, 153 sides of geometric figures, and 72 flowers?

Group Exercise

54. Group members should develop appropriate functions that model each of the projections shown in Exercise 45.

Preview Exercises

Exercises 55–57 will help you prepare for the material covered in the next section.

55. Subtract: $\dfrac{3}{x-4} - \dfrac{2}{x+2}$.

56. Add: $\dfrac{5x-3}{x^2+1} + \dfrac{2x}{(x^2+1)^2}$.

57. Solve:

$$\begin{cases} A + B = 3 \\ 2A - 2B + C = 17 \\ 4A - 2C = 14. \end{cases}$$

SECTION 5.3   Partial Fractions

Objectives

① Decompose $\dfrac{P}{Q}$, where Q has only distinct linear factors.

② Decompose $\dfrac{P}{Q}$, where Q has repeated linear factors.

③ Decompose $\dfrac{P}{Q}$, where Q has a nonrepeated prime quadratic factor.

④ Decompose $\dfrac{P}{Q}$, where Q has a prime, repeated quadratic factor.

The rising and setting of the sun suggest the obvious: Things change over time. Calculus is the study of rates of change, allowing the motion of the rising sun to be measured by "freezing the frame" at one instant in time. If you are given a function, calculus reveals its rate of change at any "frozen" instant. In this section, you will learn an algebraic technique used in calculus to find a function if its rate of change is known. The technique involves expressing a given function in terms of simpler functions.

The Idea behind Partial Fraction Decomposition

We know how to use common denominators to write a sum or difference of rational expressions as a single rational expression. For example,

$$\frac{3}{x-4} - \frac{2}{x+2} = \frac{3(x+2) - 2(x-4)}{(x-4)(x+2)}$$

$$= \frac{3x+6-2x+8}{(x-4)(x+2)} = \frac{x+14}{(x-4)(x+2)}.$$

For solving the kind of calculus problem described in the section opener, we must reverse this process:

$\dfrac{x+14}{(x-4)(x+2)}$ is expressed as the sum of two simpler fractions.

Partial fraction   Partial fraction

$$\frac{x+14}{(x-4)(x+2)} = \frac{3}{x-4} + \frac{-2}{x+2}.$$

This is the partial fraction decomposition of $\dfrac{x+14}{(x-4)(x+2)}$.

Each of the two fractions on the right is called a **partial fraction**. The sum of these fractions is called the **partial fraction decomposition** of the rational expression on the left-hand side.

Partial fraction decompositions can be written for rational expressions of the form $\dfrac{P(x)}{Q(x)}$, where P and Q have no common factors and the highest power in the numerator is less than the highest power in the denominator. In this section, we will show you how to write the partial fraction decompositions for each of the following rational expressions:

$$\frac{9x^2 - 9x + 6}{(2x - 1)(x + 2)(x - 2)}$$

> $P(x) = 9x^2 - 9x + 6$; highest power = 2
>
> $Q(x) = (2x - 1)(x + 2)(x - 2)$; multiplying factors, highest power = 3.

$$\frac{5x^3 - 3x^2 + 7x - 3}{(x^2 + 1)^2}.$$

> $P(x) = 5x^3 - 3x^2 + 7x - 3$; highest power = 3
>
> $Q(x) = (x^2 + 1)^2$; squaring the expression, highest power = 4.

The partial fraction decomposition of a rational expression depends on the factors of the denominator. We consider four cases involving different kinds of factors in the denominator:

1. The denominator is a product of distinct linear factors.

2. The denominator is a product of linear factors, some of which are repeated.

3. The denominator has prime quadratic factors, none of which is repeated.

4. The denominator has a repeated prime quadratic factor.

1 Decompose $\dfrac{P}{Q}$, where Q has only distinct linear factors.

The Partial Fraction Decomposition of a Rational Expression with Distinct Linear Factors in the Denominator

If the denominator of a rational expression has a linear factor of the form $ax + b$, then the partial fraction decomposition will contain a term of the form

$$\frac{A}{ax + b}.$$

> A — Constant
>
> $ax + b$ — Linear factor

Each distinct linear factor in the denominator produces a partial fraction of the form *constant over linear factor*. For example,

$$\frac{9x^2 - 9x + 6}{(2x - 1)(x + 2)(x - 2)} = \frac{A}{2x - 1} + \frac{B}{x + 2} + \frac{C}{x - 2}.$$

> We write a constant over each linear factor in the denominator.

The Partial Fraction Decomposition of $\dfrac{P(x)}{Q(x)}$: $Q(x)$ Has Distinct Linear Factors

The form of the partial fraction decomposition for a rational expression with distinct linear factors in the denominator is

$$\frac{P(x)}{(a_1 x + b_1)(a_2 x + b_2)(a_3 x + b_3) \cdots (a_n x + b_n)}$$

$$= \frac{A_1}{a_1 x + b_1} + \frac{A_2}{a_2 x + b_2} + \frac{A_3}{a_3 x + b_3} + \cdots + \frac{A_n}{a_n x + b_n}.$$

EXAMPLE 1 Partial Fraction Decomposition with Distinct Linear Factors

Find the partial fraction decomposition of

$$\frac{x + 14}{(x - 4)(x + 2)}.$$

SOLUTION

We begin by setting up the partial fraction decomposition with the unknown constants. Write a constant over each of the two distinct linear factors in the denominator.

$$\frac{x + 14}{(x - 4)(x + 2)} = \frac{A}{x - 4} + \frac{B}{x + 2}$$

Our goal is to find A and B. We do this by multiplying both sides of the equation by the least common denominator, $(x - 4)(x + 2)$.

$$(x - 4)(x + 2)\frac{x + 14}{(x - 4)(x + 2)} = (x - 4)(x + 2)\left(\frac{A}{x - 4} + \frac{B}{x + 2}\right)$$

We use the distributive property on the right side.

$$(x - 4)(x + 2)\frac{x + 14}{(x - 4)(x + 2)}$$

$$= (x - 4)(x + 2)\frac{A}{(x - 4)} + (x - 4)(x + 2)\frac{B}{(x + 2)}$$

Dividing out common factors in numerators and denominators, we obtain

$$x + 14 = A(x + 2) + B(x - 4).$$

To find values for A and B that make both sides equal, we will express the sides in exactly the same form by writing the variable x-terms and then writing the constant terms. Apply the distributive property on the right side.

$x + 14 = Ax + 2A + Bx - 4B$	Distribute A and B over the parentheses.
$x + 14 = Ax + Bx + 2A - 4B$	Rearrange terms.
$1x + 14 = (A + B)x + (2A - 4B)$	Rewrite to identify the coefficient of x and the constant term.

As shown by the arrows, if two polynomials are equal, coefficients of like powers of x must be equal ($A + B = 1$) and their constant terms must be equal ($2A - 4B = 14$). Consequently, A and B satisfy the following two equations:

$$\begin{cases} A + B = 1 \\ 2A - 4B = 14. \end{cases}$$

We can use the addition method to solve this linear system in two variables. By multiplying the first equation by -2 and adding equations, we obtain $A = 3$ and $B = -2$. Thus,

$$\frac{x + 14}{(x - 4)(x + 2)} = \frac{A}{x - 4} + \frac{B}{x + 2} = \frac{3}{x - 4} + \frac{-2}{x + 2} \left(\text{or } \frac{3}{x - 4} - \frac{2}{x + 2} \right).$$

• • •

Steps in Partial Fraction Decomposition

1. Set up the partial fraction decomposition with the unknown constants A, B, C, etc., in the numerators of the decomposition.
2. Multiply both sides of the resulting equation by the least common denominator.
3. Simplify the right side of the equation.
4. Write both sides in descending powers, equate coefficients of like powers of x, and equate constant terms.
5. Solve the resulting linear system for A, B, C, etc.
6. Substitute the values for A, B, C, etc., into the equation in step 1 and write the partial fraction decomposition.

GREAT QUESTION!

Is there any way to speed up the process of finding partial fraction decompositions?

Sometimes. In certain situations, you can use the equation in step 2, the identity obtained after clearing fractions, to determine the constants A, B, C, etc., needed to write the partial fraction decomposition. In Example 1, the identity obtained after fractions were cleared was

$$x + 14 = A(x + 2) + B(x - 4).$$

Using suitable choices for x, we can quickly find A and B.

$x + 14 = A(x + 2) + B(x - 4)$ $x + 14 = A(x + 2) + B(x - 4)$

> If we let $x = -2$, the term containing A drops out.
> $12 = -6B$
> $-2 = B$

> If we let $x = 4$, the term containing B drops out.
> $18 = 6A$
> $3 = A$

As in the solution to Example 1, $A = 3$ and $B = -2$. This shortcut sometimes makes life easier by letting you skip steps 3, 4, and 5 in the box. The downside: Using suitable choices for x to determine constants does not always work.

⊘ Check Point **1**   Find the partial fraction decomposition of $\dfrac{5x - 1}{(x - 3)(x + 4)}$.

② Decompose $\dfrac{P}{Q}$, where Q has repeated linear factors.

The Partial Fraction Decomposition of a Rational Expression with Linear Factors in the Denominator, Some of Which Are Repeated

Suppose that $(ax + b)^n$ is a factor of the denominator. This means that the linear factor $ax + b$ is repeated n times. When this occurs, the partial fraction decomposition will contain a sum of n fractions for this factor of the denominator.

The Partial Fraction Decomposition of $\frac{P(x)}{Q(x)}$: $Q(x)$ Has Repeated Linear Factors

The form of the partial fraction decomposition for a rational expression containing the linear factor $ax + b$ occurring n times as its denominator is

$$\frac{P(x)}{(ax + b)^n} = \frac{A_1}{ax + b} + \frac{A_2}{(ax + b)^2} + \frac{A_3}{(ax + b)^3} + \cdots + \frac{A_n}{(ax + b)^n}.$$

Include one fraction with a constant numerator for each power of $ax + b$.

EXAMPLE 2   Partial Fraction Decomposition with a Repeated Linear Factor

Find the partial fraction decomposition of $\dfrac{x - 18}{x(x - 3)^2}$.

SOLUTION

Step 1   Set up the partial fraction decomposition with the unknown constants. Because the linear factor $x - 3$ occurs twice, we must include one fraction with a constant numerator for each power of $x - 3$.

$$\frac{x - 18}{x(x - 3)^2} = \frac{A}{x} + \frac{B}{x - 3} + \frac{C}{(x - 3)^2}$$

Step 2   Multiply both sides of the resulting equation by the least common denominator. We clear fractions, multiplying both sides by $x(x - 3)^2$, the least common denominator.

$$x(x - 3)^2 \left[\frac{x - 18}{x(x - 3)^2} \right] = x(x - 3)^2 \left[\frac{A}{x} + \frac{B}{x - 3} + \frac{C}{(x - 3)^2} \right]$$

We use the distributive property on the right side.

$$x(x - 3)^2 \cdot \frac{x - 18}{x(x - 3)^2} = x(x - 3)^2 \cdot \frac{A}{x} + x(x - 3)^2 \cdot \frac{B}{(x - 3)} + x(x - 3)^2 \cdot \frac{C}{(x - 3)^2}$$

Dividing out common factors in numerators and denominators, we obtain

$$x - 18 = A(x - 3)^2 + Bx(x - 3) + Cx.$$

You can use this equation to find C (let $x = 3$) and to find A (let $x = 0$).

Step 3   Simplify the right side of the equation. Square $x - 3$. Then apply the distributive property.

$$x - 18 = A(x^2 - 6x + 9) + Bx(x - 3) + Cx \qquad$$
Square $x - 3$ using $(A - B)^2 = A^2 - 2AB + B^2$.

$$x - 18 = Ax^2 - 6Ax + 9A + Bx^2 - 3Bx + Cx \qquad$$
Apply the distributive property.

Step 4   Write both sides in descending powers, equate coefficients of like powers of x, and equate constant terms. The left side, $x - 18$, is in descending powers of x: $x - 18x^0$. We will write the right side in descending powers of x.

$$x - 18 = Ax^2 + Bx^2 - 6Ax - 3Bx + Cx + 9A \quad \text{Rearrange terms on the right side.}$$

Express both sides in the same form.

$$0x^2 + 1x - 18 = (A + B)x^2 + (-6A - 3B + C)x + 9A \quad \text{Rewrite to identify coefficients and the constant term.}$$

Equating coefficients of like powers of x and equating constant terms results in the following system of linear equations:

$$\begin{cases} A + B = 0 \\ -6A - 3B + C = 1 \\ 9A = -18. \end{cases}$$

Step 5   Solve the resulting system for $A, B,$ and C. Dividing both sides of the last equation by 9, we obtain $A = -2$. Substituting -2 for A in the first equation, $A + B = 0$, gives $-2 + B = 0$, so $B = 2$. We find C by substituting -2 for A and 2 for B in the middle equation, $-6A - 3B + C = 1$. We obtain $C = -5$.

Step 6   Substitute the values of $A, B,$ and C, and write the partial fraction decomposition. With $A = -2, B = 2,$ and $C = -5$, the required partial fraction decomposition is

$$\frac{x - 18}{x(x - 3)^2} = \frac{A}{x} + \frac{B}{x - 3} + \frac{C}{(x - 3)^2} = -\frac{2}{x} + \frac{2}{x - 3} - \frac{5}{(x - 3)^2}. \quad \bullet\bullet\bullet$$

⌀ **Check Point 2** Find the partial fraction decomposition of $\dfrac{x + 2}{x(x - 1)^2}$.

GREAT QUESTION!

In Examples 1 and 2, the denominators of the given rational expressions were factored. What do I do when I have to determine a partial fraction decomposition in which the denominator of the given rational expression is not already factored?

Begin by factoring the denominator. Then apply the steps needed to obtain the partial fraction decomposition.

③ Decompose $\dfrac{P}{Q}$, where Q has a nonrepeated prime quadratic factor.

The Partial Fraction Decomposition of a Rational Expression with Prime, Nonrepeated Quadratic Factors in the Denominator

Our final two cases of partial fraction decomposition involve prime quadratic factors of the form $ax^2 + bx + c$. Based on our work with the discriminant, we know that $ax^2 + bx + c$ is prime and cannot be factored over the integers if $b^2 - 4ac < 0$ or if $b^2 - 4ac$ is not a perfect square.

The Partial Fraction Decomposition of $\dfrac{P(x)}{Q(x)}$: $Q(x)$ Has a Nonrepeated, Prime Quadratic Factor

If $ax^2 + bx + c$ is a prime quadratic factor of $Q(x)$, the partial fraction decomposition will contain a term of the form

$$\underbrace{\frac{Ax + B}{ax^2 + bx + c}}.$$

Linear numerator

Quadratic factor

The voice balloons in the box show that each distinct prime quadratic factor in the denominator produces a partial fraction of the form *linear numerator over quadratic factor*.

Here's an example of a partial fraction decomposition containing a linear numerator over a quadratic factor:

$$\frac{3x^2 + 17x + 14}{(x - 2)(x^2 + 2x + 4)} = \frac{A}{x - 2} + \frac{Bx + C}{x^2 + 2x + 4}.$$

> We write a constant over the linear factor in the denominator.

> We write a linear numerator over the prime quadratic factor in the denominator.

Our next example illustrates how a linear system in three variables is used to determine values for A, B, and C.

EXAMPLE 3 Partial Fraction Decomposition

Find the partial fraction decomposition of

$$\frac{3x^2 + 17x + 14}{(x - 2)(x^2 + 2x + 4)}.$$

SOLUTION

Step 1   Set up the partial fraction decomposition with the unknown constants. We put a constant (A) over the linear factor and a linear expression ($Bx + C$) over the prime quadratic factor.

$$\frac{3x^2 + 17x + 14}{(x - 2)(x^2 + 2x + 4)} = \frac{A}{x - 2} + \frac{Bx + C}{x^2 + 2x + 4}$$

Step 2   Multiply both sides of the resulting equation by the least common denominator. We clear fractions, multiplying both sides by $(x - 2)(x^2 + 2x + 4)$, the least common denominator.

$$(x - 2)(x^2 + 2x + 4)\left[\frac{3x^2 + 17x + 14}{(x - 2)(x^2 + 2x + 4)}\right] = (x - 2)(x^2 + 2x + 4)\left[\frac{A}{x - 2} + \frac{Bx + C}{x^2 + 2x + 4}\right]$$

We use the distributive property on the right side.

$$(x - 2)(x^2 + 2x + 4) \cdot \frac{3x^2 + 17x + 14}{(x - 2)(x^2 + 2x + 4)}$$

$$= (x - 2)(x^2 + 2x + 4) \cdot \frac{A}{x - 2} + (x - 2)(x^2 + 2x + 4) \cdot \frac{Bx + C}{x^2 + 2x + 4}$$

Dividing out common factors in numerators and denominators, we obtain

$$3x^2 + 17x + 14 = A(x^2 + 2x + 4) + (Bx + C)(x - 2).$$

Step 3   Simplify the right side of the equation. We simplify on the right side by distributing A over each term in parentheses and multiplying $(Bx + C)(x - 2)$ using the FOIL method.

$$3x^2 + 17x + 14 = Ax^2 + 2Ax + 4A + Bx^2 - 2Bx + Cx - 2C$$

Step 4 Write both sides in descending powers, equate coefficients of like powers of x, and equate constant terms. The left side, $3x^2 + 17x + 14$, is in descending powers of x. We write the right side in descending powers of x

$$3x^2 + 17x + 14 = Ax^2 + Bx^2 + 2Ax - 2Bx + Cx + 4A - 2C$$

and express both sides in the same form.

$$3x^2 + 17x + 14 = (A + B)x^2 + (2A - 2B + C)x + (4A - 2C)$$

Equating coefficients of like powers of x and equating constant terms results in the following system of linear equations:

$$\begin{cases} A + B = 3 \\ 2A - 2B + C = 17 \\ 4A - 2C = 14. \end{cases}$$

Step 5 Solve the resulting system for $A, B,$ and C. Because the first equation involves A and B, we can obtain another equation in A and B by eliminating C from the second and third equations. Multiply the second equation by 2 and add equations. Solving in this manner, we obtain $A = 5, B = -2,$ and $C = 3$.

Step 6 Substitute the values of $A, B,$ and C, and write the partial fraction decomposition. With $A = 5, B = -2,$ and $C = 3$, the required partial fraction decomposition is

$$\frac{3x^2 + 17x + 14}{(x - 2)(x^2 + 2x + 4)} = \frac{A}{x - 2} + \frac{Bx + C}{x^2 + 2x + 4} = \frac{5}{x - 2} + \frac{-2x + 3}{x^2 + 2x + 4}. \quad \bullet \bullet \bullet$$

TECHNOLOGY

Numeric Connections

You can use the ⬚TABLE⬚ feature of a graphing utility to check a partial fraction decomposition. To check the result of Example 3, enter the given rational function and its partial fraction decomposition:

$$y_1 = \frac{3x^2 + 17x + 14}{(x - 2)(x^2 + 2x + 4)}$$

$$y_2 = \frac{5}{x - 2} + \frac{-2x + 3}{x^2 + 2x + 4}.$$

X	Y₁	Y₂
-3	.28571	.28571
-2	.5	.5
-1	0	0
0	-1.75	-1.75
1	-4.857	-4.857
2	ERROR	ERROR
3	4.8421	4.8421

X=-3

No matter how far up or down we scroll, $y_1 = y_2$, so the decomposition appears to be correct.

⬚ Check Point **3** Find the partial fraction decomposition of

$$\frac{8x^2 + 12x - 20}{(x + 3)(x^2 + x + 2)}.$$

④ Decompose $\dfrac{P}{Q}$, where Q has a prime, repeated quadratic factor.

The Partial Fraction Decomposition of a Rational Expression with a Prime, Repeated Quadratic Factor in the Denominator

Suppose that $(ax^2 + bx + c)^n$ is a factor of the denominator and that $ax^2 + bx + c$ cannot be factored further. This means that the quadratic factor $ax^2 + bx + c$ occurs n times. When this occurs, the partial fraction decomposition will contain a linear numerator for each power of $ax^2 + bx + c$.

The Partial Fraction Decomposition of $\dfrac{P(x)}{Q(x)}$: $Q(x)$ Has a Prime, Repeated Quadratic Factor

The form of the partial fraction decomposition for a rational expression containing the prime factor $ax^2 + bx + c$ occurring n times as its denominator is

$$\frac{P(x)}{(ax^2 + bx + c)^n} = \frac{A_1 x + B_1}{ax^2 + bx + c} + \frac{A_2 x + B_2}{(ax^2 + bx + c)^2} + \frac{A_3 x + B_3}{(ax^2 + bx + c)^3} + \cdots + \frac{A_n x + B_n}{(ax^2 + bx + c)^n}.$$

Include one fraction with a linear numerator for each power of $ax^2 + bx + c$.

EXAMPLE 4 Partial Fraction Decomposition with a Repeated Quadratic Factor

Find the partial fraction decomposition of

$$\frac{5x^3 - 3x^2 + 7x - 3}{(x^2 + 1)^2}.$$

GREAT QUESTION!

When setting up partial fraction decompositions, when should I use constant numerators and when should I use linear numerators?

When the denominator of a rational expression contains a **power of a linear factor**, set up the partial fraction decomposition with **constant numerators** (A, B, C, etc.). When the denominator of a rational expression contains a **power of a prime quadratic factor**, set up the partial fraction decomposition with **linear numerators** ($Ax + B$, $Cx + D$, etc.).

SOLUTION

Step 1 Set up the partial fraction decomposition with the unknown constants. Because the quadratic factor $x^2 + 1$ occurs twice, we must include one fraction with a linear numerator for each power of $x^2 + 1$.

$$\frac{5x^3 - 3x^2 + 7x - 3}{(x^2 + 1)^2} = \frac{Ax + B}{x^2 + 1} + \frac{Cx + D}{(x^2 + 1)^2}$$

Step 2 Multiply both sides of the resulting equation by the least common denominator. We clear fractions, multiplying both sides by $(x^2 + 1)^2$, the least common denominator.

$$(x^2 + 1)^2 \left[\frac{5x^3 - 3x^2 + 7x - 3}{(x^2 + 1)^2} \right] = (x^2 + 1)^2 \left[\frac{Ax + B}{x^2 + 1} + \frac{Cx + D}{(x^2 + 1)^2} \right]$$

Now we multiply and simplify.

$$5x^3 - 3x^2 + 7x - 3 = (x^2 + 1)(Ax + B) + Cx + D$$

Step 3 Simplify the right side of the equation. We multiply $(x^2 + 1)(Ax + B)$ using the FOIL method.

$$5x^3 - 3x^2 + 7x - 3 = Ax^3 + Bx^2 + Ax + B + Cx + D$$

Step 4 Write both sides in descending powers, equate coefficients of like powers of x, and equate constant terms.

$$5x^3 - 3x^2 + 7x - 3 = Ax^3 + Bx^2 + Ax + Cx + B + D$$

$$5x^3 - 3x^2 + 7x - 3 = Ax^3 + Bx^2 + (A + C)x + (B + D)$$

Equating coefficients of like powers of x and equating constant terms results in the following system of linear equations:

$$\begin{cases} A = 5 \\ B = -3 \\ A + C = 7 \quad \text{With } A = 5, \text{ we immediately obtain } C = 2. \\ B + D = -3. \quad \text{With } B = -3, \text{ we immediately obtain } D = 0. \end{cases}$$

Step 5 **Solve the resulting system for $A, B, C,$ and D.** Based on our observations in step 4, $A = 5, B = -3, C = 2,$ and $D = 0$.

Step 6 **Substitute the values of $A, B, C,$ and D, and write the partial fraction decomposition.**

$$\frac{5x^3 - 3x^2 + 7x - 3}{(x^2 + 1)^2} = \frac{Ax + B}{x^2 + 1} + \frac{Cx + D}{(x^2 + 1)^2} = \frac{5x - 3}{x^2 + 1} + \frac{2x}{(x^2 + 1)^2} \quad \cdots$$

⊘ Check Point **4** Find the partial fraction decomposition of $\dfrac{2x^3 + x + 3}{(x^2 + 1)^2}$.

GREAT QUESTION!

When a rational expression contains a power of a factor in the denominator, how many fractions do I have to include in the partial fraction decomposition?

When a rational expression contains a power of a factor in the denominator, be sure to set up the partial fraction decomposition to allow for every natural-number power of that factor less than or equal to the power. Example:

$$\frac{2x + 1}{(x - 5)^2 x^3}$$

$$= \frac{A}{x - 5} + \frac{B}{(x - 5)^2} + \frac{C}{x} + \frac{D}{x^2} + \frac{E}{x^3}$$

Although $(x - 5)^2$ and x^2 are quadratic, they are still expressed as powers of linear factors, $x - 5$ and x. Thus, the numerators are constant.

CONCEPT AND VOCABULARY CHECK

Determine whether each partial fraction decomposition is set up correctly. If the setup is incorrect, make the necessary changes to produce the correct decomposition.

1. Correct or incorrect:
$$\frac{7x}{(x + 2)(x - 3)} = \frac{A}{x + 2} + \frac{B}{x - 3} \underline{\qquad}$$

2. Correct or incorrect:
$$\frac{3x}{(x + 5)(x - 4)^2} = \frac{A}{x + 5} + \frac{B}{x - 4} + \frac{C}{x - 4} \underline{\qquad}$$

3. Correct or incorrect:
$$\frac{1}{(x + 1)(x^2 + 4)} = \frac{A}{x + 1} + \frac{B}{x^2 + 4} \underline{\qquad}$$

4. Correct or incorrect:
$$\frac{7x - 5}{(x^2 + x + 1)^2} = \frac{Ax + B}{x^2 + x + 1} + \frac{Cx + D}{(x^2 + x + 1)^2} \underline{\qquad}$$

EXERCISE SET 5.3

Practice Exercises

In Exercises 1–8, write the form of the partial fraction decomposition of the rational expression. It is not necessary to solve for the constants.

1. $\dfrac{11x - 10}{(x - 2)(x + 1)}$

2. $\dfrac{5x + 7}{(x - 1)(x + 3)}$

3. $\dfrac{6x^2 - 14x - 27}{(x + 2)(x - 3)^2}$

4. $\dfrac{3x + 16}{(x + 1)(x - 2)^2}$

5. $\dfrac{5x^2 - 6x + 7}{(x - 1)(x^2 + 1)}$

6. $\dfrac{5x^2 - 9x + 19}{(x - 4)(x^2 + 5)}$

7. $\dfrac{x^3 + x^2}{(x^2 + 4)^2}$

8. $\dfrac{7x^2 - 9x + 3}{(x^2 + 7)^2}$

In Exercises 9–42, write the partial fraction decomposition of each rational expression.

9. $\dfrac{x}{(x - 3)(x - 2)}$

10. $\dfrac{1}{x(x - 1)}$

11. $\dfrac{3x + 50}{(x - 9)(x + 2)}$

12. $\dfrac{5x - 1}{(x - 2)(x + 1)}$

13. $\dfrac{7x - 4}{x^2 - x - 12}$

14. $\dfrac{9x + 21}{x^2 + 2x - 15}$

15. $\dfrac{4}{2x^2 - 5x - 3}$

16. $\dfrac{x}{x^2 + 2x - 3}$

17. $\dfrac{4x^2 + 13x - 9}{x(x - 1)(x + 3)}$

18. $\dfrac{4x^2 - 5x - 15}{x(x + 1)(x - 5)}$

19. $\dfrac{4x^2 - 7x - 3}{x^3 - x}$

20. $\dfrac{2x^2 - 18x - 12}{x^3 - 4x}$

21. $\dfrac{6x - 11}{(x - 1)^2}$

22. $\dfrac{x}{(x + 1)^2}$

23. $\dfrac{x^2 - 6x + 3}{(x - 2)^3}$

24. $\dfrac{2x^2 + 8x + 3}{(x + 1)^3}$

25. $\dfrac{x^2 + 2x + 7}{x(x - 1)^2}$

26. $\dfrac{3x^2 + 49}{x(x + 7)^2}$

27. $\dfrac{x^2}{(x - 1)^2(x + 1)}$

28. $\dfrac{x^2}{(x - 1)^2(x + 1)^2}$

29. $\dfrac{5x^2 - 6x + 7}{(x - 1)(x^2 + 1)}$

30. $\dfrac{5x^2 - 9x + 19}{(x - 4)(x^2 + 5)}$

31. $\dfrac{5x^2 + 6x + 3}{(x + 1)(x^2 + 2x + 2)}$

32. $\dfrac{9x + 2}{(x - 2)(x^2 + 2x + 2)}$

33. $\dfrac{x + 4}{x^2(x^2 + 4)}$

34. $\dfrac{10x^2 + 2x}{(x - 1)^2(x^2 + 2)}$

35. $\dfrac{6x^2 - x + 1}{x^3 + x^2 + x + 1}$

36. $\dfrac{3x^2 - 2x + 8}{x^3 + 2x^2 + 4x + 8}$

37. $\dfrac{x^3 + x^2 + 2}{(x^2 + 2)^2}$

38. $\dfrac{x^2 + 2x + 3}{(x^2 + 4)^2}$

39. $\dfrac{x^3 - 4x^2 + 9x - 5}{(x^2 - 2x + 3)^2}$

40. $\dfrac{3x^3 - 6x^2 + 7x - 2}{(x^2 - 2x + 2)^2}$

41. $\dfrac{4x^2 + 3x + 14}{x^3 - 8}$

42. $\dfrac{3x - 5}{x^3 - 1}$

Practice Plus

In Exercises 43–46, perform each long division and write the partial fraction decomposition of the remainder term.

43. $\dfrac{x^5 + 2}{x^2 - 1}$

44. $\dfrac{x^5}{x^2 - 4x + 4}$

45. $\dfrac{x^4 - x^2 + 2}{x^3 - x^2}$

46. $\dfrac{x^4 + 2x^3 - 4x^2 + x - 3}{x^2 - x - 2}$

In Exercises 47–50, write the partial fraction decomposition of each rational expression.

47. $\dfrac{1}{x^2 - c^2}$ $\quad (c \neq 0)$

48. $\dfrac{ax + b}{x^2 - c^2}$ $\quad (c \neq 0)$

49. $\dfrac{ax + b}{(x - c)^2}$ $\quad (c \neq 0)$

50. $\dfrac{1}{x^2 - ax - bx + ab}$ $\quad (a \neq b)$

Application Exercises

51. Find the partial fraction decomposition for $\dfrac{1}{x(x + 1)}$ and use the result to find the following sum:

$$\dfrac{1}{1 \cdot 2} + \dfrac{1}{2 \cdot 3} + \dfrac{1}{3 \cdot 4} + \cdots + \dfrac{1}{99 \cdot 100}.$$

52. Find the partial fraction decomposition for $\dfrac{2}{x(x + 2)}$ and use the result to find the following sum:

$$\dfrac{2}{1 \cdot 3} + \dfrac{2}{3 \cdot 5} + \dfrac{2}{5 \cdot 7} + \cdots + \dfrac{2}{99 \cdot 101}.$$

Writing in Mathematics

53. Explain what is meant by the partial fraction decomposition of a rational expression.

54. Explain how to find the partial fraction decomposition of a rational expression with distinct linear factors in the denominator.

55. Explain how to find the partial fraction decomposition of a rational expression with a repeated linear factor in the denominator.

56. Explain how to find the partial fraction decomposition of a rational expression with a prime quadratic factor in the denominator.

57. Explain how to find the partial fraction decomposition of a rational expression with a repeated, prime quadratic factor in the denominator.

58. How can you verify your result for the partial fraction decomposition for a given rational expression without using a graphing utility?

Technology Exercise

59. Use the $\boxed{\text{TABLE}}$ feature of a graphing utility to verify any three of the decompositions that you obtained in Exercises 9–42.

Critical Thinking Exercises

Make Sense? *In Exercises 60–63, determine whether each statement makes sense or does not make sense, and explain your reasoning.*

60. Partial fraction decomposition involves finding a single rational expression for a given sum or difference of rational expressions.

61. I apply partial fraction decompositions for rational expressions of the form $\dfrac{P(x)}{Q(x)}$, where P and Q have no common factors and the degree of P is greater than the degree of Q.

62. Because $x + 5$ is linear and $x^2 - 3x + 2$ is quadratic, I set up the following partial fraction decomposition:

$$\dfrac{7x^2 + 9x + 3}{(x + 5)(x^2 - 3x + 2)} = \dfrac{A}{x + 5} + \dfrac{Bx + C}{x^2 - 3x + 2}.$$

63. Because $(x + 3)^2$ consists of two factors of $x + 3$, I set up the following partial fraction decomposition:

$$\dfrac{5x + 2}{(x + 3)^2} = \dfrac{A}{x + 3} + \dfrac{B}{x + 3}.$$

64. Use an extension of the Great Question! on page 548 to describe how to set up the partial fraction decomposition of a rational expression that contains powers of a prime cubic factor in the denominator. Give an example of such a decomposition.

65. Find the partial fraction decomposition of

$$\dfrac{4x^2 + 5x - 9}{x^3 - 6x - 9}.$$

Preview Exercises

Exercises 66–68 will help you prepare for the material covered in the next section.

66. Solve by the substitution method:

$$\begin{cases} 4x + 3y = 4 \\ y = 2x - 7. \end{cases}$$

67. Solve by the addition method:

$$\begin{cases} 2x + 4y = -4 \\ 3x + 5y = -3. \end{cases}$$

68. Graph $x - y = 3$ and $(x - 2)^2 + (y + 3)^2 = 4$ in the same rectangular coordinate system. What are the two intersection points? Show that each of these ordered pairs satisfies both equations.

SECTION 5.4

Systems of Nonlinear Equations in Two Variables

Objectives

1. Recognize systems of nonlinear equations in two variables.
2. Solve nonlinear systems by substitution.
3. Solve nonlinear systems by addition.
4. Solve problems using systems of nonlinear equations.

Scientists debate the probability that a "doomsday rock" will collide with Earth. It has been estimated that an asteroid, a tiny planet that revolves around the sun, crashes into Earth about once every 250,000 years, and that such a collision would have disastrous results. In 1908, a small fragment struck Siberia, leveling thousands of acres of trees. One theory about the extinction of dinosaurs 65 million years ago involves Earth's collision with a large asteroid and the resulting drastic changes in Earth's climate.

Understanding the path of Earth and the path of a comet is essential to detecting threatening space debris. Orbits about the sun are not described by linear equations in the form $Ax + By = C$. The ability to solve systems that contain nonlinear equations provides NASA scientists watching for troublesome asteroids with a way to locate possible collision points with Earth's orbit.

1. Recognize systems of nonlinear equations in two variables.

Systems of Nonlinear Equations and Their Solutions

A **system of** two **nonlinear equations** in two variables, also called a **nonlinear system**, contains at least one equation that cannot be expressed in the form $Ax + By = C$. Here are two examples:

$$\begin{cases} x^2 = 2y + 10 \\ 3x - y = 9 \end{cases}$$

Not in the form $Ax + By = C.$ The term x^2 is not linear.

$$\begin{cases} y = x^2 + 3 \\ x^2 + y^2 = 9. \end{cases}$$

Neither equation is in the form $Ax + By = C.$ The terms x^2 and y^2 are not linear.

A **solution** of a nonlinear system in two variables is an ordered pair of real numbers that satisfies both equations in the system. The **solution set** of the system is the set of all such ordered pairs. As with linear systems in two variables, the solution of a nonlinear system (if there is one) corresponds to the intersection point(s) of the graphs of the equations in the system. Unlike linear systems, the graphs can be circles, parabolas, or anything other than two lines. We will solve nonlinear systems using the substitution method and the addition method.

② Solve nonlinear systems by substitution.

Eliminating a Variable Using the Substitution Method

The substitution method involves converting a nonlinear system into one equation in one variable by an appropriate substitution. The steps in the solution process are exactly the same as those used to solve a linear system by substitution. However, when you obtain an equation in one variable, this equation may not be linear. In our first example, this equation is quadratic.

EXAMPLE 1 Solving a Nonlinear System by the Substitution Method

Solve by the substitution method:

$$\begin{cases} x^2 = 2y + 10 & \text{(The graph is a parabola.)} \\ 3x - y = 9. & \text{(The graph is a line.)} \end{cases}$$

SOLUTION

Step 1 Solve one of the equations for one variable in terms of the other. We begin by isolating one of the variables raised to the first power in either of the equations. By solving for y in the second equation, which has a coefficient of -1, we can avoid fractions.

$$3x - y = 9 \qquad \text{This is the second equation in the given system.}$$
$$3x = y + 9 \qquad \text{Add } y \text{ to both sides.}$$
$$3x - 9 = y \qquad \text{Subtract 9 from both sides.}$$

Step 2 Substitute the expression from step 1 into the other equation. We substitute $3x - 9$ for y in the first equation.

$$y = \boxed{3x - 9} \qquad x^2 = 2\boxed{y} + 10$$

This gives us an equation in one variable, namely,

$$x^2 = 2(3x - 9) + 10.$$

The variable y has been eliminated.

Step 3 Solve the resulting equation containing one variable.

$$x^2 = 2(3x - 9) + 10 \qquad \text{This is the equation containing one variable.}$$
$$x^2 = 6x - 18 + 10 \qquad \text{Use the distributive property.}$$
$$x^2 = 6x - 8 \qquad \text{Combine numerical terms on the right.}$$
$$x^2 - 6x + 8 = 0 \qquad \text{Move all terms to one side and set the quadratic equation equal to 0.}$$
$$(x - 4)(x - 2) = 0 \qquad \text{Factor.}$$
$$x - 4 = 0 \quad \text{or} \quad x - 2 = 0 \qquad \text{Set each factor equal to 0.}$$
$$x = 4 \qquad\qquad x = 2 \qquad \text{Solve for x.}$$

Step 4 Back-substitute the obtained values into the equation from step 1. Now that we have the x-coordinates of the solutions, we back-substitute 4 for x and 2 for x into the equation $y = 3x - 9$.

If x is 4, $\quad y = 3(4) - 9 = 3, \quad$ so $(4, 3)$ is a solution.
If x is 2, $\quad y = 3(2) - 9 = -3, \quad$ so $(2, -3)$ is a solution.

Step 5   Check the proposed solutions in both of the system's given equations. We begin by checking $(4, 3)$. Replace x with 4 and y with 3.

$x^2 = 2y + 10$	$3x - y = 9$	These are the given equations.
$4^2 \overset{?}{=} 2(3) + 10$	$3(4) - 3 \overset{?}{=} 9$	Let x = 4 and y = 3.
$16 \overset{?}{=} 6 + 10$	$12 - 3 \overset{?}{=} 9$	Simplify.
$16 = 16,$ true	$9 = 9,$ true	True statements result.

The ordered pair $(4, 3)$ satisfies both equations. Thus, $(4, 3)$ is a solution of the system. Now let's check $(2, -3)$. Replace x with 2 and y with -3 in both given equations.

$x^2 = 2y + 10$	$3x - y = 9$	These are the given equations.
$2^2 \overset{?}{=} 2(-3) + 10$	$3(2) - (-3) \overset{?}{=} 9$	Let x = 2 and y = -3.
$4 \overset{?}{=} -6 + 10$	$6 + 3 \overset{?}{=} 9$	Simplify.
$4 = 4,$ true	$9 = 9,$ true	True statements result.

The ordered pair $(2, -3)$ also satisfies both equations and is a solution of the system. The solutions are $(4, 3)$ and $(2, -3)$, and the solution set is $\{(4, 3), (2, -3)\}$.

Figure 5.9 shows the graphs of the equations in the system and the solutions as intersection points.   •••

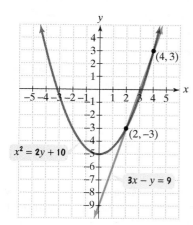

FIGURE 5.9 Points of intersection illustrate the nonlinear system's solutions.

☑ Check Point **1** Solve by the substitution method:

$$\begin{cases} x^2 = y - 1 \\ 4x - y = -1. \end{cases}$$

EXAMPLE 2   Solving a Nonlinear System by the Substitution Method

Solve by the substitution method:

$$\begin{cases} x - y = 3 & \text{(The graph is a line.)} \\ (x - 2)^2 + (y + 3)^2 = 4. & \text{(The graph is a circle.)} \end{cases}$$

GREAT QUESTION!

Why is the graph of
$(x - 2)^2 + (y + 3)^2 = 4$ **a circle?**

Recall that

$$(x - h)^2 + (y - k)^2 = r^2$$

describes a circle with center (h, k) and radius r.

SOLUTION

Graphically, we are finding the intersection of a line and a circle with center $(2, -3)$ and radius 2.

Step 1   Solve one of the equations for one variable in terms of the other. We will solve for x in the linear equation—that is, the first equation. (We could also solve for y.)

$x - y = 3$	This is the first equation in the given system.
$x = y + 3$	Add y to both sides.

Step 2   Substitute the expression from step 1 into the other equation. We substitute $y + 3$ for x in the second equation.

$$x = \boxed{y + 3} \qquad (\boxed{x} - 2)^2 + (y + 3)^2 = 4$$

This gives an equation in one variable, namely,

$$(y + 3 - 2)^2 + (y + 3)^2 = 4.$$

The variable x has been eliminated.

Step 3 Solve the resulting equation containing one variable.

$$(y + 3 - 2)^2 + (y + 3)^2 = 4 \qquad \text{This is the equation containing one variable.}$$
$$(y + 1)^2 + (y + 3)^2 = 4 \qquad \text{Combine numerical terms in the first parentheses.}$$
$$y^2 + 2y + 1 + y^2 + 6y + 9 = 4 \qquad \text{Use the formula } (A + B)^2 = A^2 + 2AB + B^2 \text{ to square } y + 1 \text{ and } y + 3.$$
$$2y^2 + 8y + 10 = 4 \qquad \text{Combine like terms on the left.}$$
$$2y^2 + 8y + 6 = 0 \qquad \text{Subtract 4 from both sides and set the quadratic equation equal to 0.}$$
$$2(y^2 + 4y + 3) = 0 \qquad \text{Factor out 2.}$$
$$2(y + 3)(y + 1) = 0 \qquad \text{Factor completely.}$$
$$y + 3 = 0 \quad \text{or} \quad y + 1 = 0 \qquad \text{Set each variable factor equal to 0.}$$
$$y = -3 \qquad\qquad y = -1 \qquad \text{Solve for } y.$$

Step 4 Back-substitute the obtained values into the equation from step 1. Now that we have the y-coordinates of the solutions, we back-substitute -3 for y and -1 for y in the equation $x = y + 3$.

If $y = -3$: $\quad x = -3 + 3 = 0, \quad$ so $(0, -3)$ is a solution.
If $y = -1$: $\quad x = -1 + 3 = 2, \quad$ so $(2, -1)$ is a solution.

Step 5 Check the proposed solutions in both of the system's given equations. Take a moment to show that each ordered pair satisfies both given equations, $x - y = 3$ and $(x - 2)^2 + (y + 3)^2 = 4$. The solutions are $(0, -3)$ and $(2, -1)$, and the solution set of the given system is $\{(0, -3), (2, -1)\}$.

Figure 5.10 shows the graphs of the equations in the system and the solutions as intersection points. • • •

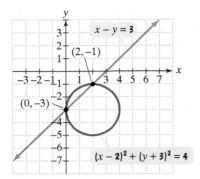

FIGURE 5.10 Points of intersection illustrate the nonlinear system's solutions.

✓ Check Point **2** Solve by the substitution method:

$$\begin{cases} x + 2y = 0 \\ (x - 1)^2 + (y - 1)^2 = 5. \end{cases}$$

3 Solve nonlinear systems by addition.

Eliminating a Variable Using the Addition Method

In solving linear systems with two variables, we learned that the addition method works well when each equation is in the form $Ax + By = C$. For nonlinear systems, the addition method can be used when each equation is in the form $Ax^2 + By^2 = C$. If necessary, we will multiply either equation or both equations by appropriate numbers so that the coefficients of x^2 or y^2 will have a sum of 0. We then add equations. The sum will be an equation in one variable.

EXAMPLE 3   Solving a Nonlinear System by the Addition Method

Solve the system:

$$\begin{cases} 4x^2 + y^2 = 13 & \text{Equation 1} \\ x^2 + y^2 = 10. & \text{Equation 2} \end{cases}$$

SOLUTION

We can use the same steps that we did when we solved linear systems by the addition method.

Step 1   Write both equations in the form $Ax^2 + By^2 = C$. Both equations are already in this form, so we can skip this step.

Step 2   If necessary, multiply either equation or both equations by appropriate numbers so that the sum of the x^2-coefficients or the sum of the y^2-coefficients is 0. We can eliminate y^2 by multiplying Equation 2 by -1.

$$\begin{cases} 4x^2 + y^2 = 13 \\ x^2 + y^2 = 10 \end{cases} \quad \xrightarrow[\text{Multiply by } -1.]{\text{No change}} \quad \begin{cases} 4x^2 + y^2 = 13 \\ -x^2 - y^2 = -10 \end{cases}$$

Steps 3 and 4   Add equations and solve for the remaining variable.

$$\begin{cases} 4x^2 + y^2 = 13 \\ \underline{-x^2 - y^2 = -10} \end{cases}$$

$$
\begin{aligned}
3x^2 &= 3 && \text{Add equations.} \\
x^2 &= 1 && \text{Divide both sides by 3.} \\
x &= \pm 1 && \text{Use the square root property:} \\
& && \text{If } x^2 = c, \text{ then } x = \pm\sqrt{c}.
\end{aligned}
$$

Step 5   Back-substitute and find the values for the other variable. We must back-substitute each value of x into either one of the original equations. Let's use $x^2 + y^2 = 10$, Equation 2. If $x = 1$,

$$
\begin{aligned}
1^2 + y^2 &= 10 && \text{Replace x with 1 in Equation 2.} \\
y^2 &= 9 && \text{Subtract 1 from both sides.} \\
y &= \pm 3. && \text{Apply the square root property.}
\end{aligned}
$$

$(1, 3)$ and $(1, -3)$ are solutions. If $x = -1$,

$$
\begin{aligned}
(-1)^2 + y^2 &= 10 && \text{Replace x with } -1 \text{ in Equation 2.} \\
y^2 &= 9 && \text{The steps are the same as before.} \\
y &= \pm 3.
\end{aligned}
$$

$(-1, 3)$ and $(-1, -3)$ are solutions.

Step 6   Check. Take a moment to show that each of the four ordered pairs satisfies the given equations, $4x^2 + y^2 = 13$ and $x^2 + y^2 = 10$. The solution set of the given system is $\{(1, 3), (1, -3), (-1, 3), (-1, -3)\}$.

Figure 5.11 shows the graphs of the equations in the system and the solutions as intersection points.   • • •

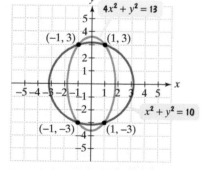

FIGURE 5.11 A system with four solutions

✓ Check Point **3** Solve the system:

$$\begin{cases} 3x^2 + 2y^2 = 35 \\ 4x^2 + 3y^2 = 48. \end{cases}$$

In solving nonlinear systems, we include only ordered pairs with real numbers in the solution set. We have seen that each of these ordered pairs corresponds to a point of intersection of the system's graphs.

EXAMPLE 4   Solving a Nonlinear System by the Addition Method

Solve the system:

$$\begin{cases} y = x^2 + 3 & \text{Equation 1 (The graph is a parabola.)} \\ x^2 + y^2 = 9. & \text{Equation 2 (The graph is a circle.)} \end{cases}$$

SOLUTION

We could use substitution because Equation 1, $y = x^2 + 3$, has y expressed in terms of x, but substituting $x^2 + 3$ for y in $x^2 + y^2 = 9$ would result in a fourth-degree equation. However, we can rewrite Equation 1 by subtracting x^2 from both sides and adding the equations to eliminate the x^2-terms.

Notice how like terms are arranged in columns.

$$\begin{cases} -x^2 + y \quad\;\; = 3 & \text{Subtract } x^2 \text{ from both sides of Equation 1.} \\ \underline{\;x^2 \qquad + y^2 = 9\;} & \text{This is Equation 2.} \end{cases}$$
$$\qquad\qquad y + y^2 = 12 \quad \text{Add the equations.}$$

We now solve this quadratic equation.

$$y + y^2 = 12 \qquad \text{This is the equation containing one variable.}$$

$$y^2 + y - 12 = 0 \qquad \text{Subtract 12 from both sides and set the quadratic equation equal to 0.}$$

$$(y + 4)(y - 3) = 0 \qquad \text{Factor.}$$

$$y + 4 = 0 \quad \text{or} \quad y - 3 = 0 \qquad \text{Set each factor equal to 0.}$$

$$y = -4 \qquad\qquad y = 3 \qquad \text{Solve for } y.$$

To complete the solution, we must back-substitute each value of y into either one of the original equations. We will use $y = x^2 + 3$, Equation 1. First, we substitute -4 for y.

$$-4 = x^2 + 3$$

$$-7 = x^2 \qquad \text{Subtract 3 from both sides.}$$

Because the square of a real number cannot be negative, the equation $x^2 = -7$ does not have real-number solutions. We will not include the imaginary solutions, $x = \pm\sqrt{-7}$, or $i\sqrt{7}$ and $-i\sqrt{7}$, in the ordered pairs that make up the solution set. Thus, we move on to our other value for y, 3, and substitute this value into Equation 1.

$$y = x^2 + 3 \qquad \text{This is Equation 1.}$$

$$3 = x^2 + 3 \qquad \text{Back-substitute 3 for } y.$$

$$0 = x^2 \qquad \text{Subtract 3 from both sides.}$$

$$0 = x \qquad \text{Solve for } x.$$

We showed that if $y = 3$, then $x = 0$. Thus, $(0, 3)$ is the solution with a real ordered pair. Take a moment to show that $(0, 3)$ satisfies the given equations, $y = x^2 + 3$ and $x^2 + y^2 = 9$. The solution set of the system is $\{(0, 3)\}$. **Figure 5.12** shows the system's graphs and the solution as an intersection point. • • •

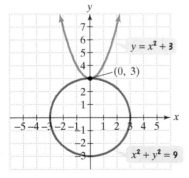

FIGURE 5.12 A system with one real solution

⊘ Check Point **4** Solve the system:

$$\begin{cases} y = x^2 + 5 \\ x^2 + y^2 = 25. \end{cases}$$

④ Solve problems using systems of nonlinear equations.

FIGURE 5.13 Building an enclosure

Applications

Many geometric problems can be modeled and solved by the use of systems of nonlinear equations. We will use our step-by-step strategy for solving problems using mathematical models that are created from verbal conditions.

EXAMPLE 5 An Application of a Nonlinear System

You have 36 yards of fencing to build the enclosure in **Figure 5.13**. Some of this fencing is to be used to build an internal divider. If you'd like to enclose 54 square yards, what are the dimensions of the enclosure?

SOLUTION

Step 1 Use variables to represent unknown quantities. Let x = the enclosure's length and y = the enclosure's width. These variables are shown in **Figure 5.13**.

Step 2 Write a system of equations modeling the problem's conditions. The first condition is that you have 36 yards of fencing.

Fencing along both lengths	plus	fencing along both widths	plus	fencing for the internal divider	equals	36 yards.
2x	+	2y	+	y	=	36

Adding like terms, we can express the equation that models the verbal conditions for the fencing as $2x + 3y = 36$.

The second condition is that you'd like to enclose 54 square yards. The rectangle's area, the product of its length and its width, must be 54 square yards.

Length	times	width	is	54 square yards.
x	·	y	=	54

Step 3 Solve the system and answer the problem's question. We must solve the system

$$\begin{cases} 2x + 3y = 36 & \text{Equation 1} \\ xy = 54. & \text{Equation 2} \end{cases}$$

We will use substitution. Because Equation 1 has no coefficients of 1 or −1, we will work with Equation 2 and solve for y. Dividing both sides of $xy = 54$ by x, we obtain

$$y = \frac{54}{x}.$$

Now we substitute $\dfrac{54}{x}$ for y in Equation 1 and solve for x.

$$2x + 3y = 36 \qquad \text{This is Equation 1.}$$
$$2x + 3 \cdot \frac{54}{x} = 36 \qquad \text{Substitute } \frac{54}{x} \text{ for } y.$$
$$2x + \frac{162}{x} = 36 \qquad \text{Multiply.}$$

$$x\left(2x + \frac{162}{x}\right) = 36 \cdot x \quad \text{Clear fractions by multiplying both sides by x.}$$

$$2x^2 + 162 = 36x \quad \text{Use the distributive property on the left side.}$$

$$2x^2 - 36x + 162 = 0 \quad \text{Subtract 36x from both sides and set the quadratic equation equal to 0.}$$

$$2(x^2 - 18x + 81) = 0 \quad \text{Factor out 2.}$$

$$2(x - 9)^2 = 0 \quad \text{Factor completely using } A^2 - 2AB + B^2 = (A - B)^2.$$

$$x - 9 = 0 \quad \text{Set the repeated factor equal to zero.}$$

$$x = 9 \quad \text{Solve for x.}$$

We back-substitute this value of x into $y = \frac{54}{x}$.

$$\text{If } x = 9, \quad y = \frac{54}{9} = 6.$$

This means that the dimensions of the enclosure in **Figure 5.13** are 9 yards by 6 yards.

Step 4   Check the proposed solution in the original wording of the problem. Take a moment to check that a length of 9 yards and a width of 6 yards results in 36 yards of fencing and an area of 54 square yards.   • • •

FIGURE 5.13 (repeated)

⊘ Check Point **5** Find the length and width of a rectangle whose perimeter is 20 feet and whose area is 21 square feet.

CONCEPT AND VOCABULARY CHECK

Fill in each blank so that the resulting statement is true.

1. A system of two equations in two variables that contains at least one equation that cannot be expressed in the form $Ax + By = C$ is called a system of _____ equations.

2. When solving
$$\begin{cases} x^2 - 4y = 4 \\ x + y = -1 \end{cases}$$
by the substitution method, we obtain $x = -4$ or $x = 0$, so the solution set is _____.

3. When solving
$$\begin{cases} 3x^2 + 2y^2 = 35 \\ 4x^2 + 3y^2 = 48 \end{cases}$$
by the addition method, we can eliminate x^2 by multiplying the first equation by -4 and the second equation by _____ and then adding the equations.

4. When solving
$$\begin{cases} x^2 + 4y^2 = 16 \\ x^2 - y^2 = 1 \end{cases}$$
by the addition method, we obtain $y^2 = 3$, so the solution set is _____.

5. When solving
$$\begin{cases} x^2 + y^2 = 13 \\ x^2 - y = 7 \end{cases}$$
by the addition method, we can eliminate x^2 by multiplying the second equation by _____ and then adding the equations. We obtain _____, a quadratic equation in y.

6. When solving
$$\begin{cases} x^2 + 4y^2 = 20 \\ xy = 4 \end{cases}$$
by the substitution method, we can eliminate y by solving the second equation for y. We obtain $y = $ _____. Then we substitute _____ for _____ in the first equation.

EXERCISE SET 5.4

Practice Exercises

In Exercises 1–18, solve each system by the substitution method.

1. $\begin{cases} x + y = 2 \\ y = x^2 - 4 \end{cases}$

2. $\begin{cases} x - y = -1 \\ y = x^2 + 1 \end{cases}$

3. $\begin{cases} x + y = 2 \\ y = x^2 - 4x + 4 \end{cases}$

4. $\begin{cases} 2x + y = -5 \\ y = x^2 + 6x + 7 \end{cases}$

5. $\begin{cases} y = x^2 - 4x - 10 \\ y = -x^2 - 2x + 14 \end{cases}$

6. $\begin{cases} y = x^2 + 4x + 5 \\ y = x^2 + 2x - 1 \end{cases}$

7. $\begin{cases} x^2 + y^2 = 25 \\ x - y = 1 \end{cases}$

8. $\begin{cases} x^2 + y^2 = 5 \\ 3x - y = 5 \end{cases}$

9. $\begin{cases} xy = 6 \\ 2x - y = 1 \end{cases}$

10. $\begin{cases} xy = -12 \\ x - 2y + 14 = 0 \end{cases}$

11. $\begin{cases} y^2 = x^2 - 9 \\ 2y = x - 3 \end{cases}$

12. $\begin{cases} x^2 + y = 4 \\ 2x + y = 1 \end{cases}$

13. $\begin{cases} xy = 3 \\ x^2 + y^2 = 10 \end{cases}$

14. $\begin{cases} xy = 4 \\ x^2 + y^2 = 8 \end{cases}$

15. $\begin{cases} x + y = 1 \\ x^2 + xy - y^2 = -5 \end{cases}$

16. $\begin{cases} x + y = -3 \\ x^2 + 2y^2 = 12y + 18 \end{cases}$

17. $\begin{cases} x + y = 1 \\ (x - 1)^2 + (y + 2)^2 = 10 \end{cases}$

18. $\begin{cases} 2x + y = 4 \\ (x + 1)^2 + (y - 2)^2 = 4 \end{cases}$

In Exercises 19–28, solve each system by the addition method.

19. $\begin{cases} x^2 + y^2 = 13 \\ x^2 - y^2 = 5 \end{cases}$

20. $\begin{cases} 4x^2 - y^2 = 4 \\ 4x^2 + y^2 = 4 \end{cases}$

21. $\begin{cases} x^2 - 4y^2 = -7 \\ 3x^2 + y^2 = 31 \end{cases}$

22. $\begin{cases} 3x^2 - 2y^2 = -5 \\ 2x^2 - y^2 = -2 \end{cases}$

23. $\begin{cases} 3x^2 + 4y^2 - 16 = 0 \\ 2x^2 - 3y^2 - 5 = 0 \end{cases}$

24. $\begin{cases} 16x^2 - 4y^2 - 72 = 0 \\ x^2 - y^2 - 3 = 0 \end{cases}$

25. $\begin{cases} x^2 + y^2 = 25 \\ (x - 8)^2 + y^2 = 41 \end{cases}$

26. $\begin{cases} x^2 + y^2 = 5 \\ x^2 + (y - 8)^2 = 41 \end{cases}$

27. $\begin{cases} y^2 - x = 4 \\ x^2 + y^2 = 4 \end{cases}$

28. $\begin{cases} x^2 - 2y = 8 \\ x^2 + y^2 = 16 \end{cases}$

In Exercises 29–42, solve each system by the method of your choice.

29. $\begin{cases} 3x^2 + 4y^2 = 16 \\ 2x^2 - 3y^2 = 5 \end{cases}$

30. $\begin{cases} x + y^2 = 4 \\ x^2 + y^2 = 16 \end{cases}$

31. $\begin{cases} 2x^2 + y^2 = 18 \\ xy = 4 \end{cases}$

32. $\begin{cases} x^2 + 4y^2 = 20 \\ xy = 4 \end{cases}$

33. $\begin{cases} x^2 + 4y^2 = 20 \\ x + 2y = 6 \end{cases}$

34. $\begin{cases} 3x^2 - 2y^2 = 1 \\ 4x - y = 3 \end{cases}$

35. $\begin{cases} x^3 + y = 0 \\ x^2 - y = 0 \end{cases}$

36. $\begin{cases} x^3 + y = 0 \\ 2x^2 - y = 0 \end{cases}$

37. $\begin{cases} x^2 + (y - 2)^2 = 4 \\ x^2 - 2y = 0 \end{cases}$

38. $\begin{cases} x^2 - y^2 - 4x + 6y - 4 = 0 \\ x^2 + y^2 - 4x - 6y + 12 = 0 \end{cases}$

39. $\begin{cases} y = (x + 3)^2 \\ x + 2y = -2 \end{cases}$

40. $\begin{cases} (x - 1)^2 + (y + 1)^2 = 5 \\ 2x - y = 3 \end{cases}$

41. $\begin{cases} x^2 + y^2 + 3y = 22 \\ 2x + y = -1 \end{cases}$

42. $\begin{cases} x - 3y = -5 \\ x^2 + y^2 - 25 = 0 \end{cases}$

In Exercises 43–46, let x represent one number and let y represent the other number. Use the given conditions to write a system of nonlinear equations. Solve the system and find the numbers.

43. The sum of two numbers is 10 and their product is 24. Find the numbers.

44. The sum of two numbers is 20 and their product is 96. Find the numbers.

45. The difference between the squares of two numbers is 3. Twice the square of the first number increased by the square of the second number is 9. Find the numbers.

46. The difference between the squares of two numbers is 5. Twice the square of the second number subtracted from three times the square of the first number is 19. Find the numbers.

Practice Plus

In Exercises 47–52, solve each system by the method of your choice.

47. $\begin{cases} 2x^2 + xy = 6 \\ x^2 + 2xy = 0 \end{cases}$

48. $\begin{cases} 4x^2 + xy = 30 \\ x^2 + 3xy = -9 \end{cases}$

49. $\begin{cases} -4x + y = 12 \\ y = x^3 + 3x^2 \end{cases}$

50. $\begin{cases} -9x + y = 45 \\ y = x^3 + 5x^2 \end{cases}$

51. $\begin{cases} \dfrac{3}{x^2} + \dfrac{1}{y^2} = 7 \\ \dfrac{5}{x^2} - \dfrac{2}{y^2} = -3 \end{cases}$

52. $\begin{cases} \dfrac{2}{x^2} + \dfrac{1}{y^2} = 11 \\ \dfrac{4}{x^2} - \dfrac{2}{y^2} = -14 \end{cases}$

In Exercises 53–54, make a rough sketch in a rectangular coordinate system of the graphs representing the equations in each system.

53. The system, whose graphs are a line with positive slope and a parabola whose equation has a positive leading coefficient, has two solutions.

54. The system, whose graphs are a line with negative slope and a parabola whose equation has a negative leading coefficient, has one solution.

Application Exercises

55. A planet's orbit follows a path described by $16x^2 + 4y^2 = 64$. A comet follows the parabolic path $y = x^2 - 4$. Where might the comet intersect the orbiting planet?

56. A system for tracking ships indicates that a ship lies on a path described by $2y^2 - x^2 = 1$. The process is repeated and the ship is found to lie on a path described by $2x^2 - y^2 = 1$. If it is known that the ship is located in the first quadrant of the coordinate system, determine its exact location.

57. Find the length and width of a rectangle whose perimeter is 36 feet and whose area is 77 square feet.

58. Find the length and width of a rectangle whose perimeter is 40 feet and whose area is 96 square feet.

Use the formula for the area of a rectangle and the Pythagorean Theorem to solve Exercises 59–60.

59. A small television has a picture with a diagonal measure of 10 inches and a viewing area of 48 square inches. Find the length and width of the screen.

60. The area of a rug is 108 square feet and the length of its diagonal is 15 feet. Find the length and width of the rug.

61. The figure shows a square floor plan with a smaller square area that will accommodate a combination fountain and pool. The floor with the fountain-pool area removed has an area of 21 square meters and a perimeter of 24 meters. Find the dimensions of the floor and the dimensions of the square that will accommodate the pool.

62. The area of the rectangular piece of cardboard shown below is 216 square inches. The cardboard is used to make an open box by cutting a 2-inch square from each corner and turning up the sides. If the box is to have a volume of 224 cubic inches, find the length and width of the cardboard that must be used.

63. The bar graph shows that compared to a century ago, work in the United States now involves mostly white-collar service jobs.

The Changing Pattern of Work in the United States, 1900–2005

Source: U.S. Department of Labor

The data can be modeled by linear and quadratic functions.

White collar $\quad 0.5x - y = -18$

Blue collar $\quad y = -0.004x^2 + 0.23x + 41$

Farming $\quad 0.4x + y = 35$

In each function, x represents the number of years after 1900 and y represents the percentage of the total U.S. labor force.

a. Based on the information in the graph, it appears that there was a year when the percentage of white-collar workers in the labor force was the same as the percentage of blue-collar workers in the labor force. According to the graph, between which two decades did this occur?

b. Solve a nonlinear system to determine the year described in part (a). Round to the nearest year. What percentage of the labor force, to the nearest percent, consisted of white-collar workers and what percentage consisted of blue-collar workers?

c. According to the graph, for which year was the percentage of white-collar workers the same as the percentage of farmers? What percentage of U.S. workers were in each of these groups?

d. Solve a linear system to determine the year described in part (c). Round to the nearest year. Use the models to find the percentage of the labor force consisting of white-collar workers and the percentage consisting of farmers. How well do your answers model the actual data specified in part (c)?

Writing in Mathematics

64. What is a system of nonlinear equations? Provide an example with your description.

65. Explain how to solve a nonlinear system using the substitution method. Use $x^2 + y^2 = 9$ and $2x - y = 3$ to illustrate your explanation.

66. Explain how to solve a nonlinear system using the addition method. Use $x^2 - y^2 = 5$ and $3x^2 - 2y^2 = 19$ to illustrate your explanation.

Technology Exercises

67. Verify your solutions to any five exercises from Exercises 1–42 by using a graphing utility to graph the two equations in the system in the same viewing rectangle. Then use the intersection feature to verify the solutions.

68. Write a system of equations, one equation whose graph is a line and the other whose graph is a parabola, that has no ordered pairs that are real numbers in its solution set. Graph the equations using a graphing utility and verify that you are correct.

Critical Thinking Exercises

Make Sense? *In Exercises 69–72, determine whether each statement makes sense or does not make sense, and explain your reasoning.*

69. I use the same steps to solve nonlinear systems as I did to solve linear systems, although I don't obtain linear equations when a variable is eliminated.

70. I graphed a nonlinear system that modeled the orbits of Earth and Mars, and the graphs indicated the system had a solution with a real ordered pair.

71. Without using any algebra, it's obvious that the nonlinear system consisting of $x^2 + y^2 = 4$ and $x^2 + y^2 = 25$ does not have real-number solutions.

72. I think that the nonlinear system consisting of $x^2 + y^2 = 36$ and $y = (x - 2)^2 - 3$ is easier to solve graphically than by using the substitution method or the addition method.

In Exercises 73–76, determine whether each statement is true or false. If the statement is false, make the necessary change(s) to produce a true statement.

73. A system of two equations in two variables whose graphs are a circle and a line can have four real ordered-pair solutions.

74. A system of two equations in two variables whose graphs are a parabola and a circle can have four real ordered-pair solutions.

75. A system of two equations in two variables whose graphs are two circles must have at least two real ordered-pair solutions.

76. A system of two equations in two variables whose graphs are a parabola and a circle cannot have only one real ordered-pair solution.

77. The points of intersection of the graphs of $xy = 20$ and $x^2 + y^2 = 41$ are joined to form a rectangle. Find the area of the rectangle.

78. Find a and b in this figure.

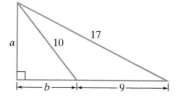

Solve the systems in Exercises 79–80.

79. $\begin{cases} \log_y x = 3 \\ \log_y(4x) = 5 \end{cases}$

80. $\begin{cases} \log x^2 = y + 3 \\ \log x = y - 1 \end{cases}$

Preview Exercises

Exercises 81–83 will help you prepare for the material covered in the next section. In each exercise, graph the linear function.

81. $2x - 3y = 6$

82. $f(x) = -\frac{2}{3}x$

83. $f(x) = -2$

CHAPTER 5 Mid-Chapter Check Point

WHAT YOU KNOW: We learned to solve systems of equations. We solved linear and nonlinear systems in two variables by the substitution method and by the addition method. We solved linear systems in three variables by eliminating a variable, reducing the system to two equations in two variables. We saw that some linear systems, called inconsistent systems, have no solution, whereas other linear systems, called dependent systems, have infinitely many solutions. We applied systems to a variety of situations, including finding the break-even point for a business, finding a quadratic function from three points on its graph, and finding a rational function's partial fraction decomposition.

In Exercises 1–12, solve each system by the method of your choice.

1. $\begin{cases} x = 3y - 7 \\ 4x + 3y = 2 \end{cases}$

2. $\begin{cases} 3x + 4y = -5 \\ 2x - 3y = 8 \end{cases}$

3. $\begin{cases} \dfrac{2x}{3} + \dfrac{y}{5} = 6 \\ \dfrac{x}{6} - \dfrac{y}{2} = -4 \end{cases}$

4. $\begin{cases} y = 4x - 5 \\ 8x - 2y = 10 \end{cases}$

5. $\begin{cases} 2x + 5y = 3 \\ 3x - 2y = 1 \end{cases}$

6. $\begin{cases} \dfrac{x}{12} - y = \dfrac{1}{4} \\ 4x - 48y = 16 \end{cases}$

7. $\begin{cases} 2x - y + 2z = -8 \\ x + 2y - 3z = 9 \\ 3x - y - 4z = 3 \end{cases}$

8. $\begin{cases} x - 3z = -5 \\ 2x - y + 2z = 16 \\ 7x - 3y - 5z = 19 \end{cases}$

9. $\begin{cases} x^2 + y^2 = 9 \\ x + 2y - 3 = 0 \end{cases}$

10. $\begin{cases} 3x^2 + 2y^2 = 14 \\ 2x^2 - y^2 = 7 \end{cases}$

11. $\begin{cases} y = x^2 - 6 \\ x^2 + y^2 = 8 \end{cases}$

12. $\begin{cases} x - 2y = 4 \\ 2y^2 + xy = 8 \end{cases}$

In Exercises 13–16, write the partial fraction decomposition of each rational expression.

13. $\dfrac{x^2 - 6x + 3}{(x - 2)^3}$

14. $\dfrac{10x^2 + 9x - 7}{(x + 2)(x^2 - 1)}$

15. $\dfrac{x^2 + 4x - 23}{(x + 3)(x^2 + 4)}$

16. $\dfrac{x^3}{(x^2 + 4)^2}$

17. A company is planning to manufacture PDAs (personal digital assistants). The fixed cost will be $400,000 and it will cost $20 to produce each PDA. Each PDA will be sold for $100.

  a. Write the cost function, C, of producing x PDAs.

  b. Write the revenue function, R, from the sale of x PDAs.

  c. Write the profit function, P, from producing and selling x PDAs.

  d. Determine the break-even point. Describe what this means.

18. Roses sell for $3 each and carnations for $1.50 each. If a mixed bouquet of 20 flowers consisting of roses and carnations costs $39, how many of each type of flower is in the bouquet?

19. Find the measure of each angle whose degree measure is represented with a variable.

20. Find the quadratic function $y = ax^2 + bx + c$ whose graph passes through the points $(-1, 0)$, $(1, 4)$, and $(2, 3)$.

21. Find the length and width of a rectangle whose perimeter is 21 meters and whose area is 20 square meters.

SECTION 5.5   Systems of Inequalities

Objectives

1. Graph a linear inequality in two variables.
2. Graph a nonlinear inequality in two variables.
3. Use mathematical models involving linear inequalities.
4. Graph a system of inequalities.

We opened the chapter noting that the modern emphasis on thinness as the ideal body shape has been suggested as a major cause of eating disorders. In this section (Example 5), as well as in the Exercise Set (Exercises 77–80), we use systems of linear inequalities in two variables that will enable you to establish a healthy weight range for your height and age.

Linear Inequalities in Two Variables and Their Solutions

We have seen that equations in the form $Ax + By = C$ are straight lines when graphed. If we change the symbol $=$ to $>$, $<$, $\geq$, or $\leq$, we obtain a **linear inequality in two variables**. Some examples of linear inequalities in two variables are $x + y > 2$, $3x - 5y \leq 15$, and $2x - y < 4$.

A **solution of an inequality in two variables**, x and y, is an ordered pair of real numbers with the following property: When the x-coordinate is substituted for x and the y-coordinate is substituted for y in the inequality, we obtain a true statement. For example, $(3, 2)$ is a solution of the inequality $x + y > 1$. When 3 is substituted for x and 2 is substituted for y, we obtain the true statement $3 + 2 > 1$, or $5 > 1$. Because there are infinitely many pairs of numbers that have a sum greater than 1, the inequality $x + y > 1$ has infinitely many solutions. Each ordered-pair solution is said to **satisfy** the inequality. Thus, $(3, 2)$ satisfies the inequality $x + y > 1$.

1 Graph a linear inequality in two variables.

The Graph of a Linear Inequality in Two Variables

We know that the graph of an equation in two variables is the set of all points whose coordinates satisfy the equation. Similarly, the **graph of an inequality in two variables** is the set of all points whose coordinates satisfy the inequality.

Let's use **Figure 5.14** to get an idea of what the graph of a linear inequality in two variables looks like. Part of the figure shows the graph of the linear equation $x + y = 2$. The line divides the points in the rectangular coordinate system into three sets. First, there is the set of points along the line, satisfying $x + y = 2$. Next, there is the set of points in the green region above the line. Points in the green region satisfy the linear inequality $x + y > 2$. Finally, there is the set of points in the purple region below the line. Points in the purple region satisfy the linear inequality $x + y < 2$.

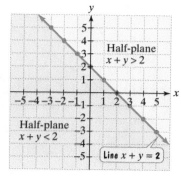

FIGURE 5.14

A **half-plane** is the set of all the points on one side of a line. In **Figure 5.14**, the green region is a half-plane. The purple region is also a half-plane. A half-plane is the graph of a linear inequality that involves $>$ or $<$. The graph of a linear inequality that involves $\geq$ or $\leq$ is a half-plane and a line. A solid line is used to show that a line is part of a solution set. A dashed line is used to show that a line is not part of a solution set.

Graphing a Linear Inequality in Two Variables

1. Replace the inequality symbol with an equal sign and graph the corresponding linear equation. Draw a solid line if the original inequality contains a $\leq$ or $\geq$ symbol. Draw a dashed line if the original inequality contains a $<$ or $>$ symbol.

2. Choose a test point from one of the half-planes. (Do not choose a point on the line.) Substitute the coordinates of the test point into the inequality.

3. If a true statement results, shade the half-plane containing this test point. If a false statement results, shade the half-plane not containing this test point.

EXAMPLE 1   Graphing a Linear Inequality in Two Variables

Graph: $2x - 3y \geq 6$.

SOLUTION

Step 1   Replace the inequality symbol by $=$ and graph the linear equation. We need to graph $2x - 3y = 6$. We can use intercepts to graph this line.

We set $y = 0$ to find the x-intercept.	We set $x = 0$ to find the y-intercept.
$2x - 3y = 6$	$2x - 3y = 6$
$2x - 3 \cdot 0 = 6$	$2 \cdot 0 - 3y = 6$
$2x = 6$	$-3y = 6$
$x = 3$	$y = -2$

The x-intercept is 3, so the line passes through $(3, 0)$. The y-intercept is -2, so the line passes through $(0, -2)$. Using the intercepts, the line is shown in **Figure 5.15** as a solid line. This is because the inequality $2x - 3y \geq 6$ contains a $\geq$ symbol, in which equality is included.

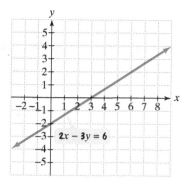

FIGURE 5.15 Preparing to graph $2x - 3y \geq 6$

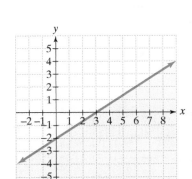

FIGURE 5.16 The graph of
$2x - 3y \geq 6$

Step 2   Choose a test point from one of the half-planes and not from the line. Substitute its coordinates into the inequality. The line $2x - 3y = 6$ divides the plane into three parts—the line itself and two half-planes. The points in one half-plane satisfy $2x - 3y > 6$. The points in the other half-plane satisfy $2x - 3y < 6$. We need to find which half-plane belongs to the solution of $2x - 3y \geq 6$. To do so, we test a point from either half-plane. The origin, $(0, 0)$, is the easiest point to test.

$$2x - 3y \geq 6 \qquad \text{This is the given inequality.}$$
$$2 \cdot 0 - 3 \cdot 0 \overset{?}{\geq} 6 \qquad \text{Test } (0, 0) \text{ by substituting 0 for } x \text{ and 0 for } y.$$
$$0 - 0 \overset{?}{\geq} 6 \qquad \text{Multiply.}$$
$$0 \geq 6 \qquad \text{This statement is false.}$$

Step 3   If a false statement results, shade the half-plane not containing the test point. Because 0 is not greater than or equal to 6, the test point, $(0, 0)$, is not part of the solution set. Thus, the half-plane below the solid line $2x - 3y = 6$ is part of the solution set. The solution set is the line and the half-plane that does not contain the point $(0, 0)$, indicated by shading this half-plane. The graph is shown using green shading and a blue line in **Figure 5.16**.   • • •

⊘ Check Point **1** Graph: $4x - 2y \geq 8$.

When graphing a linear inequality, choose a test point that lies in one of the half-planes and *not on the line dividing the half-planes*. The test point $(0, 0)$ is convenient because it is easy to calculate when 0 is substituted for each variable. However, if $(0, 0)$ lies on the dividing line and not in a half-plane, a different test point must be selected.

EXAMPLE 2   Graphing a Linear Inequality in Two Variables

Graph: $y > -\dfrac{2}{3}x$.

SOLUTION

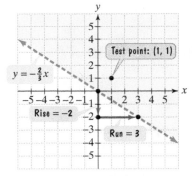

FIGURE 5.17 The graph of $y > -\frac{2}{3}x$

Step 1   Replace the inequality symbol by = and graph the linear equation. Because we are interested in graphing $y > -\frac{2}{3}x$, we begin by graphing $y = -\frac{2}{3}x$. We can use the slope and the y-intercept to graph this linear function.

$$y = -\frac{2}{3}x + 0$$

$$\text{Slope} = \frac{-2}{3} = \frac{\text{rise}}{\text{run}} \qquad y\text{-intercept} = 0$$

The y-intercept is 0, so the line passes through $(0, 0)$. Using the y-intercept and the slope, the line is shown in **Figure 5.17** as a dashed line. This is because the inequality $y > -\frac{2}{3}x$ contains a $>$ symbol, in which equality is not included.

Step 2   Choose a test point from one of the half-planes and not from the line. Substitute its coordinates into the inequality. We cannot use $(0, 0)$ as a test point because it lies on the line and not in a half-plane. Let's use $(1, 1)$, which lies in the half-plane above the line.

$$y > -\frac{2}{3}x \qquad \text{This is the given inequality.}$$
$$1 \overset{?}{>} -\frac{2}{3} \cdot 1 \qquad \text{Test } (1, 1) \text{ by substituting 1 for } x \text{ and 1 for } y.$$
$$1 > -\frac{2}{3} \qquad \text{This statement is true.}$$

Step 3 If a true statement results, shade the half-plane containing the test point. Because 1 is greater than $-\frac{2}{3}$, the test point $(1, 1)$ is part of the solution set. All the points on the same side of the line $y = -\frac{2}{3}x$ as the point $(1, 1)$ are members of the solution set. The solution set is the half-plane that contains the point $(1, 1)$, indicated by shading this half-plane. The graph is shown using green shading and a dashed blue line in **Figure 5.17**.

● ● ●

TECHNOLOGY

Most graphing utilities can graph inequalities in two variables with the ⎡SHADE⎤ feature. The procedure varies by model, so consult your manual. For most graphing utilities, you must first solve for y if it is not already isolated. The figure shows the graph of $y > -\frac{2}{3}x$. Most displays do not distinguish between dashed and solid boundary lines.

⊘ Check Point **2** Graph: $y > -\dfrac{3}{4}x.$

Graphing Linear Inequalities without Using Test Points

You can graph inequalities in the form $y > mx + b$ or $y < mx + b$ without using test points. The inequality symbol indicates which half-plane to shade.

- If $y > mx + b$, shade the half-plane above the line $y = mx + b$.
- If $y < mx + b$, shade the half-plane below the line $y = mx + b$.

Observe how this is illustrated in **Figure 5.17** in the margin on the previous page. The graph of $y > -\frac{2}{3}x$ is the half-plane above the line $y = -\frac{2}{3}x$.

It is also not necessary to use test points when graphing inequalities involving half-planes on one side of a vertical or a horizontal line.

For the Vertical Line $x = a$:	For the Horizontal Line $y = b$:
• If $x > a$, shade the half-plane to the right of $x = a$.	• If $y > b$, shade the half-plane above $y = b$.
• If $x < a$, shade the half-plane to the left of $x = a$.	• If $y < b$, shade the half-plane below $y = b$.

GREAT QUESTION!

When is it important to use test points to graph linear inequalities?

Continue using test points to graph inequalities in the form $Ax + By > C$ or $Ax + By < C$. The graph of $Ax + By > C$ can lie above or below the line given by $Ax + By = C$, depending on the values of A and B. The same comment applies to the graph of $Ax + By < C$.

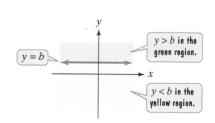

EXAMPLE 3 Graphing Inequalities without Using Test Points

Graph each inequality in a rectangular coordinate system:

a. $y \le -3$ **b.** $x > 2$.

SOLUTION

a. $y \le -3$ **b.** $x > 2$

Graph $y = -3$, a horizontal line with y-intercept −3. The line is solid because equality is included in $y \le -3$. Because of the less than part of $\le$, shade the half-plane below the horizontal line.

Graph $x = 2$, a vertical line with x-intercept **2**. The line is dashed because equality is not included in $x > 2$. Because of $>$, the greater than symbol, shade the half-plane to the right of the vertical line.

⊘ **Check Point 3** Graph each inequality in a rectangular coordinate system:

a. $y > 1$ **b.** $x \le -2$.

② Graph a nonlinear inequality in two variables.

Graphing a Nonlinear Inequality in Two Variables

Example 4 illustrates that a nonlinear inequality in two variables is graphed in the same way that we graph a linear inequality.

EXAMPLE 4 Graphing a Nonlinear Inequality in Two Variables

Graph: $x^2 + y^2 \le 9$.

SOLUTION

Step 1 Replace the inequality symbol with = and graph the nonlinear equation. We need to graph $x^2 + y^2 = 9$. The graph is a circle of radius 3 with its center at the origin. The graph is shown in **Figure 5.18** as a solid circle because equality is included in the $\le$ symbol.

Step 2 Choose a test point from one of the regions and not from the circle. Substitute its coordinates into the inequality. The circle divides the plane into three parts—the circle itself, the region inside the circle, and the region outside the circle. We need to determine whether the region inside or outside the circle is included in the solution. To do so, we will use the test point $(0, 0)$ from inside the circle.

$$x^2 + y^2 \le 9 \quad \text{This is the given inequality.}$$

$$0^2 + 0^2 \overset{?}{\le} 9 \quad \text{Test } (0, 0) \text{ by substituting 0 for } x \text{ and 0 for } y.$$

$$0 + 0 \overset{?}{\le} 9 \quad \text{Square 0: } 0^2 = 0.$$

$$0 \le 9 \quad \text{Add. This statement is true.}$$

Step 3 If a true statement results, shade the region containing the test point. The true statement tells us that all the points inside the circle satisfy $x^2 + y^2 \le 9$. The graph is shown using green shading and a solid blue circle in **Figure 5.19**.

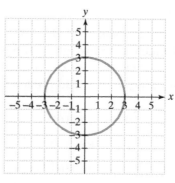

FIGURE 5.18 Preparing to graph $x^2 + y^2 \leq 9$

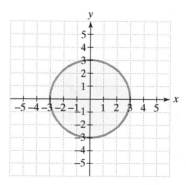

FIGURE 5.19 The graph of $x^2 + y^2 \leq 9$

• • •

⊘ Check Point **4** Graph: $x^2 + y^2 \geq 16$.

③ Use mathematical models involving linear inequalities.

Modeling with Systems of Linear Inequalities

Just as two or more linear equations make up a system of linear equations, two or more linear inequalities make up a **system of linear inequalities**. A **solution of a system of linear inequalities** in two variables is an ordered pair that satisfies each inequality in the system.

EXAMPLE 5 Does Your Weight Fit You?

The latest guidelines, which apply to both men and women, give healthy weight ranges, rather than specific weights, for your height. **Figure 5.20** shows the healthy weight region for various heights for people between the ages of 19 and 34, inclusive.

FIGURE 5.20
Source: U.S. Department of Health and Human Services

If x represents height, in inches, and y represents weight, in pounds, the healthy weight region in **Figure 5.20** can be modeled by the following system of linear inequalities:

$$\begin{cases} 4.9x - y \geq 165 \\ 3.7x - y \leq 125. \end{cases}$$

Show that point A in **Figure 5.20** is a solution of the system of inequalities that describes healthy weight.

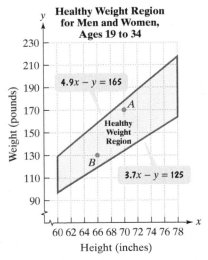

FIGURE 5.20 (repeated)

SOLUTION

Point A has coordinates $(70, 170)$. This means that if a person is 70 inches tall, or 5 feet 10 inches, and weighs 170 pounds, then that person's weight is within the healthy weight region. We can show that $(70, 170)$ satisfies the system of inequalities by substituting 70 for x and 170 for y in each inequality in the system.

$$4.9x - y \geq 165 \qquad\qquad 3.7x - y \leq 125$$
$$4.9(70) - 170 \overset{?}{\geq} 165 \qquad\qquad 3.7(70) - 170 \overset{?}{\leq} 125$$
$$343 - 170 \overset{?}{\geq} 165 \qquad\qquad 259 - 170 \overset{?}{\leq} 125$$
$$173 \geq 165, \quad \text{true} \qquad\qquad 89 \leq 125, \quad \text{true}$$

The coordinates $(70, 170)$ make each inequality true. Thus, $(70, 170)$ satisfies the system for the healthy weight region and is a solution of the system. • • •

✓ Check Point **5** Show that point B in **Figure 5.20** is a solution of the system of inequalities that describes healthy weight.

④ Graph a system of inequalities.

Graphing Systems of Linear Inequalities

The **solution set of a system of linear inequalities in two variables** is the set of all ordered pairs that satisfy each inequality in the system. Thus, to graph a system of inequalities in two variables, begin by graphing each individual inequality in the same rectangular coordinate system. Then find the region, if there is one, that is common to every graph in the system. This region of intersection gives a picture of the system's solution set.

> **EXAMPLE 6** Graphing a System of Linear Inequalities

Graph the solution set of the system:

$$\begin{cases} x - y < 1 \\ 2x + 3y \geq 12. \end{cases}$$

SOLUTION

Replacing each inequality symbol with an equal sign indicates that we need to graph $x - y = 1$ and $2x + 3y = 12$. We can use intercepts to graph these lines.

$x - y = 1$		$2x + 3y = 12$

x-intercept: $x - 0 = 1$ *Set $y = 0$ in each equation.* x-intercept: $2x + 3 \cdot 0 = 12$
$\qquad\qquad\qquad x = 1$ $\qquad\qquad\qquad\qquad\qquad\qquad\qquad\qquad 2x = 12$
The line passes through $(1, 0)$. $\qquad\qquad\qquad\qquad\qquad\qquad x = 6$
$\qquad\qquad\qquad\qquad\qquad\qquad\qquad\qquad\qquad$ The line passes through $(6, 0)$.

y-intercept: $0 - y = 1$ *Set $x = 0$ in each equation.* y-intercept: $2 \cdot 0 + 3y = 12$
$\qquad\qquad\qquad -y = 1$ $\qquad\qquad\qquad\qquad\qquad\qquad\qquad\qquad\quad 3y = 12$
$\qquad\qquad\qquad\quad y = -1$ $\qquad\qquad\qquad\qquad\qquad\qquad\qquad\qquad\quad y = 4$
The line passes through $(0, -1)$. $\qquad\qquad\qquad$ The line passes through $(0, 4)$.

Now we are ready to graph the solution set of the system of linear inequalities.

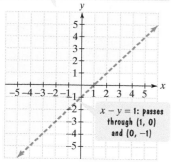

The graph of $x - y < 1$

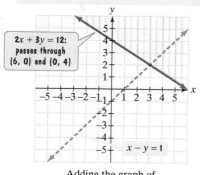

Adding the graph of
$2x + 3y \geq 12$

The graph of $x - y < 1$
and $2x + 3y \geq 12$

⦸ **Check Point 6** Graph the solution set of the system:
$$\begin{cases} x - 3y < 6 \\ 2x + 3y \geq -6. \end{cases}$$

EXAMPLE 7   Graphing a System of Inequalities

Graph the solution set of the system:
$$\begin{cases} y \geq x^2 - 4 \\ x - y \geq 2. \end{cases}$$

SOLUTION

We begin by graphing $y \geq x^2 - 4$. Because equality is included in $\geq$, we graph $y = x^2 - 4$ as a solid parabola. Because $(0, 0)$ makes the inequality $y \geq x^2 - 4$ true (we obtain $0 \geq -4$), we shade the interior portion of the parabola containing $(0, 0)$, shown in yellow in **Figure 5.21**.

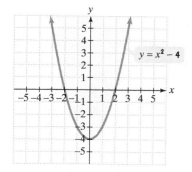

FIGURE 5.21 The graph of $y \geq x^2 - 4$

FIGURE 5.22 Adding the graph of $x - y \geq 2$

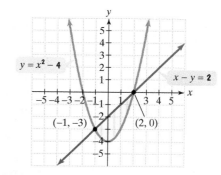

FIGURE 5.23 The graph of $y \geq x^2 - 4$ and $x - y \geq 2$

Now we graph $x - y \geq 2$ in the same rectangular coordinate system. First we graph the line $x - y = 2$ using its x-intercept, 2, and its y-intercept, -2. Because $(0, 0)$ makes the inequality $x - y \geq 2$ false (we obtain $0 \geq 2$), we shade the half-plane below the line. This is shown in **Figure 5.22** using green vertical shading.

The solution of the system is shown in **Figure 5.23** by the intersection (the overlap) of the solid yellow and green vertical shadings. The graph of the system's solution set consists of the region enclosed by the parabola and the line. To find the points of intersection of the parabola and the line, use the substitution method to solve the nonlinear system containing $y = x^2 - 4$ and $x - y = 2$. Take a moment to show that the solutions are $(-1, -3)$ and $(2, 0)$, as shown in **Figure 5.23**.   •••

GREAT QUESTION!

In Example 7, how did you graph $y = x^2 - 4$?

We used the parabola's vertex and its x-intercepts.

$$y = 1x^2 + 0x - 4$$

$$a = 1 \quad b = 0 \quad c = -4$$

- $a > 0$: opens upward
- Vertex:

$$\left(-\frac{b}{2a}, f\left(-\frac{b}{2a}\right)\right) = (0, f(0)) = (0, -4)$$

- x-intercepts:

$$x^2 - 4 = 0$$
$$x^2 = 4$$
$$x = \pm 2$$

The graph of $y = x^2 - 4$, shown in blue in **Figure 5.21** on the previous page, passes through $(-2, 0)$ and $(2, 0)$ with a vertex at $(0, -4)$.

✓ Check Point **7** Graph the solution set of the system:

$$\begin{cases} y \geq x^2 - 4 \\ x + y \leq 2. \end{cases}$$

A system of inequalities has no solution if there are no points in the rectangular coordinate system that simultaneously satisfy each inequality in the system. For example, the system

$$\begin{cases} 2x + 3y \geq 6 \\ 2x + 3y \leq 0, \end{cases}$$

whose separate graphs are shown in **Figure 5.24**, has no overlapping region. Thus, the system has no solution. The solution set is $\varnothing$, the empty set.

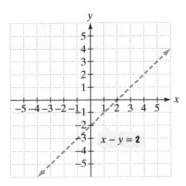

FIGURE 5.24 A system of inequalities with no solution

EXAMPLE 8   Graphing a System of Inequalities

Graph the solution set of the system:

$$\begin{cases} x - y < 2 \\ -2 \leq x < 4 \\ y < 3. \end{cases}$$

SOLUTION

We begin by graphing $x - y < 2$, the first given inequality. The line $x - y = 2$ has an x-intercept of 2 and a y-intercept of -2. The test point $(0, 0)$ makes the inequality $x - y < 2$ true, and its graph is shown in **Figure 5.25**.

Now, let's consider the second given inequality, $-2 \leq x < 4$. Replacing the inequality symbols by $=$, we obtain $x = -2$ and $x = 4$, graphed as red vertical lines in **Figure 5.26**. The line of $x = 4$ is not included. Because x is between -2 and 4, we shade the region between the vertical lines. We must intersect this region with the yellow region in **Figure 5.25**. The resulting region is shown in yellow and green vertical shading in **Figure 5.26**.

Finally, let's consider the third given inequality, $y < 3$. Replacing the inequality symbol by $=$, we obtain $y = 3$, which graphs as a horizontal line. Because of the less than symbol in $y < 3$, the graph consists of the half-plane below the line $y = 3$. We must intersect this half-plane with the region in **Figure 5.26**. The resulting region is shown in yellow and green vertical shading in **Figure 5.27**. This region represents the graph of the solution set of the given system.

FIGURE 5.25 The graph of $x - y < 2$

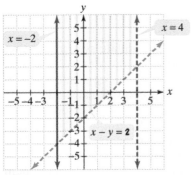

FIGURE 5.26 The graph of $x - y < 2$ and $-2 \leq x < 4$

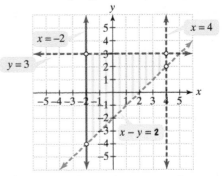

FIGURE 5.27 The graph of $x - y < 2$ and $-2 \leq x < 4$ and $y < 3$

In **Figure 5.27** it may be difficult to tell where the graph of $x - y = 2$ intersects the vertical line $x = 4$. Using the substitution method, it can be determined that this intersection point is $(4, 2)$. Take a moment to verify that the four intersection points in **Figure 5.27** are, clockwise from upper left, $(-2, 3)$, $(4, 3)$, $(4, 2)$, and $(-2, -4)$. These points are shown as open dots because none satisfies all three of the system's inequalities.

● ● ●

✓ Check Point **8** Graph the solution set of the system:

$$\begin{cases} x + y < 2 \\ -2 \le x < 1 \\ y > -3. \end{cases}$$

CONCEPT AND VOCABULARY CHECK

Fill in each blank so that the resulting statement is true.

1. The ordered pair $(3, 2)$ is a/an _____ of the inequality $x + y > 1$ because when 3 is substituted for _____ and 2 is substituted for _____, the true statement _____ is obtained.

2. The set of all points that satisfy a linear inequality in two variables is called the _____ of the inequality.

3. The set of all points on one side of a line is called a/an _____.

4. True or false: The graph of $2x - 3y > 6$ includes the line $2x - 3y = 6$. _____

5. True or false: The graph of the linear equation $2x - 3y = 6$ is used to graph the linear inequality $2x - 3y > 6$. _____

6. True or false: When graphing $4x - 2y \ge 8$, to determine which side of the line to shade, choose a test point on $4x - 2y = 8$. _____

7. When graphing $x^2 + y^2 > 25$, to determine whether to shade the region inside the circle or the region outside the circle, we can use _____ as a test point.

8. The solution set of the system

$$\begin{cases} x - y < 1 \\ 2x + 3y \ge 12. \end{cases}$$

is the set of ordered pairs that satisfy _____ and _____.

9. True or false: The graph of the solution set of the system

$$\begin{cases} x - 3y < 6 \\ 2x + 3y \ge -6. \end{cases}$$

includes the intersection point of $x - 3y = 6$ and $2x + 3y = -6$. _____

EXERCISE SET 5.5

Practice Exercises

In Exercises 1–26, graph each inequality.

1. $x + 2y \le 8$

2. $3x - 6y \le 12$

3. $x - 2y > 10$

4. $2x - y > 4$

5. $y \le \dfrac{1}{3}x$

6. $y \le \dfrac{1}{4}x$

7. $y > 2x - 1$

8. $y > 3x + 2$

9. $x \le 1$

10. $x \le -3$

11. $y > 1$

12. $y > -3$

13. $x^2 + y^2 \le 1$

14. $x^2 + y^2 \le 4$

15. $x^2 + y^2 > 25$

16. $x^2 + y^2 > 36$

17. $(x - 2)^2 + (y + 1)^2 < 9$

18. $(x + 2)^2 + (y - 1)^2 < 16$

19. $y < x^2 - 1$

20. $y < x^2 - 9$

21. $y \ge x^2 - 9$

22. $y \ge x^2 - 1$

23. $y > 2^x$

24. $y \le 3^x$

25. $y \ge \log_2(x + 1)$

26. $y \ge \log_3(x - 1)$

In Exercises 27–62, graph the solution set of each system of inequalities or indicate that the system has no solution.

27. $\begin{cases} 3x + 6y \le 6 \\ 2x + y \le 8 \end{cases}$

28. $\begin{cases} x - y \ge 4 \\ x + y \le 6 \end{cases}$

29. $\begin{cases} 2x - 5y \le 10 \\ 3x - 2y > 6 \end{cases}$

30. $\begin{cases} 2x - y \le 4 \\ 3x + 2y > -6 \end{cases}$

31. $\begin{cases} y > 2x - 3 \\ y < -x + 6 \end{cases}$

32. $\begin{cases} y < -2x + 4 \\ y < x - 4 \end{cases}$

33. $\begin{cases} x + 2y \le 4 \\ y \ge x - 3 \end{cases}$

34. $\begin{cases} x + y \le 4 \\ y \ge 2x - 4 \end{cases}$

35. $\begin{cases} x \le 2 \\ y \ge -1 \end{cases}$

36. $\begin{cases} x \le 3 \\ y \le -1 \end{cases}$

37. $-2 \le x < 5$

38. $-2 < y \le 5$

39. $\begin{cases} x - y \le 1 \\ x \ge 2 \end{cases}$

40. $\begin{cases} 4x - 5y \ge -20 \\ x \ge -3 \end{cases}$

41. $\begin{cases} x + y > 4 \\ x + y < -1 \end{cases}$

42. $\begin{cases} x + y > 3 \\ x + y < -2 \end{cases}$

43. $\begin{cases} x + y > 4 \\ x + y > -1 \end{cases}$

44. $\begin{cases} x + y > 3 \\ x + y > -2 \end{cases}$

45. $\begin{cases} y \geq x^2 - 1 \\ x - y \geq -1 \end{cases}$

46. $\begin{cases} y \geq x^2 - 4 \\ x - y \geq 2 \end{cases}$

47. $\begin{cases} x^2 + y^2 \leq 16 \\ x + y > 2 \end{cases}$

48. $\begin{cases} x^2 + y^2 \leq 4 \\ x + y > 1 \end{cases}$

49. $\begin{cases} x^2 + y^2 > 1 \\ x^2 + y^2 < 16 \end{cases}$

50. $\begin{cases} x^2 + y^2 > 1 \\ x^2 + y^2 < 9 \end{cases}$

51. $\begin{cases} (x - 1)^2 + (y + 1)^2 < 25 \\ (x - 1)^2 + (y + 1)^2 \geq 16 \end{cases}$

52. $\begin{cases} (x + 1)^2 + (y - 1)^2 < 16 \\ (x + 1)^2 + (y - 1)^2 \geq 4 \end{cases}$

53. $\begin{cases} x^2 + y^2 \leq 1 \\ y - x^2 > 0 \end{cases}$

54. $\begin{cases} x^2 + y^2 < 4 \\ y - x^2 \geq 0 \end{cases}$

55. $\begin{cases} x^2 + y^2 < 16 \\ y \geq 2^x \end{cases}$

56. $\begin{cases} x^2 + y^2 \leq 16 \\ y < 2^x \end{cases}$

57. $\begin{cases} x - y \leq 2 \\ x > -2 \\ y \leq 3 \end{cases}$

58. $\begin{cases} 3x + y \leq 6 \\ x > -2 \\ y \leq 4 \end{cases}$

59. $\begin{cases} x \geq 0 \\ y \geq 0 \\ 2x + 5y < 10 \\ 3x + 4y \leq 12 \end{cases}$

60. $\begin{cases} x \geq 0 \\ y \geq 0 \\ 2x + y < 4 \\ 2x - 3y \leq 6 \end{cases}$

61. $\begin{cases} 3x + y \leq 6 \\ 2x - y \leq -1 \\ x > -2 \\ y < 4 \end{cases}$

62. $\begin{cases} 2x + y \leq 6 \\ x + y > 2 \\ 1 \leq x \leq 2 \\ y < 3 \end{cases}$

Practice Plus

In Exercises 63–64, write each sentence as an inequality in two variables. Then graph the inequality.

63. The y-variable is at least 4 more than the product of -2 and the x-variable.

64. The y-variable is at least 2 more than the product of -3 and the x-variable.

In Exercises 65–68, write the given sentences as a system of inequalities in two variables. Then graph the system.

65. The sum of the x-variable and the y-variable is at most 4. The y-variable added to the product of 3 and the x-variable does not exceed 6.

66. The sum of the x-variable and the y-variable is at most 3. The y-variable added to the product of 4 and the x-variable does not exceed 6.

67. The sum of the x-variable and the y-variable is no more than 2. The y-variable is no less than the difference between the square of the x-variable and 4.

68. The sum of the squares of the x-variable and the y-variable is no more than 25. The sum of twice the y-variable and the x-variable is no less than 5.

In Exercises 69–70, rewrite each inequality in the system without absolute value bars. Then graph the rewritten system in rectangular coordinates.

69. $\begin{cases} |x| \leq 2 \\ |y| \leq 3 \end{cases}$

70. $\begin{cases} |x| \leq 1 \\ |y| \leq 2 \end{cases}$

*The graphs of solution sets of systems of inequalities involve finding the intersection of the solution sets of two or more inequalities. By contrast, in Exercises 71–72, you will be graphing the **union** of the solution sets of two inequalities.*

71. Graph the union of $y > \frac{3}{2}x - 2$ and $y < 4$.

72. Graph the union of $x - y \geq -1$ and $5x - 2y \leq 10$.

Without graphing, in Exercises 73–76, determine if each system has no solution or infinitely many solutions.

73. $\begin{cases} 3x + y < 9 \\ 3x + y > 9 \end{cases}$

74. $\begin{cases} 6x - y \leq 24 \\ 6x - y > 24 \end{cases}$

75. $\begin{cases} (x + 4)^2 + (y - 3)^2 \leq 9 \\ (x + 4)^2 + (y - 3)^2 \geq 9 \end{cases}$

76. $\begin{cases} (x - 4)^2 + (y + 3)^2 \leq 24 \\ (x - 4)^2 + (y + 3)^2 \geq 24 \end{cases}$

Application Exercises

The figure shows the healthy weight region for various heights for people ages 35 and older.

Source: U.S. Department of Health and Human Services

If x represents height, in inches, and y represents weight, in pounds, the healthy weight region can be modeled by the following system of linear inequalities:

$$\begin{cases} 5.3x - y \geq 180 \\ 4.1x - y \leq 140. \end{cases}$$

Use this information to solve Exercises 77–80.

77. Show that point A is a solution of the system of inequalities that describes healthy weight for this age group.

78. Show that point B is a solution of the system of inequalities that describes healthy weight for this age group.

79. Is a person in this age group who is 6 feet tall weighing 205 pounds within the healthy weight region?

80. Is a person in this age group who is 5 feet 8 inches tall weighing 135 pounds within the healthy weight region?

81. Many elevators have a capacity of 2000 pounds.

    a. If a child averages 50 pounds and an adult 150 pounds, write an inequality that describes when x children and y adults will cause the elevator to be overloaded.

    b. Graph the inequality. Because x and y must be positive, limit the graph to quadrant I only.

    c. Select an ordered pair satisfying the inequality. What are its coordinates and what do they represent in this situation?

82. A patient is not allowed to have more than 330 milligrams of cholesterol per day from a diet of eggs and meat. Each egg provides 165 milligrams of cholesterol. Each ounce of meat provides 110 milligrams.

    a. Write an inequality that describes the patient's dietary restrictions for x eggs and y ounces of meat.

    b. Graph the inequality. Because x and y must be positive, limit the graph to quadrant I only.

    c. Select an ordered pair satisfying the inequality. What are its coordinates and what do they represent in this situation?

83. On your next vacation, you will divide lodging between large resorts and small inns. Let x represent the number of nights spent in large resorts. Let y represent the number of nights spent in small inns.

    a. Write a system of inequalities that models the following conditions:

        You want to stay at least 5 nights. At least one night should be spent at a large resort. Large resorts average $200 per night and small inns average $100 per night. Your budget permits no more than $700 for lodging.

    b. Graph the solution set of the system of inequalities in part (a).

    c. Based on your graph in part (b), what is the greatest number of nights you could spend at a large resort and still stay within your budget?

84. A person with no more than $15,000 to invest plans to place the money in two investments. One investment is high risk, high yield; the other is low risk, low yield. At least $2000 is to be placed in the high-risk investment. Furthermore, the amount invested at low risk should be at least three times the amount invested at high risk. Find and graph a system of inequalities that describes all possibilities for placing the money in the high- and low-risk investments.

The graph of an inequality in two variables is a region in the rectangular coordinate system. Regions in coordinate systems have numerous applications. For example, the regions in the following two graphs indicate whether a person is obese, overweight, borderline overweight, normal weight, or underweight.

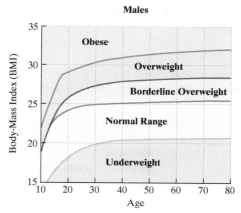

Source: Centers for Disease Control and Prevention

The horizontal axis shows a person's age. The vertical axis shows that person's body-mass index (BMI), computed using the following formula:

$$\text{BMI} = \frac{703W}{H^2}.$$

The variable W represents weight, in pounds. The variable H represents height, in inches. Use this information to solve Exercises 85–86.

85. A man is 20 years old, 72 inches (6 feet) tall, and weighs 200 pounds.

    a. Compute the man's BMI. Round to the nearest tenth.

    b. Use the man's age and his BMI to locate this information as a point in the coordinate system for males. Is this person obese, overweight, borderline overweight, normal weight, or underweight?

86. A woman is 25 years old, 66 inches (5 feet, 6 inches) tall, and weighs 105 pounds.

    a. Compute the woman's BMI. Round to the nearest tenth.

    b. Use the woman's age and her BMI to locate this information as a point in the coordinate system for females. Is this person obese, overweight, borderline overweight, normal weight, or underweight?

Writing in Mathematics

87. What is a linear inequality in two variables? Provide an example with your description.

88. How do you determine if an ordered pair is a solution of an inequality in two variables, x and y?

89. What is a half-plane?

90. What does a solid line mean in the graph of an inequality?

91. What does a dashed line mean in the graph of an inequality?

92. Compare the graphs of $3x - 2y > 6$ and $3x - 2y \leq 6$. Discuss similarities and differences between the graphs.

93. What is a system of linear inequalities?

94. What is a solution of a system of linear inequalities?

95. Explain how to graph the solution set of a system of inequalities.

96. What does it mean if a system of linear inequalities has no solution?

Technology Exercises

Graphing utilities can be used to shade regions in the rectangular coordinate system, thereby graphing an inequality in two variables. Read the section of the user's manual for your graphing utility that describes how to shade a region. Then use your graphing utility to graph the inequalities in Exercises 97–102.

97. $y \leq 4x + 4$

98. $y \geq \frac{2}{3}x - 2$

99. $y \geq x^2 - 4$

100. $y \geq \frac{1}{2}x^2 - 2$

101. $2x + y \leq 6$

102. $3x - 2y \geq 6$

103. Does your graphing utility have any limitations in terms of graphing inequalities? If so, what are they?

104. Use a graphing utility with a ⬚SHADE⬚ feature to verify any five of the graphs that you drew by hand in Exercises 1–26.

105. Use a graphing utility with a ⬚SHADE⬚ feature to verify any five of the graphs that you drew by hand for the systems in Exercises 27–62.

Critical Thinking Exercises

Make Sense? *In Exercises 106–109, determine whether each statement makes sense or does not make sense, and explain your reasoning.*

106. When graphing a linear inequality, I should always use $(0, 0)$ as a test point because it's easy to perform the calculations when 0 is substituted for each variable.

107. When graphing $3x - 4y < 12$, it's not necessary for me to graph the linear equation $3x - 4y = 12$ because the inequality contains a $<$ symbol, in which equality is not included.

108. The reason that systems of linear inequalities are appropriate for modeling healthy weight is because guidelines give healthy weight ranges, rather than specific weights, for various heights.

109. I graphed the solution set of $y \geq x + 2$ and $x \geq 1$ without using test points.

In Exercises 110–113, write a system of inequalities for each graph.

110.

111.

112. **113.**

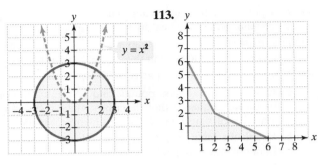

114. Write a system of inequalities whose solution set includes every point in the rectangular coordinate system.

115. Sketch the graph of the solution set for the following system of inequalities:

$$\begin{cases} y \geq nx + b \ (n < 0, b > 0) \\ y \leq mx + b \ (m > 0, b > 0). \end{cases}$$

Preview Exercises

Exercises 116–118 will help you prepare for the material covered in the next section.

116. a. Graph the solution set of the system:

$$\begin{cases} x + y \geq 6 \\ x \leq 8 \\ y \geq 5. \end{cases}$$

b. List the points that form the corners of the graphed region in part (a).

c. Evaluate $3x + 2y$ at each of the points obtained in part (b).

117. a. Graph the solution set of the system:

$$\begin{cases} x \geq 0 \\ y \geq 0 \\ 3x - 2x \leq 6 \\ y \leq -x + 7. \end{cases}$$

b. List the points that form the corners of the graphed region in part (a).

c. Evaluate $2x + 5y$ at each of the points obtained in part (b).

118. Bottled water and medical supplies are to be shipped to survivors of an earthquake by plane. The bottled water weighs 20 pounds per container and medical kits weigh 10 pounds per kit. Each plane can carry no more than 80,000 pounds. If x represents the number of bottles of water to be shipped per plane and y represents the number of medical kits per plane, write an inequality that models each plane's 80,000-pound weight restriction.

SECTION 5.6

Linear Programming

Objectives

1. Write an objective function describing a quantity that must be maximized or minimized.

2. Use inequalities to describe limitations in a situation.

3. Use linear programming to solve problems.

West Berlin children at Tempelhof airport watch fleets of U.S. airplanes bringing in supplies to circumvent the Soviet blockade. The airlift began June 28, 1948, and continued for 15 months.

The Berlin Airlift (1948–1949) was an operation by the United States and Great Britain in response to military action by the former Soviet Union: Soviet troops closed all roads and rail lines between West Germany and Berlin, cutting off supply routes to the city. The Allies used a mathematical technique developed during World War II to maximize the amount of supplies transported. During the 15-month airlift, 278,228 flights provided basic necessities to blockaded Berlin, saving one of the world's great cities.

In this section, we will look at an important application of systems of linear inequalities. Such systems arise in **linear programming**, a method for solving problems in which a particular quantity that must be maximized or minimized is limited by other factors. Linear programming is one of the most widely used tools in management science. It helps businesses allocate resources to manufacture products in a way that will maximize profit. Linear programming accounts for more than 50% and perhaps as much as 90% of all computing time used for management decisions in business. The Allies used linear programming to save Berlin.

① Write an objective function describing a quantity that must be maximized or minimized.

Objective Functions in Linear Programming

Many problems involve quantities that must be maximized or minimized. Businesses are interested in maximizing profit. An operation in which bottled water and medical kits are shipped to earthquake survivors needs to maximize the number of survivors helped by this shipment. An **objective function** is an algebraic expression in two or more variables describing a quantity that must be maximized or minimized.

EXAMPLE 1   Writing an Objective Function

Bottled water and medical supplies are to be shipped to survivors of an earthquake by plane. Each container of bottled water will serve 10 people and each medical kit will aid 6 people. If x represents the number of bottles of water to be shipped and y represents the number of medical kits, write the objective function that models the number of people that can be helped.

SOLUTION

Because each bottle of water serves 10 people and each medical kit aids 6 people, we have

The number of people helped	is	10 times the number of bottles of water	plus	6 times the number of medical kits.
$=$		$10x$	$+$	$6y.$

Using z to represent the number of people helped, the objective function is

$$z = 10x + 6y.$$

Unlike the functions that we have seen so far, the objective function is an equation in three variables. For a value of x and a value of y, there is one and only one value of z. Thus, z is a function of x and y. • • •

⊘ Check Point **1** A company manufactures bookshelves and desks for computers. Let x represent the number of bookshelves manufactured daily and y the number of desks manufactured daily. The company's profits are \$25 per bookshelf and \$55 per desk. Write the objective function that models the company's total daily profit, z, from x bookshelves and y desks. (Check Points 2 through 4 are related to this situation, so keep track of your answers.)

② Use inequalities to describe limitations in a situation.

Constraints in Linear Programming

Ideally, the number of earthquake survivors helped in Example 1 should increase without restriction so that every survivor receives water and medical supplies. However, the planes that ship these supplies are subject to weight and volume restrictions. In linear programming problems, such restrictions are called **constraints**. Each constraint is expressed as a linear inequality. The list of constraints forms a system of linear inequalities.

EXAMPLE 2   Writing a Constraint

Each plane can carry no more than 80,000 pounds. The bottled water weighs 20 pounds per container and each medical kit weighs 10 pounds. Let x represent the number of bottles of water to be shipped and y the number of medical kits. Write an inequality that models this constraint.

SOLUTION

Because each plane can carry no more than 80,000 pounds, we have

The total weight of the water bottles	plus	the total weight of the medical kits	must be less than or equal to	80,000 pounds.
$20x$	$+$	$10y$	$\leq$	$80,000.$

Each bottle weighs 20 pounds.   Each kit weighs 10 pounds.

The plane's weight constraint is modeled by the inequality

$$20x + 10y \leq 80,000.$$ • • •

⊘ Check Point **2** To maintain high quality, the company in Check Point 1 should not manufacture more than a total of 80 bookshelves and desks per day. Write an inequality that models this constraint.

In addition to a weight constraint on its cargo, each plane has a limited amount of space in which to carry supplies. Example 3 demonstrates how to express this constraint.

EXAMPLE 3   Writing a Constraint

Each plane can carry a total volume of supplies that does not exceed 6000 cubic feet. Each water bottle is 1 cubic foot and each medical kit also has a volume of 1 cubic foot. With *x* still representing the number of water bottles and *y* the number of medical kits, write an inequality that models this second constraint.

SOLUTION

Because each plane can carry a volume of supplies that does not exceed 6000 cubic feet, we have

The plane's volume constraint is modeled by the inequality $x + y \leq 6000$.   •••

In summary, here's what we have described so far in this aid-to-earthquake-survivors situation:

$$z = 10x + 6y$$ This is the objective function modeling the number of people helped with x bottles of water and y medical kits.

$$\begin{cases} 20x + 10y \leq 80,000 \\ x + y \leq 6000. \end{cases}$$ These are the constraints based on each plane's weight and volume limitations.

⊘ Check Point **3** To meet customer demand, the company in Check Point 1 must manufacture between 30 and 80 bookshelves per day, inclusive. Furthermore, the company must manufacture at least 10 and no more than 30 desks per day. Write an inequality that models each of these sentences. Then summarize what you have described about this company by writing the objective function for its profits and the three constraints.

③ Use linear programming to solve problems.

Solving Problems with Linear Programming

The problem in the earthquake situation described previously is to maximize the number of survivors who can be helped, subject to each plane's weight and volume constraints. The process of solving this problem is called *linear programming*, based on a theorem that was proven during World War II.

Solving a Linear Programming Problem

Let $z = ax + by$ be an objective function that depends on *x* and *y*. Furthermore, *z* is subject to a number of constraints on *x* and *y*. If a maximum or minimum value of *z* exists, it can be determined as follows:

1. Graph the system of inequalities representing the constraints.
2. Find the value of the objective function at each corner, or **vertex**, of the graphed region. The maximum and minimum of the objective function occur at one or more of the corner points.

EXAMPLE 4   Solving a Linear Programming Problem

Determine how many bottles of water and how many medical kits should be sent on each plane to maximize the number of earthquake survivors who can be helped.

SOLUTION

We must maximize $z = 10x + 6y$ subject to the following constraints:

$$\begin{cases} 20x + 10y \le 80{,}000 \\ \quad\ \ x + y \le 6000. \end{cases}$$

Step 1   Graph the system of inequalities representing the constraints. Because x (the number of bottles of water per plane) and y (the number of medical kits per plane) must be nonnegative, we need to graph the system of inequalities in quadrant I and its boundary only.

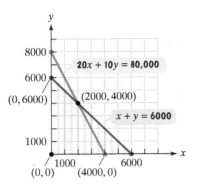

FIGURE 5.28 The region in quadrant I representing the constraints $20x + 10y \le 80{,}000$ and $x + y \le 6000$

To graph the inequality $20x + 10y \le 80{,}000$, we graph the equation $20x + 10y = 80{,}000$ as a solid blue line (**Figure 5.28**). Setting $y = 0$, the x-intercept is 4000 and setting $x = 0$, the y-intercept is 8000. Using $(0, 0)$ as a test point, the inequality is satisfied, so we shade below the blue line, as shown in yellow in **Figure 5.28**.

Now we graph $x + y \le 6000$ by first graphing $x + y = 6000$ as a solid red line. Setting $y = 0$, the x-intercept is 6000. Setting $x = 0$, the y-intercept is 6000. Using $(0, 0)$ as a test point, the inequality is satisfied, so we shade below the red line, as shown using green vertical shading in **Figure 5.28**.

We use the addition method to find where the lines $20x + 10y = 80{,}000$ and $x + y = 6000$ intersect.

$$\begin{cases} 20x + 10y = 80{,}000 \\ \quad\ x + \quad y = 6000 \end{cases} \xrightarrow[\text{Multiply by } -10.}]{\text{No change}} \begin{cases} 20x + 10y = 80{,}000 \\ -10x - 10y = -60{,}000 \end{cases}$$

$$\text{Add:}\quad \begin{aligned} 10x &= 20{,}000 \\ x &= 2000 \end{aligned}$$

Back-substituting 2000 for x in $x + y = 6000$, we find $y = 4000$, so the intersection point is $(2000, 4000)$.

The system of inequalities representing the constraints is shown by the region in which the yellow shading and the green vertical shading overlap in **Figure 5.28**. The graph of the system of inequalities is shown again in **Figure 5.29**. The red and blue line segments are included in the graph.

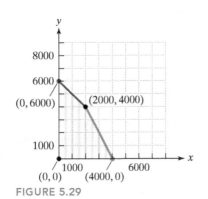

FIGURE 5.29

Step 2   Find the value of the objective function at each corner of the graphed region. The maximum and minimum of the objective function occur at one or more of the corner points. We must evaluate the objective function, $z = 10x + 6y$, at the four corners, or vertices, of the region in **Figure 5.29**.

Corner (x, y)	Objective Function $z = 10x + 6y$
$(0, 0)$	$z = 10(0) + 6(0) = 0$
$(4000, 0)$	$z = 10(4000) + 6(0) = 40{,}000$
$(2000, 4000)$	$z = 10(2000) + 6(4000) = 44{,}000 \leftarrow$ maximum
$(0, 6000)$	$z = 10(0) + 6(6000) = 36{,}000$

Thus, the maximum value of z is 44,000 and this occurs when $x = 2000$ and $y = 4000$. In practical terms, this means that the maximum number of earthquake survivors who can be helped with each plane shipment is 44,000. This can be accomplished by sending 2000 water bottles and 4000 medical kits per plane.   ●●●

⊘ Check Point **4**   For the company in Check Points 1–3, how many bookshelves and how many desks should be manufactured per day to obtain maximum profit? What is the maximum daily profit?

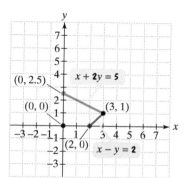

FIGURE 5.30 The graph of $x + 2y \leq 5$ and $x - y \leq 2$ in quadrant I

EXAMPLE 5 Solving a Linear Programming Problem

Find the maximum value of the objective function

$$z = 2x + y$$

subject to the following constraints:

$$\begin{cases} x \geq 0, y \geq 0 \\ x + 2y \leq 5 \\ x - y \leq 2. \end{cases}$$

SOLUTION

We begin by graphing the region in quadrant I $(x \geq 0, y \geq 0)$ formed by the constraints. The graph is shown in **Figure 5.30**.

Now we evaluate the objective function at the four vertices of this region.

Objective function: $z = 2x + y$

At $(0, 0)$: $z = 2 \cdot 0 + 0 = 0$

At $(2, 0)$: $z = 2 \cdot 2 + 0 = 4$

At $(3, 1)$: $z = 2 \cdot 3 + 1 = 7$ Maximum value of z

At $(0, 2.5)$: $z = 2 \cdot 0 + 2.5 = 2.5$

Thus, the maximum value of z is 7, and this occurs when $x = 3$ and $y = 1$. •••

We can see why the objective function in Example 5 has a maximum value that occurs at a vertex by solving the equation for y.

$$z = 2x + y$$ This is the objective function of Example 5.
$$y = -2x + z$$ Solve for y. Recall that the slope-intercept form of a line is $y = mx + b$.

Slope = -2 y-intercept = z

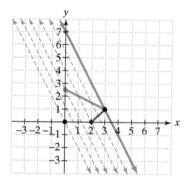

FIGURE 5.31 The line with slope -2 with the greatest y-intercept that intersects the shaded region passes through one of its vertices.

In this form, z represents the y-intercept of the objective function. The equation describes infinitely many parallel lines, each with slope -2. The process in linear programming involves finding the maximum z-value for all lines that intersect the region determined by the constraints. Of all the lines whose slope is -2, we're looking for the one with the greatest y-intercept that intersects the given region. As we see in **Figure 5.31**, such a line will pass through one (or possibly more) of the vertices of the region.

Check Point 5 Find the maximum value of the objective function $z = 3x + 5y$ subject to the constraints $x \geq 0, y \geq 0, x + y \geq 1, x + y \leq 6$.

CONCEPT AND VOCABULARY CHECK

Fill in each blank so that the resulting statement is true.

1. A method for finding the maximum or minimum value of a quantity that is subject to various limitations is called _____.

2. An algebraic expression in two or more variables describing a quantity that must be maximized or minimized is called a/an _____ function.

3. A system of linear inequalities is used to represent restrictions, or _____, on a function that must be maximized or minimized. Using the graph of such a system of inequalities, the maximum and minimum values of the function occur at one or more of the _____ points.

EXERCISE SET 5.6

Practice Exercises

In Exercises 1–4, find the value of the objective function at each corner of the graphed region. What is the maximum value of the objective function? What is the minimum value of the objective function?

1. Objective Function
$z = 5x + 6y$

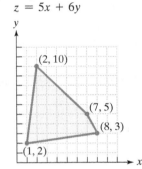

$(2, 10)$
$(7, 5)$
$(8, 3)$
$(1, 2)$

2. Objective Function
$z = 3x + 2y$

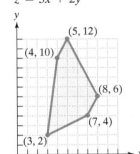

$(5, 12)$
$(4, 10)$
$(8, 6)$
$(7, 4)$
$(3, 2)$

3. Objective Function
$z = 40x + 50y$

$(4, 9)$
$(0, 8)$
$(0, 0)$
$(8, 0)$

4. Objective Function
$z = 30x + 45y$

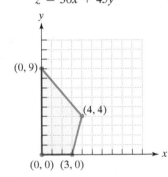

$(0, 9)$
$(4, 4)$
$(0, 0)$ $(3, 0)$

In Exercises 5–14, an objective function and a system of linear inequalities representing constraints are given.

a. *Graph the system of inequalities representing the constraints.*

b. *Find the value of the objective function at each corner of the graphed region.*

c. *Use the values in part (b) to determine the maximum value of the objective function and the values of x and y for which the maximum occurs.*

5. Objective Function
Constraints
$z = 3x + 2y$
$\begin{cases} x \geq 0, y \geq 0 \\ 2x + y \leq 8 \\ x + y \geq 4 \end{cases}$

6. Objective Function
Constraints
$z = 2x + 3y$
$\begin{cases} x \geq 0, y \geq 0 \\ 2x + y \leq 8 \\ 2x + 3y \leq 12 \end{cases}$

7. Objective Function
Constraints
$z = 4x + y$
$\begin{cases} x \geq 0, y \geq 0 \\ 2x + 3y \leq 12 \\ x + y \geq 3 \end{cases}$

8. Objective Function
Constraints
$z = x + 6y$
$\begin{cases} x \geq 0, y \geq 0 \\ 2x + y \leq 10 \\ x - 2y \geq -10 \end{cases}$

9. Objective Function
Constraints
$z = 3x - 2y$
$\begin{cases} 1 \leq x \leq 5 \\ y \geq 2 \\ x - y \geq -3 \end{cases}$

10. Objective Function
Constraints
$z = 5x - 2y$
$\begin{cases} 0 \leq x \leq 5 \\ 0 \leq y \leq 3 \\ x + y \geq 2 \end{cases}$

11. Objective Function
Constraints
$z = 4x + 2y$
$\begin{cases} x \geq 0, y \geq 0 \\ 2x + 3y \leq 12 \\ 3x + 2y \leq 12 \\ x + y \geq 2 \end{cases}$

12. Objective Function
Constraints
$z = 2x + 4y$
$\begin{cases} x \geq 0, y \geq 0 \\ x + 3y \geq 6 \\ x + y \geq 3 \\ x + y \leq 9 \end{cases}$

13. Objective Function
Constraints
$z = 10x + 12y$
$\begin{cases} x \geq 0, y \geq 0 \\ x + y \leq 7 \\ 2x + y \leq 10 \\ 2x + 3y \leq 18 \end{cases}$

14. Objective Function
Constraints
$z = 5x + 6y$
$\begin{cases} x \geq 0, y \geq 0 \\ 2x + y \geq 10 \\ x + 2y \geq 10 \\ x + y \leq 10 \end{cases}$

Application Exercises

15. A television manufacturer makes rear-projection and plasma televisions. The profit per unit is $125 for the rear-projection televisions and $200 for the plasma televisions.

a. Let $x =$ the number of rear-projection televisions manufactured in a month and let $y =$ the number of plasma televisions manufactured in a month. Write the objective function that models the total monthly profit.

b. The manufacturer is bound by the following constraints:

- Equipment in the factory allows for making at most 450 rear-projection televisions in one month.

- Equipment in the factory allows for making at most 200 plasma televisions in one month.

- The cost to the manufacturer per unit is $600 for the rear-projection televisions and $900 for the plasma televisions. Total monthly costs cannot exceed $360,000.

Write a system of three inequalities that models these constraints.

c. Graph the system of inequalities in part (b). Use only the first quadrant and its boundary, because x and y must both be nonnegative.

d. Evaluate the objective function for total monthly profit at each of the five vertices of the graphed region. [The vertices should occur at $(0, 0)$, $(0, 200)$, $(300, 200)$, $(450, 100)$, and $(450, 0)$.]

e. Complete the missing portions of this statement: The television manufacturer will make the greatest profit by manufacturing _____ rear-projection televisions each month and _____ plasma televisions each month. The maximum monthly profit is $ _____.

16. a. A student earns $10 per hour for tutoring and $7 per hour as a teacher's aide. Let x = the number of hours each week spent tutoring and let y = the number of hours each week spent as a teacher's aide. Write the objective function that models total weekly earnings.

b. The student is bound by the following constraints:

  • To have enough time for studies, the student can work no more than 20 hours per week.

  • The tutoring center requires that each tutor spend at least three hours per week tutoring.

  • The tutoring center requires that each tutor spend no more than eight hours per week tutoring.

  Write a system of three inequalities that models these constraints.

c. Graph the system of inequalities in part (b). Use only the first quadrant and its boundary, because x and y are nonnegative.

d. Evaluate the objective function for total weekly earnings at each of the four vertices of the graphed region. [The vertices should occur at $(3, 0)$, $(8, 0)$, $(3, 17)$, and $(8, 12)$.]

e. Complete the missing portions of this statement: The student can earn the maximum amount per week by tutoring for ____ hours per week and working as a teacher's aide for ____ hours per week. The maximum amount that the student can earn each week is $ ____.

Use the two steps for solving a linear programming problem, given in the box on page 577, to solve the problems in Exercises 17–23.

17. A manufacturer produces two models of mountain bicycles. The times (in hours) required for assembling and painting each model are given in the following table:

	Model A	Model B
Assembling	5	4
Painting	2	3

The maximum total weekly hours available in the assembly department and the paint department are 200 hours and 108 hours, respectively. The profits per unit are $25 for model A and $15 for model B. How many of each type should be produced to maximize profit?

18. A large institution is preparing lunch menus containing foods A and B. The specifications for the two foods are given in the following table:

Food	Units of Fat per Ounce	Units of Carbohydrates per Ounce	Units of Protein per Ounce
A	1	2	1
B	1	1	1

Each lunch must provide at least 6 units of fat per serving, no more than 7 units of protein, and at least 10 units of carbohydrates. The institution can purchase food A for $0.12 per ounce and food B for $0.08 per ounce. How many ounces of each food should a serving contain to meet the dietary requirements at the least cost?

19. Food and clothing are shipped to survivors of a natural disaster. Each carton of food will feed 12 people, while each carton of clothing will help 5 people. Each 20-cubic-foot box of food weighs 50 pounds and each 10-cubic-foot box of clothing weighs 20 pounds. The commercial carriers transporting food and clothing are bound by the following constraints:

  • The total weight per carrier cannot exceed 19,000 pounds.

  • The total volume must be less than 8000 cubic feet.

How many cartons of food and clothing should be sent with each plane shipment to maximize the number of people who can be helped?

20. On June 24, 1948, the former Soviet Union blocked all land and water routes through East Germany to Berlin. A gigantic airlift was organized using American and British planes to bring food, clothing, and other supplies to the more than 2 million people in West Berlin. The cargo capacity was 30,000 cubic feet for an American plane and 20,000 cubic feet for a British plane. To break the Soviet blockade, the Western Allies had to maximize cargo capacity but were subject to the following restrictions:

  • No more than 44 planes could be used.

  • The larger American planes required 16 personnel per flight, double that of the requirement for the British planes. The total number of personnel available could not exceed 512.

  • The cost of an American flight was $9000 and the cost of a British flight was $5000. Total weekly costs could not exceed $300,000.

Find the number of American and British planes that were used to maximize cargo capacity.

21. A theater is presenting a program for students and their parents on drinking and driving. The proceeds will be donated to a local alcohol information center. Admission is $2.00 for parents and $1.00 for students. However, the situation has two constraints: The theater can hold no more than 150 people and every two parents must bring at least one student. How many parents and students should attend to raise the maximum amount of money?

22. You are about to take a test that contains computation problems worth 6 points each and word problems worth 10 points each. You can do a computation problem in 2 minutes and a word problem in 4 minutes. You have 40 minutes to take the test and may answer no more than 12 problems. Assuming you answer all the problems attempted correctly, how many of each type of problem must you answer to maximize your score? What is the maximum score?

23. In 1978, a ruling by the Civil Aeronautics Board allowed Federal Express to purchase larger aircraft. Federal Express's options included 20 Boeing 727s that United Airlines was retiring and/or the French-built Dassault Fanjet Falcon 20. To aid in their decision, executives at Federal Express analyzed the following data:

	Boeing 727	**Falcon 20**
Direct Operating Cost	$1400 per hour	$500 per hour
Payload	42,000 pounds	6000 pounds

Federal Express was faced with the following constraints:
- Hourly operating cost was limited to $35,000.
- Total payload had to be at least 672,000 pounds.
- Only twenty 727s were available.

Given the constraints, how many of each kind of aircraft should Federal Express have purchased to maximize the number of aircraft?

Writing in Mathematics

24. What kinds of problems are solved using the linear programming method?

25. What is an objective function in a linear programming problem?

26. What is a constraint in a linear programming problem? How is a constraint represented?

27. In your own words, describe how to solve a linear programming problem.

28. Describe a situation in your life in which you would really like to maximize something, but you are limited by at least two constraints. Can linear programming be used in this situation? Explain your answer.

Critical Thinking Exercises

Make Sense? *In Exercises 29–32, determine whether each statement makes sense or does not make sense, and explain your reasoning.*

29. In order to solve a linear programming problem, I use the graph representing the constraints and the graph of the objective function.

30. I use the coordinates of each vertex from my graph representing the constraints to find the values that maximize or minimize an objective function.

31. I need to be able to graph systems of linear inequalities in order to solve linear programming problems.

32. An important application of linear programming for businesses involves maximizing profit.

33. Suppose that you inherit $10,000. The will states how you must invest the money. Some (or all) of the money must be invested in stocks and bonds. The requirements are that at least $3000 be invested in bonds, with expected returns of $0.08 per dollar, and at least $2000 be invested in stocks, with expected returns of $0.12 per dollar. Because the stocks are medium risk, the final stipulation requires that the investment in bonds should never be less than the investment in stocks. How should the money be invested so as to maximize your expected returns?

34. Consider the objective function $z = Ax + By$ ($A > 0$ and $B > 0$) subject to the following constraints: $2x + 3y \le 9, x - y \le 2, x \ge 0$, and $y \ge 0$. Prove that the objective function will have the same maximum value at the vertices $(3, 1)$ and $(0, 3)$ if $A = \frac{2}{3}B$.

Group Exercises

35. Group members should choose a particular field of interest. Research how linear programming is used to solve problems in that field. If possible, investigate the solution of a specific practical problem. Present a report on your findings, including the contributions of George Dantzig, Narendra Karmarkar, and L. G. Khachion to linear programming.

36. Members of the group should interview a business executive who is in charge of deciding the product mix for a business. How are production policy decisions made? Are other methods used in conjunction with linear programming? What are these methods? What sort of academic background, particularly in mathematics, does this executive have? Present a group report addressing these questions, emphasizing the role of linear programming for the business.

Preview Exercises

Exercises 37–39 will help you prepare for the material covered in the first section of the next chapter.

37. Solve the system:

$$\begin{cases} x + y + 2z = 19 \\ y + 2z = 13 \\ z = 5. \end{cases}$$

What makes it fairly easy to find the solution?

38. Solve the system:

$$\begin{cases} w - x + 2y - 2z = -1 \\ x - \frac{1}{3}y + z = \frac{8}{3} \\ y - z = 1 \\ z = 3. \end{cases}$$

Express the solution set in the form $\{(w, x, y, z)\}$. What makes it fairly easy to find the solution?

39. Consider the following array of numbers:

$$\begin{bmatrix} 1 & 2 & -1 \\ 4 & -3 & -15 \end{bmatrix}.$$

Rewrite the array as follows: Multiply each number in the top row by -4 and add this product to the corresponding number in the bottom row. Do not change the numbers in the top row.

SUMMARY

DEFINITIONS AND CONCEPTS	EXAMPLES

5.1 Systems of Linear Equations in Two Variables

a. Two equations in the form $Ax + By = C$ are called a system of linear equations. A solution of the system is an ordered pair that satisfies both equations in the system.

Ex. 1, p. 516

b. Systems of linear equations in two variables can be solved by eliminating a variable, using the substitution method (see the box on page 518) or the addition method (see the box on page 520).

Ex. 2, p. 518;
Ex. 3, p. 520;
Ex. 4, p. 521

c. Some linear systems have no solution and are called inconsistent systems; others have infinitely many solutions. The equations in a linear system with infinitely many solutions are called dependent. For details, see the box on page 522.

Ex. 5, p. 522;
Ex. 6, p. 523

d. Functions of Business

Ex. 7, p. 524;
Figure 5.7, p. 526

Revenue Function

$$R(x) = (\text{price per unit sold})x$$

Cost Function

$$C(x) = \text{fixed cost} + (\text{cost per unit produced})x$$

Profit Function

$$P(x) = R(x) - C(x)$$

The point of intersection of the graphs of R and C is the break-even point. The x-coordinate of the point reveals the number of units that a company must produce and sell so that the money coming in, the revenue, is equal to the money going out, the cost. The y-coordinate gives the amount of money coming in and going out.

5.2 Systems of Linear Equations in Three Variables

a. Three equations in the form $Ax + By + Cz = D$ are called a system of linear equations in three variables. A solution of the system is an ordered triple that satisfies all three equations in the system.

Ex. 1, p. 532

b. A system of linear equations in three variables can be solved by eliminating variables. Use the addition method to eliminate any variable, reducing the system to two equations in two variables. Use substitution or the addition method to solve the resulting system in two variables. Details are found in the box on page 533.

Ex. 2, p. 533;
Ex. 3, p. 535

c. Three points that do not lie on a line determine the graph of a quadratic function $y = ax^2 + bx + c$. Use the three given points to create a system of three equations. Solve the system to find a, b, and c.

Ex. 4, p. 536

5.3 Partial Fractions

a. Partial fraction decomposition is used on rational expressions in which the numerator and denominator have no common factors and the highest power in the numerator is less than the highest power in the denominator. The steps in partial fraction decomposition are given in the box on page 543.

b. Include one partial fraction with a constant numerator for each distinct linear factor in the denominator. Include one partial fraction with a constant numerator for each power of a repeated linear factor in the denominator.

Ex. 1, p. 542;
Ex. 2, p. 544

c. Include one partial fraction with a linear numerator for each distinct prime quadratic factor in the denominator. Include one partial fraction with a linear numerator for each power of a prime, repeated quadratic factor in the denominator.

Ex. 3, p. 546;
Ex. 4, p. 548

5.4 Systems of Nonlinear Equations in Two Variables

a. A system of two nonlinear equations in two variables contains at least one equation that cannot be expressed as $Ax + By = C$.

b. Systems of nonlinear equations in two variables can be solved algebraically by eliminating all occurrences of one of the variables by the substitution or addition methods.

Ex. 1, p. 552;
Ex. 2, p. 553;
Ex. 3, p. 554;
Ex. 4, p. 556

DEFINITIONS AND CONCEPTS   EXAMPLES

5.5 Systems of Inequalities

a. A linear inequality in two variables can be written in the form
$Ax + By > C, Ax + By \geq C, Ax + By < C,$ or $Ax + By \leq C.$

b. The procedure for graphing a linear inequality in two variables is given in the box on page 563. A nonlinear inequality in two variables is graphed using the same procedure.

Ex. 1, p. 563;
Ex. 2, p. 564;
Ex. 3, p. 566;
Ex. 4, p. 566

c. To graph the solution set of a system of inequalities, graph each inequality in the system in the same rectangular coordinate system. Then find the region, if there is one, that is common to every graph in the system.

Ex. 6, p. 568;
Ex. 7, p. 569;
Ex. 8, p. 570

5.6 Linear Programming

a. An objective function is an algebraic expression in three variables describing a quantity that must be maximized or minimized.

Ex. 1, p. 575

b. Constraints are restrictions, expressed as linear inequalities.

Ex. 2, p. 576;
Ex. 3, p. 577

c. Linear programming is a method for solving problems in which an objective function that must be maximized or minimized is limited by constraints. Steps for solving a linear programming problem are given in the box on page 577.

Ex. 4, p. 578;
Ex. 5, p. 579

REVIEW EXERCISES

5.1

In Exercises 1–5, solve by the method of your choice. Identify systems with no solution and systems with infinitely many solutions, using set notation to express their solution sets.

1. $\begin{cases} y = 4x + 1 \\ 3x + 2y = 13 \end{cases}$ **2.** $\begin{cases} x + 4y = 14 \\ 2x - y = 1 \end{cases}$

3. $\begin{cases} 5x + 3y = 1 \\ 3x + 4y = -6 \end{cases}$ **4.** $\begin{cases} 2y - 6x = 7 \\ 3x - y = 9 \end{cases}$

5. $\begin{cases} 4x - 8y = 16 \\ 3x - 6y = 12 \end{cases}$

6. A company is planning to manufacture computer desks. The fixed cost will be $60,000 and it will cost $200 to produce each desk. Each desk will be sold for $450.

   a. Write the cost function, C, of producing x desks.

   b. Write the revenue function, R, from the sale of x desks.

   c. Determine the break-even point. Describe what this means.

7.

Adele Bloch-Bauer, I (1907), Gustav Klimt/Neue Galerie/Art Resource, NY

Boy with a Pipe (1905), Pablo Picasso. © 2011 Picasso Estate/ARS

Talk about paintings by numbers: In 2007, this glittering Klimt set the record for the most ever paid for a painting, a title that had been held by Picasso's *Boy with a Pipe*. Combined, the two paintings sold for $239 million. The difference between the selling price for Klimt's work and the selling price for Picasso's work was $31 million. Find the amount paid for each painting.

8. The music business is evolving into a digital marketplace. The bar graph shows that from 2004 through 2009, CD album sales declined, while digital track sales grew.

Sales of Albums and Digital Tracks in the United States

Source: RIAA

a. In 2004, 142 million digital tracks were sold. For the period shown by the graph, this has increased at an average rate of 219 million digital tracks per year. Write a function that models the sale of digital tracks, y, in millions, x years after 2004.

b. The function $95x + y = 770$ models the number of albums sold, y, in millions, x years after 2004. Use this model and the model you obtained in part (a) to determine when digital track sales caught up with album sales. How many digital tracks and how many albums were sold in that year?

9. The perimeter of a rectangular table top is 34 feet. The difference between 4 times the length and 3 times the width is 33 feet. Find the dimensions.

10. A travel agent offers two package vacation plans. The first plan costs $360 and includes 3 days at a hotel and a rental car for 2 days. The second plan costs $500 and includes 4 days at a hotel and a rental car for 3 days. The daily charge for the hotel is the same under each plan, as is the daily charge for the car. Find the cost per day for the hotel and for the car.

11. The calorie-nutrient information for an apple and an avocado is given in the table. How many of each should be eaten to get exactly 1000 calories and 100 grams of carbohydrates?

	One Apple	**One Avocado**
Calories	100	350
Carbohydrates (grams)	24	14

5.2

Solve each system in Exercises 12–13.

12. $\begin{cases} 2x - y + z = 1 \\ 3x - 3y + 4z = 5 \\ 4x - 2y + 3z = 4 \end{cases}$ **13.** $\begin{cases} x + 2y - z = 5 \\ 2x - y + 3z = 0 \\ 2y + z = 1 \end{cases}$

14. Find the quadratic function $y = ax^2 + bx + c$ whose graph passes through the points $(1, 4)$, $(3, 20)$, and $(-2, 25)$.

15. 20th Century Death The greatest cause of death in the 20th century was disease, killing 1390 million people. The bar graph shows the five leading causes of death in that century, excluding disease.

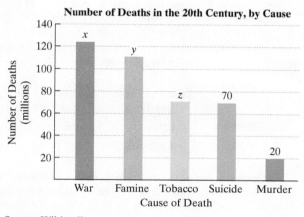

Number of Deaths in the 20th Century, by Cause

Source: Wikipedia

War, famine, and tobacco combined resulted in 306 million deaths. The difference between the number of deaths from war and famine was 13 million. The difference between the number of deaths from war and tobacco was 53 million. Find the number of 20th century deaths from war, famine, and tobacco.

5.3

In Exercises 16–24, write the partial fraction decomposition of each rational expression.

16. $\dfrac{x}{(x-3)(x+2)}$ **17.** $\dfrac{11x-2}{x^2-x-12}$

18. $\dfrac{4x^2 - 3x - 4}{x(x+2)(x-1)}$ **19.** $\dfrac{2x+1}{(x-2)^2}$

20. $\dfrac{2x-6}{(x-1)(x-2)^2}$ **21.** $\dfrac{3x}{(x-2)(x^2+1)}$

22. $\dfrac{7x^2 - 7x + 23}{(x-3)(x^2+4)}$ **23.** $\dfrac{x^3}{(x^2+4)^2}$

24. $\dfrac{4x^3 + 5x^2 + 7x - 1}{(x^2 + x + 1)^2}$

5.4

In Exercises 25–35, solve each system by the method of your choice.

25. $\begin{cases} 5y = x^2 - 1 \\ x - y = 1 \end{cases}$ **26.** $\begin{cases} y = x^2 + 2x + 1 \\ x + y = 1 \end{cases}$

27. $\begin{cases} x^2 + y^2 = 2 \\ x + y = 0 \end{cases}$ **28.** $\begin{cases} 2x^2 + y^2 = 24 \\ x^2 + y^2 = 15 \end{cases}$

29. $\begin{cases} xy - 4 = 0 \\ y - x = 0 \end{cases}$ **30.** $\begin{cases} y^2 = 4x \\ x - 2y + 3 = 0 \end{cases}$

31. $\begin{cases} x^2 + y^2 = 10 \\ y = x + 2 \end{cases}$ **32.** $\begin{cases} xy = 1 \\ y = 2x + 1 \end{cases}$

33. $\begin{cases} x + y + 1 = 0 \\ x^2 + y^2 + 6y - x = -5 \end{cases}$ **34.** $\begin{cases} x^2 + y^2 = 13 \\ x^2 - y = 7 \end{cases}$

35. $\begin{cases} 2x^2 + 3y^2 = 21 \\ 3x^2 - 4y^2 = 23 \end{cases}$

36. The perimeter of a rectangle is 26 meters and its area is 40 square meters. Find its dimensions.

37. Find the coordinates of all points (x, y) that lie on the line whose equation is $2x + y = 8$, so that the area of the rectangle shown in the figure is 6 square units.

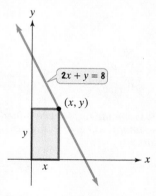

38. Two adjoining square fields with an area of 2900 square feet are to be enclosed with 240 feet of fencing. The situation is represented in the figure. Find the length of each side where a variable appears.

5.5

In Exercises 39–45, graph each inequality.

39. $3x - 4y > 12$

40. $y \leq -\dfrac{1}{2}x + 2$

41. $x < -2$

42. $y \geq 3$

43. $x^2 + y^2 > 4$

44. $y \leq x^2 - 1$

45. $y \leq 2^x$

In Exercises 46–55, graph the solution set of each system of inequalities or indicate that the system has no solution.

46. $\begin{cases} 3x + 2y \geq 6 \\ 2x + \ y \geq 6 \end{cases}$

47. $\begin{cases} 2x - \ y \geq 4 \\ \ x + 2y < 2 \end{cases}$

48. $\begin{cases} y < x \\ y \leq 2 \end{cases}$

49. $\begin{cases} x + y \leq 6 \\ y \geq 2x - 3 \end{cases}$

50. $\begin{cases} 0 \leq x \leq 3 \\ y > 2 \end{cases}$

51. $\begin{cases} 2x + y < 4 \\ 2x + y > 6 \end{cases}$

52. $\begin{cases} x^2 + y^2 \leq 16 \\ x + y < 2 \end{cases}$

53. $\begin{cases} x^2 + y^2 \leq 9 \\ y < -3x + 1 \end{cases}$

54. $\begin{cases} y > x^2 \\ x + y < 6 \\ y < x + 6 \end{cases}$

55. $\begin{cases} y \geq 0 \\ 3x + 2y \geq 4 \\ x - \ y \leq 3 \end{cases}$

5.6

56. Find the value of the objective function $z = 2x + 3y$ at each corner of the graphed region shown. What is the maximum value of the objective function? What is the minimum value of the objective function?

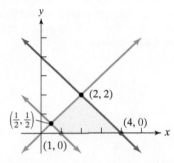

In Exercises 57–59, graph the region determined by the constraints. Then find the maximum value of the given objective function, subject to the constraints.

57. Objective Function

Constraints

$z = 2x + 3y$

$\begin{cases} x \geq 0, y \geq 0 \\ \ x + \ y \leq 8 \\ 3x + 2y \geq 6 \end{cases}$

58. Objective Function

Constraints

$z = x + 4y$

$\begin{cases} 0 \leq x \leq 5, 0 \leq y \leq 7 \\ x + y \geq 3 \end{cases}$

59. Objective Function

Constraints

$z = 5x + 6y$

$\begin{cases} x \geq 0, y \geq 0 \\ y \leq x \\ 2x + \ y \leq 12 \\ 2x + 3y \geq 6 \end{cases}$

60. A paper manufacturing company converts wood pulp to writing paper and newsprint. The profit on a unit of writing paper is $500 and the profit on a unit of newsprint is $350.

  a. Let x represent the number of units of writing paper produced daily. Let y represent the number of units of newsprint produced daily. Write the objective function that models total daily profit.

  b. The manufacturer is bound by the following constraints:
  • Equipment in the factory allows for making at most 200 units of paper (writing paper and newsprint) in a day.
  • Regular customers require at least 10 units of writing paper and at least 80 units of newsprint daily.
  Write a system of inequalities that models these constraints.

  c. Graph the inequalities in part (b). Use only the first quadrant, because x and y must both be positive. (*Suggestion:* Let each unit along the x- and y-axes represent 20.)

  d. Evaluate the objective function at each of the three vertices of the graphed region.

  e. Complete the missing portions of this statement: The company will make the greatest profit by producing _____ units of writing paper and _____ units of newsprint each day. The maximum daily profit is $_____.

61. A manufacturer of lightweight tents makes two models whose specifications are given in the following table:

	Cutting Time per Tent	Assembly Time per Tent
Model A	0.9 hour	0.8 hour
Model B	1.8 hours	1.2 hours

On a monthly basis, the manufacturer has no more than 864 hours of labor available in the cutting department and at most 672 hours in the assembly division. The profits come to $25 per tent for model A and $40 per tent for model B. How many of each should be manufactured monthly to maximize the profit?

CHAPTER 5 TEST

In Exercises 1–5, solve the system.

1. $\begin{cases} x = y + 4 \\ 3x + 7y = -18 \end{cases}$

2. $\begin{cases} 2x + 5y = -2 \\ 3x - 4y = 20 \end{cases}$

3. $\begin{cases} x + \ y + \ z = 6 \\ 3x + 4y - 7z = 1 \\ 2x - \ y + 3z = 5 \end{cases}$

4. $\begin{cases} x^2 + y^2 = 25 \\ x + y = 1 \end{cases}$

5. $\begin{cases} 2x^2 - 5y^2 = -2 \\ 3x^2 + 2y^2 = 35 \end{cases}$

6. Find the partial fraction decomposition for $\dfrac{x}{(x + 1)(x^2 + 9)}$.

In Exercises 7–10, graph the solution set of each inequality or system of inequalities.

7. $x - 2y < 8$

8. $\begin{cases} x \geq 0, y \geq 0 \\ 3x + y \leq 9 \\ 2x + 3y \geq 6 \end{cases}$

9. $\begin{cases} x^2 + y^2 > 1 \\ x^2 + y^2 < 4 \end{cases}$

10. $\begin{cases} y \leq 1 - x^2 \\ x^2 + y^2 \leq 9 \end{cases}$

11. Find the maximum value of the objective function $z = 3x + 5y$ subject to the following constraints: $x \geq 0, y \geq 0, x + y \leq 6, x \geq 2$.

12. Health experts agree that cholesterol intake should be limited to 300 mg or less each day. Three ounces of shrimp and 2 ounces of scallops contain 156 mg of cholesterol. Five ounces of shrimp and 3 ounces of scallops contain 45 mg of cholesterol less than the suggested maximum daily intake. Determine the cholesterol content in an ounce of each item.

13. A company is planning to produce and sell a new line of computers. The fixed cost will be $360,000 and it will cost $850 to produce each computer. Each computer will be sold for $1150.

  a. Write the cost function, C, of producing x computers.

  b. Write the revenue function, R, from the sale of x computers.

  c. Determine the break-even point. Describe what this means.

14. Find the quadratic function whose graph passes through the points $(-1, -2)$, $(2, 1)$, and $(-2, 1)$.

15. The rectangular plot of land shown in the figure is to be fenced along three sides using 39 feet of fencing. No fencing is to be placed along the river's edge. The area of the plot is 180 square feet. What are its dimensions?

16. A manufacturer makes two types of jet skis, regular and deluxe. The profit on a regular jet ski is $200 and the profit on the deluxe model is $250. To meet customer demand, the company must manufacture at least 50 regular jet skis per week and at least 75 deluxe models. To maintain high quality, the total number of both models of jet skis manufactured by the company should not exceed 150 per week. How many jet skis of each type should be manufactured per week to obtain maximum profit? What is the maximum weekly profit?

CUMULATIVE REVIEW EXERCISES (CHAPTERS 1–5)

The figure shows the graph of $y = f(x)$ and its two vertical asymptotes. Use the graph to solve Exercises 1–10.

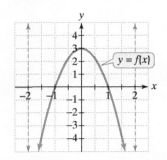

$y = f(x)$

1. Find the domain and the range of f.

2. Find the zeros.

3. What is the relative maximum and where does it occur?

4. Find the interval(s) on which f is decreasing.

5. Is $f(-0.7)$ positive or negative?

6. Find $(f \circ f)(-1)$.

7. Use arrow notation to complete this statement:

   $f(x) \rightarrow -\infty$ as _____ or as _____.

8. Does f appear to be even, odd, or neither?

9. Graph $g(x) = f(x + 2) - 1$.

10. Graph $h(x) = \frac{1}{2}f\left(\frac{1}{2}x\right)$.

In Exercises 11–21, solve each equation, inequality, or system of equations.

11. $\sqrt{x^2 - 3x} = 2x - 6$

12. $4x^2 = 8x - 7$

13. $\left| \frac{x}{3} + 2 \right| < 4$

14. $\frac{x + 5}{x - 1} > 2$

15. $2x^3 + x^2 - 13x + 6 = 0$

16. $6x - 3(5x + 2) = 4(1 - x)$

17. $\log(x + 3) + \log x = 1$

18. $3^{x+2} = 11$

19. $x^{\frac{1}{2}} - 2x^{\frac{1}{4}} - 15 = 0$

20. $\begin{cases} 3x - y = -2 \\ 2x^2 - y = 0 \end{cases}$

21. $\begin{cases} x + 2y + 3z = -2 \\ 3x + 3y + 10z = -2 \\ 2y - 5z = 6 \end{cases}$

In Exercises 22–28, graph each equation, function, or inequality in a rectangular coordinate system. If two functions are indicated, graph both in the same system.

22. $f(x) = (x + 2)^2 - 4$

23. $2x - 3y \leq 6$

24. $y = 3^{x-2}$

25. $f(x) = \frac{x^2 - x - 6}{x + 1}$

26. $f(x) = 2x - 4$ and f^{-1}

27. $(x - 2)^2 + (y - 4)^2 > 9$

28. $f(x) = |x|$ and $g(x) = -|x - 2|$

In Exercises 29–30, let $f(x) = 2x^2 - x - 1$ and $g(x) = 1 - x$.

29. Find $(f \circ g)(x)$ and $(g \circ f)(x)$.

30. Find $\dfrac{f(x + h) - f(x)}{h}$ and simplify.

In Exercises 31–32, write the linear function in slope-intercept form satisfying the given conditions.

31. Graph of f passes through $(2, 4)$ and $(4, -2)$.

32. Graph of g passes through $(-1, 0)$ and is perpendicular to the line whose equation is $x + 3y - 6 = 0$.

33. You invested $4000 in two stocks paying 12% and 14% annual interest. At the end of the year, the total interest from these investments was $508. How much was invested at each rate?

34. The length of a rectangle is 1 meter more than twice the width. If the rectangle's area is 36 square meters, find its dimensions.

35. What interest rate is required for an investment of $6000 subject to continuous compounding to grow to $18,000 in 10 years?

MATRICES AND DETERMINANTS

You are being drawn deeper into cyberspace, spending more time online each week. With constantly improving high-resolution images, cyberspace is reshaping your life by nourishing shared enthusiasms. The people who built your computer talk of bandwidth that will give you the visual experience, in high-definition 3-D format, of being in the same room with a person who is actually in another city. Rectangular arrays of numbers, called matrices, play a central role in representing computer images and in the forthcoming technology of tele-immersion.

HERE'S WHERE YOU'LL FIND THESE APPLICATIONS:

The use of rectangular arrays of numbers in the digital representation of images and the manipulation of images on a computer screen is discussed in Examples 8 and 9 in Section 6.3.

SECTION 6.1 Matrix Solutions to Linear Systems

Objectives

1. Write the augmented matrix for a linear system.
2. Perform matrix row operations.
3. Use matrices and Gaussian elimination to solve systems.
4. Use matrices and Gauss-Jordan elimination to solve systems.

In Chapter 5, we used systems of inequalities to establish healthy weight ranges for men and women of various ages and heights. Now it's time to step on the scale. The data below show the average weight of American adults, by age.

Average Weight by Age

	Ages 20–29	Ages 30–39	Ages 40–49	Ages 50–59	Ages 60–69	Ages 70–79	Ages 80+
Men	188	194	202	199	198	187	168
Women	156	165	171	172	171	156	142

Source: National Center for Health Statistics

The 14 numbers inside the brackets are arranged in two rows and seven columns. This rectangular array of 14 numbers, arranged in rows and columns and placed in brackets, is an example of a **matrix** (plural: **matrices**). The numbers inside the brackets are called **elements** of the matrix. Matrices are used to display information and to solve systems of linear equations. Because systems involving two equations in two variables can easily be solved by substitution or addition, we will focus on matrix solutions to systems of linear equations in three or more variables.

1. Write the augmented matrix for a linear system.

Augmented Matrices

A matrix gives us a shortened way of writing a system of equations. The first step in solving a system of linear equations using matrices is to write the *augmented matrix*. An **augmented matrix** has a vertical bar separating the columns of the matrix into two groups. The coefficients of each variable are placed to the left of the vertical line and the constants are placed to the right. If any variable is missing, its coefficient is 0. Here are two examples:

System of Linear Equations **Augmented Matrix**

$$\begin{cases} 3x + y + 2z = 31 \\ x + y + 2z = 19 \\ x + 3y + 2z = 25 \end{cases} \qquad \begin{bmatrix} 3 & 1 & 2 & | & 31 \\ 1 & 1 & 2 & | & 19 \\ 1 & 3 & 2 & | & 25 \end{bmatrix}$$

$$\begin{cases} x + 2y - 5z = -19 \\ y + 3z = 9 \\ z = 4 \end{cases} \qquad \begin{bmatrix} 1 & 2 & -5 & | & -19 \\ 0 & 1 & 3 & | & 9 \\ 0 & 0 & 1 & | & 4 \end{bmatrix}.$$

GREAT QUESTION!

Do linear systems have to be expressed in a special form when writing augmented matrices?

Yes. Variable terms must be on one side of each equation and constants must be on the other side. Furthermore, the variables must be in the same order in each equation.

Our goal in solving a system of linear equations in three variables using matrices is to produce a matrix with 1s down the diagonal from upper left to lower right on the left side of the vertical bar, called the **main diagonal**, and 0s below the 1s. In general, the matrix will be of the form

$$\begin{bmatrix} 1 & a & b & | & c \\ 0 & 1 & d & | & e \\ 0 & 0 & 1 & | & f \end{bmatrix},$$

where *a* through *f* represent real numbers. The third row of this matrix gives us the value of one variable. The other variables can then be found by back-substitution.

② Perform matrix row operations.

Matrix Row Operations

A matrix with 1s down the main diagonal and 0s below the 1s is said to be in **row-echelon form**. How do we produce a matrix in this form? We use **row operations** on the augmented matrix. These row operations are just like what you did when solving a linear system by the addition method. The difference is that we no longer write the variables, usually represented by x, y, and z.

Matrix Row Operations

The following row operations produce matrices that represent systems with the same solution set:

1. Two rows of a matrix may be interchanged. This is the same as interchanging two equations in a linear system.
2. The elements in any row may be multiplied by a nonzero number. This is the same as multiplying both sides of an equation by a nonzero number.
3. The elements in any row may be multiplied by a nonzero number, and these products may be added to the corresponding elements in any other row. This is the same as multiplying both sides of an equation by a nonzero number and then adding equations to eliminate a variable.

Two matrices are **row equivalent** if one can be obtained from the other by a sequence of row operations.

Each matrix row operation in the preceding box can be expressed symbolically as follows:

1. Interchange the elements in the ith and jth rows: $R_i \leftrightarrow R_j$.
2. Multiply each element in the ith row by k: kR_i.
3. Add k times the elements in row i to the corresponding elements in row j: $kR_i + R_j$.

GREAT QUESTION!

Can you clarify what I'm supposed to do to find $kR_i + R_j$? Which row do I work with and which row do I replace?

When performing the row operation

$$kR_i + R_j,$$

you use row i to find the products. However, **elements in row i do not change. It is the elements in row j that change:** Add k times the elements in row i to the corresponding elements in row j. Replace elements in row j by these sums.

EXAMPLE 1   Performing Matrix Row Operations

Use the matrix

$$\begin{bmatrix} 3 & 18 & -12 & | & 21 \\ 1 & 2 & -3 & | & 5 \\ -2 & -3 & 4 & | & -6 \end{bmatrix}$$

and perform each indicated row operation:

a. $R_1 \leftrightarrow R_2$ **b.** $\frac{1}{3}R_1$ **c.** $2R_2 + R_3$.

SOLUTION

a. The notation $R_1 \leftrightarrow R_2$ means to interchange the elements in row 1 and row 2. This results in the row-equivalent matrix

$$\begin{bmatrix} 1 & 2 & -3 & | & 5 \\ 3 & 18 & -12 & | & 21 \\ -2 & -3 & 4 & | & -6 \end{bmatrix}.$$

This was row 2; now it's row 1.

This was row 1; now it's row 2.

b. The notation $\frac{1}{3}R_1$ means to multiply each element in row 1 by $\frac{1}{3}$. This results in the row-equivalent matrix

$$\begin{bmatrix} \frac{1}{3}(3) & \frac{1}{3}(18) & \frac{1}{3}(-12) & | & \frac{1}{3}(21) \\ 1 & 2 & -3 & | & 5 \\ -2 & -3 & 4 & | & -6 \end{bmatrix} = \begin{bmatrix} 1 & 6 & -4 & | & 7 \\ 1 & 2 & -3 & | & 5 \\ -2 & -3 & 4 & | & -6 \end{bmatrix}.$$

$$\begin{bmatrix} 3 & 18 & -12 & | & 21 \\ 1 & 2 & -3 & | & 5 \\ -2 & -3 & 4 & | & -6 \end{bmatrix}$$

The given matrix (repeated)

c. The notation $2R_2 + R_3$ means to add 2 times the elements in row 2 to the corresponding elements in row 3. Replace the elements in row 3 by these sums. First, we find 2 times the elements in row 2, namely, 1, 2, −3, and 5:

$$2(1) \text{ or } 2, \qquad 2(2) \text{ or } 4, \qquad 2(-3) \text{ or } -6, \qquad 2(5) \text{ or } 10.$$

Now we add these products to the corresponding elements in row 3. Although we use row 2 to find the products, row 2 does not change. It is the elements in row 3 that change, resulting in the row-equivalent matrix

Replace row 3 by the sum of itself and 2 times row 2.

$$\begin{bmatrix} 3 & 18 & -12 & | & 21 \\ 1 & 2 & -3 & | & 5 \\ -2+2=0 & -3+4=1 & 4+(-6)=-2 & | & -6+10=4 \end{bmatrix} = \begin{bmatrix} 3 & 18 & -12 & | & 21 \\ 1 & 2 & -3 & | & 5 \\ 0 & 1 & -2 & | & 4 \end{bmatrix}.$$

• • •

☑ **Check Point 1** Use the matrix

$$\begin{bmatrix} 4 & 12 & -20 & | & 8 \\ 1 & 6 & -3 & | & 7 \\ -3 & -2 & 1 & | & -9 \end{bmatrix}$$

and perform each indicated row operation:

a. $R_1 \leftrightarrow R_2$ **b.** $\frac{1}{4}R_1$ **c.** $3R_2 + R_3$.

③ Use matrices and Gaussian elimination to solve systems.

Solving Linear Systems Using Gaussian Elimination

The process that we use to solve linear systems using matrix row operations is called **Gaussian elimination**, after the German mathematician Carl Friedrich Gauss (1777–1855). Here are the steps used in Gaussian elimination:

Solving Linear Systems of Three Equations with Three Variables Using Gaussian Elimination

1. Write the augmented matrix for the system.

2. Use matrix row operations to simplify the matrix to a row-equivalent matrix in row-echelon form, with 1s down the main diagonal from upper left to lower right, and 0s below the 1s in the first and second columns.

$$\begin{bmatrix} 1 & * & * & | & * \\ * & * & * & | & * \\ * & * & * & | & * \end{bmatrix} \rightarrow \begin{bmatrix} 1 & * & * & | & * \\ 0 & * & * & | & * \\ 0 & * & * & | & * \end{bmatrix} \rightarrow \begin{bmatrix} 1 & * & * & | & * \\ 0 & 1 & * & | & * \\ 0 & * & * & | & * \end{bmatrix} \rightarrow \begin{bmatrix} 1 & * & * & | & * \\ 0 & 1 & * & | & * \\ 0 & 0 & * & | & * \end{bmatrix} \rightarrow \begin{bmatrix} 1 & * & * & | & * \\ 0 & 1 & * & | & * \\ 0 & 0 & 1 & | & * \end{bmatrix}$$

Get 1 in the upper left-hand corner.

Use the 1 in the first column to get 0s below it.

Get 1 in the second row, second column position.

Use the 1 in the second column to get 0 below it.

Get 1 in the third row, third column position.

3. Write the system of linear equations corresponding to the matrix in step 2 and use back-substitution to find the system's solution.

EXAMPLE 2 Gaussian Elimination with Back-Substitution

Use matrices to solve the system:

$$\begin{cases} 3x + y + 2z = 31 \\ x + y + 2z = 19 \\ x + 3y + 2z = 25. \end{cases}$$

SOLUTION

Step 1   Write the augmented matrix for the system.

Linear System   **Augmented Matrix**

$$\begin{cases} 3x + y + 2z = 31 \\ x + y + 2z = 19 \\ x + 3y + 2z = 25 \end{cases} \qquad \begin{bmatrix} 3 & 1 & 2 & | & 31 \\ 1 & 1 & 2 & | & 19 \\ 1 & 3 & 2 & | & 25 \end{bmatrix}$$

Step 2   Use matrix row operations to simplify the matrix to row-echelon form, with 1s down the main diagonal from upper left to lower right, and 0s below the 1s in the first and second columns. Our first step in achieving this goal is to get 1 in the top position of the first column.

We want 1 in this position. $\begin{bmatrix} 3 & 1 & 2 & | & 31 \\ 1 & 1 & 2 & | & 19 \\ 1 & 3 & 2 & | & 25 \end{bmatrix}$

To get 1 in this position, we interchange row 1 and row 2: $R_1 \leftrightarrow R_2$. (We could also interchange row 1 and row 3 to attain our goal.)

$$\begin{bmatrix} 1 & 1 & 2 & | & 19 \\ 3 & 1 & 2 & | & 31 \\ 1 & 3 & 2 & | & 25 \end{bmatrix}$$

This was row **2**; now it's row **1**.

This was row **1**; now it's row **2**.

Now we want to get 0s below the 1 in the first column.

We want 0 in these positions. $\begin{bmatrix} 1 & 1 & 2 & | & 19 \\ 3 & 1 & 2 & | & 31 \\ 1 & 3 & 2 & | & 25 \end{bmatrix}$

To get a 0 where there is now a 3, multiply the top row of numbers by -3 and add these products to the second row of numbers: $-3R_1 + R_2$. To get a 0 where there is now a 1, multiply the top row of numbers by -1 and add these products to the third row of numbers: $-1R_1 + R_3$. Although we are using row 1 to find the products, the numbers in row 1 do not change.

Replace row 2 by $-3R_1 + R_2$.

Replace row 3 by $-1R_1 + R_3$.

$$\begin{bmatrix} 1 & 1 & 2 & | & 19 \\ -3(1) + 3 & -3(1) + 1 & -3(2) + 2 & | & -3(19) + 31 \\ -1(1) + 1 & -1(1) + 3 & -1(2) + 2 & | & -1(19) + 25 \end{bmatrix} = \begin{bmatrix} 1 & 1 & 2 & | & 19 \\ 0 & -2 & -4 & | & -26 \\ 0 & 2 & 0 & | & 6 \end{bmatrix}$$

We want 1 in this position.

We move on to the second column. To get 1 in the desired position, we multiply -2 by its reciprocal, $-\frac{1}{2}$. Therefore, we multiply all the numbers in the second row by $-\frac{1}{2}$: $-\frac{1}{2}R_2$.

$-\frac{1}{2}R_2$

$$\begin{bmatrix} 1 & 1 & 2 & | & 19 \\ -\frac{1}{2}(0) & -\frac{1}{2}(-2) & -\frac{1}{2}(-4) & | & -\frac{1}{2}(-26) \\ 0 & 2 & 0 & | & 6 \end{bmatrix} = \begin{bmatrix} 1 & 1 & 2 & | & 19 \\ 0 & 1 & 2 & | & 13 \\ 0 & 2 & 0 & | & 6 \end{bmatrix}.$$

We want 0 in this position.

$$\begin{bmatrix} 1 & 1 & 2 & | & 19 \\ 0 & 1 & 2 & | & 13 \\ 0 & 2 & 0 & | & 6 \end{bmatrix}$$

We want 0 in this position.

The matrix from the bottom
of the previous page (repeated)

So far, our matrix row operations have resulted in the matrix that we repeated in the margin. We are not yet done with the second column. The voice balloon shows that we want to get a 0 where there is now a 2. If we multiply the second row of numbers by -2 and add these products to the third row of numbers, we will get 0 in this position: $-2R_2 + R_3$. Although we are using the numbers in row 2 to find the products, the numbers in row 2 do not change.

Replace row 3 by
$-2R_2 + R_3.$
$$\begin{bmatrix} 1 & 1 & 2 & | & 19 \\ 0 & 1 & 2 & | & 13 \\ -2(0)+0 & -2(1)+2 & -2(2)+0 & | & -2(13)+6 \end{bmatrix} = \begin{bmatrix} 1 & 1 & 2 & | & 19 \\ 0 & 1 & 2 & | & 13 \\ 0 & 0 & -4 & | & -20 \end{bmatrix}$$

We want 1 in this position.

We move on to the third column. To get 1 in the desired position, we multiply -4 by its reciprocal, $-\frac{1}{4}$. Therefore, we multiply all the numbers in the third row by $-\frac{1}{4}$: $-\frac{1}{4}R_3$.

$-\frac{1}{4}R_3$
$$\begin{bmatrix} 1 & 1 & 2 & | & 19 \\ 0 & 1 & 2 & | & 13 \\ -\frac{1}{4}(0) & -\frac{1}{4}(0) & -\frac{1}{4}(-4) & | & -\frac{1}{4}(-20) \end{bmatrix} = \begin{bmatrix} 1 & 1 & 2 & | & 19 \\ 0 & 1 & 2 & | & 13 \\ 0 & 0 & 1 & | & 5 \end{bmatrix}$$

We now have the desired matrix in row-echelon form, with 1s down the main diagonal and 0s below the 1s in the first and second columns.

Step 3 Write the system of linear equations corresponding to the matrix in step 2 and use back-substitution to find the system's solution. The system represented by the matrix in step 2 is

$$\begin{bmatrix} 1 & 1 & 2 & | & 19 \\ 0 & 1 & 2 & | & 13 \\ 0 & 0 & 1 & | & 5 \end{bmatrix} \rightarrow \begin{cases} 1x + 1y + 2z = 19 \\ 0x + 1y + 2z = 13 \\ 0x + 0y + 1z = 5 \end{cases} \text{ or } \begin{cases} x + y + 2z = 19 \quad (1) \\ y + 2z = 13. \quad (2) \\ z = 5 \quad (3) \end{cases}$$

We immediately see from equation (3) that the value for z is 5. To find y, we back-substitute 5 for z in the second equation.

$y + 2z = 13$ Equation (2)

$y + 2(5) = 13$ Substitute 5 for z.

$y + 10 = 13$ Multiply.

$y = 3$ Subtract 10 from both sides and solve for y.

Finally, back-substitute 3 for y and 5 for z in the first equation.

$x + y + 2z = 19$ Equation (1)

$x + 3 + 2(5) = 19$ Substitute 3 for y and 5 for z.

$x + 13 = 19$ Multiply and add.

$x = 6$ Subtract 13 from both sides and solve for x.

With $z = 5$, $y = 3$, and $x = 6$, the solution set of the original system is $\{(6, 3, 5)\}$. Check to see that the solution satisfies all three equations in the given system. ● ● ●

✓ Check Point **2** Use matrices to solve the system:

$$\begin{cases} 2x + y + 2z = 18 \\ x - y + 2z = 9 \\ x + 2y - z = 6. \end{cases}$$

Modern supercomputers are capable of solving systems with more than 600,000 variables. The augmented matrices for such systems are huge, but the solution using matrices is exactly like what we did in Example 2. Work with the augmented matrix, one column at a time. Get 1s down the main diagonal from upper left to lower right and 0s below the 1s. Let's see how this works for a linear system involving four equations in four variables.

EXAMPLE 3 Gaussian Elimination with Back-Substitution

Use matrices to solve the system:

$$\begin{cases} 2w + x + 3y - z = 6 \\ w - x + 2y - 2z = -1 \\ w - x - y + z = -4 \\ -w + 2x - 2y - z = -7. \end{cases}$$

SOLUTION

Step 1 Write the augmented matrix for the system.

Linear System

$$\begin{cases} 2w + x + 3y - z = 6 \\ w - x + 2y - 2z = -1 \\ w - x - y + z = -4 \\ -w + 2x - 2y - z = -7 \end{cases}$$

Augmented Matrix

$$\left[\begin{array}{cccc|c} 2 & 1 & 3 & -1 & 6 \\ 1 & -1 & 2 & -2 & -1 \\ 1 & -1 & -1 & 1 & -4 \\ -1 & 2 & -2 & -1 & -7 \end{array}\right]$$

Step 2 Use matrix row operations to simplify the matrix to row-echelon form, with 1s down the main diagonal from upper left to lower right, and 0s below the 1s in the first, second, and third columns. Our first step in achieving this goal is to get 1 in the top position of the first column. To do this, we interchange row 1 and row 2: $R_1 \leftrightarrow R_2$.

We want 0s in these positions.

$$\left[\begin{array}{cccc|c} 1 & -1 & 2 & -2 & -1 \\ 2 & 1 & 3 & -1 & 6 \\ 1 & -1 & -1 & 1 & -4 \\ -1 & 2 & -2 & -1 & -7 \end{array}\right]$$

This was row 2; now it's row 1.

This was row 1; now it's row 2.

Now we use the 1 at the top of the first column to get 0s below it.

Use the previous matrix and:
Replace row 2 by $-2R_1 + R_2$.
Replace row 3 by $-1R_1 + R_3$.
Replace row 4 by $1R_1 + R_4$.

$$\left[\begin{array}{cccc|c} 1 & -1 & 2 & -2 & -1 \\ 0 & 3 & -1 & 3 & 8 \\ 0 & 0 & -3 & 3 & -3 \\ 0 & 1 & 0 & -3 & -8 \end{array}\right]$$

We want 1 in this position.

We move on to the second column. We can obtain 1 in the desired position by multiplying the numbers in the second row by $\frac{1}{3}$, the reciprocal of 3.

$$\left[\begin{array}{cccc|c} 1 & -1 & 2 & -2 & -1 \\ \frac{1}{3}(0) & \frac{1}{3}(3) & \frac{1}{3}(-1) & \frac{1}{3}(3) & \frac{1}{3}(8) \\ 0 & 0 & -3 & 3 & -3 \\ 0 & 1 & 0 & -3 & -8 \end{array}\right] = \left[\begin{array}{cccc|c} 1 & -1 & 2 & -2 & -1 \\ 0 & 1 & -\frac{1}{3} & 1 & \frac{8}{3} \\ 0 & 0 & -3 & 3 & -3 \\ 0 & 1 & 0 & -3 & -8 \end{array}\right] \quad \frac{1}{3}R_2$$

We want 0s in these positions.
The top position already has a 0.

$$\begin{bmatrix} 1 & -1 & 2 & -2 & | & -1 \\ 0 & 1 & -\frac{1}{3} & 1 & | & \frac{8}{3} \\ 0 & 0 & -3 & 3 & | & -3 \\ 0 & 1 & 0 & -3 & | & -8 \end{bmatrix}$$

We want 0s in these positions. The top position already has a 0.

The matrix from the bottom of the previous page (repeated)

So far, our matrix row operations have resulted in the matrix that we repeated in the margin. Now we use the 1 in the second row, second column position to get 0s below it.

Replace row 4 in the previous matrix by $-1R_2 + R_4$.

$$\begin{bmatrix} 1 & -1 & 2 & -2 & | & -1 \\ 0 & 1 & -\frac{1}{3} & 1 & | & \frac{8}{3} \\ 0 & 0 & -3 & 3 & | & -3 \\ 0 & 0 & \frac{1}{3} & -4 & | & -\frac{32}{3} \end{bmatrix}$$ **We want 1 in this position.**

We move on to the third column. We can obtain 1 in the desired position by multiplying the numbers in the third row by $-\frac{1}{3}$, the reciprocal of -3.

$$\begin{bmatrix} 1 & -1 & 2 & -2 & | & -1 \\ 0 & 1 & -\frac{1}{3} & 1 & | & \frac{8}{3} \\ -\frac{1}{3}(0) & -\frac{1}{3}(0) & -\frac{1}{3}(-3) & -\frac{1}{3}(3) & | & -\frac{1}{3}(-3) \\ 0 & 0 & \frac{1}{3} & -4 & | & -\frac{32}{3} \end{bmatrix} = \begin{bmatrix} 1 & -1 & 2 & -2 & | & -1 \\ 0 & 1 & -\frac{1}{3} & 1 & | & \frac{8}{3} \\ 0 & 0 & 1 & -1 & | & 1 \\ 0 & 0 & \frac{1}{3} & -4 & | & -\frac{32}{3} \end{bmatrix}$$ $-\frac{1}{3}R_3$

We want 0 in this position.

Now we use the 1 in the third column to get 0 below it.

Replace row 4 in the previous matrix by $-\frac{1}{3}R_3 + R_4$.

$$\begin{bmatrix} 1 & -1 & 2 & -2 & | & -1 \\ 0 & 1 & -\frac{1}{3} & 1 & | & \frac{8}{3} \\ 0 & 0 & 1 & -1 & | & 1 \\ 0 & 0 & 0 & -\frac{11}{3} & | & -11 \end{bmatrix}$$ **We want 1 in this position.**

We move on to the fourth column. Because we want 1s down the diagonal from upper left to lower right, we want 1 where there is now $-\frac{11}{3}$. We can obtain 1 in this position by multiplying the numbers in the fourth row by $-\frac{3}{11}$.

$$\begin{bmatrix} 1 & -1 & 2 & -2 & | & -1 \\ 0 & 1 & -\frac{1}{3} & 1 & | & \frac{8}{3} \\ 0 & 0 & 1 & -1 & | & 1 \\ -\frac{3}{11}(0) & -\frac{3}{11}(0) & -\frac{3}{11}(0) & -\frac{3}{11}(-\frac{11}{3}) & | & -\frac{3}{11}(-11) \end{bmatrix}$$

$$= \begin{bmatrix} 1 & -1 & 2 & -2 & | & -1 \\ 0 & 1 & -\frac{1}{3} & 1 & | & \frac{8}{3} \\ 0 & 0 & 1 & -1 & | & 1 \\ 0 & 0 & 0 & 1 & | & 3 \end{bmatrix}$$ $-\frac{3}{11}R_4$

We now have the desired matrix in row-echelon form, with 1s down the main diagonal and 0s below the 1s. An equivalent row-echelon matrix can be obtained using a graphing utility and the $\boxed{\text{REF}}$ command on the augmented matrix.

Step 3   Write the system of linear equations corresponding to the matrix in step 2 and use back-substitution to find the system's solution. The system represented by the matrix in step 2 is

$$\begin{bmatrix} 1 & -1 & 2 & -2 & | & -1 \\ 0 & 1 & -\frac{1}{3} & 1 & | & \frac{8}{3} \\ 0 & 0 & 1 & -1 & | & 1 \\ 0 & 0 & 0 & 1 & | & 3 \end{bmatrix} \rightarrow \begin{cases} 1w - 1x + 2y - 2z = -1 \\ 0w + 1x - \frac{1}{3}y + 1z = \frac{8}{3} \\ 0w + 0x + 1y - 1z = 1 \\ 0w + 0x + 0y + 1z = 3 \end{cases}$$ or $$\begin{cases} w - x + 2y - 2z = -1 \\ x - \frac{1}{3}y + z = \frac{8}{3} \\ y - z = 1 \\ z = 3. \end{cases}$$

We immediately see that the value for z is 3. We can now use back-substitution to find the values for y, x, and w.

These are the four equations from the last column.

$z = 3$ | $y - z = 1$ | $x - \dfrac{1}{3}y + z = \dfrac{8}{3}$ | $w - x + 2y - 2z = -1$

$y - 3 = 1$ | $x - \dfrac{1}{3}(4) + 3 = \dfrac{8}{3}$ | $w - 1 + 2(4) - 2(3) = -1$

$y = 4$ | $x + \dfrac{5}{3} = \dfrac{8}{3}$ | $w - 1 + 8 - 6 = -1$

$x = 1$ | $w + 1 = -1$

$w = -2$

Let's agree to write the solution for the system in the alphabetical order of the variables from left to right, namely (w, x, y, z). Thus, the solution set is $\{(-2, 1, 4, 3)\}$. We can verify the solution by substituting the value for each variable into the original system of equations and obtaining four true statements.   • • •

⊘ Check Point **3** Use matrices to solve the system:

$$\begin{cases} w - 3x - 2y + z = -3 \\ 2w - 7x - y + 2z = 1 \\ 3w - 7x - 3y + 3z = -5 \\ 5w + x + 4y - 2z = 18. \end{cases}$$

④ Use matrices and Gauss-Jordan elimination to solve systems.

Solving Linear Systems Using Gauss-Jordan Elimination

Using Gaussian elimination, we obtain a matrix in row-echelon form, with 1s down the main diagonal and 0s below the 1s. A second method, called **Gauss-Jordan elimination**, after Carl Friedrich Gauss and Wilhelm Jordan (1842–1899), continues the process until a matrix with 1s down the main diagonal and 0s in every position *above and below* each 1 is found. Such a matrix is said to be in **reduced row-echelon form**. For a system of three linear equations in three variables, x, y, and z, we must get the augmented matrix into the form

$$\begin{bmatrix} 1 & 0 & 0 & | & a \\ 0 & 1 & 0 & | & b \\ 0 & 0 & 1 & | & c \end{bmatrix}.$$

Based on this matrix, we conclude that $x = a$, $y = b$, and $z = c$.

Solving Linear Systems Using Gauss-Jordan Elimination

1. Write the augmented matrix for the system.
2. Use matrix row operations to simplify the matrix to a row-equivalent matrix in reduced row-echelon form, with 1s down the main diagonal from upper left to lower right, and 0s above and below the 1s.
   a. Get 1 in the upper left-hand corner.
   b. Use the 1 in the first column to get 0s below it.
   c. Get 1 in the second row, second column.
   d. Use the 1 in the second column to make the remaining entries in the second column 0.
   e. Get 1 in the third row, third column.
   f. Use the 1 in the third column to make the remaining entries in the third column 0.
   g. Continue this procedure as far as possible.
3. Use the reduced row-echelon form of the matrix in step 2 to write the system's solution set. (Back-substitution is not necessary.)

TECHNOLOGY

Most graphing utilities can convert a matrix to reduced row-echelon form. Enter the system's augmented matrix and name it A. Then use the $\boxed{\text{RREF}}$ (reduced row-echelon form) command on matrix A.

This is the augmented matrix for the system in Example 4.

This is the matrix in reduced row-echelon form we obtained in Example 4.

EXAMPLE 4   Using Gauss-Jordan Elimination

Use Gauss-Jordan elimination to solve the system:

$$\begin{cases} 3x + y + 2z = 31 \\ x + y + 2z = 19 \\ x + 3y + 2z = 25. \end{cases}$$

SOLUTION

In Example 2, we used Gaussian elimination to obtain the following matrix:

We want 0s in these positions.

$$\begin{bmatrix} 1 & 1 & 2 & | & 19 \\ 0 & 1 & 2 & | & 13 \\ 0 & 0 & 1 & | & 5 \end{bmatrix}.$$

To use Gauss-Jordan elimination, we need 0s both above and below the 1s in the main diagonal. We use the 1 in the second row, second column to get a 0 above it.

Replace row 1 in the previous matrix by $-1R_2 + R_1$.

$$\begin{bmatrix} 1 & 0 & 0 & | & 6 \\ 0 & 1 & 2 & | & 13 \\ 0 & 0 & 1 & | & 5 \end{bmatrix}$$

We want 0s in these positions.

We use the 1 in the third column to get 0s above it.

$$\begin{bmatrix} 1 & 0 & 0 & | & 6 \\ 0 & 1 & 0 & | & 3 \\ 0 & 0 & 1 & | & 5 \end{bmatrix}$$

Replace row 2 in the previous matrix by $-2R_3 + R_2$.

This last matrix corresponds to

$$x = 6, \quad y = 3, \quad z = 5.$$

As we found in Example 2, the solution set is $\{(6, 3, 5)\}$.   • • •

Check Point **4** Solve the system in Check Point 2 using Gauss-Jordan elimination. Begin by working with the matrix that you obtained in Check Point 2.

CONCEPT AND VOCABULARY CHECK

Fill in each blank so that the resulting statement is true.

1. A rectangular array of numbers, arranged in rows and columns and placed in brackets, is called a/an _____. The numbers inside the brackets are called _____.

2. Consider the matrix

$$\begin{bmatrix} 1 & 1 & -1 & | & -2 \\ -3 & -4 & 2 & | & 4 \\ 2 & 1 & 1 & | & 6 \end{bmatrix}.$$

We can obtain 0 in the position shaded by a rectangle if we multiply the top row of numbers by _____ and add these products to the _____ row of numbers. We can obtain 0 in the position shaded by an oval if we multiply the top row of numbers by _____ and add these products to the _____ row of numbers.

3. The augmented matrix for the system

$$\begin{cases} 2x + y + 4z = -4 \\ 3x + z = 1 \\ 4x + 3y + z = 8 \end{cases}$$

is $\begin{bmatrix} - & - & - & | & - \\ - & - & - & | & - \\ - & - & - & | & - \end{bmatrix}.$

4. Using Gauss-Jordan elimination to solve the system

$$\begin{cases} x - y + z = -4 \\ 5x + y - 2z = 12, \\ 2x - 3y + 4z = -15 \end{cases}$$

we obtain the matrix

$$\begin{bmatrix} 1 & 0 & 0 & | & 1 \\ 0 & 1 & 0 & | & 3 \\ 0 & 0 & 1 & | & -2 \end{bmatrix}.$$

The system's solution set is _____.

5. True or false: Back-substitution is required to solve linear systems using Gaussian elimination. _____

6. True or false: Back-substitution is required to solve linear systems using Gauss-Jordan elimination. _____

EXERCISE SET 6.1

Practice Exercises

In Exercises 1–8, write the augmented matrix for each system of linear equations.

1. $\begin{cases} 2x + y + 2z = 2 \\ 3x - 5y - z = 4 \\ x - 2y - 3z = -6 \end{cases}$

2. $\begin{cases} 3x - 2y + 5z = 31 \\ x + 3y - 3z = -12 \\ -2x - 5y + 3z = 11 \end{cases}$

3. $\begin{cases} x - y + z = 8 \\ y - 12z = -15 \\ z = 1 \end{cases}$

4. $\begin{cases} x - 2y + 3z = 9 \\ y + 3z = 5 \\ z = 2 \end{cases}$

5. $\begin{cases} 5x - 2y - 3z = 0 \\ x + y = 5 \\ 2x - 3z = 4 \end{cases}$

6. $\begin{cases} x - 2y + z = 10 \\ 3x + y = 5 \\ 7x + 2z = 2 \end{cases}$

7. $\begin{cases} 2w + 5x - 3y + z = 2 \\ 3x + y = 4 \\ w - x + 5y = 9 \\ 5w - 5x - 2y = 1 \end{cases}$

8. $\begin{cases} 4w + 7x - 8y + z = 3 \\ 5x + y = 5 \\ w - x - y = 17 \\ 2w - 2x + 11y = 4 \end{cases}$

In Exercises 9–12, write the system of linear equations represented by the augmented matrix. Use x, y, and z, or, if necessary, w, x, y, and z, for the variables.

9. $\begin{bmatrix} 5 & 0 & 3 & | & -11 \\ 0 & 1 & -4 & | & 12 \\ 7 & 2 & 0 & | & 3 \end{bmatrix}$

10. $\begin{bmatrix} 7 & 0 & 4 & | & -13 \\ 0 & 1 & -5 & | & 11 \\ 2 & 7 & 0 & | & 6 \end{bmatrix}$

11. $\begin{bmatrix} 1 & 1 & 4 & 1 & | & 3 \\ -1 & 1 & -1 & 0 & | & 7 \\ 2 & 0 & 0 & 5 & | & 11 \\ 0 & 0 & 12 & 4 & | & 5 \end{bmatrix}$

12. $\begin{bmatrix} 4 & 1 & 5 & 1 & | & 6 \\ 1 & -1 & 0 & -1 & | & 8 \\ 3 & 0 & 0 & 7 & | & 4 \\ 0 & 0 & 11 & 5 & | & 3 \end{bmatrix}$

In Exercises 13–18, perform each matrix row operation and write the new matrix.

13. $\begin{bmatrix} 2 & -6 & 4 & | & 10 \\ 1 & 5 & -5 & | & 0 \\ 3 & 0 & 4 & | & 7 \end{bmatrix} \quad \frac{1}{2}R_1$

14. $\begin{bmatrix} 3 & -12 & 6 & | & 9 \\ 1 & -4 & 4 & | & 0 \\ 2 & 0 & 7 & | & 4 \end{bmatrix} \quad \frac{1}{3}R_1$

15. $\begin{bmatrix} 1 & -3 & 2 & | & 0 \\ 3 & 1 & -1 & | & 7 \\ 2 & -2 & 1 & | & 3 \end{bmatrix} \quad -3R_1 + R_2$

16. $\begin{bmatrix} 1 & -1 & 5 & | & -6 \\ 3 & 3 & -1 & | & 10 \\ 1 & 3 & 2 & | & 5 \end{bmatrix} \quad -3R_1 + R_2$

17. $\begin{bmatrix} 1 & -1 & 1 & 1 & | & 3 \\ 0 & 1 & -2 & -1 & | & 0 \\ 2 & 0 & 3 & 4 & | & 11 \\ 5 & 1 & 2 & 4 & | & 6 \end{bmatrix} \quad \begin{matrix} -2R_1 + R_3 \\ -5R_1 + R_4 \end{matrix}$

18. $\begin{bmatrix} 1 & -5 & 2 & -2 & | & 4 \\ 0 & 1 & -3 & -1 & | & 0 \\ 3 & 0 & 2 & -1 & | & 6 \\ -4 & 1 & 4 & 2 & | & -3 \end{bmatrix} \quad \begin{matrix} -3R_1 + R_3 \\ 4R_1 + R_4 \end{matrix}$

In Exercises 19–20, a few steps in the process of simplifying the given matrix to row-echelon form, with 1s down the diagonal from upper left to lower right, and 0s below the 1s, are shown. Fill in the missing numbers in the steps that are shown.

19. $\begin{bmatrix} 1 & -1 & 1 & | & 8 \\ 2 & 3 & -1 & | & -2 \\ 3 & -2 & -9 & | & 9 \end{bmatrix} \rightarrow \begin{bmatrix} 1 & -1 & 1 & | & 8 \\ 0 & 5 & \square & | & \square \\ 0 & 1 & \square & | & \square \end{bmatrix}$

$$\rightarrow \begin{bmatrix} 1 & -1 & 1 & | & 8 \\ 0 & 1 & \square & | & \square \\ 0 & 1 & \square & | & \square \end{bmatrix}$$

20. $\begin{bmatrix} 1 & -2 & 3 & | & 4 \\ 2 & 1 & -4 & | & 3 \\ -3 & 4 & -1 & | & -2 \end{bmatrix} \rightarrow \begin{bmatrix} 1 & -2 & 3 & | & 4 \\ 0 & 5 & \square & | & \square \\ 0 & -2 & \square & | & \square \end{bmatrix}$

$$\rightarrow \begin{bmatrix} 1 & -2 & 3 & | & 4 \\ 0 & 1 & \square & | & \square \\ 0 & -2 & \square & | & \square \end{bmatrix}$$

In Exercises 21–38, solve each system of equations using matrices. Use Gaussian elimination with back-substitution or Gauss-Jordan elimination.

21. $\begin{cases} x + y - z = -2 \\ 2x - y + z = 5 \\ -x + 2y + 2z = 1 \end{cases}$

22. $\begin{cases} x - 2y - z = 2 \\ 2x - y + z = 4 \\ -x + y - 2z = -4 \end{cases}$

23. $\begin{cases} x + 3y = 0 \\ x + y + z = 1 \\ 3x - y - z = 11 \end{cases}$

24. $\begin{cases} 3y - z = -1 \\ x + 5y - z = -4 \\ -3x + 6y + 2z = 11 \end{cases}$

25. $\begin{cases} 2x - y - z = 4 \\ x + y - 5z = -4 \\ x - 2y = 4 \end{cases}$ **26.** $\begin{cases} x - 3z = -2 \\ 2x + 2y + z = 4 \\ 3x + y - 2z = 5 \end{cases}$

27. $\begin{cases} x + y + z = 4 \\ x - y - z = 0 \\ x - y + z = 2 \end{cases}$ **28.** $\begin{cases} 3x + y - z = 0 \\ x + y + 2z = 6 \\ 2x + 2y + 3z = 10 \end{cases}$

29. $\begin{cases} x + 2y = z - 1 \\ x = 4 + y - z \\ x + y - 3z = -2 \end{cases}$ **30.** $\begin{cases} 2x + y = z + 1 \\ 2x = 1 + 3y - z \\ x + y + z = 4 \end{cases}$

31. $\begin{cases} 3a - b - 4c = 3 \\ 2a - b + 2c = -8 \\ a + 2b - 3c = 9 \end{cases}$ **32.** $\begin{cases} 3a + b - c = 0 \\ 2a + 3b - 5c = 1 \\ a - 2b + 3c = -4 \end{cases}$

33. $\begin{cases} 2x + 2y + 7z = -1 \\ 2x + y + 2z = 2 \\ 4x + 6y + z = 15 \end{cases}$ **34.** $\begin{cases} 3x + 2y + 3z = 3 \\ 4x - 5y + 7z = 1 \\ 2x + 3y - 2z = 6 \end{cases}$

35. $\begin{cases} w + x + y + z = 4 \\ 2w + x - 2y - z = 0 \\ w - 2x - y - 2z = -2 \\ 3w + 2x + y + 3z = 4 \end{cases}$

36. $\begin{cases} w + x + y + z = 5 \\ w + 2x - y - 2z = -1 \\ w - 3x - 3y - z = -1 \\ 2w - x + 2y - z = -2 \end{cases}$

37. $\begin{cases} 3w - 4x + y + z = 9 \\ w + x - y - z = 0 \\ 2w + x + 4y - 2z = 3 \\ -w + 2x + y - 3z = 3 \end{cases}$

38. $\begin{cases} 2w + y - 3z = 8 \\ w - x + 4z = -10 \\ 3w + 5x - y - z = 20 \\ w + x - y - z = 6 \end{cases}$

Practice Plus

39. Find the quadratic function $f(x) = ax^2 + bx + c$ for which $f(-2) = -4, f(1) = 2,$ and $f(2) = 0$.

40. Find the quadratic function $f(x) = ax^2 + bx + c$ for which $f(-1) = 5, f(1) = 3,$ and $f(2) = 5$.

41. Find the cubic function $f(x) = ax^3 + bx^2 + cx + d$ for which $f(-1) = 0, f(1) = 2, f(2) = 3,$ and $f(3) = 12$.

42. Find the cubic function $f(x) = ax^3 + bx^2 + cx + d$ for which $f(-1) = 3, f(1) = 1, f(2) = 6,$ and $f(3) = 7$.

43. Solve the system:

$$\begin{cases} 2 \ln w + \ln x + 3 \ln y - 2 \ln z = -6 \\ 4 \ln w + 3 \ln x + \ln y - \ln z = -2 \\ \ln w + \ln x + \ln y + \ln z = -5 \\ \ln w + \ln x - \ln y - \ln z = 5. \end{cases}$$

(*Hint:* Let $A = \ln w, B = \ln x, C = \ln y,$ and $D = \ln z$. Solve the system for $A, B, C,$ and D. Then use the logarithmic equations to find $w, x, y,$ and z.)

44. Solve the system:

$$\begin{cases} \ln w + \ln x + \ln y + \ln z = -1 \\ -\ln w + 4 \ln x + \ln y - \ln z = 0 \\ \ln w - 2 \ln x + \ln y - 2 \ln z = 11 \\ -\ln w - 2 \ln x + \ln y + 2 \ln z = -3. \end{cases}$$

(*Hint:* Let $A = \ln w, B = \ln x, C = \ln y,$ and $D = \ln z$. Solve the system for $A, B, C,$ and D. Then use the logarithmic equations to find $w, x, y,$ and z.)

Application Exercises

45. A ball is thrown straight upward. A position function

$$s(t) = \tfrac{1}{2}at^2 + v_0 t + s_0$$

can be used to describe the ball's height, $s(t)$, in feet, after t seconds.

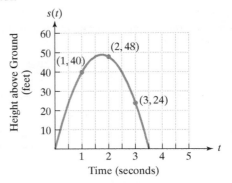

  a. Use the points labeled in the graph to find the values of $a, v_0,$ and s_0. Solve the system of linear equations involving $a, v_0,$ and s_0 using matrices.

  b. Find and interpret $s(3.5)$. Identify your solution as a point on the graph shown.

  c. After how many seconds does the ball reach its maximum height? What is its maximum height?

46. A football is kicked straight upward. A position function

$$s(t) = \tfrac{1}{2}at^2 + v_0 t + s_0$$

can be used to describe the ball's height, $s(t)$, in feet, after t seconds.

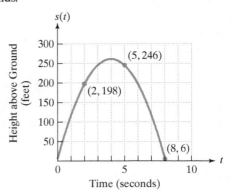

  a. Use the points labeled in the graph to find the values of $a, v_0,$ and s_0. Solve the system of linear equations involving $a, v_0,$ and s_0 using matrices.

  b. Find and interpret $s(7)$. Identify your solution as a point on the graph shown.

  c. After how many seconds does the ball reach its maximum height? What is its maximum height?

Write a system of linear equations in three or four variables to solve Exercises 47–50. Then use matrices to solve the system.

47. Three foods have the following nutritional content per ounce.

	Calories	Protein (in grams)	Vitamin C (in milligrams)
Food A	40	5	30
Food B	200	2	10
Food C	400	4	300

If a meal consisting of the three foods allows exactly 660 calories, 25 grams of protein, and 425 milligrams of vitamin C, how many ounces of each kind of food should be used?

48. A furniture company produces three types of desks: a children's model, an office model, and a deluxe model. Each desk is manufactured in three stages: cutting, construction, and finishing. The time requirements for each model and manufacturing stage are given in the following table.

	Children's Model	Office Model	Deluxe Model
Cutting	2 hr	3 hr	2 hr
Construction	2 hr	1 hr	3 hr
Finishing	1 hr	1 hr	2 hr

Each week the company has available a maximum of 100 hours for cutting, 100 hours for construction, and 65 hours for finishing. If all available time must be used, how many of each type of desk should be produced each week?

49. Imagine the entire global population as a village of precisely 200 people. The bar graph shows some numeric observations based on this scenario.

Earth's Population as a Village of 200 People

Source: Gary Rimmer, *Number Freaking*, The Disinformation Company Ltd., 2006

Combined, there are 183 Asians, Africans, Europeans, and Americans in the village. The number of Asians exceeds the number of Africans and Europeans by 70. The difference between the number of Europeans and Americans is 15. If the number of Africans is doubled, their population exceeds the number of Europeans and Americans by 23. Determine the number of Asians, Africans, Europeans, and Americans in the global village.

50. The bar graph shows the number of rooms, bathrooms, fireplaces, and elevators in the U.S. White House.

The U.S. White House by the Numbers

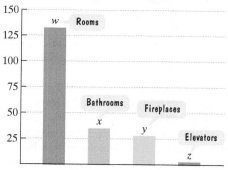

Source: The White House

Combined, there are 198 rooms, bathrooms, fireplaces, and elevators. The number of rooms exceeds the number of bathrooms and fireplaces by 69. The difference between the number of fireplaces and elevators is 25. If the number of bathrooms is doubled, it exceeds the number of fireplaces and elevators by 39. Determine the number of rooms, bathrooms, fireplaces, and elevators in the U.S. White House.

Writing in Mathematics

51. What is a matrix?

52. Describe what is meant by the augmented matrix of a system of linear equations.

53. In your own words, describe each of the three matrix row operations. Give an example with each of the operations.

54. Describe how to use row operations and matrices to solve a system of linear equations.

55. What is the difference between Gaussian elimination and Gauss-Jordan elimination?

Technology Exercises

56. Most graphing utilities can perform row operations on matrices. Consult the owner's manual for your graphing utility to learn proper keystrokes for performing these operations. Then duplicate the row operations of any three exercises that you solved from Exercises 13–18.

57. If your graphing utility has a $\boxed{\text{REF}}$ (row-echelon form) command or a $\boxed{\text{RREF}}$ (reduced row-echelon form) command, use this feature to verify your work with any five systems that you solved from Exercises 21–38.

58. Solve using a graphing utility's $\boxed{\text{REF}}$ or $\boxed{\text{RREF}}$ command:

$$\begin{cases} 2x_1 - 2x_2 + 3x_3 - x_4 = 12 \\ x_1 + 2x_2 - x_3 + 2x_4 - x_5 = -7 \\ x_1 + x_3 + x_4 - 5x_5 = 1 \\ -x_1 + x_2 - x_3 - 2x_4 - 3x_5 = 0 \\ x_1 - x_2 - x_4 + x_5 = 4. \end{cases}$$

Critical Thinking Exercises

Make Sense? *In Exercises 59–62, determine whether each statement makes sense or does not make sense, and explain your reasoning.*

59. Matrix row operations remind me of what I did when solving a linear system by the addition method, although I no longer write the variables.

60. When I use matrices to solve linear systems, the only arithmetic involves multiplication or a combination of multiplication and addition.

61. When I use matrices to solve linear systems, I spend most of my time using row operations to express the system's augmented matrix in row-echelon form.

62. Using row operations on an augmented matrix, I obtain a row in which 0s appear to the left of the vertical bar, but 6 appears on the right, so the system I'm working with has no solution.

In Exercises 63–66, determine whether each statement is true or false. If the statement is false, make the necessary change(s) to produce a true statement.

63. A matrix row operation such as $-\frac{4}{5}R_1 + R_2$ is not permitted because of the negative fraction.

64. The augmented matrix for the system

$$\begin{cases} x - 3y = 5 \\ y - 2z = 7 \\ 2x + z = 4 \end{cases} \text{ is } \begin{bmatrix} 1 & -3 & | & 5 \\ 1 & -2 & | & 7 \\ 2 & 1 & | & 4 \end{bmatrix}.$$

65. In solving a linear system of three equations in three variables, we begin with the augmented matrix and use row operations to obtain a row-equivalent matrix with 0s down the diagonal from left to right and 1s below each 0.

66. The row operation $kR_i + R_j$ indicates that it is the elements in row i that change.

67. The table shows the daily production level and profit for a business.

x (Number of Units Produced Daily)	30	50	100
y (Daily Profit)	$5900	$7500	$4500

Use the quadratic function $y = ax^2 + bx + c$ to determine the number of units that should be produced each day for maximum profit. What is the maximum daily profit?

Preview Exercises

Exercises 68–70 will help you prepare for the material covered in the next section. In each exercise, refer to the following system:

$$\begin{cases} 3x - 4y + 4z = 7 \\ x - y - 2z = 2 \\ 2x - 3y + 6z = 5. \end{cases}$$

68. Show that $(12z + 1, 10z - 1, z)$ satisfies the system for $z = 0$.

69. Show that $(12z + 1, 10z - 1, z)$ satisfies the system for $z = 1$.

70. a. Select a value for z other than 0 or 1 and show that $(12z + 1, 10z - 1, z)$ satisfies the system.

b. Based on your work in Exercises 68–70(a), how does this system differ from those in Exercises 21–34?

SECTION 6.2

Inconsistent and Dependent Systems and Their Applications

Objectives

① Apply Gaussian elimination to systems without unique solutions.

② Apply Gaussian elimination to systems with more variables than equations.

③ Solve problems involving systems without unique solutions.

① Apply Gaussian elimination to systems without unique solutions.

Traffic jams getting you down? Powerful computers, able to solve systems with hundreds of thousands of variables in a single bound, may promise a gridlock-free future. The computer in your car could be linked to a central computer that manages traffic flow by controlling traffic lights, rerouting you away from traffic congestion, issuing weather reports, and selecting the best route to your destination. New technologies could eventually drive your car at a steady 75 miles per hour along automated highways as you comfortably nap. In this section, we look at the role of linear systems without unique solutions in a future free of traffic jams.

Linear systems can have one solution, no solution, or infinitely many solutions. We can use Gaussian elimination on systems with three or more variables to determine how many solutions such systems may have. In the case of systems with no solution or infinitely many solutions, it is impossible to rewrite the augmented matrix in the desired form with 1s down the main diagonal from upper left to lower right, and 0s below the 1s. Let's see what this means by looking at a system that has no solution.

EXAMPLE 1   A System with No Solution

Use Gaussian elimination to solve the system:

$$\begin{cases} x - y - 2z = 2 \\ 2x - 3y + 6z = 5 \\ 3x - 4y + 4z = 12. \end{cases}$$

SOLUTION

DISCOVERY

Use the addition method to solve Example 1. Describe what happens. Why does this mean that there is no solution?

Step 1   Write the augmented matrix for the system.

Linear System

$$\begin{cases} x - y - 2z = 2 \\ 2x - 3y + 6z = 5 \\ 3x - 4y + 4z = 12 \end{cases}$$

Augmented Matrix

$$\left[\begin{array}{ccc|c} 1 & -1 & -2 & 2 \\ 2 & -3 & 6 & 5 \\ 3 & -4 & 4 & 12 \end{array}\right]$$

Step 2   Attempt to simplify the matrix to row-echelon form, with 1s down the main diagonal and 0s below the 1s. Notice that the augmented matrix already has a 1 in the top position of the first column. Now we want 0s below the 1. To get the first 0, multiply row 1 by −2 and add these products to row 2. To get the second 0, multiply row 1 by −3 and add these products to row 3. Performing these operations, we obtain the following matrix:

We want 1 in this position.

$$\left[\begin{array}{ccc|c} 1 & -1 & -2 & 2 \\ 0 & -1 & 10 & 1 \\ 0 & -1 & 10 & 6 \end{array}\right]$$

Use the augmented matrix and:
Replace row 2 by $-2R_1 + R_2$.
Replace row 3 by $-3R_1 + R_3$.

Moving on to the second column, we obtain 1 in the desired position by multiplying row 2 by −1.

$$\left[\begin{array}{ccc|c} 1 & -1 & -2 & 2 \\ -1(0) & -1(-1) & -1(10) & -1(1) \\ 0 & -1 & 10 & 6 \end{array}\right] = \left[\begin{array}{ccc|c} 1 & -1 & -2 & 2 \\ 0 & 1 & -10 & -1 \\ 0 & -1 & 10 & 6 \end{array}\right] \quad -1R_2$$

We want 0 in this position.

Now we want a 0 below the 1 in column 2. To get the 0, multiply row 2 by 1 and add these products to row 3. (Equivalently, add row 2 to row 3.) We obtain the following matrix:

$$\left[\begin{array}{ccc|c} 1 & -1 & -2 & 2 \\ 0 & 1 & -10 & -1 \\ 0 & 0 & 0 & 5 \end{array}\right]$$

Replace row 3 in the previous matrix by $1R_2 + R_3$.

It is impossible to convert this last matrix to the desired form of 1s down the main diagonal. If we translate the last row back into equation form, we get

$$0x + 0y + 0z = 5,$$

There are no values of x, y, and z for which $0 = 5$.

which is false. Regardless of which values we select for x, y, and z, the last equation can never be a true statement. Consequently, the system has no solution. The solution set is ∅, the empty set.   • • •

✓ Check Point **1**   Use Gaussian elimination to solve the system:

$$\begin{cases} x - 2y - z = -5 \\ 2x - 3y - z = 0 \\ 3x - 4y - z = 1. \end{cases}$$

Recall that the graph of a system of three linear equations in three variables consists of three planes. When these planes intersect in a single point, the system has precisely one ordered-triple solution. When the planes have no point in common, the system has no solution, like the one in Example 1. **Figure 6.1** illustrates some of the geometric possibilities for these inconsistent systems.

Three planes are parallel with no common intersection point.

Two planes are parallel with no common intersection point.

Planes intersect two at a time. There is no intersection point common to all three planes.

FIGURE 6.1 Three planes may have no common point of intersection.

Now let's see what happens when we apply Gaussian elimination to a system with infinitely many solutions. Representing the solution set for these systems can be a bit tricky.

EXAMPLE 2   A System with an Infinite Number of Solutions

Use Gaussian elimination to solve the following system:

$$\begin{cases} 3x - 4y + 4z = 7 \\ x - y - 2z = 2 \\ 2x - 3y + 6z = 5. \end{cases}$$

SOLUTION

As always, we start with the augmented matrix.

$$\begin{bmatrix} 3 & -4 & 4 & | & 7 \\ 1 & -1 & -2 & | & 2 \\ 2 & -3 & 6 & | & 5 \end{bmatrix} \xrightarrow[\text{Interchange rows}]{\substack{R_1 \leftrightarrow R_2 \\ \text{1 and 2.}}} \begin{bmatrix} 1 & -1 & -2 & | & 2 \\ 3 & -4 & 4 & | & 7 \\ 2 & -3 & 6 & | & 5 \end{bmatrix} \xrightarrow{\substack{\text{Replace row 2} \\ \text{by } -3R_1 + R_2. \\ \text{Replace row 3} \\ \text{by } -2R_1 + R_3.}}$$

$$\begin{bmatrix} 1 & -1 & -2 & | & 2 \\ 0 & -1 & 10 & | & 1 \\ 0 & -1 & 10 & | & 1 \end{bmatrix} \xrightarrow[\text{Multiply row 2}]{\substack{-1R_2 \\ \text{by } -1.}} \begin{bmatrix} 1 & -1 & -2 & | & 2 \\ 0 & 1 & -10 & | & -1 \\ 0 & -1 & 10 & | & 1 \end{bmatrix} \xrightarrow{\substack{\text{Replace row 3} \\ \text{by } 1R_2 + R_3.}}$$

$$\begin{bmatrix} 1 & -1 & -2 & | & 2 \\ 0 & 1 & -10 & | & -1 \\ 0 & 0 & 0 & | & 0 \end{bmatrix}$$

If we translate row 3 of the matrix into equation form, we obtain

$$0x + 0y + 0z = 0$$

or

$$0 = 0.$$

This equation results in a true statement regardless of which values we select for x, y, and z. Consequently, the equation $0x + 0y + 0z = 0$ is *dependent* on the other two equations in the system in the sense that it adds no new information about the variables. Thus, we can drop it from the system, which can now be expressed in the form

$$\begin{bmatrix} 1 & -1 & -2 & | & 2 \\ 0 & 1 & -10 & | & -1 \end{bmatrix}.$$ This is the last matrix from above with row 3 omitted.

The original system is equivalent to the system

$$\begin{cases} x - y - 2z = 2 \\ \quad\ \ y - 10z = -1. \end{cases}$$

This is the system represented by the matrix at the bottom of the previous page.

Although neither of these equations gives a value for z, we can use them to express x and y in terms of z. From the last equation, we obtain

$$y = 10z - 1. \qquad \text{Add } 10z \text{ to both sides and isolate } y.$$

Back-substituting for y into the first equation obtained from the final matrix, we can find x in terms of z.

$$x - y - 2z = 2 \qquad \text{This is the first equation obtained from the final matrix.}$$
$$x - (10z - 1) - 2z = 2 \qquad \text{Because } y = 10z - 1, \text{ substitute } 10z - 1 \text{ for } y.$$
$$x - 10z + 1 - 2z = 2 \qquad \text{Apply the distributive property.}$$
$$x - 12z + 1 = 2 \qquad \text{Combine like terms.}$$
$$x = 12z + 1 \qquad \text{Solve for } x \text{ in terms of } z.$$

We have now found two equations expressing x and y in terms of z:

$$x = 12z + 1$$
$$y = 10z - 1.$$

Because no value is determined for z, we can find a solution of the system by letting z equal any real number and then using these equations to obtain x and y. For example, if $z = 1$, then

$$x = 12z + 1 = 12(1) + 1 = 13 \text{ and}$$
$$y = 10z - 1 = 10(1) - 1 = 9.$$

Consequently, $(13, 9, 1)$ is a solution of the system. On the other hand, if we let $z = -1$, then

$$x = 12z + 1 = 12(-1) + 1 = -11 \text{ and}$$
$$y = 10z - 1 = 10(-1) - 1 = -11.$$

Thus, $(-11, -11, -1)$ is another solution of the system.

We see that for any arbitrary choice of z, every ordered triple of the form $(12z + 1, 10z - 1, z)$ is a solution of the system. The solution set of this system with dependent equations is

$$\{(12z + 1, 10z - 1, z)\}. \qquad \bullet\bullet\bullet$$

We have seen that when three planes have no point in common, the corresponding system has no solution. When the system has infinitely many solutions, like the one in Example 2, the three planes intersect in more than one point. **Figure 6.2** illustrates geometric possibilities for systems with dependent equations.

The planes intersect
along a common line.   The planes coincide.

FIGURE 6.2 Three planes may intersect at infinitely many points.

☑ Check Point **2** Use Gaussian elimination to solve the following system:

$$\begin{cases} x - 2y - z = 5 \\ 2x - 5y + 3z = 6 \\ x - 3y + 4z = 1. \end{cases}$$

② Apply Gaussian elimination to systems with more variables than equations.

Nonsquare Systems

Up to this point, we have encountered only *square* systems in which the number of equations is equal to the number of variables. In a **nonsquare system**, the number of variables differs from the number of equations. In Example 3, we have two equations and three variables.

EXAMPLE 3   A System with Fewer Equations Than Variables

Use Gaussian elimination to solve the system:

$$\begin{cases} 3x + 7y + 6z = 26 \\ x + 2y + z = 8. \end{cases}$$

SOLUTION

We begin with the augmented matrix.

$$\begin{bmatrix} 3 & 7 & 6 & | & 26 \\ 1 & 2 & 1 & | & 8 \end{bmatrix} \xrightarrow{R_1 \leftrightarrow R_2} \begin{bmatrix} 1 & 2 & 1 & | & 8 \\ 3 & 7 & 6 & | & 26 \end{bmatrix} \xrightarrow[\text{by } -3R_1 + R_2.]{\text{Replace row 2}} \begin{bmatrix} 1 & 2 & 1 & | & 8 \\ 0 & 1 & 3 & | & 2 \end{bmatrix}$$

Because the matrix $\begin{bmatrix} 1 & 2 & 1 & | & 8 \\ 0 & 1 & 3 & | & 2 \end{bmatrix}$ has 1s down the diagonal that begins with the upper-left entry and a 0 below the leading 1, we translate this matrix back into equation form.

$$\begin{cases} x + 2y + z = 8 & \text{Equation 1} \\ y + 3z = 2 & \text{Equation 2} \end{cases}$$

We can let z equal any real number and use back-substitution to express x and y in terms of z.

<table>
<tr><td align="center">**Equation 2**</td><td align="center">**Equation 1**</td></tr>
<tr><td align="center">$y + 3z = 2$</td><td align="center">$x + 2y + z = 8$</td></tr>
<tr><td align="center">$y = -3z + 2$</td><td align="center">$x + 2(-3z + 2) + z = 8$</td></tr>
<tr><td></td><td align="center">$x - 6z + 4 + z = 8$</td></tr>
<tr><td></td><td align="center">$x - 5z + 4 = 8$</td></tr>
<tr><td></td><td align="center">$x = 5z + 4$</td></tr>
</table>

For any arbitrary choice of z, every ordered triple of the form $(5z + 4, -3z + 2, z)$ is a solution of the system. We can express the system's solution set as

$$\{(5z + 4, -3z + 2, z)\}. \qquad \bullet\bullet\bullet$$

DISCOVERY

Let $z = 1$ for the solution

$$(5z + 4, -3z + 2, z).$$

What solution do you obtain? Substitute these three values in the two original equations:

$$\begin{cases} 3x + 7y + 6z = 26 \\ x + 2y + z = 8. \end{cases}$$

Show that each equation is satisfied. Repeat this process for two other values of z.

☑ Check Point **3** Use Gaussian elimination to solve the system:

$$\begin{cases} x + 2y + 3z = 70 \\ x + y + z = 60. \end{cases}$$

③ Solve problems involving systems without unique solutions.

Applications

How will computers be programmed to control traffic flow and avoid congestion? They will be required to solve systems continually based on the following premise: If traffic is to keep moving, during any period of time the number of cars entering an intersection must equal the number of cars leaving that intersection. Let's see what this means by looking at the intersections of four one-way city streets.

EXAMPLE 4 Traffic Control

300 Cars/hr 900 Cars/hr

Palm Drive

700 Cars/hr

200 Cars/hr

200 Cars/hr

400 Cars/hr

400 Cars/hr 300 Cars/hr

FIGURE 6.3 The intersections of four one-way streets

Figure 6.3 shows the intersections of four one-way streets. As you study the figure, notice that 300 cars per hour want to enter intersection I_1 from the north on 27th Avenue. Also, 200 cars per hour want to head east from intersection I_2 on Palm Drive. The letters $w, x, y,$ and z stand for the number of cars passing between the intersections.

a. If the traffic is to keep moving, at each intersection the number of cars entering per hour must equal the number of cars leaving per hour. Use this idea to set up a linear system of equations involving $w, x, y,$ and z.

b. Use Gaussian elimination to solve the system.

c. If construction on 27th Avenue limits z to 50 cars per hour, how many cars per hour must pass between the other intersections to keep traffic flowing?

SOLUTION

a. Set up the system by considering one intersection at a time, referring to **Figure 6.3**.

For Intersection I_1: Because $300 + 700 = 1000$ cars enter I_1 and $w + z$ cars leave the intersection, then $w + z = 1000$.

For Intersection I_2: Because $w + x$ cars enter the intersection and $200 + 900 = 1100$ cars leave I_2, then $w + x = 1100$.

For Intersection I_3: **Figure 6.3** indicates that $300 + 400 = 700$ cars enter and $x + y$ leave, so $x + y = 700$.

For Intersection I_4: With $y + z$ cars entering and $200 + 400 = 600$ cars exiting, traffic will keep flowing if $y + z = 600$.

The system of equations that models this situation is given by

$$\begin{cases} w + z = 1000 \\ w + x = 1100 \\ x + y = 700 \\ y + z = 600. \end{cases}$$

b. To solve this system using Gaussian elimination, we begin with the augmented matrix.

System of Linear Equations (showing missing variables with 0 coefficients)

$$\begin{cases} 1w + 0x + 0y + 1z = 1000 \\ 1w + 1x + 0y + 0z = 1100 \\ 0w + 1x + 1y + 0z = 700 \\ 0w + 0x + 1y + 1z = 600 \end{cases}$$

Augmented Matrix

$$\begin{bmatrix} 1 & 0 & 0 & 1 & | & 1000 \\ 1 & 1 & 0 & 0 & | & 1100 \\ 0 & 1 & 1 & 0 & | & 700 \\ 0 & 0 & 1 & 1 & | & 600 \end{bmatrix}$$

We can now use row operations to obtain the following matrix:

$$\left[\begin{array}{cccc|c} 1 & 0 & 0 & 1 & 1000 \\ 0 & 1 & 0 & -1 & 100 \\ 0 & 0 & 1 & 1 & 600 \\ 0 & 0 & 0 & 0 & 0 \end{array}\right].$$

$w + z = 1000$
$x - z = 100$
$y + z = 600$

The last row of the matrix shows that the system in the voice balloons has dependent equations and infinitely many solutions. To write the solution set containing these infinitely many solutions, let z equal any real number. Use the three equations in the voice balloons to express w, x, and y in terms of z:

$$w = 1000 - z, \quad x = 100 + z, \quad \text{and} \quad y = 600 - z.$$

With z arbitrary, the alphabetically ordered solution (w, x, y, z) enables us to express the system's solution set as

$$\{(1000 - z, 100 + z, 600 - z, z)\}.$$

c. We are given that construction limits z to 50 cars per hour. Because $z = 50$, we substitute 50 for z in the system's ordered solution:

$(1000 - z, 100 + z, 600 - z, z)$ Use the system's solution.

$= (1000 - 50, 100 + 50, 600 - 50, 50)$ $z = 50$

$= (950, 150, 550, 50)$.

Thus, $w = 950$, $x = 150$, and $y = 550$. (See **Figure 6.4**.) With construction on 27th Avenue, this means that to keep traffic flowing, 950 cars per hour must be routed between I_1 and I_2, 150 per hour between I_3 and I_2, and 550 per hour between I_3 and I_4. ●●●

FIGURE 6.4 With z limited to 50 cars per hour, values for w, x, and y are determined.

⊘ Check Point **4** **Figure 6.5** shows a system of four one-way streets. The numbers in the figure denote the number of cars per minute that travel in the direction shown.

a. Use the requirement that the number of cars entering each of the intersections per minute must equal the number of cars leaving per minute to set up a system of equations in w, x, y, and z.

b. Use Gaussian elimination to solve the system.

c. If construction limits z to 10 cars per minute, how many cars per minute must pass between the other intersections to keep traffic flowing?

FIGURE 6.5

CONCEPT AND VOCABULARY CHECK

Fill in each blank so that the resulting statement is true.

Using Gaussian elimination on linear systems in three variables, we obtained each of the matrices shown in Exercises 1 through 3. State whether the linear system has one solution, no solution, or infinitely many solutions.

1. $\left[\begin{array}{ccc|c} 1 & 1 & 1 & 6 \\ 0 & 1 & 1 & -6 \\ 0 & 0 & 0 & -27 \end{array}\right]$ _____

2. $\left[\begin{array}{ccc|c} 1 & 1 & 2 & 19 \\ 0 & 1 & 2 & 13 \\ 0 & 0 & 1 & 5 \end{array}\right]$ _____

3. $\left[\begin{array}{ccc|c} 1 & -1 & -2 & 2 \\ 0 & 1 & -10 & -1 \\ 0 & 0 & 0 & 0 \end{array}\right]$ _____

4. True or false: If $\{(2z + 3, 5z - 1, z)\}$ is the solution set of a system with dependent equations, then $(5, 4, 1)$ is a solution of this system. _____

5. Using Gaussian elimination to solve

$$\begin{cases} 3x + 2y - 2z = 0 \\ x - y + z = 5, \end{cases}$$

we obtain the matrix

$$\begin{bmatrix} 1 & -1 & 1 & | & 5 \\ 0 & 1 & -1 & | & -3 \end{bmatrix}.$$

Translating this matrix back into equation form gives

Solving Equation 2 for y in terms of z results in $y = $ _____. Substituting this expression for y in Equation 1 gives $x = $ _____. The system's solution set is _____.

EXERCISE SET 6.2

Practice Exercises

In Exercises 1–24, use Gaussian elimination to find the complete solution to each system of equations, or show that none exists.

1. $\begin{cases} 5x + 12y + z = 10 \\ 2x + 5y + 2z = -1 \\ x + 2y - 3z = 5 \end{cases}$

2. $\begin{cases} 2x - 4y + z = 3 \\ x - 3y + z = 5 \\ 3x - 7y + 2z = 12 \end{cases}$

3. $\begin{cases} 5x + 8y - 6z = 14 \\ 3x + 4y - 2z = 8 \\ x + 2y - 2z = 3 \end{cases}$

4. $\begin{cases} 5x - 11y + 6z = 12 \\ -x + 3y - 2z = -4 \\ 3x - 5y + 2z = 4 \end{cases}$

5. $\begin{cases} 3x + 4y + 2z = 3 \\ 4x - 2y - 8z = -4 \\ x + y - z = 3 \end{cases}$

6. $\begin{cases} 2x - y - z = 0 \\ x + 2y + z = 3 \\ 3x + 4y + 2z = 8 \end{cases}$

7. $\begin{cases} 8x + 5y + 11z = 30 \\ -x - 4y + 2z = 3 \\ 2x - y + 5z = 12 \end{cases}$

8. $\begin{cases} x + y - 10z = -4 \\ x - 7z = -5 \\ 3x + 5y - 36z = -10 \end{cases}$

9. $\begin{cases} w - 2x - y - 3z = -9 \\ w + x - y = 0 \\ 3w + 4x + z = 6 \\ 2x - 2y + z = 3 \end{cases}$

10. $\begin{cases} 2w + x - 2y - z = 3 \\ w - 2x + y + z = 4 \\ -w - 8x + 7y + 5z = 13 \\ 3w + x - 2y + 2z = 6 \end{cases}$

11. $\begin{cases} 2w + x - y = 3 \\ w - 3x + 2y = -4 \\ 3w + x - 3y + z = 1 \\ w + 2x - 4y - z = -2 \end{cases}$

12. $\begin{cases} 2w - x + 3y + z = 0 \\ 3w + 2x + 4y - z = 0 \\ 5w - 2x - 2y - z = 0 \\ 2w + 3x - 7y - 5z = 0 \end{cases}$

13. $\begin{cases} w - 3x + y - 4z = 4 \\ -2w + x + 2y = -2 \\ 3w - 2x + y - 6z = 2 \\ -w + 3x + 2y - z = -6 \end{cases}$

14. $\begin{cases} 3w + 2x - y + 2z = -12 \\ 4w - x + y + 2z = 1 \\ w + x + y + z = -2 \\ -2w + 3x + 2y - 3z = 10 \end{cases}$

15. $\begin{cases} 2x + y - z = 2 \\ 3x + 3y - 2z = 3 \end{cases}$

16. $\begin{cases} 3x + 2y - z = 5 \\ x + 2y - z = 1 \end{cases}$

17. $\begin{cases} x + 2y + 3z = 5 \\ y - 5z = 0 \end{cases}$

18. $\begin{cases} 3x - y + 4z = 8 \\ y + 2z = 1 \end{cases}$

19. $\begin{cases} x + y - 2z = 2 \\ 3x - y - 6z = -7 \end{cases}$

20. $\begin{cases} -2x - 5y + 10z = 19 \\ x + 2y - 4z = 12 \end{cases}$

21. $\begin{cases} w + x - y + z = -2 \\ 2w - x + 2y - z = 7 \\ -w + 2x + y + 2z = -1 \end{cases}$

22. $\begin{cases} 2w - 3x + 4y + z = 7 \\ w - x + 3y - 5z = 10 \\ 3w + x - 2y - 2z = 6 \end{cases}$

23. $\begin{cases} w + 2x + 3y - z = 7 \\ 2x - 3y + z = 4 \\ w - 4x + y = 3 \end{cases}$

24. $\begin{cases} w - x + z = 0 \\ w - 4x + y + 2z = 0 \\ 3w - y + 2z = 0 \end{cases}$

Practice Plus

In Exercises 25–28, the first screen shows the augmented matrix, A, for a nonsquare linear system of three equations in four variables, w, x, y, and z. The second screen shows the reduced row-echelon form of matrix A. For each exercise,

    a. *Write the system represented by A.*

    b. *Use the reduced row-echelon form of A to find the system's complete solution.*

25.

26.

27.

28.

Application Exercises

The figure for Exercises 29–32 shows the intersections of three one-way streets. To keep traffic moving, the number of cars per minute entering an intersection must equal the number exiting that intersection. For intersection I_1, $x + 10$ cars enter and $y + 14$ cars exit per minute. Thus, $x + 10 = y + 14$.

29. Write an equation for intersection I_2 that keeps traffic moving.

30. Write an equation for intersection I_3 that keeps traffic moving.

31. Use Gaussian elimination to solve the system formed by the equation given prior to Exercise 29 and the two equations that you obtained in Exercises 29–30.

32. Use your ordered solution obtained in Exercise 31 to solve this exercise. If construction limits z to 4 cars per minute, how many cars per minute must pass between the other intersections to keep traffic flowing?

33. The figure shows the intersections of four one-way streets.

a. Set up a system of equations that keeps traffic moving.

b. Use Gaussian elimination to solve the system.

c. If construction limits z to 50 cars per hour, how many cars per hour must pass between the other intersections to keep traffic moving?

34. The vitamin content per ounce for three foods is given in the following table.

	Milligrams per Ounce		
	Thiamin	**Riboflavin**	**Niacin**
Food A	3	7	1
Food B	1	5	3
Food C	3	8	2

a. Use matrices to show that no combination of these foods can provide exactly 14 mg of thiamin, 32 mg of riboflavin, and 9 mg of niacin.

b. Use matrices to describe in practical terms what happens if the riboflavin requirement is increased by 5 mg and the other requirements stay the same.

35. Three foods have the following nutritional content per ounce.

	Units per Ounce		
	Vitamin A	**Iron**	**Calcium**
Food 1	20	20	10
Food 2	30	10	10
Food 3	10	10	30

a. A diet must consist precisely of 220 units of vitamin A, 180 units of iron, and 340 units of calcium. However, the dietician runs out of Food 1. Use a matrix approach to show that under these conditions the dietary requirements cannot be met.

b. Now suppose that all three foods are available. Use matrices to give two possible ways to meet the iron and calcium requirements with the three foods.

36. A company that manufactures products A, B, and C does both manufacturing and testing. The hours needed to manufacture and test each product are shown in the table.

	Hours Needed Weekly to Manufacture	Hours Needed Weekly to Test
Product A	7	2
Product B	6	2
Product C	3	1

The company has exactly 67 hours per week available for manufacturing and 20 hours per week available for testing. Give two different combinations for the number of products that can be manufactured and tested weekly.

Writing in Mathematics

37. Describe what happens when Gaussian elimination is used to solve an inconsistent system.

38. Describe what happens when Gaussian elimination is used to solve a system with dependent equations.

39. In solving a system of dependent equations in three variables, one student simply said that there are infinitely many solutions. A second student expressed the solution set as $\{(4z + 3, 5z - 1, z)\}$. Which is the better form of expressing the solution set and why?

Technology Exercise

40. a. The figure shows the intersections of a number of one-way streets. The numbers given represent traffic flow at a peak period (from 4 P.M. to 5:30 P.M.). Use the figure to write a linear system of six equations in seven variables based on the idea that at each intersection the number of cars entering must equal the number of cars leaving.

b. Use a graphing utility with a $\boxed{\text{REF}}$ or $\boxed{\text{RREF}}$ command to find the complete solution to the system.

Critical Thinking Exercises

Make Sense? *In Exercises 41–44, determine whether each statement makes sense or does not make sense, and explain your reasoning.*

41. I omitted row 3 from $\begin{bmatrix} 1 & -1 & -2 & 2 \\ 0 & 1 & -10 & -1 \\ 0 & 0 & 0 & 5 \end{bmatrix}$ and expressed the system in the form $\begin{bmatrix} 1 & -1 & -2 & 2 \\ 0 & 1 & -10 & -1 \end{bmatrix}$.

42. I omitted row 3 from $\begin{bmatrix} 1 & -1 & -2 & 2 \\ 0 & 1 & -10 & -1 \\ 0 & 0 & 0 & 0 \end{bmatrix}$ and expressed the system in the form $\begin{bmatrix} 1 & -1 & -2 & 2 \\ 0 & 1 & -10 & -1 \end{bmatrix}$.

43. I solved a nonsquare system in which the number of equations was the same as the number of variables.

44. Models for controlling traffic flow are based on an equal number of cars entering an intersection and leaving that intersection.

45. Consider the linear system

$$\begin{cases} x + 3y + z = a^2 \\ 2x + 5y + 2az = 0 \\ x + y + a^2z = -9. \end{cases}$$

For which values of a will the system be inconsistent?

Group Exercise

46. Before beginning this exercise, the group needs to read and solve Exercise 40.

a. A political group is planning a demonstration on 95th Street between 113th Place and 117th Court for 5 P.M. Wednesday. The problem becomes one of minimizing traffic flow on 95th Street (between 113th and 117th) without causing traffic tie-ups on other streets. One possible solution is to close off traffic on 95th Street between 113th and 117th (let $x_6 = 0$). What can group members conclude about x_7 under these conditions?

b. Working with a matrix allows us to simplify the problem caused by the political demonstration, but it did not actually solve the problem. There are an infinite number of solutions; each value of x_7 we choose gives us a new picture. We also assumed x_6 was equal to 0; changing that assumption would also lead to different solutions. With your group, design another solution to the traffic flow problem caused by the political demonstration.

Preview Exercises

Exercises 47–49 will help you prepare for the material covered in the next section. In each exercise, perform the indicated operation or operations.

47. $-6 - (-5)$

48. $1(-4) + 2(5) + 3(-6)$

49. $\frac{1}{2}[8 - (-8)]$

Objectives

1. Use matrix notation.
2. Understand what is meant by equal matrices.
3. Add and subtract matrices.
4. Perform scalar multiplication.
5. Solve matrix equations.
6. Multiply matrices.
7. Model applied situations with matrix operations.

Use your smartphone to read your e-mail. Turn on your computer to write a paper. When you need to do research, use the Internet to browse through art museums and photography exhibits. When you need a break, load a flight simulator program and fly through a photorealistic computer world. As different as these experiences may be, they all share one thing—you're looking at images based on matrices. Matrices have applications in numerous fields, including the technology of digital photography in which pictures are represented by numbers rather than film. In this section, we turn our attention to matrix algebra and some of its applications.

① Use matrix notation.

Notations for Matrices

We have seen that an array of numbers, arranged in rows and columns and placed in brackets, is called a matrix. We can represent a matrix in two different ways.

- A capital letter, such as A, B, or C, can denote a matrix.
- A lowercase letter enclosed in brackets, such as that shown below, can denote a matrix.

$$A = [a_{ij}] \quad \text{Matrix } A \text{ with elements } a_{ij}$$

A general element in matrix A is denoted by a_{ij}. This refers to the element in the ith row and jth column. For example, a_{32} is the element of A located in the third row, second column.

A matrix of **order $m \times n$** has m rows and n columns. If $m = n$, a matrix has the same number of rows as columns and is called a **square matrix**.

EXAMPLE 1 Matrix Notation

Let

$$A = \begin{bmatrix} 3 & 2 & 0 \\ -4 & -5 & -\frac{1}{5} \end{bmatrix}.$$

a. What is the order of A?
b. If $A = [a_{ij}]$, identify a_{23} and a_{12}.

SOLUTION

a. The matrix has 2 rows and 3 columns, so it is of order 2×3.

b. The element a_{23} is in the second row and third column. Thus, $a_{23} = -\frac{1}{5}$. The element a_{12} is in the first row and second column. Consequently, $a_{12} = 2$.

● ● ●

⊘ Check Point **1** Let

$$A = \begin{bmatrix} 5 & -2 \\ -3 & \pi \\ 1 & 6 \end{bmatrix}.$$

a. What is the order of A?　　**b.** Identify a_{12} and a_{31}.

② Understand what is meant by equal matrices.

Equality of Matrices

Two matrices are **equal** if and only if they have the same order and corresponding elements are equal.

> ### Definition of Equality of Matrices
>
> Two matrices A and B are **equal** if and only if they have the same order $m \times n$ and $a_{ij} = b_{ij}$ for $i = 1, 2, \ldots, m$ and $j = 1, 2, \ldots, n$.

For example, if $A = \begin{bmatrix} x & y+1 \\ z & 6 \end{bmatrix}$ and $B = \begin{bmatrix} 1 & 5 \\ 3 & 6 \end{bmatrix}$, then $A = B$ if and only if $x = 1, y + 1 = 5$ (so $y = 4$), and $z = 3$.

③ Add and subtract matrices.

Matrix Addition and Subtraction

Table 6.1 shows that matrices of the same order can be added or subtracted by simply adding or subtracting corresponding elements.

Table 6.1　Adding and Subtracting Matrices

Let $A = [a_{ij}]$ and $B = [b_{ij}]$ be matrices of order $m \times n$.

Definition	The Definition in Words	Example
Matrix Addition $A + B = [a_{ij} + b_{ij}]$	Matrices of the same order are added by adding the elements in corresponding positions.	$\begin{bmatrix} 1 & -2 \\ 3 & 5 \end{bmatrix} + \begin{bmatrix} -1 & 6 \\ 0 & 4 \end{bmatrix}$ $= \begin{bmatrix} 1 + (-1) & -2 + 6 \\ 3 + 0 & 5 + 4 \end{bmatrix} = \begin{bmatrix} 0 & 4 \\ 3 & 9 \end{bmatrix}$
Matrix Subtraction $A - B = [a_{ij} - b_{ij}]$	Matrices of the same order are subtracted by subtracting the elements in corresponding positions.	$\begin{bmatrix} 1 & -2 \\ 3 & 5 \end{bmatrix} - \begin{bmatrix} -1 & 6 \\ 0 & 4 \end{bmatrix}$ $= \begin{bmatrix} 1 - (-1) & -2 - 6 \\ 3 - 0 & 5 - 4 \end{bmatrix} = \begin{bmatrix} 2 & -8 \\ 3 & 1 \end{bmatrix}$

The sum or difference of two matrices of different orders is undefined. For example, consider the matrices

$$A = \begin{bmatrix} 0 & 3 \\ 4 & 3 \end{bmatrix} \quad \text{and} \quad B = \begin{bmatrix} 1 & 9 \\ 4 & 5 \\ 2 & 3 \end{bmatrix}.$$

The order of A is 2×2; the order of B is 3×2. These matrices are of different orders and cannot be added or subtracted.

TECHNOLOGY

Graphing utilities can add and subtract matrices. Enter the matrices and name them $[A]$ and $[B]$. Then use a keystroke sequence similar to

$\boxed{[A]}\ \boxed{+}\ \boxed{[B]}\ \boxed{\text{ENTER}}$

$\boxed{[A]}\ \boxed{-}\ \boxed{[B]}\ \boxed{\text{ENTER}}$

Consult your manual and verify the results in Example 2.

EXAMPLE 2   Adding and Subtracting Matrices

Perform the indicated matrix operations:

a. $\begin{bmatrix} 0 & 5 & 3 \\ -2 & 6 & -8 \end{bmatrix} + \begin{bmatrix} -2 & 3 & 5 \\ 7 & -9 & 6 \end{bmatrix}$

b. $\begin{bmatrix} -6 & 7 \\ 2 & -3 \end{bmatrix} - \begin{bmatrix} -5 & 6 \\ 0 & -4 \end{bmatrix}.$

SOLUTION

a.
$$\begin{bmatrix} 0 & 5 & 3 \\ -2 & 6 & -8 \end{bmatrix} + \begin{bmatrix} -2 & 3 & 5 \\ 7 & -9 & 6 \end{bmatrix}$$

$$= \begin{bmatrix} 0 + (-2) & 5 + 3 & 3 + 5 \\ -2 + 7 & 6 + (-9) & -8 + 6 \end{bmatrix}$$ Add the corresponding elements in the 2 × 3 matrices.

$$= \begin{bmatrix} -2 & 8 & 8 \\ 5 & -3 & -2 \end{bmatrix}$$ Simplify.

b.
$$\begin{bmatrix} -6 & 7 \\ 2 & -3 \end{bmatrix} - \begin{bmatrix} -5 & 6 \\ 0 & -4 \end{bmatrix}$$

$$= \begin{bmatrix} -6 - (-5) & 7 - 6 \\ 2 - 0 & -3 - (-4) \end{bmatrix}$$ Subtract the corresponding elements in the 2 × 2 matrices.

$$= \begin{bmatrix} -1 & 1 \\ 2 & 1 \end{bmatrix}$$ Simplify.   • • •

✓ Check Point **2** Perform the indicated matrix operations:

a. $\begin{bmatrix} -4 & 3 \\ 7 & -6 \end{bmatrix} + \begin{bmatrix} 6 & -3 \\ 2 & -4 \end{bmatrix}$ **b.** $\begin{bmatrix} 5 & 4 \\ -3 & 7 \\ 0 & 1 \end{bmatrix} - \begin{bmatrix} -4 & 8 \\ 6 & 0 \\ -5 & 3 \end{bmatrix}.$

A matrix whose elements are all equal to 0 is called a **zero matrix**. If A is an $m \times n$ matrix and 0 is the $m \times n$ zero matrix, then $A + 0 = A$. For example,

$$\begin{bmatrix} -5 & 2 \\ 3 & 6 \end{bmatrix} + \begin{bmatrix} 0 & 0 \\ 0 & 0 \end{bmatrix} = \begin{bmatrix} -5 & 2 \\ 3 & 6 \end{bmatrix}.$$

The $m \times n$ zero matrix is called the **additive identity** for $m \times n$ matrices.

For any matrix A, the **additive inverse** of A, written $-A$, is the matrix with the same order as A such that every element of $-A$ is the opposite of the corresponding element of A. Because corresponding elements are added in matrix addition, $A + (-A)$ is a zero matrix. For example,

$$\begin{bmatrix} -5 & 2 \\ 3 & 6 \end{bmatrix} + \begin{bmatrix} 5 & -2 \\ -3 & -6 \end{bmatrix} = \begin{bmatrix} 0 & 0 \\ 0 & 0 \end{bmatrix}.$$

Properties of matrix addition are similar to properties for adding real numbers.

Properties of Matrix Addition

If A, B, and C are $m \times n$ matrices and 0 is the $m \times n$ zero matrix, then the following properties are true.

1. $A + B = B + A$ Commutative property of addition

2. $(A + B) + C = A + (B + C)$ Associative property of addition

3. $A + 0 = 0 + A = A$ Additive identity property

4. $A + (-A) = (-A) + A = 0$ Additive inverse property

④ Perform scalar multiplication.

Scalar Multiplication

A matrix of order 1×1, such as [6], contains only one entry. To distinguish this matrix from the number 6, we refer to 6 as a **scalar**. In general, in our work with matrices, we will refer to real numbers as scalars.

To multiply a matrix A by a scalar c, we multiply each entry in A by c. For example,

$$4\underset{\text{Matrix}}{\underbrace{\begin{bmatrix} 2 & 5 \\ -3 & 0 \end{bmatrix}}} = \begin{bmatrix} 4(2) & 4(5) \\ 4(-3) & 4(0) \end{bmatrix} = \begin{bmatrix} 8 & 20 \\ -12 & 0 \end{bmatrix}.$$

Scalar   Matrix

Definition of Scalar Multiplication

If $A = [a_{ij}]$ is a matrix of order $m \times n$ and c is a scalar, then the matrix cA is the $m \times n$ matrix given by

$$cA = [ca_{ij}].$$

This matrix is obtained by multiplying each element of A by the real number c. We call cA a **scalar multiple** of A.

EXAMPLE 3   Scalar Multiplication

If $A = \begin{bmatrix} -1 & 4 \\ 3 & 0 \end{bmatrix}$ and $B = \begin{bmatrix} 2 & -3 \\ 5 & -6 \end{bmatrix}$, find the following matrices:

a. $-5B$ **b.** $2A + 3B$.

SOLUTION

a. $-5B = -5\begin{bmatrix} 2 & -3 \\ 5 & -6 \end{bmatrix} = \begin{bmatrix} -5(2) & -5(-3) \\ -5(5) & -5(-6) \end{bmatrix} = \begin{bmatrix} -10 & 15 \\ -25 & 30 \end{bmatrix}$

Multiply each element by −5.

b. $2A + 3B = 2\begin{bmatrix} -1 & 4 \\ 3 & 0 \end{bmatrix} + 3\begin{bmatrix} 2 & -3 \\ 5 & -6 \end{bmatrix}$

$$= \begin{bmatrix} 2(-1) & 2(4) \\ 2(3) & 2(0) \end{bmatrix} + \begin{bmatrix} 3(2) & 3(-3) \\ 3(5) & 3(-6) \end{bmatrix}$$

Multiply each element in A by **2**.   Multiply each element in B by **3**.

$$= \begin{bmatrix} -2 & 8 \\ 6 & 0 \end{bmatrix} + \begin{bmatrix} 6 & -9 \\ 15 & -18 \end{bmatrix} = \begin{bmatrix} -2+6 & 8+(-9) \\ 6+15 & 0+(-18) \end{bmatrix}$$

Perform the addition of these 2 x 2 matrices by adding corresponding elements.

$$= \begin{bmatrix} 4 & -1 \\ 21 & -18 \end{bmatrix}$$

• • •

TECHNOLOGY

You can verify the algebraic solution in Example 3(b) by first entering the matrices [A] and [B] into your graphing utility. The screen below shows the required computation.

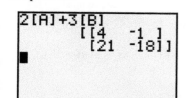

```
2[A]+3[B]
       [[4   -1 ]
        [21  -18]]
■
```

✓ Check Point **3** If $A = \begin{bmatrix} -4 & 1 \\ 3 & 0 \end{bmatrix}$ and $B = \begin{bmatrix} -1 & -2 \\ 8 & 5 \end{bmatrix}$, find the following matrices:

a. $-6B$ **b.** $3A + 2B$.

Properties of scalar multiplication are similar to properties for multiplying real numbers.

Properties of Scalar Multiplication

If A and B are $m \times n$ matrices, and c and d are scalars, then the following properties are true.

1. $(cd)A = c(dA)$ Associative property of scalar multiplication

2. $1A = A$ Scalar identity property

3. $c(A + B) = cA + cB$ Distributive property

4. $(c + d)A = cA + dA$ Distributive property

⑤ Solve matrix equations.

Have you noticed the many similarities between addition of real numbers and matrix addition, subtraction of real numbers and matrix subtraction, and multiplication of real numbers and scalar multiplication? Example 4 shows how these similarities can be used to solve matrix equations involving matrix addition, matrix subtraction, and scalar multiplication.

EXAMPLE 4   Solving a Matrix Equation

Solve for X in the matrix equation

$$2X + A = B,$$

where $A = \begin{bmatrix} 1 & -5 \\ 0 & 2 \end{bmatrix}$ and $B = \begin{bmatrix} -6 & 5 \\ 9 & 1 \end{bmatrix}.$

SOLUTION

We begin by solving the matrix equation for X.

$$2X + A = B \qquad \text{This is the given matrix equation.}$$

$$2X = B - A \qquad \text{Subtract matrix } A \text{ from both sides.}$$

We multiply both sides by $\frac{1}{2}$ rather than divide both sides by 2. This is in anticipation of performing scalar multiplication.

$$X = \frac{1}{2}(B - A) \qquad \text{Multiply both sides by } \frac{1}{2} \text{ and solve for matrix } X.$$

Now we use the matrices A and B to find the matrix X.

$$X = \frac{1}{2}\left(\begin{bmatrix} -6 & 5 \\ 9 & 1 \end{bmatrix} - \begin{bmatrix} 1 & -5 \\ 0 & 2 \end{bmatrix} \right) \qquad \text{Substitute the matrices into } X = \frac{1}{2}(B - A).$$

$$= \frac{1}{2}\begin{bmatrix} -7 & 10 \\ 9 & -1 \end{bmatrix} \qquad \text{Subtract matrices by subtracting corresponding elements.}$$

$$= \begin{bmatrix} -\dfrac{7}{2} & 5 \\ \dfrac{9}{2} & -\dfrac{1}{2} \end{bmatrix} \qquad \text{Perform the scalar multiplication by multiplying each element by } \frac{1}{2}.$$

Take a few minutes to show that this matrix satisfies the given equation $2X + A = B$. Substitute the matrix for X and the given matrices for A and B into the equation. The matrices on each side of the equal sign, $2X + A$ and B, should be equal. • • •

⊘ Check Point **4** Solve for X in the matrix equation $3X + A = B$, where

$$A = \begin{bmatrix} 2 & -8 \\ 0 & 4 \end{bmatrix} \quad \text{and} \quad B = \begin{bmatrix} -10 & 1 \\ -9 & 17 \end{bmatrix}.$$

⑥ Multiply matrices.

Matrix Multiplication

We do not multiply two matrices by multiplying the corresponding entries of the matrices. Instead, we must think of matrix multiplication as *row-by-column multiplication*. To better understand how this works, let's begin with the definition of matrix multiplication for matrices of order 2×2.

Definition of Matrix Multiplication: 2 × 2 Matrices

| Row 1 of A × Column 1 of B | Row 1 of A × Column 2 of B |

$$AB = \begin{bmatrix} a & b \\ c & d \end{bmatrix} \begin{bmatrix} e & f \\ g & h \end{bmatrix} = \begin{bmatrix} ae + bg & af + bh \\ ce + dg & cf + dh \end{bmatrix}$$

| Row 2 of A × Column 1 of B | Row 2 of A × Column 2 of B |

Notice that we obtain the element in the ith row and jth column in AB by performing computations with elements in the ith row of A and the jth column of B. For example, we obtain the element in the first row and first column of AB by performing computations with elements in the first row of A and the first column of B.

First row of A First column of B

$$\begin{bmatrix} a & b \end{bmatrix} \begin{bmatrix} e \\ g \end{bmatrix} = \begin{bmatrix} ae + bg & \end{bmatrix}$$

1. Multiply each element in row 1 of A by the corresponding element in column 1 of B.

2. Add these products.

3. Record the sum as the element in row 1, column 1 of the product matrix.

Corresponding elements

Corresponding elements

FIGURE 6.6 Finding corresponding elements when multiplying matrices

You may wonder how to find the corresponding elements in step 1 in the voice balloon. The element at the far left of row 1 corresponds to the element at the top of column 1. The second element from the left of row 1 corresponds to the second element from the top of column 1. This is illustrated in **Figure 6.6**.

EXAMPLE 5 Multiplying Matrices

Find AB, given

$$A = \begin{bmatrix} 2 & 3 \\ 4 & 7 \end{bmatrix} \quad \text{and} \quad B = \begin{bmatrix} 0 & 1 \\ 5 & 6 \end{bmatrix}.$$

SOLUTION

We will perform a row-by-column computation.

$$AB = \begin{bmatrix} 2 & 3 \\ 4 & 7 \end{bmatrix}\begin{bmatrix} 0 & 1 \\ 5 & 6 \end{bmatrix}$$

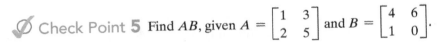

Row 1 of A × Column 1 of B Row 1 of A × Column 2 of B

$$= \begin{bmatrix} 2(0) + 3(5) & 2(1) + 3(6) \\ 4(0) + 7(5) & 4(1) + 7(6) \end{bmatrix} = \begin{bmatrix} 15 & 20 \\ 35 & 46 \end{bmatrix}$$

Row 2 of A × Column 1 of B Row 2 of A × Column 2 of B • • •

✓ Check Point **5** Find AB, given $A = \begin{bmatrix} 1 & 3 \\ 2 & 5 \end{bmatrix}$ and $B = \begin{bmatrix} 4 & 6 \\ 1 & 0 \end{bmatrix}$.

We can generalize the process of Example 5 to multiply an $m \times n$ matrix and an $n \times p$ matrix. **For the product of two matrices to be defined, the number of columns of the first matrix must equal the number of rows of the second matrix.**

First Matrix   Second Matrix

$m \times n$ $n \times p$

The number of columns in the first matrix must be the same as the number of rows in the second matrix.

GREAT QUESTION!

Is there a diagram I can use to determine the order of the matrix product AB?

Yes. The following diagram illustrates the first sentence in the box defining matrix multiplication.

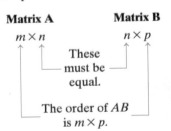

Matrix A   Matrix B

$m \times n$ $n \times p$

These
must be
equal.

The order of AB
is $m \times p$.

Definition of Matrix Multiplication

The **product** of an $m \times n$ matrix, A, and an $n \times p$ matrix, B, is an $m \times p$ matrix, AB, whose elements are found as follows: The element in the ith row and jth column of AB is found by multiplying each element in the ith row of A by the corresponding element in the jth column of B and adding the products.

To find a product AB, each row of A must have the same number of elements as each column of B. We obtain p_{ij}, the element in the ith row and jth column in AB, by performing computations with elements in the ith row of A and the jth column of B:

ith row of A jth column of B Element in the ith row and jth column of AB

When multiplying corresponding elements, keep in mind that the element at the far left of row i corresponds to the element at the top of column j. The element second from the left in row i corresponds to the element second from the top in column j. Likewise, the element third from the left in row i corresponds to the element third from the top in column j, and so on.

EXAMPLE 6   Multiplying Matrices

Matrices A and B are defined as follows:

$$A = \begin{bmatrix} 1 & 2 & 3 \end{bmatrix} \qquad B = \begin{bmatrix} 4 \\ 5 \\ 6 \end{bmatrix}.$$

Find each product: **a.** AB **b.** BA.

SOLUTION

a. Matrix A is a 1×3 matrix and matrix B is a 3×1 matrix. Thus, the product AB is a 1×1 matrix.

$$A = [1 \quad 2 \quad 3] \quad B = \begin{bmatrix} 4 \\ 5 \\ 6 \end{bmatrix}$$

Matrix A   **Matrix B**

1×3 3×1

These are equal.

The order of AB is 1×1.

$$AB = [1 \quad 2 \quad 3] \begin{bmatrix} 4 \\ 5 \\ 6 \end{bmatrix}$$

We will perform a row-by-column computation.

$$= [(1)(4) + (2)(5) + (3)(6)]$$

Multiply elements in row 1 of A by corresponding elements in column 1 of B and add the products.

$$= [4 + 10 + 18]$$ Perform the multiplications.

$$= [32]$$ Add.

b. Matrix B is a 3×1 matrix and matrix A is a 1×3 matrix. Thus, the product BA is a 3×3 matrix.

$$B = \begin{bmatrix} 4 \\ 5 \\ 6 \end{bmatrix} \quad A = [1 \quad 2 \quad 3]$$

Matrix B   **Matrix A**

3×1 1×3

These are equal.

The order of BA is 3×3.

$$BA = \begin{bmatrix} 4 \\ 5 \\ 6 \end{bmatrix} [1 \quad 2 \quad 3]$$

We perform a row-by-column computation.

$$= \begin{bmatrix} (4)(1) & (4)(2) & (4)(3) \\ (5)(1) & (5)(2) & (5)(3) \\ (6)(1) & (6)(2) & (6)(3) \end{bmatrix}$$

Row 1 of $B \times$ Column 1 of A Row 1 of $B \times$ Column 2 of A Row 1 of $B \times$ Column 3 of A

Row 2 of $B \times$ Column 1 of A Row 2 of $B \times$ Column 2 of A Row 2 of $B \times$ Column 3 of A

Row 3 of $B \times$ Column 1 of A Row 3 of $B \times$ Column 2 of A Row 3 of $B \times$ Column 3 of A

$$= \begin{bmatrix} 4 & 8 & 12 \\ 5 & 10 & 15 \\ 6 & 12 & 18 \end{bmatrix}$$ Simplify.

• • •

In Example 6, did you notice that AB and BA are different matrices? For most matrices A and B, $AB \neq BA$. Because **matrix multiplication is not commutative**, be careful about the order in which matrices appear when performing this operation.

✓ Check Point **6** If $A = [2 \quad 0 \quad 4]$ and $B = \begin{bmatrix} 1 \\ 3 \\ 7 \end{bmatrix}$, find AB and BA.

TECHNOLOGY

The screens illustrate the solution of Example 6 using a graphing utility.

EXAMPLE 7 Multiplying Matrices

Where possible, find each product:

a. $\begin{bmatrix} 4 & 2 \\ 1 & 3 \end{bmatrix}\begin{bmatrix} 1 & 2 & 3 & 4 \\ 0 & 2 & -1 & 6 \end{bmatrix}$ **b.** $\begin{bmatrix} 1 & 2 & 3 & 4 \\ 0 & 2 & -1 & 6 \end{bmatrix}\begin{bmatrix} 4 & 2 \\ 1 & 3 \end{bmatrix}.$

SOLUTION

a. The first matrix is a 2×2 matrix and the second is a 2×4 matrix. The product will be a 2×4 matrix.

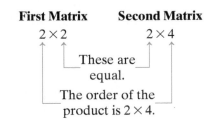

$$\begin{bmatrix} 4 & 2 \\ 1 & 3 \end{bmatrix}\begin{bmatrix} 1 & 2 & 3 & 4 \\ 0 & 2 & -1 & 6 \end{bmatrix}$$ We perform a row-by-column computation.

$$= \begin{bmatrix} 4(1) + 2(0) & 4(2) + 2(2) & 4(3) + 2(-1) & 4(4) + 2(6) \\ 1(1) + 3(0) & 1(2) + 3(2) & 1(3) + 3(-1) & 1(4) + 3(6) \end{bmatrix}$$

$$= \begin{bmatrix} 4 + 0 & 8 + 4 & 12 - 2 & 16 + 12 \\ 1 + 0 & 2 + 6 & 3 - 3 & 4 + 18 \end{bmatrix}$$

$$= \begin{bmatrix} 4 & 12 & 10 & 28 \\ 1 & 8 & 0 & 22 \end{bmatrix}$$

b. $\begin{bmatrix} 1 & 2 & 3 & 4 \\ 0 & 2 & -1 & 6 \end{bmatrix}\begin{bmatrix} 4 & 2 \\ 1 & 3 \end{bmatrix}$ First matrix 2×4 Second matrix 2×2

These numbers must be the same to multiply the matrices.

The number of columns in the first matrix does not equal the number of rows in the second matrix. Thus, the product of these two matrices is undefined. • • •

✓ Check Point **7** Where possible, find each product:

a. $\begin{bmatrix} 1 & 3 \\ 0 & 2 \end{bmatrix}\begin{bmatrix} 2 & 3 & -1 & 6 \\ 0 & 5 & 4 & 1 \end{bmatrix}$ **b.** $\begin{bmatrix} 2 & 3 & -1 & 6 \\ 0 & 5 & 4 & 1 \end{bmatrix}\begin{bmatrix} 1 & 3 \\ 0 & 2 \end{bmatrix}.$

Although matrix multiplication is not commutative, it does obey many of the properties of real numbers.

Properties of Matrix Multiplication

If A, B, and C are matrices and c is a scalar, then the following properties are true. (Assume the order of each matrix is such that all operations in these properties are defined.)

1. $(AB)C = A(BC)$ — Associative property of matrix multiplication
2. $A(B + C) = AB + AC$ — Distributive properties of matrix multiplication
   $(A + B)C = AC + BC$
3. $c(AB) = (cA)B$ — Associative property of scalar multiplication

Applications

⑦ Model applied situations with matrix operations.

All of the still images that you see on the Web have been created or manipulated on a computer in a digital format—made up of hundreds of thousands, or even millions, of tiny squares called **pixels**. Pixels are created by dividing an image into a grid. The computer can change the brightness of every square or pixel in this grid. A digital camera captures photos in this digital format. Also, you can scan pictures to convert them into digital format. Example 8 illustrates the role that matrices play in this technology.

EXAMPLE 8 Matrices and Digital Photography

The letter L in **Figure 6.7** is shown using 9 pixels in a 3×3 grid. The colors possible in the grid are shown in **Figure 6.8**. Each color is represented by a specific number: 0, 1, 2, or 3.

FIGURE 6.7 The letter L

White Light gray Dark gray Black

0   1   2   3

FIGURE 6.8 Color levels

a. Find a matrix that represents a digital photograph of this letter L.

b. Increase the contrast of the letter L by changing the dark gray to black and the light gray to white. Use matrix addition to accomplish this.

SOLUTION

a. Look at the L and the background in **Figure 6.7**. Because the L is dark gray, color level 2, and the background is light gray, color level 1, a digital photograph of **Figure 6.7** can be represented by the matrix

$$\begin{bmatrix} 2 & 1 & 1 \\ 2 & 1 & 1 \\ 2 & 2 & 1 \end{bmatrix}.$$

b. We can make the L black, color level 3, by increasing each 2 in the above matrix to 3. We can make the background white, color level 0, by decreasing each 1 in the above matrix to 0. This is accomplished using the following matrix addition:

$$\begin{bmatrix} 2 & 1 & 1 \\ 2 & 1 & 1 \\ 2 & 2 & 1 \end{bmatrix} + \begin{bmatrix} 1 & -1 & -1 \\ 1 & -1 & -1 \\ 1 & 1 & -1 \end{bmatrix} = \begin{bmatrix} 3 & 0 & 0 \\ 3 & 0 & 0 \\ 3 & 3 & 0 \end{bmatrix}.$$

The picture corresponding to the matrix sum to the right of the equal sign is shown in **Figure 6.9**. • • •

FIGURE 6.9 Changing contrast: the letter L

Check Point **8** Change the contrast of the letter L in **Figure 6.7** on the previous page by making the L light gray and the background black. Use matrix addition to accomplish this.

Blitzer Bonus || Images of Space

Photographs sent back from space use matrices with thousands of pixels. Each pixel is assigned a number from 0 to 63 representing its color—0 for pure white and 63 for pure black. In the image of Saturn shown here, matrix operations provide false colors that emphasize the banding of the planet's upper atmosphere.

We have seen how functions can be transformed using translations, reflections, stretching, and shrinking. In a similar way, matrix operations are used to transform and manipulate computer graphics.

EXAMPLE 9   Transformations of an Image

The quadrilateral in **Figure 6.10** can be represented by the matrix

Coordinates of vertices

$$A = \begin{bmatrix} -2 & -1 & 3 & 1 \\ -3 & 2 & 4 & -2 \end{bmatrix}.$$

x-coordinates

y-coordinates

Each column in the matrix gives the coordinates of a vertex, or corner, of the quadrilateral. Use matrix operations to perform the following transformations:

a. Move the quadrilateral 4 units to the right and 1 unit down.

b. Shrink the quadrilateral to half its perimeter.

c. Let $B = \begin{bmatrix} -1 & 0 \\ 0 & 1 \end{bmatrix}$. Find BA. What effect does this have on the quadrilateral in **Figure 6.10**?

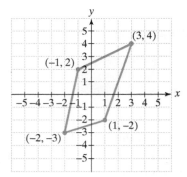

FIGURE 6.10

SOLUTION

a. We translate the quadrilateral 4 units right and 1 unit down by adding 4 to each *x*-coordinate and subtracting 1 from each *y*-coordinate. This is accomplished using the following matrix addition:

$$\begin{bmatrix} -2 & -1 & 3 & 1 \\ -3 & 2 & 4 & -2 \end{bmatrix} + \begin{bmatrix} 4 & 4 & 4 & 4 \\ -1 & -1 & -1 & -1 \end{bmatrix} = \begin{bmatrix} 2 & 3 & 7 & 5 \\ -4 & 1 & 3 & -3 \end{bmatrix}.$$

This matrix represents the original quadrilateral.

Shift 4 units to the right and 1 unit down.

This matrix represents the translated quadrilateral.

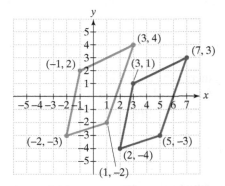

FIGURE 6.11 Shifting the quadrilateral 4 units right and 1 unit down

Each column in the matrix on the right gives the coordinates of a vertex of the translated quadrilateral. The original quadrilateral and the translated image are shown in **Figure 6.11**.

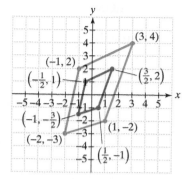

FIGURE 6.12 Shrinking the quadrilateral to half the original perimeter

b. We shrink the quadrilateral in **Figure 6.10**, shown in blue in **Figure 6.12**, to half its perimeter by multiplying each x-coordinate and each y-coordinate by $\frac{1}{2}$. This is accomplished using the following scalar multiplication:

$$\frac{1}{2}\begin{bmatrix} -2 & -1 & 3 & 1 \\ -3 & 2 & 4 & -2 \end{bmatrix} = \begin{bmatrix} -1 & -\frac{1}{2} & \frac{3}{2} & \frac{1}{2} \\ -\frac{3}{2} & 1 & 2 & -1 \end{bmatrix}.$$

This matrix represents the original quadrilateral.   This matrix represents the quadrilateral with half the original perimeter.

Each column in the matrix on the right gives the coordinates of a vertex of the reduced quadrilateral. The original quadrilateral and the reduced image are shown in **Figure 6.12**.

c. We begin by finding BA. Keep in mind that A represents the original quadrilateral, shown in blue in **Figure 6.13**.

$$BA = \begin{bmatrix} -1 & 0 \\ 0 & 1 \end{bmatrix}\begin{bmatrix} -2 & -1 & 3 & 1 \\ -3 & 2 & 4 & -2 \end{bmatrix}$$

$$= \begin{bmatrix} (-1)(-2)+0(-3) & (-1)(-1)+0(2) & (-1)(3)+0(4) & (-1)(1)+0(-2) \\ 0(-2)+1(-3) & 0(-1)+1(2) & 0(3)+1(4) & 0(1)+1(-2) \end{bmatrix}$$

$$= \begin{bmatrix} 2 & 1 & -3 & -1 \\ -3 & 2 & 4 & -2 \end{bmatrix}$$

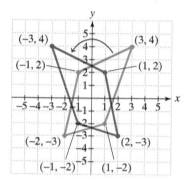

FIGURE 6.13

Each column in the matrix multiplication gives the coordinates of a vertex of the transformed image. The original quadrilateral and this transformed image are shown in **Figure 6.13**. Notice that each x-coordinate on the original blue image is replaced with its opposite on the transformed red image. We can conclude that multiplication by $\begin{bmatrix} -1 & 0 \\ 0 & 1 \end{bmatrix}$ reflected the blue quadrilateral about the y-axis.   • • •

⊘ Check Point **9** Consider the triangle represented by the matrix

$$A = \begin{bmatrix} 0 & 3 & 4 \\ 0 & 5 & 2 \end{bmatrix}.$$

Use matrix operations to perform the following transformations:

a. Move the triangle 3 units to the left and 1 unit down.

b. Enlarge the triangle to twice its original perimeter.

Illustrate your results in parts (a) and (b) by showing the original triangle and the transformed image in a rectangular coordinate system.

c. Let $B = \begin{bmatrix} 1 & 0 \\ 0 & -1 \end{bmatrix}$. Find BA. What effect does this have on the original triangle?

CONCEPT AND VOCABULARY CHECK

Fill in each blank so that the resulting statement is true.

1. The notation a_{34} refers to the element in the _____ row and _____ column of a matrix.

2. The order of $A = [2 \quad 3 \quad 7]$ is _____.

3. A matrix that has the same number of rows as columns is called a/an _____ matrix.

4. If $\begin{bmatrix} 3 & x \\ y & -7 \end{bmatrix} = \begin{bmatrix} 3 & -10 \\ 6 & -7 \end{bmatrix}$, then $x =$ _____ and $y =$ _____.

5. True or false: Matrix addition is commutative. _____

6. True or false: Matrices of different orders can be added. _____

7. True or false: The scalar multiple $-4A$ is obtained by multiplying each element of A by -4. _____

8. If A is an $m \times n$ matrix and B is an $n \times p$ matrix, then AB is defined as an ____ $\times$ ____ matrix. To find the product AB, the number of _____ in matrix A must equal the number of _____ in matrix B.

9. True or false: Matrices of different orders can sometimes be multiplied. _____

10. True or false: Matrix multiplication is commutative. _____

EXERCISE SET 6.3

Practice Exercises

In Exercises 1–4,

   a. Give the order of each matrix.

   b. If $A = [a_{ij}]$, identify a_{32} and a_{23}, or explain why identification is not possible.

1. $\begin{bmatrix} 4 & -7 & 5 \\ -6 & 8 & -1 \end{bmatrix}$
2. $\begin{bmatrix} -6 & 4 & -1 \\ -9 & 0 & \frac{1}{2} \end{bmatrix}$

3. $\begin{bmatrix} 1 & -5 & \pi & e \\ 0 & 7 & -6 & -\pi \\ -2 & \frac{1}{2} & 11 & -\frac{1}{5} \end{bmatrix}$
4. $\begin{bmatrix} -4 & 1 & 3 & -5 \\ 2 & -1 & \pi & 0 \\ 1 & 0 & -e & \frac{1}{5} \end{bmatrix}$

In Exercises 5–8, find values for the variables so that the matrices in each exercise are equal.

5. $\begin{bmatrix} x \\ 4 \end{bmatrix} = \begin{bmatrix} 6 \\ y \end{bmatrix}$
6. $\begin{bmatrix} x \\ 7 \end{bmatrix} = \begin{bmatrix} 11 \\ y \end{bmatrix}$

7. $\begin{bmatrix} x & 2y \\ z & 9 \end{bmatrix} = \begin{bmatrix} 4 & 12 \\ 3 & 9 \end{bmatrix}$
8. $\begin{bmatrix} x & y + 3 \\ 2z & 8 \end{bmatrix} = \begin{bmatrix} 12 & 5 \\ 6 & 8 \end{bmatrix}$

In Exercises 9–16, find the following matrices:

   a. $A + B$ *b. $A - B$*
   c. $-4A$ *d. $3A + 2B$.*

9. $A = \begin{bmatrix} 4 & 1 \\ 3 & 2 \end{bmatrix}$, $B = \begin{bmatrix} 5 & 9 \\ 0 & 7 \end{bmatrix}$

10. $A = \begin{bmatrix} -2 & 3 \\ 0 & 1 \end{bmatrix}$, $B = \begin{bmatrix} 8 & 1 \\ 5 & 4 \end{bmatrix}$

11. $A = \begin{bmatrix} 1 & 3 \\ 3 & 4 \\ 5 & 6 \end{bmatrix}$, $B = \begin{bmatrix} 2 & -1 \\ 3 & -2 \\ 0 & 1 \end{bmatrix}$

12. $A = \begin{bmatrix} 3 & 1 & 1 \\ -1 & 2 & 5 \end{bmatrix}$, $B = \begin{bmatrix} 2 & -3 & 6 \\ -3 & 1 & -4 \end{bmatrix}$

13. $A = \begin{bmatrix} 2 \\ -4 \\ 1 \end{bmatrix}$, $B = \begin{bmatrix} -5 \\ 3 \\ -1 \end{bmatrix}$

14. $A = [6 \quad 2 \quad -3]$, $B = [4 \quad -2 \quad 3]$

15. $A = \begin{bmatrix} 2 & -10 & -2 \\ 14 & 12 & 10 \\ 4 & -2 & 2 \end{bmatrix}$, $B = \begin{bmatrix} 6 & 10 & -2 \\ 0 & -12 & -4 \\ -5 & 2 & -2 \end{bmatrix}$

16. $A = \begin{bmatrix} 6 & -3 & 5 \\ 6 & 0 & -2 \\ -4 & 2 & -1 \end{bmatrix}$, $B = \begin{bmatrix} -3 & 5 & 1 \\ -1 & 2 & -6 \\ 2 & 0 & 4 \end{bmatrix}$

In Exercises 17–26, let

$$A = \begin{bmatrix} -3 & -7 \\ 2 & -9 \\ 5 & 0 \end{bmatrix} \text{ and } B = \begin{bmatrix} -5 & -1 \\ 0 & 0 \\ 3 & -4 \end{bmatrix}.$$

Solve each matrix equation for X.

17. $X - A = B$
18. $X - B = A$
19. $2X + A = B$
20. $3X + A = B$
21. $3X + 2A = B$
22. $2X + 5A = B$
23. $B - X = 4A$
24. $A - X = 4B$
25. $4A + 3B = -2X$
26. $4B + 3A = -2X$

In Exercises 27–36, find (if possible) the following matrices:

   a. AB   *b. BA.*

27. $A = \begin{bmatrix} 1 & 3 \\ 5 & 3 \end{bmatrix}$, $B = \begin{bmatrix} 3 & -2 \\ -1 & 6 \end{bmatrix}$

28. $A = \begin{bmatrix} 3 & -2 \\ 1 & 5 \end{bmatrix}$, $B = \begin{bmatrix} 0 & 0 \\ 5 & -6 \end{bmatrix}$

29. $A = [1 \quad 2 \quad 3 \quad 4]$, $B = \begin{bmatrix} 1 \\ 2 \\ 3 \\ 4 \end{bmatrix}$

30. $A = \begin{bmatrix} -1 \\ -2 \\ -3 \end{bmatrix}$, $B = [1 \quad 2 \quad 3]$

31. $A = \begin{bmatrix} 1 & -1 & 4 \\ 4 & -1 & 3 \\ 2 & 0 & -2 \end{bmatrix}$, $B = \begin{bmatrix} 1 & 1 & 0 \\ 1 & 2 & 4 \\ 1 & -1 & 3 \end{bmatrix}$

32. $A = \begin{bmatrix} 1 & -1 & 1 \\ 5 & 0 & -2 \\ 3 & -2 & 2 \end{bmatrix}$, $B = \begin{bmatrix} 1 & 1 & 0 \\ 1 & -4 & 5 \\ 3 & -1 & 2 \end{bmatrix}$

33. $A = \begin{bmatrix} 4 & 2 \\ 6 & 1 \\ 3 & 5 \end{bmatrix}$, $B = \begin{bmatrix} 2 & 3 & 4 \\ -1 & -2 & 0 \end{bmatrix}$

34. $A = \begin{bmatrix} 2 & 4 \\ 3 & 1 \\ 4 & 2 \end{bmatrix}$, $B = \begin{bmatrix} 3 & 2 & 0 \\ -1 & -3 & 5 \end{bmatrix}$

35. $A = \begin{bmatrix} 2 & -3 & 1 & -1 \\ 1 & 1 & -2 & 1 \end{bmatrix}$, $B = \begin{bmatrix} 1 & 2 \\ -1 & 1 \\ 5 & 4 \\ 10 & 5 \end{bmatrix}$

36. $A = \begin{bmatrix} 2 & -1 & 3 & 2 \\ 1 & 0 & -2 & 1 \end{bmatrix}$, $B = \begin{bmatrix} -1 & 2 \\ 1 & 1 \\ 3 & -4 \\ 6 & 5 \end{bmatrix}$

In Exercises 37–44, perform the indicated matrix operations given that A, B, and C are defined as follows. If an operation is not defined, state the reason.

$$A = \begin{bmatrix} 4 & 0 \\ -3 & 5 \\ 0 & 1 \end{bmatrix} \quad B = \begin{bmatrix} 5 & 1 \\ -2 & -2 \end{bmatrix} \quad C = \begin{bmatrix} 1 & -1 \\ -1 & 1 \end{bmatrix}$$

37. $4B - 3C$ **38.** $5C - 2B$

39. $BC + CB$ **40.** $A(B + C)$

41. $A - C$ **42.** $B - A$

43. $A(BC)$ **44.** $A(CB)$

Practice Plus

In Exercises 45–50, let

$$A = \begin{bmatrix} 1 & 0 \\ 0 & 1 \end{bmatrix}, \quad B = \begin{bmatrix} 1 & 0 \\ 0 & -1 \end{bmatrix}, \quad C = \begin{bmatrix} -1 & 0 \\ 0 & 1 \end{bmatrix},$$

$$D = \begin{bmatrix} -1 & 0 \\ 0 & -1 \end{bmatrix}.$$

45. Find the product of the sum of A and B and the difference between C and D.

46. Find the product of the difference between A and B and the sum of C and D.

47. Use any three of the matrices to verify a distributive property.

48. Use any three of the matrices to verify an associative property.

In Exercises 49–50, suppose that the vertices of a computer graphic are points, (x, y), represented by the matrix

$$Z = \begin{bmatrix} x \\ y \end{bmatrix}.$$

49. Find BZ and explain why this reflects the graphic about the x-axis.

50. Find CZ and explain why this reflects the graphic about the y-axis.

Application Exercises

The + sign in the figure is shown using 9 pixels in a 3 × 3 grid. The color levels are given to the right of the figure. Each color is represented by a specific number: 0, 1, 2, or 3. Use this information to solve Exercises 51–52.

51. a. Find a matrix that represents a digital photograph of the + sign.

   b. Adjust the contrast by changing the black to dark gray and the light gray to white. Use matrix addition to accomplish this.

   c. Adjust the contrast by changing the black to light gray and the light gray to dark gray. Use matrix addition to accomplish this.

52. a. Find a matrix that represents a digital photograph of the + sign.

   b. Adjust the contrast by changing the black to dark gray and the light gray to black. Use matrix addition to accomplish this.

   c. Adjust the contrast by leaving the black alone and changing the light gray to white. Use matrix addition to accomplish this.

The figure shows the letter L in a rectangular coordinate system.

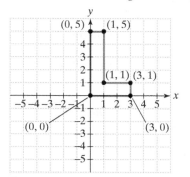

The figure can be represented by the matrix

$$B = \begin{bmatrix} 0 & 3 & 3 & 1 & 1 & 0 \\ 0 & 0 & 1 & 1 & 5 & 5 \end{bmatrix}.$$

Each column in the matrix describes a point on the letter. The order of the columns shows the direction in which a pencil must move to draw the letter. The L is completed by connecting the last point in the matrix, $(0, 5)$, to the starting point, $(0, 0)$. Use these ideas to solve Exercises 53–60.

53. Use matrix operations to move the L 2 units to the left and 3 units down. Then graph the letter and its transformation in a rectangular coordinate system.

54. Use matrix operations to move the L 2 units to the right and 3 units down. Then graph the letter and its transformation in a rectangular coordinate system.

55. Reduce the L to half its perimeter and move the reduced image 1 unit up. Then graph the letter and its transformation.

56. Reduce the L to half its perimeter and move the reduced image 2 units up. Then graph the letter and its transformation.

57. a. If $A = \begin{bmatrix} 1 & 0 \\ 0 & -1 \end{bmatrix}$, find AB.

   b. Graph the object represented by matrix AB. What effect does the matrix multiplication have on the letter L represented by matrix B?

58. a. If $A = \begin{bmatrix} -1 & 0 \\ 0 & 1 \end{bmatrix}$, find AB.

   b. Graph the object represented by matrix AB. What effect does the matrix multiplication have on the letter L represented by matrix B?

(In Exercises 59–60, be sure to refer to matrix B described in the second column on the previous page.)

59. a. If $A = \begin{bmatrix} 0 & -1 \\ 1 & 0 \end{bmatrix}$, find AB.

   b. Graph the object represented by matrix AB. What effect does the matrix multiplication have on the letter L represented by matrix B?

60. a. If $A = \begin{bmatrix} 2 & 0 \\ 0 & 1 \end{bmatrix}$, find AB.

   b. Graph the object represented by matrix AB. What effect does the matrix multiplication have on the letter L represented by matrix B?

61. Completing the transition to adulthood is measured by one or more of the following: leaving home, finishing school, getting married, having a child, or being financially independent. The bar graph shows the percentage of Americans, ages 20 and 30, who had completed the transition to adulthood in 1960 and in 2000.

Percentage Having Completed the Transition to Adulthood

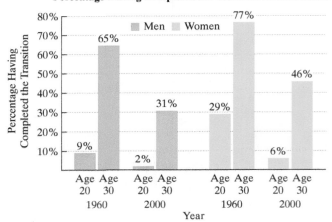

Source: James M. Henslin, *Sociology,* Eleventh Edition, Pearson, 2012.

   a. Use a 2 × 2 matrix to represent the data for 2000. Entries in the matrix should be percents that are organized as follows:

$$\begin{array}{c} \\ \text{Age 20} \\ \text{Age 30} \end{array} \overset{\displaystyle \text{Men} \quad \text{Women}}{\begin{bmatrix} & \\ & \end{bmatrix}}$$

Call this matrix A.

   b. Use a 2 × 2 matrix to represent the data for 1960. Call this matrix B.

   c. Find $B - A$. What does this matrix represent?

62. The table gives an estimate of basic caloric needs for different age groups and activity levels.

Age Range	Sedentary		Moderately Active		Active	
	Men	Women	Men	Women	Men	Women
19 – 30	2400	2000	2700	2100	3000	2400
31 – 50	2200	1800	2500	2000	2900	2200
51 +	2000	1600	2300	1800	2600	2100

Source: *USA Today*

   a. Use a 3 × 3 matrix to represent the daily caloric needs, by age and activity level, for men. Call this matrix M.

   b. Use a 3 × 3 matrix to represent the daily caloric needs, by age and activity level, for women. Call this matrix W.

   c. Find $M - W$. What does this matrix represent?

63. The final grade in a particular course is determined by grades on the midterm and final. The grades for five students and the two grading systems are modeled by the following matrices. Call the first matrix A and the second B.

$$\begin{array}{c} \text{Student 1} \\ \text{Student 2} \\ \text{Student 3} \\ \text{Student 4} \\ \text{Student 5} \end{array} \overset{\displaystyle \text{Midterm} \quad \text{Final}}{\begin{bmatrix} 76 & 92 \\ 74 & 84 \\ 94 & 86 \\ 84 & 62 \\ 58 & 80 \end{bmatrix}} \qquad \begin{array}{c} \text{Midterm} \\ \text{Final} \end{array} \overset{\displaystyle \begin{array}{cc} \text{System} & \text{System} \\ 1 & 2 \end{array}}{\begin{bmatrix} 0.5 & 0.3 \\ 0.5 & 0.7 \end{bmatrix}}$$

   a. Describe the grading system that is represented by matrix B.

   b. Compute the matrix AB and assign each of the five students a final course grade first using system 1 and then using system 2. ($89.5 - 100 = A$, $79.5 - 89.4 = B$, $69.5 - 79.4 = C$, $59.5 - 69.4 = D$, below $59.5 = F$)

64. In a certain county, the proportion of voters in each age group registered as Republicans, Democrats, or Independents is given by the following matrix, which we'll call A.

$$\begin{array}{c} \text{Republicans} \\ \text{Democrats} \\ \text{Independents} \end{array} \overset{\displaystyle \begin{array}{ccc} \multicolumn{3}{c}{\text{Age}} \\ \text{18–30} & \text{31–50} & \text{Over 50} \end{array}}{\begin{bmatrix} 0.40 & 0.30 & 0.70 \\ 0.30 & 0.60 & 0.25 \\ 0.30 & 0.10 & 0.05 \end{bmatrix}}$$

The distribution, by age and gender, of this county's voting population is given by the following matrix, which we'll call B.

$$\begin{array}{c} \\ \text{18–30} \\ \text{Age} \quad \text{31–50} \\ \text{Over 50} \end{array} \overset{\displaystyle \text{Male} \qquad \text{Female}}{\begin{bmatrix} 6000 & 8000 \\ 12,000 & 14,000 \\ 14,000 & 16,000 \end{bmatrix}}$$

   a. Calculate the product AB.

   b. How many female Democrats are there?

   c. How many male Republicans are there?

Writing in Mathematics

65. What is meant by the order of a matrix? Give an example with your explanation.

66. What does a_{ij} mean?

67. What are equal matrices?

68. How are matrices added?

69. Describe how to subtract matrices.

70. Describe matrices that cannot be added or subtracted.

71. Describe how to perform scalar multiplication. Provide an example with your description.

72. Describe how to multiply matrices.

73. Describe when the multiplication of two matrices is not defined.

74. If two matrices can be multiplied, describe how to determine the order of the product.

75. Low-resolution digital photographs use 262,144 pixels in a 512×512 grid. If you enlarge a low-resolution digital photograph enough, describe what will happen.

Technology Exercise

76. Use the matrix feature of a graphing utility to verify each of your answers to Exercises 37–44.

Critical Thinking Exercises

Make Sense? *In Exercises 77–80, determine whether each statement makes sense or does not make sense, and explain your reasoning.*

77. I added matrices of the same order by adding corresponding elements.

78. I multiplied an $m \times n$ matrix and an $n \times p$ matrix by multiplying corresponding elements.

79. I'm working with two matrices that can be added but not multiplied.

80. I'm working with two matrices that can be multiplied but not added.

81. Find two matrices A and B such that $AB = BA$.

82. Consider a square matrix such that each element that is not on the diagonal from upper left to lower right is zero. Experiment with such matrices (call each matrix A) by finding AA. Then write a sentence or two describing a method for multiplying this kind of matrix by itself.

83. If $AB = -BA$, then A and B are said to be anticommutative.

Are $A = \begin{bmatrix} 0 & -1 \\ 1 & 0 \end{bmatrix}$ and $B = \begin{bmatrix} 1 & 0 \\ 0 & -1 \end{bmatrix}$ anticommutative?

Group Exercise

84. The interesting and useful applications of matrix theory are nearly unlimited. Applications of matrices range from representing digital photographs to predicting long-range trends in the stock market. Members of the group should research an application of matrices that they find intriguing. The group should then present a seminar to the class about this application.

Preview Exercises

Exercises 85–87 will help you prepare for the material covered in the next section.

85. Multiply:

$$\begin{bmatrix} a_{11} & a_{12} \\ a_{21} & a_{22} \end{bmatrix} \begin{bmatrix} 1 & 0 \\ 0 & 1 \end{bmatrix}.$$

After performing the multiplication, describe what happens to the elements in the first matrix.

86. Use Gauss-Jordan elimination to solve the system:

$$\begin{cases} -x - y - z = 1 \\ 4x + 5y \quad\quad = 0 \\ \quad\quad y - 3z = 0. \end{cases}$$

87. Multiply and write the linear system represented by the following matrix multiplication:

$$\begin{bmatrix} a_1 & b_1 & c_1 \\ a_2 & b_2 & c_2 \\ a_3 & b_3 & c_3 \end{bmatrix} \begin{bmatrix} x \\ y \\ z \end{bmatrix} = \begin{bmatrix} d_1 \\ d_2 \\ d_3 \end{bmatrix}.$$

CHAPTER 6   Mid-Chapter Check Point

WHAT YOU KNOW: We learned to use matrices to solve systems of linear equations. Gaussian elimination required simplifying the augmented matrix to one with 1s down the main diagonal and 0s below the 1s. Gauss-Jordan elimination simplified the augmented matrix to one with 1s down the main diagonal and 0s above and below each 1. Such a matrix, in reduced row-echelon form, did not require back-substitution to solve the system. We applied Gaussian elimination to systems with no solution, as well as to represent the solution set for systems with infinitely many solutions, including nonsquare systems. We learned how to perform operations with matrices, including matrix addition, matrix subtraction, scalar multiplication, and matrix multiplication.

In Exercises 1–5, use matrices to find the complete solution to each system of equations, or show that none exists.

1. $\begin{cases} x + 2y - 3z = -7 \\ 3x - y + 2z = 8 \\ 2x - y + z = 5 \end{cases}$

2. $\begin{cases} 2x + 4y + 5z = 2 \\ x + y + 2z = 1 \\ 3x + 5y + 7z = 4 \end{cases}$

3. $\begin{cases} x - 2y + 2z = -2 \\ 2x + 3y - z = 1 \end{cases}$

4. $\begin{cases} w + x + y + z = 6 \\ w - x + 3y + z = -14 \\ w + 2x \quad - 3z = 12 \\ 2w + 3x + 6y + z = 1 \end{cases}$

5. $\begin{cases} 2x - 2y + 2z = 5 \\ x - y + z = 2 \\ 2x + y - z = 1 \end{cases}$

In Exercises 6–10, perform the indicated matrix operations or solve the matrix equation for X given that A, B, and C are defined as follows. If an operation is not defined, state the reason.

$$A = \begin{bmatrix} 0 & 2 \\ -1 & 3 \\ 1 & 0 \end{bmatrix} \quad B = \begin{bmatrix} 4 & 1 \\ -6 & -2 \end{bmatrix} \quad C = \begin{bmatrix} -1 & 0 \\ 0 & 1 \end{bmatrix}$$

6. $2C - \frac{1}{2}B$ **7.** $A(B + C)$ **8.** $A(BC)$

9. $A + C$ **10.** $2X - 3C = B$

SECTION 6.4

Multiplicative Inverses of Matrices and Matrix Equations

Objectives

① Find the multiplicative inverse of a square matrix.

② Use inverses to solve matrix equations.

③ Encode and decode messages.

In 1939, Britain's secret service hired top chess players, mathematicians, and other masters of logic to break the code used by the Nazis in communications between headquarters and troops. The project, which employed over 10,000 people, broke the code less than a year later, providing the Allies with information about Nazi troop movements throughout World War II.

Messages must often be sent in such a way that the real meaning is hidden from everyone but the sender and the recipient. In this section, we will look at the role that matrices and their inverses play in this process.

The Multiplicative Identity Matrix

For the real numbers, we know that 1 is the multiplicative identity because $a \cdot 1 = 1 \cdot a = a$. Is there a similar property for matrix multiplication? That is, is there a matrix I such that $AI = A$ and $IA = A$? The answer is yes. A square matrix with 1s down the main diagonal from upper left to lower right and 0s elsewhere does not change the elements in a matrix in products with that matrix. In the case of 2×2 matrices,

$$\begin{bmatrix} a_{11} & a_{12} \\ a_{21} & a_{22} \end{bmatrix} \begin{bmatrix} 1 & 0 \\ 0 & 1 \end{bmatrix} = \begin{bmatrix} a_{11} & a_{12} \\ a_{21} & a_{22} \end{bmatrix}$$

The elements in the matrix do not change.

$$\text{and} \quad \begin{bmatrix} 1 & 0 \\ 0 & 1 \end{bmatrix} \begin{bmatrix} a_{11} & a_{12} \\ a_{21} & a_{22} \end{bmatrix} = \begin{bmatrix} a_{11} & a_{12} \\ a_{21} & a_{22} \end{bmatrix}.$$

The elements in the matrix do not change.

The $n \times n$ square matrix with 1s down the main diagonal from upper left to lower right and 0s elsewhere is called the **multiplicative identity matrix of order n**. This matrix is designated by I_n. For example,

$$I_2 = \begin{bmatrix} 1 & 0 \\ 0 & 1 \end{bmatrix}, \quad I_3 = \begin{bmatrix} 1 & 0 & 0 \\ 0 & 1 & 0 \\ 0 & 0 & 1 \end{bmatrix},$$

and so on.

① Find the multiplicative inverse of a square matrix.

The Multiplicative Inverse of a Matrix

The multiplicative identity matrix, I_n, will help us to define a new concept: the multiplicative inverse of a matrix. To do so, let's consider a similar concept, the multiplicative inverse of a nonzero number, a. Recall that the multiplicative inverse of a is $\frac{1}{a}$. The multiplicative inverse has the following property:

$$a \cdot \tfrac{1}{a} = 1 \quad \text{and} \quad \tfrac{1}{a} \cdot a = 1.$$

We can define the multiplicative inverse of a square matrix in a similar manner.

> ### Definition of the Multiplicative Inverse of a Square Matrix
>
> Let A be an $n \times n$ matrix. If there exists an $n \times n$ matrix A^{-1} (read: "A inverse") such that
>
> $$AA^{-1} = I_n \quad \text{and} \quad A^{-1}A = I_n,$$
>
> then A^{-1} is the **multiplicative inverse** of A.

We have seen that matrix multiplication is not commutative. Thus, to show that a matrix B is the multiplicative inverse of the matrix A, find both AB and BA. If B is the multiplicative inverse of A, both products (AB and BA) will be the multiplicative identity matrix, I_n.

EXAMPLE 1   The Multiplicative Inverse of a Matrix

Show that B is the multiplicative inverse of A, where

$$A = \begin{bmatrix} -1 & 3 \\ 2 & -5 \end{bmatrix} \quad \text{and} \quad B = \begin{bmatrix} 5 & 3 \\ 2 & 1 \end{bmatrix}.$$

SOLUTION

To show that B is the multiplicative inverse of A, we must find the products AB and BA. If B is the multiplicative inverse of A, then AB will be the multiplicative identity matrix and BA will be the multiplicative identity matrix. Because A and B are 2×2 matrices, $n = 2$. Thus, we denote the multiplicative identity matrix as I_2; it is also a 2×2 matrix. We must show that

- $AB = I_2 = \begin{bmatrix} 1 & 0 \\ 0 & 1 \end{bmatrix}$ and

- $BA = I_2 = \begin{bmatrix} 1 & 0 \\ 0 & 1 \end{bmatrix}$.

Let's first show $AB = I_2$.

$$AB = \begin{bmatrix} -1 & 3 \\ 2 & -5 \end{bmatrix}\begin{bmatrix} 5 & 3 \\ 2 & 1 \end{bmatrix}$$

$$= \begin{bmatrix} -1(5) + 3(2) & -1(3) + 3(1) \\ 2(5) + (-5)(2) & 2(3) + (-5)(1) \end{bmatrix} = \begin{bmatrix} 1 & 0 \\ 0 & 1 \end{bmatrix}$$

Let's now show $BA = I_2$.

$$BA = \begin{bmatrix} 5 & 3 \\ 2 & 1 \end{bmatrix}\begin{bmatrix} -1 & 3 \\ 2 & -5 \end{bmatrix}$$

$$= \begin{bmatrix} 5(-1) + 3(2) & 5(3) + 3(-5) \\ 2(-1) + 1(2) & 2(3) + 1(-5) \end{bmatrix} = \begin{bmatrix} 1 & 0 \\ 0 & 1 \end{bmatrix}$$

Both products give the multiplicative identity matrix. Thus, B is the multiplicative inverse of A and we can designate B as $A^{-1} = \begin{bmatrix} 5 & 3 \\ 2 & 1 \end{bmatrix}$.   • • •

✓ Check Point **1** Show that B is the multiplicative inverse of A, where

$$A = \begin{bmatrix} 2 & 1 \\ 1 & 1 \end{bmatrix} \quad \text{and} \quad B = \begin{bmatrix} 1 & -1 \\ -1 & 2 \end{bmatrix}.$$

One method for finding the multiplicative inverse of a matrix A is to begin by denoting the elements in A^{-1} with variables. Using the equation $AA^{-1} = I_n$, we can find a value for each element in the multiplicative inverse that is represented by a variable. Example 2 shows how this is done.

EXAMPLE 2 Finding the Multiplicative Inverse of a Matrix

Find the multiplicative inverse of

$$A = \begin{bmatrix} 2 & 1 \\ 5 & 3 \end{bmatrix}.$$

SOLUTION

Let us denote the multiplicative inverse by

$$A^{-1} = \begin{bmatrix} w & x \\ y & z \end{bmatrix}.$$

Because A is a 2×2 matrix, we use the equation $AA^{-1} = I_2$ to find values for $w, x, y,$ and z.

$$\underset{A}{\begin{bmatrix} 2 & 1 \\ 5 & 3 \end{bmatrix}} \underset{A^{-1}}{\begin{bmatrix} w & x \\ y & z \end{bmatrix}} = \underset{I_2}{\begin{bmatrix} 1 & 0 \\ 0 & 1 \end{bmatrix}}$$

$$\begin{bmatrix} 2w + y & 2x + z \\ 5w + 3y & 5x + 3z \end{bmatrix} = \begin{bmatrix} 1 & 0 \\ 0 & 1 \end{bmatrix}$$

Use row-by-column matrix multiplication on the left side of $\begin{bmatrix} 2 & 1 \\ 5 & 3 \end{bmatrix} \begin{bmatrix} w & x \\ y & z \end{bmatrix} = \begin{bmatrix} 1 & 0 \\ 0 & 1 \end{bmatrix}.$

We now equate corresponding elements to obtain the following two systems of linear equations:

$$\begin{cases} 2w + y = 1 \\ 5w + 3y = 0 \end{cases} \quad \text{and} \quad \begin{cases} 2x + z = 0 \\ 5x + 3z = 1. \end{cases}$$

Each of these systems can be solved using the addition method.

$$\begin{cases} 2w + y = 1 \\ 5w + 3y = 0 \end{cases} \quad \begin{array}{l} \text{Multiply by } -3. \\ \text{No change} \end{array} \quad \begin{array}{r} -6w - 3y = -3 \\ 5w + 3y = 0 \\ \hline \text{Add:} \quad -w = -3 \\ w = 3 \\ y = -5 \end{array}$$

Use back-substitution.

$$\begin{cases} 2x + z = 0 \\ 5x + 3z = 1 \end{cases} \quad \begin{array}{l} \text{Multiply by } -3. \\ \text{No change} \end{array} \quad \begin{array}{r} -6x - 3z = 0 \\ 5x + 3z = 1 \\ \hline \text{Add:} \quad -x = 1 \\ x = -1 \\ z = 2 \end{array}$$

Use back-substitution.

Using these values, we have

$$A^{-1} = \begin{bmatrix} w & x \\ y & z \end{bmatrix} = \begin{bmatrix} 3 & -1 \\ -5 & 2 \end{bmatrix}.$$

$\bullet\bullet\bullet$

TECHNOLOGY

You can use a graphing utility to find the inverse of the matrix in Example 2. Enter the matrix and name it A. The screens show A and A^{-1}. Verify that this is correct by showing that

$$AA^{-1} = I_2 \quad \text{and} \quad A^{-1}A = I_2.$$

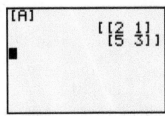

⌀ Check Point **2** Find the multiplicative inverse of $A = \begin{bmatrix} 5 & 7 \\ 2 & 3 \end{bmatrix}.$

Only square matrices of order $n \times n$ have multiplicative inverses, but not every square matrix possesses a multiplicative inverse. For example, suppose that you apply the procedure of Example 2 to $A = \begin{bmatrix} -6 & 4 \\ -3 & 2 \end{bmatrix}$:

This is
A.

This represents
A^{-1}.

This is the
multiplicative
identity matrix.

$$\begin{bmatrix} -6 & 4 \\ -3 & 2 \end{bmatrix} \begin{bmatrix} w & x \\ y & z \end{bmatrix} = \begin{bmatrix} 1 & 0 \\ 0 & 1 \end{bmatrix}.$$

Multiplying matrices on the left and equating corresponding elements results in inconsistent systems with no solutions. There are no values for $w, x, y,$ and z. This shows that matrix A does not have a multiplicative inverse.

A nonsquare matrix, one with a different number of rows than columns, cannot have a multiplicative inverse. If A is an $m \times n$ matrix and B is an $n \times m$ matrix ($n \neq m$), then the products AB and BA are of different orders. This means that they could not be equal to each other, so that AB and BA could not both equal the multiplicative identity matrix.

If a square matrix has a multiplicative inverse, that inverse is unique. This means that the square matrix has no more than one inverse. If a square matrix has a multiplicative inverse, it is said to be **invertible** or **nonsingular**. If a square matrix has no multiplicative inverse, it is called **singular**.

A Quick Method for Finding the Multiplicative Inverse of a 2 × 2 Matrix

The same method used in Example 2 can be used to develop the general form of the multiplicative inverse of a 2 × 2 matrix. The following rule enables us to calculate the multiplicative inverse, if there is one:

> **Multiplicative Inverse of a 2 × 2 Matrix**
>
> If $A = \begin{bmatrix} a & b \\ c & d \end{bmatrix}$, then $A^{-1} = \dfrac{1}{ad - bc} \begin{bmatrix} d & -b \\ -c & a \end{bmatrix}$.
>
> The matrix A is invertible if and only if $ad - bc \neq 0$. If $ad - bc = 0$, then A does not have a multiplicative inverse.

EXAMPLE 3 Using the Quick Method to Find a Multiplicative Inverse

Find the multiplicative inverse of

$$A = \begin{bmatrix} -1 & -2 \\ 3 & 4 \end{bmatrix}.$$

SOLUTION

a b

$$A = \begin{bmatrix} -1 & -2 \\ 3 & 4 \end{bmatrix}$$

This is the given matrix. We've designated the elements a, b, c, and d.

c d

$$A = \begin{bmatrix} \overset{a}{-1} & \overset{b}{-2} \\ \underset{c}{3} & \underset{d}{4} \end{bmatrix}$$

The given matrix (repeated)

$$A^{-1} = \frac{1}{ad - bc}\begin{bmatrix} d & -b \\ -c & a \end{bmatrix}$$

This is the formula for the inverse of $\begin{bmatrix} a & b \\ c & d \end{bmatrix}$.

$$= \frac{1}{(-1)(4) - (-2)(3)}\begin{bmatrix} 4 & -(-2) \\ -3 & -1 \end{bmatrix}$$

Apply the formula with $a = -1$, $b = -2$, $c = 3$, and $d = 4$.

$$= \frac{1}{2}\begin{bmatrix} 4 & 2 \\ -3 & -1 \end{bmatrix}$$

Simplify.

$$= \begin{bmatrix} 2 & 1 \\ -\frac{3}{2} & -\frac{1}{2} \end{bmatrix}$$

Perform the scalar multiplication by multiplying each element in the matrix by $\frac{1}{2}$.

The inverse of $A = \begin{bmatrix} -1 & -2 \\ 3 & 4 \end{bmatrix}$ is $A^{-1} = \begin{bmatrix} 2 & 1 \\ -\frac{3}{2} & -\frac{1}{2} \end{bmatrix}$.

We can verify this result by showing that $AA^{-1} = I_2$ and $A^{-1}A = I_2$.   • • •

✓ Check Point **3** Find the multiplicative inverse of

$$A = \begin{bmatrix} 3 & -2 \\ -1 & 1 \end{bmatrix}.$$

Finding Multiplicative Inverses of $n \times n$ Matrices with n Greater Than 2

To find the multiplicative inverse of a 3×3 invertible matrix, we begin by denoting the elements in the multiplicative inverse with variables. Here is an example:

$$\begin{bmatrix} -1 & -1 & -1 \\ 4 & 5 & 0 \\ 0 & 1 & -3 \end{bmatrix}\begin{bmatrix} x_1 & x_2 & x_3 \\ y_1 & y_2 & y_3 \\ z_1 & z_2 & z_3 \end{bmatrix} = \begin{bmatrix} 1 & 0 & 0 \\ 0 & 1 & 0 \\ 0 & 0 & 1 \end{bmatrix}.$$

This is matrix A whose inverse we wish to find.   This represents A^{-1}.   This is the multiplicative identity matrix, I_3.

We multiply the matrices on the left, using the row-by-column definition of matrix multiplication.

$$\begin{bmatrix} -x_1 - y_1 - z_1 & -x_2 - y_2 - z_2 & -x_3 - y_3 - z_3 \\ 4x_1 + 5y_1 + 0z_1 & 4x_2 + 5y_2 + 0z_2 & 4x_3 + 5y_3 + 0z_3 \\ 0x_1 + 1y_1 - 3z_1 & 0x_2 + 1y_2 - 3z_2 & 0x_3 + 1y_3 - 3z_3 \end{bmatrix} = \begin{bmatrix} 1 & 0 & 0 \\ 0 & 1 & 0 \\ 0 & 0 & 1 \end{bmatrix}$$

We now equate corresponding entries to obtain the following three systems of linear equations:

$$\begin{cases} -x_1 - y_1 - z_1 = 1 \\ 4x_1 + 5y_1 + 0z_1 = 0 \\ 0x_1 + y_1 - 3z_1 = 0 \end{cases} \quad \begin{cases} -x_2 - y_2 - z_2 = 0 \\ 4x_2 + 5y_2 + 0z_2 = 1 \\ 0x_2 + y_2 - 3z_2 = 0 \end{cases} \quad \begin{cases} -x_3 - y_3 - z_3 = 0 \\ 4x_3 + 5y_3 + 0z_3 = 0 \\ 0x_3 + y_3 - 3z_3 = 1. \end{cases}$$

Notice that the variables on the left of the equal signs have the same coefficients in each system. We can use Gauss-Jordan elimination to solve all three systems at once. Form an augmented matrix that contains the coefficients of the three systems to the left of the vertical line and the constants for the systems to the right.

$$\left[\begin{array}{ccc|ccc} -1 & -1 & -1 & 1 & 0 & 0 \\ 4 & 5 & 0 & 0 & 1 & 0 \\ 0 & 1 & -3 & 0 & 0 & 1 \end{array}\right]$$

Coefficients of the three systems   Constants on the right in each of the three systems

To solve all three systems using Gauss-Jordan elimination, we must obtain $\left[\begin{array}{ccc} 1 & 0 & 0 \\ 0 & 1 & 0 \\ 0 & 0 & 1 \end{array}\right]$ to the left of the vertical line. Use matrix row operations, working one column at a time. Obtain 1 in the required position. Then obtain 0s in the other two positions. Using these operations, we obtain the matrix

$$\left[\begin{array}{ccc|ccc} 1 & 0 & 0 & 15 & 4 & -5 \\ 0 & 1 & 0 & -12 & -3 & 4 \\ 0 & 0 & 1 & -4 & -1 & 1 \end{array}\right].$$

This augmented matrix provides the solutions to the three systems of equations. They are given by

$$\left[\begin{array}{ccc|c} 1 & 0 & 0 & 15 \\ 0 & 1 & 0 & -12 \\ 0 & 0 & 1 & -4 \end{array}\right] \quad \begin{array}{l} x_1 = 15 \\ y_1 = -12 \\ z_1 = -4 \end{array}$$

and $\left[\begin{array}{ccc|c} 1 & 0 & 0 & 4 \\ 0 & 1 & 0 & -3 \\ 0 & 0 & 1 & -1 \end{array}\right]$ $\begin{array}{l} x_2 = 4 \\ y_2 = -3 \\ z_2 = -1 \end{array}$ and $\left[\begin{array}{ccc|c} 1 & 0 & 0 & -5 \\ 0 & 1 & 0 & 4 \\ 0 & 0 & 1 & 1 \end{array}\right]$ $\begin{array}{l} x_3 = -5 \\ y_3 = 4 \\ z_3 = 1. \end{array}$

Using the preceding nine values, the inverse matrix is

$$\left[\begin{array}{ccc} x_1 & x_2 & x_3 \\ y_1 & y_2 & y_3 \\ z_1 & z_2 & z_3 \end{array}\right] = \left[\begin{array}{ccc} 15 & 4 & -5 \\ -12 & -3 & 4 \\ -4 & -1 & 1 \end{array}\right].$$

Take a second look at the matrix obtained at the point where Gauss-Jordan elimination was completed. This matrix is shown, again, below. Notice that the 3×3 matrix to the right of the vertical bar is the multiplicative inverse of A. Also notice that the multiplicative identity matrix, I_3 is the matrix that appears to the left of the vertical bar.

$$\left[\begin{array}{ccc|ccc} 1 & 0 & 0 & 15 & 4 & -5 \\ 0 & 1 & 0 & -12 & -3 & 4 \\ 0 & 0 & 1 & -4 & -1 & 1 \end{array}\right]$$

This is the multiplicative identity, I_3.   This is the multiplicative inverse of A.

The observations in the voice balloons and the procedures followed above give us a general method for finding the multiplicative inverse of an invertible matrix. This method is given at the top of the next page.

GREAT QUESTION!

Should I use the procedure in the box for finding the multiplicative inverse of a 2 × 2 matrix?

No. Because we have a quick method for finding the multiplicative inverse of a 2 × 2 matrix, the procedure on the right is recommended for matrices of order 3 × 3 or greater when a graphing utility is not being used.

Procedure for Finding the Multiplicative Inverse of an Invertible Matrix

To find A^{-1} for any $n \times n$ matrix A for which A^{-1} exists,

1. Form the augmented matrix $[A \,|\, I_n]$, where I_n is the multiplicative identity matrix of the same order as the given matrix A.
2. Perform row operations on $[A \,|\, I_n]$ to obtain a matrix of the form $[I_n \,|\, B]$. This is equivalent to using Gauss-Jordan elimination to change A into the identity matrix.
3. Matrix B is A^{-1}.
4. Verify the result by showing that $AA^{-1} = I_n$ and $A^{-1}A = I_n$.

EXAMPLE 4 Finding the Multiplicative Inverse of a 3 × 3 Matrix

Find the multiplicative inverse of

$$A = \begin{bmatrix} 1 & -1 & 1 \\ 0 & -2 & 1 \\ -2 & -3 & 0 \end{bmatrix}.$$

SOLUTION

Step 1 Form the augmented matrix $[A \,|\, I_3]$.

$$\left[\begin{array}{ccc|ccc} 1 & -1 & 1 & 1 & 0 & 0 \\ 0 & -2 & 1 & 0 & 1 & 0 \\ -2 & -3 & 0 & 0 & 0 & 1 \end{array} \right]$$

This is matrix A.

This is I_3, the multiplicative identity matrix, with 1s down the main diagonal and 0s elsewhere.

Step 2 Perform row operations on $[A \,|\, I_3]$ to obtain a matrix of the form $[I_3 \,|\, B]$. To the left of the vertical dividing line, we want 1s down the diagonal from upper left to lower right and 0s elsewhere.

$$\left[\begin{array}{ccc|ccc} 1 & -1 & 1 & 1 & 0 & 0 \\ 0 & -2 & 1 & 0 & 1 & 0 \\ -2 & -3 & 0 & 0 & 0 & 1 \end{array} \right] \xrightarrow[\text{by } 2R_1 + R_3.]{\text{Replace row 3}} \left[\begin{array}{ccc|ccc} 1 & -1 & 1 & 1 & 0 & 0 \\ 0 & -2 & 1 & 0 & 1 & 0 \\ 0 & -5 & 2 & 2 & 0 & 1 \end{array} \right] \xrightarrow{-\frac{1}{2}R_2}$$

$$\left[\begin{array}{ccc|ccc} 1 & -1 & 1 & 1 & 0 & 0 \\ 0 & 1 & -\frac{1}{2} & 0 & -\frac{1}{2} & 0 \\ 0 & -5 & 2 & 2 & 0 & 1 \end{array} \right] \xrightarrow[\text{Replace row 3 by } 5R_2 + R_3.]{\text{Replace row 1 by } 1R_2 + R_1.} \left[\begin{array}{ccc|ccc} 1 & 0 & \frac{1}{2} & 1 & -\frac{1}{2} & 0 \\ 0 & 1 & -\frac{1}{2} & 0 & -\frac{1}{2} & 0 \\ 0 & 0 & -\frac{1}{2} & 2 & -\frac{5}{2} & 1 \end{array} \right] \xrightarrow{-2R_3}$$

$$\left[\begin{array}{ccc|ccc} 1 & 0 & \frac{1}{2} & 1 & -\frac{1}{2} & 0 \\ 0 & 1 & -\frac{1}{2} & 0 & -\frac{1}{2} & 0 \\ 0 & 0 & 1 & -4 & 5 & -2 \end{array} \right] \xrightarrow[\text{Replace row 2 by } \frac{1}{2}R_3 + R_2.]{\text{Replace row 1 by } -\frac{1}{2}R_3 + R_1.} \left[\begin{array}{ccc|ccc} 1 & 0 & 0 & 3 & -3 & 1 \\ 0 & 1 & 0 & -2 & 2 & -1 \\ 0 & 0 & 1 & -4 & 5 & -2 \end{array} \right]$$

This is the multiplicative identity, I_3.

This is the multiplicative inverse of A.

TECHNOLOGY

We can use a graphing utility to verify the inverse matrix we found in Example 4. Enter the elements in matrix A and press $\boxed{x^{-1}}$ to display A^{-1}.

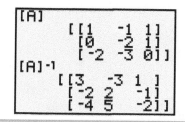

TECHNOLOGY

The matrix

$$A = \begin{bmatrix} 4 & 6 \\ 2 & 3 \end{bmatrix} = \begin{bmatrix} a & b \\ c & d \end{bmatrix}$$

has no multiplicative inverse because

$$ad - bc = 4 \cdot 3 - 6 \cdot 2$$
$$= 12 - 12 = 0.$$

When we try to find the inverse with a graphing utility, an ERROR message occurs, indicating the matrix is singular.

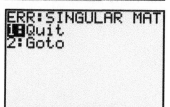

Step 3 Matrix B is A^{-1}. The last matrix shown at the bottom of the previous page is in the form $[I_3 \mid B]$. The multiplicative identity matrix is on the left of the vertical bar. Matrix B, the multiplicative inverse of A, is on the right. Thus, the multiplicative inverse of A is

$$A^{-1} = \begin{bmatrix} 3 & -3 & 1 \\ -2 & 2 & -1 \\ -4 & 5 & -2 \end{bmatrix}.$$

Step 4 Verify the result by showing that $AA^{-1} = I_3$ and $A^{-1}A = I_3$. Try confirming the result by multiplying A and A^{-1} to obtain I_3. Do you obtain I_3 if you reverse the order of the multiplication?　• • •

We have seen that not all square matrices have multiplicative inverses. If the row operations in step 2 result in all zeros in a row or column to the left of the vertical line, the given matrix does not have a multiplicative inverse.

✓ Check Point **4** Find the multiplicative inverse of

$$A = \begin{bmatrix} 1 & 0 & 2 \\ -1 & 2 & 3 \\ 1 & -1 & 0 \end{bmatrix}.$$

Summary: Finding Multiplicative Inverses for Invertible Matrices

Use a graphing utility with matrix capabilities, or

a. If the matrix is 2×2: The inverse of $A = \begin{bmatrix} a & b \\ c & d \end{bmatrix}$ is

$$A^{-1} = \frac{1}{ad - bc} \begin{bmatrix} d & -b \\ -c & a \end{bmatrix}.$$

b. If the matrix A is $n \times n$ where $n > 2$: Use the procedure on page 634. Form $[A \mid I_n]$ and use row transformations to obtain $[I_n \mid B]$. Then $A^{-1} = B$.

Solving Systems of Equations Using Multiplicative Inverses of Matrices

Matrix multiplication can be used to represent a system of linear equations.

Linear System

$$\begin{cases} a_1 x + b_1 y + c_1 z = d_1 \\ a_2 x + b_2 y + c_2 z = d_2 \\ a_3 x + b_3 y + c_3 z = d_3 \end{cases}$$

Matrix Form of the System

$$\begin{bmatrix} a_1 & b_1 & c_1 \\ a_2 & b_2 & c_2 \\ a_3 & b_3 & c_3 \end{bmatrix} \begin{bmatrix} x \\ y \\ z \end{bmatrix} = \begin{bmatrix} d_1 \\ d_2 \\ d_3 \end{bmatrix}$$

The matrix contains the system's coefficients.　The matrix contains the system's variables.　The matrix contains the system's constants.

You can work with the matrix form of the system and obtain the form of the linear system on the left. To do so, perform the matrix multiplication on the left side of the matrix equation. Then equate the corresponding elements.

The matrix equation

$$\begin{bmatrix} a_1 & b_1 & c_1 \\ a_2 & b_2 & c_2 \\ a_3 & b_3 & c_3 \end{bmatrix} \begin{bmatrix} x \\ y \\ z \end{bmatrix} = \begin{bmatrix} d_1 \\ d_2 \\ d_3 \end{bmatrix}$$

$$\downarrow \qquad \downarrow \quad \downarrow \quad \downarrow$$
$$A \qquad X \ = \ B$$

is abbreviated as $AX = B$, where A is the **coefficient matrix** of the system, and X and B are matrices containing one column, called **column matrices**. The matrix B is called the **constant matrix**.

Here is a specific example of a linear system and its matrix form:

Linear System

$$\begin{cases} x - y + z = 2 \\ -2y + z = 2 \\ -2x - 3y = \frac{1}{2} \end{cases}$$

Matrix Form

Coefficients

$$\begin{bmatrix} 1 & -1 & 1 \\ 0 & -2 & 1 \\ -2 & -3 & 0 \end{bmatrix} \begin{bmatrix} x \\ y \\ z \end{bmatrix} = \begin{bmatrix} 2 \\ 2 \\ \frac{1}{2} \end{bmatrix}$$ Constants

A, the coefficient matrix X B, the constant matrix

The matrix equation $AX = B$ can be solved using A^{-1} if it exists.

$AX = B$ This is the matrix equation.

$A^{-1}AX = A^{-1}B$ Multiply both sides by A^{-1}. Because matrix multiplication is not commutative, put A^{-1} in the same left position on both sides.

$I_nX = A^{-1}B$ The multiplicative inverse property tells us that $A^{-1}A = I_n$.

$X = A^{-1}B$ Because I_n is the multiplicative identity, $I_nX = X$.

We see that if $AX = B$, then $X = A^{-1}B$.

② Use inverses to solve matrix equations.

Solving a System Using A^{-1}

If $AX = B$ has a unique solution, then $X = A^{-1}B$. To solve a linear system of equations, multiply A^{-1} and B to find X.

EXAMPLE 5   Using the Inverse of a Matrix to Solve a System

Solve the system by using A^{-1}, the inverse of the coefficient matrix:

$$\begin{cases} x - y + z = 2 \\ -2y + z = 2 \\ -2x - 3y = \frac{1}{2}. \end{cases}$$

TECHNOLOGY

We can use a graphing utility to solve a linear system with a unique solution by entering the elements in A, the coefficient matrix, and B, the column matrix. Then find the product of A^{-1} and B. The screen below verifies our solution in Example 5.

```
[A]⁻¹*[B]
              [[.5 ]
               [-.5]
               [1  ]]
```

This verifies that $x = .5$, or $\frac{1}{2}$, $y = -.5$, or $-\frac{1}{2}$, and $z = 1$.

SOLUTION

The linear system can be written as

$$\underbrace{\begin{bmatrix} 1 & -1 & 1 \\ 0 & -2 & 1 \\ -2 & -3 & 0 \end{bmatrix}}_{A} \underbrace{\begin{bmatrix} x \\ y \\ z \end{bmatrix}}_{X} = \underbrace{\begin{bmatrix} 2 \\ 2 \\ \frac{1}{2} \end{bmatrix}}_{B}.$$

The solution is given by $X = A^{-1}B$. Consequently, we must find A^{-1}. We found the inverse of matrix A in Example 4. Using this result,

$$X = A^{-1}B = \begin{bmatrix} 3 & -3 & 1 \\ -2 & 2 & -1 \\ -4 & 5 & -2 \end{bmatrix} \begin{bmatrix} 2 \\ 2 \\ \frac{1}{2} \end{bmatrix} = \begin{bmatrix} 3 \cdot 2 + (-3) \cdot 2 + 1 \cdot \frac{1}{2} \\ -2 \cdot 2 + 2 \cdot 2 + (-1) \cdot \frac{1}{2} \\ -4 \cdot 2 + 5 \cdot 2 + (-2) \cdot \frac{1}{2} \end{bmatrix} = \begin{bmatrix} \frac{1}{2} \\ -\frac{1}{2} \\ 1 \end{bmatrix}.$$

Thus, $x = \frac{1}{2}$, $y = -\frac{1}{2}$, and $z = 1$. The solution set is $\{(\frac{1}{2}, -\frac{1}{2}, 1)\}$.   • • •

⊘ Check Point **5** Solve the system by using A^{-1}, the inverse of the coefficient matrix that you found in Check Point 4:

$$\begin{cases} x + 2z = 6 \\ -x + 2y + 3z = -5 \\ x - y = 6. \end{cases}$$

③ Encode and decode messages.

Applications of Matrix Inverses to Coding

A **cryptogram** is a message written so that no one other than the intended recipient can understand it. To encode a message, we begin by assigning a number to each letter in the alphabet: $A = 1, B = 2, C = 3, \ldots, Z = 26$, and a space $= 0$. For example, the numerical equivalent of the word MATH is $13, 1, 20, 8$. The numerical equivalent of the message is then converted into a matrix. Finally, an invertible matrix can be used to convert the message into code. The multiplicative inverse of this matrix can be used to decode the message.

> ### Encoding a Word or Message
> 1. Express the word or message numerically.
> 2. List the numbers in step 1 by columns and form a square matrix. If you do not have enough numbers to form a square matrix, put zeros in any remaining spaces in the last column.
> 3. Select any square invertible matrix, called the **coding matrix**, the same size as the matrix in step 2. Multiply the coding matrix by the square matrix that expresses the message numerically. The resulting matrix is the **coded matrix**.
> 4. Use the numbers, by columns, from the coded matrix in step 3 to write the encoded message.

EXAMPLE 6   Encoding a Word

Use matrices to encode the word MATH.

SOLUTION

Step 1 Express the word numerically. As shown previously, the numerical equivalent of MATH is $13, 1, 20, 8$.

Step 2 List the numbers in step 1 by columns and form a square matrix. The 2×2 matrix for the numerical equivalent of MATH, $13, 1, 20, 8$, is

$$\begin{bmatrix} 13 & 20 \\ 1 & 8 \end{bmatrix}.$$

Step 3 Multiply the matrix in step 2 by a square invertible matrix. We will use $\begin{bmatrix} -2 & -3 \\ 3 & 4 \end{bmatrix}$ as the coding matrix.

$$\begin{bmatrix} -2 & -3 \\ 3 & 4 \end{bmatrix} \begin{bmatrix} 13 & 20 \\ 1 & 8 \end{bmatrix} = \begin{bmatrix} -2(13) - 3(1) & -2(20) - 3(8) \\ 3(13) + 4(1) & 3(20) + 4(8) \end{bmatrix}$$

Coding matrix   Numerical representation of MATH

$$= \begin{bmatrix} -29 & -64 \\ 43 & 92 \end{bmatrix}$$

Coded matrix

Step 4 Use the numbers, by columns, from the coded matrix in step 3 to write the encoded message. The encoded message is $-29, 43, -64, 92$.   • • •

⊘ Check Point **6** Use the coding matrix in Example 6, $\begin{bmatrix} -2 & -3 \\ 3 & 4 \end{bmatrix}$, to encode the word BASE.

The inverse of a coding matrix can be used to decode a word or message that was encoded.

Decoding a Word or Message That Was Encoded

1. Find the multiplicative inverse of the coding matrix.
2. Multiply the multiplicative inverse of the coding matrix and the coded matrix.
3. Express the numbers, by columns, from the matrix in step 2 as letters.

EXAMPLE 7   Decoding a Word

Decode $-29, 43, -64, 92$ from Example 6.

SOLUTION

Step 1   Find the inverse of the coding matrix. The coding matrix in Example 6 was $\begin{bmatrix} -2 & -3 \\ 3 & 4 \end{bmatrix}$. We use the formula for the multiplicative inverse of a 2×2 matrix to find the multiplicative inverse of this matrix. It is $\begin{bmatrix} 4 & 3 \\ -3 & -2 \end{bmatrix}$.

Step 2   Multiply the multiplicative inverse of the coding matrix and the coded matrix.

$$\underbrace{\begin{bmatrix} 4 & 3 \\ -3 & -2 \end{bmatrix}}_{\substack{\text{Multiplicative inverse} \\ \text{of the coding matrix}}} \underbrace{\begin{bmatrix} -29 & -64 \\ 43 & 92 \end{bmatrix}}_{\substack{\text{Coded} \\ \text{matrix}}} = \begin{bmatrix} 4(-29) + 3(43) & 4(-64) + 3(92) \\ -3(-29) - 2(43) & -3(-64) - 2(92) \end{bmatrix}$$

$$= \begin{bmatrix} 13 & 20 \\ 1 & 8 \end{bmatrix}$$

Step 3   Express the numbers, by columns, from the matrix in step 2 as letters. The numbers are $13, 1, 20$, and 8. Using letters, the decoded message is MATH.   • • •

 Check Point **7** Decode the word that you encoded in Check Point 6.

Decoding is simple for an authorized receiver who knows the coding matrix. Because any invertible matrix can be used for the coding matrix, decoding a cryptogram for an unauthorized receiver who does not know this matrix is extremely difficult.

CONCEPT AND VOCABULARY CHECK

Fill in each blank so that the resulting statement is true.

1. The multiplicative identity matrix of order 2 is
$$I_2 = \underline{\quad\quad}.$$

2. The multiplicative identity matrix of order 3 is
$$I_3 = \underline{\quad\quad}.$$

3. For $n \times n$ matrices A and B, if $AB = I_n$ and $BA = I_n$, then B is called the _____ of A.

4. True or false: Only square matrices have multiplicative inverses. _____

5. If $A = \begin{bmatrix} a & b \\ c & d \end{bmatrix}$, the matrix A is invertible if and only if _____.

6. If a square matrix does not have a multiplicative inverse, it is called _____.

7. True or false: $A = \begin{bmatrix} 3 & 2 \\ 9 & 6 \end{bmatrix}$ is invertible. _____

8. To find the multiplicative inverse of an invertible matrix A, we perform row operations on $[A \,|\, I_n]$ to obtain a matrix of the form $[I_n \,|\, B]$, where $B = $ _____.

9. If the matrix equation $AX = B$ has a unique solution, then we can solve the equation using $X = $ _____.

EXERCISE SET 6.4

Practice Exercises

In Exercises 1–12, find the products AB and BA to determine whether B is the multiplicative inverse of A.

1. $A = \begin{bmatrix} 4 & -3 \\ -5 & 4 \end{bmatrix}$, $B = \begin{bmatrix} 4 & 3 \\ 5 & 4 \end{bmatrix}$

2. $A = \begin{bmatrix} -2 & -1 \\ -1 & 1 \end{bmatrix}$, $B = \begin{bmatrix} 1 & 1 \\ 1 & 2 \end{bmatrix}$

3. $A = \begin{bmatrix} -4 & 0 \\ 1 & 3 \end{bmatrix}$, $B = \begin{bmatrix} -2 & 4 \\ 0 & 1 \end{bmatrix}$

4. $A = \begin{bmatrix} -2 & 4 \\ 1 & -2 \end{bmatrix}$, $B = \begin{bmatrix} 1 & 2 \\ -1 & -2 \end{bmatrix}$

5. $A = \begin{bmatrix} -2 & 1 \\ \frac{3}{2} & -\frac{1}{2} \end{bmatrix}$, $B = \begin{bmatrix} 1 & 2 \\ 3 & 4 \end{bmatrix}$

6. $A = \begin{bmatrix} 4 & 5 \\ 2 & 3 \end{bmatrix}$, $B = \begin{bmatrix} \frac{3}{2} & -\frac{5}{2} \\ -1 & 2 \end{bmatrix}$

7. $A = \begin{bmatrix} 0 & 1 & 0 \\ 0 & 0 & 1 \\ 1 & 0 & 0 \end{bmatrix}$, $B = \begin{bmatrix} 0 & 0 & 1 \\ 1 & 0 & 0 \\ 0 & 1 & 0 \end{bmatrix}$

8. $A = \begin{bmatrix} -2 & 1 & -1 \\ -5 & 2 & -1 \\ 3 & -1 & 1 \end{bmatrix}$, $B = \begin{bmatrix} 1 & 0 & 1 \\ 2 & 1 & 3 \\ -1 & 1 & 1 \end{bmatrix}$

9. $A = \begin{bmatrix} 1 & 2 & 3 \\ 1 & 3 & 4 \\ 1 & 4 & 3 \end{bmatrix}$, $B = \begin{bmatrix} \frac{7}{2} & -3 & \frac{1}{2} \\ -\frac{1}{2} & 0 & \frac{1}{2} \\ -\frac{1}{2} & 1 & -\frac{1}{2} \end{bmatrix}$

10. $A = \begin{bmatrix} 0 & 2 & 0 \\ 3 & 3 & 2 \\ 2 & 5 & 1 \end{bmatrix}$, $B = \begin{bmatrix} -3.5 & -1 & 2 \\ 0.5 & 0 & 0 \\ 4.5 & 2 & -3 \end{bmatrix}$

11. $A = \begin{bmatrix} 0 & 0 & -2 & 1 \\ -1 & 0 & 1 & 1 \\ 0 & 1 & -1 & 0 \\ 1 & 0 & 0 & -1 \end{bmatrix}$, $B = \begin{bmatrix} 1 & 2 & 0 & 3 \\ 0 & 1 & 1 & 1 \\ 0 & 1 & 0 & 1 \\ 1 & 2 & 0 & 2 \end{bmatrix}$

12. $A = \begin{bmatrix} 1 & -2 & 1 & 0 \\ 0 & 1 & -2 & 1 \\ 0 & 0 & 1 & -2 \\ 0 & 0 & 0 & 1 \end{bmatrix}$, $B = \begin{bmatrix} 1 & 2 & 3 & 4 \\ 0 & 1 & 2 & 3 \\ 0 & 0 & 1 & 2 \\ 0 & 0 & 0 & 1 \end{bmatrix}$

In Exercises 13–18, use the fact that if $A = \begin{bmatrix} a & b \\ c & d \end{bmatrix}$, then $A^{-1} = \frac{1}{ad - bc} \begin{bmatrix} d & -b \\ -c & a \end{bmatrix}$ to find the inverse of each matrix, if possible. Check that $AA^{-1} = I_2$ and $A^{-1}A = I_2$.

13. $A = \begin{bmatrix} 2 & 3 \\ -1 & 2 \end{bmatrix}$

14. $A = \begin{bmatrix} 0 & 3 \\ 4 & -2 \end{bmatrix}$

15. $A = \begin{bmatrix} 3 & -1 \\ -4 & 2 \end{bmatrix}$

16. $A = \begin{bmatrix} 2 & -6 \\ 1 & -2 \end{bmatrix}$

17. $A = \begin{bmatrix} 10 & -2 \\ -5 & 1 \end{bmatrix}$

18. $A = \begin{bmatrix} 6 & -3 \\ -2 & 1 \end{bmatrix}$

In Exercises 19–28, find A^{-1} by forming $[A\,|\,I]$ and then using row operations to obtain $[I\,|\,B]$, where $A^{-1} = [B]$. Check that $AA^{-1} = I$ and $A^{-1}A = I$.

19. $A = \begin{bmatrix} 2 & 0 & 0 \\ 0 & 4 & 0 \\ 0 & 0 & 6 \end{bmatrix}$

20. $A = \begin{bmatrix} 3 & 0 & 0 \\ 0 & 6 & 0 \\ 0 & 0 & 9 \end{bmatrix}$

21. $A = \begin{bmatrix} 1 & 2 & -1 \\ -2 & 0 & 1 \\ 1 & -1 & 0 \end{bmatrix}$

22. $A = \begin{bmatrix} 1 & -1 & 1 \\ 0 & 2 & -1 \\ 2 & 3 & 0 \end{bmatrix}$

23. $A = \begin{bmatrix} 2 & 2 & -1 \\ 0 & 3 & -1 \\ -1 & -2 & 1 \end{bmatrix}$

24. $A = \begin{bmatrix} 2 & 4 & -4 \\ 1 & 3 & -4 \\ 2 & 4 & -3 \end{bmatrix}$

25. $A = \begin{bmatrix} 5 & 0 & 2 \\ 2 & 2 & 1 \\ -3 & 1 & -1 \end{bmatrix}$

26. $A = \begin{bmatrix} 3 & 2 & 6 \\ 1 & 1 & 2 \\ 2 & 2 & 5 \end{bmatrix}$

27. $A = \begin{bmatrix} 1 & 0 & 0 & 0 \\ 0 & -1 & 0 & 0 \\ 0 & 0 & 3 & 0 \\ 1 & 0 & 0 & 1 \end{bmatrix}$

28. $A = \begin{bmatrix} 2 & 0 & 0 & 1 \\ 0 & 1 & 0 & 0 \\ 0 & 0 & -1 & 0 \\ 0 & 0 & 0 & 2 \end{bmatrix}$

In Exercises 29–32, write each linear system as a matrix equation in the form $AX = B$, where A is the coefficient matrix and B is the constant matrix.

29. $\begin{cases} 6x + 5y = 13 \\ 5x + 4y = 10 \end{cases}$

30. $\begin{cases} 7x + 5y = 23 \\ 3x + 2y = 10 \end{cases}$

31. $\begin{cases} x + 3y + 4z = -3 \\ x + 2y + 3z = -2 \\ x + 4y + 3z = -6 \end{cases}$

32. $\begin{cases} x + 4y - z = 3 \\ x + 3y - 2z = 5 \\ 2x + 7y - 5z = 12 \end{cases}$

In Exercises 33–36, write each matrix equation as a system of linear equations without matrices.

33. $\begin{bmatrix} 4 & -7 \\ 2 & -3 \end{bmatrix} \begin{bmatrix} x \\ y \end{bmatrix} = \begin{bmatrix} -3 \\ 1 \end{bmatrix}$

34. $\begin{bmatrix} 3 & 0 \\ -3 & 1 \end{bmatrix} \begin{bmatrix} x \\ y \end{bmatrix} = \begin{bmatrix} 6 \\ -7 \end{bmatrix}$

35. $\begin{bmatrix} 2 & 0 & -1 \\ 0 & 3 & 0 \\ 1 & 1 & 0 \end{bmatrix} \begin{bmatrix} x \\ y \\ z \end{bmatrix} = \begin{bmatrix} 6 \\ 9 \\ 5 \end{bmatrix}$

36. $\begin{bmatrix} -1 & 0 & 1 \\ 0 & -1 & 0 \\ 0 & 1 & 1 \end{bmatrix} \begin{bmatrix} x \\ y \\ z \end{bmatrix} = \begin{bmatrix} -4 \\ 2 \\ 4 \end{bmatrix}$

In Exercises 37–42,

a. *Write each linear system as a matrix equation in the form $AX = B$.*

b. *Solve the system using the inverse that is given for the coefficient matrix.*

37. $\begin{cases} 2x + 6y + 6z = 8 \\ 2x + 7y + 6z = 10 \\ 2x + 7y + 7z = 9 \end{cases}$
The inverse of $\begin{bmatrix} 2 & 6 & 6 \\ 2 & 7 & 6 \\ 2 & 7 & 7 \end{bmatrix}$ is $\begin{bmatrix} \frac{7}{2} & 0 & -3 \\ -1 & 1 & 0 \\ 0 & -1 & 1 \end{bmatrix}$.

The inverse of

38. $\begin{cases} x + 2y + 5z = 2 \\ 2x + 3y + 8z = 3 \\ -x + y + 2z = 3 \end{cases}$ $\begin{bmatrix} 1 & 2 & 5 \\ 2 & 3 & 8 \\ -1 & 1 & 2 \end{bmatrix}$ is $\begin{bmatrix} 2 & -1 & -1 \\ 12 & -7 & -2 \\ -5 & 3 & 1 \end{bmatrix}$.

The inverse of

39. $\begin{cases} x - y + z = 8 \\ 2y - z = -7 \\ 2x + 3y = 1 \end{cases}$ $\begin{bmatrix} 1 & -1 & 1 \\ 0 & 2 & -1 \\ 2 & 3 & 0 \end{bmatrix}$ is $\begin{bmatrix} 3 & 3 & -1 \\ -2 & -2 & 1 \\ -4 & -5 & 2 \end{bmatrix}$.

The inverse of

40. $\begin{cases} x - 6y + 3z = 11 \\ 2x - 7y + 3z = 14 \\ 4x - 12y + 5z = 25 \end{cases}$ $\begin{bmatrix} 1 & -6 & 3 \\ 2 & -7 & 3 \\ 4 & -12 & 5 \end{bmatrix}$ is $\begin{bmatrix} 1 & -6 & 3 \\ 2 & -7 & 3 \\ 4 & -12 & 5 \end{bmatrix}$.

41. $\begin{cases} w - x + 2y = -3 \\ x - y + z = 4 \\ -w + x - y + 2z = 2 \\ -x + y - 2z = -4 \end{cases}$

The inverse of

$\begin{bmatrix} 1 & -1 & 2 & 0 \\ 0 & 1 & -1 & 1 \\ -1 & 1 & -1 & 2 \\ 0 & -1 & 1 & -2 \end{bmatrix}$ is $\begin{bmatrix} 0 & 0 & -1 & -1 \\ 1 & 4 & 1 & 3 \\ 1 & 2 & 1 & 2 \\ 0 & -1 & 0 & -1 \end{bmatrix}$.

42. $\begin{cases} 2w + y + z = 6 \\ 3w + z = 9 \\ -w + x - 2y + z = 4 \\ 4w - x + y = 6 \end{cases}$

The inverse of

$\begin{bmatrix} 2 & 0 & 1 & 1 \\ 3 & 0 & 0 & 1 \\ -1 & 1 & -2 & 1 \\ 4 & -1 & 1 & 0 \end{bmatrix}$ is $\begin{bmatrix} -1 & 2 & -1 & -1 \\ -4 & 9 & -5 & -6 \\ 0 & 1 & -1 & -1 \\ 3 & -5 & 3 & 3 \end{bmatrix}$.

Practice Plus

In Exercises 43–44, find A^{-1} and check.

43. $A = \begin{bmatrix} e^x & e^{3x} \\ -e^{3x} & e^{5x} \end{bmatrix}$

44. $A = \begin{bmatrix} e^{2x} & -e^x \\ e^{3x} & e^{2x} \end{bmatrix}$

In Exercises 45–46, if I is the multiplicative identity matrix of order 2, find $(I - A)^{-1}$ for the given matrix A.

45. $\begin{bmatrix} 8 & -5 \\ -3 & 2 \end{bmatrix}$

46. $\begin{bmatrix} 7 & -5 \\ -4 & 3 \end{bmatrix}$

In Exercises 47–48, find $(AB)^{-1}$, $A^{-1}B^{-1}$, and $B^{-1}A^{-1}$. What do you observe?

47. $A = \begin{bmatrix} 2 & 1 \\ 3 & 1 \end{bmatrix}$ $B = \begin{bmatrix} 4 & 7 \\ 1 & 2 \end{bmatrix}$

48. $A = \begin{bmatrix} 2 & -9 \\ 1 & -4 \end{bmatrix}$ $B = \begin{bmatrix} 9 & 5 \\ 7 & 4 \end{bmatrix}$

49. Prove the following statement:

If $A = \begin{bmatrix} a & 0 & 0 \\ 0 & b & 0 \\ 0 & 0 & c \end{bmatrix}$, $a \neq 0, b \neq 0, c \neq 0$,

then $A^{-1} = \begin{bmatrix} \frac{1}{a} & 0 & 0 \\ 0 & \frac{1}{b} & 0 \\ 0 & 0 & \frac{1}{c} \end{bmatrix}$.

50. Prove the following statement:

If $A = \begin{bmatrix} a & b \\ c & d \end{bmatrix}$ and $ad - bc \neq 0$,

then $A^{-1} = \dfrac{1}{ad - bc} \begin{bmatrix} d & -b \\ -c & a \end{bmatrix}$.

(*Hint:* Use the method of Example 2 on page 630.)

Application Exercises

In Exercises 51–52, use the coding matrix

$$A = \begin{bmatrix} 4 & -1 \\ -3 & 1 \end{bmatrix} \text{ and its inverse } A^{-1} = \begin{bmatrix} 1 & 1 \\ 3 & 4 \end{bmatrix}$$

to encode and then decode the given message.

51. HELP

52. LOVE

In Exercises 53–54, use the coding matrix

$$A = \begin{bmatrix} 1 & -1 & 0 \\ 3 & 0 & 2 \\ -1 & 0 & -1 \end{bmatrix} \text{ and its inverse}$$

$$A^{-1} = \begin{bmatrix} 0 & 1 & 2 \\ -1 & 1 & 2 \\ 0 & -1 & -3 \end{bmatrix} \text{ to write a cryptogram for each}$$

message. Check your result by decoding the cryptogram.

53. S   E   N   D   _   C   A   S   H
   19   5   14   4   0   3   1   19   8

   Use $\begin{bmatrix} 19 & 4 & 1 \\ 5 & 0 & 19 \\ 14 & 3 & 8 \end{bmatrix}$.

54. S   T   A   Y   _   W   E   L   L
   19   20   1   25   0   23   5   12   12

   Use $\begin{bmatrix} 19 & 25 & 5 \\ 20 & 0 & 12 \\ 1 & 23 & 12 \end{bmatrix}$.

Writing in Mathematics

55. What is the multiplicative identity matrix?

56. If you are given two matrices, A and B, explain how to determine if B is the multiplicative inverse of A.

57. Explain why a matrix that does not have the same number of rows and columns cannot have a multiplicative inverse.

58. Explain how to find the multiplicative inverse for a 2×2 invertible matrix.

59. Explain how to find the multiplicative inverse for a 3×3 invertible matrix.

60. Explain how to write a linear system of three equations in three variables as a matrix equation.

61. Explain how to solve the matrix equation $AX = B$.

62. What is a cryptogram?

63. It's January 1, and you've written down your major goal for the year. You do not want those closest to you to see what you've written in case you do not accomplish your objective. Consequently, you decide to use a coding matrix to encode your goal. Explain how this can be accomplished.

64. A year has passed since Exercise 63. (Time flies when you're solving exercises in algebra books.) It's been a terrific year and so many wonderful things have happened that you can't remember your goal from a year ago. You consult your personal journal and you find the encoded message and the coding matrix. How can you use these to find your original goal?

Technology Exercises

In Exercises 65–70, use a graphing utility to find the multiplicative inverse of each matrix. Check that the displayed inverse is correct.

65. $\begin{bmatrix} 3 & -1 \\ -2 & 1 \end{bmatrix}$

66. $\begin{bmatrix} -4 & 1 \\ 6 & -2 \end{bmatrix}$

67. $\begin{bmatrix} -2 & 1 & -1 \\ -5 & 2 & -1 \\ 3 & -1 & 1 \end{bmatrix}$

68. $\begin{bmatrix} 1 & 1 & -1 \\ -3 & 2 & -1 \\ 3 & -3 & 2 \end{bmatrix}$

69. $\begin{bmatrix} 7 & -3 & 0 & 2 \\ -2 & 1 & 0 & -1 \\ 4 & 0 & 1 & -2 \\ -1 & 1 & 0 & -1 \end{bmatrix}$

70. $\begin{bmatrix} 1 & 2 & 0 & 0 \\ 0 & 0 & 1 & 0 \\ 1 & 3 & 0 & 1 \\ 4 & 0 & 0 & 2 \end{bmatrix}$

In Exercises 71–76, write each system in the form $AX = B$. Then solve the system by entering A and B into your graphing utility and computing $A^{-1}B$.

71. $\begin{cases} x - y + z = -6 \\ 4x + 2y + z = 9 \\ 4x - 2y + z = -3 \end{cases}$

72. $\begin{cases} y + 2z = 0 \\ -x + y = 1 \\ 2x - y + z = -1 \end{cases}$

73. $\begin{cases} 3x - 2y + z = -2 \\ 4x - 5y + 3z = -9 \\ 2x - y + 5z = -5 \end{cases}$

74. $\begin{cases} x - y = 1 \\ 6x + y + 20z = 14 \\ y + 3z = 1 \end{cases}$

75. $\begin{cases} v - 3x + z = -3 \\ w + y = -1 \\ x + z = 7 \\ v + w - x + 4y = -8 \\ v + w + x + y + z = 8 \end{cases}$

76. $\begin{cases} w + x + y + z = 4 \\ w + 3x - 2y + 2z = 7 \\ 2w + 2x + y + z = 3 \\ w - x + 2y + 3z = 5 \end{cases}$

In Exercises 77–78, use a coding matrix A of your choice. Use a graphing utility to find the multiplicative inverse of your coding matrix. Write a cryptogram for each message. Check your result by decoding the cryptogram. Use your graphing utility to perform all necessary matrix multiplications.

77.

A	R	R	I	V	E	D	_	S	A	F	E	L	Y
1	18	18	9	22	5	4	0	19	1	6	5	12	25

78.

A	R	T	_	E	N	R	I	C	H	E	S
1	18	20	0	5	14	18	9	3	8	5	19

Critical Thinking Exercises

Make Sense? *In Exercises 79–82, determine whether each statement makes sense or does not make sense, and explain your reasoning.*

79. I found the multiplicative inverse of a 2×3 matrix.

80. I used Gauss-Jordan elimination to find the multiplicative inverse of a 3×3 matrix.

81. I used matrix multiplication to represent a system of linear equations.

82. I made an encoding error by selecting the wrong square invertible matrix.

In Exercises 83–88, determine whether each statement is true or false. If the statement is false, make the necessary change(s) to produce a true statement.

83. All square 2×2 matrices have inverses because there is a formula for finding these inverses.

84. Two 2×2 invertible matrices can have a matrix sum that is not invertible.

85. To solve the matrix equation $AX = B$ for X, multiply A and the inverse of B.

86. $(AB)^{-1} = A^{-1}B^{-1}$, assuming A, B, and AB are invertible.

87. $(A + B)^{-1} = A^{-1} + B^{-1}$, assuming A, B, and $A + B$ are invertible.

88. $\begin{bmatrix} 1 & -3 \\ -1 & 3 \end{bmatrix}$ is an invertible matrix.

89. Give an example of a 2×2 matrix that is its own inverse.

90. If $A = \begin{bmatrix} 3 & 5 \\ 2 & 4 \end{bmatrix}$, find $(A^{-1})^{-1}$.

91. Find values of a for which the following matrix is not invertible:

$$\begin{bmatrix} 1 & a + 1 \\ a - 2 & 4 \end{bmatrix}.$$

Group Exercise

92. Each person in the group should work with one partner. Send a coded word or message to each other by giving your partner the coded matrix and the coding matrix that you selected. Once messages are sent, each person should decode the message received.

Preview Exercises

Exercises 93–95 will help you prepare for the material covered in the next section. Simplify the expression in each exercise.

93. $2(-5) - (-3)(4)$

94. $\dfrac{2(-5) - 1(-4)}{5(-5) - 6(-4)}$

95. $2(-30 - (-3)) - 3(6 - 9) + (-1)(1 - 15)$

SECTION 6.5

Determinants and Cramer's Rule

Objectives

1. Evaluate a second-order determinant.
2. Solve a system of linear equations in two variables using Cramer's Rule.
3. Evaluate a third-order determinant.
4. Solve a system of linear equations in three variables using Cramer's Rule.
5. Evaluate higher-order determinants.

A portion of Charles Babbage's unrealized difference engine

As cyberspace absorbs more and more of our work, play, shopping, and socializing, where will it all end? Which activities will still be offline in 2025?

Our technologically transformed lives can be traced back to the English inventor Charles Babbage (1792–1871). Babbage knew of a method for solving linear systems called *Cramer's Rule*, in honor of the Swiss geometer Gabriel Cramer (1704–1752). Cramer's Rule was simple but involved numerous multiplications for large systems. Babbage designed a machine, called the "difference engine" that consisted of toothed wheels on shafts for performing these multiplications. Despite the fact that only one-seventh of the functions ever worked, Babbage's invention demonstrated how complex calculations could be handled mechanically. In 1944, scientists at IBM used the lessons of the difference engine to create the world's first computer.

Those who invented computers hoped to relegate the drudgery of repeated computation to a machine. In this section, we look at a method for solving linear systems that played a critical role in this process. The method uses real numbers, called *determinants*, that are associated with arrays of numbers. As with matrix methods, solutions are obtained by writing down the coefficients and constants of a linear system and performing operations with them.

① Evaluate a second-order determinant.

The Determinant of a 2 × 2 Matrix

Associated with every square matrix is a real number, called its **determinant**. The determinant for a 2 × 2 square matrix is defined as follows:

GREAT QUESTION!

What does the definition of a determinant mean? What am I supposed to do?

To evaluate a second-order determinant, find the difference of the product of the two diagonals.

$$\begin{vmatrix} a_1 & b_1 \\ a_2 & b_2 \end{vmatrix} = a_1b_2 - a_2b_1$$

Definition of the Determinant of a 2 × 2 Matrix

The determinant of the matrix $\begin{bmatrix} a_1 & b_1 \\ a_2 & b_2 \end{bmatrix}$ is denoted by $\begin{vmatrix} a_1 & b_1 \\ a_2 & b_2 \end{vmatrix}$ and is defined by

$$\begin{vmatrix} a_1 & b_1 \\ a_2 & b_2 \end{vmatrix} = a_1b_2 - a_2b_1.$$

We also say that the **value** of the **second-order determinant** $\begin{vmatrix} a_1 & b_1 \\ a_2 & b_2 \end{vmatrix}$ is $a_1b_2 - a_2b_1$.

Example 1 illustrates that the determinant of a matrix may be positive or negative. A determinant can also have 0 as its value.

EXAMPLE 1   Evaluating the Determinant of a 2 × 2 Matrix

Evaluate the determinant of each of the following matrices:

a. $\begin{bmatrix} 5 & 6 \\ 7 & 3 \end{bmatrix}$ **b.** $\begin{bmatrix} 2 & 4 \\ -3 & -5 \end{bmatrix}$.

DISCOVERY

Write and then evaluate three determinants, one whose value is positive, one whose value is negative, and one whose value is 0.

SOLUTION

We multiply and subtract as indicated.

a. $\begin{vmatrix} 5 & 6 \\ 7 & 3 \end{vmatrix} = 5 \cdot 3 - 7 \cdot 6 = 15 - 42 = -27$ *The value of the second-order determinant is -27.*

b. $\begin{vmatrix} 2 & 4 \\ -3 & -5 \end{vmatrix} = 2(-5) - (-3)(4) = -10 + 12 = 2$ *The value of the second-order determinant is 2.* • • •

⊘ Check Point **1**   Evaluate the determinant of each of the following matrices:

a. $\begin{bmatrix} 10 & 9 \\ 6 & 5 \end{bmatrix}$ **b.** $\begin{bmatrix} 4 & 3 \\ -5 & -8 \end{bmatrix}$.

② Solve a system of linear equations in two variables using Cramer's Rule.

Solving Systems of Linear Equations in Two Variables Using Determinants

Determinants can be used to solve a linear system in two variables. In general, such a system appears as

$$\begin{cases} a_1 x + b_1 y = c_1 \\ a_2 x + b_2 y = c_2. \end{cases}$$

Let's first solve this system for x using the addition method. We can solve for x by eliminating y from the equations. Multiply the first equation by b_2 and the second equation by $-b_1$. Then add the two equations:

$$\begin{cases} a_1 x + b_1 y = c_1 \\ a_2 x + b_2 y = c_2 \end{cases}$$
$\xrightarrow{\text{Multiply by } b_2.}$
$\xrightarrow{\text{Multiply by } -b_1.}$

$$\begin{cases} a_1 b_2 x + b_1 b_2 y = c_1 b_2 \\ -a_2 b_1 x - b_1 b_2 y = -c_2 b_1 \end{cases}$$

Add: $(a_1 b_2 - a_2 b_1)x = c_1 b_2 - c_2 b_1$

$$x = \frac{c_1 b_2 - c_2 b_1}{a_1 b_2 - a_2 b_1}.$$

Because

$$\begin{vmatrix} c_1 & b_1 \\ c_2 & b_2 \end{vmatrix} = c_1 b_2 - c_2 b_1 \quad \text{and} \quad \begin{vmatrix} a_1 & b_1 \\ a_2 & b_2 \end{vmatrix} = a_1 b_2 - a_2 b_1,$$

we can express our answer for x as the quotient of two determinants:

$$x = \frac{c_1 b_2 - c_2 b_1}{a_1 b_2 - a_2 b_1} = \frac{\begin{vmatrix} c_1 & b_1 \\ c_2 & b_2 \end{vmatrix}}{\begin{vmatrix} a_1 & b_1 \\ a_2 & b_2 \end{vmatrix}}.$$

Similarly, we could use the addition method to solve our system for y, again expressing y as the quotient of two determinants. This method of using determinants to solve the linear system, called **Cramer's Rule**, is summarized in the box at the top of the next page.

Solving a Linear System in Two Variables Using Determinants
Cramer's Rule

If

$$\begin{cases} a_1x + b_1y = c_1 \\ a_2x + b_2y = c_2, \end{cases}$$

then

$$x = \frac{\begin{vmatrix} c_1 & b_1 \\ c_2 & b_2 \end{vmatrix}}{\begin{vmatrix} a_1 & b_1 \\ a_2 & b_2 \end{vmatrix}} \quad \text{and} \quad y = \frac{\begin{vmatrix} a_1 & c_1 \\ a_2 & c_2 \end{vmatrix}}{\begin{vmatrix} a_1 & b_1 \\ a_2 & b_2 \end{vmatrix}},$$

where

$$\begin{vmatrix} a_1 & b_1 \\ a_2 & b_2 \end{vmatrix} \neq 0.$$

Here are some helpful tips when solving

$$\begin{cases} a_1x + b_1y = c_1 \\ a_2x + b_2y = c_2 \end{cases}$$

using determinants:

1. Three different determinants are used to find x and y. The determinants in the denominators for x and y are identical. The determinants in the numerators for x and y differ. In abbreviated notation, we write

$$x = \frac{D_x}{D} \quad \text{and} \quad y = \frac{D_y}{D}, \text{where } D \neq 0.$$

2. The elements of D, the determinant in the denominator, are the coefficients of the variables in the system.

$$D = \begin{vmatrix} a_1 & b_1 \\ a_2 & b_2 \end{vmatrix}$$

3. D_x, the determinant in the numerator of x, is obtained by replacing the x-coefficients, in D, a_1 and a_2, with the constants on the right sides of the equations, c_1 and c_2.

$$D = \begin{vmatrix} a_1 & b_1 \\ a_2 & b_2 \end{vmatrix} \quad \text{and} \quad D_x = \begin{vmatrix} c_1 & b_1 \\ c_2 & b_2 \end{vmatrix} \quad \begin{array}{l} \text{Replace the column with } a_1 \text{ and } a_2 \\ \text{with the constants } c_1 \text{ and } c_2 \text{ to get } D_x. \end{array}$$

4. D_y, the determinant in the numerator for y, is obtained by replacing the y-coefficients, in D, b_1 and b_2, with the constants on the right sides of the equations, c_1 and c_2.

$$D = \begin{vmatrix} a_1 & b_1 \\ a_2 & b_2 \end{vmatrix} \quad \text{and} \quad D_y = \begin{vmatrix} a_1 & c_1 \\ a_2 & c_2 \end{vmatrix} \quad \begin{array}{l} \text{Replace the column with } b_1 \text{ and } b_2 \\ \text{with the constants } c_1 \text{ and } c_2 \text{ to get } D_y. \end{array}$$

EXAMPLE 2 Using Cramer's Rule to Solve a Linear System

Use Cramer's Rule to solve the system:

$$\begin{cases} 5x - 4y = 2 \\ 6x - 5y = 1. \end{cases}$$

SOLUTION

Because

$$x = \frac{D_x}{D} \quad \text{and} \quad y = \frac{D_y}{D},$$

we will set up and evaluate the three determinants D, D_x, and D_y.

1. D, the determinant in both denominators, consists of the x- and y-coefficients.

$$D = \begin{vmatrix} 5 & -4 \\ 6 & -5 \end{vmatrix} = (5)(-5) - (6)(-4) = -25 + 24 = -1$$

Because this determinant is not zero, we continue to use Cramer's Rule to solve the system.

2. D_x, the determinant in the numerator for x, is obtained by replacing the x-coefficients in D, 5 and 6, by the constants on the right sides of the equations, 2 and 1.

$$D_x = \begin{vmatrix} 2 & -4 \\ 1 & -5 \end{vmatrix} = (2)(-5) - (1)(-4) = -10 + 4 = -6$$

3. D_y, the determinant in the numerator for y, is obtained by replacing the y-coefficients in D, -4 and -5, by the constants on the right sides of the equations, 2 and 1.

$$D_y = \begin{vmatrix} 5 & 2 \\ 6 & 1 \end{vmatrix} = (5)(1) - (6)(2) = 5 - 12 = -7$$

4. Thus,

$$x = \frac{D_x}{D} = \frac{-6}{-1} = 6 \quad \text{and} \quad y = \frac{D_y}{D} = \frac{-7}{-1} = 7.$$

As always, the solution $(6, 7)$ can be checked by substituting these values into the original equations. The solution set is $\{(6, 7)\}$.   • • •

✓ Check Point **2** Use Cramer's Rule to solve the system:

$$\begin{cases} 5x + 4y = 12 \\ 3x - 6y = 24. \end{cases}$$

③ Evaluate a third-order determinant.

The Determinant of a 3 × 3 Matrix

Associated with every square matrix is a real number called its determinant. The determinant for a 3 × 3 matrix is defined as follows:

Definition of a Third-Order Determinant

$$\begin{vmatrix} a_1 & b_1 & c_1 \\ a_2 & b_2 & c_2 \\ a_3 & b_3 & c_3 \end{vmatrix} = a_1b_2c_3 + b_1c_2a_3 + c_1a_2b_3 - a_3b_2c_1 - b_3c_2a_1 - c_3a_2b_1$$

The six terms and the three factors in each term in this complicated evaluation formula, $a_1b_2c_3 + b_1c_2a_3 + c_1a_2b_3 - a_3b_2c_1 - b_3c_2a_1 - c_3a_2b_1$, can be rearranged, and then we can apply the distributive property. We obtain

$$a_1b_2c_3 - a_1b_3c_2 - a_2b_1c_3 + a_2b_3c_1 + a_3b_1c_2 - a_3b_2c_1$$
$$= a_1(b_2c_3 - b_3c_2) - a_2(b_1c_3 - b_3c_1) + a_3(b_1c_2 - b_2c_1)$$
$$= a_1\begin{vmatrix} b_2 & c_2 \\ b_3 & c_3 \end{vmatrix} - a_2\begin{vmatrix} b_1 & c_1 \\ b_3 & c_3 \end{vmatrix} + a_3\begin{vmatrix} b_1 & c_1 \\ b_2 & c_2 \end{vmatrix}.$$

You can evaluate each of the second-order determinants and obtain the three expressions in parentheses in the second step.

In summary, we now have arranged the definition of a third-order determinant as follows:

Definition of the Determinant of a 3 × 3 Matrix

A third-order determinant is defined by

Each a on the right comes from the first column.

Here are some tips that may be helpful when evaluating the determinant of a 3 × 3 matrix:

Evaluating the Determinant of a 3 × 3 Matrix

1. Each of the three terms in the definition contains two factors—a numerical factor and a second-order determinant.
2. The numerical factor in each term is an element from the first column of the third-order determinant.
3. The minus sign precedes the second term.
4. The second-order determinant that appears in each term is obtained by crossing out the row and the column containing the numerical factor.

$$a_1\begin{vmatrix} b_2 & c_2 \\ b_3 & c_3 \end{vmatrix} - a_2\begin{vmatrix} b_1 & c_1 \\ b_3 & c_3 \end{vmatrix} + a_3\begin{vmatrix} b_1 & c_1 \\ b_2 & c_2 \end{vmatrix}$$

The **minor** of an element is the determinant that remains after deleting the row and column of that element. For this reason, we call this method **expansion by minors**.

EXAMPLE 3 Evaluating the Determinant of a 3 × 3 Matrix

Evaluate the determinant of the following matrix:

$$\begin{bmatrix} 4 & 1 & 0 \\ -9 & 3 & 4 \\ -3 & 8 & 1 \end{bmatrix}.$$

SOLUTION

We know that each of the three terms in the determinant contains a numerical factor and a second-order determinant. The numerical factors are from the first column of the given matrix. They are highlighted in red in the following matrix:

$$\begin{bmatrix} 4 & 1 & 0 \\ -9 & 3 & 4 \\ -3 & 8 & 1 \end{bmatrix}.$$

We find the minor for each numerical factor by deleting the row and column of that element:

The minor for 4 is $\begin{vmatrix} 3 & 4 \\ 8 & 1 \end{vmatrix}$.

The minor for -9 is $\begin{vmatrix} 1 & 0 \\ 8 & 1 \end{vmatrix}$.

The minor for -3 is $\begin{vmatrix} 1 & 0 \\ 3 & 4 \end{vmatrix}$.

Now we have three numerical factors, 4, −9, and −3, and three second-order determinants. We multiply each numerical factor by its second-order determinant to find the three terms of the third-order determinant:

$$4\begin{vmatrix} 3 & 4 \\ 8 & 1 \end{vmatrix}, \quad -9\begin{vmatrix} 1 & 0 \\ 8 & 1 \end{vmatrix}, \quad -3\begin{vmatrix} 1 & 0 \\ 3 & 4 \end{vmatrix}.$$

Based on the preceding definition, we subtract the second term from the first term and add the third term:

Don't forget to supply the minus sign.

$$\begin{vmatrix} 4 & 1 & 0 \\ -9 & 3 & 4 \\ -3 & 8 & 1 \end{vmatrix} = 4\begin{vmatrix} 3 & 4 \\ 8 & 1 \end{vmatrix} - (-9)\begin{vmatrix} 1 & 0 \\ 8 & 1 \end{vmatrix} - 3\begin{vmatrix} 1 & 0 \\ 3 & 4 \end{vmatrix}$$

Begin by evaluating the three second-order determinants.

$= 4(3 \cdot 1 - 8 \cdot 4) + 9(1 \cdot 1 - 8 \cdot 0) - 3(1 \cdot 4 - 3 \cdot 0)$

$= 4(3 - 32) + 9(1 - 0) - 3(4 - 0)$ Multiply within parentheses.

$= 4(-29) + 9(1) - 3(4)$ Subtract within parentheses.

$= -116 + 9 - 12$ Multiply.

$= -119$ Add and subtract as indicated. ●●●

TECHNOLOGY

A graphing utility can be used to evaluate the determinant of a matrix. Enter the matrix and call it A. Then use the determinant command. The screen below verifies our result in Example 3.

```
[A]
     [[4   1  0]
      [-9  3  4]
      [-3  8  1]]
det([A])
              -119
■
```

✓ **Check Point 3** Evaluate the determinant of the following matrix:

$$\begin{bmatrix} 2 & 1 & 7 \\ -5 & 6 & 0 \\ -4 & 3 & 1 \end{bmatrix}.$$

The six terms in the definition of a third-order determinant can be rearranged and factored in a variety of ways. Thus, it is possible to expand a determinant by minors about any row or any column. *Minus signs must be supplied preceding any element appearing in a position where the sum of its row and its column is an odd number.* For example, expanding about the elements in column 2 gives us

$$\begin{vmatrix} a_1 & b_1 & c_1 \\ a_2 & b_2 & c_2 \\ a_3 & b_3 & c_3 \end{vmatrix} = -b_1\begin{vmatrix} a_2 & c_2 \\ a_3 & c_3 \end{vmatrix} + b_2\begin{vmatrix} a_1 & c_1 \\ a_3 & c_3 \end{vmatrix} - b_3\begin{vmatrix} a_1 & c_1 \\ a_2 & c_2 \end{vmatrix}.$$

Minus sign is supplied because b_1 appears in row 1 and column 2; $1 + 2 = 3$, an odd number.

Minus sign is supplied because b_3 appears in row 3 and column 2; $3 + 2 = 5$, an odd number.

Expanding by minors about column 3, we obtain

$$\begin{vmatrix} a_1 & b_1 & c_1 \\ a_2 & b_2 & c_2 \\ a_3 & b_3 & c_3 \end{vmatrix} = c_1 \begin{vmatrix} a_2 & b_2 \\ a_3 & b_3 \end{vmatrix} - c_2 \begin{vmatrix} a_1 & b_1 \\ a_3 & b_3 \end{vmatrix} + c_3 \begin{vmatrix} a_1 & b_1 \\ a_2 & b_2 \end{vmatrix}.$$

Minus sign must be supplied because c_2 appears in row **2** and column **3**; $2 + 3 = 5$, an odd number.

When evaluating a 3 × 3 determinant using expansion by minors, you can expand about any row or column. To simplify the arithmetic, if a row or column contains one or more 0s, expand about that row or column.

EXAMPLE 4   Evaluating a Third-Order Determinant

Evaluate:

$$\begin{vmatrix} 9 & 5 & 0 \\ -2 & -3 & 0 \\ 1 & 4 & 2 \end{vmatrix}.$$

SOLUTION

Note that the last column has two 0s. We will expand the determinant about the elements in that column.

$$\begin{vmatrix} 9 & 5 & 0 \\ -2 & -3 & 0 \\ 1 & 4 & 2 \end{vmatrix} = 0 \begin{vmatrix} -2 & -3 \\ 1 & 4 \end{vmatrix} - 0 \begin{vmatrix} 9 & 5 \\ 1 & 4 \end{vmatrix} + 2 \begin{vmatrix} 9 & 5 \\ -2 & -3 \end{vmatrix}$$

$$= 0 - 0 + 2[9(-3) - (-2)5]$$ Evaluate the second-order
$$= 2(-27 + 10)$$ determinant whose numerical
$$= 2(-17)$$ factor is not 0.
$$= -34$$ ● ● ●

☑ Check Point **4** Evaluate:

$$\begin{vmatrix} 6 & 4 & 0 \\ -3 & -5 & 3 \\ 1 & 2 & 0 \end{vmatrix}.$$

④ Solve a system of linear equations in three variables using Cramer's Rule.

Solving Systems of Linear Equations in Three Variables Using Determinants

Cramer's Rule can be applied to solving systems of linear equations in three variables. The determinants in the numerator and denominator of all variables are third-order determinants.

Solving Three Equations in Three Variables Using Determinants Cramer's Rule

If

$$\begin{cases} a_1x + b_1y + c_1z = d_1 \\ a_2x + b_2y + c_2z = d_2 \\ a_3x + b_3y + c_3z = d_3 \end{cases}$$

then

$$x = \frac{D_x}{D}, y = \frac{D_y}{D}, \text{ and } z = \frac{D_z}{D}, \text{ where } D \neq 0.$$

These four third-order determinants are given by

$$D = \begin{vmatrix} a_1 & b_1 & c_1 \\ a_2 & b_2 & c_2 \\ a_3 & b_3 & c_3 \end{vmatrix}$$ These are the coefficients of the variables x, y, and z.

$$D_x = \begin{vmatrix} d_1 & b_1 & c_1 \\ d_2 & b_2 & c_2 \\ d_3 & b_3 & c_3 \end{vmatrix}$$ Replace x-coefficients in D with the constants on the right of the three equations.

$$D_y = \begin{vmatrix} a_1 & d_1 & c_1 \\ a_2 & d_2 & c_2 \\ a_3 & d_3 & c_3 \end{vmatrix}$$ Replace y-coefficients in D with the constants on the right of the three equations.

$$D_z = \begin{vmatrix} a_1 & b_1 & d_1 \\ a_2 & b_2 & d_2 \\ a_3 & b_3 & d_3 \end{vmatrix}$$ Replace z-coefficients in D with the constants on the right of the three equations.

EXAMPLE 5 Using Cramer's Rule to Solve a Linear System in Three Variables

Use Cramer's Rule to solve:

$$\begin{cases} x + 2y - z = -4 \\ x + 4y - 2z = -6 \\ 2x + 3y + z = 3. \end{cases}$$

SOLUTION

Because

$$x = \frac{D_x}{D}, \quad y = \frac{D_y}{D}, \quad \text{and} \quad z = \frac{D_z}{D},$$

we need to set up and evaluate four determinants.

Step 1   Set up the determinants.

1. D, the determinant in all three denominators, consists of the x-, y-, and z-coefficients.

$$D = \begin{vmatrix} 1 & 2 & -1 \\ 1 & 4 & -2 \\ 2 & 3 & 1 \end{vmatrix}$$

2. D_x, the determinant in the numerator for x, is obtained by replacing the x-coefficients in D, 1, 1, and 2, with the constants on the right sides of the equations, $-4, -6,$ and 3.

$$D_x = \begin{vmatrix} -4 & 2 & -1 \\ -6 & 4 & -2 \\ 3 & 3 & 1 \end{vmatrix}$$

3. D_y, the determinant in the numerator for y, is obtained by replacing the y-coefficients in D, 2, 4, and 3, with the constants on the right sides of the equations, $-4, -6,$ and 3.

$$D_y = \begin{vmatrix} 1 & -4 & -1 \\ 1 & -6 & -2 \\ 2 & 3 & 1 \end{vmatrix}$$

4. D_z, the determinant in the numerator for z, is obtained by replacing the z-coefficients in D, $-1, -2,$ and 1, with the constants on the right sides of the equations, $-4, -6,$ and 3.

$$D_z = \begin{vmatrix} 1 & 2 & -4 \\ 1 & 4 & -6 \\ 2 & 3 & 3 \end{vmatrix}$$

Step 2   Evaluate the four determinants.

$$D = \begin{vmatrix} 1 & 2 & -1 \\ 1 & 4 & -2 \\ 2 & 3 & 1 \end{vmatrix} = 1\begin{vmatrix} 4 & -2 \\ 3 & 1 \end{vmatrix} - 1\begin{vmatrix} 2 & -1 \\ 3 & 1 \end{vmatrix} + 2\begin{vmatrix} 2 & -1 \\ 4 & -2 \end{vmatrix}$$

$$= 1(4 + 6) - 1(2 + 3) + 2(-4 + 4)$$

$$= 1(10) - 1(5) + 2(0) = 5$$

Using the same technique to evaluate each determinant, we obtain

$$D_x = -10, \quad D_y = 5, \quad \text{and} \quad D_z = 20.$$

Step 3   Substitute these four values and solve the system.

$$x = \frac{D_x}{D} = \frac{-10}{5} = -2$$

$$y = \frac{D_y}{D} = \frac{5}{5} = 1$$

$$z = \frac{D_z}{D} = \frac{20}{5} = 4$$

The solution $(-2, 1, 4)$ can be checked by substitution into the original three equations. The solution set is $\{(-2, 1, 4)\}$.   • • •

GREAT QUESTION!

Can I use D, the determinant in each denominator, to find the determinants in the numerators?

No. To find D_x, D_y, and D_z, you'll need to apply the evaluation process for a 3×3 determinant three more times. The values of D_x, D_y, and D_z cannot be obtained from the number that occurs in the computation of D.

✓ Check Point **5**   Use Cramer's Rule to solve the system:

$$\begin{cases} 3x - 2y + z = 16 \\ 2x + 3y - z = -9 \\ x + 4y + 3z = 2. \end{cases}$$

GREAT QUESTION!

What should I do if D, the determinant in the denominator of Cramer's Rule, is zero?

If $D = 0$, the system is inconsistent or contains dependent equations. Use a method other than Cramer's Rule to determine the solution set. For systems in two variables, use the substitution method or the addition method. For systems in three variables, use Gaussian elimination.

Speaking of Cramer meltdown, there's another situation in which Cramer's Rule is useless. This involves nonsquare systems such as

$$\begin{cases} 3x + 7y + 6z = 26 \\ x + 2y + z = 8. \end{cases}$$

Determinants are only associated with square matrices. Gaussian elimination must be used to solve systems with fewer equations than variables. (This system is solved in Example 3 on page 606.)

In essence, the use of Cramer's Rule to determine solution sets is only an alternative to Gaussian elimination in some situations.

⑤ Evaluate higher-order determinants.

The Determinant of Any $n \times n$ Matrix

The determinant of a matrix with n rows and n columns is said to be an **nth-order determinant**. The value of an nth-order determinant ($n > 2$) can be found in terms of determinants of order $n - 1$. For example, we found the value of a third-order determinant in terms of determinants of order 2.

We can generalize this idea for fourth-order determinants and higher. We have seen that the **minor** of the element a_{ij} is the determinant obtained by deleting the ith row and the jth column in the given array of numbers. The **cofactor** of the element a_{ij} is $(-1)^{i+j}$ times the minor of a_{ij}. If the sum of the row and column $(i + j)$ is even, the cofactor is the same as the minor. If the sum of the row and column $(i + j)$ is odd, the cofactor is the opposite of the minor.

Let's see what this means in the case of a fourth-order determinant.

EXAMPLE 6   Evaluating the Determinant of a 4 × 4 Matrix

Evaluate the determinant of the following matrix:

$$A = \begin{bmatrix} 1 & -2 & 3 & 0 \\ -1 & 1 & 0 & 2 \\ 0 & 2 & 0 & -3 \\ 2 & 3 & -4 & 1 \end{bmatrix}.$$

SOLUTION

$$|A| = \begin{vmatrix} 1 & -2 & 3 & 0 \\ -1 & 1 & 0 & 2 \\ 0 & 2 & 0 & -3 \\ 2 & 3 & -4 & 1 \end{vmatrix}$$

With two 0s in the third column, we will expand along the third column.

$$= (-1)^{1+3}(3)\begin{vmatrix} -1 & 1 & 2 \\ 0 & 2 & -3 \\ 2 & 3 & 1 \end{vmatrix} + (-1)^{4+3}(-4)\begin{vmatrix} 1 & -2 & 0 \\ -1 & 1 & 2 \\ 0 & 2 & -3 \end{vmatrix}$$

3 is in row 1, column 3.

−4 is in row 4, column 3.

$$= 3\begin{vmatrix} -1 & 1 & 2 \\ 0 & 2 & -3 \\ 2 & 3 & 1 \end{vmatrix} + 4\begin{vmatrix} 1 & -2 & 0 \\ -1 & 1 & 2 \\ 0 & 2 & -3 \end{vmatrix}$$

The determinant that follows 3 is obtained by crossing out the row and the column (row 1, column 3) in the original determinant. The minor for −4 is obtained in a similar manner.

Evaluate the two third-order determinants to get

$$|A| = 3(-25) + 4(-1) = -79.$$

● ● ●

✓ Check Point **6** Evaluate the determinant of the following matrix:

$$A = \begin{bmatrix} 0 & 4 & 0 & -3 \\ -1 & 1 & 5 & 2 \\ 1 & -2 & 0 & 6 \\ 3 & 0 & 0 & 1 \end{bmatrix}.$$

If a linear system has n equations, Cramer's Rule requires you to compute $n + 1$ determinants of nth order. The excessive number of calculations required to perform Cramer's Rule for systems with four or more equations makes it an inefficient method for solving large systems.

CONCEPT AND VOCABULARY CHECK

Fill in each blank so that the resulting statement is true.

1. $\begin{vmatrix} 5 & 4 \\ 2 & 3 \end{vmatrix} = \underline{\quad} \cdot \underline{\quad} - \underline{\quad} \cdot \underline{\quad} = \underline{\quad} - \underline{\quad} = \underline{\quad}$

The value of this second-order _____

is _____.

2. Using Cramer's Rule to solve

$$\begin{cases} x + y = 8 \\ x - y = -2 \end{cases},$$

we obtain

$$x = \dfrac{\begin{vmatrix} \underline{\ } & \underline{\ } \\ \underline{\ } & \underline{\ } \end{vmatrix}}{\begin{vmatrix} \underline{\ } & \underline{\ } \\ \underline{\ } & \underline{\ } \end{vmatrix}} \quad \text{and} \quad y = \dfrac{\begin{vmatrix} \underline{\ } & \underline{\ } \\ \underline{\ } & \underline{\ } \end{vmatrix}}{\begin{vmatrix} \underline{\ } & \underline{\ } \\ \underline{\ } & \underline{\ } \end{vmatrix}}.$$

3. $\begin{vmatrix} 3 & 2 & 1 \\ 4 & 3 & 1 \\ 5 & 1 & 1 \end{vmatrix} = 3 \begin{vmatrix} \underline{\ } & \underline{\ } \\ \underline{\ } & \underline{\ } \end{vmatrix} - 4 \begin{vmatrix} \underline{\ } & \underline{\ } \\ \underline{\ } & \underline{\ } \end{vmatrix} + 5 \begin{vmatrix} \underline{\ } & \underline{\ } \\ \underline{\ } & \underline{\ } \end{vmatrix}$

4. Using Cramer's Rule to solve

$$\begin{cases} 3x + y + 4z = -8 \\ 2x + 3y - 2z = 11 \\ x - 3y - 2z = 4 \end{cases}$$

for y, we obtain

$$y = \frac{}{}.$$

5. The easiest way to evaluate

$$\begin{vmatrix} 3 & 2 & 8 \\ 5 & -4 & 0 \\ -6 & 7 & 0 \end{vmatrix}$$

is to expand about the elements in

_____.

EXERCISE SET 6.5

Practice Exercises

Evaluate each determinant in Exercises 1–10.

1. $\begin{vmatrix} 5 & 7 \\ 2 & 3 \end{vmatrix}$

2. $\begin{vmatrix} 4 & 8 \\ 5 & 6 \end{vmatrix}$

3. $\begin{vmatrix} -4 & 1 \\ 5 & 6 \end{vmatrix}$

4. $\begin{vmatrix} 7 & 9 \\ -2 & -5 \end{vmatrix}$

5. $\begin{vmatrix} -7 & 14 \\ 2 & -4 \end{vmatrix}$

6. $\begin{vmatrix} 1 & -3 \\ -8 & 2 \end{vmatrix}$

7. $\begin{vmatrix} -5 & -1 \\ -2 & -7 \end{vmatrix}$

8. $\begin{vmatrix} \frac{1}{5} & \frac{1}{6} \\ -6 & 5 \end{vmatrix}$

9. $\begin{vmatrix} \frac{1}{2} & \frac{1}{2} \\ \frac{1}{8} & -\frac{3}{4} \end{vmatrix}$

10. $\begin{vmatrix} \frac{2}{3} & \frac{1}{3} \\ -\frac{1}{2} & \frac{3}{4} \end{vmatrix}$

For Exercises 11–22, use Cramer's Rule to solve each system.

11. $\begin{cases} x + y = 7 \\ x - y = 3 \end{cases}$

12. $\begin{cases} 2x + y = 3 \\ x - y = 3 \end{cases}$

13. $\begin{cases} 12x + 3y = 15 \\ 2x - 3y = 13 \end{cases}$

14. $\begin{cases} x - 2y = 5 \\ 5x - y = -2 \end{cases}$

15. $\begin{cases} 4x - 5y = 17 \\ 2x + 3y = 3 \end{cases}$

16. $\begin{cases} 3x + 2y = 2 \\ 2x + 2y = 3 \end{cases}$

17. $\begin{cases} x + 2y = 3 \\ 3x - 4y = 4 \end{cases}$

18. $\begin{cases} 2x - 9y = 5 \\ 3x - 3y = 11 \end{cases}$

19. $\begin{cases} 3x - 4y = 4 \\ 2x + 2y = 12 \end{cases}$

20. $\begin{cases} 3x = 7y + 1 \\ 2x = 3y - 1 \end{cases}$

21. $\begin{cases} 2x = 3y + 2 \\ 5x = 51 - 4y \end{cases}$

22. $\begin{cases} y = -4x + 2 \\ 2x = 3y + 8 \end{cases}$

Evaluate each determinant in Exercises 23–28.

23. $\begin{vmatrix} 3 & 0 & 0 \\ 2 & 1 & -5 \\ 2 & 5 & -1 \end{vmatrix}$

24. $\begin{vmatrix} 4 & 0 & 0 \\ 3 & -1 & 4 \\ 2 & -3 & 5 \end{vmatrix}$

25. $\begin{vmatrix} 3 & 1 & 0 \\ -3 & 4 & 0 \\ -1 & 3 & -5 \end{vmatrix}$

26. $\begin{vmatrix} 2 & -4 & 2 \\ -1 & 0 & 5 \\ 3 & 0 & 4 \end{vmatrix}$

27. $\begin{vmatrix} 1 & 1 & 1 \\ 2 & 2 & 2 \\ -3 & 4 & -5 \end{vmatrix}$

28. $\begin{vmatrix} 1 & 2 & 3 \\ 2 & 2 & -3 \\ 3 & 2 & 1 \end{vmatrix}$

In Exercises 29–36, use Cramer's Rule to solve each system.

29. $\begin{cases} x + y + z = 0 \\ 2x - y + z = -1 \\ -x + 3y - z = -8 \end{cases}$

30. $\begin{cases} x - y + 2z = 3 \\ 2x + 3y + z = 9 \\ -x - y + 3z = 11 \end{cases}$

31. $\begin{cases} 4x - 5y - 6z = -1 \\ x - 2y - 5z = -12 \\ 2x - y = 7 \end{cases}$

32. $\begin{cases} x - 3y + z = -2 \\ x + 2y = 8 \\ 2x - y = 1 \end{cases}$

33. $\begin{cases} x + y + z = 4 \\ x - 2y + z = 7 \\ x + 3y + 2z = 4 \end{cases}$

34. $\begin{cases} 2x + 2y + 3z = 10 \\ 4x - y + z = -5 \\ 5x - 2y + 6z = 1 \end{cases}$

35. $\begin{cases} x + 2z = 4 \\ 2y - z = 5 \\ 2x + 3y = 13 \end{cases}$

36. $\begin{cases} 3x + 2z = 4 \\ 5x - y = -4 \\ 4y + 3z = 22 \end{cases}$

Evaluate each determinant in Exercises 37–40.

37. $\begin{vmatrix} 4 & 2 & 8 & -7 \\ -2 & 0 & 4 & 1 \\ 5 & 0 & 0 & 5 \\ 4 & 0 & 0 & -1 \end{vmatrix}$

38. $\begin{vmatrix} 3 & -1 & 1 & 2 \\ -2 & 0 & 0 & 0 \\ 2 & -1 & -2 & 3 \\ 1 & 4 & 2 & 3 \end{vmatrix}$

39. $\begin{vmatrix} -2 & -3 & 3 & 5 \\ 1 & -4 & 0 & 0 \\ 1 & 2 & 2 & -3 \\ 2 & 0 & 1 & 1 \end{vmatrix}$ **40.** $\begin{vmatrix} 1 & -3 & 2 & 0 \\ -3 & -1 & 0 & -2 \\ 2 & 1 & 3 & 1 \\ 2 & 0 & -2 & 0 \end{vmatrix}$

Practice Plus

In Exercises 41–42, evaluate each determinant.

41. $\begin{vmatrix} \begin{vmatrix} 3 & 1 \\ -2 & 3 \end{vmatrix} & \begin{vmatrix} 7 & 0 \\ 1 & 5 \end{vmatrix} \\ \begin{vmatrix} 3 & 0 \\ 0 & 7 \end{vmatrix} & \begin{vmatrix} 9 & -6 \\ 3 & 5 \end{vmatrix} \end{vmatrix}$ **42.** $\begin{vmatrix} \begin{vmatrix} 5 & 0 \\ 4 & -3 \end{vmatrix} & \begin{vmatrix} -1 & 0 \\ 0 & -1 \end{vmatrix} \\ \begin{vmatrix} 7 & -5 \\ 4 & 6 \end{vmatrix} & \begin{vmatrix} 4 & 1 \\ -3 & 5 \end{vmatrix} \end{vmatrix}$

In Exercises 43–44, write the system of linear equations for which Cramer's Rule yields the given determinants.

43. $D = \begin{vmatrix} 2 & -4 \\ 3 & 5 \end{vmatrix}, \quad D_x = \begin{vmatrix} 8 & -4 \\ -10 & 5 \end{vmatrix}$

44. $D = \begin{vmatrix} 2 & -3 \\ 5 & 6 \end{vmatrix}, \quad D_x = \begin{vmatrix} 8 & -3 \\ 11 & 6 \end{vmatrix}$

In Exercises 45–48, solve each equation for x.

45. $\begin{vmatrix} -2 & x \\ 4 & 6 \end{vmatrix} = 32$ **46.** $\begin{vmatrix} x+3 & -6 \\ x-2 & -4 \end{vmatrix} = 28$

47. $\begin{vmatrix} 1 & x & -2 \\ 3 & 1 & 1 \\ 0 & -2 & 2 \end{vmatrix} = -8$ **48.** $\begin{vmatrix} 2 & x & 1 \\ -3 & 1 & 0 \\ 2 & 1 & 4 \end{vmatrix} = 39$

Application Exercises

Determinants are used to find the area of a triangle whose vertices are given by three points in a rectangular coordinate system. The area of a triangle with vertices (x_1, y_1), (x_2, y_2), and (x_3, y_3) is

$$\text{Area} = \pm \frac{1}{2} \begin{vmatrix} x_1 & y_1 & 1 \\ x_2 & y_2 & 1 \\ x_3 & y_3 & 1 \end{vmatrix},$$

where the $\pm$ symbol indicates that the appropriate sign should be chosen to yield a positive area. Use this information to work Exercises 49–50.

49. Use determinants to find the area of the triangle whose vertices are $(3, -5)$, $(2, 6)$, and $(-3, 5)$.

50. Use determinants to find the area of the triangle whose vertices are $(1, 1)$, $(-2, -3)$, and $(11, -3)$.

Determinants are used to show that three points lie on the same line (are collinear). If

$$\begin{vmatrix} x_1 & y_1 & 1 \\ x_2 & y_2 & 1 \\ x_3 & y_3 & 1 \end{vmatrix} = 0,$$

then the points (x_1, y_1), (x_2, y_2), and (x_3, y_3) are collinear. If the determinant does not equal 0, then the points are not collinear. Use this information to work Exercises 51–52.

51. Are the points $(3, -1)$, $(0, -3)$, and $(12, 5)$ collinear?

52. Are the points $(-4, -6)$, $(1, 0)$, and $(11, 12)$ collinear?

Determinants are used to write an equation of a line passing through two points. An equation of the line passing through the distinct points (x_1, y_1) and (x_2, y_2) is given by

$$\begin{vmatrix} x & y & 1 \\ x_1 & y_1 & 1 \\ x_2 & y_2 & 1 \end{vmatrix} = 0.$$

Use this information to work Exercises 53–54.

53. Use the determinant to write an equation of the line passing through $(3, -5)$ and $(-2, 6)$. Then expand the determinant, expressing the line's equation in slope-intercept form.

54. Use the determinant to write an equation of the line passing through $(-1, 3)$ and $(2, 4)$. Then expand the determinant, expressing the line's equation in slope-intercept form.

Writing in Mathematics

55. Explain how to evaluate a second-order determinant.

56. Describe the determinants D_x and D_y in terms of the coefficients and constants in a system of two equations in two variables.

57. Explain how to evaluate a third-order determinant.

58. When expanding a determinant by minors, when is it necessary to supply minus signs?

59. Without going into too much detail, describe how to solve a linear system in three variables using Cramer's Rule.

60. In applying Cramer's Rule, what should you do if $D = 0$?

61. The process of solving a linear system in three variables using Cramer's Rule can involve tedious computation. Is there a way of speeding up this process, perhaps using Cramer's Rule to find the value for only one of the variables? Describe how this process might work, presenting a specific example with your description. Remember that your goal is still to find the value for each variable in the system.

62. If you could use only one method to solve linear systems in three variables, which method would you select? Explain why this is so.

Technology Exercises

63. Use the feature of your graphing utility that evaluates the determinant of a square matrix to verify any five of the determinants that you evaluated by hand in Exercises 1–10, 23–28, or 37–40.

In Exercises 64–65, use a graphing utility to evaluate the determinant for the given matrix.

64. $\begin{bmatrix} 3 & -2 & -1 & 4 \\ -5 & 1 & 2 & 7 \\ 2 & 4 & 5 & 0 \\ -1 & 3 & -6 & 5 \end{bmatrix}$ **65.** $\begin{bmatrix} 8 & 2 & 6 & -1 & 0 \\ 2 & 0 & -3 & 4 & 7 \\ 2 & 1 & -3 & 6 & -5 \\ -1 & 2 & 1 & 5 & -1 \\ 4 & 5 & -2 & 3 & -8 \end{bmatrix}$

66. What is the fastest method for solving a linear system with your graphing utility?

Critical Thinking Exercises

Make Sense? *In Exercises 67–70, determine whether each statement makes sense or does not make sense, and explain your reasoning.*

67. I'm solving a linear system using a determinant that contains two rows and three columns.

68. I can speed up the tedious computations required by Cramer's Rule by using the value of D to determine the value of D_x.

69. When using Cramer's Rule to solve a linear system, the number of determinants that I set up and evaluate is the same as the number of variables in the system.

70. Using Cramer's Rule to solve a linear system, I found the value of D to be zero, so the value of each variable is zero.

71. a. Evaluate: $\begin{vmatrix} a & a \\ 0 & a \end{vmatrix}$.

b. Evaluate: $\begin{vmatrix} a & a & a \\ 0 & a & a \\ 0 & 0 & a \end{vmatrix}$.

c. Evaluate: $\begin{vmatrix} a & a & a & a \\ 0 & a & a & a \\ 0 & 0 & a & a \\ 0 & 0 & 0 & a \end{vmatrix}$.

d. Describe the pattern in the given determinants.

e. Describe the pattern in the evaluations.

72. Evaluate: $\begin{vmatrix} 2 & 0 & 0 & 0 & 0 \\ 0 & 3 & 0 & 0 & 0 \\ 0 & 0 & 2 & 0 & 0 \\ 0 & 0 & 0 & 1 & 0 \\ 0 & 0 & 0 & 0 & 4 \end{vmatrix}$.

73. What happens to the value of a second-order determinant if the two columns are interchanged?

74. Consider the system

$$\begin{cases} a_1x + b_1y = c_1 \\ a_2x + b_2y = c_2. \end{cases}$$

Use Cramer's Rule to prove that if the first equation of the system is replaced by the sum of the two equations, the resulting system has the same solution as the original system.

75. Show that the equation of a line through (x_1, y_1) and (x_2, y_2) is given by the determinant equation in Exercises 53–54.

Group Exercise

76. We have seen that determinants can be used to solve linear equations, give areas of triangles in rectangular coordinates, and determine equations of lines. Not impressed with these applications? Members of the group should research an application of determinants that they find intriguing. The group should then present a seminar to the class about this application.

Preview Exercises

Exercises 77–79 will help you prepare for the material covered in the first section of the next chapter.

77. Consider the equation $\dfrac{x^2}{9} + \dfrac{y^2}{4} = 1$.

a. Set $y = 0$ and find the x-intercepts.

b. Set $x = 0$ and find the y-intercepts.

78. Divide both sides of $25x^2 + 16y^2 = 400$ by 400 and simplify.

79. Complete the square and write the circle's equation in standard form:

$$x^2 + y^2 - 2x + 4y = 4.$$

Then give the center and radius of the circle and graph the equation.

CHAPTER 6   Summary, Review, and Test

SUMMARY

DEFINITIONS AND CONCEPTS	EXAMPLES
6.1 Matrix Solutions to Linear Systems	
a. Matrix row operations are described in the box on page 591.	Ex. 1, p. 591
b. To solve a linear system using Gaussian elimination, begin with the system's augmented matrix. Use matrix row operations to get 1s down the main diagonal from upper left to lower right, and 0s below the 1s. Such a matrix is in row-echelon form. Details are in the box on page 592.	Ex. 2, p. 592; Ex. 3, p. 595
c. To solve a linear system using Gauss-Jordan elimination, use the procedure of Gaussian elimination, but obtain 0s above and below the 1s in the main diagonal from upper left to lower right. Such a matrix is in reduced row-echelon form. Details are in the box on page 597.	Ex. 4, p. 598

6.2 Inconsistent and Dependent Systems and Their Applications

a. If Gaussian elimination results in a matrix with a row containing all 0s to the left of the vertical line and a nonzero number to the right, the system has no solution (is inconsistent).

Ex. 1, p. 603

b. In a square system, if Gaussian elimination results in a matrix with a row with all 0s, but not a row like the one in part (a), the system has an infinite number of solutions (contains dependent equations).

Ex. 2, p. 604

c. In nonsquare systems, the number of variables differs from the number of equations.

Ex. 3, p. 606

6.3 Matrix Operations and Their Applications

a. A matrix of order $m \times n$ has m rows and n columns. Two matrices are equal if and only if they have the same order and corresponding elements are equal.

Ex. 1, p. 612

b. Matrix Addition and Subtraction: Matrices of the same order are added or subtracted by adding or subtracting corresponding elements. Properties of matrix addition are given in the box on page 614.

Ex. 2, p. 614

c. Scalar Multiplication: If A is a matrix and c is a scalar, then cA is the matrix formed by multiplying each element in A by c. Properties of scalar multiplication are given in the box on page 616.

Ex. 3, p. 615;
Ex. 4, p. 616

d. Matrix Multiplication: The product of an $m \times n$ matrix A and an $n \times p$ matrix B is an $m \times p$ matrix AB. The element in the ith row and jth column of AB is found by multiplying each element in the ith row of A by the corresponding element in the jth column of B and adding the products. Matrix multiplication is not commutative: $AB \neq BA$. Properties of matrix multiplication are given in the box on page 621.

Ex. 5, p. 617;
Ex. 6, p. 618;
Ex. 7, p. 620

6.4 Multiplicative Inverses of Matrices and Matrix Equations

a. The multiplicative identity matrix I_n is an $n \times n$ matrix with 1s down the main diagonal from upper left to lower right and 0s elsewhere.

b. Let A be an $n \times n$ square matrix. If there is a square matrix A^{-1} such that $AA^{-1} = I_n$ and $A^{-1}A = I_n$, then A^{-1} is the multiplicative inverse of A.

Ex. 1, p. 629

c. If a square matrix has a multiplicative inverse, it is invertible or nonsingular. Methods for finding multiplicative inverses for invertible matrices, including a formula for 2×2 matrices, are given in the box on page 635.

Ex. 2, p. 630;
Ex. 3, p. 631;
Ex. 4, p. 634

d. Linear systems can be represented by matrix equations of the form $AX = B$ in which A is the coefficient matrix and B is the constant matrix. If $AX = B$ has a unique solution, then $X = A^{-1}B$.

Ex. 5, p. 636

6.5 Determinants and Cramer's Rule

a. Value of a second-order determinant:

Ex. 1, p. 643

$$\begin{vmatrix} a_1 & b_1 \\ a_2 & b_2 \end{vmatrix} = a_1 b_2 - a_2 b_1$$

b. Cramer's Rule for solving systems of linear equations in two variables uses three second-order determinants and is stated in the box on page 644.

Ex. 2, p. 645

c. To evaluate an nth-order determinant, where $n > 2$,

Ex. 3, p. 646;
Ex. 4, p. 648;
Ex. 6, p. 651

1. Select a row or column about which to expand.

2. Multiply each element a_{ij} in the row or column by $(-1)^{i+j}$ times the determinant obtained by deleting the ith row and the jth column in the given array of numbers.

3. The value of the determinant is the sum of the products found in step 2.

d. Cramer's Rule for solving systems of linear equations in three variables uses four third-order determinants and is stated in the box beginning on page 648.

Ex. 5, p. 649

e. Cramer's Rule cannot be used to determine solution sets with inconsistent or dependent systems.

REVIEW EXERCISES

6.1

In Exercises 1–2, perform each matrix row operation and write the new matrix.

1. $\begin{bmatrix} 1 & 2 & 2 & | & 2 \\ 0 & 1 & -1 & | & 2 \\ 0 & 5 & 4 & | & 1 \end{bmatrix}$ $-5R_2 + R_3$

2. $\begin{bmatrix} 2 & -2 & 1 & | & -1 \\ 1 & 2 & -1 & | & 2 \\ 6 & 4 & 3 & | & 5 \end{bmatrix}$ $\frac{1}{2}R_1$

In Exercises 3–5, solve each system of equations using matrices. Use Gaussian elimination with back-substitution or Gauss-Jordan elimination.

3. $\begin{cases} x + 2y + 3z = -5 \\ 2x + y + z = 1 \\ x + y - z = 8 \end{cases}$

4. $\begin{cases} x - 2y + z = 0 \\ y - 3z = -1 \\ 2y + 5z = -2 \end{cases}$

5. $\begin{cases} 3x_1 + 5x_2 - 8x_3 + 5x_4 = -8 \\ x_1 + 2x_2 - 3x_3 + x_4 = -7 \\ 2x_1 + 3x_2 - 7x_3 + 3x_4 = -11 \\ 4x_1 + 8x_2 - 10x_3 + 7x_4 = -10 \end{cases}$

6. The table shows the pollutants in the air in a city on a typical summer day.

x (Hours after 6 A.M.)	y (Amount of Pollutants in the Air, in parts per million)
2	98
4	138
10	162

a. Use the function $y = ax^2 + bx + c$ to model the data. Use either Gaussian elimination with back-substitution or Gauss-Jordan elimination to find the values for a, b, and c.

b. Use the function to find the time of day at which the city's air pollution level is at a maximum. What is the maximum level?

7. Sociologists Joseph Kahl and Dennis Gilbert developed a six-tier model to portray the class structure of the United States. The bar graph represents the percentage of Americans who are members of each of the six social classes.

The United States Social Class Ladder

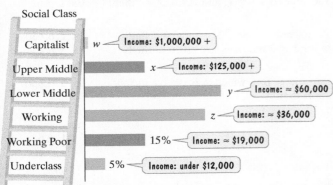

Social Class

Percentage of the Population

Source: James Henslin, *Sociology*, Ninth Edition, Allyn and Bacon, 2011.

Combined, members of the capitalist class, the upper-middle class, the lower-middle class, and the working class make up 80% of the U.S. population. The percentage of the population belonging to the lower-middle class exceeds the percentage belonging to capitalist and upper-middle classes by 18%. The difference between the percentage belonging to the lower-middle class and the working class is 4%. If the percentage belonging to the upper-middle class is tripled, it exceeds the percentage belonging to the capitalist and lower-middle classes by 10%. Determine the percentage of the U.S. population who are members of the capitalist class, the upper-middle class, the lower-middle class, and the working class.

6.2

In Exercises 8–11, use Gaussian elimination to find the complete solution to each system, or show that none exists.

8. $\begin{cases} 2x - 3y + z = 1 \\ x - 2y + 3z = 2 \\ 3x - 4y - z = 1 \end{cases}$

9. $\begin{cases} x - 3y + z = 1 \\ -2x + y + 3z = -7 \\ x - 4y + 2z = 0 \end{cases}$

10. $\begin{cases} x_1 + 4x_2 + 3x_3 - 6x_4 = 5 \\ x_1 + 3x_2 + x_3 - 4x_4 = 3 \\ 2x_1 + 8x_2 + 7x_3 - 5x_4 = 11 \\ 2x_1 + 5x_2 \quad\quad - 6x_4 = 4 \end{cases}$

11. $\begin{cases} 2x + 3y - 5z = 15 \\ x + 2y - z = 4 \end{cases}$

12. The figure shows the intersections of three one-way streets. The numbers given represent traffic flow, in cars per hour, at a peak period (from 4 P.M. to 6 P.M.).

a. Use the idea that the number of cars entering each intersection per hour must equal the number of cars leaving per hour to set up a system of linear equations involving x, y, and z.

b. Use Gaussian elimination to solve the system.

c. If construction limits the value of z to 400, how many cars per hour must pass between the other intersections to keep traffic flowing?

6.3

13. Find values for x, y, and z so that the following matrices are equal:

$$\begin{bmatrix} 2x & y + 7 \\ z & 4 \end{bmatrix} = \begin{bmatrix} -10 & 13 \\ 6 & 4 \end{bmatrix}.$$

In Exercises 14–27, perform the indicated matrix operations given that A, B, C, and D are defined as follows. If an operation is not defined, state the reason.

$$A = \begin{bmatrix} 2 & -1 & 2 \\ 5 & 3 & -1 \end{bmatrix} \quad B = \begin{bmatrix} 0 & -2 \\ 3 & 2 \\ 1 & -5 \end{bmatrix}$$

$$C = \begin{bmatrix} 1 & 2 & 3 \\ -1 & 1 & 2 \\ -1 & 2 & 1 \end{bmatrix} \quad D = \begin{bmatrix} -2 & 3 & 1 \\ 3 & -2 & 4 \end{bmatrix}$$

14. $A + D$
15. $2B$
16. $D - A$
17. $B + C$
18. $3A + 2D$
19. $-2A + 4D$
20. $-5(A + D)$
21. AB
22. BA
23. BD
24. DB
25. $AB - BA$
26. $(A - D)C$
27. $B(AC)$

28. Solve for X in the matrix equation

$$3X + A = B,$$

where $A = \begin{bmatrix} 4 & 6 \\ -5 & 0 \end{bmatrix}$ and $B = \begin{bmatrix} -2 & -12 \\ 4 & 1 \end{bmatrix}.$

In Exercises 29–30, use nine pixels in a 3 × 3 grid and the color levels shown.

29. Write a 3×3 matrix that represents a digital photograph of the letter T in dark gray on a light gray background.

30. Find a matrix B so that $A + B$ increases the contrast of the letter T by changing the dark gray to black and the light gray to white.

The figure shows a right triangle in a rectangular coordinate system.

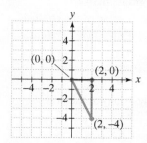

The figure can be represented by the matrix

$$B = \begin{bmatrix} 0 & 2 & 2 \\ 0 & 0 & -4 \end{bmatrix}.$$

Use the triangle and the matrix that represents it to solve Exercises 31–36.

31. Use matrix operations to move the triangle 2 units to the left and 1 unit up. Then graph the triangle and its transformation in a rectangular coordinate system.

32. Use matrix operations to reduce the triangle to half its perimeter and move the reduced image 2 units down. Then graph the triangle and its transformation in a rectangular coordinate system.

In Exercises 33–36, find AB and graph the resulting image. What effect does the multiplication have on the triangle represented by matrix B?

33. $A = \begin{bmatrix} 1 & 0 \\ 0 & -1 \end{bmatrix}$

34. $A = \begin{bmatrix} -1 & 0 \\ 0 & 1 \end{bmatrix}$

35. $A = \begin{bmatrix} 0 & -1 \\ 1 & 0 \end{bmatrix}$

36. $A = \begin{bmatrix} 2 & 0 \\ 0 & 1 \end{bmatrix}$

6.4

In Exercises 37–38, find the products AB and BA to determine whether B is the multiplicative inverse of A.

37. $A = \begin{bmatrix} 2 & 7 \\ 1 & 4 \end{bmatrix}$, $B = \begin{bmatrix} 4 & -7 \\ -1 & 3 \end{bmatrix}$

38. $A = \begin{bmatrix} 1 & 0 & 0 \\ 0 & 2 & -7 \\ 0 & -1 & 4 \end{bmatrix}$, $B = \begin{bmatrix} 1 & 0 & 0 \\ 0 & 4 & 7 \\ 0 & 1 & 2 \end{bmatrix}$

In Exercises 39–42, find A^{-1}. Check that $AA^{-1} = I$ and $A^{-1}A = I$.

39. $A = \begin{bmatrix} 1 & -1 \\ -2 & 3 \end{bmatrix}$

40. $A = \begin{bmatrix} 0 & 1 \\ 5 & 3 \end{bmatrix}$

41. $A = \begin{bmatrix} 1 & 0 & -2 \\ 2 & 1 & 0 \\ 1 & 0 & -3 \end{bmatrix}$

42. $A = \begin{bmatrix} 1 & 3 & -2 \\ 4 & 13 & -7 \\ 5 & 16 & -8 \end{bmatrix}$

In Exercises 43–44,

    a. *Write each linear system as a matrix equation in the form $AX = B$.*

    b. *Solve the system using the inverse that is given for the coefficient matrix.*

43. $\begin{cases} x + y + 2z = 7 \\ y + 3z = -2 \\ 3x - 2z = 0 \end{cases}$ The inverse of $\begin{bmatrix} 1 & 1 & 2 \\ 0 & 1 & 3 \\ 3 & 0 & -2 \end{bmatrix}$ is $\begin{bmatrix} -2 & 2 & 1 \\ 9 & -8 & -3 \\ -3 & 3 & 1 \end{bmatrix}$.

44. $\begin{cases} x - y + 2z = 12 \\ y - z = -5 \\ x + 2z = 10 \end{cases}$ The inverse of $\begin{bmatrix} 1 & -1 & 2 \\ 0 & 1 & -1 \\ 1 & 0 & 2 \end{bmatrix}$ is $\begin{bmatrix} 2 & 2 & -1 \\ -1 & 0 & 1 \\ -1 & -1 & 1 \end{bmatrix}$.

45. Use the coding matrix $A = \begin{bmatrix} 3 & 2 \\ 4 & 3 \end{bmatrix}$ and its inverse $A^{-1} = \begin{bmatrix} 3 & -2 \\ -4 & 3 \end{bmatrix}$ to encode and then decode the word RULE.

6.5

In Exercises 46–51, evaluate each determinant.

46. $\begin{vmatrix} 3 & 2 \\ -1 & 5 \end{vmatrix}$

47. $\begin{vmatrix} -2 & -3 \\ -4 & -8 \end{vmatrix}$

48. $\begin{vmatrix} 2 & 4 & -3 \\ 1 & -1 & 5 \\ -2 & 4 & 0 \end{vmatrix}$

49. $\begin{vmatrix} 4 & 7 & 0 \\ -5 & 6 & 0 \\ 3 & 2 & -4 \end{vmatrix}$

50. $\begin{vmatrix} 1 & 1 & 0 & 2 \\ 0 & 3 & 2 & 1 \\ 0 & -2 & 4 & 0 \\ 0 & 3 & 0 & 1 \end{vmatrix}$

51. $\begin{vmatrix} 2 & 2 & 2 & 2 \\ 0 & 2 & 2 & 2 \\ 0 & 0 & 2 & 2 \\ 0 & 0 & 0 & 2 \end{vmatrix}$

In Exercises 52–55, use Cramer's Rule to solve each system.

52. $\begin{cases} x - 2y = 8 \\ 3x + 2y = -1 \end{cases}$

53. $\begin{cases} 7x + 2y = 0 \\ 2x + y = -3 \end{cases}$

54. $\begin{cases} x + 2y + 2z = 5 \\ 2x + 4y + 7z = 19 \\ -2x - 5y - 2z = 8 \end{cases}$

55. $\begin{cases} 2x + y = -4 \\ y - 2z = 0 \\ 3x - 2z = -11 \end{cases}$

56. Use the quadratic function $y = ax^2 + bx + c$ to model the following data:

x (Age of a Driver)	y (Average Number of Automobile Accidents per Day in the United States)
20	400
40	150
60	400

Use Cramer's Rule to determine values for a, b, and c. Then use the model to write a statement about the average number of automobile accidents in which 30-year-olds and 50-year-olds are involved daily.

CHAPTER 6 TEST

In Exercises 1–2, solve each system of equations using matrices.

1. $\begin{cases} x + 2y - z = -3 \\ 2x - 4y + z = -7 \\ -2x + 2y - 3z = 4 \end{cases}$

2. $\begin{cases} x - 2y + z = 2 \\ 2x - y - z = 1 \end{cases}$

In Exercises 3–6, let

$$A = \begin{bmatrix} 3 & 1 \\ 1 & 0 \\ 2 & 1 \end{bmatrix}, \quad B = \begin{bmatrix} 1 & -1 \\ 2 & 1 \end{bmatrix}, \quad \text{and} \quad C = \begin{bmatrix} 1 & 2 \\ -1 & 3 \end{bmatrix}.$$

Carry out the indicated operations.

3. $2B + 3C$

4. AB

5. C^{-1}

6. $BC - 3B$

7. If $A = \begin{bmatrix} 1 & 2 & 2 \\ 2 & 3 & 3 \\ 1 & -1 & -2 \end{bmatrix}$ and $B = \begin{bmatrix} -3 & 2 & 0 \\ 7 & -4 & 1 \\ -5 & 3 & -1 \end{bmatrix}$, show that B is the inverse of A.

8. Consider the system

$$\begin{cases} 3x + 5y = 9 \\ 2x - 3y = -13. \end{cases}$$

a. Express the system in the form $AX = B$, where A, X, and B are appropriate matrices.

b. Find A^{-1}, the inverse of the coefficient matrix.

c. Use A^{-1} to solve the given system.

9. Evaluate: $\begin{vmatrix} 4 & -1 & 3 \\ 0 & 5 & -1 \\ 5 & 2 & 4 \end{vmatrix}$.

10. Solve for x only using Cramer's Rule:

$$\begin{cases} 3x + y - 2z = -3 \\ 2x + 7y + 3z = 9 \\ 4x - 3y - z = 7. \end{cases}$$

CUMULATIVE REVIEW EXERCISES (CHAPTERS 1–6)

Solve each equation or inequality in Exercises 1–6.

1. $2x^2 = 4 - x$

2. $5x + 8 \le 7(1 + x)$

3. $\sqrt{2x + 4} - \sqrt{x + 3} - 1 = 0$

4. $3x^3 + 8x^2 - 15x + 4 = 0$

5. $e^{2x} - 14e^x + 45 = 0$

6. $\log_3 x + \log_3(x + 2) = 1$

7. Use matrices to solve this system:

$$\begin{cases} x - y + z = 17 \\ 2x + 3y + z = 8 \\ -4x + y + 5z = -2. \end{cases}$$

8. Solve for y using Cramer's Rule:

$$\begin{cases} x - 2y + z = 7 \\ 2x + y - z = 0 \\ 3x + 2y - 2z = -2. \end{cases}$$

9. If $f(x) = \sqrt{4x - 7}$, find $f^{-1}(x)$.

10. Graph: $f(x) = \dfrac{x}{x^2 - 16}$.

11. Use the graph of $f(x) = 4x^4 - 4x^3 - 25x^2 + x + 6$ shown in the figure to factor the polynomial completely.

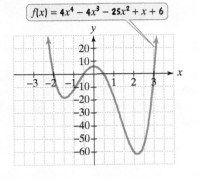

$f(x) = 4x^4 - 4x^3 - 25x^2 + x + 6$

12. Graph $y = \log_2 x$ and $y = \log_2(x + 1)$ in the same rectangular coordinate system.

13. Use the exponential decay model $A = A_0 e^{kt}$ to solve this problem. A radioactive substance has a half-life of 40 days. There are initially 900 grams of the substance.

a. Find the decay model for this substance. Round k to the nearest thousandth.

b. How much of the substance will remain after 10 days? Round to the nearest hundredth of a gram.

14. Multiply the matrices: $\begin{bmatrix} 1 & -1 & 0 \\ 2 & 1 & 3 \end{bmatrix} \begin{bmatrix} 4 & -1 \\ 2 & 0 \\ 1 & 1 \end{bmatrix}$.

15. Find the partial fraction decomposition of

$$\frac{3x^2 + 17x - 38}{(x - 3)(x - 2)(x + 2)}.$$

In Exercises 16–19, graph each equation, function, or inequality in a rectangular coordinate system.

16. $y = -\frac{2}{3}x - 1$

17. $3x - 5y < 15$

18. $f(x) = x^2 - 2x - 3$

19. $(x - 1)^2 + (y + 1)^2 = 9$

20. Use synthetic division to divide $x^3 - 6x + 4$ by $x - 2$.

APPENDIX

Where Did That Come From?
Selected Proofs

Properties of Logarithms

The Product Rule

Let b, M, and N be positive real numbers with $b \neq 1$.

$$\log_b(MN) = \log_b M + \log_b N$$

Proof

We begin by letting $\log_b M = R$ and $\log_b N = S$.
Now we write each logarithm in exponential form.

$$\log_b M = R \quad \text{means} \quad b^R = M.$$
$$\log_b N = S \quad \text{means} \quad b^S = N.$$

By substituting and using a property of exponents, we see that

$$MN = b^R b^S = b^{R+S}.$$

Now we change $MN = b^{R+S}$ to logarithmic form.

$$MN = b^{R+S} \quad \text{means} \quad \log_b(MN) = R + S.$$

Finally, substituting $\log_b M$ for R and $\log_b N$ for S gives us

$$\log_b(MN) = \log_b M + \log_b N,$$

the property that we wanted to prove.

The quotient and power rules for logarithms are proved using similar procedures.

The Change-of-Base Property

For any logarithmic bases a and b, and any positive number M,

$$\log_b M = \frac{\log_a M}{\log_a b}.$$

Proof

To prove the change-of-base property, we let x equal the logarithm on the left side:

$$\log_b M = x.$$

Now we rewrite this logarithm in exponential form.

$$\log_b M = x \quad \text{means} \quad b^x = M.$$

Because b^x and M are equal, the logarithms with base a for each of these expressions must be equal. This means that

$$\log_a b^x = \log_a M$$

$$x \log_a b = \log_a M \qquad \text{Apply the power rule for logarithms on the left side.}$$

$$x = \frac{\log_a M}{\log_a b} \qquad \text{Solve for x by dividing both sides by } \log_a b.$$

In our first step we let x equal $\log_b M$. Replacing x on the left side by $\log_b M$ gives us

$$\log_b M = \frac{\log_a M}{\log_a b},$$

which is the change-of-base property.

SECTION 7.1   The Ellipse

The Standard Form of the Equation of an Ellipse with a Horizontal Major Axis Centered at the Origin

Proof

Refer to **Figure A.1**.

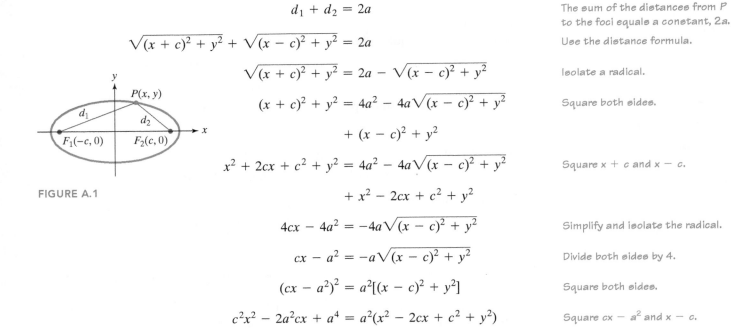

FIGURE A.1

$d_1 + d_2 = 2a$	The sum of the distances from P to the foci equals a constant, $2a$.
$\sqrt{(x+c)^2 + y^2} + \sqrt{(x-c)^2 + y^2} = 2a$	Use the distance formula.
$\sqrt{(x+c)^2 + y^2} = 2a - \sqrt{(x-c)^2 + y^2}$	Isolate a radical.
$(x+c)^2 + y^2 = 4a^2 - 4a\sqrt{(x-c)^2 + y^2}$ $\qquad + (x-c)^2 + y^2$	Square both sides.
$x^2 + 2cx + c^2 + y^2 = 4a^2 - 4a\sqrt{(x-c)^2 + y^2}$ $\qquad + x^2 - 2cx + c^2 + y^2$	Square $x + c$ and $x - c$.
$4cx - 4a^2 = -4a\sqrt{(x-c)^2 + y^2}$	Simplify and isolate the radical.
$cx - a^2 = -a\sqrt{(x-c)^2 + y^2}$	Divide both sides by 4.
$(cx - a^2)^2 = a^2[(x-c)^2 + y^2]$	Square both sides.
$c^2x^2 - 2a^2cx + a^4 = a^2(x^2 - 2cx + c^2 + y^2)$	Square $cx - a^2$ and $x - c$.
$c^2x^2 - 2a^2cx + a^4 = a^2x^2 - 2a^2cx + a^2c^2 + a^2y^2$	Use the distributive property.
$c^2x^2 + a^4 = a^2x^2 + a^2c^2 + a^2y^2$	Add $2a^2cx$ to both sides.
$c^2x^2 - a^2x^2 - a^2y^2 = a^2c^2 - a^4$	Rearrange the terms.
$(c^2 - a^2)x^2 - a^2y^2 = a^2(c^2 - a^2)$	Factor out x^2 and a^2, respectively.
$(a^2 - c^2)x^2 + a^2y^2 = a^2(a^2 - c^2)$	Multiply both sides by -1.

Refer to the discussion on page 662. Let $b^2 = a^2 - c^2$ in the preceding equation.

$b^2x^2 + a^2y^2 = a^2b^2$	
$\dfrac{x^2}{a^2} + \dfrac{y^2}{b^2} = 1$	Divide both sides by a^2b^2.

SECTION 7.2   The Hyperbola

The Asymptotes of a Hyperbola Centered at the Origin

The hyperbola

$$\frac{x^2}{a^2} - \frac{y^2}{b^2} = 1$$

with a horizontal transverse axis has the two asymptotes

$$y = \frac{b}{a}x \quad \text{and} \quad y = -\frac{b}{a}x.$$

Proof

Begin by solving the hyperbola's equation for y.

$$\frac{x^2}{a^2} - \frac{y^2}{b^2} = 1$$ This is the standard form of the equation of a hyperbola.

$$\frac{y^2}{b^2} = \frac{x^2}{a^2} - 1$$ We isolate the term involving y^2 to solve for y.

$$y^2 = \frac{b^2x^2}{a^2} - b^2$$ Multiply both sides by b^2.

$$y^2 = \frac{b^2x^2}{a^2}\left(1 - \frac{a^2}{x^2}\right)$$ Factor out $\frac{b^2x^2}{a^2}$ on the right. Verify that this result is correct by multiplying using the distributive property and obtaining the previous step.

$$y = \pm\sqrt{\frac{b^2x^2}{a^2}\left(1 - \frac{a^2}{x^2}\right)}$$ Solve for y using the square root property: If $u^2 = d$, then $u = \pm\sqrt{d}$.

$$y = \pm\frac{b}{a}x\sqrt{1 - \frac{a^2}{x^2}}$$ Simplify.

As $|x| \to \infty$, the value of $\frac{a^2}{x^2}$ approaches 0. Consequently, the value of y can be approximated by

$$y = \pm\frac{b}{a}x.$$

This means that the lines whose equations are $y = \frac{b}{a}x$ and $y = -\frac{b}{a}x$ are asymptotes for the graph of the hyperbola.

ANSWERS TO SELECTED EXERCISES

CHAPTER 2

Section 2.1

Check Point Exercises

1. domain: $\{0, 10, 20, 30, 40\}$; range: $\{9.1, 6.7, 10.7, 13.2, 21.2\}$ **2. a.** not a function   **b.** function   **3. a.** $y = 6 - 2x$; function
b. $y = \pm\sqrt{1 - x^2}$; not a function   **4. a.** 42   **b.** $x^2 + 6x + 15$ **c.** $x^2 + 2x + 7$
5. ; The graph of g is the graph of f shifted down by 3 units.
           6. a. function   **b.** not a function   **c.** function   **d.** not a function   **7. a.** 400   **b.** 9   **c.** approximately 425
           8. a. domain: $\{x \mid -2 \le x \le 1\}$ or $[-2, 1]$; range: $\{y \mid 0 \le y \le 3\}$ or $[0, 3]$
           b. domain: $\{x \mid -2 < x \le 1\}$ or $(-2, 1]$; range: $\{y \mid -1 \le y < 2\}$ or $[-1, 2)$
           c. domain: $\{x \mid -3 \le x < 0\}$ or $[-3, 0)$; range: $\{-3, -2, -1\}$

Concept and Vocabulary Check

1. relation; domain; range   **2.** function   **3.** f; x **4.** true   **5.** false   **6.** x; $x + 6$ **7.** ordered pairs   **8.** more than once; function
9. $[0, 3)$; domain   **10.** $[1, \infty)$; range   **11.** 0; 0; zeros   **12.** false

Exercise Set 2.1

1. function; $\{1, 3, 5\}$; $\{2, 4, 5\}$ **3.** not a function; $\{3, 4\}$; $\{4, 5\}$ **5.** function; $\{3, 4, 5, 7\}$; $\{-2, 1, 9\}$ **7.** function; $\{-3, -2, -1, 0\}$; $\{-3, -2, -1, 0\}$
9. not a function; $\{1\}$; $\{4, 5, 6\}$ **11.** y is a function of x.   **13.** y is a function of x.   **15.** y is not a function of x.   **17.** y is not a function of x.
19. y is a function of x.   **21.** y is a function of x.   **23.** y is a function of x.   **25.** y is a function of x.   **27. a.** 29   **b.** $4x + 9$ **c.** $-4x + 5$
29. a. 2   **b.** $x^2 + 12x + 38$ **c.** $x^2 - 2x + 3$ **31. a.** 13   **b.** 1   **c.** $x^4 - x^2 + 1$ **d.** $81a^4 - 9a^2 + 1$ **33. a.** 3   **b.** 7   **c.** $\sqrt{x} + 3$
35. a. $\dfrac{15}{4}$ **b.** $\dfrac{15}{4}$ **c.** $\dfrac{4x^2 - 1}{x^2}$ **37. a.** 1   **b.** -1 **c.** 1

39.

The graph of g is the graph of f shifted up by 3 units.

41.

The graph of g is the graph of f shifted down by 1 unit.

43.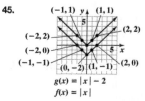

The graph of g is the graph of f shifted up by 1 unit.

45.

The graph of g is the graph of f shifted down by 2 units.

47.

$f(x) = x^3$
$g(x) = x^3 + 2$
(0, 2)
(-1, 1)
(2, 10)
(2, 8)
(1, 3)
(1, 1)
(0, 0)
(-1, -1)
(-2, -6)
(-2, -8)

The graph of g is the graph of f shifted up by 2 units.

49.

(0, 5)
(-1, 5)
(-2, 5)
(1, 5)
(2, 5)
$g(x) = 5$
(2, 3)
$f(x) = 3$
(-2, 3)
(-1, 3)
(0, 3)
(1, 3)

The graph of g is the graph of f shifted up by 2 units.

51.

(4, 2)   (9, 3)
(1, 1)
(0, 0)
$f(x) = \sqrt{x}$
$g(x) = \sqrt{x} - 1$
(0, -1)
(1, 0)   (4, 1)   (9, 2)

The graph of g is the graph of f shifted down by 1 unit.

53.

(4, 2)   (9, 3)
(1, 1)
$f(x) = \sqrt{x}$
$g(x) = \sqrt{x - 1}$
(10, 3)
(0, 0)
(1, 0)   (2, 1)   (5, 2)

The graph of g is the graph of f shifted to the right by 1 unit.

55. function   **57.** function   **59.** not a function   **61.** function   **63.** function   **65.** -4 **67.** 4   **69.** 0   **71.** 2   **73.** 2
75. -2 **77. a.** $(-\infty, \infty)$ **b.** $[-4, \infty)$ **c.** -3 and 1   **d.** -3 **e.** $f(-2) = -3$ and $f(2) = 5$ **79. a.** $(-\infty, \infty)$ **b.** $[1, \infty)$ **c.** none
d. 1   **e.** $f(-1) = 2$ and $f(3) = 4$ **81. a.** $[0, 5)$ **b.** $[-1, 5)$ **c.** 2   **d.** -1 **e.** $f(3) = 1$ **83. a.** $[0, \infty)$ **b.** $[1, \infty)$ **c.** none
d. 1   **e.** $f(4) = 3$ **85. a.** $[-2, 6]$ **b.** $[-2, 6]$ **c.** 4   **d.** 4   **e.** $f(-1) = 5$ **87. a.** $(-\infty, \infty)$ **b.** $(-\infty, -2]$ **c.** none
d. -2 **e.** $f(-4) = -5$ and $f(4) = -2$ **89. a.** $(-\infty, \infty)$ **b.** $(0, \infty)$ **c.** none   **d.** 1.5   **e.** $f(4) = 6$ **91. a.** $\{-5, -2, 0, 1, 3\}$
b. $\{2\}$ **c.** none   **d.** 2   **e.** $f(-5) + f(3) = 4$ **93.** $-2; 10$ **95.** -38 **97.** $-2x^3 - 2x$
99. a. {(Philippines, 12), (Spain, 13), (Italy, 14), (Germany, 14), (Russia, 16)}   **b.** yes; Each country corresponds to exactly one age.
c. {(12, Philippines), (13, Spain), (14, Italy), (14, Germany), (16, Russia)}   **d.** no; 14 in the domain corresponds to two members of the range, Italy and
Germany.   **101. a.** 83; The chance that a 60-year-old will survive to age 70 is 83%.   **b.** 76; The chance that a 60-year-old will survive to age 70 is 76%.
c. f **103. a.** 81; In 2010, the wage gap was 81%.; (30, 81)   **b.** underestimates by 2%   **105.** $C = 100,000 + 100x$, where x is the number of
bicycles produced; $C(90) = 109,000$; It costs \$109,000 to produce 90 bicycles.   **107.** $T = \dfrac{40}{x} + \dfrac{40}{x + 30}$, where x is the rate on the outgoing trip;
$T(30) = 2$; It takes 2 hours, traveling 30 mph outgoing and 60 mph returning.   **119.** does not make sense   **121.** does not make sense
123. false   **125.** false   **127.** Answers will vary; an example is {(1, 1), (2, 1)}.   **129.** 36; For 100 calling minutes, the monthly cost is \$36.
130.   **131.** $4xh + 2h^2 + 3h$

$f(x) = x + 2, x \le 1$
(1, 3)
(-2, -0)
(-5, -3)

Section 2.2

Check Point Exercises

1. increasing on $(-\infty, -1)$, decreasing on $(-1, 1)$, increasing on $(1, \infty)$ **2. a.** even   **b.** odd   **c.** neither
3. a. 20; With 40 calling minutes, the cost is \$20.; (40, 20)   **b.** 28; With 80 calling minutes, the cost is \$28.; (80, 28)
4.

(-4, 3)
(-1, 3)
(2, 0)
(-1, -3)

$f(x) = \begin{cases} 3 & \text{if } x \le -1 \\ x - 2 & \text{if } x > -1 \end{cases}$

5. a. $-2x^2 - 4xh - 2h^2 + x + h + 5$ **b.** $-4x - 2h + 1, h \ne 0$

Concept and Vocabulary Check

1. $< f(x_2); > f(x_2); = f(x_2)$ **2.** maximum; minimum   **3.** $f(x); y$-axis   **4.** $-f(x)$; origin   **5.** piecewise   **6.** less than or equal to x; $2; -3; 0$
7. difference quotient; $x + h; f(x); h; h$ **8.** false   **9.** false

Exercise Set 2.2

1. a. $(-1, \infty)$ **b.** $(-\infty, -1)$ **c.** none   **3. a.** $(0, \infty)$ **b.** none   **c.** none   **5. a.** none   **b.** $(-2, 6)$ **c.** none   **7. a.** $(-\infty, -1)$
b. none   **c.** $(-1, \infty)$ **9. a.** $(-\infty, 0)$ or $(1.5, 3)$ **b.** $(0, 1.5)$ or $(3, \infty)$ **c.** none   **11. a.** $(-2, 4)$ **b.** none   **c.** $(-\infty, -2)$ or $(4, \infty)$

13. a. 0; $f(0) = 4$ **b.** $-3, 3; f(-3) = f(3) = 0$ **15. a.** $-2; f(-2) = 21$ **b.** 1; $f(1) = -6$ **17.** odd   **19.** neither   **21.** even   **23.** even
25. even   **27.** odd   **29.** even   **31.** odd   **33. a.** $(-\infty, \infty)$ **b.** $[-4, \infty)$ **c.** 1 and 7   **d.** 4   **e.** $(4, \infty)$ **f.** $(0, 4)$ **g.** $(-\infty, 0)$
h. 4   **i.** -4 **j.** 4   **k.** 2 and 6   **l.** neither   **35. a.** $(-\infty, 3]$ **b.** $(-\infty, 4]$ **c.** -3 and 3   **d.** 3   **e.** $(-\infty, 1)$ **f.** $(1, 3)$ **g.** $(-\infty, -3]$
h. A relative maximum of 4 occurs at 1.   **i.** 1   **j.** positive   **37. a.** -1 **b.** 7   **c.** 19   **39. a.** 3   **b.** 3   **c.** 0   **41. a.** 8   **b.** 3   **c.** 6

43. a.

$f(x) = \begin{cases} -x \text{ if } x < 0 \\ x \text{ if } x \geq 0 \end{cases}$

b. $[0, \infty)$

45. a.

$f(x) = \begin{cases} 2x \text{ if } x \leq 0 \\ 2 \text{ if } x > 0 \end{cases}$

b. $(-\infty, 0] \cup \{2\}$

47. a.

$f(x) = \begin{cases} x + 3 \text{ if } x < -2 \\ x - 3 \text{ if } x \geq -2 \end{cases}$

b. $(-\infty, \infty)$

49. a.

$f(x) = \begin{cases} 3 \text{ if } x \leq -1 \\ -3 \text{ if } x > -1 \end{cases}$

b. $\{-3, 3\}$

51. a.

$f(x) = \begin{cases} \frac{1}{2}x^2 \text{ if } x < 1 \\ 2x - 1 \text{ if } x \geq 1 \end{cases}$

b. $[0, \infty)$

53. a.

$f(x) = \begin{cases} 0 \text{ if } x < -4 \\ -x \text{ if } -4 \leq x < 0 \\ x^2 \text{ if } x \geq 0 \end{cases}$

b. $[0, \infty)$

55. $4, h \neq 0$ **57.** $3, h \neq 0$ **59.** $2x + h, h \neq 0$ **61.** $2x + h - 4, h \neq 0$ **63.** $4x + 2h + 1, h \neq 0$ **65.** $-2x - h + 2, h \neq 0$
67. $-4x - 2h + 5, h \neq 0$ **69.** $-4x - 2h - 1, h \neq 0$ **71.** $0, h \neq 0$ **73.** $-\dfrac{1}{x(x + h)}, h \neq 0$ **75.** $\dfrac{1}{\sqrt{x + h} + \sqrt{x}}, h \neq 0$ **77.** -18

79. $0.30t - 6$

81. $C(t) = \begin{cases} 50 & \text{if } 0 \leq t \leq 400 \\ 50 + 0.30(t - 400) & \text{if } t > 400 \end{cases}$

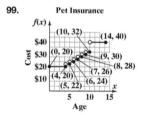

83. increasing: $(25, 55)$; decreasing: $(55, 75)$ **85.** 55 years old; 38%   **87.** domain: $[25, 75]$; range: $[34, 38]$ **89.** men
91. 2575; A single taxpayer with taxable income of $20,000 owes $2575.   **93.** $42,449 + 0.33(x - 174,400)$
95. 0.85; It costs $0.85 to mail a 3-ounce first-class letter.   **97.** $0.65

99.

107.

increasing: $(-\infty, 1)$ or $(3, \infty)$
decreasing: $(1, 3)$

109.

increasing: $(2, \infty)$
decreasing: $(-\infty, -2)$
constant: $(-2, 2)$

111.

increasing: $(0, \infty)$
decreasing: $(-\infty, 0)$
c. increasing: $(0, \infty)$; decreasing: $(-\infty, 0)$

113. a.

b.

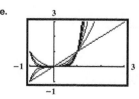

d. $f(x) = x^n$ is increasing for $(-\infty, \infty)$ when n is positive and odd.   **e.**

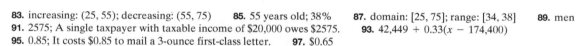

115. makes sense   **117.** makes sense   **122.** 3   **123.** $\left(\dfrac{3}{2}, 0\right)$ and $(0, -2)$
124. $y = \dfrac{-3x + 4}{2}$ or $y = -\dfrac{3}{2}x + 2$

As n increases the steepness
increases.

Section 2.3
Check Point Exercises

1. a. 6   **b.** $-\dfrac{7}{5}$ **2.** $y + 5 = 6(x - 2); y = 6x - 17$ **3.** $y + 1 = -5(x + 2)$ or $y + 6 = -5(x + 1); y = -5x - 11$

4.

$f(x) = \dfrac{3}{5}x + 1$

5.

6.

7. slope: $-\dfrac{1}{2}$; y-intercept: 2

$3x + 6y - 12 = 0$

8.

$3x - 2y - 6 = 0$

9. $f(x) = 0.016x + 52.0; 61.6°F$

Concept and Vocabulary Check

1. scatter plot; regression   **2.** $\dfrac{y_2 - y_1}{x_2 - x_1}$ **3.** positive   **4.** negative   **5.** zero   **6.** undefined   **7.** $y - y_1 = m(x - x_1)$

8. $y = mx + b$; slope; y-intercept   **9.** $(0, 3); 2; 5$ **10.** horizontal   **11.** vertical   **12.** general

Exercise Set 2.3

1. $\dfrac{3}{4}$; rises   **3.** $\dfrac{1}{4}$; rises   **5.** 0; horizontal   **7.** -5; falls   **9.** undefined; vertical   **11.** $y - 5 = 2(x - 3); y = 2x - 1$

13. $y - 5 = 6(x + 2); y = 6x + 17$ **15.** $y + 3 = -3(x + 2); y = -3x - 9$ **17.** $y - 0 = -4(x + 4); y = -4x - 16$

19. $y + 2 = -1\left(x + \dfrac{1}{2}\right); y = -x - \dfrac{5}{2}$ **21.** $y - 0 = \dfrac{1}{2}(x - 0); y = \dfrac{1}{2}x$ **23.** $y + 2 = -\dfrac{2}{3}(x - 6); y = -\dfrac{2}{3}x + 2$

25. using $(1, 2), y - 2 = 2(x - 1); y = 2x$ **27.** using $(-3, 0), y - 0 = 1(x + 3); y = x + 3$ **29.** using $(-3, -1), y + 1 = 1(x + 3); y = x + 2$

31. using $(-3, -2), y + 2 = \dfrac{4}{3}(x + 3); y = \dfrac{4}{3}x + 2$ **33.** using $(-3, -1), y + 1 = 0(x + 3); y = -1$ **35.** using $(2, 4), y - 4 = 1(x - 2); y = x + 2$

37. using $(0, 4), y - 4 = 8(x - 0); y = 8x + 4$

39. $m = 2; b = 1$

$y = 2x + 1$

41. $m = -2; b = 1$

$f(x) = -2x + 1$

43. $m = \dfrac{3}{4}; b = -2$

$f(x) = \dfrac{3}{4}x - 2$

45. $m = -\dfrac{3}{5}; b = 7$

$y = -\dfrac{3}{5}x + 7$

47. $m = -\dfrac{1}{2}; b = 0$

$g(x) = -\dfrac{1}{2}x$

49. $y = -2$

51. $x = -3$

53. $y = 0$

55. $f(x) = 1$

57.

$3x - 18 = 0$

59. a. $y = -3x + 5$ **b.** $m = -3; b = 5$ **c.**

$3x + y - 5 = 0$

61. a. $y = -\dfrac{2}{3}x + 6$ **b.** $m = -\dfrac{2}{3}; b = 6$ **c.**

$2x + 3y - 18 = 0$

63. a. $y = 2x - 3$ **b.** $m = 2; b = -3$ **c.**

$8x - 4y - 12 = 0$

65. a. $y = 3$ **b.** $m = 0; b = 3$ **c.**

$3y - 9 = 0$

67.

$6x - 2y - 12 = 0$

69. $2x + 3y + 6 = 0$

71. $8x - 2y + 12 = 0$

73. $m = -\dfrac{a}{b}$; falls

75. undefined slope; vertical

77. $m = -\dfrac{A}{B}; b = \dfrac{C}{B}$

79. -2

81. $3x - 4f(x) - 6 = 0$

83. 5

85. m_1, m_3, m_2, m_4

87. a. $y - 31.1 = 0.78(x - 10)$ or $y - 38.9 = 0.78(x - 20)$ **b.** $f(x) = 0.78x + 23.3$ **c.** 54.5%

89. a & b. Life Expectancy for United States; $E(x) = 0.215x + 65.7$

c. 78.6 yr

91. Answers will vary; an example is $y = -2.3x + 255$, where x is the percentage of adult females who are literate and y is under-five mortality per thousand.; Predictions will vary.

101. $m = -3$

103. $m = \dfrac{3}{4}$

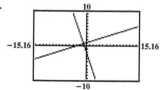

105. does not make sense **107.** does not make sense
109. false **111.** true
113. coefficient of x: -6; coefficient of y: 3
118. $y = 2x + 7$ or $f(x) = 2x + 7$
119. $4x - y - 17 = 0$ **120.** 5

Section 2.4

Check Point Exercises

1. $y - 5 = 3(x + 2)$; $y = 3x + 11$ or $f(x) = 3x + 11$ **2. a.** 3 **b.** $3x - y = 0$ **3.** $m \approx 0.32$; The number of men living alone increased at a rate of 0.32 million per year. The rate of change is 0.32 million men per year. **4. a.** 1 **b.** 7 **c.** 4 **5.** 0.01 mg per 100 ml per hr

Concept and Vocabulary Check

1. the same **2.** -1 **3.** $-\dfrac{1}{3}$; 3 **4.** -2; $\dfrac{1}{2}$ **5.** y; x **6.** $\dfrac{f(x_2) - f(x_1)}{x_2 - x_1}$

Exercise Set 2.4

1. $y - 2 = 2(x - 4)$; $y = 2x - 6$ or $f(x) = 2x - 6$ **3.** $y - 4 = -\dfrac{1}{2}(x - 2)$; $y = -\dfrac{1}{2}x + 5$ or $f(x) = -\dfrac{1}{2}x + 5$

5. $y + 10 = -4(x + 8)$; $y = -4x - 42$ **7.** $y + 3 = -5(x - 2)$; $y = -5x + 7$ **9.** $y - 2 = \dfrac{2}{3}(x + 2)$; $2x - 3y + 10 = 0$

11. $y + 7 = -2(x - 4)$; $2x + y - 1 = 0$ **13.** 3 **15.** 10 **17.** $\dfrac{1}{5}$ **19.** $f(x) = 5$ **21.** $f(x) = -\dfrac{1}{2}x + 1$ **23.** $f(x) = -\dfrac{2}{3}x - 2$

25. $p(x) = -0.25x + 22$ **27.** 137; There was an average increase of approximately 137 discharges per year.
29. a. 142 **b.** overestimates by 5 discharges per year
37. a. The product of their slopes is -1.
b. ; no **c.** ; The lines now appear to be perpendicular.

39. makes sense **41.** makes sense **43.** $-\dfrac{3}{7}$

44. a. $f(x) = |x|$ **b.** **c.** The graph in part (b) is the graph in part (a) shifted down 4 units.

45. a. $f(x) = x^2$ **b.** **c.** The graph in part (b) is the graph in part (a) shifted to the right 2 units.

46. a. **b.** **c.** The graph in part (b) is the graph in part (a) reflected across the y-axis.

Mid-Chapter 2 Check Point

1. not a function; domain: $\{1, 2\}$; range: $\{-6, 4, 6\}$ **2.** function; domain: $\{0, 2, 3\}$; range: $\{1, 4\}$ **3.** function; domain: $\{x \mid -2 \le x < 2\}$ or $[-2, 2)$; range: $\{y \mid 0 \le y \le 3\}$ or $[0, 3]$ **4.** not a function; domain: $\{x \mid -3 < x \le 4\}$ or $(-3, 4]$; range: $\{y \mid -1 \le y \le 2\}$ or $[-1, 2]$ **5.** not a function; domain: $\{-2, -1, 0, 1, 2\}$; range: $\{-2, -1, 1, 3\}$ **6.** function; domain: $\{x \mid x \le 1\}$ or $(-\infty, 1]$; range: $\{y \mid y \ge -1\}$ or $[-1, \infty)$ **7.** y is a function of x. **8.** y is not a function of x. **9.** No vertical line intersects the graph in more than one point. **10.** $(-\infty, \infty)$ **11.** $(-\infty, 4]$ **12.** -6 and 2 **13.** 3 **14.** $(-\infty, -2)$ **15.** $(-2, \infty)$ **16.** -2 **17.** 4 **18.** 3 **19.** -7 and 3 **20.** -6 and 2 **21.** $(-6, 2)$ **22.** negative **23.** neither **24.** -1

25. $y = -2x$ **26.** $y = -2$ **27.** $x + y = -2$ **28.** $y = \frac{1}{3}x - 2$ **29.** $x = 3.5$

30. $4x - 2y = 8$ **31.** $f(x) = x^2 - 4$ **32.** $f(x) = x - 4$ **33.** $f(x) = |x| - 4$ **34.** $5y = -3x$

35. $5y = 20$ **36.** $f(x) = \begin{cases} -1 \text{ if } x \le 0 \\ 2x + 1 \text{ if } x > 0 \end{cases}$

37. a. $f(-x) = -2x^2 - x - 5$; neither **b.** $-4x - 2h + 1, h \ne 0$ **38. a.** 30 **b.** 50 **39.** $f(x) = -2x - 5$ **40.** $f(x) = 2x - 3$ **41.** $f(x) = 3x - 13$ **42.** $f(x) = -\frac{5}{2}x - 13$ **43.** The lines are parallel. **44. a.** 0.16 **b.** $0.16; 0.16$; minute of brisk walking **45.** 2

Section 2.5

Check Point Exercises

1. **2.** **3.** **4.** **5.**

6. **7. a.** $g(x) = f(2x)$ **b.** $h(x) = f\left(\frac{1}{2}x\right)$ **8.** $y = -\frac{1}{3}f(x + 1) - 2$ **9.** $g(x) = 2(x - 1)^2 + 3$

Concept and Vocabulary Check

1. vertical; down **2.** horizontal; to the right **3.** x-axis **4.** y-axis **5.** vertical; y **6.** horizontal; x **7.** false

Exercise Set 2.5

1. $g(x) = f(x) + 1$ **3.** $g(x) = f(x + 1)$ **5.** $g(x) = f(x - 1) - 2$ **7.** $g(x) = f(-x)$ **9.** $g(x) = -f(x) + 3$

11. $g(x) = \frac{1}{2}f(x)$ **13.** $g(x) = f\left(\frac{1}{2}x\right)$ **15.** $g(x) = -f\left(\frac{1}{2}x\right) + 1$ **17.** $g(x) = f(x) - 1$ **19.** $g(x) = f(x - 1)$

21.

(−3, 2) (3, 4) (1, 2) (5, 2) (−1, 0)

$g(x) = f(x − 1) + 2$

23.

(−2, 2) (4, 0) (−4, 0) (0, 0) (2, −2)

$g(x) = −f(x)$

25.

(−2, 3) (−4, 1) (4, 1) (0, 1) (2, −1)

$g(x) = f(−x) + 1$

27.

(2, 4) (−4, 0) (0, 0) (4, 0) (−2, −4)

$g(x) = 2f(x)$

29.

(1, 2) (−2, 0) (2, 0) (0, 0) (−1, −2)

$g(x) = f(2x)$

31.

(0, 5) (−6, 1) (−2, 1) (2, 1) (−4, −3)

$g(x) = 2f(x + 2) + 1$

33.

(−4, 2) (0, 2) (0, 0) (4, 0)

$g(x) = f(x) + 2$

35.

(−6, 0) (−2, 0) (−2, −2) (2, −2)

$g(x) = f(x + 2)$

37.

(−2, 2) (2, 2) (−6, 0) (−2, 0)

$g(x) = −f(x + 2)$

39.

(−2, 1) (2, 1) (−6, 0) (−2, 0)

$g(x) = −\frac{1}{2}f(x + 2)$

41.

(−2, −1) (−6, −2) (2, −1) (−2, −2)

$g(x) = −\frac{1}{2}f(x + 2) − 2$

43.

(−2, 0) (0, 0) (0, −1) (2, −1)

$g(x) = \frac{1}{2}f(2x)$

45.

(1, 1) (3, 1) (−1, −1) (−3, −3) (5, −1)

$g(x) = f(x − 1) − 1$

47.

(−3, 3) (3, −1) (5, 1) (−1, 1) (1, −1)

$g(x) = −f(x − 1) + 1$

49.

(0, 4) (4, 4) (−4, 0) (8, 0) (−8, −4)

$g(x) = 2f\left(\frac{1}{2}x\right)$

51.

(−1, 1) (1, 1) (−5, −1) (−3, 0) (3, 0)

$g(x) = \frac{1}{2}f(x + 1)$

53.

(0, 0) (−2, 4) (2, 4) (−2, 2) (2, 2) (0, −2) *fg*

55.

(0, 4) (2, 4) (−2, 4) (4, 4) (0, 0) (2, 0) *f g*

57.

(−2, 4) (2, 4) (0, 0) (2, 0) (0, −4) (4, −4) *f h*

59.

(1, 2) (−1, 1) (3, 2) (0, 0) (1, 1) (2, 1) *f h*

61.

(1, 2) (−1, 1) (3, 2) (0, 0) (2, 0) (1, 1) *f g*

63.

(1, 1) (−1, 1) (3, 1) (0, 0) (2, −1) *f h*

65.

(−1, 1) (1, 1) (−2, −1) (0, −1) *f* *h*

67.

(1, 3) (4, 4) (0, 2) (4, 2) (0, 0) (1, 1) *g* *f*

69.

(2, 2) (4, 2) (−1, 1) (1, 1) (−2, 0) (0, 0) *g f*

71.

(1, 1) (0, 0) (4, 2) (−2, 0) (−1, −1) (2, −2) *f* *h*

73.

(−2, 2) (1, 1) (4, 2) (0, 0) (2, 0) *h* *f*

75.

(4, 2) (−2, 0) (0, 0) (2, 1) *f g*

77.

(1, 1) (4, 2) (0, 0) (−1, −1) (2, 0) (−2, −2) *f h*

79.

(2, 2) (−1, 0) (4, 2) (0, 0) (1, 1) (−2, −2) *g f*

81.

(−2, 6) (2, 6) (0, 4) (−2, 2) (2, 2) (0, 0) *g f*

83.

(−2, 2) (−6, 0) (−4, 0) (2, 2) (0, 0) *g f*

85.

(−2, 2) (−6, 0) (−4, −2) (2, 2) (−2, 0) *h f*

87.

(−1, 1) (0, 0) (−4, 0) (−5, −1) (1, 1) (−3, −1) *f* *h*

89.

(−1, 1) (0, 0) (−4, 1) (−5, 0) (1, 1) (−3, 0) *f* *g*

91.

(−3, 2) (−1, 1) (−5, 2) (−4, 0) (1, 1) (0, 0) *h* *f*

93.

(−2, 2) (−4, 1) (2, 2) (−6, −3) (0, 0) (−2, −3) *f* *g*

95.

(1, 1) (0, 0) (−1, −1) (1, −2) (−1, −4) (0, −3) *f g*

97.

(1, 1) (0, 0) (4, 1) (−1, −1) (3, 0) (2, −1) *f* *g*

99.

(−1, 1) (1, 1) (−1, −1) (1, −1) (0, 0) *h* *f* *f* *h*

101.

(1, 1) (1, ½) (0, 0) (−1, −½) (−1, −1) *f h*

103.

(1, 1) (3, 2) (0, 0) (2, 1) (4, 3) (−1, −1) *f r*

105.

(1, 1) (0, 0) (−1, −1) (2, −5/2) (3, −2) (4, −3/2) *f h*

107.

(0, 2) (1, 3) (−1, 1) (1, 1) (−1, −1) *g f*

109.

(−1, 1) (−2, 0) (1, 1) (−3, −1) (0, 0) (−1, −1) *g f*

111.

(−1, ½) (−2, 0) (1, 1) (−3, −½) (0, 0) (−1, −1) *f h*

113.

(0, 0) (1, 1) (−1, −1) (−3, −5/2) (−2, 2) (−1, −3/2) *f r*

115.

(−2, 0) (0, 0) (−3, 1) (1, 1) (−1, −1) *f h*

117.

(0, 0) (−3, 1) (1, 1) (−2, 0) (−1, −1) *f g*

119.

(1, 4) (0, 2) (−1, 0) (−2, −2) (−3, −4)

$g(x) = 2\,\text{int}\,(x + 1)$

121. $(-1, 2)$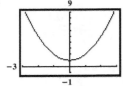

$h(x) = \text{int}(-x) + 1$

123. $y = \sqrt{x - 2}$ **125.** $y = (x + 1)^2 - 4$
127. a. First, vertically stretch the graph of $f(x) = \sqrt{x}$ by the factor 2.9; then, shift the result up 20.1 units.   **b.** 40.2 in.; very well
c. 0.9 in. per month   **d.** 0.2 in. per month; This is a much smaller rate of change; The graph is not as steep between 50 and 60 as it is between 0 and 10.

135. a.

b.

137. makes sense   **139.** does not make sense   **141.** false   **143.** false   **145.** $g(x) = -(x + 4)^2$ **147.** $g(x) = -\sqrt{x - 2} + 2$

149. $(-a, b)$ **151.** $(a + 3, b)$ **153.** $2x^3 + x^2 - 5x + 2$ **154.** $9x^2 - 30x + 30$ **155.** $\dfrac{2x}{3 - x}$

Section 2.6

Check Point Exercises

1. a. $(-\infty, \infty)$ **b.** $(-\infty, -7) \cup (-7, 7) \cup (7, \infty)$ **c.** $[3, \infty)$ **d.** $(-\infty, 8)$ **2. a.** $(f + g)(x) = x^2 + x - 6; (-\infty, \infty)$

b. $(f - g)(x) = -x^2 + x - 4; (-\infty, \infty)$ **c.** $(fg)(x) = x^3 - 5x^2 - x + 5; (-\infty, \infty)$ **d.** $\left(\dfrac{f}{g}\right)(x) = \dfrac{x - 5}{x^2 - 1}; (-\infty, -1) \cup (-1, 1) \cup (1, \infty)$

3. a. $(f + g)(x) = \sqrt{x - 3} + \sqrt{x + 1}$ **b.** $[3, \infty)$ **4. a.** $(B + D)(x) = -3.2x^2 + 56x + 6406$ **b.** 6545.2 thousand   **c.** overestimates by

7.2 thousand   **5. a.** $(f \circ g)(x) = 10x^2 - 5x + 1$ **b.** $(g \circ f)(x) = 50x^2 + 115x + 65$ **c.** 16   **6. a.** $(f \circ g)(x) = \dfrac{4x}{1 + 2x}$

b. $\left(-\infty, -\dfrac{1}{2}\right) \cup \left(-\dfrac{1}{2}, 0\right) \cup (0, \infty)$ **7.** If $f(x) = \sqrt{x}$ and $g(x) = x^2 + 5$, then $h(x) = (f \circ g)(x)$.

Concept and Vocabulary Check

1. zero   **2.** negative   **3.** $f(x) + g(x)$ **4.** $f(x) - g(x)$ **5.** $f(x) \cdot g(x)$ **6.** $\dfrac{f(x)}{g(x)}; g(x)$ **7.** $(-\infty, \infty)$ **8.** $(2, \infty)$ **9.** $(0, 3); (3, \infty)$

10. composition; $f(g(x))$ **11.** $f; g(x)$ **12.** composition; $g(f(x))$ **13.** $g; f(x)$ **14.** false   **15.** false   **16.** 2

Exercise Set 2.6

1. $(-\infty, \infty)$ **3.** $(-\infty, 4) \cup (4, \infty)$ **5.** $(-\infty, \infty)$ **7.** $(-\infty, -3) \cup (-3, 5) \cup (5, \infty)$ **9.** $(-\infty, -7) \cup (-7, 9) \cup (9, \infty)$
11. $(-\infty, -1) \cup (-1, 1) \cup (1, \infty)$ **13.** $(-\infty, 0) \cup (0, 3) \cup (3, \infty)$ **15.** $(-\infty, 1) \cup (1, 3) \cup (3, \infty)$ **17.** $[3, \infty)$ **19.** $(3, \infty)$ **21.** $[-7, \infty)$
23. $(-\infty, 12]$ **25.** $[2, \infty)$ **27.** $[2, 5) \cup (5, \infty)$ **29.** $(-\infty, -2) \cup (-2, 2) \cup (2, 5) \cup (5, \infty)$

31. $(f + g)(x) = 3x + 2$; domain: $(-\infty, \infty)$; $(f - g)(x) = x + 4$; domain: $(-\infty, \infty)$; $(fg)(x) = 2x^2 + x - 3$; domain: $(-\infty, \infty)$; $\left(\dfrac{f}{g}\right)(x) = \dfrac{2x + 3}{x - 1}$;
domain: $(-\infty, 1) \cup (1, \infty)$ **33.** $(f + g)(x) = 3x^2 + x - 5$; domain: $(-\infty, \infty)$; $(f - g)(x) = -3x^2 + x - 5$; domain: $(-\infty, \infty)$; $(fg)(x) = 3x^3 - 15x^2$;
domain: $(-\infty, \infty)$; $\left(\dfrac{f}{g}\right)(x) = \dfrac{x - 5}{3x^2}$; domain: $(-\infty, 0) \cup (0, \infty)$ **35.** $(f + g)(x) = 2x^2 - 2$; domain: $(-\infty, \infty)$; $(f - g)(x) = 2x^2 - 2x - 4$;
domain: $(-\infty, \infty)$; $(fg)(x) = 2x^3 + x^2 - 4x - 3$; domain: $(-\infty, \infty)$; $\left(\dfrac{f}{g}\right)(x) = 2x - 3$; domain: $(-\infty, -1) \cup (-1, \infty)$
37. $(f + g)(x) = 2x - 12$; domain: $(-\infty, \infty)$; $(f - g)(x) = -2x^2 - 2x + 18$; domain: $(-\infty, \infty)$; $(fg)(x) = -x^4 - 2x^3 + 18x^2 + 6x - 45$;
domain: $(-\infty, \infty)$; $\left(\dfrac{f}{g}\right)(x) = \dfrac{3 - x^2}{x^2 + 2x - 15}$; domain: $(-\infty, -5) \cup (-5, 3) \cup (3, \infty)$
39. $(f + g)(x) = \sqrt{x} + x - 4$; domain: $[0, \infty)$; $(f - g)(x) = \sqrt{x} - x + 4$; domain: $[0, \infty)$; $(fg)(x) = \sqrt{x}(x - 4)$; domain: $[0, \infty)$; $\left(\dfrac{f}{g}\right)(x) = \dfrac{\sqrt{x}}{x - 4}$;
domain: $[0, 4) \cup (4, \infty)$ **41.** $(f + g)(x) = \dfrac{2x + 2}{x}$; domain: $(-\infty, 0) \cup (0, \infty)$; $(f - g)(x) = 2$; domain: $(-\infty, 0) \cup (0, \infty)$; $(fg)(x) = \dfrac{2x + 1}{x^2}$;
domain: $(-\infty, 0) \cup (0, \infty)$; $\left(\dfrac{f}{g}\right)(x) = 2x + 1$; domain: $(-\infty, 0) \cup (0, \infty)$ **43.** $(f + g)(x) = \dfrac{9x - 1}{x^2 - 9}$; domain:
$(-\infty, -3) \cup (-3, 3) \cup (3, \infty)$; $(f - g)(x) = \dfrac{x + 3}{x^2 - 9} = \dfrac{1}{x - 3}$; domain: $(-\infty, -3) \cup (-3, 3) \cup (3, \infty)$; $(fg)(x) = \dfrac{20x^2 - 6x - 2}{(x^2 - 9)^2}$;
domain: $(-\infty, -3) \cup (-3, 3) \cup (3, \infty)$; $\left(\dfrac{f}{g}\right)(x) = \dfrac{5x + 1}{4x - 2}$; domain: $(-\infty, -3) \cup \left(-3, \dfrac{1}{2}\right) \cup \left(\dfrac{1}{2}, 3\right) \cup (3, \infty)$ **45.** $(f + g)(x) = \dfrac{8x^2 + 30x - 12}{(x - 2)(x + 3)}$;
domain: $(-\infty, -3) \cup (-3, 2) \cup (2, \infty)$; $(f - g)(x) = \dfrac{8x^2 + 18x + 12}{(x - 2)(x + 3)}$; domain: $(-\infty, -3) \cup (-3, 2) \cup (2, \infty)$; $(fg)(x) = \dfrac{48x}{(x - 2)(x + 3)}$;
domain: $(-\infty, -3) \cup (-3, 2) \cup (2, \infty)$; $\left(\dfrac{f}{g}\right)(x) = \dfrac{4x(x + 3)}{3(x - 2)}$; domain: $(-\infty, -3) \cup (-3, 2) \cup (2, \infty)$ **47.** $(f + g)(x) = \sqrt{x + 4} + \sqrt{x - 1}$;
domain: $[1, \infty)$; $(f - g)(x) = \sqrt{x + 4} - \sqrt{x - 1}$; domain: $[1, \infty)$; $(fg)(x) = \sqrt{x^2 + 3x - 4}$; domain: $[1, \infty)$; $\left(\dfrac{f}{g}\right)(x) = \dfrac{\sqrt{x + 4}}{\sqrt{x - 1}}$; domain: $(1, \infty)$

49. $(f + g)(x) = \sqrt{x - 2} + \sqrt{2 - x}$; domain: $\{2\}$; $(f - g)(x) = \sqrt{x - 2} - \sqrt{2 - x}$; domain: $\{2\}$; $(fg)(x) = \sqrt{x - 2} \cdot \sqrt{2 - x}$; domain: $\{2\}$; $\left(\dfrac{f}{g}\right)(x) = \dfrac{\sqrt{x - 2}}{\sqrt{2 - x}}$; domain: $\varnothing$ **51. a.** $(f \circ g)(x) = 2x + 14$ **b.** $(g \circ f)(x) = 2x + 7$ **c.** $(f \circ g)(2) = 18$ **d.** $(g \circ f)(2) = 11$
53. a. $(f \circ g)(x) = 2x + 5$ **b.** $(g \circ f)(x) = 2x + 9$ **c.** $(f \circ g)(2) = 9$ **d.** $(g \circ f)(2) = 13$ **55. a.** $(f \circ g)(x) = 20x^2 - 11$
b. $(g \circ f)(x) = 80x^2 - 120x + 43$ **c.** $(f \circ g)(2) = 69$ **d.** $(g \circ f)(2) = 123$ **57. a.** $(f \circ g)(x) = x^4 - 4x^2 + 6$ **b.** $(g \circ f)(x) = x^4 + 4x^2 + 2$
c. $(f \circ g)(2) = 6$ **d.** $(g \circ f)(2) = 34$ **59. a.** $(f \circ g)(x) = -2x^2 - x - 1$ **b.** $(g \circ f)(x) = 2x^2 - 17x + 41$ **c.** $(f \circ g)(2) = -11$ **d.** $(g \circ f)(2) = 15$
61. a. $(f \circ g)(x) = \sqrt{x - 1}$ **b.** $(g \circ f)(x) = \sqrt{x} - 1$ **c.** $(f \circ g)(2) = 1$ **d.** $(g \circ f)(2) = \sqrt{2} - 1$ **63. a.** $(f \circ g)(x) = x$ **b.** $(g \circ f)(x) = x$
c. $(f \circ g)(2) = 2$ **d.** $(g \circ f)(2) = 2$ **65. a.** $(f \circ g)(x) = x$ **b.** $(g \circ f)(x) = x$ **c.** 2   **d.** $(g \circ f)(2) = 2$ **67. a.** $(f \circ g)(x) = \dfrac{2x}{1 + 3x}$
b. $\left(-\infty, -\dfrac{1}{3}\right) \cup \left(-\dfrac{1}{3}, 0\right) \cup (0, \infty)$ **69. a.** $(f \circ g)(x) = \dfrac{4}{4 + x}$ **b.** $(-\infty, -4) \cup (-4, 0) \cup (0, \infty)$ **71. a.** $(f \circ g)(x) = \sqrt{x - 2}$ **b.** $[2, \infty)$
73. a. $(f \circ g)(x) = 5 - x$ **b.** $(-\infty, 1]$ **75.** $f(x) = x^4, g(x) = 3x - 1$ **77.** $f(x) = \sqrt[3]{x}, g(x) = x^2 - 9$ **79.** $f(x) = |x|, g(x) = 2x - 5$
81. $f(x) = \dfrac{1}{x}, g(x) = 2x - 3$ **83.** 5   **85.** -1 **87.** $[-4, 3]$

89.   **91.** 1   **93.** -6 **95.** 1 and 2   **97. a.** $(M + F)(x) = 2.99x + 235.5$ **b.** 295.3 million   **c.** underestimates by 2.7 million

99. $(R - C)(20,000) = -200,000$; The company loses \$200,000 when 20,000 radios are sold.; $(R - C)(30,000) = 0$; The company breaks even when 30,000 radios are sold.; $(R - C)(40,000) = 200,000$; The company makes a profit of \$200,000 when 40,000 radios are sold.   **101. a.** f gives the price of the computer after a \$400 discount. g gives the price of the computer after a 25% discount.   **b.** $(f \circ g)(x) = 0.75x - 400$; This models the price of a computer after first a 25% discount and then a \$400 discount.   **c.** $(g \circ f)(x) = 0.75(x - 400)$; This models the price of a computer after first a \$400 discount and then a 25% discount.   **d.** $f \circ g$ because $0.75x - 400 < 0.75(x - 400)$

109.

111. makes sense   **113.** does not make sense   **115.** false   **117.** true
119. Answers will vary; One possible answer is $f(x) = x + 1$ and $g(x) = x - 1$.
120. $\{(4, -2), (1, -1), (1, 1), (4, 2)\}$; no   **121.** $y = \dfrac{5}{x - 4}$ **122.** $y = \sqrt{x + 1}$

Domain: $[0, 4]$

Section 2.7

Check Point Exercises

1. $f(g(x)) = 4\left(\dfrac{x + 7}{4}\right) - 7 = x + 7 - 7 = x; g(f(x)) = \dfrac{(4x - 7) + 7}{4} = \dfrac{4x}{4} = x$ **2.** $f^{-1}(x) = \dfrac{x - 7}{2}$ **3.** $f^{-1}(x) = \sqrt[3]{\dfrac{x + 1}{4}}$
4. $f^{-1}(x) = \dfrac{3}{x + 1}$ **5.** (b) and (c)
6.   **7.** $f^{-1}(x) = \sqrt{x - 1}$

Concept and Vocabulary Check

1. inverse   **2.** $x; x$ **3.** horizontal; one-to-one   **4.** $y = x$

Exercise Set 2.7

1. $f(g(x)) = x; g(f(x)) = x; f$ and g are inverses.   **3.** $f(g(x)) = x; g(f(x)) = x; f$ and g are inverses.
5. $f(g(x)) = \dfrac{5x - 56}{9}; g(f(x)) = \dfrac{5x - 4}{9}; f$ and g are not inverses.   **7.** $f(g(x)) = x; g(f(x)) = x; f$ and g are inverses.
9. $f(g(x)) = x; g(f(x)) = x; f$ and g are inverses.   **11.** $f^{-1}(x) = x - 3$ **13.** $f^{-1}(x) = \dfrac{x}{2}$ **15.** $f^{-1}(x) = \dfrac{x - 3}{2}$ **17.** $f^{-1}(x) = \sqrt[3]{x - 2}$
19. $f^{-1}(x) = \sqrt[3]{x} - 2$ **21.** $f^{-1}(x) = \dfrac{1}{x}$ **23.** $f^{-1}(x) = x^2, x \geq 0$ **25.** $f^{-1}(x) = \dfrac{7}{x + 3}$ **27.** $f^{-1}(x) = \dfrac{3x + 1}{x - 2}; x \neq 2$
29. The function is not one-to-one, so it does not have an inverse function.   **31.** The function is not one-to-one, so it does not have an inverse function.
33. The function is one-to-one, so it does have an inverse function.
35.   **37.**

39. a. $f^{-1}(x) = \dfrac{x + 1}{2}$

b.

c. domain of f = range of $f^{-1} = (-\infty, \infty)$;
range of f = domain of $f^{-1} = (-\infty, \infty)$

41. a. $f^{-1}(x) = \sqrt{x + 4}$

b.

c. domain of f = range of $f^{-1} = [0, \infty)$;
range of f = domain of $f^{-1} = [-4, \infty)$

43. a. $f^{-1}(x) = -\sqrt{x} + 1$

b.

d. domain of f = range of $f^{-1} = (-\infty, 1]$;
range of f = domain of $f^{-1} = [0, \infty)$

45. a. $f^{-1}(x) = \sqrt[3]{x + 1}$

b.

c. domain of f = range of $f^{-1} = (-\infty, \infty)$;
range of f = domain of $f^{-1} = (-\infty, \infty)$

47. a. $f^{-1}(x) = \sqrt[3]{x} - 2$

b.

c. domain of f = range of $f^{-1} = (-\infty, \infty)$;
range of f = domain of $f^{-1} = (-\infty, \infty)$

49. a. $f^{-1}(x) = x^2 + 1, x \geq 0$

b.

c. domain of f = range of $f^{-1} = [1, \infty)$;
range of f = domain of $f^{-1} = [0, \infty)$

51. a. $f^{-1}(x) = (x - 1)^3$

b.

c. domain of f = range of $f^{-1} = (-\infty, \infty)$;
range of f = domain of $f^{-1} = (-\infty, \infty)$

53. 5   **55.** 1   **57.** 2   **59.** -7 **61.** 3   **63.** 11

65. a. {(Zambia, 4.2), (Colombia, 4.5), (Poland, 3.3), (Italy, 3.3), (United States, 2.5)}
b. {(4.2, Zambia), (4.5, Colombia), (3.3, Poland), (3.3, Italy), (2.5, United States)}; no; The inverse of f is not a function.   **67. a.** f is a one-to-one function.   **b.** $f^{-1}(0.25)$ is the number of people in a room for a 25% probability of two people sharing a birthday. $f^{-1}(0.5)$ is the number of people in a room for a 50% probability of two people sharing a birthday. $f^{-1}(0.7)$ is the number of people in a room for a 70% probability of two people sharing a birthday.

69. $f(g(x)) = \dfrac{9}{5}\left[\dfrac{5}{9}(x - 32)\right] + 32 = x$ and $g(f(x)) = \dfrac{5}{9}\left[\left(\dfrac{9}{5}x + 32\right) - 32\right] = x$

77.

one-to-one

79.

not one-to-one

81.

not one-to-one

83.

not one-to-one

85.

f and g are inverses.

87. makes sense   **89.** makes sense   **91.** false   **93.** false
95. $(f \circ g)^{-1}(x) = \dfrac{x - 15}{3}$; $(g^{-1} \circ f^{-1})(x) = \dfrac{x}{3} - 5 = \dfrac{x - 15}{3}$
97. No; The spacecraft was at the same height, $s(t)$, for two different values of t–once during the ascent and once again during the descent.
100. $3\sqrt{5}$ **101.**   **102.** $\{3 \pm \sqrt{13}\}$

Section 2.8

Check Point Exercises

1. $3\sqrt{5} \approx 6.71$ **2.** $\left(4, -\dfrac{1}{2}\right)$ **3.** $x^2 + y^2 = 16$ **4.** $x^2 + (y + 6)^2 = 100$

5. a. center: $(-3, 1)$; radius: 2   **6.** $(x + 2)^2 + (y - 2)^2 = 9$
b.

$(x + 3)^2 + (y - 1)^2 = 4$

$x^2 + y^2 + 4x - 4y - 1 = 0$

c. domain: $[-5, -1]$;
range: $[-1, 3]$

Concept and Vocabulary Check

1. $\sqrt{(x_2 - x_1)^2 + (y_2 - y_1)^2}$ **2.** $\dfrac{x_1 + x_2}{2}; \dfrac{y_1 + y_2}{2}$ **3.** circle; center; radius   **4.** $(x - h)^2 + (y - k)^2 = r^2$ **5.** general   **6.** 4; 16

Exercise Set 2.8

1. 13   **3.** $2\sqrt{29} \approx 10.77$ **5.** 5   **7.** $\sqrt{29} \approx 5.39$ **9.** $4\sqrt{2} \approx 5.66$ **11.** $2\sqrt{5} \approx 4.47$ **13.** $2\sqrt{2} \approx 2.83$ **15.** $\sqrt{93} \approx 9.64$

17. $\sqrt{5} \approx 2.24$ **19.** $(4, 6)$ **21.** $(-4, -5)$ **23.** $\left(\dfrac{3}{2}, -6\right)$ **25.** $(-3, -2)$ **27.** $(1, 5\sqrt{5})$ **29.** $(2\sqrt{2}, 0)$ **31.** $x^2 + y^2 = 49$

33. $(x - 3)^2 + (y - 2)^2 = 25$ **35.** $(x + 1)^2 + (y - 4)^2 = 4$ **37.** $(x + 3)^2 + (y + 1)^2 = 3$ **39.** $(x + 4)^2 + y^2 = 100$

41. center: $(0, 0)$
radius: 4
domain: $[-4, 4]$
range: $[-4, 4]$

$x^2 + y^2 = 16$

43. center: $(3, 1)$
radius: 6
domain: $[-3, 9]$
range: $[-5, 7]$

$(x - 3)^2 + (y - 1)^2 = 36$

45. center: $(-3, 2)$
radius: 2
domain: $[-5, -1]$
range: $[0, 4]$

$(x + 3)^2 + (y - 2)^2 = 4$

47. center: $(-2, -2)$
radius: 2
domain: $[-4, 0]$
range: $[-4, 0]$

$(x + 2)^2 + (y + 2)^2 = 4$

49. center: $(0, 1)$
radius: 1
domain: $[-1, 1]$
range: $[0, 2]$

$x^2 + (y - 1)^2 = 1$

51. center: $(-1, 0)$
radius: 5
domain: $[-6, 4]$
range: $[-5, 5]$

$(x + 1)^2 + y^2 = 25$

53. $(x + 3)^2 + (y + 1)^2 = 4$
center: $(-3, -1)$
radius: 2

$x^2 + y^2 + 6x + 2y + 6 = 0$

55. $(x - 5)^2 + (y - 3)^2 = 64$
center: $(5, 3)$
radius: 8

$x^2 + y^2 - 10x - 6y - 30 = 0$

57. $(x + 4)^2 + (y - 1)^2 = 25$
center: $(-4, 1)$
radius: 5

$x^2 + y^2 + 8x - 2y - 8 = 0$

59. $(x - 1)^2 + y^2 = 16$

center: $(1, 0)$

radius: 4

$x^2 - 2x + y^2 - 15 = 0$

61. $\left(x - \dfrac{1}{2}\right)^2 + (y + 1)^2 = \dfrac{1}{4}$

center: $\left(\dfrac{1}{2}, -1\right)$

radius: $\dfrac{1}{2}$

$x^2 + y^2 - x + 2y + 1 = 0$

63. $\left(x + \dfrac{3}{2}\right)^2 + (y - 1)^2 = \dfrac{17}{4}$

center: $\left(-\dfrac{3}{2}, 1\right)$

radius: $\dfrac{\sqrt{17}}{2}$

$x^2 + y^2 + 3x - 2y - 1 = 0$

65. a. $(5, 10)$ **b.** $\sqrt{5}$
c. $(x - 5)^2 + (y - 10)^2 = 5$
67. $\{(0, -4), (4, 0)\}$

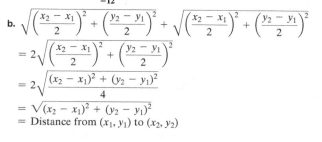

$x^2 + y^2 = 16$
$x - y = 4$

69. $\{(0, -3), (2, -1)\}$

$(x - 2)^2 + (y + 3)^2 = 4$
$y = x - 3$

71. 2693 mi   **73.** $(x + 2.4)^2 + (y + 2.7)^2 = 900$

83.

85.

87. makes sense
89. makes sense
91. false
93. false

95. a. Distance between (x_1, y_1) and $\left(\dfrac{x_1 + x_2}{2}, \dfrac{y_1 + y_2}{2}\right)$

$= \sqrt{\left(\dfrac{x_1 + x_2}{2} - x_1\right)^2 + \left(\dfrac{y_1 + y_2}{2} - y_1\right)^2}$

$= \sqrt{\left(\dfrac{x_1 + x_2 - 2x_1}{2}\right)^2 + \left(\dfrac{y_1 + y_2 - 2y_1}{2}\right)^2}$

$= \sqrt{\left(\dfrac{x_2 - x_1}{2}\right)^2 + \left(\dfrac{y_2 - y_1}{2}\right)^2}$

$= \sqrt{\dfrac{x_2^2 - 2x_1x_2 + x_1^2}{4} + \dfrac{y_2^2 - 2y_1y_2 + y_1^2}{4}}$

$= \sqrt{\dfrac{x_1^2 - 2x_1x_2 + x_2^2}{4} + \dfrac{y_1^2 - 2y_1y_2 + y_2^2}{4}}$

$= \sqrt{\left(\dfrac{x_1 - x_2}{2}\right)^2 + \left(\dfrac{y_1 - y_2}{2}\right)^2}$

$= \sqrt{\left(\dfrac{x_1 + x_2 - 2x_2}{2}\right)^2 + \left(\dfrac{y_1 + y_2 - 2y_2}{2}\right)^2}$

$= \sqrt{\left(\dfrac{x_1 + x_2}{2} - x_2\right)^2 + \left(\dfrac{y_1 + y_2}{2} - y_2\right)^2}$

$=$ Distance between (x_2, y_2) and $\left(\dfrac{x_1 + x_2}{2}, \dfrac{y_1 + y_2}{2}\right)$

b. $\sqrt{\left(\dfrac{x_2 - x_1}{2}\right)^2 + \left(\dfrac{y_2 - y_1}{2}\right)^2} + \sqrt{\left(\dfrac{x_2 - x_1}{2}\right)^2 + \left(\dfrac{y_2 - y_1}{2}\right)^2}$

$= 2\sqrt{\left(\dfrac{x_2 - x_1}{2}\right)^2 + \left(\dfrac{y_2 - y_1}{2}\right)^2}$

$= 2\sqrt{\dfrac{(x_2 - x_1)^2 + (y_2 - y_1)^2}{4}}$

$= \sqrt{(x_2 - x_1)^2 + (y_2 - y_1)^2}$

$=$ Distance from (x_1, y_1) to (x_2, y_2)

97. $y + 4 = \dfrac{3}{4}(x - 3)$ **98.** $\{1, 5\}$ **99.** $\{-1 \pm \sqrt{2}\}$ **100.**

$f(x) = x^2$
$g(x) = (x + 3)^2 + 1$

Chapter 2 Review Exercises

1. function; domain: $\{2, 3, 5\}$; range: $\{7\}$ **2.** function; domain: $\{1, 2, 13\}$; range: $\{10, 500, \pi\}$ **3.** not a function; domain: $\{12, 14\}$; range: $\{13, 15, 19\}$
4. y is a function of x.   **5.** y is a function of x.   **6.** y is not a function of x.   **7. a.** $f(4) = -23$ **b.** $f(x + 3) = -7x - 16$
c. $f(-x) = 5 + 7x$ **8. a.** $g(0) = 2$ **b.** $g(-2) = 24$ **c.** $g(x - 1) = 3x^2 - 11x + 10$ **d.** $g(-x) = 3x^2 + 5x + 2$ **9. a.** $g(13) = 3$
b. $g(0) = 4$ **c.** $g(-3) = 7$ **10. a.** -1 **b.** 12 **c.** 3 **11.** not a function   **12.** function   **13.** function   **14.** not a function
15. not a function   **16.** function   **17. a.** $[-3, 5)$ **b.** $[-5, 0]$ **c.** -3 **d.** -2 **e.** increasing: $(-2, 0)$ or $(3, 5)$; decreasing: $(-3, -2)$
or $(0, 3)$ **f.** $f(-2) = -3$ and $f(3) = -5$ **18. a.** $(-\infty, \infty)$ **b.** $(-\infty, 3]$ **c.** -2 and 3 **d.** 3 **e.** increasing: $(-\infty, 0)$;
decreasing: $(0, \infty)$ **f.** $f(-2) = 0$ and $f(6) = -3$ **19. a.** $(-\infty, \infty)$ **b.** $[-2, 2]$ **c.** 0 **d.** 0 **e.** increasing: $(-2, 2)$;
constant: $(-\infty, -2)$ or $(2, \infty)$ **f.** $f(-9) = -2$ and $f(14) = 2$ **20. a.** $0; f(0) = -2$ **b.** $-2, 3; f(-2) = -3, f(3) = -5$
21. a. $0; f(0) = 3$ **b.** none   **22.** odd; symmetric with respect to the origin   **23.** even; symmetric with respect to the y-axis
24. odd; symmetric with respect to the origin
25. ; $\{-3, 5\}$ **26.** ; $(-\infty, 0]$

$f(x) = \begin{cases} 5 \text{ if } x \le -1 \\ -3 \text{ if } x > -1 \end{cases}$

$f(x) = \begin{cases} 2x \text{ if } x < 0 \\ -x \text{ if } x \ge 0 \end{cases}$

27. 8 **28.** $-4x - 2h + 1$ **29. a.** yes; The graph passes the vertical line test.   **b.** $(3, 12)$; The eagle descended.
c. $(0, 3)$ and $(12, 17)$; The eagle's height held steady during the first 3 seconds and the eagle was on the ground for 5 seconds.
d. $(17, 30)$; The eagle was ascending.

30.

31. $-\dfrac{1}{2}$; falls   **32.** 1; rises   **33.** 0; horizontal   **34.** undefined; vertical
35. $y - 2 = -6(x + 3); y = -6x - 16$ **36.** using $(1, 6), y - 6 = 2(x - 1); y = 2x + 4$
37. $y + 7 = -3(x - 4); y = -3x + 5$ **38.** $y - 6 = -3(x + 3); y = -3x - 3$ **39.** $x + 6y + 18 = 0$

40. Slope: $\dfrac{2}{5}$; y-intercept: -1 **41.** Slope: -4; y-intercept: 5 **42.** Slope: $-\dfrac{2}{3}$; y-intercept: -2 **43.** Slope: 0; y-intercept: 4

$y = \dfrac{2}{5}x - 1$ $f(x) = -4x + 5$ $2x + 3y + 6 = 0$ $2y - 8 = 0$

44.   **45.** $2x - 10 = 0$

$2x - 5y - 10 = 0$

46. a. $y - 2.3 = 0.116(x - 15)$ or $y - 11 = 0.116(x - 90)$ **b.** $f(x) = 0.116x + 0.56$ **c.** approximately 5 deaths per 100,000 persons
d. 4.3 deaths per 100,000 persons; underestimates by 0.7 death per 100,000 persons; The line passes below the point for France.
47. a. -0.48 **b.** $0.48; -0.48\%$; year   **48.** 10
49.   **50.**   **51.**   **52.**   **53.**

54.

55.

56.

57.

58.

59.

60.

61.

62.

63.

64.

65.

66.

67.

68. $\left(-\dfrac{1}{2}, 1\right)$

69.

70. $(-\infty, \infty)$ **71.** $(-\infty, 7) \cup (7, \infty)$ **72.** $(-\infty, 4]$ **73.** $(-\infty, -7) \cup (-7, 3) \cup (3, \infty)$

74. $[2, 5) \cup (5, \infty)$ **75.** $[1, \infty)$ **76.** $(f + g)(x) = 4x - 6$; domain: $(-\infty, \infty)$; $(f - g)(x) = 2x + 4$;

domain: $(-\infty, \infty)$; $(fg)(x) = 3x^2 - 16x + 5$; domain: $(-\infty, \infty)$; $\left(\dfrac{f}{g}\right)(x) = \dfrac{3x - 1}{x - 5}$; domain: $(-\infty, 5) \cup (5, \infty)$

77. $(f + g)(x) = 2x^2 + x$; domain: $(-\infty, \infty)$; $(f - g)(x) = x + 2$; domain: $(-\infty, \infty)$; $(fg)(x) = x^4 + x^3 - x - 1$;

domain: $(-\infty, \infty)$; $\left(\dfrac{f}{g}\right)(x) = \dfrac{x^2 + x + 1}{x^2 - 1}$; domain: $(-\infty, -1) \cup (-1, 1) \cup (1, \infty)$

78. $(f + g)(x) = \sqrt{x + 7} + \sqrt{x - 2}$; domain: $[2, \infty)$; $(f - g)(x) = \sqrt{x + 7} - \sqrt{x - 2}$; domain: $[2, \infty)$; $(fg)(x) = \sqrt{x^2 + 5x - 14}$; domain:

$[2, \infty)$; $\left(\dfrac{f}{g}\right)(x) = \dfrac{\sqrt{x + 7}}{\sqrt{x - 2}}$; domain: $(2, \infty)$ **79. a.** $(f \circ g)(x) = 16x^2 - 8x + 4$ **b.** $(g \circ f)(x) = 4x^2 + 11$ **c.** $(f \circ g)(3) = 124$

80. a. $(f \circ g)(x) = \sqrt{x + 1}$ **b.** $(g \circ f)(x) = \sqrt{x} + 1$ **c.** $(f \circ g)(3) = 2$ **81. a.** $(f \circ g)(x) = \dfrac{1 + x}{1 - 2x}$ **b.** $(-\infty, 0) \cup \left(0, \dfrac{1}{2}\right) \cup \left(\dfrac{1}{2}, \infty\right)$

82. a. $(f \circ g)(x) = \sqrt{x + 2}$ **b.** $[-2, \infty)$ **83.** $f(x) = x^4, g(x) = x^2 + 2x - 1$ **84.** $f(x) = \sqrt[3]{x}, g(x) = 7x + 4$ **85.** $f(g(x)) = x - \dfrac{7}{10}$;

$g(f(x)) = x - \dfrac{7}{6}$; f and g are not inverses of each other.   **86.** $f(g(x)) = x$; $g(f(x)) = x$; f and g are inverses of each other.   **87.** $f^{-1}(x) = \dfrac{x + 3}{4}$

88. $f^{-1}(x) = \sqrt[3]{\dfrac{x - 1}{8}}$ or $\dfrac{\sqrt[3]{x - 1}}{2}$ **89.** $f^{-1}(x) = \dfrac{2}{x - 5}$ **90.** Inverse function exists.   **91.** Inverse function does not exist.

92. Inverse function exists.   **93.** Inverse function does not exist.

94.

95. $f^{-1}(x) = \sqrt{1 - x}$

96. $f^{-1}(x) = (x - 1)^2, x \geq 1$

97. 13   **98.** $2\sqrt{2} \approx 2.83$

99. $(-5, 5)$ **100.** $\left(-\dfrac{11}{2}, -2\right)$

101. $x^2 + y^2 = 9$

102. $(x + 2)^2 + (y - 4)^2 = 36$

103. center: $(0, 0)$; radius: 1
domain: $[-1, 1]$; range: $[-1, 1]$

104. center: $(-2, 3)$; radius: 3
domain: $[-5, 1]$; range: $[0, 6]$

105. center: $(2, -1)$; radius: 3
domain: $[-1, 5]$; range: $[-4, 2]$

$x^2 + y^2 = 1$

$(x + 2)^2 + (y - 3)^2 = 9$

$x^2 + y^2 - 4x + 2y - 4 = 0$

Chapter 2 Test

1. b, c, d   **2. a.** $f(4) - f(-3) = 5$ **b.** $(-5, 6]$ **c.** $[-4, 5]$ **d.** $(-1, 2)$ **e.** $(-5, -1)$ or $(2, 6)$ **f.** $2; f(2) = 5$ **g.** $-1; f(-1) = -4$
h. $-4, 1,$ and 5 **i.** -3 **3. a.** -2 and 2 **b.** -1 and 1 **c.** 0 **d.** even   **e.** no   **f.** relative minimum

g.

h.

i.

j. $-\dfrac{1}{3}$

4. $x + y = 4$

domain: $(-\infty, \infty)$;
range: $(-\infty, \infty)$

5. $x^2 + y^2 = 4$

domain: $[-2, 2]$;
range: $[-2, 2]$

6. $f(x) = 4$

domain: $(-\infty, \infty)$;
range: $\{4\}$

7.

$f(x) = -\dfrac{1}{3}x + 2$

domain: $(-\infty, \infty)$;
range: $(-\infty, \infty)$

8.

$(x + 2)^2 + (y - 1)^2 = 9$

domain: $[-5, 1]$;
range: $[-2, 4]$

9.

$f(x) = \begin{cases} 2 \text{ if } x \le 0 \\ -1 \text{ if } x > 0 \end{cases}$

domain: $(-\infty, \infty)$;
range: $\{-1, 2\}$

10.

$x^2 + y^2 + 4x - 6y - 3 = 0$

domain: $[-6, 2]$;
range: $[-1, 7]$

11.

domain of f = domain of g = $(-\infty, \infty)$;
range of f = $[0, \infty)$; range of g = $[-2, \infty)$

12.

domain of f = domain of g = $(-\infty, \infty)$;
range of f = $[0, \infty)$; range of g = $(-\infty, 4]$

13.

domain of f = range of f^{-1} = $(-\infty, \infty)$;
range of f = domain of f^{-1} = $(-\infty, \infty)$

14.

domain of f = range of f^{-1} = $(-\infty, \infty)$;
range of f = domain of f^{-1} = $(-\infty, \infty)$

15.

domain of f = range of f^{-1} = $[0, \infty)$;
range of f = domain of f^{-1} = $[-1, \infty)$

16. $f(x - 1) = x^2 - 3x - 2$ **17.** $2x + h - 1$ **18.** $(g - f)(x) = -x^2 + 3x - 2$

19. $\left(\dfrac{f}{g}\right)(x) = \dfrac{x^2 - x - 4}{2x - 6}$; $(-\infty, 3) \cup (3, \infty)$ **20.** $(f \circ g)(x) = 4x^2 - 26x + 38$ **21.** $(g \circ f)(x) = 2x^2 - 2x - 14$

22. -10 **23.** $f(-x) = x^2 + x - 4$; neither   **24.** using $(2, 1)$, $y - 1 = 3(x - 2)$; $y = 3x - 5$

25. $y - 6 = 4(x + 4)$; $y = 4x + 22$ **26.** $2x + y + 24 = 0$ **27. a.** using $(1, 4571)$, $y - 4571 = 433(x - 1)$

b. $f(x) = 433x + 4138$ **c.** 8468 deaths   **28.** 48   **29.** $g(-1) = 4$; $g(7) = 2$ **30.** $(-\infty, -5) \cup (-5, 1) \cup (1, \infty)$

31. $[1, \infty)$ **32.** $\dfrac{7x}{2 - 4x}$; domain: $(-\infty, 0) \cup \left(0, \dfrac{1}{2}\right) \cup \left(\dfrac{1}{2}, \infty\right)$ **33.** $f(x) = x^7$, $g(x) = 2x + 3$ **34.** 5; $\left(\dfrac{7}{2}, 0\right)$ or $(3.5, 0)$

Cumulative Review Exercises (Chapters 1–2)

1. domain: $[0, 2)$; range: $[0, 2]$ **2.** $\dfrac{1}{2}$ and $\dfrac{3}{2}$ **3.** 2

4.

$g(x) = f(x - 1) + 1$

5.

$h(x) = -2f\left(\dfrac{1}{2}x\right)$

6. $\{-4, 5\}$

7. $\left\{\dfrac{25}{18}\right\}$

8. $\{4\}$

9. $\{-8, 27\}$

10. $(-\infty, 20]$

11.

$3x - 6y - 12 = 0$

domain: $(-\infty, \infty)$;
range: $(-\infty, \infty)$

12.

$(x - 2)^2 + (y + 1)^2 = 4$

domain: $[0, 4]$;
range: $[-3, 1]$

13.

domain of f = domain of g = $(-\infty, \infty)$;
range of f = range of g = $(-\infty, \infty)$

14.

domain of f = range of f^{-1} = $[3, \infty)$;
range of f = domain of f^{-1} = $[2, \infty)$

15. $-2x - h$ **16.** -7 and -3 **17.** $y - 5 = 4(x + 2)$; $y = 4x + 13$; $4x - y + 13 = 0$ **18.** \$1500 at 7%; \$4500 at 9%   **19.** \$2000

20. 3 ft by 8 ft

CHAPTER 3

Section 3.1

Check Point Exercises

1.

$f(x) = -(x - 1)^2 + 4$

2.

$f(x) = (x - 2)^2 + 1$

3.

$f(x) = -x^2 + 4x + 1$
domain: $(-\infty, \infty)$; range: $(-\infty, 5]$

4. a. minimum   **b.** Minimum is 984 at $x = 2$.
c. domain: $(-\infty, \infty)$; range: $[984, \infty)$
5. a. 205 ft; 200 ft   **b.** 402 ft
c.

6. $4, -4; -16$ **7.** 30 ft by 30 ft; 900 sq ft

Concept and Vocabulary Check

1. standard; parabola; (h, k); > 0; < 0 **2.** $-\dfrac{b}{2a}; f\left(-\dfrac{b}{2a}\right); -\dfrac{b}{2a}; f\left(-\dfrac{b}{2a}\right)$ **3.** true   **4.** false   **5.** true   **6.** $x - 8; x^2 - 8x$
7. $40 - x; -x^2 + 40x$

Exercise Set 3.1

1. $h(x) = (x - 1)^2 + 1$ **3.** $j(x) = (x - 1)^2 - 1$ **5.** $h(x) = x^2 - 1$ **7.** $g(x) = x^2 - 2x + 1$ **9.** $(3, 1)$ **11.** $(-1, 5)$
13. $(2, -5)$ **15.** $(-1, 9)$

17. domain: $(-\infty, \infty)$
range: $[-1, \infty)$
axis of symmetry: $x = 4$

$f(x) = (x - 4)^2 - 1$

19. domain: $(-\infty, \infty)$
range: $[2, \infty)$
axis of symmetry: $x = 1$
$f(x) = (x - 1)^2 + 2$

21. domain: $(-\infty, \infty)$
range: $[1, \infty)$
axis of symmetry: $x = 3$
$y - 1 = (x - 3)^2$

23. domain: $(-\infty, \infty)$
range: $[-1, \infty)$
axis of symmetry: $x = -2$

$f(x) = 2(x + 2)^2 - 1$

25. domain: $(-\infty, \infty)$
range: $(-\infty, 4]$
axis of symmetry: $x = 1$

$f(x) = 4 - (x - 1)^2$

27. domain: $(-\infty, \infty)$
range: $[-4, \infty)$
axis of symmetry: $x = 1$

$f(x) = x^2 - 2x - 3$

29. domain: $(-\infty, \infty)$
range: $\left[-\dfrac{49}{4}, \infty\right)$
axis of symmetry: $x = -\dfrac{3}{2}$
$f(x) = x^2 + 3x - 10$

31. domain: $(-\infty, \infty)$
range: $(-\infty, 4]$
axis of symmetry: $x = 1$
$f(x) = 2x - x^2 + 3$

33. domain: $(-\infty, \infty)$
range: $[-6, \infty)$
axis of symmetry: $x = -3$

$f(x) = x^2 + 6x + 3$

35. domain: $(-\infty, \infty)$
range: $[-5, \infty)$
axis of symmetry: $x = -1$

$f(x) = 2x^2 + 4x - 3$

37. domain: $(-\infty, \infty)$
range: $(-\infty, -1]$
axis of symmetry: $x = 1$

$f(x) = 2x - x^2 - 2$

39. a. minimum   **b.** Minimum is -13 at $x = 2$.   **c.** domain: $(-\infty, \infty)$; range: $[-13, \infty)$ **41. a.** maximum   **b.** Maximum is 1 at $x = 1$.
c. domain: $(-\infty, \infty)$; range: $(-\infty, 1]$ **43. a.** minimum   **b.** Minimum is $-\dfrac{5}{4}$ at $x = \dfrac{1}{2}$.   **c.** domain: $(-\infty, \infty)$; range: $\left[-\dfrac{5}{4}, \infty\right)$
45. domain: $(-\infty, \infty)$; range: $[-2, \infty)$ **47.** domain: $(-\infty, \infty)$; range: $(-\infty, -6]$ **49.** $f(x) = 2(x - 5)^2 + 3$ **51.** $f(x) = 2(x + 10)^2 - 5$
53. $f(x) = -3(x + 2)^2 + 4$ **55.** $f(x) = 3(x - 11)^2$ **57. a.** 18.35 ft; 35 ft   **b.** 77.8 ft   **c.** 6.1 ft

59. a. 7.8 ft; 1.5 ft   **b.** 4.6 ft   **c.**

61. 8 and 8; 64   **63.** 8, −8; −64

65. length: 300 ft; width: 150 ft; maximum area: 45,000 sq ft   **67.** 12.5 yd by 12.5 yd; 156.25 sq yd   **69.** 150 ft by 100 ft; 15,000 sq ft
71. 5 in.; 50 sq in.   **73. a.** $C(x) = 0.55x + 525$ **b.** $P(x) = -0.001x^2 + 2.45x - 525$ **c.** 1225 roast beef sandwiches; $\approx \$975.63$

81. a.

You can only see a little of the parabola.

b. $(20.5, -120.5)$
c. Ymax = 750
d. You can choose Xmin and Xmax so the x-value of the vertex is in the center of the graph. Choose Ymin to include the y-value of the vertex.

83. $(2.5, 185)$

85. $(-30, 91)$

87. does not make sense   **89.** does not make sense   **91.** true   **93.** false   **95.** $x = -2; (-3, -2)$ **97.** $f(x) = \frac{1}{2}(x + 3)^2 - 4$

99. $x = 166\frac{2}{3}$ ft, $y = 125$ ft; approximately 20,833 ft²   **102.** $(x + 3)(x + 1)(x - 1)$ **103.** $f(2) = -1; f(3) = 16$; The graph passes through $(2, -1)$, which is below the x-axis, and $(3, 16)$, which is above the x-axis. Since the graph of f is continuous, it must cross the x-axis somewhere between 2 and 3 to get from one of these points to the other.   **104.** even; symmetric with respect to the y-axis

Section 3.2

Check Point Exercises

1. The graph rises to the left and to the right.   **2.** The graph falls to the left and rises to the right.   **3.** Since n is odd and the leading coefficient is negative, the graph falls to the right. Since the ratio cannot be negative, the model won't be appropriate.   **4.** No; the graph should fall to the left but doesn't appear to do so.   **5.** −2 and 2   **6.** −2, 0, and 2   **7.** $-\frac{1}{2}$ with multiplicity 2 and 5 with multiplicity 3; touches and turns at $-\frac{1}{2}$ and crosses at 5
8. $f(-3) = -42; f(-2) = 5$ **9.**

$f(x) = x^3 - 3x^2$

10.

$f(x) = 2(x + 2)^2 (x - 3)$

Concept and Vocabulary Check

1. 5; −2   **2.** false   **3.** end; leading   **4.** falls; rises   **5.** rises; falls   **6.** rises; rises   **7.** falls; falls   **8.** true   **9.** true
10. x-intercept   **11.** turns around; crosses   **12.** 0; Intermediate Value   **13.** $n - 1$

Exercise Set 3.2

1. polynomial function; degree: 3   **3.** polynomial function; degree: 5   **5.** not a polynomial function   **7.** not a polynomial function
9. not a polynomial function   **11.** could be polynomial function   **13.** not a polynomial function   **15.** b   **17.** a
19. falls to the left and rises to the right   **21.** rises to the left and to the right   **23.** falls to the left and to the right
25. $x = 5$ has multiplicity 1; The graph crosses the x-axis; $x = -4$ has multiplicity 2; The graph touches the x-axis and turns around.
27. $x = 3$ has multiplicity 1; The graph crosses the x-axis; $x = -6$ has multiplicity 3; The graph crosses the x-axis.
29. $x = 0$ has multiplicity 1; The graph crosses the x-axis; $x = 1$ has multiplicity 2; The graph touches the x-axis and turns around.
31. $x = 2, x = -2$ and $x = -7$ have multiplicity 1; The graph crosses the x-axis.   **33.** $f(1) = -1; f(2) = 5$ **35.** $f(-1) = -1; f(0) = 1$
37. $f(-3) = -11; f(-2) = 1$ **39.** $f(-3) = -42; f(-2) = 5$
41. a. $f(x)$ rises to the right and falls to the left.
b. $x = -2, x = 1, x = -1$;
   $f(x)$ crosses the x-axis at each.
c. The y-intercept is −2.
d. neither
e.

$f(x) = x^3 + 2x^2 - x - 2$

43. a. $f(x)$ rises to the left and the right.
b. $x = 0, x = 3, x = -3$;
   $f(x)$ crosses the x-axis at −3 and 3;
   $f(x)$ touches the x-axis at 0.
c. The y-intercept is 0.
d. y-axis symmetry
e.

$f(x) = x^4 - 9x^2$

45. a. $f(x)$ falls to the left and the right.
b. $x = 0, x = 4, x = -4$;
  $f(x)$ crosses the x-axis at -4 and 4;
  $f(x)$ touches the x-axis at 0.
c. The y-intercept is 0.
d. y-axis symmetry
e.

$$f(x) = -x^4 + 16x^2$$

49. a. $f(x)$ falls to the left and the right.
b. $x = 0, x = 2$;
  $f(x)$ crosses the x-axis at 0 and 2.
c. The y-intercept is 0.
d. neither
e.

$$f(x) = -2x^4 + 4x^3$$

53. a. $f(x)$ rises to the left and falls to the right.
b. $x = 0, x = 3$;
  $f(x)$ crosses the x-axis at 3;
  $f(x)$ touches the x-axis at 0.
c. The y-intercept is 0.
d. neither
e.

$$f(x) = 3x^2 - x^3$$

57. a. $f(x)$ rises to the left and the right.
b. $x = -2, x = 0, x = 1$;
  $f(x)$ crosses the x-axis at -2 and 1;
  $f(x)$ touches the x-axis at 0.
c. The y-intercept is 0.
d. neither
e.

$$f(x) = x^2(x - 1)^3(x + 2)$$

61. a. $f(x)$ falls to the left and the right.
b. $x = -5, x = 0, x = 1$;
  $f(x)$ crosses the x-axis at -5 and 0;
  $f(x)$ touches the x-axis at 1.
c. The y-intercept is 0.
d. neither
e.

$$f(x) = -2x^3(x - 1)^2(x + 5)$$

47. a. $f(x)$ rises to the left and the right.
b. $x = 0, x = 1$;
  $f(x)$ touches the x-axis at 0 and 1.
c. The y-intercept is 0.
d. neither
e.

$$f(x) = x^4 - 2x^3 + x^2$$

51. a. $f(x)$ rises to the left and falls to the right.
b. $x = 0, x = \pm\sqrt{3}$;
  $f(x)$ crosses the x-axis at 0;
  $f(x)$ touches the x-axis at $\sqrt{3}$ and $-\sqrt{3}$.
c. The y-intercept is 0.
d. origin symmetry
e.

$$f(x) = 6x^3 - 9x - x^5$$

55. a. $f(x)$ falls to the left and the right.
b. $x = 1, x = -2, x = 2$;
  $f(x)$ crosses the x-axis at -2 and 2;
  $f(x)$ touches the x-axis at 1.
c. The y-intercept is 12.
d. neither
e.

$$f(x) = -3(x - 1)^2(x^2 - 4)$$

59. a. $f(x)$ falls to the left and the right.
b. $x = -3, x = 0, x = 1$;
  $f(x)$ crosses the x-axis at -3 and 1;
  $f(x)$ touches the x-axis at 0.
c. The y-intercept is 0.
d. neither
e.

$$f(x) = -x^2(x - 1)(x + 3)$$

63. a. $f(x)$ rises to the left and the right.
b. $x = -4, x = 1, x = 2$;
  $f(x)$ crosses the x-axis at -4 and 1;
  $f(x)$ touches the x-axis at 2.
c. The y-intercept is -16.
d. neither
e.

$$f(x) = (x - 2)^2(x + 4)(x - 1)$$

65. a. -2, odd; 1, odd; 4, odd **b.** $f(x) = (x + 2)(x - 1)(x - 4)$ **c.** 8 **67. a.** -1, odd; 3, even **b.** $f(x) = (x + 1)(x - 3)^2$ **c.** 9
69. a. -3, even; 2, even **b.** $f(x) = -(x + 3)^2(x - 2)^2$ **c.** -36 **71. a.** -2, even; -1, odd; 1, odd **b.** $f(x) = (x + 2)^2(x + 1)(x - 1)^3$
c. -4 **73. a.** 3167; The world tiger population in 2010 was approximately 3167.; $(40, 3167)$ **b.** underestimates by 33 **c.** rises to the right; no;
The model indicates an increasing world tiger population that will actually decrease without conservation efforts. **75. a.** from 1 through 4 min and
from 8 through 10 min **b.** from 4 through 8 min and from 10 through 12 min **c.** 3 **d.** 4 **e.** negative; The graph falls to the left and falls to
the right. **f.** 116 ± 1 beats per min; 10 min **g.** 64 ± 1 beats per min; 8 min

95. **97.** **99.**

101. does not make sense **103.** makes sense **105.** false **107.** false **109.** $f(x) = x^3 - 2x^2$

110. $35\dfrac{2}{21}$ **111.** $6x^3 - x^2 - 5x + 4$ **112.** $(x - 3)(2x - 1)(x + 2)$

Section 3.3

Check Point Exercises

1. $x + 5$ **2.** $2x^2 + 3x - 2 + \dfrac{1}{x - 3}$ **3.** $2x^2 + 7x + 14 + \dfrac{21x - 10}{x^2 - 2x}$ **4.** $x^2 - 2x - 3$ **5.** -105 **6.** $\left\{-1, -\dfrac{1}{3}, \dfrac{2}{5}\right\}$

Concept and Vocabulary Check

1. $2x^3 + 0x^2 + 6x - 4$ **2.** $6x^3; 3x; 2x^2; 7x^2$ **3.** $2x^2; 5x - 2; 10x^3 - 4x^2; 10x^3 + 6x^2$ **4.** $6x^2 - 10x; 6x^2 + 8x; 18x; -4; 18x - 4$
5. $9; 3x - 5; 9; 3x - 5 + \dfrac{9}{2x + 1}$ **6.** divisor; quotient; remainder; dividend **7.** $4; 1; 5; -7; 1$ **8.** $-5; 4; 0; -8; -2$ **9.** true
10. $f(c)$ **11.** $x - c$

Exercise Set 3.3

1. $x + 3$ **3.** $x^2 + 3x + 1$ **5.** $2x^2 + 3x + 5$ **7.** $4x + 3 + \dfrac{2}{3x - 2}$ **9.** $2x^2 + x + 6 - \dfrac{38}{x + 3}$ **11.** $4x^3 + 16x^2 + 60x + 246 + \dfrac{984}{x - 4}$
13. $2x + 5$ **15.** $6x^2 + 3x - 1 - \dfrac{3x - 1}{3x^2 + 1}$ **17.** $2x + 5$ **19.** $3x - 8 + \dfrac{20}{x + 5}$ **21.** $4x^2 + x + 4 + \dfrac{3}{x - 1}$
23. $6x^4 + 12x^3 + 22x^2 + 48x + 93 + \dfrac{187}{x - 2}$ **25.** $x^3 - 10x^2 + 51x - 260 + \dfrac{1300}{x + 5}$ **27.** $x^4 + x^3 + 2x^2 + 2x + 2$ **29.** $x^3 + 4x^2 + 16x + 64$
31. $2x^4 - 7x^3 + 15x^2 - 31x + 64 - \dfrac{129}{x + 2}$ **33.** -25 **35.** -133 **37.** 240 **39.** 1 **41.** $x^2 - 5x + 6; x = -1, x = 2, x = 3$
43. $\left\{-\dfrac{1}{2}, 1, 2\right\}$ **45.** $\left\{-\dfrac{3}{2}, -\dfrac{1}{3}, \dfrac{1}{2}\right\}$ **47.** 2; The remainder is zero; $\{-3, -1, 2\}$ **49.** 1; The remainder is zero; $\left\{\dfrac{1}{3}, \dfrac{1}{2}, 1\right\}$
51. a. The remainder is 0. **b.** 3 mm **53.** $0.5x^2 - 0.4x + 0.3$ **55. a.** 70; When the tax rate is 30%, tax revenue is \$700 billion.; $(30, 70)$
b. $80 + \dfrac{800}{x - 110}; f(30) = 70$; yes **c.** No, f is a rational function because it is a quotient of two polynomials. **67.** makes sense
69. does not make sense **71.** true **73.** false **75.** $x - 2$ **79.** $\{-2 \pm \sqrt{5}\}$ **80.** $\{-2 \pm i\sqrt{2}\}$ **81.** -3

Section 3.4

Check Point Exercises

1. $\pm 1, \pm 2, \pm 3, \pm 6$ **2.** $\pm 1, \pm 3, \pm\dfrac{1}{2}, \pm\dfrac{1}{4}, \pm\dfrac{3}{2}, \pm\dfrac{3}{4}$ **3.** $-5, -4,$ and 1 **4.** $2, \dfrac{-3 - \sqrt{5}}{2},$ and $\dfrac{-3 + \sqrt{5}}{2}$ **5.** $\{1, 2 - 3i, 2 + 3i\}$
6. $f(x) = x^3 + 3x^2 + x + 3$ **7.** 4, 2, or 0 positive zeros, no possible negative zeros

Concept and Vocabulary Check

1. $a_0; a_n$ **2.** true **3.** false **4.** n **5.** $a - bi$ **6.** $-6; (x + 6)(2x^2 - x - 1) = 0$ **7.** $n; 1$ **8.** false **9.** true **10.** true

Exercise Set 3.4

1. $\pm 1, \pm 2, \pm 4$ **3.** $\pm 1, \pm 2, \pm 3, \pm 6, \pm\dfrac{1}{3}, \pm\dfrac{2}{3}$ **5.** $\pm 1, \pm 2, \pm 3, \pm 6, \pm\dfrac{1}{2}, \pm\dfrac{1}{4}, \pm\dfrac{3}{2}, \pm\dfrac{3}{4}$ **7.** $\pm 1, \pm 2, \pm 3, \pm 4, \pm 6, \pm 12$ **9. a.** $\pm 1, \pm 2, \pm 4$
b. $-2, -1,$ or 2 **c.** $-2, -1,$ and 2 **11. a.** $\pm 1, \pm 2, \pm 3, \pm 6, \pm\dfrac{1}{2}, \pm\dfrac{3}{2}$ **b.** $-2, \dfrac{1}{2},$ or 3 **c.** $-2, \dfrac{1}{2},$ and 3 **13. a.** $\pm 1, \pm 2, \pm 3, \pm 6$
b. -1 **c.** $-1, \dfrac{-3 - \sqrt{33}}{2},$ and $\dfrac{-3 + \sqrt{33}}{2}$ **15. a.** $\pm 1, \pm\dfrac{1}{2}, \pm 2$ **b.** -2 **c.** $-2, \dfrac{-1 + i}{2},$ and $\dfrac{-1 - i}{2}$ **17. a.** $\pm 1, \pm 2, \pm 3, \pm 4, \pm 6, \pm 12$
b. $-3, 1,$ or 4 **c.** $\{-3, 1, 4\}$ **19. a.** $\pm 1, \pm 2, \pm 3, \pm 4, \pm 6, \pm 12$ **b.** -2 **c.** $\{-2, 1 + \sqrt{7}, 1 - \sqrt{7}\}$ **21. a.** $\pm 1, \pm 5, \pm\dfrac{1}{2}, \pm\dfrac{5}{2}, \pm\dfrac{1}{3}, \pm\dfrac{5}{3}, \pm\dfrac{1}{6}, \pm\dfrac{5}{6}$
b. $-5, \dfrac{1}{3},$ or $\dfrac{1}{2}$ **c.** $\left\{-5, \dfrac{1}{3}, \dfrac{1}{2}\right\}$ **23. a.** $\pm 1, \pm 2, \pm 4$ **b.** -2 or 2 **c.** $\{-2, 2, 1 + \sqrt{2}, 1 - \sqrt{2}\}$ **25.** $f(x) = 2x^3 - 2x^2 + 50x - 50$
27. $f(x) = x^3 - 3x^2 - 15x + 125$ **29.** $f(x) = x^4 + 10x^2 + 9$ **31.** $f(x) = x^4 - 9x^3 + 21x^2 + 21x - 130$ **33.** no positive real roots;
3 or 1 negative real roots **35.** 3 or 1 positive real roots; no negative real roots **37.** 2 or 0 positive real roots; 2 or 0 negative real roots

39. $-2, 5,$ and 1 **41.** $\left\{-\dfrac{1}{2}, \dfrac{1 + \overline{\mp} \sqrt{17}}{2}, \dfrac{1 \overline{-} \sqrt{17}}{2}\right\}$ **43.** $-1, 2 + 2i,$ and $2 - 2i$ **45.** $\{-1, -2, 3 + \sqrt{13}, 3 - \sqrt{13}\}$

47. $-1, 2, -\dfrac{1}{3},$ and 3 **49.** $\left\{1, -\dfrac{3}{4}, i\sqrt{2}, -i\sqrt{2}\right\}$ **51.** $\left\{-2, \dfrac{1}{2}, \sqrt{2}, -\sqrt{2}\right\}$

53. a. $-4, 1,$ and 4 **55. a.** -1 and $\dfrac{3}{2}$ **57. a.** $\dfrac{1}{2}, 3, -1 \pm i$ **59. a.** $-2, -1, -\dfrac{2}{3}, 1,$ and 2

b.

$f(x) = -x^3 + x^2 + 16x - 16$

b.

$f(x) = 4x^3 - 8x^2 - 3x + 9$

b.

$f(x) = 2x^4 - 3x^3 - 7x^2 - 8x + 6$

b.

$f(x) = 3x^5 + 2x^4 - 15x^3 - 10x^2 + 12x + 8$

61. 7.8 in., 10 in.   **63. a.** $(7.8, 2000), (10, 2000)$ **b.** $(0, 15)$ **73.** $\left\{\dfrac{1}{2}, \dfrac{2}{3}, 2\right\}$ **75.** $\left\{\pm\dfrac{1}{2}\right\}$ **77.** $5, 3,$ or 1 positive real zeros; no negative real zeros

79.

1 real zero, 2 nonreal complex zeros

81.

2 real zeros, 2 nonreal complex zeros

83. makes sense   **85.** makes sense   **87.** false
89. true   **91.** 3 in.   **93.** 3   **95.** 5
98. $x = 1$ and $x = 2$ **99.** $x = 1$ **100.** $y = 0$

Mid-Chapter 3 Check Point

1.

$f(x) = (x - 3)^2 - 4$
domain: $(-\infty, \infty)$
range: $[-4, \infty)$

2.

$f(x) = 5 - (x + 2)^2$
domain: $(-\infty, \infty)$
range: $(-\infty, 5]$

3.
$f(x) = -x^2 - 4x + 5$
domain: $(-\infty, \infty)$
range: $(-\infty, 9]$

4.
$f(x) = 3x^2 - 6x + 1$
domain: $(-\infty, \infty)$
range: $[-2, \infty)$

5. -1 and 2 **6.** -1 and 2 **7.** $-2, 1,$ and 2 **8.** $-2, -1, 1,$ and 2

$f(x) = (x - 2)^2 (x + 1)^3$

$f(x) = -(x - 2)^2 (x + 1)^2$

$f(x) = x^3 - x^2 - 4x + 4$

$f(x) = x^4 - 5x^2 + 4$

9. -1 **10.** $-\dfrac{1}{3}, \dfrac{1}{2},$ and 1 **11.** $-1, 0,$ and 1 **12.** $0, 1 \pm 5i$

$f(x) = -(x + 1)^6$

$f(x) = -6x^3 + 7x^2 - 1$

$f(x) = 2x^3 - 2x$

$f(x) = x^3 - 2x^2 + 26x$

13. $3, 1 \pm \sqrt{2}$

$f(x) = -x^3 + 5x^2 - 5x - 3$

14. $\{-2, 1\}$ **15.** $\left\{\dfrac{1}{3}, \dfrac{1}{2}, 1\right\}$ **16.** $\left\{-\dfrac{1}{2}, \dfrac{2}{3}, \dfrac{7}{2}\right\}$ **17.** $\left\{-10, -\dfrac{5}{2}, 10\right\}$ **18.** $\{-3, 4, \pm i\}$

19. $\left\{-3, \dfrac{1}{2}, 1 \pm \sqrt{3}\right\}$ **20.** 75 cabinets per day; $1200   **21.** $-9, -9; 81$ **22.** 10 in.; 100 sq in.

23. $2x^2 - x - 3 + \dfrac{x + 1}{3x^2 - 1}$ **24.** $2x^3 - 5x^2 - 3x + 6$ **25.** $f(x) = -2x^3 + 2x^2 - 2x + 2$

26. $f(x) = x^4 - 4x^3 + 13x^2 - 36x + 36$ **27.** yes

Section 3.5

Check Point Exercises

1. a. $\{x \mid x \neq 5\}$ or $(-\infty, 5) \cup (5, \infty)$ **b.** $\{x \mid x \neq -5, x \neq 5\}$ or $(-\infty, -5) \cup (-5, 5) \cup (5, \infty)$ **c.** all real numbers or $(-\infty, \infty)$
2. a. $x = 1, x = -1$ **b.** $x = -1$ **c.** none   **3. a.** $y = 3$ **b.** $y = 0$ **c.** none

4.
$$g(x) = \frac{1}{x+2} - 1$$

5.
$$f(x) = \frac{3x-3}{x-2}$$

6.
$$f(x) = \frac{2x^2}{x^2-9}$$

7.
$$f(x) = \frac{x^4}{x^2+2}$$

8. $y = 2x - 1$ **9. a.** $C(x) = 500{,}000 + 400x$ **b.** $\overline{C}(x) = \dfrac{500{,}000 + 400x}{x}$ **c.** $\overline{C}(1000) = 900$: The average cost per wheelchair of producing 1000 wheelchairs per month is \$900.; $\overline{C}(10{,}000) = 450$: The average cost per wheelchair of producing 10,000 wheelchairs per month is \$450.; $\overline{C}(100{,}000) = 405$: The average cost per wheelchair of producing 100,000 wheelchairs per month is \$405.   **d.** $y = 400$; The cost per wheelchair approaches \$400 as more wheelchairs are produced.

Concept and Vocabulary Check

1. polynomial   **2.** false   **3.** true   **4.** vertical asymptote; $x = -5$ **5.** horizontal asymptote; $y = 0$; $y = \dfrac{1}{3}$ **6.** true
7. left; down   **8.** one more than   **9.** $y = 3x + 5$

Exercise Set 3.5

1. $\{x \mid x \neq 4\}$ **3.** $\{x \mid x \neq 5, x \neq -4\}$ **5.** $\{x \mid x \neq 7, x \neq -7\}$ **7.** all real numbers   **9.** $-\infty$ **11.** $-\infty$ **13.** 0 **15.** $+\infty$
17. $-\infty$ **19.** 1 **21.** vertical asymptote: $x = -4$; no holes   **23.** vertical asymptotes: $x = -4$, $x = 0$; no holes   **25.** vertical asymptote: $x = -4$; hole at $x = 0$ **27.** no vertical asymptotes; no holes   **29.** no vertical asymptotes; hole at $x = 3$ **31.** vertical asymptote: $x = -3$; hole at $x = 3$
33. vertical asymptote: $x = 3$; hole at $x = -7$ **35.** no vertical asymptotes; hole at $x = -7$ **37.** $y = 0$ **39.** $y = 4$

41. no horizontal asymptote   **43.** $y = -\dfrac{2}{3}$

45.
$$g(x) = \frac{1}{x-1}$$

47.
$$h(x) = \frac{1}{x} + 2$$

49.
$$g(x) = \frac{1}{x+1} - 2$$

51.
$$g(x) = \frac{1}{(x+2)^2}$$

53.
$$h(x) = \frac{1}{x^2} - 4$$

55.
$$h(x) = \frac{1}{(x-3)^2} + 1$$

57.
$$f(x) = \frac{4x}{x-2}$$

59.
$$f(x) = \frac{2x}{x^2-4}$$

61.
$$f(x) = \frac{2x^2}{x^2-1}$$

63.
$$f(x) = \frac{-x}{x+1}$$

65.
$$f(x) = -\frac{1}{x^2-4}$$

67.
$$f(x) = \frac{2}{x^2+x-2}$$

69.
$$f(x) = \frac{2x^2}{x^2+4}$$

71.
$$f(x) = \frac{x+2}{x^2+x-6}$$

73.
$$f(x) = \frac{x-2}{x^2-4}$$

75.
$$f(x) = \frac{x^4}{x^2+2}$$

77.
$$f(x) = \frac{x^2+x-12}{x^2-4}$$

79.
$$f(x) = \frac{3x^2+x-4}{2x^2-5x}$$

81. a. Slant asymptote: $y = x$
b.
$$f(x) = \frac{x^2-1}{x}$$

83. a. Slant asymptote: $y = x$
b.
$$f(x) = \frac{x^2+1}{x}$$

85. a. Slant asymptote: $y = x + 4$
b.

$$f(x) = \frac{x^2 + x - 6}{x - 3}$$

87. a. Slant asymptote: $y = x - 2$
b.

$$f(x) = \frac{x^3 + 1}{x^2 + 2x}$$

89.

$$f(x) = \frac{x + 2}{2x(x - 2)}$$

91.

$$f(x) = \frac{x - 6}{2(x - 3)}$$

93.

$$f(x) = \frac{x - 2}{x + 2}$$

95. $g(x) = \dfrac{1}{x + 3} + 2$

$$g(x) = \frac{1}{x + 3} + 2$$

97. $g(x) = \dfrac{-1}{x - 2} + 3$

$$g(x) = \frac{-1}{x - 2} + 3$$

99. a. $C(x) = 100x + 100,000$ **b.** $\overline{C}(x) = \dfrac{100x + 100,000}{x}$ **c.** $\overline{C}(500) = 300$, when 500 bicycles are produced, it costs $300 to produce each bicycle; $\overline{C}(1000) = 200$, when 1000 bicycles are produced, it costs $200 to produce each bicycle; $\overline{C}(2000) = 150$, when 2000 bicycles are produced, it costs $150 to produce each bicycle; $\overline{C}(4000) = 125$, when 4000 bicycles are produced, it costs $125 to produce each bicycle. **d.** $y = 100$; The cost per bicycle approaches $100 as more bicycles are produced. **101. a.** 6.0 **b.** after 6 minutes; about 4.8 **c.** 6.5 **d.** $y = 6.5$; Over time, the pH level rises back to normal. **e.** It quickly drops below normal and then slowly begins to approach the normal level.
103. 90; An incidence ratio of 10 means 90% of the deaths are smoking related. **105.** $y = 100$; The percentage of deaths cannot exceed 100% as the incidence ratios increase. **107. a.** $f(x) = \dfrac{1.75x^2 - 15.9x + 160}{2.1x^2 - 3.5x + 296}$ **b.** 67% **c.** 66%; underestimates by 1% **d.** $y = \dfrac{1.75}{2.1}$; 83%

119.

−3   3
0

The graph approaches the horizontal asymptote faster and the vertical asymptote slower as n increases.

121. a.

400

0   70
0

b. The graph increases and reaches a maximum of about 356 arrests per 100,000 drivers at age 25.
c. at age 25, about 356 arrests

123. does not make sense **125.** does not make sense **127.** true **129.** true **134.** $\left\{-3, \dfrac{5}{2}\right\}$ **135.** $\{-2, -1, 2\}$ **136.** $\dfrac{-x - 5}{x + 3}$ or $-\dfrac{x + 5}{x + 3}$

Section 3.6

Check Point Exercises

1. $\{x \mid x < -4 \text{ or } x > 5\}$ or $(-\infty, -4) \cup (5, \infty)$

2. $\left\{x \,\middle|\, \dfrac{-3 - \sqrt{7}}{2} \le x \le \dfrac{-3 + \sqrt{7}}{2}\right\}$ or $\left[\dfrac{-3 - \sqrt{7}}{2}, \dfrac{-3 + \sqrt{7}}{2}\right]$

3. $\{x \mid x \le -3 \text{ or } -1 \le x \le 1\}$ or $(-\infty, -3] \cup [-1, 1]$

4. $\{x \mid x < -1 \text{ or } x \ge 1\}$ or $(-\infty, -1) \cup [1, \infty)$

5. between 1 and 4 seconds, excluding $t = 1$ and $t = 4$

Concept and Vocabulary Check

1. $x^2 + 8x + 15 = 0$; boundary **2.** $(-\infty, -5); (-5, -3); (-3, \infty)$ **3.** true **4.** true **5.** $(-\infty, -2) \cup [1, \infty)$

Exercise Set 3.6

1. $(-\infty, -2) \cup (4, \infty)$

−2   4

3. $[-3, 7]$

−3   7

5. $(-\infty, 1) \cup (4, \infty)$

1   4

7. $(-\infty, -4) \cup (-1, \infty)$

−4   −1

9. $\varnothing$

11. $\left[-4, \dfrac{2}{3}\right]$

−4 $\dfrac{2}{3}$

13. $\left(-3, \dfrac{5}{2}\right)$

−3 $\dfrac{5}{2}$

15. $\left(-1, -\dfrac{3}{4}\right)$

−1 $-\dfrac{3}{4}$

17. $\left[-2, \dfrac{1}{3}\right]$

19. $(-\infty, 0] \cup [4, \infty)$

21. $\left(-\infty, -\dfrac{3}{2}\right) \cup (0, \infty)$

23. $[0, 1]$

25. $[2 - \sqrt{2}, 2 + \sqrt{2}]$

27. $\varnothing$

29. $[1, 2] \cup [3, \infty)$

31. $[0, 3] \cup [5, \infty)$

33. $(-\infty, 2) \cup \left(2, \dfrac{7}{2}\right)$

35. $[-2, -1] \cup [1, \infty)$

37. $(-\infty, -3)$

39. $(-1, \infty)$

41. $\{0\} \cup [9, \infty)$

43. $(-\infty, -3) \cup (4, \infty)$

45. $(-4, -3)$

47. $[2, 4)$

49. $\left(-\infty, -\dfrac{4}{3}\right) \cup [2, \infty)$

51. $(-\infty, 0) \cup (3, \infty)$

53. $(-\infty, -4] \cup (-2, 1]$

55. $(-\infty, -5) \cup (-3, \infty)$

57. $\left(-\infty, \dfrac{1}{2}\right) \cup \left[\dfrac{7}{5}, \infty\right)$

59. $(-\infty, -6] \cup (-2, \infty)$

61. $\left(-\infty, \dfrac{1}{2}\right] \cup [2, \infty)$

63. $(-\infty, -1) \cup [1, \infty)$

65. $(-\infty, -8) \cup (-6, 4) \cup (6, \infty)$

67. $(-3, 2)$

69. $(-\infty, -1) \cup (1, 2) \cup (3, \infty)$

71. $\left[-6, -\dfrac{1}{2}\right] \cup [1, \infty)$ **73.** $(-\infty, -2) \cup [-1, 2)$ **75.** between 0 and $\dfrac{1}{2}$ second **77. a.** dry: 160 ft; wet: 185 ft **b.** dry pavement: graph (b); wet pavement: graph (a) **c.** extremely well; Function values and data are identical. **d.** speeds exceeding 76 miles per hour; points on (b) to the right of $(76, 540)$ **79.** The sides (in feet) are in $(0, 6]$ or $[19, 25)$. **87.** $\left[-3, \dfrac{1}{2}\right]$ **89.** $(1, 4]$ **91.** $(-4, -1) \cup [2, \infty)$

93. a. $f(x) = 0.1375x^2 + 0.7x + 37.8$ **b.** speeds exceeding 52 miles per hour **95.** does not make sense **97.** does not make sense

99. false **101.** true **103.** Answers may vary. One possible solution is $\dfrac{x - 3}{x + 4} \geq 0$. **105.** $\{2\}$ **107.** $(-\infty, 2) \cup (2, \infty)$

109. $27 - 3x^2 \geq 0$
$$3x^2 \leq 27$$
$$x^2 \leq 9$$
$$-3 \leq x \leq 3$$

110. a. 16 **b.** $y = 16x^2$ **c.** 400 **111. a.** 96 **b.** $y = \dfrac{96}{x}$ **c.** 32 **112.** 8

Section 3.7

Check Point Exercises

1. 66 gal **2.** 9375 lb **3.** 512 cycles per second **4.** 24 min **5.** 96π cubic feet

Concept and Vocabulary Check

1. $y = kx$; constant of variation **2.** $y = kx^n$ **3.** $y = \dfrac{k}{x}$ **4.** $y = \dfrac{kx}{z}$ **5.** $y = kxz$ **6.** directly; inversely **7.** jointly; inversely

Exercise Set 3.7

1. 156 **3.** 30 **5.** $\dfrac{5}{6}$ **7.** 240 **9.** 50 **11.** $x = kyz; y = \dfrac{x}{kz}$ **13.** $x = \dfrac{kz^3}{y}; y = \dfrac{kz^3}{x}$ **15.** $x = \dfrac{kyz}{\sqrt{w}}; y = \dfrac{x\sqrt{w}}{kz}$

17. $x = kz(y + w); y = \dfrac{x - kzw}{kz}$ **19.** $x = \dfrac{kz}{y - w}; y = \dfrac{xw + kz}{x}$ **21.** 5.4 ft **23.** 80 in. **25.** about 607 lb **27.** 32°

29. 90 milliroentgens per hour **31.** This person has a BMI of 24.4 and is not overweight. **33.** 1800 Btu per hour

35. $\dfrac{1}{4}$ of what it was originally **37. a.** $C = \dfrac{kP_1P_2}{d^2}$ **b.** $k \approx 0.02; C = \dfrac{0.02\, P_1P_2}{d^2}$ **c.** 39,813 daily phone calls

39. a.

b. Current varies inversely as resistance. **c.** $R = \dfrac{6}{I}$

49. does not make sense **51.** makes sense **53.** The destructive power is four times as much. **55.** Reduce the resistance by a factor of $\frac{1}{3}$.

58.

$f(x) = 2^x$

59.

$g(x) = f(-x) = 2^{-x}$

60.

$h(x) = f(x) + 1 = 2^x + 1$

Chapter 3 Review Exercises

1.

$f(x) = -(x + 1)^2 + 4$

axis of symmetry; $x = -1$
domain: $(-\infty, \infty)$; range: $(-\infty, 4]$

2.

$f(x) = (x + 4)^2 - 2$

axis of symmetry: $x = -4$
domain: $(-\infty, \infty)$; range: $[-2, \infty)$

3.

$f(x) = -x^2 + 2x + 3$

axis of symmetry: $x = 1$
domain: $(-\infty, \infty)$; range: $(-\infty, 4]$

4.

$f(x) = 2x^2 - 4x - 6$

axis of symmetry: $x = 1$
domain: $(-\infty, \infty)$; range: $[-8, \infty)$

5. a. maximum is -57 at $x = 7$ **b.** domain: $(-\infty, \infty)$; range: $(-\infty, -57]$ **6. a.** minimum is 685 at $x = -3$ **b.** domain: $(-\infty, \infty)$; range: $[685, \infty)$
7. a. 16 ft; 20 yd   **b.** 6 ft   **c.** 45.3 yd   **d.**

$f(x) = -0.025x^2 + x + 6$

8. 250 yd by 500 yd; 125,000 sq yard   **9.** -7 and 7; -49

10. c   **11.** b   **12.** a   **13.** d   **14. a.** rises to the right   **b.** no; The model indicates increasing deforestation despite a declining rate in which the forest is being cut down.   **c.** falls to the right   **d.** no; The model indicates the amount of forest cleared, in square kilometers, will eventually be negative, which is not possible.   **15.** No; the graph falls to the right, so eventually there would be a negative number of thefts, which is not possible.
16. $x = 1$, multiplicity 1, crosses; $x = -2$, multiplicity 2, touches; $x = -5$, multiplicity 3, crosses
17. $x = -5$, multiplicity 1, crosses; $x = 5$, multiplicity 2, touches
18. $f(1)$ is negative and $f(2)$ is positive, so by the Intermediate Value Theorem, f has a real zero between 1 and 2.
19. a. The graph falls to the left and rises to the right.   **b.** no symmetry   **c.**

$f(x) = x^3 - x^2 - 9x + 9$

20. a. The graph rises to the left and falls to the right.   **b.** origin symmetry   **c.**

$f(x) = 4x - x^3$

21. a. The graph falls to the left and rises to the right.   **b.** no symmetry   **c.**

$f(x) = 2x^3 + 3x^2 - 8x - 12$

22. a. The graph falls to the left and to the right.   **b.** y-axis symmetry   **c.**

$f(x) = -x^4 + 25x^2$

23. a. The graph falls to the left and to the right.   **b.** no symmetry   **c.**

$f(x) = -x^4 + 6x^3 - 9x^2$

24. a. The graph rises to the left and to the right.   **b.** no symmetry   **c.**

$f(x) = 3x^4 - 15x^3$

25.

$f(x) = 2x^2 (x - 1)^3 (x + 2)$

26.

$f(x) = -x^3 (x + 4)^2 (x - 1)$

27. $4x^2 - 7x + 5 - \dfrac{4}{x + 1}$

28. $2x^2 - 4x + 1 - \dfrac{10}{5x - 3}$

29. $2x^2 + 3x - 1$ **30.** $3x^3 - 4x^2 + 7$

31. $3x^3 + 6x^2 + 10x + 10 + \dfrac{20}{x - 2}$ **32.** -5697

33. $2, \dfrac{1}{2}, -3$ **34.** $\{4, -2 \pm \sqrt{5}\}$ **35.** $\pm 1, \pm 5$ **36.** $\pm 1, \pm 2, \pm 4, \pm 8, \pm\dfrac{8}{3}, \pm\dfrac{4}{3}, \pm\dfrac{2}{3}, \pm\dfrac{1}{3}$ **37.** 2 or 0 positive real zeros; no negative real zeros

38. 3 or 1 positive real zeros; 2 or 0 negative real zeros   **39.** No sign variations exist for either $f(x)$ or $f(-x)$, so no real roots exist.

40. a. $\pm 1, \pm 2, \pm 4$ **b.** 1 positive real zero; 2 or no negative real zeros   **c.** -2 or 1 **d.** $-2, 1$

41. a. $\pm 1, \pm\dfrac{1}{2}, \pm\dfrac{1}{3}, \pm\dfrac{1}{6}$ **b.** 2 or 0 positive real zeros; 1 negative real zero   **c.** $-1, \dfrac{1}{3}$, or $\dfrac{1}{2}$ **d.** $-1, \dfrac{1}{3}, \dfrac{1}{2}$

42. a. $\pm 1, \pm 3, \pm 5, \pm 15, \pm\dfrac{1}{2}, \pm\dfrac{1}{4}, \pm\dfrac{1}{8}, \pm\dfrac{3}{2}, \pm\dfrac{3}{4}, \pm\dfrac{3}{8}, \pm\dfrac{5}{2}, \pm\dfrac{5}{4}, \pm\dfrac{5}{8}, \pm\dfrac{15}{2}, \pm\dfrac{15}{4}, \pm\dfrac{15}{8}$ **b.** 3 or 1 positive real solutions; no negative real solutions

c. $\dfrac{1}{2}, \dfrac{3}{2}$, or $\dfrac{5}{2}$ **d.** $\left\{\dfrac{1}{2}, \dfrac{3}{2}, \dfrac{5}{2}\right\}$ **43. a.** $\pm 1, \pm\dfrac{1}{2}$ **b.** 2 or 0 positive real solutions; 1 negative solution   **c.** $\dfrac{1}{2}$ **d.** $\left\{\dfrac{1}{2}, \dfrac{-5 - \sqrt{29}}{2}, \dfrac{-5 + \sqrt{29}}{2}\right\}$

44. a. $\pm 1, \pm 2, \pm 3, \pm 6$ **b.** 2 or zero positive real solutions; 2 or zero negative real solutions   **c.** $-2, -1, 1$, or 3 **d.** $\{-2, -1, 1, 3\}$

45. a. $\pm 1, \pm 2, \pm\dfrac{1}{2}, \pm\dfrac{1}{4}$ **b.** 1 positive real root; 1 negative real root   **c.** $-\dfrac{1}{2}$ or $\dfrac{1}{2}$ **d.** $\left\{-\dfrac{1}{2}, \dfrac{1}{2}, i\sqrt{2}, -i\sqrt{2}\right\}$

46. a. $\pm 1, \pm 2, \pm 4, \pm\dfrac{1}{2}$ **b.** 2 or no positive zeros; 2 or no negative zeros   **c.** $-2, -1, \dfrac{1}{2}$, or 2 **d.** $-2, -1, \dfrac{1}{2}, 2$

47. $f(x) = x^3 - 6x^2 + 21x - 26$ **48.** $f(x) = 2x^4 + 12x^3 + 20x^2 + 12x + 18$ **49.** $-2, \dfrac{1}{2}, \pm i; f(x) = (x - i)(x + i)(x + 2)(2x - 1)$

50. $-1, 4; g(x) = (x + 1)^2(x - 4)^2$ **51.** 4 real zeros, one with multiplicity two   **52.** 3 real zeros; 2 nonreal complex zeros

53. 2 real zeros, one with multiplicity two; 2 nonreal complex zeros   **54.** 1 real zero; 4 nonreal complex zeros

55.

$g(x) = \dfrac{1}{(x + 2)^2} - 1$

56.

$h(x) = \dfrac{1}{x - 1} + 3$

57. Vertical asymptotes: $x = 3$ and $x = -3$
horizontal asymptote: $y = 0$

$f(x) = \dfrac{2x}{x^2 - 9}$

58. Vertical asymptote: $x = -3$
horizontal asymptote: $y = 2$

$f(x) = \dfrac{2x - 4}{x + 3}$

59. Vertical asymptotes: $x = 3$ and $x = -2$
horizontal asymptote: $y = 1$

$h(x) = \dfrac{x^2 - 3x - 4}{x^2 - x - 6}$

60. Vertical asymptote: $x = -2$
horizontal asymptote: $y = 1$

$r(x) = \dfrac{x^2 + 4x + 3}{(x + 2)^2}$

61. Vertical asymptote: $x = -1$
no horizontal asymptote
slant asymptote: $y = x - 1$

$y = \dfrac{x^2}{x + 1}$

62. Vertical asymptote: $x = 3$
no horizontal asymptote
slant asymptote: $y = x + 5$

$y = \dfrac{x^2 + 2x - 3}{x - 3}$

63. No vertical asymptote
no horizontal asymptote
slant asymptote: $y = -2x$

$f(x) = \dfrac{-2x^3}{x^2 + 1}$

64. Vertical asymptote: $x = \dfrac{3}{2}$
no horizontal asymptote
slant asymptote: $y = 2x - 5$

$g(x) = \dfrac{4x^2 - 16x + 16}{2x - 3}$

65. a. $C(x) = 25x + 50,000$
b. $\overline{C}(x) = \dfrac{25x + 50,000}{x}$
c. $\overline{C}(50) = 1025$, when 50 calculators are manufactured, it costs \$1025 to manufacture each; $\overline{C}(100) = 525$, when 100 calculators are manufactured, it costs \$525 to manufacture each; $\overline{C}(1000) = 75$, when 1000 calculators are manufactured, it costs \$75 to manufacture each; $\overline{C}(100,000) = 25.5$, when 100,000 calculators are manufactured, it costs \$25.50 to manufacture each.
d. $y = 25$; costs will approach \$25.

66. $y = 3000$; The number of fish in the pond approaches 3000.
67. $y = 0$; As the number of years of education increases the percentage rate of unemployment approaches zero.

68. a. $P(x) = 2.99x + 235.5$ **b.** $R(x) = \dfrac{1.53x + 114.8}{2.99x + 235.5}$ **c.** $y = 0.51$; Over time the percentage of men in the U.S. population will approach 51%.

69. $\left(-3, \dfrac{1}{2}\right)$

70. $(-\infty, -4] \cup \left[-\dfrac{1}{2}, \infty\right)$

71. $(-3, 0) \cup (1, \infty)$

72. $(-\infty, -2) \cup (6, \infty)$

73. $[-1, 1) \cup [2, \infty)$

74. $(-\infty, 4) \cup \left[\dfrac{23}{4}, \infty\right)$

75. a. 261 ft; overestimates by 1 ft   **b.** speeds exceeding 40 miles per hour   **76.** from 1 to 2 sec   **77.** 134.4 cm³   **78.** 1600 ft

79. 440 vibrations per second   **80.** 112 decibels   **81.** 16 hr   **82.** 800 ft³   **83. a.** $L = \dfrac{1890}{R}$ **b.** an approximate model   **c.** 70 yr

Chapter 3 Test

1.

$f(x) = (x + 1)^2 + 4$

axis of symmetry: $x = -1$
domain: $(-\infty, \infty)$; range: $[4, \infty)$

2.

$f(x) = x^2 - 2x - 3$

axis of symmetry: $x = 1$
domain: $(-\infty, \infty)$; range: $[-4, \infty)$

3. a. maximum of 2 at $x = 3$;
b. domain: $(-\infty, \infty)$; range: $(-\infty, 2]$
4. 23 computers;
maximum daily profit $= \$16{,}900$
5. 7 and 7; 49

6. a. $5, 2, -2$
b.

$f(x) = x^3 - 5x^2 - 4x + 20$

7. Since the degree of the polynomial is odd and the leading coefficient is positive, the graph of f should fall to the left and rise to the right. The x-intercepts should be $-1, 0$, and 1.

8. a. 2   **b.** $\dfrac{1}{2}, \dfrac{2}{3}$ **9.** $\pm1, \pm2, \pm3, \pm6, \pm\dfrac{1}{2}, \pm\dfrac{3}{2}$

10. 3 or 1 positive real zeros; no negative real zeros

11. $\{-3, -3 - \sqrt{11}, -3 + \sqrt{11}\}$ **12. a.** $\pm1, \pm3, \pm5, \pm15, \pm\dfrac{1}{2}, \pm\dfrac{3}{2}, \pm\dfrac{5}{2}, \pm\dfrac{15}{2}$ **b.** $-\sqrt{5}, -1, \dfrac{3}{2}$, and $\sqrt{5}$ **13.** $(x - 1)(x + 2)^2$

14. $f(x) = 2x^4 - 2$ **15.** -1 and $\dfrac{2}{3}$

$f(x) = -3x^3 - 4x^2 + x + 2$

16. domain: $\{x \mid x \ne -3\}$

$f(x) = \dfrac{1}{(x + 3)^2}$

17. domain: $\{x \mid x \ne 1\}$

$f(x) = \dfrac{1}{x - 1} + 2$

18. domain: $\{x \mid x \ne 4, x \ne -4\}$

$f(x) = \dfrac{x}{x^2 - 16}$

19. domain: $\{x \mid x \ne 2\}$

$f(x) = \dfrac{x^2 - 9}{x - 2}$

20. domain: $\{x \mid x \ne -3, x \ne 1\}$

$f(x) = \dfrac{x + 1}{x^2 + 2x - 3}$

21. domain: all real numbers

$f(x) = \dfrac{4x^2}{x^2 + 3}$

22. a. $\overline{C}(x) = \dfrac{300{,}000 + 10x}{x}$ **b.** $y = 10$; As the number of satellite radio players increases, the average cost approaches \$10.

23. $(-3, 4)$

24. $(-\infty, 3) \cup [10, \infty)$

25. 45 foot-candles

Cumulative Review Exercises (Chapters 1–3)

1. domain: $(-2, 2)$; range: $[0, \infty)$ **2.** -1 and 1, both of multiplicity 2   **3.** 0   **4.** 3   **5.** $x \to -2^+$; $x \to 2^-$

6.

$g(x) = f(x + 2) + 1$

7. $\{2, -1\}$ **8.** $\left\{\dfrac{5 + \sqrt{13}}{6}, \dfrac{5 - \sqrt{13}}{6}\right\}$ **9.** $\left\{\dfrac{1}{3}, -\dfrac{2}{3}\right\}$ **10.** $\{-3, -1, 2\}$ **11.** $(-\infty, 1) \cup (4, \infty)$

12. $(-\infty, -1) \cup \left(\dfrac{5}{3}, \infty\right)$ **13.**

$f(x) = x^3 - 4x^2 - x + 4$

14.

$f(x) = x^2 + 2x - 8$

15.

$f(x) = x^2(x - 3)$

16.
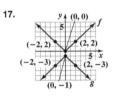
$f(x) = \dfrac{x - 1}{x - 2}$

17.

18.

$x^2 + y^2 - 2x + 4y - 4 = 0$

19. $(f \circ g)(x) = 32x^2 - 20x + 2$ **20.** $4x + 2h - 1$

CHAPTER 4

Section 4.1

Check Point Exercises

1. approximately $160; overestimates by $11

2.

$f(x) = 3^x$

3.

$f(x) = \left(\dfrac{1}{3}\right)^x$

4.

$f(x) = 3^x$
$g(x) = 3^x - 1$

5.

$f(x) = 2^x$
$g(x) = 2^x + 1$

6. approximately 4446   **7. a.** $14,859.47   **b.** $14,918.25

Concept and Vocabulary Check

1. b^x; $(-\infty, \infty)$; $(0, \infty)$ **2.** x; $y = 0$; horizontal   **3.** e; natural; 2.72   **4.** A; P; r; n **5.** semiannually; quarterly; continuous

Exercise Set 4.1

1. 10.556   **3.** 11.665   **5.** 0.125   **7.** 9.974   **9.** 0.387

11.

$f(x) = 4^x$

13.

$g(x) = \left(\dfrac{3}{2}\right)^x$

15.

$h(x) = \left(\dfrac{1}{2}\right)^x$

17.
$f(x) = (0.6)^x$

19. $H(x) = -3^{-x}$
21. $F(x) = -3^x$
23. $h(x) = 3^x - 1$

25.

$f(x) = 2^x$
$g(x) = 2^x + 1$
asymptote: $y = 0$
domain: $(-\infty, \infty)$
range: $(0, \infty)$

27.

$f(x) = 2^x$
$g(x) = 2^x - 1$
asymptote: $y = -1$
domain: $(-\infty, \infty)$
range: $(-1, \infty)$

29.
$f(x) = 2^x$
$h(x) = 2^{x+1} - 1$
asymptote: $y = -1$
domain: $(-\infty, \infty)$
range: $(-1, \infty)$

31.

$f(x) = 2^x$
$g(x) = -2^x$
asymptote: $y = 0$
domain: $(-\infty, \infty)$
range: $(-\infty, 0)$

33.
$f(x) = 2^x$
$g(x) = 2 \cdot 2^x$
asymptote: $y = 0$
domain: $(-\infty, \infty)$
range: $(0, \infty)$

35.

$g(x) = e^{x-1}$

asymptote: $y = 0$
domain: $(-\infty, \infty)$
range: $(0, \infty)$

37.

$g(x) = e^x + 2$

asymptote: $y = 2$
domain: $(-\infty, \infty)$
range: $(2, \infty)$

39.

$h(x) = e^{x-1} + 2$

asymptote: $y = 2$
domain: $(-\infty, \infty)$
range: $(2, \infty)$

41.

$h(x) = e^{-x}$

asymptote: $y = 0$
domain: $(-\infty, \infty)$
range: $(0, \infty)$

43.

$g(x) = 2e^x$

asymptote: $y = 0$
domain: $(-\infty, \infty)$
range: $(0, \infty)$

45.

$h(x) = e^{2x} + 1$

asymptote: $y = 1$
domain: $(-\infty, \infty)$
range: $(1, \infty)$

47.

$f(x) = 3^x$
$g(x) = 3^{-x}$

asymptote of f: $y = 0$
asymptote of g: $y = 0$

49.

$f(x) = 3^x$
$g(x) = \dfrac{1}{3} \cdot 3^x$

asymptote of f: $y = 0$
asymptote of g: $y = 0$

51.

$f(x) = \left(\dfrac{1}{2}\right)^x$

$g(x) = \left(\dfrac{1}{2}\right)^{x-1} + 1$

asymptote of f: $y = 0$
asymptote of g: $y = 1$

53. a. \$13,116.51
b. \$13,140.67
c. \$13,157.04
d. \$13,165.31
55. 7% compounded monthly

57. $(0, 1)$

59.

$g(x) = 2^{-x}$ $f(x) = 2^x$

61. $y = 4^x$ **63.** $y = -e^x$ **65. a.** 574 million **b.** 1148 million
c. 2295 million **d.** 4590 million **e.** It appears to double. **67.** \$832,744
69. 3.249009585; 3.317278183; 3.321880096; 3.321995226; 3.321997068; $2^{\sqrt{3}} \approx 3.321997085$;
The closer the exponent is to $\sqrt{3}$, the closer the value is to $2^{\sqrt{3}}$.
71. a. \$15,166 **b.** \$16,037 **c.** linear model **73. a.** 100% **b.** $\approx 68.5\%$
c. $\approx 30.8\%$ **d.** $\approx 20\%$ **75.** the function g

81. a. $A = 10,000\left(1 + \dfrac{0.05}{4}\right)^{4t}$; $A = 10,000\left(1 + \dfrac{0.045}{12}\right)^{12t}$

b. 24,000

83. does not make sense
85. does not make sense
87. false
89. false
91. $y = 3^x$ is (d); $y = 5^x$ is (c); $y = \left(\dfrac{1}{3}\right)^x$ is (a); $y = \left(\dfrac{1}{5}\right)^x$ is (b).

5% interest compounded quarterly

93. a. $\cosh(-x) = \dfrac{e^{-x} + e^{-(-x)}}{2} = \dfrac{e^{-x} + e^x}{2} = \dfrac{e^x + e^{-x}}{2} = \cosh x$

b. $\sinh(-x) = \dfrac{e^{-x} - e^{-(-x)}}{2} = \dfrac{e^{-x} - e^x}{2} = -\dfrac{e^x - e^{-x}}{2} = -\sinh x$

c. $\left(\dfrac{e^x + e^{-x}}{2}\right)^2 - \left(\dfrac{e^x - e^{-x}}{2}\right)^2 \overset{?}{=} 1$

$\dfrac{e^{2x} + 2 + e^{-2x}}{4} - \dfrac{e^{2x} - 2 + e^{-2x}}{4} \overset{?}{=} 1$

$\dfrac{e^{2x} + 2 + e^{-2x} - e^{2x} + 2 - e^{-2x}}{4} \overset{?}{=} 1$

$\dfrac{4}{4} \overset{?}{=} 1$

$1 = 1$

94. We don't know how to solve $x = 2^y$ for y. **95.** $\dfrac{1}{2}$ **96.** $(-\infty, 3) \cup (3, \infty)$

Section 4.2

Check Point Exercises

1. a. $7^3 = x$ **b.** $b^2 = 25$ **c.** $4^y = 26$ **2. a.** $5 = \log_2 x$ **b.** $3 = \log_b 27$ **c.** $y = \log_e 33$ **3. a.** 2 **b.** -3 **c.** $\dfrac{1}{2}$ **d.** $\dfrac{1}{7}$
4. a. 1 **b.** 0 **5. a.** 8 **b.** 17 **6.**

$f(x) = 3^x$
$g(x) = \log_3 x$

7. $(5, \infty)$ **8.** 80% **9.** 4.0 **10. a.** $(-\infty, 4)$ **b.** $(-\infty, 0) \cup (0, \infty)$
11. 34°; extremely well

Concept and Vocabulary Check

1. $b^y = x$ **2.** logarithmic; b **3.** 1 **4.** 0 **5.** x **6.** x **7.** $(0, \infty)$; $(-\infty, \infty)$ **8.** y; $x = 0$; vertical **9.** up 5 units
10. to the left 5 units **11.** x-axis **12.** y-axis **13.** $5 - x > 0$ **14.** common; $\log x$ **15.** natural; $\ln x$

Exercise Set 4.2

1. $2^4 = 16$ **3.** $3^2 = x$ **5.** $b^5 = 32$ **7.** $6^y = 216$ **9.** $\log_2 8 = 3$ **11.** $\log_2 \frac{1}{16} = -4$ **13.** $\log_8 2 = \frac{1}{3}$ **15.** $\log_{13} x = 2$

17. $\log_b 1000 = 3$ **19.** $\log_7 200 = y$ **21.** 2 **23.** 6 **25.** -1 **27.** -3 **29.** $\frac{1}{2}$ **31.** $-\frac{1}{2}$ **33.** $\frac{1}{2}$ **35.** 1 **37.** 0 **39.** 7 **41.** 19

43.

45.

47. $H(x) = 1 - \log_3 x$ **49.** $h(x) = \log_3 x - 1$ **51.** $g(x) = \log_3(x - 1)$

53.

$f(x) = \log_2 x$
$g(x) = \log_2(x+1)$
vertical asymptote: $x = -1$
domain: $(-1, \infty)$
range: $(-\infty, \infty)$

55.
$f(x) = \log_2 x$
$h(x) = 1 + \log_2 x$
vertical asymptote: $x = 0$
domain: $(0, \infty)$
range: $(-\infty, \infty)$

57.
$f(x) = \log_2 x$
$g(x) = \frac{1}{2} \log_2 x$
vertical asymptote: $x = 0$
domain: $(0, \infty)$
range: $(-\infty, \infty)$

59.
$g(x) = \log(x - 1)$
asymptote: $x = 1$
domain: $(1, \infty)$
range: $(-\infty, \infty)$

61.

$h(x) = \log x - 1$
asymptote: $x = 0$
domain: $(0, \infty)$
range: $(-\infty, \infty)$

63.
$g(x) = 1 - \log x$
asymptote: $x = 0$
domain: $(0, \infty)$
range: $(-\infty, \infty)$

65.
$g(x) = \ln(x + 2)$
asymptote: $x = -2$
domain: $(-2, \infty)$
range: $(-\infty, \infty)$

67.
$h(x) = \ln(2x)$
asymptote: $x = 0$
domain: $(0, \infty)$
range: $(-\infty, \infty)$

69.

$g(x) = 2 \ln x$
asymptote: $x = 0$
domain: $(0, \infty)$
range: $(-\infty, \infty)$

71.
$h(x) = -\ln x$
asymptote: $x = 0$
domain: $(0, \infty)$
range: $(-\infty, \infty)$

73.

$g(x) = 2 - \ln x$
asymptote: $x = 0$
domain: $(0, \infty)$
range: $(-\infty, \infty)$

75. $(-4, \infty)$ **77.** $(-\infty, 2)$ **79.** $(-\infty, 2) \cup (2, \infty)$ **81.** 2 **83.** 7 **85.** 33 **87.** 0 **89.** 6 **91.** -6 **93.** 125 **95.** $9x$

97. $5x^2$ **99.** $\sqrt{x}$ **101.** $3^2 = x - 1$; $\{10\}$ **103.** $4^{-3} = x$; $\left\{\frac{1}{64}\right\}$ **105.** 0 **107.** 2 **109.** $(-\infty, -1) \cup (2, \infty)$ **111.** $(-\infty, -1) \cup (5, \infty)$

113. 95.4% **115. a.** 25.5%; underestimates by 0.7% **b.** 24.2% **117.** ≈ 188 db; yes

119. a. 88
b. 71.5; 63.9; 58.8; 55; 52; 49.5
c.

Material retention decreases as
time passes.

129.

$g(x)$ is $f(x)$ shifted upward
3 units.

131.

$g(x)$ is $f(x)$ shifted right 2 units
and upward 1 unit.

133. a.   **b.**

c.   **d.** They are the same.
$\log_b M + \log_b N$
e. the sum of the logarithms of its factors

135. makes sense   **137.** makes sense   **139.** false   **141.** false   **143.** $\dfrac{4}{5}$ **145.** $\log_3 40 > \log_4 60$

147. a. 5   **b.** 5   **c.** $\log_2(8 \cdot 4) = \log_2 8 + \log_2 4$ **148. a.** 4   **b.** 4   **c.** $\log_2\left(\dfrac{32}{2}\right) = \log_2 32 - \log_2 2$

149. a. 4   **b.** 4   **c.** $\log_3 9^2 = 2\log_3 9$

Section 4.3
Check Point Exercises

1. a. $\log_6 7 + \log_6 11$ **b.** $2 + \log x$ **2. a.** $\log_8 23 - \log_8 x$ **b.** $5 - \ln 11$ **3. a.** $9\log_6 3$ **b.** $\dfrac{1}{3}\ln x$ **c.** $2\log(x+4)$

4. a. $4\log_b x + \dfrac{1}{3}\log_b y$ **b.** $\dfrac{1}{2}\log_5 x - 2 - 3\log_5 y$ **5. a.** $\log 100 = 2$ **b.** $\log\dfrac{7x+6}{x}$ **6. a.** $\ln x^2\sqrt[3]{x+5}$ **b.** $\log\dfrac{(x-3)^2}{x}$

c. $\log_b\dfrac{\sqrt[4]{x}}{25y^{10}}$ **7.** 4.02   **8.** 4.02

Concept and Vocabulary Check

1. $\log_b M + \log_b N$; sum   **2.** $\log_b M - \log_b N$; difference   **3.** $p\log_b M$; product   **4.** $\dfrac{\log_a M}{\log_a b}$

Exercise Set 4.3

1. $\log_5 7 + \log_5 3$ **3.** $1 + \log_7 x$ **5.** $3 + \log x$ **7.** $1 - \log_7 x$ **9.** $\log x - 2$ **11.** $3 - \log_4 y$ **13.** $2 - \ln 5$ **15.** $3\log_b x$

17. $-6\log N$ **19.** $\dfrac{1}{5}\ln x$ **21.** $2\log_b x + \log_b y$ **23.** $\dfrac{1}{2}\log_4 x - 3$ **25.** $2 - \dfrac{1}{2}\log_6(x+1)$ **27.** $2\log_b x + \log_b y - 2\log_b z$

29. $1 + \dfrac{1}{2}\log x$ **31.** $\dfrac{1}{3}\log x - \dfrac{1}{3}\log y$ **33.** $\dfrac{1}{2}\log_b x + 3\log_b y - 3\log_b z$ **35.** $\dfrac{2}{3}\log_5 x + \dfrac{1}{3}\log_5 y - \dfrac{2}{3}$ **37.** $3\ln x + \dfrac{1}{2}\ln(x^2+1) - 4\ln(x+1)$

39. $1 + 2\log x + \dfrac{1}{3}\log(1-x) - \log 7 - 2\log(x+1)$ **41.** 1   **43.** $\ln(7x)$ **45.** 5   **47.** $\log\left(\dfrac{2x+5}{x}\right)$ **49.** $\log(xy^3)$

51. $\ln(x^{1/2}y)$ or $\ln(y\sqrt{x})$ **53.** $\log_b(x^2y^3)$ **55.** $\ln\left(\dfrac{x^5}{y^2}\right)$ **57.** $\ln\left(\dfrac{x^3}{y^{1/3}}\right)$ or $\ln\left(\dfrac{x^3}{\sqrt[3]{y}}\right)$ **59.** $\ln\dfrac{(x+6)^4}{x^3}$ **61.** $\ln\left(\dfrac{x^3y^5}{z^6}\right)$ **63.** $\log\sqrt{xy}$

65. $\log_5\left(\dfrac{\sqrt{xy}}{(x+1)^2}\right)$ **67.** $\ln\sqrt[3]{\dfrac{(x+5)^2}{x(x^2-4)}}$ **69.** $\log\dfrac{x(x^2-1)}{7(x+1)} = \log\dfrac{x(x-1)}{7}$ **71.** 1.5937   **73.** 1.6944   **75.** -1.2304 **77.** 3.6193

79.   **81.**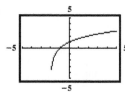

83. $C - A$ **85.** $3A$ **87.** $\dfrac{1}{2}A - \dfrac{3}{2}C$ **89.** false; $\ln e = 1$ **91.** false; $\log_4(2x)^3 = 3\log_4(2x)$ **93.** true   **95.** true

97. false; $\log(x+3) - \log(2x) = \log\left(\dfrac{x+3}{2x}\right)$ **99.** true   **101.** true   **103. a.** $D = 10\log\dfrac{I}{I_0}$ **b.** 20 decibels louder

113. a.   **b.** $y = 2 + \log_3 x$ shifts the graph of $y = \log_3 x$ two units upward; $y = \log_3(x+2)$ shifts the graph of $y = \log_3 x$ two units left; $y = -\log_3 x$ reflects the graph of $y = \log_3 x$ about the x-axis.

115.

a. top graph: $y = \log_{100} x$; bottom graph: $y = \log_3 x$
b. top graph: $y = \log_3 x$; bottom graph: $y = \log_{100} x$
c. The graph of the equation with the largest b will be on the top in the interval $(0, 1)$ and on the bottom in the interval $(1, \infty)$.

121. makes sense   **123.** makes sense   **125.** true   **127.** false   **129.** $\log e = \log_{10} e = \dfrac{\ln e}{\ln 10} = \dfrac{1}{\ln 10}$ **131.** $4x^3$

133. Let $\log_b M = R$ and $\log_b N = S$.
Then $\log_b M = R$ means $b^R = M$ and $\log_b N = S$ means $b^S = N$.
$$\frac{M}{N} = \frac{b^R}{b^S} = b^{R-S}$$
$$\log_b \frac{M}{N} = \log_b b^{R-S} = R - S = \log_b M - \log_b N$$

134. $x = \dfrac{2a + 3b}{a - 2b}$ **135.** $\left\{ \dfrac{7 \pm \sqrt{61}}{2} \right\}$ **136.** $\{-1, 3\}$

Mid-Chapter 4 Check Point

1.

$f(x) = 2^x$
$g(x) = 2^x - 3$

asymptote of f: $y = 0$
asymptote of g: $y = -3$
domain of f = domain of $g = (-\infty, \infty)$
range of $f = (0, \infty)$; range of $g = (-3, \infty)$

2.

$f(x) = \left(\dfrac{1}{2}\right)^x$
$g(x) = \left(\dfrac{1}{2}\right)^{x-1}$

asymptote of f: $y = 0$
asymptote of g: $y = 0$
domain of f = domain of $g = (-\infty, \infty)$
range of f = range of $g = (0, \infty)$

3.

$f(x) = e^x$
$g(x) = \ln x$

asymptote of f: $y = 0$
asymptote of g: $x = 0$
domain of f = range of $g = (-\infty, \infty)$
range of f = domain of $g = (0, \infty)$

4.

$f(x) = \log_2 x$
$g(x) = \log_2 (x - 1) + 1$

asymptote of f: $x = 0$
asymptote of g: $x = 1$
domain of $f = (0, \infty)$; domain of $g = (1, \infty)$
range of f = range of $g = (-\infty, \infty)$

5.

$f(x) = \log_{1/2} x$
$g(x) = -2 \log_{1/2} x$

asymptote of f: $x = 0$
asymptote of g: $x = 0$
domain of f = domain of $g = (0, \infty)$
range of f = range of $g = (-\infty, \infty)$

6. $(-6, \infty)$ **7.** $(0, \infty)$ **8.** $(-\infty, -6) \cup (-6, \infty)$ **9.** $(-\infty, \infty)$ **10.** 5   **11.** -2 **12.** $\dfrac{1}{2}$ **13.** $\dfrac{1}{3}$ **14.** 2

15. Evaluation not possible; $\log_2 \dfrac{1}{8} = -3$ and $\log_3(-3)$ is undefined.   **16.** 5   **17.** $\sqrt{7}$ **18.** 13   **19.** $-\dfrac{1}{2}$ **20.** $\sqrt{\pi}$

21. $\dfrac{1}{2}\log x + \dfrac{1}{2}\log y - 3$ **22.** $19 + 20 \ln x$ **23.** $\log_7 \left(\dfrac{x^8}{\sqrt[3]{y}} \right)$ **24.** $\log_5 x^9$ **25.** $\ln \left[\dfrac{\sqrt{x}}{y^3(z - 2)} \right]$ **26.** \$8

Section 4.4

Check Point Exercises

1. a. $\{3\}$ **b.** $\{-12\}$ **2. a.** $\left\{ \dfrac{\ln 134}{\ln 5} \right\}$; ≈ 3.04 **b.** $\{\log 8000\}$; ≈ 3.90 **3.** $\left\{ \dfrac{\ln 9}{2} \right\}$; ≈ 1.10 **4.** $\left\{ \dfrac{\ln 3 + \ln 7}{2 \ln 3 - \ln 7} \right\}$; ≈ 12.11

5. $\{0, \ln 7\}$; $\ln 7 \approx 1.95$ **6. a.** $\{12\}$ **b.** $\left\{ \dfrac{e^2}{3} \right\}$ **7.** $\{5\}$ **8.** $\{4, 5\}$ **9.** 0.01   **10.** 16.2 yr   **11.** 14

Concept and Vocabulary Check

1. $M = N$ **2.** $4x - 1$ **3.** $\dfrac{\ln 20}{\ln 9}$ **4.** $\ln 6$ **5.** 5^3 **6.** $(x^2 + x)$ **7.** $\dfrac{7x - 23}{x + 1}$

8. false   **9.** true   **10.** false   **11.** true

Exercise Set 4.4

1. $\{6\}$ **3.** $\{3\}$ **5.** $\{3\}$ **7.** $\{2\}$ **9.** $\left\{\dfrac{3}{5}\right\}$ **11.** $\left\{\dfrac{3}{2}\right\}$ **13.** $\{4\}$ **15.** $\{5\}$ **17.** $\left\{-\dfrac{1}{4}\right\}$ **19.** $\{13\}$ **21.** $\{-2\}$

23. $\left\{\dfrac{\ln 3.91}{\ln 10}\right\}; \approx 0.59$ **25.** $\{\ln 5.7\}; \approx 1.74$ **27.** $\left\{\dfrac{\ln 17}{\ln 5}\right\}; \approx 1.76$ **29.** $\left\{\ln \dfrac{23}{5}\right\}; \approx 1.53$ **31.** $\left\{\dfrac{\ln 659}{5}\right\}; \approx 1.30$

33. $\left\{\dfrac{\ln 793 - 1}{-5}\right\}; \approx -1.14$ **35.** $\left\{\dfrac{\ln 10,478 + 3}{5}\right\}; \approx 2.45$ **37.** $\left\{\dfrac{\ln 410}{\ln 7} - 2\right\}; \approx 1.09$ **39.** $\left\{\dfrac{\ln 813}{0.3 \ln 7}\right\}; \approx 11.48$ **41.** $\left\{\dfrac{3 \ln 5 + \ln 3}{\ln 3 - 2 \ln 5}\right\}; \approx -2.80$

43. $\{0, \ln 2\}; \ln 2 \approx 0.69$ **45.** $\left\{\dfrac{\ln 3}{2}\right\}; \approx 0.55$ **47.** $\{0\}$ **49.** $\{81\}$ **51.** $\{e^2\}; \approx 7.39$ **53.** $\{59\}$ **55.** $\{-9\}$ **57.** $\left\{-\dfrac{107}{27}\right\}$ **59.** $\left\{\dfrac{62}{3}\right\}$

61. $\left\{\dfrac{e^4}{2}\right\}; \approx 27.30$ **63.** $\{e^{-1/2}\}; \approx 0.61$ **65.** $\{e^2 - 3\}; \approx 4.39$ **67.** $\left\{\dfrac{5}{4}\right\}$ **69.** $\{-3\}$ **71.** $\{6\}$ **73.** $\{5\}$ **75.** $\{12\}$ **77.** $\left\{\dfrac{4}{3}\right\}$ **79.** $\varnothing$

81. $\{5\}$ **83.** $\left\{\dfrac{2}{9}\right\}$ **85.** $\{28\}$ **87.** $\{2\}$ **89.** $\varnothing$ **91.** $\left\{\dfrac{11}{3}\right\}$ **93.** $\left\{\dfrac{1}{2}\right\}$ **95.** $\{e^3, e^{-3}\}$ **97.** $\left\{\pm\sqrt{\dfrac{\ln 45}{\ln 3}}\right\}$ **99.** $\left\{\dfrac{5 + \sqrt{37}}{2}\right\}$

101. $\{-2, 6\}$ **103. a.** 37.3 million   **b.** 2017   **105.** 118 ft; by the point $(118, 1)$ **107.** 8.2 yr   **109.** 2.0 yr   **111.** 8.7 yr   **113.** 7.0 yr
115. a. 17.0%; underestimates by 0.3%   **b.** 2016   **117.** 2.8 days; $(2.8, 50)$ **119. a.** $10^{-5.6}$ mole per liter   **b.** $10^{-2.4}$ mole per liter
c. $10^{3.2}$ times greater   **125.** $\{2\}$ **127.** $\{4\}$ **129.** $\{2\}$ **131.** $\{-1.391606, 1.6855579\}$

133.

As distance from eye increases, barometric
air pressure increases.

135.

about 7.9 min

137. does not make sense   **139.** makes sense   **141.** false   **143.** true   **145.** after 36 yr   **147.** $\{10^{-2}, 10^{3/2}\}$, $10^{3/2} = 10\sqrt{10} \approx 31.62$
150. a. 10 million; 9.97 million; 9.94 million; 9.91 million   **b.** decreasing   **151. a.** 3   **b.** $e^{(\ln 3)x}$
152.

Section 4.5

Check Point Exercises

1. a. $A = 807e^{0.024t}$ **b.** 2038   **2. a.** $A = A_0 e^{-0.0248t}$ **b.** about 72 yr   **3. a.** 0.4 correct responses   **b.** 0.7 correct responses
c. 0.8 correct responses

4.

; logarithmic function

5.

; exponential function, although answers may vary

6. a. the exponential function g **b.** the linear function f **7.** $y = 4e^{(\ln 7.8)x}$; $y = 4e^{2.054x}$

Concept and Vocabulary Check

1. $> 0; < 0$ **2.** $A_0; A$ **3.** $A; c$ **4.** logarithmic   **5.** exponential   **6.** linear   **7.** $\ln 5$

Exercise Set 4.5

1. 127.3 million   **3.** Iraq; 1.9%   **5.** 2030   **7. a.** $A = 6.04e^{0.01t}$ **b.** 2040   **9.** 146.1 million   **11.** 0.0088   **13.** -0.0039
15. approximately 8 grams   **17.** 8 grams after 10 seconds; 4 grams after 20 seconds; 2 grams after 30 seconds; 1 gram after 40 seconds; 0.5 gram
after 50 seconds   **19.** approximately 15,679 years old   **21.** 12.6 yr   **23.** -0.000428; 0.0428% per year   **25.** -0.039608; 3.9608% per day

27. a. $\dfrac{1}{2} = e^{1.31k}$ yields $k = \dfrac{\ln\left(\dfrac{1}{2}\right)}{1.31} \approx -0.52912.$ **b.** about 0.1069 billion or 106,900,000 years old   **29.** 7.1 yr   **31.** 5.5 hr

33. $2A_0 = A_0 e^{kt}; 2 = e^{kt}; \ln 2 = \ln e^{kt}; \ln 2 = kt; \dfrac{\ln 2}{k} = t$ **35. a.** 1%   **b.** about 69 yr   **37. a.** about 20 people   **b.** about 1080 people

c. 100,000 people   **39.** quite well   **41.** 2025   **43.** about 3.7%   **45.** about 48 years old

47. a.

b. exponential function

49. a.

b. logarithmic function

51. a.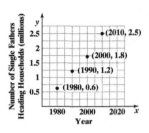

b. linear function

53. $y = 100e^{(\ln 4.6)x}$; $y = 100e^{1.526x}$ **55.** $y = 2.5e^{(\ln 0.7)x}$; $y = 2.5e^{-0.357x}$ **67.** $y = 191.9 + 24.569 \ln x$; $r \approx 0.870$; Fit is ok, but not great.

69. $y = 195.056x^{0.100}$; $r \approx 0.896$; Fits data fairly well.   **71. a.** $y = 3.46(1.02)^x$ **b.** $y = 3.46e^{(\ln 1.02)x}$; $y = 3.46e^{0.02x}$; by approximately 2%

73. does not make sense   **75.** makes sense   **77.** true   **79.** true   **81.** about 126° F   **83. a.** yes   **b.** yes

84. ; $(4, -1)$ **85.** $\{4\}$

$x + 2y = 2$
$x - 2y = 6$

Chapter 4 Review Exercises

1. $g(x) = 4^{-x}$ **2.** $h(x) = -4^{-x}$ **3.** $r(x) = -4^{-x} + 3$ **4.** $f(x) = 4^x$

5.

$f(x) = 2^x$
$g(x) = 2^{x-1}$

asymptote of f: $y = 0$
asymptote of g: $y = 0$
domain of f = domain of g = $(-\infty, \infty)$
range of f = range of g = $(0, \infty)$

6.

$f(x) = 3^x$
$g(x) = 3^x - 1$

asymptote of f: $y = 0$
asymptote of g: $y = -1$
domain of f = domain of g = $(-\infty, \infty)$
range of f = $(0, \infty)$; range of g = $(-1, \infty)$

7.

$f(x) = 3^x$
$g(x) = -3^x$

asymptote of f: $y = 0$
asymptote of g: $y = 0$
domain of f = domain of g = $(-\infty, \infty)$
range of f = $(0, \infty)$; range of g = $(-\infty, 0)$

8.

$f(x) = \left(\dfrac{1}{2}\right)^x$

$g(x) = \left(\dfrac{1}{2}\right)^{-x}$

asymptote of f: $y = 0$
asymptote of g: $y = 0$
domain of f = domain of g = $(-\infty, \infty)$
range of f = range of g = $(0, \infty)$

9.

$f(x) = e^x$
$g(x) = 2e^{x/2}$

asymptote of f: $y = 0$
asymptote of g: $y = 0$
domain of f = domain of g = $(-\infty, \infty)$
range of f = range of g = $(0, \infty)$

10. 5.5% compounded semiannually   **11.** 7% compounded monthly   **12. a.** 200°   **b.** 120°; 119°   **c.** 70°; The temperature in the room is 70°.

13. $49^{1/2} = 7$ **14.** $4^3 = x$ **15.** $3^y = 81$ **16.** $\log_6 216 = 3$ **17.** $\log_b 625 = 4$ **18.** $\log_{13} 874 = y$ **19.** 3   **20.** -2 **21.** undefined;

$\log_b x$ is defined only for $x > 0$.   **22.** $\dfrac{1}{2}$ **23.** 1   **24.** 8   **25.** 5   **26.** $-\dfrac{1}{2}$ **27.** -2 **28.** -3 **29.** 0

30.

$f(x) = 2^x$
$g(x) = \log_2 x$

domain of f = range of g = $(-\infty, \infty)$
range of f = domain of g = $(0, \infty)$

31.

$f(x) = \left(\dfrac{1}{3}\right)^x$

$g(x) = \log_{1/3} x$

domain of f = range of g = $(-\infty, \infty)$
range of f = domain of g = $(0, \infty)$

32. $g(x) = \log(-x)$
33. $r(x) = 1 + \log(2 - x)$
34. $h(x) = \log(2 - x)$
35. $f(x) = \log x$

36.

$f(x) = \log_2 x$
$g(x) = \log_2(x - 2)$

x-intercept: $(3, 0)$
vertical asymptote: $x = 2$
domain: $(2, \infty)$; range: $(-\infty, \infty)$

37.

$f(x) = \log_2 x$
$h(x) = -1 + \log_2 x$

x-intercept: $(2, 0)$
vertical asymptote: $x = 0$
domain: $(0, \infty)$; range: $(-\infty, \infty)$

38.

$f(x) = \log_2 x$
$r(x) = \log_2(-x)$

x-intercept: $(-1, 0)$
vertical asymptote: $x = 0$
domain: $(-\infty, 0)$; range: $(-\infty, \infty)$

39.

$f(x) = \log x$
$g(x) = -\log(x + 3)$

asymptote of f: $x = 0$
asymptote of g: $x = -3$
domain of $f = (0, \infty)$; domain of $g = (-3, \infty)$
range of f = range of $g = (-\infty, \infty)$

40.

$f(x) = \ln x$
$g(x) = -\ln(2x)$

asymptote of f: $x = 0$
asymptote of g: $x = 0$
domain of f = domain of $g = (0, \infty)$
range of f = range of $g = (-\infty, \infty)$

41. $(-5, \infty)$
42. $(-\infty, 3)$
43. $(-\infty, 1) \cup (1, \infty)$
44. $6x$
45. $\sqrt{x}$
46. $4x^2$
47. 3.0

48. a. 76 **b.** ≈ 67, ≈ 63, ≈ 61, ≈ 59, ≈ 56

c.

49. about 9 weeks **50.** $2 + 3\log_6 x$ **51.** $\frac{1}{2}\log_4 x - 3$

52. $\log_2 x + 2\log_2 y - 6$ **53.** $\frac{1}{3}\ln x - \frac{1}{3}$ **54.** $\log_b 21$ **55.** $\log\frac{3}{x^3}$

56. $\ln(x^3 y^4)$ **57.** $\ln\frac{\sqrt{x}}{y}$ **58.** 6.2448 **59.** -0.1063

60. true **61.** false; $\log(x + 9) - \log(x + 1) = \log\left(\frac{x + 9}{x + 1}\right)$

62. false; $4\log_2 x = \log_2 x^4$ **63.** true **64.** $\{2\}$ **65.** $\left\{\frac{2}{3}\right\}$ **66.** $\{\log 7000\}$; ≈ 3.85

67. $\left\{-\frac{4}{5}\right\}$ **68.** $\left\{\frac{\ln 12{,}143}{\ln 8}\right\}$; ≈ 4.52 **69.** $\left\{\frac{1}{5}\ln 141\right\}$; ≈ 0.99 **70.** $\left\{\frac{12 - \ln 130}{5}\right\}$; ≈ 1.43 **71.** $\left\{\frac{\ln 37{,}500 - 2\ln 5}{4\ln 5}\right\}$; ≈ 1.14

72. $\left\{\frac{\ln 7 + 4\ln 3}{2\ln 7 - \ln 3}\right\}$; ≈ 2.27 **73.** $\{\ln 3\}$; ≈ 1.10 **74.** $\{23\}$ **75.** $\left\{\frac{e^3}{2}\right\}$; ≈ 10.04 **76.** $\{5\}$ **77.** $\varnothing$ **78.** $\{2\}$ **79.** $\{4\}$

80. 5.5 mi **81.** 2013 **82. a.** 2031 **b.** 1994 **83.** 7.3 yr **84.** 14.6 yr **85.** about 22% **86. a.** 0.036 **b.** 60.6 million **c.** 2019
87. 325 days **88. a.** 200 people **b.** about 45,411 people **c.** 500,000 people

89. a.

b. linear function

90. a.

b. logarithmic function

91. a.

b. exponential function

92. $y = 73e^{(\ln 2.6)x}$; $y = 73e^{0.956x}$ **93.** $y = 6.5e^{(\ln 0.43)x}$; $y = 6.5e^{-0.844x}$

Chapter 4 Test

1.

$f(x) = 2^x$
$g(x) = 2^x + 1$

2.

$f(x) = \log_2 x$
$g(x) = \log_2(x - 1)$

3. $5^3 = 125$ **4.** $\log_{36} 6 = \frac{1}{2}$ **5.** $(-\infty, 3)$ **6.** $3 + 5\log_4 x$

7. $\frac{1}{3}\log_3 x - 4$ **8.** $\log(x^6 y^2)$ **9.** $\ln\frac{7}{x^3}$ **10.** 1.5741 **11.** $\{-10\}$

12. $\left\{\frac{\ln 1.4}{\ln 5}\right\}$ **13.** $\left\{\frac{\ln 4}{0.005}\right\}$ **14.** $\{0, \ln 5\}$ **15.** $\{54.25\}$

16. $\left\{\frac{e^4}{3}\right\}$ **17.** $\{5\}$ **18.** $\varnothing$ **19.** 120 db **20.** $5x$ **21.** 1 **22.** 0

23. 6.5% compounded semiannually; $221 more **24.** 13.9 years **25.** about 6.9%

26. a. 82.3 million **b.** decreasing; The growth rate, -0.004, is negative. **c.** 2020 **27.** $A = 4121e^{0.006t}$ **28.** 12.5 days **29. a.** 14 elk
b. about 51 elk **c.** 140 elk **30.** linear **31.** logarithmic **32.** exponential **33.** quadratic **34.** $y = 96e^{(\ln 0.38)x}$; $y = 96e^{-0.968x}$

Cumulative Review Exercises (Chapters 1–4)

1. $\left\{\frac{2}{3}, 2\right\}$ **2.** $\{3, 7\}$ **3.** $\{-2, -1, 1\}$ **4.** $\left\{\frac{\ln 128}{5}\right\}$ **5.** $\{3\}$ **6.** $\varnothing$ **7.** $(-\infty, 4]$ **8.** $[1, 3]$

9.

$(x - 3)^2 + (y + 2)^2 = 4$

10.

$f(x) = (x - 2)^2 - 1$

11.

$f(x) = \dfrac{x^2 - 1}{x^2 - 4}$

12.

$f(x) = (x - 2)^2(x + 1)$

13.

$f(x) = 2x - 4$
$f^{-1}(x) = \dfrac{x + 4}{2}$

14.

$f(x) = \ln x$
$g(x) = \ln(x - 2) + 1$

15. using $(1, 3)$, $y - 3 = -3(x - 1)$; $y = -3x + 6$
16. $(f \circ g)(x) = (x + 2)^2$; $(g \circ f)(x) = x^2 + 2$
17. You can expect to sleep 2 hours.
18. after 2 sec; 69 ft
19. 4.1 sec
20. $12 per hr

CHAPTER 5

Section 5.1

Check Point Exercises

1. a. solution   **b.** not a solution   **2.** $\{(-2, 5)\}$ **3.** $\{(2, -1)\}$ **4.** $\left\{\left(\frac{60}{17}, -\frac{11}{17}\right)\right\}$ **5.** no solution or $\varnothing$

6. $\{(x, y) \mid x = 4y - 8\}$ or $\{(x, y) \mid 5x - 20y = -40\}$ **7. a.** $C(x) = 300{,}000 + 30x$ **b.** $R(x) = 80x$ **c.** $(6000, 480{,}000)$; The company will break even if it produces and sells 6000 pairs of shoes.

Concept and Vocabulary Check

1. satisfies both equations in the system   **2.** the intersection point   **3.** $\left\{\left(\frac{1}{3}, -2\right)\right\}$ **4.** -2 **5.** -3 **6.** $\varnothing$; inconsistent; parallel
7. $\{(x, y) \mid x = 3y + 2\}$ or $\{(x, y) \mid 5x - 15y = 10\}$; dependent; are identical or coincide   **8.** revenue; profit   **9.** break-even point

Exercise Set 5.1

1. solution   **3.** not a solution   **5.** $\{(1, 3)\}$ **7.** $\{(5, 1)\}$ **9.** $\{(-22, -5)\}$ **11.** $\{(0, 0)\}$ **13.** $\{(3, -2)\}$ **15.** $\{(5, 4)\}$ **17.** $\{(7, 3)\}$

19. $\{(2, -1)\}$ **21.** $\{(3, 0)\}$ **23.** $\{(-4, 3)\}$ **25.** $\{(3, 1)\}$ **27.** $\{(1, -2)\}$ **29.** $\left\{\left(\frac{7}{25}, -\frac{1}{25}\right)\right\}$ **31.** $\varnothing$ **33.** $\{(x, y) \mid y = 3x - 5\}$

35. $\{(1, 4)\}$ **37.** $\{(x, y) \mid x + 3y = 2\}$ **39.** $\{(-5, -1)\}$ **41.** $\left\{\left(\frac{29}{22}, -\frac{5}{11}\right)\right\}$ **43.** $x + y = 7$; $x - y = -1$; 3 and 4

45. $3x - y = 1$; $x + 2y = 12$; 2 and 5   **47.** $\{(6, -1)\}$ **49.** $\left\{\left(\frac{1}{a}, 3\right)\right\}$ **51.** $m = -4$, $b = 3$ **53.** $y = x - 4$; $y = -\frac{1}{3}x + 4$

55. 500 radios   **57.** -6000; When the company produces and sells 200 radios, the loss is $6000.   **59. a.** $P(x) = 20x - 10{,}000$ **b.** $190{,}000
61. a. $C(x) = 18{,}000 + 20x$ **b.** $R(x) = 80x$ **c.** $(300, 24{,}000)$; When 300 canoes are produced and sold, both revenue and cost are $24,000.
63. a. $C(x) = 30{,}000 + 2500x$ **b.** $R(x) = 3125x$ **c.** $(48, 150{,}000)$; For 48 sold-out performances, both cost and revenue are $150,000.
65. a. 4 million workers; $4.50 per hour   **b.** $4.50; 4; 4   **c.** 2 million   **d.** 5.7 million   **e.** 3.7 million   **67. a.** 2039; 37%
b. by the intersection point $(69, 37)$ **69. a.** $y = 0.45x + 0.8$ **b.** $y = 0.15x + 2.6$ **c.** week 6; 3.5 symptoms; by the intersection point $(6, 3.5)$
71. a. $y = 0.2x + 5$ **b.** $y = -0.4x + 47$ **c.** 2030; 19%   **73.** Mr. Goodbar: 264 cal; Mounds: 258 cal   **75.** 3 Mr. Goodbars and 2 Mounds bars
77. 50 rooms with kitchen facilities, 150 rooms without kitchen facilities   **79.** 100 ft long by 80 ft wide   **81.** rate rowing in still water: 6 mph;
rate of the current: 2 mph   **83.** $80°, 50°, 50°$ **95.** makes sense   **97.** makes sense   **99.** $y = \dfrac{a_1c_2 - a_2c_1}{a_1b_2 - a_2b_1}$; $x = \dfrac{b_2c_1 - b_1c_2}{a_1b_2 - a_2b_1}$

101. Yes; 8 hexagons and 4 squares   **103.** yes   **104.** $11x + 4y = -3$ **105.** $1682 = 16a + 4b + c$

Section 5.2

Check Point Exercises

1. $(-1) - 2(-4) + 3(5) = 22$; $2(-1) - 3(-4) - 5 = 5$; $3(-1) + (-4) - 5(5) = -32$ **2.** $\{(1, 4, -3)\}$ **3.** $\{(4, 5, 3)\}$ **4.** $y = 3x^2 - 12x + 13$

Concept and Vocabulary Check

1. triple; all   **2.** -2; -4 **3.** z; add Equations 1 and 3

Exercise Set 5.2

1. solution   **3.** solution   **5.** $\{(2, 3, 3)\}$ **7.** $\{(2, -1, 1)\}$ **9.** $\{(1, 2, 3)\}$ **11.** $\{(3, 1, 5)\}$ **13.** $\{(1, 0, -3)\}$ **15.** $\{(1, -5, -6)\}$

17. $\left\{\left(\dfrac{1}{2}, \dfrac{1}{3}, -1\right)\right\}$ **19.** $y = 2x^2 - x + 3$ **21.** $y = 2x^2 + x - 5$ **23.** 7, 4, and 5   **25.** $\{(4, 8, 6)\}$ **27.** $y = -\dfrac{3}{4}x^2 + 6x - 11$

29. $\left\{\left(\dfrac{8}{a}, -\dfrac{3}{b}, -\dfrac{5}{c}\right)\right\}$ **31. a.** $y = -16x^2 + 40x + 200$ **b.** $y = 0$ when $x = 5$; The ball hits the ground after 5 seconds.

33. housing: \$6133; vehicles/gas: \$2269; health care: \$5438   **35.** milk: \$3.50; water: \$1.50; chips: \$0.75   **37.** 200 \$8 tickets; 150 \$10 tickets; 50 \$12 tickets

39. \$1200 at 8%, \$2000 at 10%, and \$3500 at 12%   **41.** $x = 60, y = 55, z = 65$ **49.** does not make sense   **51.** makes sense

53. 13 triangles, 21 rectangles, and 6 pentagons   **55.** $\dfrac{x + 14}{(x - 4)(x + 2)}$ **56.** $\dfrac{5x^3 - 3x^2 + 7x - 3}{(x^2 + 1)^2}$ **57.** $\{(5, -2, 3)\}$

Section 5.3

Check Point Exercises

1. $\dfrac{2}{x - 3} + \dfrac{3}{x + 4}$ **2.** $\dfrac{2}{x} - \dfrac{2}{x - 1} + \dfrac{3}{(x - 1)^2}$ **3.** $\dfrac{2}{x + 3} + \dfrac{6x - 8}{x^2 + x + 2}$ **4.** $\dfrac{2x}{x^2 + 1} + \dfrac{-x + 3}{(x^2 + 1)^2}$

Concept and Vocabulary Check

1. correct   **2.** incorrect   **3.** incorrect   **4.** correct

Exercise Set 5.3

1. $\dfrac{A}{x - 2} + \dfrac{B}{x + 1}$ **3.** $\dfrac{A}{x + 2} + \dfrac{B}{x - 3} + \dfrac{C}{(x - 3)^2}$ **5.** $\dfrac{A}{x - 1} + \dfrac{Bx + C}{x^2 + 1}$ **7.** $\dfrac{Ax + B}{x^2 + 4} + \dfrac{Cx + D}{(x^2 + 4)^2}$ **9.** $\dfrac{3}{x - 3} - \dfrac{2}{x - 2}$

11. $\dfrac{7}{x - 9} - \dfrac{4}{x + 2}$ **13.** $\dfrac{24}{7(x - 4)} + \dfrac{25}{7(x + 3)}$ **15.** $\dfrac{4}{7(x - 3)} - \dfrac{8}{7(2x + 1)}$ **17.** $\dfrac{3}{x} + \dfrac{2}{x - 1} - \dfrac{1}{x + 3}$ **19.** $\dfrac{3}{x} + \dfrac{4}{x + 1} - \dfrac{3}{x - 1}$

21. $\dfrac{6}{x - 1} - \dfrac{5}{(x - 1)^2}$ **23.** $\dfrac{1}{x - 2} - \dfrac{2}{(x - 2)^2} - \dfrac{5}{(x - 2)^3}$ **25.** $\dfrac{7}{x} - \dfrac{6}{x - 1} + \dfrac{10}{(x - 1)^2}$ **27.** $\dfrac{1}{4(x + 1)} + \dfrac{3}{4(x - 1)} + \dfrac{1}{2(x - 1)^2}$

29. $\dfrac{3}{x - 1} + \dfrac{2x - 4}{x^2 + 1}$ **31.** $\dfrac{2}{x + 1} + \dfrac{3x - 1}{x^2 + 2x + 2}$ **33.** $\dfrac{1}{4x} + \dfrac{1}{x^2} - \dfrac{x + 4}{4(x^2 + 4)}$ **35.** $\dfrac{4}{x + 1} + \dfrac{2x - 3}{x^2 + 1}$ **37.** $\dfrac{x + 1}{x^2 + 2} - \dfrac{2x}{(x^2 + 2)^2}$

39. $\dfrac{x - 2}{x^2 - 2x + 3} + \dfrac{2x + 1}{(x^2 - 2x + 3)^2}$ **41.** $\dfrac{3}{x - 2} + \dfrac{x - 1}{x^2 + 2x + 4}$ **43.** $x^3 + x - \dfrac{1}{2(x + 1)} + \dfrac{3}{2(x - 1)}$ **45.** $x + 1 - \dfrac{2}{x} - \dfrac{2}{x^2} + \dfrac{2}{x - 1}$

47. $\dfrac{\frac{1}{2c}}{x - c} - \dfrac{\frac{1}{2c}}{x + c}$ **49.** $\dfrac{a}{x - c} + \dfrac{ac + b}{(x - c)^2}$ **51.** $\dfrac{1}{x} - \dfrac{1}{x + 1}; \dfrac{99}{100}$ **61.** does not make sense   **63.** does not make sense

65. $\dfrac{2}{x - 3} + \dfrac{2x + 5}{x^2 + 3x + 3}$ **66.** $\{(2.5, -2)\}$ **67.** $\{(4, -3)\}$

68.

$; (0, -3)$ and $(2, -1); 0 - (-3) = 3$ and $(0 - 2)^2 + (-3 + 3)^2 = 4$ are true;
$2 - (-1) = 3$ and $(2 - 2)^2 + (-1 + 3)^2 = 4$ are true.

Section 5.4

Check Point Exercises

1. $\{(0, 1), (4, 17)\}$ **2.** $\left\{\left(-\dfrac{6}{5}, \dfrac{3}{5}\right), (2, -1)\right\}$ **3.** $\{(3, 2), (3, -2), (-3, 2), (-3, -2)\}$ **4.** $\{(0, 5)\}$ **5.** length: 7 ft; width: 3 ft or length: 3 ft; width: 7 ft

Concept and Vocabulary Check

1. nonlinear   **2.** $\{(-4, 3), (0, 1)\}$ **3.** 3   **4.** $\{(2, \sqrt{3}), (2, -\sqrt{3}), (-2, \sqrt{3}), (-2, -\sqrt{3})\}$ **5.** $-1; y^2 + y = 6$ **6.** $\dfrac{4}{x}, \dfrac{4}{x}; y$

Exercise Set 5.4

1. $\{(-3, 5), (2, 0)\}$ **3.** $\{(1, 1), (2, 0)\}$ **5.** $\{(4, -10), (-3, 11)\}$ **7.** $\{(4, 3), (-3, -4)\}$ **9.** $\left\{\left(-\dfrac{3}{2}, -4\right), (2, 3)\right\}$ **11.** $\{(-5, -4), (3, 0)\}$

13. $\{(3, 1), (-3, -1), (1, 3), (-1, -3)\}$ **15.** $\{(4, -3), (-1, 2)\}$ **17.** $\{(0, 1), (4, -3)\}$ **19.** $\{(3, 2), (3, -2), (-3, 2), (-3, -2)\}$

21. $\{(3, 2), (3, -2), (-3, 2), (-3, -2)\}$ **23.** $\{(2, 1), (2, -1), (-2, 1), (-2, -1)\}$ **25.** $\{(3, 4), (3, -4)\}$

27. $\{(0, 2), (0, -2), (-1, \sqrt{3}), (-1, -\sqrt{3})\}$ **29.** $\{(2, 1), (2, -1), (-2, 1), (-2, -1)\}$ **31.** $\{(-2\sqrt{2}, -\sqrt{2}), (-1, -4), (1, 4), (2\sqrt{2}, \sqrt{2})\}$

33. $\{(2, 2), (4, 1)\}$ **35.** $\{(0, 0), (-1, 1)\}$ **37.** $\{(0, 0), (-2, 2), (2, 2)\}$ **39.** $\left\{(-4, 1), \left(-\dfrac{5}{2}, \dfrac{1}{4}\right)\right\}$ **41.** $\left\{\left(\dfrac{12}{5}, -\dfrac{29}{5}\right), (-2, 3)\right\}$

43. 4 and 6   **45.** 2 and 1, 2 and -1, -2 and 1, or -2 and -1

47. $\{(2, -1), (-2, 1)\}$ **49.** $\{(2, 20), (-2, 4), (-3, 0)\}$ **51.** $\left\{\left(-1, -\dfrac{1}{2}\right), \left(-1, \dfrac{1}{2}\right), \left(1, -\dfrac{1}{2}\right), \left(1, \dfrac{1}{2}\right)\right\}$

53.

55. $(0, -4), (-2, 0), (2, 0)$ **57.** 11 ft and 7 ft   **59.** width: 6 in.; length: 8 in.
61. $x = 5 \text{ m}, y = 2 \text{ m}$

63. a. between the 1940s and the 1960s   **b.** 1949; 43%; 43%   **c.** 1920; 28%   **d.** 1919; white collar: 27.5%; farmers: 27.4%; fairly well, although answers may vary.   **69.** makes sense   **71.** makes sense   **73.** false   **75.** false   **77.** 18 sq units   **79.** $\{(8, 2)\}$

81.   **82.**   **83.**

Mid-Chapter 5 Check Point

1. $\{(-1, 2)\}$ **2.** $\{(1, -2)\}$ **3.** $\{(6, 10)\}$ **4.** $\{(x, y) \mid y = 4x - 5\}$ or $\{(x, y) \mid 8x - 2y = 10\}$ **5.** $\left\{\left(\dfrac{11}{19}, \dfrac{7}{19}\right)\right\}$ **6.** $\varnothing$ **7.** $\{(-1, 2, -2)\}$

8. $\{(4, -2, 3)\}$ **9.** $\left\{\left(-\dfrac{9}{5}, \dfrac{12}{5}\right), (3, 0)\right\}$ **10.** $\{(-2, -1), (-2, 1), (2, -1), (2, 1)\}$ **11.** $\{(-\sqrt{7}, 1), (-2, -2), (2, -2), (\sqrt{7}, 1)\}$

12. $\{(0, -2), (6, 1)\}$ **13.** $\dfrac{1}{x - 2} - \dfrac{2}{(x - 2)^2} - \dfrac{5}{(x - 2)^3}$ **14.** $\dfrac{5}{x + 2} + \dfrac{3}{x + 1} + \dfrac{2}{x - 1}$ **15.** $-\dfrac{2}{x + 3} + \dfrac{3x - 5}{x^2 + 4}$ **16.** $\dfrac{x}{x^2 + 4} - \dfrac{4x}{(x^2 + 4)^2}$

17. a. $C(x) = 400{,}000 + 20x$ **b.** $R(x) = 100x$ **c.** $P(x) = 80x - 400{,}000$ **d.** $(5000, 500{,}000)$; The company will break even when it produces and sells 5000 PDAs. At this level, both revenue and cost are $500,000.   **18.** 6 roses and 14 carnations   **19.** $x = 55°, y = 35°$
20. $y = -x^2 + 2x + 3$ **21.** length: 8 m; width: 2.5 m

Section 5.5

Check Point Exercises

1.   **2.**   **3. a.**   **b.**   **4.**

5. Point $B = (66, 130)$; $4.9(66) - 130 \geq 165$, or $193.4 \geq 165$, is true; $3.7(66) - 130 \leq 125$, or $114.2 \leq 125$, is true.

6.   **7.**   **8.**

Concept and Vocabulary Check

1. solution; x; y; $5 > 1$ **2.** graph   **3.** half-plane   **4.** false   **5.** true   **6.** false   **7.** $(0, 0)$, although answers will vary
8. $x - y < 1$; $2x + 3y \geq 12$ **9.** false

Exercise Set 5.5

1.   **3.**   **5.**   **7.**   **9.**

11.   **13.**   **15.**   **17.**   **19.**

21.
$y \geq x^2 - 9$

23.
$y > 2^x$

25. $x = -1$
$y \geq \log_2 (x + 1)$

27. $\begin{cases} 3x + 6y \leq 6 \\ 2x + y \leq 8 \end{cases}$

29. $\begin{cases} 2x - 5y \leq 10 \\ 3x - 2y > 6 \end{cases}$

31. $\begin{cases} y > 2x - 3 \\ y < -x + 6 \end{cases}$

33. $\begin{cases} x + 2y \leq 4 \\ y \geq x - 3 \end{cases}$

35. $\begin{cases} x \leq 2 \\ y \geq -1 \end{cases}$

37. $-2 \leq x < 5$

39. $\begin{cases} x - y \leq 1 \\ x \geq 2 \end{cases}$

41. $\varnothing$

43. $\begin{cases} x + y > 4 \\ x + y > -1 \end{cases}$

45.
$\begin{cases} y \geq x^2 - 1 \\ x - y \geq -1 \end{cases}$

47.
$\begin{cases} x^2 + y^2 \leq 16 \\ x + y > 2 \end{cases}$

49.
$\begin{cases} x^2 + y^2 > 1 \\ x^2 + y^2 < 16 \end{cases}$

51.
$\begin{cases} (x - 1)^2 + (y + 1)^2 < 25 \\ (x - 1)^2 + (y + 1)^2 \geq 16 \end{cases}$

53.
$\begin{cases} x^2 + y^2 \leq 1 \\ y - x^2 > 0 \end{cases}$

55.
$\begin{cases} x^2 + y^2 < 16 \\ y \geq 2^x \end{cases}$

57. $\begin{cases} x - y \geq 2 \\ x > -2 \\ y \leq 3 \end{cases}$

59. $\begin{cases} x \geq 0 \\ y \geq 0 \\ 2x + 5y < 10 \\ 3x + 4y \leq 12 \end{cases}$

61. $\begin{cases} 3x + y \leq 6 \\ 2x - y \leq -1 \\ x > -2 \\ y < 4 \end{cases}$

63. $y \geq -2x + 4$

65. $\begin{cases} x + y \leq 4 \\ 3x + y \leq 6 \end{cases}$

67.
$\begin{cases} x + y \leq 2 \\ y \geq x^2 - 4 \end{cases}$

69. $\begin{cases} -2 \leq x \leq 2 \\ -3 \leq y \leq 3 \end{cases}$

71.
$y > \frac{3}{2}x - 2 \text{ or } y < 4$

73. no solution
75. infinitely many solutions
77. Point $A = (66, 160)$; $5.3(66) - 160 \geq 180$, or $189.8 \geq 180$, is true; $4.1(66) - 160 \leq 140$, or $110.6 \leq 140$, is true.
79. no

81. a. $50x + 150y > 2000$
b.
$50x + 150y > 2000$
c. Answers may vary. Example:
$(20, 20)$: 20 children and 20 adults
will cause the elevator to be overloaded.

83. a. $\begin{cases} y \geq 0 \\ x + y \geq 5 \\ x \geq 1 \\ 200x + 100y \leq 700 \end{cases}$

b. $\begin{cases} y \geq 0 \\ x + y \geq 5 \\ x \geq 1 \\ 200x + 100y \leq 700 \end{cases}$ **c.** 2 nights

85. a. 27.1   **b.** overweight

97.

99.

101.

107. does not make sense   **109.** makes sense   **111.** $\begin{cases} y > x - 3 \\ y \leq x \end{cases}$ **113.** $x + 2y \leq 6$ or $2x + y \leq 6$

115. $y \geq nx + b$ $y = mx + b$
$y \leq mx + b$

$(0, b)$
$y = nx + b$

116. a.
$(1, 5)$ $(8, 5)$
$(8, -2)$
$x + y \geq 6$
$x \leq 8$
$y \leq 5$

b. $(1, 5), (8, 5), (8, -2)$

c. at $(1, 5)$: 13; at $(8, 5)$: 34; at $(8, -2)$: 20

117. a.
$(0, 7)$
$(4, 3)$
$(0, 0)$ $(2, 0)$
$x \geq 0$
$y \geq 0$
$3x - 2y \leq 6$
$y \leq -x + 7$

b. $(0, 0), (2, 0), (4, 3), (0, 7)$

c. at $(0, 0)$: 0; at $(2, 0)$: 4; at $(4, 3)$: 23; $(0, 7)$: 35

118. $20x + 10y \leq 80,000$

Section 5.6

Check Point Exercises

1. $z = 25x + 55y$ **2.** $x + y \leq 80$ **3.** $30 \leq x \leq 80$; $10 \leq y \leq 30$; objective function: $z = 25x + 55y$; constraints: $\begin{cases} x + y \leq 80 \\ 30 \leq x \leq 80 \\ 10 \leq y \leq 30 \end{cases}$

4. 50 bookshelves and 30 desks; $2900   **5.** 30

Concept and Vocabulary Check

1. linear programming   **2.** objective   **3.** constraints; corner

Exercise Set 5.6

1. $(1, 2)$: 17; $(2, 10)$: 70; $(7, 5)$: 65; $(8, 3)$: 58; maximum: $z = 70$; minimum: $z = 17$
3. $(0, 0)$: 0; $(0, 8)$: 400; $(4, 9)$: 610; $(8, 0)$: 320; maximum: $z = 610$; minimum: $z = 0$

5. a.
$(0, 8)$
$(0, 4)$
$(4, 0)$

b. $(0, 8)$: 16; $(0, 4)$: 8; $(4, 0)$: 12
c. maximum value: 16 at $x = 0$ and and $y = 8$

7. a.
$(0, 4)$
$(0, 3)$
$(6, 0)$
$(3, 0)$

b. $(0, 4)$: 4; $(0, 3)$: 3; $(3, 0)$: 12; $(6, 0)$: 24
c. maximum value: 24 at $x = 6$ and $y = 0$

9. a.
$(5, 8)$
$(1, 4)$
$(5, 2)$
$(1, 2)$

b. $(1, 2)$: -1; $(1, 4)$: -5; $(5, 8)$: -1; $(5, 2)$: 11
c. maximum value: 11 at $x = 5$ and $y = 2$

11. a.
$\left(\dfrac{12}{5}, \dfrac{12}{5}\right)$
$(0, 4)$
$(0, 2)$ $(2, 0)$ $(4, 0)$

b. $(0, 4)$: 8; $(0, 2)$: 4; $(2, 0)$: 8; $(4, 0)$: 16; $\left(\dfrac{12}{5}, \dfrac{12}{5}\right)$: $\dfrac{72}{5}$
c. maximum value: 16 at $x = 4$ and $y = 0$

13. a.
$(0, 6)$
$(3, 4)$
$(0, 0)$ $(5, 0)$

b. $(0, 6)$: 72; $(0, 0)$: 0; $(5, 0)$: 50; $(3, 4)$: 78
c. maximum value: 78 at $x = 3$ and $y = 4$

15. a. $z = 125x + 200y$ **b.** $\begin{cases} x \leq 450 \\ y \leq 200 \\ 600x + 900y \leq 360,000 \end{cases}$

c.
$(0, 200)$
$(300, 200)$
$(450, 100)$
$(450, 0)$
$(0, 0)$

d. $(0, 0)$: 0; $(0, 200)$: 40,000; $(300, 200)$: 77,500; $(450, 100)$: 76,250; $(450, 0)$: 56,250
e. 300; 200; $77,500

17. 40 model A bicycles and no model B bicycles
19. 300 cartons of food and 200 cartons of clothing
21. 50 students and 100 parents
23. 10 Boeing 727s and 42 Falcon 20s

29. does not make sense   **31.** makes sense   **33.** $5000 in stocks and $5000 in bonds   **37.** $\{(6, 3, 5)\}$; Answers may vary.

38. $\{(-2, 1, 4, 3)\}$; Answers may vary.   **39.** $\begin{bmatrix} 1 & 2 & -1 \\ 0 & -11 & -11 \end{bmatrix}$

Chapter 5 Review Exercises

1. $\{(1, 5)\}$ **2.** $\{(2, 3)\}$ **3.** $\{(2, -3)\}$ **4.** $\varnothing$ **5.** $\{(x, y) \mid 3x - 6y = 12\}$ **6. a.** $C(x) = 60,000 + 200x$ **b.** $R(x) = 450x$
c. $(240, 108,000)$; This means the company will break even if it produces and sells 240 desks.   **7.** Klimt: $135 million; Picasso: $104 million
8. a. $y = 219x + 142$ **b.** 2006; 580 million of each   **9.** 12 ft by 5 ft   **10.** $80 per day for the room, $60 per day for the car
11. 3 apples and 2 avocados   **12.** $\{(0, 1, 2)\}$ **13.** $\{(2, 1, -1)\}$ **14.** $y = 3x^2 - 4x + 5$ **15.** war: 124 million; famine: 111 million; tobacco: 71 million

16. $\dfrac{3}{5(x-3)} + \dfrac{2}{5(x+2)}$ **17.** $\dfrac{6}{x-4} + \dfrac{5}{x+3}$ **18.** $\dfrac{2}{x} + \dfrac{3}{x+2} - \dfrac{1}{x-1}$ **19.** $\dfrac{2}{x-2} + \dfrac{5}{(x-2)^2}$ **20.** $-\dfrac{4}{x-1} + \dfrac{4}{x-2} - \dfrac{2}{(x-2)^2}$

21. $\dfrac{6}{5(x-2)} + \dfrac{-6x+3}{5(x^2+1)}$ **22.** $\dfrac{5}{x-3} + \dfrac{2x-1}{x^2+4}$ **23.** $\dfrac{x}{x^2+4} - \dfrac{4x}{(x^2+4)^2}$ **24.** $\dfrac{4x+1}{x^2+x+1} + \dfrac{2x-2}{(x^2+x+1)^2}$ **25.** $\{(4,3),(1,0)\}$

26. $\{(0,1),(-3,4)\}$ **27.** $\{(1,-1),(-1,1)\}$ **28.** $\{(3,\sqrt{6}),(3,-\sqrt{6}),(-3,\sqrt{6}),(-3,-\sqrt{6})\}$ **29.** $\{(2,2),(-2,-2)\}$ **30.** $\{(9,6),(1,2)\}$

31. $\{(-3,-1),(1,3)\}$ **32.** $\left\{\left(\dfrac{1}{2},2\right),(-1,-1)\right\}$ **33.** $\left\{\left(\dfrac{5}{2},-\dfrac{7}{2}\right),(0,-1)\right\}$ **34.** $\{(2,-3),(-2,-3),(3,2),(-3,2)\}$

35. $\{(3,1),(3,-1),(-3,1),(-3,-1)\}$ **36.** 8 m and 5 m **37.** $(1,6),(3,2)$ **38.** $x=46$ and $y=28$ or $x=50$ and $y=20$

39.
$3x - 4y > 12$

40.
$y \le -\dfrac{1}{2}x + 2$

41.
$x < -2$

42.
$y \ge 3$

43.
$x^2 + y^2 > 4$

44.
$y \le x^2 - 1$

45.
$y \le 2^x$

46.
$\begin{cases} 3x + 2y \ge 6 \\ 2x + y \ge 6 \end{cases}$

47.
$\begin{cases} 2x - y \ge 4 \\ x + 2y < 2 \end{cases}$

48.
$\begin{cases} y < x \\ y \le 2 \end{cases}$

49.
$\begin{cases} x + y \le 6 \\ y \ge 2x - 3 \end{cases}$

50.
$\begin{cases} 0 \le x \le 3 \\ y > 2 \end{cases}$

51. no solution

52.
$\begin{cases} x^2 + y^2 \le 16 \\ x + y < 2 \end{cases}$

53.
$\begin{cases} x^2 + y^2 \le 9 \\ y < -3x + 1 \end{cases}$

54.
$\begin{cases} y > x^2 \\ x + y < 6 \\ y < x + 6 \end{cases}$

55.
$\begin{cases} y \ge 0 \\ 3x + 2y \ge 4 \\ x - y \le 3 \end{cases}$

56. $(2,2)$: 10; $(4,0)$: 8; $\left(\dfrac{1}{2},\dfrac{1}{2}\right)$: $\dfrac{5}{2}$; $(1,0)$: 2; maximum value: 10; minimum value: 2

57.
$x \ge 0,\ y \ge 0$
$x + y \le 8$
$3x + 2y \ge 6$
Maximum is 24 at $x = 0$, $y = 8$.

58.
$0 \le x \le 5$
$0 \le y \le 7$
$x + y \ge 3$
Maximum is 33 at $x = 5$, $y = 7$.

59.
$x \ge 0,\ y \ge 0$
$y \le x$
$2x + y \le 12$
$2x + 3y \ge 6$
Maximum is 44 at $x = y = 4$.

60. a. $z = 500x + 350y$
b. $\begin{cases} x + y \le 200 \\ x \ge 10 \\ y \ge 80 \end{cases}$
c.
$x + y \le 200$
$x \ge 10,\ y \ge 80$
d. $(10,80)$: 33,000; $(10,190)$: 71,500; $(120,80)$: 88,000
e. 120; 80; 88,000

61. 480 of model A and 240 of model B

Chapter 5 Test

1. $\{(1,-3)\}$ **2.** $\{(4,-2)\}$ **3.** $\{(1,3,2)\}$ **4.** $\{(4,-3),(-3,4)\}$ **5.** $\{(3,2),(3,-2),(-3,2),(-3,-2)\}$ **6.** $\dfrac{-1}{10(x+1)} + \dfrac{x+9}{10(x^2+9)}$

7.
$x - 2y < 8$

8.
$\begin{cases} x \ge 0,\ y \ge 0 \\ 3x + y \le 9 \\ 2x + 3y \ge 6 \end{cases}$

9.
$\begin{cases} x^2 + y^2 > 1 \\ x^2 + y^2 < 4 \end{cases}$

10.
$\begin{cases} y \le 1 - x^2 \\ x^2 + y^2 \le 9 \end{cases}$

11. 26   **12.** shrimp: 42 mg; scallops: 15 mg   **13. a.** $C(x) = 360{,}000 + 850x$ **b.** $R(x) = 1150x$ **c.** $(1200, 1{,}380{,}000)$; The company will break even if it produces and sells 1200 computers.   **14.** $y = x^2 - 3$ **15.** $x = 7.5$ ft and $y = 24$ ft or $x = 12$ ft and $y = 15$ ft
16. 50 regular and 100 deluxe jet skis; \$35,000

Cumulative Review Exercises (Chapters 1–5)

1. domain: $(-2, 2)$; range: $(-\infty, 3]$ **2.** -1 and 1 **3.** maximum of 3 at $x = 0$ **4.** $(0, 2)$
5. positive   **6.** 3   **7.** $x \to -2^+; x \to 2^-$ **8.** even

9.
$g(x) = f(x + 2) - 1$

10.
$h(x) = \frac{1}{2} f\left(\frac{1}{2} x\right)$

11. $\{3, 4\}$ **12.** $\left\{\dfrac{2 + i\sqrt{3}}{2}, \dfrac{2 - i\sqrt{3}}{2}\right\}$

13. $(-18, 6)$ **14.** $(1, 7)$

15. $\left\{-3, \dfrac{1}{2}, 2\right\}$ **16.** $\{-2\}$

17. $\{2\}$ **18.** $\{-2 + \log_3 11\}$

19. $\{625\}$ **20.** $\left\{\left(-\dfrac{1}{2}, \dfrac{1}{2}\right), (2, 8)\right\}$ **21.** $\{(8, -2, -2)\}$

22.
$f(x) = (x + 2)^2 - 4$

23.
$2x - 3y \le 6$

24.
$y = 3^{x-2}$

25.
$f(x) = \dfrac{x^2 - x - 6}{x + 1}$

26.
$f(x) = 2x - 4$
$f^{-1}(x) = \dfrac{x + 4}{2}$

27.
$(x - 2)^2 + (y - 4)^2 > 9$

28.
$f(x) = |x|$
$g(x) = -|x - 2|$

29. $(f \circ g)(x) = 2x^2 - 3x$; $(g \circ f)(x) = -2x^2 + x + 2$
30. $4x + 2h - 1$
31. $y = -3x + 10$
32. $y = 3x + 3$
33. \$2600 at 12%; \$1400 at 14%
34. 4 m by 9 m
35. 10.99%

CHAPTER 6

Section 6.1

Check Point Exercises

1. a. $\begin{bmatrix} 1 & 6 & -3 & | & 7 \\ 4 & 12 & -20 & | & 8 \\ -3 & -2 & 1 & | & -9 \end{bmatrix}$ **b.** $\begin{bmatrix} 1 & 3 & -5 & | & 2 \\ 1 & 6 & -3 & | & 7 \\ -3 & -2 & 1 & | & -9 \end{bmatrix}$ **c.** $\begin{bmatrix} 4 & 12 & -20 & | & 8 \\ 1 & 6 & -3 & | & 7 \\ 0 & 16 & -8 & | & 12 \end{bmatrix}$ **2.** $\{(5, 2, 3)\}$ **3.** $\{(1, -1, 2, -3)\}$ **4.** $\{(5, 2, 3)\}$

Concept and Vocabulary Check

1. matrix; elements   **2.** 3; second; -2; third   **3.** $\begin{bmatrix} 2 & 1 & 4 & | & -4 \\ 3 & 0 & 1 & | & 1 \\ 4 & 3 & 1 & | & 8 \end{bmatrix}$ **4.** $\{(1, 3, -2)\}$ **5.** true   **6.** false

Exercise Set 6.1

1. $\begin{bmatrix} 2 & 1 & 2 & | & 2 \\ 3 & -5 & -1 & | & 4 \\ 1 & -2 & -3 & | & -6 \end{bmatrix}$ **3.** $\begin{bmatrix} 1 & -1 & 1 & | & 8 \\ 0 & 1 & -12 & | & -15 \\ 0 & 0 & 1 & | & 1 \end{bmatrix}$ **5.** $\begin{bmatrix} 5 & -2 & -3 & | & 0 \\ 1 & 1 & 0 & | & 5 \\ 2 & 0 & -3 & | & 4 \end{bmatrix}$ **7.** $\begin{bmatrix} 2 & 5 & -3 & 1 & | & 2 \\ 0 & 3 & 1 & 0 & | & 4 \\ 1 & -1 & 5 & 0 & | & 9 \\ 5 & -5 & -2 & 0 & | & 1 \end{bmatrix}$ **9.** $\begin{cases} 5x + 3z = -11 \\ y - 4z = 12 \\ 7x + 2y = 3 \end{cases}$

11. $\begin{cases} w + x + 4y + z = 3 \\ -w + x - y = 7 \\ 2w + 5z = 11 \\ 12y + 4z = 5 \end{cases}$ **13.** $\begin{bmatrix} 1 & -3 & 2 & | & 5 \\ 1 & 5 & -5 & | & 0 \\ 3 & 0 & 4 & | & 7 \end{bmatrix}$ **15.** $\begin{bmatrix} 1 & -3 & 2 & | & 0 \\ 0 & 10 & -7 & | & 7 \\ 2 & -2 & 1 & | & 3 \end{bmatrix}$ **17.** $\begin{bmatrix} 1 & -1 & 1 & 1 & | & 3 \\ 0 & 1 & -2 & -1 & | & 0 \\ 0 & 2 & 1 & 2 & | & 5 \\ 0 & 6 & -3 & -1 & | & -9 \end{bmatrix}$

19. R_2: $-3, -18$; R_3: $-12, -15$; R_2: $-\dfrac{3}{5}, -\dfrac{18}{5}$; R_3: $-12, -15$ **21.** $\{(1, -1, 2)\}$ **23.** $\{(3, -1, -1)\}$ **25.** $\{(2, -1, 1)\}$ **27.** $\{(2, 1, 1)\}$
29. $\{(2, -1, 1)\}$ **31.** $\{(-1, 2, -2)\}$ **33.** $\{(1, 2, -1)\}$ **35.** $\{(1, 2, 3, -2)\}$ **37.** $\{(0, -3, 0, -3)\}$ **39.** $f(x) = -x^2 + x + 2$
41. $f(x) = x^3 - 2x^2 + 3$ **43.** $\{(e^{-1}, e, e^{-3}, e^{-2})\}$ **45. a.** $a = -32$, $v_0 = 56$, $s_0 = 0$ **b.** 0; The ball hits the ground 3.5 seconds after it is thrown; $(3.5, 0)$.
c. 1.75 sec; 49 ft   **47.** 4 oz of Food A; $\dfrac{1}{2}$ oz of Food B; 1 oz of Food C **49.** Asians: 122; Africans: 28; Europeans: 24; Americans: 9   **59.** makes sense
61. makes sense   **63.** false   **65.** false   **67.** 60 units: \$7700
68. For $z = 0$, $(12z + 1, 10z - 1, z)$ is $(1, -1, 0)$; $3(1) - 4(-1) + 4(0) = 7$ is true; $1 - (-1) - 2(0) = 2$ is true; $2(1) - 3(-1) + 6(0) = 5$ is true.
69. For $z = 1$, $(12z + 1, 10z - 1, z)$ is $(13, 9, 1)$; $3(13) - 4(9) + 4(1) = 7$ is true; $13 - 9 - 2(1) = 2$ is true; $2(13) - 3(9) + 6(1) = 5$ is true.
70. a. Answers may vary.   **b.** This system has more than one solution.

Section 6.2

Check Point Exercises

1. $\varnothing$ **2.** $\{(11t + 13, 5t + 4, t)\}$ **3.** $\{(t + 50, -2t + 10, t)\}$

4. a. $\begin{cases} w + z = 15 \\ w + x = 30 \\ x + y = 45 \\ y + z = 30 \end{cases}$ **b.** $\{(-t + 15, t + 15, -t + 30, t)\}$ **c.** $w = 5; x = 25; y = 20$

Concept and Vocabulary Check

1. no solution   **2.** one solution   **3.** infinitely many solutions   **4.** true

5. $\begin{cases} x - y + z = 5 \\ y - z = -3 \end{cases}$; $z - 3; 2; \{(2, z - 3, z)\}$

Exercise Set 6.2

1. $\varnothing$ **3.** $\left\{\left(-2t + 2, 2t + \dfrac{1}{2}, t\right)\right\}$ **5.** $\{(-3, 4, -2)\}$ **7.** $\{(5 - 2t, -2 + t, t)\}$ **9.** $\{(-1, 2, 1, 1)\}$ **11.** $\{(1, 3, 2, 1)\}$

13. $\{(1, -2, 1, 1)\}$ **15.** $\left\{\left(1 + \dfrac{1}{3}t, \dfrac{1}{3}t, t\right)\right\}$ **17.** $\{(-13t + 5, 5t, t)\}$ **19.** $\left\{\left(2t - \dfrac{5}{4}, \dfrac{13}{4}, t\right)\right\}$ **21.** $\{(1, -t - 1, 2, t)\}$

23. $\left\{\left(-\dfrac{2}{11}t + \dfrac{81}{11}, \dfrac{1}{22}t + \dfrac{10}{11}, \dfrac{4}{11}t - \dfrac{8}{11}, t\right)\right\}$

25. a. $4w - 2x + 2y - 3z = 0; 7w - x - y - 3z = 0; w + x + y - z = 0$ **b.** $\{(0.5t, 0, 0.5t, t)\}$

27. a. $w + 2x + 5y + 5z = -3; w + x + 3y + 4z = -1; w - x - y + 2z = 3$ **b.** $\{(1 - 3s - t, -2 - s - 2t, t, s)\}$

29. $z + 12 = x + 6$ **31.** $\{(t + 6, t + 2, t)\}$

33. a. $\begin{cases} w + z = 380 \\ w + x = 600 \\ x - y = 170 \\ y - z = 50 \end{cases}$ **b.** $\{(380 - t, 220 + t, 50 + t, t)\}$ **c.** $w = 330, x = 270, y = 100$

35. a. The system has no solution, so there is no way to satisfy these dietary requirements with no Food 1 available.

　　b. 4 oz of Food 1, 0 oz of Food 2, 10 oz of Food 3; 2 oz of Food 1, 5 oz of Food 2, 9 oz of Food 3 (other answers are possible).

41. does not make sense   **43.** does not make sense   **45.** $a = 1$ or $a = 3$ **47.** -1 **48.** -12 **49.** 8

Section 6.3

Check Point Exercises

1. a. 3×2 **b.** $a_{12} = -2; a_{31} = 1$ **2. a.** $\begin{bmatrix} 2 & 0 \\ 9 & -10 \end{bmatrix}$ **b.** $\begin{bmatrix} 9 & -4 \\ -9 & 7 \\ 5 & -2 \end{bmatrix}$ **3. a.** $\begin{bmatrix} 6 & 12 \\ -48 & -30 \end{bmatrix}$ **b.** $\begin{bmatrix} -14 & -1 \\ 25 & 10 \end{bmatrix}$ **4.** $\begin{bmatrix} -4 & 3 \\ -3 & \dfrac{13}{3} \end{bmatrix}$

5. $\begin{bmatrix} 7 & 6 \\ 13 & 12 \end{bmatrix}$ **6.** $[30]; \begin{bmatrix} 2 & 0 & 4 \\ 6 & 0 & 12 \\ 14 & 0 & 28 \end{bmatrix}$ **7. a.** $\begin{bmatrix} 2 & 18 & 11 & 9 \\ 0 & 10 & 8 & 2 \end{bmatrix}$ **b.** The product is undefined.

8. $\begin{bmatrix} 2 & 1 & 1 \\ 2 & 1 & 1 \\ 2 & 2 & 1 \end{bmatrix} + \begin{bmatrix} -1 & 2 & 2 \\ -1 & 2 & 2 \\ -1 & -1 & 2 \end{bmatrix} = \begin{bmatrix} 1 & 3 & 3 \\ 1 & 3 & 3 \\ 1 & 1 & 3 \end{bmatrix}$

9. a. $\begin{bmatrix} 0 & 3 & 4 \\ 0 & 5 & 2 \end{bmatrix} + \begin{bmatrix} -3 & -3 & -3 \\ -1 & -1 & -1 \end{bmatrix} = \begin{bmatrix} -3 & 0 & 1 \\ -1 & 4 & 1 \end{bmatrix}$ **b.** $2\begin{bmatrix} 0 & 3 & 4 \\ 0 & 5 & 2 \end{bmatrix} = \begin{bmatrix} 0 & 6 & 8 \\ 0 & 10 & 4 \end{bmatrix}$

c. $\begin{bmatrix} 0 & 3 & 4 \\ 0 & -5 & -2 \end{bmatrix}$; Multiplying by B reflects the triangle over the x-axis.

Concept and Vocabulary Check

1. third; fourth   **2.** 1×3 **3.** square   **4.** $-10; 6$ **5.** true   **6.** false   **7.** true   **8.** $m; p$; columns; rows   **9.** true   **10.** false

Exercise Set 6.3

1. a. 2×3 **b.** a_{32} does not exist; $a_{23} = -1$ **3. a.** 3×4 **b.** $a_{32} = \dfrac{1}{2}; a_{23} = -6$ **5.** $x = 6; y = 4$ **7.** $x = 4; y = 6; z = 3$

9. a. $\begin{bmatrix} 9 & 10 \\ 3 & 9 \end{bmatrix}$ **b.** $\begin{bmatrix} -1 & -8 \\ 3 & -5 \end{bmatrix}$ **c.** $\begin{bmatrix} -16 & -4 \\ -12 & -8 \end{bmatrix}$ **d.** $\begin{bmatrix} 22 & 21 \\ 9 & 20 \end{bmatrix}$ **11. a.** $\begin{bmatrix} 3 & 2 \\ 6 & 2 \\ 5 & 7 \end{bmatrix}$ **b.** $\begin{bmatrix} -1 & 4 \\ 0 & 6 \\ 5 & 5 \end{bmatrix}$ **c.** $\begin{bmatrix} -4 & -12 \\ -12 & -16 \\ -20 & -24 \end{bmatrix}$ **d.** $\begin{bmatrix} 7 & 7 \\ 15 & 8 \\ 15 & 20 \end{bmatrix}$

13. a. $\begin{bmatrix} -3 \\ -1 \\ 0 \end{bmatrix}$ **b.** $\begin{bmatrix} 7 \\ -7 \\ 2 \end{bmatrix}$ **c.** $\begin{bmatrix} -8 \\ 16 \\ -4 \end{bmatrix}$ **d.** $\begin{bmatrix} -4 \\ -6 \\ 1 \end{bmatrix}$ **15. a.** $\begin{bmatrix} 8 & 0 & -4 \\ 14 & 0 & 6 \\ -1 & 0 & 0 \end{bmatrix}$ **b.** $\begin{bmatrix} -4 & -20 & 0 \\ 14 & 24 & 14 \\ 9 & -4 & 4 \end{bmatrix}$ **c.** $\begin{bmatrix} -8 & 40 & 8 \\ -56 & -48 & -40 \\ -16 & 8 & -8 \end{bmatrix}$ **d.** $\begin{bmatrix} 18 & -10 & -10 \\ 42 & 12 & 22 \\ 2 & -2 & 2 \end{bmatrix}$

17. $\begin{bmatrix} -8 & -8 \\ 2 & -9 \\ 8 & -4 \end{bmatrix}$ **19.** $\begin{bmatrix} -1 & 3 \\ -1 & \frac{9}{2} \\ -1 & -2 \end{bmatrix}$ **21.** $\begin{bmatrix} \frac{1}{3} & \frac{13}{3} \\ -\frac{4}{3} & 6 \\ -\frac{7}{3} & -\frac{4}{3} \end{bmatrix}$ **23.** $\begin{bmatrix} 7 & 27 \\ -8 & 36 \\ -17 & -4 \end{bmatrix}$ **25.** $\begin{bmatrix} \frac{27}{2} & \frac{31}{2} \\ -4 & 18 \\ -\frac{29}{2} & 6 \end{bmatrix}$ **27. a.** $\begin{bmatrix} 0 & 16 \\ 12 & 8 \end{bmatrix}$ **b.** $\begin{bmatrix} -7 & 3 \\ 29 & 15 \end{bmatrix}$

29. a. [30] **b.** $\begin{bmatrix} 1 & 2 & 3 & 4 \\ 2 & 4 & 6 & 8 \\ 3 & 6 & 9 & 12 \\ 4 & 8 & 12 & 16 \end{bmatrix}$ **31. a.** $\begin{bmatrix} 4 & -5 & 8 \\ 6 & -1 & 5 \\ 0 & 4 & -6 \end{bmatrix}$ **b.** $\begin{bmatrix} 5 & -2 & 7 \\ 17 & -3 & 2 \\ 3 & 0 & -5 \end{bmatrix}$ **33. a.** $\begin{bmatrix} 6 & 8 & 16 \\ 11 & 16 & 24 \\ 1 & -1 & 12 \end{bmatrix}$ **b.** $\begin{bmatrix} 38 & 27 \\ -16 & -4 \end{bmatrix}$

35. a. $\begin{bmatrix} 0 & 0 \\ 0 & 0 \end{bmatrix}$ **b.** $\begin{bmatrix} 4 & -1 & -3 & 1 \\ -1 & 4 & -3 & 2 \\ 14 & -11 & -3 & -1 \\ 25 & -25 & 0 & -5 \end{bmatrix}$ **37.** $\begin{bmatrix} 17 & 7 \\ -5 & -11 \end{bmatrix}$ **39.** $\begin{bmatrix} 11 & -1 \\ -7 & -3 \end{bmatrix}$

41. $A - C$ is not defined because A is 3×2 and C is 2×2. **43.** $\begin{bmatrix} 16 & -16 \\ -12 & 12 \\ 0 & 0 \end{bmatrix}$ **45.** $\begin{bmatrix} 0 & 0 \\ 0 & 0 \end{bmatrix}$

47. Answers will vary.; Example:

$A(B + C) = \begin{bmatrix} 1 & 0 \\ 0 & 1 \end{bmatrix}\left(\begin{bmatrix} 1 & 0 \\ 0 & -1 \end{bmatrix} + \begin{bmatrix} -1 & 0 \\ 0 & 1 \end{bmatrix}\right) = \begin{bmatrix} 1 & 0 \\ 0 & 1 \end{bmatrix}\begin{bmatrix} 0 & 0 \\ 0 & 0 \end{bmatrix} = \begin{bmatrix} 0 & 0 \\ 0 & 0 \end{bmatrix}$

$AB + AC = \begin{bmatrix} 1 & 0 \\ 0 & 1 \end{bmatrix}\begin{bmatrix} 1 & 0 \\ 0 & -1 \end{bmatrix} + \begin{bmatrix} 1 & 0 \\ 0 & 1 \end{bmatrix}\begin{bmatrix} -1 & 0 \\ 0 & 1 \end{bmatrix} = \begin{bmatrix} 1 & 0 \\ 0 & -1 \end{bmatrix} + \begin{bmatrix} -1 & 0 \\ 0 & 1 \end{bmatrix} = \begin{bmatrix} 0 & 0 \\ 0 & 0 \end{bmatrix}$

So, $A(B + C) = AB + AC$.

49. $\begin{bmatrix} x \\ -y \end{bmatrix}$; It changes the sign of the y-coordinate.

51. a. $\begin{bmatrix} 1 & 3 & 1 \\ 3 & 3 & 3 \\ 1 & 3 & 1 \end{bmatrix}$ **b.** $\begin{bmatrix} 1 & 3 & 1 \\ 3 & 3 & 3 \\ 1 & 3 & 1 \end{bmatrix} + \begin{bmatrix} -1 & -1 & -1 \\ -1 & -1 & -1 \\ -1 & -1 & -1 \end{bmatrix} = \begin{bmatrix} 0 & 2 & 0 \\ 2 & 2 & 2 \\ 0 & 2 & 0 \end{bmatrix}$ **c.** $\begin{bmatrix} 1 & 3 & 1 \\ 3 & 3 & 3 \\ 1 & 3 & 1 \end{bmatrix} + \begin{bmatrix} 1 & -2 & 1 \\ -2 & -2 & -2 \\ 1 & -2 & 1 \end{bmatrix} = \begin{bmatrix} 2 & 1 & 2 \\ 1 & 1 & 1 \\ 2 & 1 & 2 \end{bmatrix}$

53. $\begin{bmatrix} -2 & 1 & 1 & -1 & -1 & -2 \\ -3 & -3 & -2 & -2 & 2 & 2 \end{bmatrix}$ **55.** $\begin{bmatrix} 0 & \frac{3}{2} & \frac{3}{2} & \frac{1}{2} & \frac{1}{2} & 0 \\ 1 & 1 & \frac{3}{2} & \frac{3}{2} & \frac{7}{2} & \frac{7}{2} \end{bmatrix}$ **57. a.** $\begin{bmatrix} 0 & 3 & 3 & 1 & 1 & 0 \\ 0 & 0 & -1 & -1 & -5 & -5 \end{bmatrix}$

b. The effect is a reflection across the x-axis.

59. a. $\begin{bmatrix} 0 & 0 & -1 & -1 & -5 & -5 \\ 0 & 3 & 3 & 1 & 1 & 0 \end{bmatrix}$

b.

The effect is a 90° counterclockwise rotation about the origin.

61. a. $A = \begin{bmatrix} 2 & 6 \\ 31 & 46 \end{bmatrix}$ **b.** $B = \begin{bmatrix} 9 & 29 \\ 65 & 77 \end{bmatrix}$

c. $B - A = \begin{bmatrix} 7 & 23 \\ 34 & 31 \end{bmatrix}$

The difference between the percentage of people completing the transition to adulthood in 1960 and 2000 by age and gender

63. a. System 1: The midterm and final both count for 50% of the course grade. System 2: The midterm counts for 30% of the course grade and the final counts for 70%.

b. $\begin{bmatrix} 84 & 87.2 \\ 79 & 81 \\ 90 & 88.4 \\ 73 & 68.6 \\ 69 & 73.4 \end{bmatrix}$ System 1 grades are listed first (if different). Student 1: B; Student 2: C or B; Student 3: A or B; Student 4: C or D; Student 5: D or C

77. makes sense **79.** makes sense **83.** $AB = -BA$ so they are anticommutative.

85. $\begin{bmatrix} a_{11} & a_{12} \\ a_{21} & a_{22} \end{bmatrix}$; Nothing happens to the elements in the first matrix.   **86.** $\{(15, -12, -4)\}$ **87.** $\begin{cases} a_1x + b_1y + c_1z = d_1 \\ a_2x + b_2y + c_2z = d_2 \\ a_3x + b_3y + c_3z = d_3 \end{cases}$

Mid-Chapter 6 Check Point

1. $\{(1, -1, 2)\}$ **2.** $\varnothing$ **3.** $\left\{\left(-\frac{4}{7} - \frac{4}{7}t, \frac{5}{7} + \frac{5}{7}t, t\right)\right\}$ **4.** $\{(3, 6, -4, 1)\}$ **5.** $\varnothing$ **6.** $\begin{bmatrix} -4 & -\frac{1}{2} \\ 3 & 3 \end{bmatrix}$ **7.** $\begin{bmatrix} -12 & -2 \\ -21 & -4 \\ 3 & 1 \end{bmatrix}$ **8.** $\begin{bmatrix} 12 & -4 \\ 22 & -7 \\ -4 & 1 \end{bmatrix}$

9. $A + C$ does not exist because A is 3×2 and C is 2×2.   **10.** $\begin{bmatrix} \frac{1}{2} & \frac{1}{2} \\ -3 & \frac{1}{2} \end{bmatrix}$

Section 6.4

Check Point Exercises

1. $AB = I_2$; $BA = I_2$ **2.** $\begin{bmatrix} 3 & -7 \\ -2 & 5 \end{bmatrix}$ **3.** $\begin{bmatrix} 1 & 2 \\ 1 & 3 \end{bmatrix}$ **4.** $\begin{bmatrix} 3 & -2 & -4 \\ 3 & -2 & -5 \\ -1 & 1 & 2 \end{bmatrix}$ **5.** $\{(4, -2, 1)\}$ **6.** The encoded message is $-7, 10, -53, 77$.

7. The decoded message is 2, 1, 19, 5 or BASE.

Concept and Vocabulary Check

1. $\begin{bmatrix} 1 & 0 \\ 0 & 1 \end{bmatrix}$ **2.** $\begin{bmatrix} 1 & 0 & 0 \\ 0 & 1 & 0 \\ 0 & 0 & 1 \end{bmatrix}$ **3.** multiplicative inverse   **4.** true   **5.** $ad - bc \neq 0$

6. singular   **7.** false   **8.** A^{-1} **9.** $A^{-1}B$

Exercise Set 6.4

1. $AB = I_2$; $BA = I_2$; $B = A^{-1}$ **3.** $AB = \begin{bmatrix} 8 & -16 \\ -2 & 7 \end{bmatrix}$; $BA = \begin{bmatrix} 12 & 12 \\ 1 & 3 \end{bmatrix}$; $B \neq A^{-1}$ **5.** $AB = I_2$; $BA = I_2$; $B = A^{-1}$

7. $AB = I_3$; $BA = I_3$; $B = A^{-1}$ **9.** $AB = I_3$; $BA = I_3$; $B = A^{-1}$ **11.** $AB = I_4$; $BA = I_4$; $B = A^{-1}$

13. $\begin{bmatrix} \frac{2}{7} & -\frac{3}{7} \\ \frac{1}{7} & \frac{2}{7} \end{bmatrix}$ **15.** $\begin{bmatrix} 1 & \frac{1}{2} \\ 2 & \frac{3}{2} \end{bmatrix}$ **17.** A does not have an inverse.   **19.** $\begin{bmatrix} \frac{1}{2} & 0 & 0 \\ 0 & \frac{1}{4} & 0 \\ 0 & 0 & \frac{1}{6} \end{bmatrix}$ **21.** $\begin{bmatrix} 1 & 1 & 2 \\ 1 & 1 & 1 \\ 2 & 3 & 4 \end{bmatrix}$ **23.** $\begin{bmatrix} 1 & 0 & 1 \\ 1 & 1 & 2 \\ 3 & 2 & 6 \end{bmatrix}$

25. $\begin{bmatrix} -3 & 2 & -4 \\ -1 & 1 & -1 \\ 8 & -5 & 10 \end{bmatrix}$ **27.** $\begin{bmatrix} 1 & 0 & 0 & 0 \\ 0 & -1 & 0 & 0 \\ 0 & 0 & \frac{1}{3} & 0 \\ -1 & 0 & 0 & 1 \end{bmatrix}$ **29.** $\begin{bmatrix} 6 & 5 \\ 5 & 4 \end{bmatrix}\begin{bmatrix} x \\ y \end{bmatrix} = \begin{bmatrix} 13 \\ 10 \end{bmatrix}$ **31.** $\begin{bmatrix} 1 & 3 & 4 \\ 1 & 2 & 3 \\ 1 & 4 & 3 \end{bmatrix}\begin{bmatrix} x \\ y \\ z \end{bmatrix} = \begin{bmatrix} -3 \\ -2 \\ -6 \end{bmatrix}$ **33.** $\begin{cases} 4x - 7y = -3 \\ 2x - 3y = 1 \end{cases}$

35. $\begin{cases} 2x - z = 6 \\ 3y = 9 \\ x + y = 5 \end{cases}$ **37. a.** $\begin{bmatrix} 2 & 6 & 6 \\ 2 & 7 & 6 \\ 2 & 7 & 7 \end{bmatrix}\begin{bmatrix} x \\ y \\ z \end{bmatrix} = \begin{bmatrix} 8 \\ 10 \\ 9 \end{bmatrix}$ **b.** $\{(1, 2, -1)\}$ **39. a.** $\begin{bmatrix} 1 & -1 & 1 \\ 0 & 2 & -1 \\ 2 & 3 & 0 \end{bmatrix}\begin{bmatrix} x \\ y \\ z \end{bmatrix} = \begin{bmatrix} 8 \\ -7 \\ 1 \end{bmatrix}$ **b.** $\{(2, -1, 5)\}$

41. a. $\begin{bmatrix} 1 & -1 & 2 & 0 \\ 0 & 1 & -1 & 1 \\ -1 & 1 & -1 & 2 \\ 0 & -1 & 1 & -2 \end{bmatrix}\begin{bmatrix} w \\ x \\ y \\ z \end{bmatrix} = \begin{bmatrix} -3 \\ 4 \\ 2 \\ -4 \end{bmatrix}$ **b.** $\{(2, 3, -1, 0)\}$ **43.** $\begin{bmatrix} \frac{1}{2}e^{-x} & -\frac{1}{2}e^{-3x} \\ \frac{1}{2}e^{-3x} & \frac{1}{2}e^{-5x} \end{bmatrix}$ **45.** $\begin{bmatrix} \frac{1}{8} & \frac{5}{8} \\ \frac{3}{8} & \frac{7}{8} \end{bmatrix}$

47. $(AB)^{-1} = \begin{bmatrix} -23 & 16 \\ 13 & -9 \end{bmatrix}$; $A^{-1}B^{-1} = \begin{bmatrix} -3 & 11 \\ 8 & -29 \end{bmatrix}$; $B^{-1}A^{-1} = \begin{bmatrix} -23 & 16 \\ 13 & -9 \end{bmatrix}$; $(AB)^{-1} = B^{-1}A^{-1}$ **49.** $AA^{-1} = I_3$ and $A^{-1}A = I_3$

51. The encoded message is $27, -19, 32, -20.$; The decoded message is 8, 5, 12, 16 or HELP.

53. The encoded message is $14, 85, -33, 4, 18, -7, -18, 19, -9.$

65. $\begin{bmatrix} 1 & 1 \\ 2 & 3 \end{bmatrix}$ **67.** $\begin{bmatrix} 1 & 0 & 1 \\ 2 & 1 & 3 \\ -1 & 1 & 1 \end{bmatrix}$ **69.** $\begin{bmatrix} 0 & -1 & 0 & 1 \\ -1 & -5 & 0 & 3 \\ -2 & -4 & 1 & -2 \\ -1 & -4 & 0 & 1 \end{bmatrix}$ **71.** $\{(2, 3, -5)\}$ **73.** $\{(1, 2, -1)\}$ **75.** $\{(2, 1, 3, -2, 4)\}$

79. does not make sense   **81.** makes sense   **83.** false   **85.** false   **87.** false   **91.** $a = 3$ or $a = -2$ **93.** 2   **94.** 6   **95.** -31

Section 6.5

Check Point Exercises

1. a. -4 **b.** -17 **2.** $\{(4, -2)\}$ **3.** 80   **4.** -24 **5.** $\{(2, -3, 4)\}$ **6.** -250

Concept and Vocabulary Check

1. $5 \cdot 3 - 2 \cdot 4 = 15 - 8 = 7$; determinant; 7

2. $x = \dfrac{\begin{vmatrix} 8 & 1 \\ -2 & -1 \end{vmatrix}}{\begin{vmatrix} 1 & 1 \\ 1 & -1 \end{vmatrix}}$; $y = \dfrac{\begin{vmatrix} 1 & 8 \\ 1 & -2 \end{vmatrix}}{\begin{vmatrix} 1 & 1 \\ 1 & -1 \end{vmatrix}}$

3. $3\begin{vmatrix} 3 & 1 \\ 1 & 1 \end{vmatrix} - 4\begin{vmatrix} 2 & 1 \\ 1 & 1 \end{vmatrix} + 5\begin{vmatrix} 2 & 1 \\ 3 & 1 \end{vmatrix}$

4. $\dfrac{\begin{vmatrix} 3 & -8 & 4 \\ 2 & 11 & -2 \\ 1 & 4 & -2 \end{vmatrix}}{\begin{vmatrix} 3 & 1 & 4 \\ 2 & 3 & -2 \\ 1 & -3 & -2 \end{vmatrix}}$ 5. column 3/the last column

Exercise Set 6.5

1. 1   3. −29   5. 0   7. 33   9. $-\dfrac{7}{16}$ 11. $\{(5, 2)\}$ 13. $\{(2, -3)\}$ 15. $\{(3, -1)\}$ 17. $\left\{\left(2, \dfrac{1}{2}\right)\right\}$ 19. $\{(4, 2)\}$

21. $\{(7, 4)\}$ 23. 72   25. −75   27. 0   29. $\{(-5, -2, 7)\}$ 31. $\{(2, -3, 4)\}$ 33. $\{(3, -1, 2)\}$ 35. $\{(2, 3, 1)\}$ 37. −200   39. 195

41. −42   43. $2x - 4y = 8$; $3x + 5y = -10$ 45. −11   47. 4   49. 28 sq units   51. yes   53. The equation of the line is $y = -\dfrac{11}{5}x + \dfrac{8}{5}$.

65. 13,200   67. does not make sense   69. does not make sense   71. **a.** a^2 **b.** a^3 **c.** a^4 **d.** Each determinant has zeros below the main diagonal and a's everywhere else.   **e.** Each determinant equals a raised to the power equal to the order of the determinant.

73. The sign of the value is changed when 2 columns are interchanged in a 2nd order determinant.

75. $\begin{vmatrix} x & y & 1 \\ x_1 & y_1 & 1 \\ x_2 & y_2 & 1 \end{vmatrix} = x(y_1 - y_2) - y(x_1 - x_2) + (x_1y_2 - x_2y_1) = 0$; solving for y, $y = \dfrac{y_1 - y_2}{x_1 - x_2}x + \dfrac{x_1y_2 - x_2y_1}{x_1 - x_2}$, and $m = \dfrac{y_1 - y_2}{x_1 - x_2}$ and $b = \dfrac{x_1y_2 - x_2y_1}{x_1 - x_2}$.

77. **a.** −3 and 3   **b.** −2 and 2   78. $\dfrac{x^2}{16} + \dfrac{y^2}{25} = 1$ 79. $(x - 1)^2 + (y + 2)^2 = 9$; center: $(1, -2)$; radius: 3;

Chapter 6 Review Exercises

1. $\begin{bmatrix} 1 & 2 & 2 & | & 2 \\ 0 & 1 & -1 & | & 2 \\ 0 & 0 & 9 & | & -9 \end{bmatrix}$ 2. $\begin{bmatrix} 1 & -1 & \frac{1}{2} & | & -\frac{1}{2} \\ 1 & 2 & -1 & | & 2 \\ 6 & 4 & 3 & | & 5 \end{bmatrix}$ 3. $\{(1, 3, -4)\}$ 4. $\{(-2, -1, 0)\}$ 5. $\{(2, -2, 3, 4)\}$

6. **a.** $a = -2$; $b = 32$; $c = 42$ **b.** 2:00 p.m.; 170 parts per million   7. capitalist: 1%; upper middle: 15%; lower middle: 34%; working: 30%

8. $\varnothing$ 9. $\{(2t + 4, t + 1, t)\}$ 10. $\{(-37t + 2, 16t, -7t + 1, t)\}$ 11. $\{(7t + 18, -3t - 7, t)\}$

12. **a.** $\begin{cases} x + z = 750 \\ y - z = -250 \\ x + y = 500 \end{cases}$ **b.** $\{(-t + 750, t - 250, t)\}$ **c.** $x = 350$; $y = 150$ 13. $x = -5$; $y = 6$; $z = 6$ 14. $\begin{bmatrix} 0 & 2 & 3 \\ 8 & 1 & 3 \end{bmatrix}$ 15. $\begin{bmatrix} 0 & -4 \\ 6 & 4 \\ 2 & -10 \end{bmatrix}$

16. $\begin{bmatrix} -4 & 4 & -1 \\ -2 & -5 & 5 \end{bmatrix}$ 17. Not possible since B is 3×2 and C is 3×3.   18. $\begin{bmatrix} 2 & 3 & 8 \\ 21 & 5 & 5 \end{bmatrix}$ 19. $\begin{bmatrix} -12 & 14 & 0 \\ 2 & -14 & 18 \end{bmatrix}$ 20. $\begin{bmatrix} 0 & -10 & -15 \\ -40 & -5 & -15 \end{bmatrix}$

21. $\begin{bmatrix} -1 & -16 \\ 8 & 1 \end{bmatrix}$ 22. $\begin{bmatrix} -10 & -6 & 2 \\ 16 & 3 & 4 \\ -23 & -16 & 7 \end{bmatrix}$ 23. $\begin{bmatrix} -6 & 4 & -8 \\ 0 & 5 & 11 \\ -17 & 13 & -19 \end{bmatrix}$ 24. $\begin{bmatrix} 10 & 5 \\ -2 & -30 \end{bmatrix}$ 25. Not possible since AB is 2×2 and BA is 3×3.

26. $\begin{bmatrix} 7 & 6 & 5 \\ 2 & -1 & 11 \end{bmatrix}$ 27. $\begin{bmatrix} -6 & -22 & -40 \\ 9 & 43 & 58 \\ -14 & -48 & -94 \end{bmatrix}$ 28. $\begin{bmatrix} -2 & -6 \\ 3 & \frac{1}{3} \end{bmatrix}$ 29. $\begin{bmatrix} 2 & 2 & 2 \\ 1 & 2 & 1 \\ 1 & 2 & 1 \end{bmatrix}$ 30. $\begin{bmatrix} 1 & 1 & 1 \\ -1 & 1 & -1 \\ -1 & 1 & -1 \end{bmatrix}$

31. $\begin{bmatrix} -2 & 0 & 0 \\ 1 & 1 & -3 \end{bmatrix}$ 32. $\begin{bmatrix} 0 & 1 & 1 \\ -2 & -2 & -4 \end{bmatrix}$ 33. $\begin{bmatrix} 0 & 2 & 2 \\ 0 & 0 & 4 \end{bmatrix}$

The effect is a reflection over the x-axis

34. $\begin{bmatrix} 0 & -2 & -2 \\ 0 & 0 & -4 \end{bmatrix}$

The effect is a reflection over the y-axis.

35. $\begin{bmatrix} 0 & 0 & 4 \\ 0 & 2 & 2 \end{bmatrix}$

The effect is a 90° counterclockwise rotation about the origin.

36. $\begin{bmatrix} 0 & 4 & 4 \\ 0 & 0 & -4 \end{bmatrix}$

The effect is a horizontal stretch by a factor of 2.

37. $AB = \begin{bmatrix} 1 & 7 \\ 0 & 5 \end{bmatrix}$; $BA = \begin{bmatrix} 1 & 0 \\ 1 & 5 \end{bmatrix}$; $B \neq A^{-1}$ **38.** $AB = I_3$; $BA = I_3$; $B = A^{-1}$ **39.** $\begin{bmatrix} 3 & 1 \\ 2 & 1 \end{bmatrix}$ **40.** $\begin{bmatrix} -\dfrac{3}{5} & \dfrac{1}{5} \\ 1 & 0 \end{bmatrix}$ **41.** $\begin{bmatrix} 3 & 0 & -2 \\ -6 & 1 & 4 \\ 1 & 0 & -1 \end{bmatrix}$

42. $\begin{bmatrix} 8 & -8 & 5 \\ -3 & 2 & -1 \\ -1 & -1 & 1 \end{bmatrix}$ **43. a.** $\begin{bmatrix} 1 & 1 & 2 \\ 0 & 1 & 3 \\ 3 & 0 & -2 \end{bmatrix}\begin{bmatrix} x \\ y \\ z \end{bmatrix} = \begin{bmatrix} 7 \\ -2 \\ 0 \end{bmatrix}$ **b.** $\{(-18, 79, -27)\}$ **44. a.** $\begin{bmatrix} 1 & -1 & 2 \\ 0 & 1 & -1 \\ 1 & 0 & 2 \end{bmatrix}\begin{bmatrix} x \\ y \\ z \end{bmatrix} = \begin{bmatrix} 12 \\ -5 \\ 10 \end{bmatrix}$

b. $\{(4, -2, 3)\}$ **45.** The encoded message is 96, 135, 46, 63; The decoded message is 18, 21, 12, 5 or RULE.   **46.** 17   **47.** 4

48. -86 **49.** -236 **50.** 4   **51.** 16   **52.** $\left\{\left(\dfrac{7}{4}, -\dfrac{25}{8}\right)\right\}$ **53.** $\{(2, -7)\}$ **54.** $\{(23, -12, 3)\}$ **55.** $\{(-3, 2, 1)\}$

56. $a = \dfrac{5}{8}$; $b = -50$; $c = 1150$; 30- and 50-year-olds are involved in an average of 212.5 automobile accidents per day.

Chapter 6 Test

1. $\left\{\left(-3, \dfrac{1}{2}, 1\right)\right\}$ **2.** $\{(t, t - 1, t)\}$ **3.** $\begin{bmatrix} 5 & 4 \\ 1 & 11 \end{bmatrix}$ **4.** $\begin{bmatrix} 5 & -2 \\ 1 & -1 \\ 4 & -1 \end{bmatrix}$ **5.** $\begin{bmatrix} \dfrac{3}{5} & -\dfrac{2}{5} \\ \dfrac{1}{5} & \dfrac{1}{5} \end{bmatrix}$ **6.** $\begin{bmatrix} -1 & 2 \\ -5 & 4 \end{bmatrix}$ **7.** $AB = I_3$; $BA = I_3$

8. a. $\begin{bmatrix} 3 & 5 \\ 2 & -3 \end{bmatrix}\begin{bmatrix} x \\ y \end{bmatrix} = \begin{bmatrix} 9 \\ -13 \end{bmatrix}$ **b.** $\begin{bmatrix} \dfrac{3}{19} & \dfrac{5}{19} \\ \dfrac{2}{19} & -\dfrac{3}{19} \end{bmatrix}$ **c.** $\{(-2, 3)\}$ **9.** 18   **10.** $x = 2$

Cumulative Review Exercises (Chapters 1–6)

1. $\left\{\dfrac{-1 + \sqrt{33}}{4}, \dfrac{-1 - \sqrt{33}}{4}\right\}$ **2.** $\left[\dfrac{1}{2}, \infty\right)$ **3.** $\{6\}$ **4.** $\left\{-4, \dfrac{1}{3}, 1\right\}$ **5.** $\{\ln 5, \ln 9\}$ **6.** $\{1\}$ **7.** $\{(7, -4, 6)\}$

8. $y = -1$ **9.** $f^{-1}(x) = \dfrac{x^2 + 7}{4}$ $(x \geq 0)$

10.

11. $f(x) = (x + 2)(x - 3)(2x + 1)(2x - 1)$ **12.**

13. a. $A = 900e^{-0.017t}$ **b.** 759.30 g

14. $\begin{bmatrix} 2 & -1 \\ 13 & 1 \end{bmatrix}$ **15.** $\dfrac{8}{x - 3} + \dfrac{-2}{x - 2} + \dfrac{-3}{x + 2}$ **16.**

17.

18.

19.

20. $x^2 + 2x - 2$

SUBJECT INDEX

PHOTO CREDITS

Definitions, Rules, and Formulas

THE REAL NUMBERS

Natural Numbers: $\{1, 2, 3, \ldots\}$
Whole Numbers: $\{0, 1, 2, 3, \ldots\}$
Integers: $\{\ldots, -3, -2, -1, 0, 1, 2, 3, \ldots\}$
Rational Numbers: $\left\{\frac{a}{b} \mid a \text{ and } b \text{ are integers}, b \neq 0\right\}$
Irrational Numbers: $\{x \mid x \text{ is real and not rational}\}$

PROPERTIES OF ADDITION AND MULTIPLICATION

Commutative: $a + b = b + a; ab = ba$
Associative: $(a + b) + c = a + (b + c);$
$\qquad\qquad (ab)c = a(bc)$
Distributive: $a(b + c) = ab + ac; a(b - c) = ab - ac$
Identity: $a + 0 = a; a \cdot 1 = a$
Inverse: $a + (-a) = 0; a \cdot \frac{1}{a} = 1 \ (a \neq 0)$
Multiplication Properties: $(-1)a = -a;$
$(-1)(-a) = a; a \cdot 0 = 0; (-a)(b) = (a)(-b) = -ab;$
$(-a)(-b) = ab$

EXPONENTS

Definitions of Rational Exponents

1. $a^{\frac{1}{n}} = \sqrt[n]{a}$ **2.** $a^{\frac{m}{n}} = \left(\sqrt[n]{a}\right)^m \text{ or } \sqrt[n]{a^m}$

3. $a^{-\frac{m}{n}} = \dfrac{1}{a^{\frac{m}{n}}}$

Properties of Rational Exponents

If m and n are rational exponents, and a and b are real numbers for which the following expressions are defined, then

1. $b^m \cdot b^n = b^{m+n}$ **2.** $\dfrac{b^m}{b^n} = b^{m-n}$

3. $(b^m)^n = b^{mn}$ **4.** $(ab)^n = a^n b^n$

5. $\left(\dfrac{a}{b}\right)^n = \dfrac{a^n}{b^n}$

RADICALS

If $\sqrt[n]{a}$ and $\sqrt[n]{b}$ are real numbers, then
1. If n is even, then $\sqrt[n]{a^n} = |a|$.
2. If n is odd, then $\sqrt[n]{a^n} = a$.
3. The product rule: $\sqrt[n]{a} \cdot \sqrt[n]{b} = \sqrt[n]{ab}$
4. The quotient rule: $\dfrac{\sqrt[n]{a}}{\sqrt[n]{b}} = \sqrt[n]{\dfrac{a}{b}}$

INTERVAL NOTATION, SET-BUILDER NOTATION, AND GRAPHS

$(a, b) = \{x \mid a < x < b\}$

$[a, b) = \{x \mid a \leq x < b\}$

$(a, b] = \{x \mid a < x \leq b\}$

$[a, b] = \{x \mid a \leq x \leq b\}$

$(-\infty, b) = \{x \mid x < b\}$

$(-\infty, b] = \{x \mid x \leq b\}$

$(a, \infty) = \{x \mid x > a\}$

$[a, \infty) = \{x \mid x \geq a\}$

$(-\infty, \infty) = \{x \mid x \text{ is a real number}\} = \{x \mid x \in R\}$

SLOPE FORMULA

$$\text{slope } (m) = \frac{\text{change in } y}{\text{change in } x} = \frac{y_2 - y_1}{x_2 - x_1}, \quad (x_1 \neq x_2)$$

EQUATIONS OF LINES

1. *Slope-intercept form:* $y = mx + b$
m is the line's slope and b is its y-intercept.
2. *General form:* $Ax + By + C = 0$
3. *Point-slope form:* $y - y_1 = m(x - x_1)$
m is the line's slope and (x_1, y_1) is a fixed point on the line.
4. *Horizontal line parallel to the x-axis:* $y = b$
5. *Vertical line parallel to the y-axis:* $x = a$

ABSOLUTE VALUE

1. $|x| = \begin{cases} x & \text{if } x \geq 0 \\ -x & \text{if } x < 0 \end{cases}$
2. If $|x| = c$, then $x = c$ or $x = -c$. $(c > 0)$
3. If $|x| < c$, then $-c < x < c$. $(c > 0)$
4. If $|x| > c$, then $x < -c$ or $x > c$. $(c > 0)$

SPECIAL FACTORIZATIONS

1. *Difference of two squares:*
$$A^2 - B^2 = (A + B)(A - B)$$

2. *Perfect square trinomials:*
$$A^2 + 2AB + B^2 = (A + B)^2$$
$$A^2 - 2AB + B^2 = (A - B)^2$$

3. *Sum of two cubes:*
$$A^3 + B^3 = (A + B)(A^2 - AB + B^2)$$

4. *Difference of two cubes:*
$$A^3 - B^3 = (A - B)(A^2 + AB + B^2)$$

ALGEBRA'S COMMON GRAPHS

Identity Function

Absolute Value Function

Standard Quadratic Function

Square Root Function

Standard Cubic Function

Cube Root Function

Greatest Integer Function

Reciprocal Function

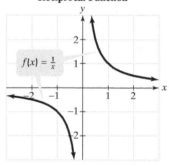

TRANSFORMATIONS

In each case, c represents a positive real number.

	Function	Draw the graph of f and:
Vertical translations	$\begin{cases} y = f(x) + c \\ y = f(x) - c \end{cases}$	Shift f upward c units. Shift f downward c units.
Horizontal translations	$\begin{cases} y = f(x - c) \\ y = f(x + c) \end{cases}$	Shift f to the right c units. Shift f to the left c units.
Reflections	$\begin{cases} y = -f(x) \\ y = f(-x) \end{cases}$	Reflect f about the x-axis. Reflect f about the y-axis.
Vertical Stretching or Shrinking	$\begin{cases} y = cf(x); c > 1 \\ y = cf(x): 0 < c < 1 \end{cases}$	Vertically stretch f, multiplying each of its y-coordinates by c. Vertically shrink f, multiplying each of its y-coordinates by c.
Horizontal Stretching or Shrinking	$\begin{cases} y = f(cx); c > 1 \\ y = f(cx); 0 < c < 1 \end{cases}$	Horizontally shrink f, dividing each of its x-coordinates by c. Horizontally stretch f, dividing each of its x-coordinates by c.

DISTANCE AND MIDPOINT FORMULAS

1. The distance from (x_1, y_1) to (x_2, y_2) is

$$\sqrt{(x_2 - x_1)^2 + (y_2 - y_1)^2}.$$

2. The midpoint of the line segment with endpoints (x_1, y_1) and (x_2, y_2) is

$$\left(\frac{x_1 + x_2}{2}, \frac{y_1 + y_2}{2}\right).$$

QUADRATIC FORMULA

The solutions of $ax^2 + bx + c = 0$ with $a \neq 0$ are

$$x = \frac{-b \pm \sqrt{b^2 - 4ac}}{2a}.$$

FUNCTIONS

1. Linear Function: $f(x) = mx + b$
   Graph is a line with slope m and y-intercept b.

2. Quadratic Function: $f(x) = ax^2 + bx + c, a \neq 0$

   Graph is a parabola with vertex at $x = -\dfrac{b}{2a}$.

   Quadratic Function: $f(x) = a(x - h)^2 + k$
   In this form, the parabola's vertex is (h, k).

3. nth-Degree Polynomial Function:

   $$f(x) = a_n x^n + a_{n-1} x^{n-1} + a_{n-2} x^{n-2} + \cdots + a_1 x + a_0, a_n \neq 0$$

   For n odd and $a_n > 0$, graph falls to the left and rises to the right.

   For n odd and $a_n < 0$, graph rises to the left and falls to the right.

   For n even and $a_n > 0$, graph rises to the left and rises to the right.

   For n even and $a_n < 0$, graph falls to the left and falls to the right.

4. Rational Function: $f(x) = \dfrac{p(x)}{q(x)}, p(x)$ and $q(x)$ are polynomials, $q(x) \neq 0$

5. Exponential Function: $f(x) = b^x, b > 0, b \neq 1$

   Graphs:

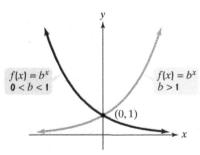

PROPERTIES OF LOGARITHMS

1. $\log_b(MN) = \log_b M + \log_b N$

2. $\log_b\left(\dfrac{M}{N}\right) = \log_b M - \log_b N$

3. $\log_b M^p = p \log_b M$

4. $\log_b M = \dfrac{\log_a M}{\log_a b} = \dfrac{\ln M}{\ln b} = \dfrac{\log M}{\log b}$

5. $\log_b b^x = x; \quad \ln e^x = x$

6. $b^{\log_b x} = x; \quad e^{\ln x} = x$

INVERSE OF A 2 × 2 MATRIX

If $A = \begin{bmatrix} a & b \\ c & d \end{bmatrix}$, then $A^{-1} = \dfrac{1}{ad - bc}\begin{bmatrix} d & -b \\ -c & a \end{bmatrix}$, where $ad - bc \neq 0$.

CRAMER'S RULE

If

$$a_{11}x_1 + a_{12}x_2 + a_{13}x_3 + \cdots + a_{1n}x_n = b_1$$
$$a_{21}x_1 + a_{22}x_2 + a_{23}x_3 + \cdots + a_{2n}x_n = b_2$$
$$a_{31}x_1 + a_{32}x_2 + a_{33}x_3 + \cdots + a_{3n}x_n = b_3$$
$$\vdots$$
$$a_{n1}x_1 + a_{n2}x_2 + a_{n3}x_3 + \cdots + a_{nn}x_n = b_n$$

then $x_i = \dfrac{D_i}{D}, D \neq 0$.

D: determinant of the system's coefficients

D_i: determinant in which coefficients of x_1 are replaced by $b_1, b_2, b_3, \ldots, b_n$.

6. Logarithmic Function: $f(x) = \log_b x, b > 0, b \neq 1$
   $y = \log_b x$ is equivalent to $x = b^y$.

   Graph:

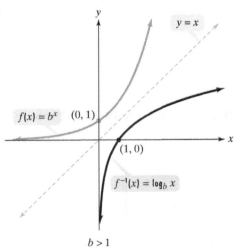

$b > 1$